The chemistry of
the ether linkage

THE CHEMISTRY OF FUNCTIONAL GROUPS

A series of advanced treatises under the general editorship of
Professor Saul Patai

The chemistry of alkenes
The chemistry of the carbonyl group
The chemistry of the ether linkage

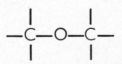

The chemistry of
the ether linkage

Edited by

SAUL PATAI

The Hebrew University
Jerusalem, Israel

1967

INTERSCIENCE PUBLISHERS

a division of John Wiley & Sons

LONDON – NEW YORK – SYDNEY

First published by John Wiley & Sons Ltd. 1967

Library of Congress catalog card number 66–30401

Text set in Monotype Baskerville 11 on 12 point, with formu-
lae in Gill Sans Light 8 point.   Made and printed in Great
Britain by William Clowes and Sons Ltd, London and Beccles

Contributing authors

J. F. Arens   University of Utrecht, Holland

L. Brandsma   University of Utrecht, Holland

D. L. Dalrymple   University of Vermont, U.S.A.

Hans Diekmann   Department of Biochemistry, University of Freiburg, Germany

Inge Eichhorn   German Academy of Sciences, Berlin-Adlershof, G.D.R.

Dov Elad   The Weizmann Institute of Science, Rehovoth, Israel

Henry Feuer   Purdue University, Lafayette, Indiana, U.S.A.

James S. Fritz   Iowa State University, Ames, U.S.A.

Jürgen Gosselck   The University, Giessen, Germany

Roy J. Gritter   IBM Research Laboratory, San Jose, California, U.S.A.

John Hooz   University of Alberta, Edmonton, Canada

Václav Horák   Charles University, Prague, Czechoslovakia

G. Kohnstam   University of Durham, England

T. L. Kruger   University of Vermont, U.S.A.

K. J. Laidler   University of Ottawa, Canada

D. J. McKenney   University of Windsor, Canada

Franz Patat   Institute of Technical Chemistry, München, Germany

David Peters   Royal Holloway College, London, England

Charles C. Price   University of Pennsylvania, Philadelphia, U.S.A.

Ernst Schmitz   German Academy of Sciences, Berlin-Adlershof, G.D.R.

Scott Searles, Jr.   Department of Chemistry, University of Missouri, U.S.A.

v

Contributing authors—*cont.*

Eberhard Staude   Institute of Technical Chemistry, München, Germany

N. V. Steere   University of Minnesota, U.S.A.

Milton Tamres   Department of Chemistry, University of Michigan, U.S.A.

Kurt Wallenfels   Department of Biochemistry, University of Freiburg, Germany

W. N. White   University of Vermont, U.S.A.

D. L. H. Williams   University of Durham, England

Foreword

This volume, the third in the series 'The Chemistry of the Functional Groups', follows in general the pattern established in the previous two volumes. The task which the authors were asked to fulfil remained as summarized in the foreword to the second volume: 'The authors of the chapters were asked to concentrate their efforts on a critical discussion of their subjects, emphasizing recent advances and new developments and addressing themselves mainly to postgraduate students and research workers. Material appearing in modern textbooks or reviewed satisfactorily in easily available sources was to be covered briefly and only then if it was considered to be necessary for the balance of the presentation. Nevertheless, each author was asked to treat his subject monographically and a certain amount of overlap between the chapters was accepted in order to preserve their structural unity and to spare the reader from too frequent recourse to different chapters of the book.'

In two aspects this volume differs from its predecessors. Firstly, while several chapters included in the plan of the previous two volumes did not materialize and had to be omitted from the books, in the present volume all authors delivered their manuscripts, so that any incompleteness in the structure of this book is my own responsibility. Secondly, owing to continued efforts on the part of the publisher's editorial office in London, the interval between the receipt of the manuscripts and their appearance in print has been shortened, compared to previous volumes. In the forthcoming volumes of the series (two of which, 'The Chemistry of the Amino Group' and 'The Chemistry of Carboxylic Acids and Esters' are already in advanced stages of preparation) it will be attempted to shorten again as far as possible the publishing schedule.

It is a pleasure to acknowledge my indebtedness to several of my younger colleagues of the Hebrew University; to Mrs. Zdenka Grunbaum, to Mr. Chaim Gilon and to Dr. Michael Michman, who took on themselves some of the more laborious tasks of the preparation of this volume, such as translating and indexing.

Jerusalem, September 1966 SAUL PATAI

Contents

coordinate system is shown in Figure 1 (note the choice of x and y axes to conform with the IUPAP recommendation[5] and that $2p_{xO}$ may be written $2p\pi_O$). This coordinate system will be used throughout. The

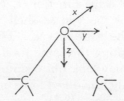

FIGURE 1.

$\widehat{\text{COC}}$ bond angle is $112°$ and the C—O bond length is $1\cdot41$ Å in dimethyl ether[6]. The bond strength[7] is 83–85 kcal/mole and the force constant of the carbon–oxygen bond[8] is about 5 mdyn/Å.

It is often helpful to use the local symmetry when working within a small region of a large molecule. In doing this we assume that the distant parts of the molecule (the remote methyl groups in diethyl ether, say) have only a small effect on the properties of the ether linkage itself. The local symmetry in the neighbourhood of the ether linkage is C_{2v} and the character table of this group[9] is given in Table 1.

TABLE 1. The character table of the C_{2v} group.

		E	C_2	$\sigma_{v(xz)}$	$\sigma_{v(yz)}$
$1s_O, 2s_O, 2p_{zO}$	a_1	1	1	1	1
	a_2	1	1	-1	-1
$2p_{xO}$	b_1	1	-1	1	-1
$2p_{yO}, (2s_C - 2s_{C'})$	b_2	1	-1	-1	1

The atomic orbitals and the linear combinations of atomic orbitals which belong to the irreducible representations of the group are shown on the left of Table 1. Notice that if a molecular orbital is of symmetry b_2, say, it can only contain $2p_{yO}$, $(2s_C - 2s_{C'})$, etc., and it cannot contain any other atomic orbital or linear combination of atomic orbitals. This is the essential group-theory result that we need.

There are two different ways of representing the *same* wave function in molecular-orbital theory. In the first the wave function is written down in terms of the delocalized molecular orbitals. In the second it is written down in terms of the localized molecular orbitals which correspond to the chemical bonds and the lone pairs[10]. It is essential to realize that these two descriptions are only two different ways of writing down the same total wave function[11]. Notice that this result is only valid, in general, for the 'closed shell' ground states of singlet molecules and not for the general case. The reason for using two different ways of representing the same total wave function is that a particular phenomenon may look quite simple in terms of one set of molecular orbitals but rather involved in terms of the other set. Details on this point are given elsewhere[10, 11].

The only important units required here are the electon volt (ev) and the kilocalorie. The relationship between them is as shown in equation (1).

$$1.0 \text{ ev/molecule} = 23.06 \text{ kcal/mole} \tag{1}$$

The physical constants quoted in this chapter are taken from reference 12 unless otherwise specified.

II. THE ISOLATED OXYGEN ATOM

The nucleus of the oxygen atom contains eight protons and eight, nine, or ten neutrons giving the stable isotopes ^{16}O, ^{17}O, and ^{18}O, with ^{16}O making up 99.76% of the natural abundance. The nuclei of ^{16}O and ^{18}O have no spin and so for all chemical purposes they behave as charged mass points. The ^{17}O nucleus has a spin of $\frac{5}{2}$ (in units of $h/2\pi$) and so it behaves as a magnet and as an electric quadrupole. This means that there is an energy of interaction between this nucleus and the magnetic and electric fields created by the rest of the molecule or an externally applied field and this is potentially a valuable source of information, via paramagnetic and quadrupole resonance experiments, about the electron organization in and around the ether linkage. There are difficulties in realizing this possibility and little attention has yet been given to it[13].

The eight electrons of the oxygen atom are first described by the statement of their configuration, which is $(1s)^2(2s)^2(2p)^4$. This is the crudest possible description; if electrons did not interact with each other through coulomb and exchange forces, this configuration statement would describe the single level of the ground state of the oxygen atom. It would be highly degenerate because there are many ways of arranging the four $2p$ electrons among the six $2p$ atomic orbitals. When

we allow for the interaction between the electrons, for the Pauli
principle and for the indistinguishability of the electrons[14], it turns out
that this single state is replaced by three states, usually written ^3P,
^1D and ^1S. The triplet state lies lowest (Hund's rule), the ^1D state lies
2·0 ev higher and the ^1S state 2·2 ev higher again. The first excited
state, built from the configuration $(1s)^2(2s)^2(2p)^3(3s)^1$, lies about
10 ev higher than the ^3P ground state, the exact number depending on
what one takes for the energy of a configuration. There is an additional
interaction between the magnetic moments of the spin and orbital
angular momenta which creates further splittings, such as that of the
ground state into $^3P_2$, $^3P_1$, and $^3P_0$ but these are small (about 0·02 ev)
compared with typical bond energies (about 3 ev).

The important energy quantity of the atom is the ionization energy
of the valence electrons. The experimentally lowest ionization
energy[14] of the ^3P ground state is 13·6 ev but this number is partly

$$O,\ ^3P_2(1s^22s^22p^4) \xrightarrow{\ 13\cdot6\ \text{ev}\ } O^+,\ ^4S^0(1s^22s^22p^3) \tag{2}$$

determined by the complicated spin and orbital angular momentum
coupling in the neutral atom and in the ion. It is better to use the
ionization energy of the 'valence state' of the atom in the molecule, in
which this coupling has been averaged over all the states of the atom.
This condition of the atom then corresponds more closely with that in
the molecule where the electric fields from the other atoms quench this
coupling. There are two different models for the atom in the molecule.
The first model[14] gives a value of 15·9 ev for the ionization energy of
the $2p$ electron of oxygen. The second model[15] gives values of 17·3 ev
for the ionization energy of the valence $2p$ electron and 14·6 ev for that
of the lone-pair electron. This is a large ionization energy for a valence
electron and it is the reason for the high electronegativity of the oxygen
atom, if we use Mulliken's definition[16] of this quantity as the mean of
the ionization energy and the electron affinity (which is small).

The electronegativity of an element is usually thought of as a property of the atom[17], although it is difficult to see how this comes about
for a property which is so closely related to both bond energy and
bond polarity when these are determined by the molecule as a whole.
Nevertheless, the idea of electronegativity has been remarkably successful and we make use of it here. The results of the accurate wave
functions[10b] certainly seem to agree with the general idea of electronegativity at least in so far as bond polarity goes. Its connection with
bond energies is less clear at the moment.

III. BONDING IN SIMPLE ETHERS

The clearest way to describe bonding in simple ethers is to start with the simplest description and work our way up to the most refined description of the electron organization in the ethers. In this way it is possible to have continuous gradation of theory and to see how the simpler ideas are related to the more sophisticated ones. All of the simpler descriptions are in terms of localized bonding and the more elaborate ones in terms of delocalized bonding.

The most elementary picture of the bonding in the simple ethers is that found in chemistry texts and is depicted in Figure 2. The important implication of this picture is that we can divide up the eight

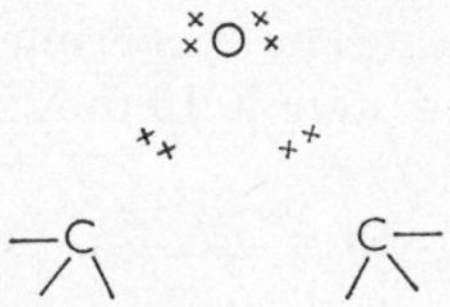

FIGURE 2.

valence electrons into four pairs, one pair for each bond and two lone pairs. This division of the electrons into pairs (but see reference 18) is one of the central assumptions of chemical valence theory and it is only recently that this has been confirmed by the modern wave functions[10].

The next more refined statement is that the bonds are formed from the $1s$ atomic orbital of the hydrogen atoms and the $2p$ atomic orbitals (properly directed) of the oxygen atom, while the lone pairs are formed from the $2s$ and the $2p_x$ atomic orbitals of oxygen. Such bonds may be represented by the valence-bond wave function (equation 3), or by the

$$\psi_{\text{VB}} = [(1s_{\text{H}})^1(2p_{\text{O}})^2 + (1s_{\text{H}})^2(2p_{\text{O}})^1][\alpha^1\beta^2 - \alpha^2\beta^1] \qquad (3)$$

molecular-orbital wave function (equation 4), where α and β are the

$$\psi_{\text{MO}} = [(1s_{\text{H}} + 2p_{\text{O}})^1(1s_{\text{H}} + 2p_{\text{O}})^2][\alpha^1\beta^2 - \alpha^2\beta^1] \qquad (4)$$

usual spin functions and the electron label is written as a superscript. The functions as written are not normalized. The complete wave function for a large molecule is then obtained by writing down a product of such functions and then antisymmetrizing this product for the exchange of electrons between the bonds and lone pairs.

Such a description of the bonding is the simplest possible quantitative statement. We might call such a bond the 'standard bond'. This is built from the pure atomic orbitals of the atoms; it is perfectly localized and it is non-polar. It is important to realize that this is probably accurate enough a picture to explain bond formation and to give something like one-half of the bond energy. We cannot prove this contention yet and in saying it we are assuming that the correlation of the two electrons of the bond is somehow allowed for, and that the electron kinetic energy is also increased over that given by a simple molecular-orbital wave function. The remainder of the bond energy is provided by three additional correction factors, each of which probably contributes some 5 to 10 kilocalories per mole to the bond energy. We will shortly discuss these in turn.

Before doing that, we must connect up this picture with that of the oxygen atom given in section II. The point here is that we have to 'unpair' the electrons of the triplet ground state of the free atom before the two electrons are free to form bonds. After the spins are unpaired, the oxygen atom is in a condition which is not a pure state but which is a mixture of the ^3P, ^1D and ^1S states. This is called the valence state [4] (a better term would be the valence condition) of the oxygen atom and to put the atom into this state requires some energy (about 1 ev here). This is the promotion energy of the atom. This increase in the total energy of the system is outweighed by the decrease in the total energy when the two bonds are formed.

We return now to the three correction factors which increase the bond energy over that of the standard bond. The first of these is the polarity of the bond. Bonds certainly are polar, so there must be a lowering of the total energy of the system when we go from the standard non-polar bond to the real polar bond (variation principle). The question is whether the two electrons of the carbon–oxygen bond are equally shared between carbon and oxygen or whether the carbon atom has, say, 0·9 electrons and the oxygen atom has 1·1 electrons. This is often answered by saying that molecules such as diethyl ether have a dipole moment so the bonds must be polar and that the theoretical explanation of this is that the electronegativity of oxygen is higher than that of carbon. Since it is not quite clear just what role electronegativity plays in determining bond energies, it is simpler to look at the results [10b, 10c] of recent calculations [3, 19] on the OH radical and the water molecule. These results gave the charge diagrams shown in Figure 3. Then if we replace the hydrogen atoms by methyl groups, say, and remember that an sp^3 carbon hybrid atomic orbital is a little more electronegative than a hydrogen atom[10, 15], we conclude that the polarity of the carbon–oxygen bond of a typical ether will be such that the oxygen atom carries 1·1 electrons and the carbon atom 0·9 electrons. This is not a precise statement, because atomic charges are not precisely defined quantities since their numerical values depend on what one means by an electron being 'on' an atom, but the result agrees with both electronegativity ideas and with chemical experience.

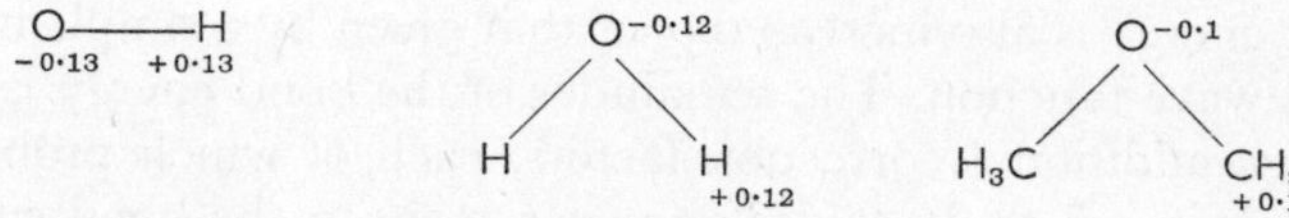

$$\underset{-0\cdot13}{O}\text{———}\underset{+0\cdot13}{H} \qquad \overset{O^{-0\cdot12}}{\underset{\underset{H\;\;\;\;\;\;\;\;\underset{+0\cdot12}{H}}{\diagup\;\;\;\diagdown}}{}} \qquad \overset{O^{-0\cdot1}}{\underset{\underset{H_3C\;\;\;\;\;\;\;\underset{+0\cdot1}{CH_3}}{\diagup\;\;\;\diagdown}}{}}$$

FIGURE 3.

It is tempting to try to check this result by comparing it with the dipole moment of the simple ethers (1·1–1·3 D[6, 20]). This simple equating of bond dipole with observed dipole moment may well be an oversimplification, because there are other sources of electric moments in such molecules, particularly in the hybridization of the valence electrons and the lone pairs[1, 10], so that the experimental dipole moment will be a sum of several electric moments all of similar size and of both signs. It happens, however, that the above charges do give a reasonable estimate of the dipole moment (0·8 D) so perhaps we are overestimating the importance of the hybridization dipoles. There is some reason to think that we are, because molecular-orbital wave functions make no allowance for the fact that the atom will resist deformation beyond the point necessary to form the bonds. So perhaps the bond dipoles are the main contributors to the observed dipole moment.

The second correction factor is concerned with hybridization. The question is whether the valence and lone-pair atomic orbitals of the oxygen atom are appreciably hybridized. It is often said[21], for example, that the valence and lone-pair atomic orbitals of the oxygen atom are sp^3 hybrids. The available results[10c] do not settle this question because they do not establish hybridizations accurately enough, but there is a strong tendency in the results for hybridizations to be small. This is the best we can say at the moment. There must be some stabilizing of the molecule as a result of hybridization, but we cannot do more than guess that it will be a few kilocalories per mole.

The third and the most subtle of the three correction factors is the electron delocalization. This concept is familiar under the names of conjugation, hyperconjugation and departure from perfect pairing in a valence-bond scheme. All these terms describe the same physical thing. It is clear enough that the lowering of the total energy which results from the electron delocalization cannot be large in the simple σ-bonded molecules, otherwise we would not have chemical bonds in the first place, but it is still very difficult to make non-empirical calculations of this quantity. Some approximate results[22] suggest that the upper limit to this delocalization energy is a few kilocalories per mole per bond.

The third correction factor differs from the other two in that it may be thought of as an interaction between localized bonds. There are other interaction effects to be considered, such as the simple dipole–dipole interaction, the interaction between non-bonded atoms, and the more subtle dispersion forces between different pairs of electrons in different bonds or lone pairs[23]. It seems fair to say that we understand these factors very poorly and that we generally assume that they are small.

Most of the above remarks refer to the localized molecular-orbital description of the bonding. In an electron excitation or ionization experiment, however, we supply the molecule with such a large amount of energy (5–10 ev) that the factors responsible for holding the electrons into the bonds and lone pairs are swamped and then we have to use the more general delocalized description of the electron organization. The best available estimate that we have for the forms of the delocalized molecular orbitals of the simple ethers is the set of molecular orbitals for the water molecule[3]. It is likely that those of the simple ethers will not differ too greatly from these. The molecular orbitals are given in Table 2.

TABLE 2. Delocalized valence molecular orbitals of the water molecule[3].

	$(-\varepsilon)^{3a}$	$(-\varepsilon)^{3b}$	$(-\varepsilon)^{3c}$
$1a_1 = 0.845(2s_O) + 0.1328(2p_{zO}) + 0.1259(1s_H + 1s_{H'})$	36·19	37·27	36·08
$b_2 = 0.5428(2p_{yO}) + 0.5486(1s_H - 1s_{H'})$	18·55	19·21	18·54
$2a_1 = 0.4601(2s_O) - 0.8277(2p_{zO}) - 0.2362(1s_H + 1s_{H'})$	13·20	15·21	15·13
$b_1 = 1.0(2p_{xO})$	11·79	13·59	13·48

These molecular orbitals are from reference 3a. Those from references 3b and 3c are certainly more accurate, but they are less easy to interpret. The $1s_O$ atomic orbital has been dropped out of these molecular orbitals so they may not be accurately normalized. The $1s_O$-like inner-shell molecular orbital is also omitted from the table.

1*

The molecular orbital b_1 is just the lone pair again, but there will be important modifications of this in the others (see below). The two a_1 molecular orbitals and the b_2 one have replaced the $2s$-like lone pair and the two bonds. The quantities in the right-hand columns of Table 2 are the ionization energies of the molecular orbitals and are expected (Koopmans' theorem) [24] to represent the observable ionization energies of the molecule. The total energy which is obtained from calculations such as these is not usually very useful because it contains the large correlation error [25]. The more useful information is contained in the forms of the molecular orbitals and in the ionization energy estimates. One of the important pieces of information which these give us is an idea of how strongly bonding, non-bonding or antibonding is the molecular orbital. This is obtained either by evaluating the overlap population (bond order) [26] both for the complete molecular orbital and for the various pairs of atoms or by evaluating the increase in the ionization energy $(-\delta\varepsilon)$ of the molecular orbital on molecule formation [10d]. To work out the increase in the ionization energy of the molecular orbital, we take the difference of $(-\varepsilon)$ and the average ionization energy of the atomic orbitals which make up the molecular orbital, weighted according to their population in the molecular orbital. The details of this are given elsewhere for the localized bond; the extension to the delocalized bond is simple [10d]. It is true that the overlapping of the atomic orbitals is only part of the full story [27] but we may hope that it will be qualitatively correct. The results are given in Table 3. If the

TABLE 3. Overlap populations and ionization energy increments in the water molecule [26].

	Overlap populations				Ionization energy increments (ev)		
	$2s_O:1s_H$	$2p_{zO}:1s_H$	$H_1:H_2$	$2p_{yO}:1s_H$ Total/MO	$(-\delta\varepsilon)^{3a}$	$(-\delta\varepsilon)^{3b}$	$(-\delta\varepsilon)^{3c}$
$1a_1$	0·21	0·01	0·01	— 0·47	7·1	8·2	7·1
b_2	—	—	−0·45	0·33 0·21	3·9	4·6	3·9
$2a_1$	−0·22	0·17	0·08	— −0·02	−4·1	−2·1	−2·2
b_2	—	—	—	— 0·0	−4·0	−2·3	−2·4

overlap population between a pair of atomic orbitals is large and positive, the atoms are said to be bonded. If the total overlap population of a molecular orbital is large and positive, the molecular orbital is said to be bonding. If the ionization energy increment is large and positive, the molecular orbital is said to be bonding. When these numbers are small, or large and negative, the terms non-bonding and antibonding are used appropriately.

From the table, it is clear that both methods of judging the bonding character of a molecular orbital give the same result. Notice that the bonding occurs in the lowest-energy molecular orbital of a given symmetry species, the b_1 orbital apart. This is generally the case, the higher-energy molecular orbitals being quite close to non-bonding or even slightly antibonding. In other words, by using the delocalized molecular orbitals, we replace two bonds and one lone pair with two bonding molecular orbitals and one non-bonding one. Despite the fact that the appearance of the molecular orbitals changes drastically when using delocalized molecular orbitals, the description of the bonding has not changed so markedly.

One important example in which we need to know which molecular orbital is bonding is when we consider excited or ionized states, because then we can draw some inferences about the geometry of the excited state or ion and about the photochemical reaction routes of the molecule[28].

Finally, we should mention the more recent developments in molecular-structure theory which will influence our chemical valence theory in the future. The first of these is concerned with the problem of choosing the best forms for the atomic orbitals of the atom in the molecule and in studying how these differ from the free-atom atomic orbitals[29]. Another problem is that of the celebrated correlation energy of the electrons[25]. It is clear that points such as these will soon be of major importance in our theory of the ether linkage, remote though they seem at the moment.

Looking at the experimental facts, the bond energy of the ether linkage[7] is 83–85 kcal/mole and the bond-dissociation energy is rather smaller than this at 77 kcal/mole. The average bond energy is smaller than that in water, partly because of the greater polarity of the bond in water but partly for other reasons which are not understood yet. We cannot yet compute such a bond energy with useful accuracy, but we can compute the bond length and the bond angle of such a molecule as water quite satisfactorily[3b], so that the geometry of the simple ethers will soon be within our computational facilities.

IV. BONDING IN CONJUGATED ETHERS

We take the non-cyclic conjugated ethers first and deal with the cyclic ones later. The conjugation in such molecules as the aryl ethers was one of the first cases in which conjugation was noticed[30]. It was represented then in valence-bond language by the interaction of the resonance structures such as **1** and **2** in the case of the vinyl ethers. We say that

$$\begin{array}{cc} \diagup\hspace{-0.5em}C{=}C{-}O & \diagup\hspace{-0.5em}\overset{-}{C}{-}C{=}\overset{+}{O} \\ \diagup \quad\; | & \diagup \quad\; | \\ \quad\; R & \quad\; R \\ (\mathbf{1}) & (\mathbf{2}) \end{array}$$

there is a lowering of the total energy under the resonance. This also suggests that there is a transfer of electrons (perhaps about $0\cdot1$ electrons) away from the oxygen atom.

The molecular-orbital statement of the same physical effect is essentially the same as in the delocalized bonding case for the simple ethers (section III). Taking the vinyl ether case and writing π for the ethylene π molecular orbital, the localized or non-conjugated wave function is as shown in equation (5), where the other molecular orbitals

$$\Psi_{\text{loc.}} = \left| \ldots \pi\bar{\pi}2p\pi_O\overline{2p\pi_O}\ldots \right| \tag{5}$$

are represented by dots and the presence of a bar over the symbol denotes β spin and the absence of a bar α spin. The vertical lines represent the determinant which antisymmetrizes the whole function for electron exchange. The conjugated or delocalized counterpart is written in equation (6), where ϕ_1 and ϕ_2 must be obtained by solving a secular

$$\Psi_{\text{deloc.}} = \left| \ldots \phi_1\bar{\phi}_1\phi_2\bar{\phi}_2\ldots \right| \tag{6}$$

equation, although it is clear that these two molecular orbitals will be *closely related* to π and $2p_{xO}$. The molecular orbitals ϕ_1 and ϕ_2 will not be *exactly* related to π and $2p_{xO}$ by an orthogonal transformation, otherwise there would be no change in the total energy of the system on going from one representation to the other.

This introduces the familiar Hückel-type secular equation and determinant[31]. The vinyl and aryl ethers have been treated by this theory[1,32] and the results are certainly interesting but they must be accepted with caution. They are best thought of as constructive speculation. One of the difficulties is that, in molecules as complicated as the aryl ethers, one has to choose the numerical values for a number of parameters at the beginning of the calculation and the results depend critically on these choices. Indeed, there is sometimes a clear disagreement between the semiempirical methods and the self-consistent field method even as to the sign of the π electron charge on certain atoms. The self-consistent field results show[10b] that, in the π bond of the carbonyl and nitrile groups, the π electrons accumulate on the carbon atom and not on the oxygen or nitrogen atoms. The reason for this is that the σ electrons accumulate on the oxygen or nitrogen atoms to such an extent as to reduce its effective electronegativity towards the π electrons below that of the carbon atom. In this circumstance it is best to think of the Hückel method as dealing with some mixture of the σ and π electrons and to think of the so-called π charges as total atomic charges. Some typical examples of these calculated charge distributions are given in the standard texts[1, 32].

The question of the conjugation in cyclic ethers such as furan is also in a somewhat unsettled state. It seems at first sight that there could well be a large benzene-like resonance energy in furan. Whether[33] or not[7b] there is a resonance energy depends upon how the term is defined; the present situation with regard to resonance energies is so confused (even for benzene[34]) that it is generally felt that the term should not be used. Perhaps we should return to the old-fashioned definition of the term 'aromatic' as a function of chemical reactivity[35].

The ultraviolet spectrum of furan (see below) is quite similar to that of the acyclic analogues so there is no evidence for extensive electron delocalization there. The most persuasive evidence for the existence of some aromatic character in furan is its low chemical reactivity as compared with the acyclic analogues, but it is equally true that this may have little or no direct bearing on how the π electrons of the molecule behave.

Several computations have been carried out on furan, the most thoroughgoing of which is still semiempirical in nature[36]. The results of this computation seem to agree well with both the energies of the excited states and with the chemical reactivity, if this is thought of as a π-electron problem. The π-electron populations which this calculation leads to are shown in Figure 4. The low π-electron population on

FIGURE 4. Calculated π-electron populations in furan[36].

oxygen seems a little odd since it requires about 7 ev to remove one-half of an electron from the oxygen atom and it seems fair to say that the question of electron delocalization in furan is open to further work.

V. BONDING IN STRAINED CYCLIC ETHERS

The natural example here is the ethylene oxide molecule, and the valence problem of this is obviously very like that of cyclopropane, modified by the fact that the bond angle at oxygen is naturally smaller than that at carbon and by the electronegativity of the oxygen atom. There have been several calculations on the cyclopropane molecule[37], none of them really accurate, but they all agree that the ring bonds are heavily bent, that the valence atomic orbitals used by the carbon atoms to form the ring bonds contain an unusually large amount of $2p$ character, and that the carbon–hydrogen bonds are rather like the ethylene ones. The source of the unsaturated character of the molecule is still somewhat obscure, although the fact that the ring carbon–carbon bonds are built from atomic orbitals which contain an unusually large amount of $2p$ character certainly suggests the possibility of ethylene-like conjugation.

The ionization potential of the oxygen $2p\pi$ lone pair (10·6–10·8 ev)[46] is rather higher than that of dimethyl ether (see below) so the delocalization of the carbon–hydrogen bonds with the $2p\pi$ lone pair may be less effective in ethylene oxide than in the simple ethers. There is also experimental evidence of charge migration away from the oxygen atom in ethylene oxide[38] and this could also increase the ionization potential of the $2p\pi$ lone pair electrons.

VI. ELECTRONIC EXCITED STATES, ULTRAVIOLET SPECTRA, AND IONIZATION POTENTIALS OF ETHERS

The excited states of the simple ethers are only now being examined in the sort of detail which is necessary to establish the nature of the excited states with certainty[39]. It is known[40, 41] that these compounds, like all molecules of any complexity, have several absorption bands below 2000 Å and some of these are certainly Rydberg transitions in which the $2p_{xO}$ lone-pair electron is being excited to orbitals of principal quantum number 3, 4, ... but the lower energy ones may be wholly or in part transitions to the antibonding valence-shell molecular orbitals of symmetry a_1 or b_2. The transition to the a_1 orbital from $2p_{xO}$ is an allowed transition; that to the b_2 orbital is forbidden. It is interesting to notice that there should be triplet states of these two transitions rather lower in energy (5–6 ev, say) and this should lead to some interesting photochemistry of the simple ethers[24]. This may be important because it is not easy to break the ether linkage by conventional means.

The ultraviolet spectra of the simple aryl ethers such as anisole have been examined thoroughly[42]. These spectra are essentially those of the parent hydrocarbon, the perturbing effect of the alkoxyl group shifting the bands to the red and intensifying them. It is generally agreed[43] that the inductive effect of the alkoxyl group is not important here, because even the —NH$_3$$^+$ substituent has remarkably little effect on the benzene spectrum, and even the conjugative effect is not large. This is because the ionization energy of the $2p_x$ lone pair of the oxygen atom is several electron volts greater than that of the carbon atom and it is a general principle of molecular-orbital theory[1] that two atomic orbitals can only interact when their energies are close together. Alternatively, we may emphasize the charge-transfer nature of the alkoxyl group by writing the resonance structures such as **3** for both

(**3**)

ground and excited states and supposing that this effect is more important in the excited state.

The reported computations[43] on the ultraviolet spectra of the aryl ethers are semiempirical and accurate computations are not yet possible for molecules as large as these.

The cyclic 'conjugated' ethers such as furan have an ultraviolet spectrum which is rather like the acyclic analogues[44] so that even in the excited state there is rather little interaction with the oxygen lone-pair electrons. One interesting type of ether spectrum is the charge-transfer one observed[45] with the ether–iodine complex. It is natural to suppose that the lone-pair electrons of oxygen act as donor to the iodine molecule. The observed charge-transfer band is at 440–460 mμ (2·75 ev).

The first ionization potentials of the simple oxygen compounds, including ethers, have been measured with the results shown in Table 4. That these are the ionization potentials of the $2p_{xo}$ lone-pair electron is confirmed by the results of the water molecule calculations[3] which show that the lone-pair electron is the least tightly bound one. The numbers in the table show that the electron delocalization is much more effective in lowering the ionization potential than in lowering the bond energies. This illustrates another principle of theory which is that

TABLE 4. Ionization energies of simple oxygen
compounds[41,46] (ev).

H_2O	MeOH	EtOH	Me_2O	Et_2O
12·6	10·85	10·5	10·0	9·5

when two orbitals interact, one goes up and one goes down (on the energy scale). The decrease in the ionization energy is then quite drastic, but the change in the total energy, which is the sum of the two energy changes, may be quite small. We are neglecting the two electron contribution to the total energy in these remarks[10,22].

VI. CHEMICAL REACTIVITY OF ETHERS

Like most chemical reactivity problems, that of the ethers has received very little theoretical attention so far. The difficulty is that the semi-empirical theories cannot cope with large changes in bond length because they ignore the two-electron terms which are just as important as the one-electron terms in determining bond energies[10f]. On the other hand, the thoroughgoing theories have not yet been used on the problem, so little progress has been made outside of the use of the qualitative (but, in its clearest forms, very useful) organic reaction-mechanism theory.

Some qualitative remarks can be made. The chemistry of the ether linkage is dominated by the behaviour of the $2p_{xo}$ lone-pair electrons. These form the basic site for the addition of protons and other Lewis acids and for the formation of the oxonium salts[47]. The effect of an added proton is obviously to withdraw electrons from the oxygen atom and perhaps from the carbon atoms, exposing the latter to attack by solvent and nucleophiles. The other general case in which the lone-pair electrons are important is when partial carbonium ion character is developed at the adjacent carbon atom as in the reactions of the α-halo ethers[48]. Then there is a pronounced stabilizing of the system by the lone-pair electrons of oxygen.

VIII. THIOETHERS

Much of our understanding of these compounds is by analogy with the simple ethers. The sulphur shell has the configuration $(3s)^2 (3p)^4$ and many of the points about oxygen carry over directly. The important point of difference is that the ionization energy of the sulphur $3p$ lone-pair electron ($11 \cdot 74$ ev [14], $12 \cdot 4$–$11 \cdot 1$ ev [15]) is much lower than that of the oxygen lone pair and very much closer to the ionization energy of the carbon atom. This means that the interaction between carbon and sulphur may be quite large in the π-electron situation, particularly if the sulphur orbital is shrunk somewhat, and this may be the reason why thiophene is closer to benzene in its general chemistry than is furan. Moreover, the thioethers absorb at longer wavelength than do the simple ethers [49] and this may be simply a consequence of the lower ionization energy of the sulphur $3p$ electron. The question of the role of the $3d$ atomic orbitals in the bonding of the sulphur atom is unsettled, some recent and direct evidence suggesting that the $3d$ atomic orbitals are unimportant in this connection [50]. The ultraviolet spectra of the thioethers have been reviewed recently [49].

IX. REFERENCES

1. C. A. Coulson, *Valence*, 2nd ed., Oxford University Press, London, 1961; R. Daudel, R. Lefebvre, and C. Moser, *Quantum Chemistry*, Interscience Publishers, New York, 1959; A. Streitwieser, *Molecular Orbital Theory for Organic Chemists*, John Wiley and Sons, New York, 1961.
2. E.g. E. Clementi, *J. Chem. Phys.*, **36**, 33 (1962).
3. (a) F. O. Ellison and H. Shull, *J. Chem. Phys.*, **23**, 2348 (1955); (b) M. Krauss, *J. Res. Natl. Bur. Std.*, *A*, **68**, 635 (1964); (c) R. Moccia, *J. Chem. Phys.*, **40**, 2186 (1964).
4. J. H. Van Vleck, *J. Chem. Phys.*, **2**, 20 (1934).
5. R. S. Mulliken, *J. Chem. Phys.*, **23**, 2002 (1955).
6. U. Blukis, P. H. Kasai, and R. Myers, *J. Chem. Phys.*, **38**, 2753 (1963).
7. (a) G. Glocker, *J. Phys. Chem.*, **62**, 1049 (1958); (b) P. C. Cass, S. E. Fletcher, C. T. Mortimer, A. D. Springall, and T. R. White, *J. Chem. Soc.*, 1406 (1958); (c) T. L. Cottrell, *The Strengths of Chemical Bonds*, 2nd ed., Butterworths, London, 1958, p. 244.
8. E. B. Wilson, J. C. Decius, and P. C. Cross, *Molecular Vibrations*, McGraw-Hill Book Co., New York, 1955, p. 175.
9. H. Eyring, J. Walter, and G. E. Kimball, *Quantum Chemistry*, John Wiley and Sons, New York, 1944.
10. D. Peters, *J. Chem. Soc.* (a) 2003 (1963); (b) 2015 (1963); (c) 4017 (1963); (d) 2901 (1964); (e) 2908 (1964); (f) 2916 (1964).
11. J. Lennard-Jones, *Proc. Roy. Soc.* (*London*), *Ser. A*, **198**, 1, 14 (1949); C. C. J. Roothaan, *Rev. Mod. Phys.*, **23**, 69 (1951).
12. *Handbook of Chemistry and Physics*, 41st ed., Chemical Rubber Publishing Co., Cleveland, Ohio, 1959.
13. P. C. Lauterbur in *Determination of Organic Structures by Physical Methods*, Vol. 2 (Ed. F. C. Nachod and W. D. Phillips), Academic Press, New York, 1962, p. 509.

14. J. C. Slater, *Quantum Theory of Atomic Structure*, Vol. 1, McGraw-Hill Book Co., New York, 1960, p. 206.
15. J. Hinze and H. H. Jaffé, *J. Am. Chem. Soc.*, **84**, 540 (1962).
16. R. S. Mulliken, *J. Chem. Phys.*, **2**, 782 (1934).
17. L. Pauling, *The Nature of the Chemical Bond*, 3rd ed., Cornell University Press, Ithaca, New York, 1960.
18. J. W. Linnett, *The Electronic Structure of Molecules*, Methuen and Co., London, 1964.
19. M. Krauss, *J. Chem. Phys.*, **28**, 1021 (1958).
20. R. A. Spurr and H. Zeitlin, *J. Am. Chem. Soc.*, **72**, 4832 (1950); G. A. Barclay and R. J. W. LeFevre, *J. Chem. Soc.*, 1643 (1952).
21. J. A. Pople, *Quart. Rev. (London)*, **11**, 273 (1957); E. Cartmell and G. W. A. Fowles, *Valency and Molecular Structure*, Butterworths, London, 1961, p. 176.
22. D. Peters, *J. Chem. Soc.*, 3026 (1965).
23. K. S. Pitzer and E. Catalano, *J. Am. Chem. Soc.*, **78**, 4844 (1956).
24. T. Koopmans, *Physica*, **1**, 104 (1933); J. C. Lorquet, *Rev. Mod. Phys.*, **32**, 312 (1960).
25. P. O. Lowdin, *Advan. Chem. Phys.*, **2**, 207 (1959).
26. R. S. Mulliken, *J. Chem. Phys.*, **23**, 1833, 1841, 2338, 2343 (1955).
27. D. Peters, *Trans. Faraday Soc.*, **60**, 1193 (1964).
28. D. Peters, *Trans. Faraday Soc.*, **59**, 1121 (1963).
29. R. S. Mulliken, *J. Chem. Phys.*, **36**, 3428 (1962).
30. G. W. Wheland, *Resonance in Organic Chemistry*, John Wiley and Sons, New York, 1955.
31. A. Streitwieser, *Molecular Orbital Theory for Organic Chemists*, John Wiley and Sons, New York, 1961, Chap. 2.
32. E.g. H. Zimmermann, *Tetrahedron*, **16**, 169 (1962).
33. C. T. Mortimer, *Reaction Heats and Bond Strengths*, Pergamon Press, Oxford, 1962, p. 81.
34. A. Streitwieser, reference 31, p. 246.
35. D. Peters, *J. Chem. Soc.*, 1274 (1960).
36. M. K. Orloff and D. D. Fitts, *J. Chem. Phys.*, **38**, 2334 (1963); R. D. Brown, *Australian J. Chem.*, **12**, 152 (1963).
37. C. A. Coulson and W. Moffitt, *Phil. Mag.*, **40**, 1 (1949); D. Peters, *Tetrahedron*, **19**, 1539 (1963).
38. H. S. Gutowsky, R. L. Routledge, M. Tamres, and S. Searles, *J. Am. Chem. Soc.*, **76**, 4242 (1954).
39. D. A. Ramsey in *Determination of Organic Structures by Physical Methods*, Vol. 2 (Ed. F. C. Wachod and W. D. Phillips), Academic Press, New York, 1962, Chap. 4.
40. G. Fleming, M. M. Anderson, A. J. Harrison, and L. W. Pickett, *J. Chem. Phys.*, **30**, 351, 357 (1959).
41. G. J. Hernandez, *J. Chem. Phys.*, **38**, 1644 (1963); **39**, 1355 (1963).
42. L. Doub and J. M. Vandenbelt, *J. Am. Chem. Soc.*, **69**, 2714 (1947).
43. A. Streitwieser, reference 31, p. 230.
44. L. W. Pickett, *J. Chem. Phys.*, **8**, 293 (1940).
45. M. Brandon, M. Tamres, and S. Searles, *J. Am. Chem. Soc.*, **82**, 2129, 2134 (1960).

46. K. Wanatabe, *J. Chem. Phys.*, **26**, 542 (1957); A. Lowrey and K. Wanatabe, *J. Chem. Phys.*, **28**, 208 (1958).
47. R. L. Burwell, *Chem. Rev.*, **54**, 615 (1954).
48. L. Summers, *Chem. Rev.*, **55**, 301 (1955).
49. R. C. Passerini in *Organic Sulphur Compounds*, Vol. 1 (Ed. N. Kharasch), Pergamon Press, Oxford, 1961, Chap. 7.
50. R. Gerdil and E. A. C. Lucken, *J. Am. Chem. Soc.*, **87**, 213 (1965).

CHAPTER **2**

Cleavage of the C—O—C bond

EBERHARD STAUDE and FRANZ PATAT

Institute of Technical Chemistry, München, Germany

I. INTRODUCTION

The various possibilities for the cleavage of phenyl ethers have been comprehensively summarized by Lüttringhaus[1]. The remarkably extensive work of Burwell[2] surveys most of the field of acyclic ethers, giving special importance to studies where mechanistic interpretations are presented, but reactions like the splitting of isocholesteryl ethers, vinyl ethers and ring-opening reactions of cyclic ethers are not included. Lately, Parker[3] has studied the cleavage and rearrangement reactions of oxiranes.

This chapter will review the present state of knowledge on ether cleavage reactions based on recent work. For this purpose, reactions of both cyclic and acyclic ethers will be described, but some selection regarding the ether and the splitting reagent was found to be unavoidable. Detailed results dealing with further possible splitting reagents have been presented by Burwell[2].

II. ACID-CATALYZED CLEAVAGE

A. Kinetic Measurements of the Acidic Cleavage and Related Mechanisms

For the acid-catalyzed hydrolysis of ethers, the rate equation (1) will generally be valid. The order for ether (m) is usually one.

$$\frac{d[\text{ether}]}{dt} = k[\text{ether}]^m [\text{H}^+]^n \tag{1}$$

It is assumed that the first step in the reaction is the quick establishment of a preequilibrium. A proton is transferred from the hydronium ion to the ether and the conjugated acid is thus formed (reaction 2). The second rate-determining step proceeds either as a unimolecular cleavage, $A1$ (reaction 3), or as a bimolecular displacement, $A2$ (reaction 4).

$$(C_2H_5)_2O + H_3O^+ \rightleftharpoons (C_2H_5)_2OH^+ + H_2O \tag{2}$$

$$(C_2H_5)_2OH^+ \xrightarrow{\text{Slow}} C_2H_5OH + C_2H_5^+ \tag{3a}$$

$$C_2H_5^+ + 2\,H_2O \xrightarrow{\text{Fast}} C_2H_5OH + H_3O^+ \tag{3b}$$

$$(C_2H_5)OH^+ + H_2O \xrightarrow{\text{Slow}} C_2H_5OH + C_2H_5OH_2^+ \tag{4a}$$

$$C_2H_5OH_2^+ + H_2O \xrightarrow{\text{Fast}} C_2H_5OH + H_3O^+ \tag{4b}$$

As already noted by Burwell[2] much work has been done in order to determine the reaction mechanism. In the following section several methods will be studied which could well lead to a conclusion between the two mechanisms based on kinetic data.

From the calculated value of the entropy of activation, which should be positive[4] for the ether hydrolysis, it has been suggested by Long and Paul[5] that primary and secondary ethers are cleaved via an $A1$ mechanism. The activation entropy is calculated from equation (5).

$$K = (kT/h) \exp (\Delta S^{\ddagger}/R) \exp (-\Delta H^{\ddagger}/RT) \qquad (5)$$

For ester hydrolysis, $\Delta S^{\ddagger}$ values range from 0 to $+10$ and from -15 to -30 cal/deg mole for the $A1$ and $A2$ mechanisms, respectively, so that generally an increase in the entropy of activation entails a change from $A1$ to $A2$ mechanism, with the $A1$ mechanism being more probable when $\Delta S^{\ddagger} > 0$. As shown by Whalley[6], however, this hypothesis is by no means exclusive as the $A2$ step can, in fact, have a positive entropy of activation[7].

More recent kinetic measurements of the hydrolysis of diethyl ether at pressures up to 3000 atm indicate an $A2$ mechanism[8]. As a criterion for this, use is made of the change in activation volumes, which can be calculated from the measured rate coefficient (equation 6).

$$\left(\frac{\delta \ln k}{\delta p}\right)_T = \frac{-\Delta V^*}{RT} \qquad (6)$$

Here $\Delta V^* = V^* - V_{\text{init.}}$, i.e. the difference in partial volumes between the transition state (including any solvents if present) and the initial state. This question has been examined in detail by Whalley[7,9]. The mechanism can be determined from the volume of activation since the anticipated ΔV^* for the $A1$ mechanism should be positive or only slightly negative, and ΔV^* for the $A2$ mechanism is expected to be significantly negative. For the above-mentioned scheme the difference in the volumes of activation will be the volume difference in the formation of the conjugate acid and in the rate-determining step. If the negligibly small volume change resulting from the formation of the conjugate acid is disregarded, then, for reaction (3a) the volume of the intermediates is found to be larger than that of the reactants with the result that ΔV^* is equal to or larger than zero. According to reaction (4a), an interaction of the van der Waals type takes place in the transition state between water and the conjugate acid, and a volume contraction results. ΔV^* is then negative for values ranging from

−5 to − 10 ml/mole. Hence the ethers in Table 1 undergo an $A2$ type acid-catalyzed hydrolysis.

TABLE 1. Volumes of activation ΔV^* ml/mole at 1 atm.

Ether	ΔV^*	Temp.(°c)	Ref.
Diethyl ether	−8·5 ± 2	161·2	8
Ethylene oxide	−5·9 ± 1	0	10
Propylene oxide	−8·4 ± 1·3	0	10
Isobutylene oxide	−9·2 ± 1·7	0	10
Epichlorohydrin	−8·5 ± 3	25	11
Trimethylene oxide	−5·5 ± 3	25	11

An additional criterion for the $A2$ mechanism in the acid hydrolysis of ethers is that as the acid concentration is increased the reaction rate first increases, and after passing through a maximum, decreases. The maximum value lies in the range where the acidity function is equal to the pK of the substrate. This change of rates can be explained by the fact that water, which takes part in the rate-determining step, becomes less available at the higher acid concentrations. In very strongly acidic media a shift to the $A1$ mechanism will take place, so that there is no decrease in the reaction rate, as shown in the investigation of the hydrolysis of diethyl ether in the presence of concentrated sulfuric acid[12] (see Table 9).

Kinetic data concerning alkyl aryl ethers have been obtained by Bunnett[13,14]. The hydrolysis has been carried out with HCl and $HClO_4$. Plotting the rate coefficients against the acid concentration indeed shows a maximum, a fact which may be interpreted as an indication of an $A2$ reaction. Bunnett pointed out a further criterion which is indicative of an $A2$ reaction[15]. The classification, made possible by his w and w^* values is, in fact, more reliable than the one that the Zucker–Hammett hypothesis suggests[16]. This hypothesis postulates that water is needed for the reaction of the protonated substrate (SH^+); hence the reaction is bimolecular, if a linear relationship will result from the plotting of log k_ψ against log [HX], k_ψ being the rate coefficient of pseudo-first order. The reaction is unimolecular, however, when a linear relationship is found between log k_ψ and the acidity function $H_0 = - \log h_0$.

Recently, however, some doubt has arisen regarding this sort of classification[8,17]. According to Bunnett, the values of log k_ψ − log

$[h_0/(h_0 + K_{SH^+})]$ are plotted against log a_{H_2O} and w is calculated from the slope of the line. Similarly, the plot of log k_ψ − log $[(HX)/(h_0 + K_{SH^+})]$ against log a_{H_2O} should yield the w^* parameter. Considering the results obtained up to now, this method seems to be valid in concentrations ranging from 1·0 to 9·3 mole of acid. It can be concluded from the positive values of w that the ethers listed in Table 2 react through an $A2$ mechanism. Lower w values of about +2 indicate nucleophilic attack by water, followed by formation of the transition state. Higher values suggest that water acts as a protonating agent.

TABLE 2. w-Values according to Bunnett[15].

Ether	Acid	Temp.(°c)	w	Ref.
Diethyl ether	HClO$_4$	120·1	+2·72	8
4-(p-Sulfophenylazo)-1-naphthyl methyl ether	HClO$_4$	46·0	+8·2	13
4-(p-Sulfophenylazo)-1-phenyl methyl ether	HClO$_4$	95·1	+4·9	13
1-Methoxy-3,5-dihydroxybenzene	HClO$_4$	50	+2·0	18

According to Parker[19], the results obtained from the chloride ion catalyzed hydrolysis of propylene oxide under acidic and neutral conditions do not clearly indicate a definite $A2$ mechanism. A bimolecular reaction route is assumed, which may be considered a 'borderline' case of the S_N2 mechanism. The same kinetics were found for both the normal and abnormal reactions, the overall reaction following a second-order rate equation (7), where $m = 1$.

$$-\frac{d[ether]}{dt} = k_1 [ether] = k_s . k[H_3O^+]^n[ether]^m \qquad (7)$$

Compared with those instances of acidic ether hydrolysis which may now be considered fully understood, the number of cases which appear doubtful from the kinetic point of view is still relatively large, e.g. as yet no valid information on secondary aliphatic ethers has been obtained[20].

B. Methods of Ether Cleavage

I. Acyclic ethers

Cleavage of alkoxy compounds has been achieved for the first time by Butlerow[21], who used aqueous hydrogen iodide in order to split α-ethoxypropionic acid. In later years hydrogen iodide proved to be an excellent cleaving reagent (cf. determination of methoxy groups by the Zeisel method[22]). Constant-boiling hydrobromic acid is considered preferable to hydrogen iodide for the cleavage of *t*-butyl aryl ethers, as less than 2% of the butyl bromide formed is found to decompose to butene and hydrogen bromide[23]. The extent of cleavage found for *t*-butyl phenyl ether, *t*-butyl naphthyl ether and *t*-butyl *p*-tolyl ether, after three hours of reaction is 96·2%, 97·5% and 95·6%, respectively. Decomposition of *t*-butyl aryl ethers, resulting in formation of the respective hydroxy aromatic compounds, is observed at high temperatures under the influence of catalytic amounts of *p*-toluenesulfonic acid[24]. *t*-Butyl phenyl ethers are easily dealkylated by *p*-toluenesulfonic acid, but in contrast to the cases in which other cleavage reagents, e.g. $AlCl_3$, are used no alkylation of the aromatic nucleus is observed[25].

The cleavage of alkyl ethers has been extensively investigated by Lippert[26]. According to his results the reaction is as shown in equation (8) where the more bulky alkyl group gives the alcohol; i.e. the

$$R^1\!-\!O\!-\!R^2 + HX \longrightarrow R^1OH + R^2X \tag{8}$$

C—O bond is broken between the oxygen and the smaller alkyl group. However, bond cleavage is often observed between oxygen and tertiary alkyl groups, owing to the higher reactivity of the latter. Likewise the reaction of benzyl ethers with hydrogen halides leads to cleavage[27]. Besides being used in the form of constant-boiling aqueous acids[20], hydrogen halides can also be employed in organic solvents such as alcohols or organic acids.

Other inorganic acids are capable of splitting the ether linkage. Thus, 2-bromo-4-nitrophenetole is hydrolyzed to the corresponding phenol at 100° by 80% sulfuric acid[28]. Often only catalytic amounts of sulfuric acid are necessary, as in the case of aryl benzyl ethers in acetic anhydride[29]. Sulfuric acid in various concentrations, from dilute to strong solutions, will effect the hydrolysis of diethyl ether under normal conditions[12], or under pressure[8]. HCl and $HClO_4$ may also be used for the hydrolysis under pressure. The chlorine-catalyzed demethylation of aryl methyl ethers is regarded by the authors as an acid-catalyzed cleavage, in which the usual role of the proton is taken over by the chlorine molecule in aqueous solution (reaction 9)[30].

Similar solvolyses have been discovered by Ingold and coworkers, e.g. in the nitration of aryl methyl ethers in acetic acid[31]. Aryl vinyl ethers are decomposed to the corresponding aldehydes by 70% ethereal perchloric acid[32].

$$Cl^- \cdots Cl^+ : OCH_3 \cdots OH_2 \longrightarrow Cl^- + \underset{ClO}{\bigcirc} + CH_3OH + H^+ \xrightarrow{H_2O}$$

$$\underset{OH}{\bigcirc} + HOCl \quad (9)$$

Alkyl transfer is observed when ethers react in the presence of boron hydride and mercaptans[33]. A four-centered transition state is presumably established, in which the previously formed ether and the mercaptoborane take part (reaction 10).

$$R^1SBH_2 + R^2OR^3 \longrightarrow \underset{R^2 \cdots OR^3}{\overset{\overset{\displaystyle H}{R^1S \cdots BH}}{\vdots \quad \vdots}} \longrightarrow R^1SR^2 + BH_2OR^3 \quad (10)$$

The mechanism suggested by Gerrard[34], involving a carbonium ion, does not seem applicable in this case.

2. Cyclic ethers

Oxiranes, such as propylene oxide, react in aqueous solutions of HCl and HBr (reaction 11)[35].

$$\underset{(1)}{RCH\overset{\displaystyle O}{-\!\!\!\triangle\!\!\!-}CH_2} \xrightarrow{HX} \underset{(1)}{RCH(OH)CH_2X} + \underset{(2)}{RCHXCH_2OH} \quad (11)$$

Normally, the least-substituted carbon atom is attacked with the subsequent formation of a primary halide (1). Changes in the reaction conditions will, however, effect an increase in the yield of the abnormal product (2). Thus, the yield of the secondary halohydrin is only 11% when the reaction is carried out in ethereal HCl at $-55°$, but it increases to 44% in aqueous HCl at 83°. However, the yield of the abnormal reaction product is not solely determined by the reaction conditions. Other factors, such as steric effects and the ability of electron-donating groups to stabilize a positive charge on the adjacent carbon atom may also effect the result. This occurs according to the two possible transition states **3** and **4**, where N is the nucleophilic agent.

(3)   (4)

Ring-opening by acetic acid yields a mixture of both products[36]. On the other hand, use of phenol results in formation of the normal product. H_2SO_4 in allyl alcohol is employed for the ring opening of styrene oxide. In this case the secondary carbon atom is attacked[37]. Splitting of the primary C—O bond has been observed when phosgene[38] or acetic acid was used as the reagent[39]. In the reaction of 2,3-epoxy-2,3-dimethylbutane[39] with organic acids the abnormal product is also formed. However, it has been noted by Cohen[36] that the normal ring opening is the dominant reaction, resulting in the formation of **5**, the latter being slowly transformed into the abnormal product (**6**) under the reaction conditions (reaction 12).

This rearrangement includes an oxygen to oxygen acyl transfer as has been shown for epoxy ethers[40]. Much research on the cleavage of epoxy compounds has been carried out by Stevens[41]. The nature of the ring-opening process under the influence of various organic acids proved to be highly specific, and retention of the configuration of the carbon atom adjacent to the ether group was observed. Displacement of an acyl group followed the fission of the cyclic ethereal bond[42]. Contrary to these results, racemization occurred after ring opening of epoxy compounds when aqueous HCl or acetic acid was used[43].

Oxetanes are cleaved by nucleophilic reagents not, however, quite as easily as oxiranes. Chloro- or bromopropanol is obtained from trimethylene oxide and aqueous HCl or HBr[44] and an A2 mechanism is assumed. On the other hand, an A1 mechanism was deduced for the cleavage of trimethylene oxide by Long and coworkers[45] from the value of the entropy of activation which was found to be

$\Delta S = -3 \cdot 9$ cal/deg mole. 2-Methyloxethane reacts with HCl to yield 94% of the primary and 6% of the secondary halide, but in the case of 2-phenyloxethane cleavage of the 1,2-bond results in formation of 3-chloro-3-phenyl-1-propanol[44]. Ring enlargement is observed in the case of 2-oxaspiro[3.4]hexane which yields cyclobutane in dilute hydrochloric acid at 0°. The ring system seems to enhance the migration aptitude of a carbon atom with its electron pair in the carbonium ion transition state (reaction 13)[46].

$$\tag{13}$$

Dry hydrogen bromide in benzene does not bring about ring enlargement, the only consequence of the reaction being simple bond fission. Obviously, solvation of the ions by benzene is too slight (reaction 14).

$$\tag{14}$$

1,2-Ring opening takes place easily when the oxetanes are substituted at $C_{(3)}$. In these cases the normal reaction is observed; e.g. a primary halide is formed when HCl reacts with 3,3-diethyloxetane[47].

Five-membered cyclic ethers undergo ring opening under acidic conditions. Tetrahydrofuran should therefore yield the corresponding 1,4-derivative[48]. According to recent results, the dihalide can be obtained by reaction with thionyl chloride in the presence of $ZnCl_2$, whereas the reaction of tetrahydrofuran with HCl at room temperature results mainly in the formation of 4-chloro-1-butanol[49]. 2-Phenyltetrahydrofuran is split in acetic acid–acetic anhydride solution in the presence of catalytic amounts of $HClO_4$[50].

Like 1,2-oxiranes, 1,4-oxiranes react with dilute acids. 1,4-Epoxy-1,4-dihydronaphthalene isomerizes quantitatively into 1-naphthol (reaction 15)[51]. The 4-methyl-substituted compound reacts in exactly

$$(15)$$

the same manner[52]. Yet, when both the 1- and 4-positions are methylated, 2-naphthols are formed by isomerization (reaction 16)[53].

$$(16)$$

C. Further Investigations of Mechanisms

Criteria concerning the reaction mechanisms, and derivations from kinetic data, have been summarized in section II.A. A more detailed account of studies, leading to the present state of knowledge of acid hydrolysis through kinetic and analytical data, is given in this section.

I. Acyclic ethers

Even in concentrated acids, the cleavage rate of acyclic ethers is very small[2]. The half-life value for diethyl ether in the reaction with 1 mole of p-toluenesulfonic acid at 25° is 903,000 years; this was calculated by Skrabal[4,54].

Successful rate measurements of the reaction of ethers with hydrogen bromide in acetic acid[27] were carried out by Hughes and Ingold[55] who found that when an ether contains two primary groups, the splitting will proceed via the $A2$ mechanism, while the presence of a secondary or a tertiary group will cause a shift to the $A1$ route.

Further information is available through Burwell's work[56]. Cleavage of optically active s-butyl methyl ethers with HBr at 50° results in formation of methyl bromide and s-butyl alcohol with retained configuration. Consequently, the splitting of the methyl–oxygen bond seems to occur either through a dialkyl hydronium ion or via formation of a nonionized complex, i.e. by an S_N2 mechanism.

Naturally the splitting of unsymmetrical ethers is of competitive character as shown in reaction (17). Besides the conjugate acid $R^1R^2OH^+$, the negative ion $BrHBr^-$ is formed. The rates of these competitive reactions, relative to the value obtained for the ethyl group, are given in Table 3[20].

$$R^1OR^2 + HBr \longrightarrow (R^2Br,\ R^1Br) + (R^1OH,\ R^2OH) \tag{17}$$

No accurate kinetic results are available regarding these cases. It is assumed by the authors that 10% of the reaction is completed after 5 to 6 minutes with n-butyl methyl ether, as opposed to 110 minutes needed to affect isobutyl n-butyl ether to the same extent. The first five ethers listed react via an $A2$ mechanism; the following three cleave via the $A1$ reaction. No mechanistic conclusions can yet be derived regarding secondary ethers, although the authors presume that to a considerable extent an $A1$ mechanism is involved.

TABLE 3. Relative rates of cleavage of aliphatic ethers with anhydrous HBr at 26°, according to Burwell[20].

Ether	Relative rates of cleavage
Butyl ethyl ether	1·0
Butyl propyl ether	1·0
Butyl methyl ether	11·1
Isobutyl propyl ether	0·053
Isobutyl butyl ether	0·93
Isopropyl propyl ether	0·87
Cyclopentyl propyl ether	3·8
3-Pentyl propyl ether	4·2

The rate equation (18) is valid for the cleavage of diethyl ether by HBr in chlorobenzene, toluene and chloroform[57]. The reaction is

$$-\frac{d\,[(C_2H_5)_2O]}{dt} = k[HBr]^2[(C_2H_5)_2O] \tag{18}$$

accelerated when alcohol is added, the expression being altered to give

$$-\frac{d\,[(C_2H_5)_2O]}{dt} = k'[HBr][(C_2H_5)_2O][C_2H_5OH] \tag{19}$$

equation (19). Quite a different interdependence is obtained in chloroform (equation 20).

$$-\frac{d\,[(C_2H_5)_2O]}{dt} = k''\,[HBr]^{\frac{3}{2}}[(C_2H_5)_2O]^{\frac{3}{2}} \qquad (20)$$

The same reaction orders for the various reactants have been found for the reaction of benzyl phenyl ether with HBr in nitrobenzene[58]. The initial reaction rates have been measured up to 10% reaction, and a rate coefficient has been obtained of $k_3 = 0.058$ (l^2/mole^2 min) at 25°. It has been suggested that formation of a complex (7) takes place as a first step in the cleavage reaction, with the subsequent rate-determining step being an S_N2 attack by a further HBr molecule at the methylene carbon (reaction 21). Hoffmeister's

$$PhCH_2OPh + HBr \rightleftharpoons PhCH_2 \quad\quad HBr \xrightarrow{HBr} PhCH_2Br + PhOH + HBr \qquad (21)$$

$$O$$

$$Ph$$

$$(7)$$

results do, in fact, support this mechanism[59]. He found that diphenyl ether is stable to hydrogen bromide. In contrast to the results in chloroform quoted above the mechanism for the benzyl ether cleavage becomes more complicated and the rate diminishes. Whereas for the initial rates no change of order is observed, in the case of the acid a complex interrelationship has been found, namely, that an increase in concentration brings about an increase in order. Substituted ammonium bromide catalysts do not affect the kinetics. A stable R_3NHBr–HBr complex seems to be present, which may influence both the attacking and departing ions. The rate equation is shown by equation (22), where [HBr] is the concentration of hydrogen bromide

$$-\frac{d\,[HBr]}{dt} = k'\,[HBr]^2\,[ether] \qquad (22)$$

not bound in the complex. Overall second-order kinetics are observed in the gas-phase reaction of *t*-butyl methyl ether with HBr at temperatures ranging from 255–371°. The rate coefficient is proportional to the pressure[60].

According to Burwell, the first step in the cleavage reactions involves the formation of an oxonium ion which subsequently dissociates into a carbonium ion and an alcohol or phenol molecule[56]. Thereby racemization, and to a small extent inversion, are observed alongside the C—O bond splitting. The second step may also be a bimolecular nucleophilic substitution with inversion by an alcohol or phenol. This obviously includes inversion as well. This suggested S_N2 mechanism cannot be considered altogether valid based on the recent work on the hydrolysis of optically active ethers with hydrochloric acid. Considering his experiments with α-phenylethyl aryl ethers Burwell suggested a somewhat different mechanism which yields phenylethyl chloride. The latter will retain its configuration of at least 38% optical purity (reaction 23) [61]. Reactions have been carried out in the neat substance as

$$
\text{Cl}^- \rightarrow \underset{\underset{\text{CH}_3}{|}}{\overset{\overset{+}{\text{HOC}_6\text{H}_5}}{\underset{|}{\overset{|}{\text{C}}}}} \text{—H} \quad \longrightarrow \quad \underset{\underset{\text{CH}_3}{\diagdown}}{\overset{\overset{\text{Cl}}{|}}{\text{C}}} \text{—H} + \text{C}_6\text{H}_5\text{OH} \qquad (23)
$$

well as in solutions of benzene, acetone and dibutyl ether. Further experiments have shown that cleavage of optically active α-phenylethyl phenyl ethers with hydrogen chloride at 40° results in 85–80% retention [62]. An S_N2 ion-pair mechanism is assumed; the author designates it as an S_Ni mechanism. This contradicts the mechanism proposed for the hydrolysis of benzyl ethers [58], which demands inversion of the aliphatic carbon atom of the benzyl group; in the phenylethyl system inversion is not observed. Both are first-order reactions. The influence of solvents is shown in Table 4, which gives the increase in the rate coefficient k_2 with ascending values of dielectric constants of the solvents.

TABLE 4. Rate coefficients k_2 obtained for the cleavage of α-phenylethyl phenyl ether with HCl at 40° in solvents having various dielectric constants.

Solvent	$10^5 k_2$ (l/mole sec)	Dielectric constant
Toluene	$1 \cdot 33 \pm 0 \cdot 05$	$2 \cdot 379$ (25°)
3-Pentanone	$2 \cdot 41 \pm 0 \cdot 03$	$17 \cdot 0$ (20°)
2-Methylpropanol	$3 \cdot 23 \pm 0 \cdot 12$	$15 \cdot 8$ (25°)

The results described above are further supported by the fact that cis- and trans-oxiranes [63] undergo acid cleavage with retention of configuration. cis- and trans-stilbene oxides yield the expected threo- and

2 + C.E.L.

erythro-chlorohydrin, presumably through an oxonium ion-pair intermediate (reaction 24).

$$(24)$$

Most alkyl aryl ethers resist acid-catalyzed hydrolysis. Azophenyl ethers are split by dilute or moderately concentrated acids. A protonated azo group seems to make a nucleophilic aromatic substitution of the ether possible[13,14]. This reaction was discovered as early as 1892[64]. Unlike the normal ether cleavages, this reaction proceeds swiftly in dilute or moderately concentrated acids, and does not need the use of strongly nucleophilic anions like bromide and iodide. 4-(*p*-Sulfophenylazo)-1-naphthyl methyl ether and 4-(sulfophenylazo)-anisole were split in hydrochloric acid and perchloric acid, respectively. The reactions were found to be of first order in the ethers. Table 5 shows the pseudo first-order rate coefficients.

TABLE 5. Dependence of the rate coefficients k_1 of the hydrolysis of naphthyl ether at 46·0° and phenyl ether at 95·1° on the acid concentration.

Naphthyl ether		Phenyl ether	
$HClO_4$ (mole/l)	$10^2 k_1$ (l/sec)	$HClO_4$ (mole/l)	$10^4 k_1$ (l/sec)
0·13	0·166	1·0	1·38
2·14	1·421	3·85	4·1
4·10	0·357	5·95	1·00
HCl (mole/l)		HCl (mole/l)	
1·02	1·08	1·01	1·49
2·54	2·15	5·08	12·6
8·12	0·142	9·30	2·23

Bunnett's parameters[65] for the azonaphthyl methyl ether are $w = +8\cdot2$, $w^* = +0\cdot9$ in $HClO_4$ and $w = +4\cdot5$, $w^* = -0\cdot9$ in HCl. The intermediate (**8**) formed by the attack of water on an aromatic carbon subsequently yields the naphthol.

$$Ar\!-\!\underset{\underset{H}{|}}{N}\!-\!N\!=\!\!\left\langle\!=\!\!\right\rangle\!\!\begin{smallmatrix}OCH_3\\OH_2^+\end{smallmatrix}$$

(**8**)

The values for azophenyl methyl ether are $w = +4\cdot9$, $w^* = -0\cdot93$ in $HClO_4$ and $w = +2\cdot8$, $w^* = -2\cdot2$ in HCl. In order to account for these low values an S_N2 mechanism was suggested, which involves a nucleophilic attack on the alkyl carbon atom (**9**).

$$Ar\!-\!\overset{+}{\underset{\underset{H}{|}}{N}}\!=\!N\!-\!\!\left\langle\!=\!\!\right\rangle\!-\!O\cdots CH_3 \cdots OH_2$$

(**9**)

In this case bond fission should take place between the alkyl group and the oxygen atom[14], but evidence for the previously proposed mechanism is provided by hydrolysis studies in $H_2{}^{18}O$. The azonaphthol formed is indeed the carrier of the ^{18}O atoms, proving that splitting of the aryl–oxygen bond occurs[13]. Obviously, the same should hold true for phenyl ether.

Results dealing with cleavage of alkoxy ethers of heteroaromatic compounds indicate a prevailing attack on the aromatic carbon atom. Nucleophilic attack on the aliphatic carbon atom also occurs to a minor extent. α- or γ-Alkoxypyrimidines are more susceptible to acid hydrolysis than the corresponding carbocyclic compounds, owing to easier nucleophilic displacement on the former than on the latter[65]. As in the case of azoaryl ethers two reaction routes are possible, namely, either a nucleophilic attack on the α- or γ-position followed by the elimination of the available functional group, or the heterolytic fission of the alkyl–oxygen bond. In order to decide between the alternatives 2-methoxy-^{18}O-pyrimidine was chosen as the starting material. If the hydrolysis occurs through a nucleophilic attack on the aromatic ring $CH_3{}^{18}OH$ should be produced. Hydrolysis with sulfuric acid at 105°, or with hydrochloric acid at 100°, gave yields of about

75% after 4 hours. The methanol produced indeed contained 91·8% of the ^{18}O. Yet the remaining 8·2% of the ^{18}O present in the other reaction product clearly indicates that the alternative reaction route does also operate[66]. The high polarizability of the C—O bond of the methoxy group in the pyrimidinium ether makes the compound accessible to a nucleophilic attack (reaction 25).

(25)

The rate of hydrolysis of 3,5-dihydroxy-1-methoxybenzene and of 1,3,5-trimethoxybenzene exhibits a pronounced dependence on the acidity. The reaction is strongly accelerated when the acidity is increased. Presumably[18] monoprotonation takes place at lower acid concentrations, while diprotonation appears at higher acidities. This interdependence of rate and acidity is shown in Table 6 which, however, does not give all measurements.

TABLE 6. Dependence on acid concentration of the rate coefficients k_1 for 3,5-dihydroxy-1-methoxybenzene and for 1,3,5-trimethoxybenzene.

3,5-Dihydroxy-1-methoxy-benzene 50°		1,3,5-Trimethoxybenzene			
		60°		90°	
% $HClO_4$	$10^4 k_1$ (l/sec)	% $HClO_4$	$10^4 k_1$ (l/sec)	% $HClO_4$	$10^4 k_1$ (l/sec)
50	1·88	52·4	1·20	44·7	1·20
58	8·91	57·9	8·10	50·2	9·59
63·5	24·9	61·2	30·4	54·2	36·0

The w-value obtained for the 1-methoxy ether is $+2\cdot0$. This value lies in the range assumed for reactions where water may act as a nucleophile in the rate-determining step, but it is lower than those found by Bunnett. No accurate results are available for the 1,3,5-trimethoxy ether. As pointed out by the authors, the values in this case generally tend to be positive. Tracer studies using ^{18}O have shown that the aryl–oxygen bond is cleaved. From the results of Long and Paul[5] and the substantially negative value obtained for the entropy of activation, $\Delta S^{\ddagger}\ (25°) = -15\cdot2$ cal/deg mole, it has been suggested that the reaction is of the $A2$ type, although the two-proton step will mean a certain restriction on the reaction in this case.

As previously shown for the hydrolysis of diethyl ether, negative values of volumes of activation suggest an $A2$ mechanism. The measurements were carried out at pressures up to 3000 atm and at temperatures from 120–160°. Table 7 represents the dependence of the second-order rate coefficients on pressure at $161\cdot2°$ in a $0\cdot099$ M solution of perchloric acid.

TABLE 7. Dependence on
pressure of the rate
coefficients k_2.

p(atm)	$10^5 k_2$ (l/mole sec)
50	$8\cdot1$
400	$7\cdot9$
1000	$10\cdot2$
2000	$11\cdot2$
3000	$13\cdot2$

Temperature also affects the reaction rate. At 50 atm and a concentration of $0\cdot19$ M the second-order rate coefficient changes from $1\cdot46 \times 10^{-6}$ to 75×10^{-6} l/mole sec when the temperature increases from 119 to $161\cdot2°$. The experimental error is of the order of 10%. The entropy of activation is $-9\cdot0 \pm 2\cdot5$ cal/deg mole, and the volume of activation is $-8\cdot5 \pm 2$ ml/mole at $161\cdot2°$ and 1 atm.

The overall rate of the solvolysis of alkyl ethers in concentrated sulfuric acid is proportional to the sulfur trioxide concentration. It has been proposed by Jaques and Leisten[67] that the reaction consists of a two-stage mechanism. First a preequilibrium is established in which a complex is formed between the sulfur trioxide and the conjugate acid of the ether (reaction 26). This is then followed by heterolysis into a

$$R^1R^2OH^+ + SO_3 \longrightarrow [R^1R^2SO_4H]^+ \qquad (26)$$

carbonium ion and alkyl hydrogen sulfate. Constitutional factors influence this stage (reaction 27). The carbonium ion reacts rapidly with

$$R^1 \overset{+}{\underset{SO_3H}{\overset{}{O}}} R^2 \longrightarrow R^{1+} + R^2HSO_4 \tag{27}$$

another hydrogen sulfate ion. The solvolysis in 99·6% sulfuric acid fits the overall equation (28). It has been possible to follow the reaction by

$$R^1R^2O + 3\,H_2SO_4 \longrightarrow R^1HSO_4 + R^2HSO_4 + H_3O^+ + HSO_4^- \tag{28}$$

measuring the change of the freezing-point depression; the first-order rate coefficients obtained are shown in Table 8.

TABLE 8. Rate coefficients k_1 in 99·6% sulfuric acid.

Ether	10^3k_1 (l/min)	Temp. (°c)
Dimethyl ether	3·41	90
Ethyl methyl ether	13·8	55
2-Chloromethyl methyl ether	3·4	65
Diethyl ether	6·93	55
2,2'-Dichlorodiethyl ether	4·96	65
Ethyl 2-ethylsulfonyl ether	24·2	55
n-Dibutyl ether	6·0	25
Diisopropyl ether	40·0	25
n-Butyl methyl ether	16·0	25

A comparison of constitutional influences shows that dimethyl ether reaches at 90° a rate similar to that of n-butyl methyl ether at 25°. It can also be seen from Table 8 that the stability of the carbonium ion diminishes in the order: isopropyl, n-butyl, ethyl, 2-chloroethyl, 2-ethylsulphenyl and methyl. In the mixed ethers mentioned in Table 8 it is always the first group which appears as a carbonium ion in the reaction.

Alkyl aryl ethers split by a simple $A1$ mechanism, where heterolysis of the conjugate acid occurs. The observed orders are very similar to those found in alkyl ether cleavage. Under the same reaction conditions used for the alkyl ethers, the rate coefficients for 2,4-dinitroanisole and 2,4-dinitrophenetole were found to be $k_1 = 32·1 \times 10^{-3}$ l/min at 85° and $k_1 = 38·7 \times 10^{-3}$ l/min at 25·6°, respectively. It can be concluded that bond fission takes place between the oxygen and the alkyl group. However, the values of the freezing-point depression support a simple mechanism with formation of phenol, and not of phenyl hydrogen sulfate (reaction 29).

$$R\text{—}O\text{—}Ar + H_2SO_4 \longrightarrow RHSO_4 + ArOH \qquad (29)$$

The rate coefficients for the hydrolysis of diethyl ether are shown in Table 9. The maximum should lie at the point where the pK value for the oxonium ion is -3.5. This is not the case, and therefore a shift from $A2$ to an $A1$ mechanism has been assumed at high acid concentrations[12]. Additional data[8] support this shift of mechanism: in the hydrolysis of diethyl ether the rate coefficients ($10^3 k_1$ (1/min)) are found to increase from 0.92 in H_2SO_4 containing no SO_3, to 250 in H_2SO_4 containing 1.24% SO_3, whereas only an increase from 3.11 to 5.03 is observed in 60.6 and 72.2% perchloric acid, respectively. By plotting Bunnett's constants in the range of 61 to 90% sulfuric acid, the authors assumed that the terminal slopes point to an $A2$ mechanism, but this is not conclusive evidence for the case discussed.

TABLE 9. Dependence of the rate coefficients k_1 of the hydrolysis of $(C_2H_5)_2O$ on the acid concentration.

%H_2SO_4	$10^3 k_1$ (1/min)	Temp. (°c)
61	0.43	94.7
71.4	1.97	94.7
75.4	3.06	94.7
80.2	4.84	94.7
84.4	5.53	94.7
90.0	5.71	94.7
95.3	13.1	94.7
98.4	68.6	94.7
98.4	9.30	74.8
98.4	1.01	54.8
99.9	26.3	54.8
100.0	57.8	54.8

A unimolecular S_N1 cleavage is presumed in the reaction of *para*-substituted *t*-butyl phenyl ethers with HCl at 70° and HBr at 19° in phenol–dioxane solutions[68]. The reaction is first order in both the ether and the hydrogen halide. The coefficient k_2 reaches higher values when the phenol content increases.

For the hydrolysis of vinyl ethers in acidic solutions a rate-determining step consisting of carbonium ion formation is suggested (reaction 30). Use of $H_2^{18}O$ has proved[69] that in the acid hydrolysis of

$$CH{-}OR \atop \underset{CH_2}{\|} \quad + H_3O^+ \longrightarrow \quad \begin{matrix} CH{-}OR \\ \| \\ CH_2\cdots H\cdots O \end{matrix} \begin{matrix} H \\ / \\ \diagdown \\ H \end{matrix} \longrightarrow \quad CH_3\overset{+}{C}HOR \longrightarrow$$

$$H_2O + CH_3CHO + ROH + H_3O^+ \quad (30)$$

alkyl vinyl ethers the alkyl–oxygen bond is not severed. Dilute sulfuric acid was used for the splitting of ethyl, isopropyl and butyl vinyl ethers; the alcohol formed contained no ^{18}O. A possible intermediate is the hemiacetal (10). The rate coefficients for the acid hydrolysis of

$$\underset{OH}{\overset{RCH_2CHOR}{|}}$$

(10)

vinyl ethers with $HClO_4$ in dioxane–water solution are given in Table 10[70].

TABLE 10. Rate coefficient k_2 for vinyl ethers ($CH_2{=}CHOR$) at 25°.

R in $CH_2{=}CHOR$	$10^4 k_2$ (l/mole sec)
t-Butyl	3885
Isopropyl	1557
Ethyl	530
Isobutyl	409
n-Butyl	366
Tolyl	81

The high reactivity of the vinyl ethers is explained by a mesomeric effect, which results in the β-carbon atom of the vinyl group obtaining a partial negative charge, enabling easy protonation. An electron-donating alkyl group increases this effect.

Naturally, the hydrolysis rate diminishes under the influence of groups which oppose the mesomeric effect. Thus, at 25°, k_2 (l/mole sec) for $CH_2{=}C(CH_3)OC_2H_5$ is found to be $1{\cdot}031 \times 10^{-7}$ compared to 91×10^4 for $C_2H_5CH{=}CHOC_2H_5$.

The exact picture of the mechanism of vinyl ether hydrolysis seems still somewhat elusive. 2-Ethoxy-1-cyclopentene-1-carboxylic acid reacted with hydrochloric acid in the pH range from 1·85 to 7·0. The second-order rate coefficients for the hydrolysis of this ether at 30° in dioxane–water are shown in Table 11.

TABLE 11. Rate coefficients for 2-ethoxy-1-cyclopentene-1-carboxylic acid at various pH values in H_2O and D_2O at 30°.

	H_2O	D_2O
pH < 3, k_2 (1/mole min)	13·2	4·57
pH > 3, k_2 (1/mole min)	2762	1140
Uncatalyzed k_1 (1/min)	6·33 × 10^{-3}	7·71 × 10^{-3}

It can be seen from these values that at a relatively low pH, where the carboxylic acid may be considered undissociated, the reaction is catalyzed by hydronium ions[71].

The ratio of k_{D_2O}/k_{H_2O} (0·35) is too low to distinguish between an $A2$ and an $A1$ mechanism. As a rule in the case of an $A2$ mechanism, when the protonated intermediate is attacked by a water molecule to yield the products, the reaction should be accelerated by a factor from 1·4 to 1·7 when D_2O is used instead of H_2O (reaction 31). The $\Delta S^{\ddagger}$

$$(31)$$

value of $-14·5$ cal/deg mole suggests an $A2$ mechanism. At high pH values, the rate-determining step consists either of protonation of the anion by a hydronium ion or, alternatively, protonation takes place simultaneously with the nucleophilic attack by the anion, as an anion-catalyzed reaction according to reaction (32). From the kinetic point of view these two possibilities cannot be distinguished.

$$(32)$$

2*

No results are available regarding the substituent effects on the rate of hydrolysis of alkyl aryl ethers. The splitting of halogen-substituted phenoxyacetic acids with hydroiodic acid shows only a small substituent effect (Table 12) [72].

TABLE 12. Rate coefficients k_1 for substituted phenoxy-acetic acids.

Substituent	10^6k_1 at 100° (l/sec)	10^6k_1 at 115° (l/sec)
Unsubstituted	2·23	10·85
2-Fluoro-	2·23	9·14
4-Fluoro-	2·36	10·87
2,4-Difluoro-	2·42	10·14
2-Chloro-	2·01	8·90
4-Chloro-	1·74	7·61
2,4-Dichloro-	1·61	6·68

The rates are of the same order as those for the hydrolysis of chloro- and bromoanisole with aqueous HCl at 120° in acetic acid [73].

2. Cyclic ethers

Based on recent results an $A2$ mechanism has been suggested for the acid-catalyzed cleavage of oxiranes. An account of the different opinions on this subject seems appropriate here. As in the case of diethyl ether, an equilibrium is established between the oxirane and its conjugate acid. The latter is more reactive than the oxirane and consequently the reaction occurs by an $A1$ or an $A2$ mechanism (Scheme 1).

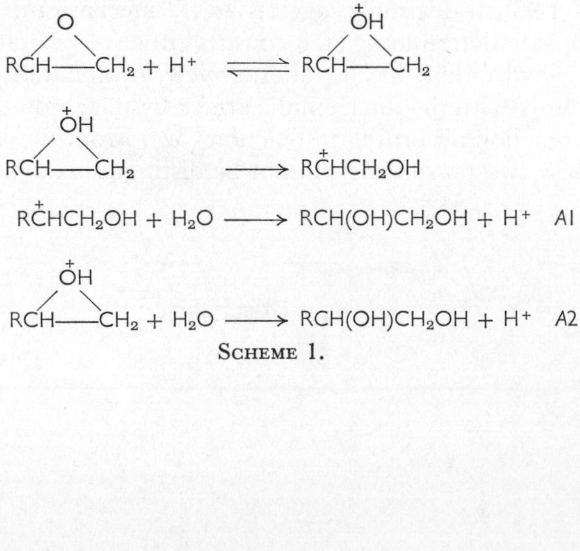

SCHEME 1.

An $A1$ mechanism is favored by the results of Long and coworkers[74], and by consideration of the Hammett relationship. In the cleavage of ten simple oxiranes with $HClO_4$ the first-order rate coefficients when plotted against H_0 offer evidence for an $A1$ reaction, since the slopes obtained have values between 0·86 and 1·06. These results ought to be referred to with a certain amount of scepticism as unsymmetrical oxiranes seldom yield a single product. Moreover, experiments with substituted oxiranes resulted in inversion, a fact that strongly suggests an $A2$ mechanism[75].

The method used in the case of acyclic ethers for determination of the reaction mechanism through the values of activation entropies encounters difficulties in the present case. The values obtained for the hydrolysis of ethylene oxide, propylene oxide and isobutylene oxide are $\Delta S^{\ddagger} = -6·1$, $-4·3$ and -4 cal/deg mole, respectively[45]. These values give no clear evidence for either mechanism, since the values expected for $A1$ and $A2$ reactions are $\Delta S^{\ddagger} = 0$ to $+10$ cal/deg mole and $\Delta S^{\ddagger} = -15$ to -30 cal/deg mole, respectively. Consequently, the result was considered to fit a modified $A2$ step. The ratio of K_{D_2O}/K_{H_2O} of 1·9 to 2·2 favors an $A1$ mechanism[76], since acceleration of solvolysis in D_2O is generally taken as evidence for an $A1$ mechanism.

In the hydrolysis of epichlorohydrin with aqueous sulfuric acid a change in the unimolecular process is observed on the addition of alcohol[17]. Consideration of the solvent composition and of the acidity gives another criterion for determining the mechanism[77]. Plotting the appropriate parameters yields a linear relationship in the case of an $A1$ mechanism. Since a parabolic curve is obtained for the epichlorohydrin reaction, it is assumed by the authors that an $A1$ step does not fit this case. Either a solvent molecule or an additional nucleophile takes part in the ring opening (reaction 33).

$$\tag{33}$$

Further objections concerning the applicability of the Hammett equation have been expressed by Whalley[6,8], who examined the hydrolysis of oxiranes under pressure[10]. As mentioned already[78], a negative volume of activation is expected for an $A2$ reaction as a result of the simultaneous shortening of the C—O bond and the decrease in distance between the carbon atom and the solvent molecule in the transition state. Lengthening of the C—O bond in the $A1$ transition state results in a positive value. The hydrolysis is carried out with 0·002 to 0·01 M $HClO_4$ at 0 to 40° and at pressures up to 3000 atm. For ethylene oxide a value of $\Delta S^\ddagger = -7\cdot5$ cal/deg mole has been calculated for the entropy of activation, which corresponds with Long's[45] result. The rate coefficients found for the hydrolyses at 0° are $0\cdot526 \times 10^{-3}$ for ethylene oxide and $2\cdot48 \times 10^{-3}$ l/mole sec for propylene oxide. From the negative values of the activation volumes it is concluded that an $A2$ mechanism operates (cf. Table 1).

The hydrolysis of epichlorohydrin and trimethylene oxide with $HClO_4$ at 25° and at pressures up to 7000 atm exhibits the characteristic features of an $A2$ displacement reaction. The activation volumes, calculated from the rate coefficients (first order in ether), are $\Delta V^\ddagger = -5\cdot5 \pm 3$ ml/mole for trimethylene oxide and $\Delta V^\ddagger = -8\cdot5 \pm 3$ ml/mole for epichlorohydrin[11]. These results seem plausible considering that large cyclic molecules undergo a volume diminution of 7 to 10 ml/mole[79].

Detailed kinetic studies on the product formation in the hydrolysis have been carried out with propylene oxide[18]. The latter reacts with chloride ions in water–dioxane mixtures, in acid and neutral media, to yield both isomers, 1-chloropropanol and 2-chloropropanol. The results obtained are shown in Table 13.

TABLE 13. pH dependency of the rate coefficients k_2 at 40°.

pH	$10^6 k_2$	$10^6 k_n$ (l/mole sec)	$10^6 k_a$ (l/mole sec)	% Product Normal	Abnormal
7·0	21·4	18·4	3·0	86	14
4·5	43·7	31·5	12·2	72	28
3·8	151	97	54	64	36
3·6	226	145	81	64	36

From the equations (34) and (35), where the subscript n stands for

$$k_n = k_{wn} + k_{hn}[H^+] \tag{34}$$

$$k_a = k_{wa} + k_{ha}[H^+] \tag{35}$$

normal, a for abnormal, w for water, h for acid, the k_w and k_h values are obtainable. The two possible intermediates **11** and **12** result

$$
\begin{array}{cc}
\overset{\delta+}{O}H & \overset{\delta+}{O}H \\
CH_3\overset{\cdots}{CH}\!\!-\!\!\overset{\delta+}{CH_2} & CH_3\overset{\delta+}{CH}\!\!-\!\!CH_2 \\
\vdots & \vdots \\
Cl^{\delta-} & Cl^{\delta+} \\
\textbf{(11)} & \textbf{(12)}
\end{array}
$$

from a bimolecular reaction between the chloride anion and the pro-tonated oxirane. The intermediates for the uncatalyzed reaction are **13** and **14**.

$$
\begin{array}{cc}
\overset{\delta-}{O} & \overset{\delta-}{O} \\
CH_3\overset{\cdots}{CH}\!\!-\!\!\overset{\delta+}{CH_2} & CH_3\overset{\delta+}{CH}\!\!-\!\!CH_2 \\
\vdots & \vdots \\
Cl^{\delta-} & Cl^{\delta-} \\
\textbf{(13)} & \textbf{(14)}
\end{array}
$$

It is suggested, on the basis of kinetic results, that both the normal and abnormal reactions should be considered as borderline cases of an $S_N 2$ mechanism with respect to the rate-determining step. The same borderline $S_N 2$ mechanism should also hold true for the uncatalyzed reaction, but with an intermediate which is even more different from that in an $S_N 1$ step. Thus it has been concluded that in the inter-mediate of the neutral reaction partial bonds exist between C—Cl and C—O shorter than those in the intermediate of the acid-catalyzed reaction.

Substituent effects have been kinetically estimated for the hydrolysis of substituted 1,2-oxiranes in acetic acid, using an HBr–pyridine complex[80]. Half-life values have been calculated from the second-order rate coefficients. For epoxysuccinonitrile the value of 65 minutes has been found and for epoxysuccinamide 1975.

Kinetic measurements concerning the polar effects of substituents on the ring opening of simple oxiranes are also available[81]. The rate co-efficients were determined under neutral conditions and in the pre-sence of HCl at 40°. Under neutral conditions electron-attracting substituents accelerate the normal reaction and slow down the ab-normal one. Hence for epichlorohydrin with $\sigma = +1.05$, k_n is found to be 6.3×10^{-5}, and k_a to be 0.13×10^{-5} l/mole sec. Contrary to this the values of k_n and k_a for propylene oxide with $\sigma = \pm 0$ are 1.84×10^{-5} and 0.3×10^{-5} l/mole sec, respectively. In acid media both normal and abnormal reactions are slower, hence, both reactions have a negative polar reaction coefficient. For both the normal and the abnormal reactions an S_N2 borderline description seems likely for the rate-determining step. The overall reaction may be classified as a borderline $A2$ case.

III. BASE-CATALYZED CLEAVAGE

A. Mechanism

Kinetic results on the base-catalyzed cleavage of acyclic ethers are comparatively rare. In reactions (36) the second step is rate determining. The overall rate is given by equation (37).

$$
\begin{aligned}
\text{HS} + \text{B} &\rightleftharpoons \text{S}^- + \text{BH}^+ \\
\text{S}^- + \text{R} &\longrightarrow \text{Products}
\end{aligned}
\tag{36}
$$

$$
v = k[\text{S}^-][\text{R}] = kK\frac{[\text{SH}][\text{B}][\text{R}]}{[\text{BH}^+]}
\tag{37}
$$

For the base-catalyzed splitting of oxirane an anionic mechanism was suggested by Ingold[82]. This is strongly supported by the observed first-order dependence on the catalyst concentration. In measurements carried out by Parker[83] on the reaction of benzylamine and styrene oxide in alcohol bimolecular cleavage was also postulated. The same conclusion was made by Whalley[84] who found a negative volume of activation ($\Delta V^{\ddagger} = -7\cdot0$ ml/mole) for the reaction of ethylene oxide at 60°, as expected for a bimolecular reaction. The ionic ring opening can be written as in reaction (38).

$$
\underset{\text{CH}_2}{\overset{\text{CH}_2}{\diagdown}}\!\!\diagup\text{O} \xrightarrow{+\text{OH}^-} \underset{\text{CH}_2\text{O}^-}{\overset{\text{CH}_2\text{OH}}{|}} \xrightarrow{+\text{H}_2\text{O}} \underset{\text{CH}_2\text{OH}}{\overset{\text{CH}_2\text{OH}}{|}} + \text{OH}^-
\tag{38}
$$

The studies of Patat and coworkers[85] indicate that the ring opening is a multicentered reaction. Investigation of the addition of ethylene oxide and propylene oxide to phenols, in the presence of alkali phenolates or amines as catalysts, has shown that the reaction passes through a transition state in which all the reactants take part. Measurements of dielectric constants, infrared absorption spectra, vapor-pressure and conductivity on the oxirane–phenol-catalyst system have been carried out, and the results support the suggestion previously based on kinetic studies that the reaction may be formulated as in reaction (39).

According to Patat[86], the first step of the addition of ethylene oxide to phenol demonstrates a general rule concerning ethylene oxide condensations. According to this, the classification of the additions into anionic and cationic reactions is a purely formal one, and both can be explained by the formation of a basically identical complex. This opinion is also presented in the studies of Ishii[87]. An example of a nonionic ring opening is the addition of ethylene oxide to Lewis acids[88,89].

B. Methods of Cleavage

I. Acyclic ethers

Alkyl ethers are stable to alkaline hydrolysis. Alkyl phenyl ethers react with potassium hydroxide in ethanol. Nevertheless, the cleavage demands quite drastic conditions. Anisole gives a 15% yield of phenol at 180–200° in excess KOH[90] after 15 hours, while a 20% KOH solution in ethanol gives 7% cleavage after 7 hours[91]. The tendency of alkyl aryl ethers to react under alkaline conditions increases under the influence of electron-attracting substituents on the aromatic ring, such as chloro, bromo and nitro groups[2,92,93]. Similarly, the splitting of alkyl aryl ethers is also made easier by the effect of substituents on the alkyl part of the molecule. After heating glycidyl guaiacyl ether for 2 hours at 170° with 2 N NaOH, an 80% yield of guaiacol is obtained, the cleavage product being practically stable in the reaction conditions[94]. In the case of the cleavage of β-hydroxyalkyl aryl ethers the formation of an intermediate oxirane compound is postulated. The cleavage, in

2 N KOH, of diphenyl ethers in which one aromatic nucleus carries three adjacent hydroxy groups is especially easy. The suggested mechanism is a β-elimination[95]. In liquid ammonia 2- and 4-nitrophenyl benzyl ether were cleaved by sodium hydroxide with subsequent formation of benzyl alcohol[96]. Unsubstituted ethers are also indifferent to amines. Nitro groups increase the cleavage of alkyl aryl ethers in aqueous ammonia[97]. Kinetic data are available concerning the cleavage of methyl picryl ether by dimethylaniline at room temperature[98]. Here the aryl–oxygen bond is split.

There are, as yet, few works which deal with the reaction between ethers and amide ions. Phenyl ethers are cleaved by sodamide in boiling pyridine to yield the corresponding phenols[99]. During studies on the stereochemistry of electrophilic substitution benzyl ethers have been treated with potassium N-methylanilide in methylaniline solution[100]. It has been found that 2-benzyloxy-2-phenylbutane yielded 2-phenylbutane. This reaction occurred with retention of configuration and with a stereospecifity of at least 26%.

In general the base-catalyzed cleavage of benzyl ethers can occur in two directions, the first corresponding to reaction (40). This mechan-

$$
\begin{array}{c}
CH_3 \\
C_2H_5 \rightarrow \overset{\cdot}{C}OCH_2C_6H_5 + H{-}B \longrightarrow \\
C_6H_5 \; B^-
\end{array}
$$

$$
\begin{array}{c}
CH_3 \quad\quad\quad\quad H \\
C_2H_5 \rightarrow CH + O{=}C{-}C_6H_5 + HB + B^- \quad (40) \\
C_6H_5
\end{array}
$$

ism may also be applied to the cleavage of alkyl benzyl and benzyl phenyl ethers with potassium amide in ethanol (reaction 41)[101]. The formation of the carbinols results from a 1,2-shift (a). β-Elimination

$$(C_6H_5CH_2)_2O \xrightarrow{\text{KNH}_2}$$

$$
C_6H_5\overset{-\;K^+}{C}HOCH_2C_6H_5
\begin{array}{l}
\xrightarrow{(a)} \;\; C_6H_5\overset{\displaystyle CH_2C_6H_5}{\underset{|}{C}}HO^-K^+ \\
\xrightarrow{(b)} \;\; C_6H_5CHO + C_6H_5CH_2^-K^+
\end{array}
\quad (41)
$$

further explains the formation of toluene and benzaldehyde (b). The same mechanism explains the formation of benzaldehyde, toluene, desoxybenzoin, benzyl alcohol and benzoic acid; all of these are formed from dibenzyl ether with potassium *t*-butoxide which acts as a strong base on the intermediate carbinol[102].

On the other hand, reductive cleavage similar to the Birch reduction[103] may also occur. This consists of several steps, the first being the addition of one or more metal atoms to the unsaturated system (reaction 42).

$$
\begin{array}{c}
\text{(structures)}
\end{array}
$$

This reaction is dependent both on the metal and on the solvent. While inversion occurs during the reaction of 2-methoxy-2-phenyl-butane[100] with potassium in *t*-butyl alcohol, complete racemization is observed when potassium reacts with the same ether in *N*-methyl-amine solution, or when sodium in methanol is used in liquid ammonia. Retention of configuration prevails when aprotic solvents, i.e. benzene or diethyl ether, are used with a sodium–potassium alloy. Obviously, the stereochemical behavior of the carbanion formed is strongly determined by the properties of the environment and the reaction is therefore far more complex than shown by equation (42).

2. Cyclic ethers

Whereas the acid-catalyzed cleavage of oxiranes can lead to the formation of both normal and abnormal products, the base-catalyzed reaction is found to be more clear-cut.

Sodium hydroxide in ethanol splits propylene oxide solely by attacking the primary carbon atom[104]. The preferential formation of the normal isomer results when other basic reagents are used. Hence it is most likely that the reaction occurs through an S_N2 mechanism. A bimolecular step has also been assumed by Whalley[84], who obtained negative volumes of activation for the cleavage of ethylene oxide and propylene oxide at 3000 atm using NaOH.

Table 14 shows the experimental rate coefficients obtained at 60° for the basic and the uncatalyzed cleavages of ethylene oxide. In the latter case reactions were carried out at pH 7·3 in a 2,4,6-trimethylpyridine–2,4,6-trimethylpyridinium perchlorate buffer.

TABLE 14. Pressure dependency of rate coefficients of the uncatalyzed and base-catalyzed cleavage of ethylene oxide.

p(atm)	$10^6 k_{uncat.}$ (1/sec)	$10^3 k_{base-cat.}$ (l/mole sec)
1	19·2	2·76
500	27·2	3·19
1000	36·6	3·64
2000	59·1	4·31
3000	86·5	5·33

The volumes of activation obtained at 60° are $\Delta V^{\ddagger} = -18·9$ ml/mole for the uncatalyzed, and $\Delta V^{\ddagger} = -7$ ml/mole for the base-catalyzed reaction.

Much work has been done on the reactions of substituted styrene oxides with benzylamine in ethanol [83] in order to clarify the question of the formation of normal and abnormal products (reaction 43). It

$$\underset{\text{PhCH}\overline{\hspace{1em}}\text{CH}_2}{\overset{O}{\diagup\diagdown}} + \text{PhCH}_2\text{NH}_2 \underset{k_n}{\overset{k_a}{\Bigg\langle}} \begin{array}{l} \text{PhCHCH}_2\text{OH} \\ \phantom{\text{PhCH}}| \\ \phantom{\text{PhCH}}\text{NHCH}_2\text{Ph} \\ \text{PhCH(OH)CH}_2\text{NHCH}_2\text{Ph} \end{array} \tag{43}$$

has been concluded, since the reaction was first order in each of the reactants, that both reactions consist of a bimolecular process. The kinetic measurements (Table 15) clearly indicate an increase in the

TABLE 15. Rate coefficients k_2 and activation entropies for the cleavage of styrene oxides with various substituents.

Substituent	$10^3 k_{normal}$ (l/mole sec)	$\Delta S^{\ddagger}$ (cal/deg mole)
3,4-Dimethyl	1·41	− 33·2
Unsubstituted	4·9	− 37·3
m-Chloro	7·28	− 40·0
	$10^5 k_{abnormal}$ (l/mole sec)	$\Delta S^{\ddagger}$ (cal/deg mole)
3,4-Dimethyl	5·50	− 35·0
Unsubstituted	1·38	− 30·9
m-Chloro	0·66	− 24·9

normal reaction rate under the influence of electron-attracting substituents and inhibition with electron-donating substituents; the opposite is true in the abnormal reaction.

In other words the ρ values of the Hammett equation are positive ($\rho = +0.87$) for the normal reaction and negative ($\rho = -1.15$) for the abnormal reaction, the dominating factor being the bond cleavage. The low values of the entropy of activation $\Delta S^{\ddagger}_{exp.}$ suggest that two neutral molecules form a charged transition state. The same mechanism may therefore be applied to both the normal and abnormal reactions, in spite of the opposite signs of the ρ values. The rate coefficients are larger in methanol than in ethanol for almost all substituted products[105]: k_2 for the abnormal reaction of 3,4-dimethyl-styrene oxide is 8.26×10^{-5} l/mole sec and for m-chlorostyrene oxide it is 2.48×10^{-5} l/mole sec.

Less energy is necessary for the formation of the transition state in a solvent with a relatively high dielectric constant. Also the various changes in energy requirements caused by a change of substituents are smaller in methanol, i.e. the reactions in methanol are faster and less influenced by substituents[105,106].

The ratio ρ_n/ρ_a ($\rho_n = +0.30$, $\rho_a = -0.70$) is 0.43 in methanol, compared with a ratio of 0.76 ($\rho_n = 0.87$, $\rho_a = -1.15$) in ethanol. This means that the selectivity in methanol is smaller. A decrease in the steric effect of the solvent is shown by the increase in yield of the abnormal product from 22% in ethanol to 38% in methanol. Besides this, an electronic factor also operates in the case of styrene oxides, e.g. the yield of the abnormal product with 3,4-dimethylstyrene oxide is 80% in ethanol and 70% in methanol. Here the reaction site in the normal reaction is further removed from the substituents, resulting in a larger charge separation in the transition state, which is then better stabilized by solvents of higher dielectric constant. This leads to a relatively higher yield of the normal product. A further electronic effect must be considered, namely that the greater ease of combination of the oxirane with the more acidic methanol will accelerate the abnormal reaction.

Different products are obtained when the diastereoisomers of 2-methyl-1-phenylethylene oxide are hydrolyzed under basic conditions. In the *cis* isomer the ring opening occurs at the $C_{(2)}$ atom with subsequent formation of the *threo* compound. The $C_{(1)}$ atom is attacked in the case of the *trans* isomer resulting in ring opening to give the *erythro* compound[107].

The opinion expressed by Boyd and Marle[108] that in the alkaline ring opening of oxirane anions take part as intermediates[82,109] has been contradicted by the studies of Patat and coworkers[110-112]. According to the latter the first step in the addition of oxiranes to a phenol consists of the formation of a complex, the further reaction is characterized by insertion[113].

Assuming that all the phenol appears in the system as a phenol–oxirane associate, a formulation of the reaction can be adopted which is similar to that suggested by Michaelis and Menten for fermentation reactions (reaction 44), where EO is the ethylene oxide and ME the

$$\text{Catalyst} + C_6H_5OH + EO \underset{k_{-1}}{\overset{k_1}{\rightleftharpoons}} \text{Transition state} \xrightarrow{k_2} ME + \text{Catalyst} \quad (44)$$

phenyl monoethylene glycol ether. The rate-determining step consists of the reversible reaction between the binary phenol–ethylene oxide associate and the catalyst. The products are then formed from the reaction of the catalyst–substrate complex. The reaction rate is given by equation (45). The unimolecular decomposition coefficient of

$$V = \frac{d[C_6H_5OH]}{dt} = \frac{k_1[C_6H_5OH]\,[\text{catalyst}]}{k_2 + k_1' + k_1[C_6H OH]}\,k_2 \quad (45)$$

the transition state k_2 has different values when different catalysts are used (Table 16).

TABLE 16. Dependence of rate coefficients for the cleavage of ethylene oxide and of propylene oxide on various catalysts.

Catalyst	Ethylene oxide k_2[1/min] 70°	Propylene oxide k_2[1/min] 80°
Sodium phenolate	0·35	0·37
Potassium phenolate	0·46	—
Cesium phenolate	0·53	—
Triethylamine	0·33	0·55
Tributylamine	0·38	0·78

The reaction of glycidyl phenyl ether with protonating agents such as phenol or benzoic acid in xylene or in nitrobenzene solution, in the presence of catalysts like sodium phenolate or tributylamine, shows that the reaction does not occur through an ionic mechanism, but through a ternary transition complex which is involved in the ring opening[87]. The reaction is third order according to equation (46).

$$-\frac{d[\text{oxirane}]}{dt} = k_2\,[\text{catalyst}]\,[\text{oxirane}]\,[\text{attacking agent}] \quad (46)$$

IV. CLEAVAGE BY METAL HALIDES

A. Acyclic Ethers

Ethers yield complexes with Lewis acids which when heated lead to decomposition of the ether. The first example of such a reaction was the reaction of anisole with $AlCl_3$[114]. When molar equivalents (1:1) of aryl ether and aluminum halide are used a satisfactory yield of aryloxy aluminum halides can be obtained. This reaction was successfully adapted for the removal of alkoxy groups from aromatic compounds. The 1:1 complex of diethyl ether with aluminum chloride decomposes when heated to give ethyl chloride, hydrogen chloride and ethylene[115]. Aluminum bromide can be used in a similar manner.

The reactivity of phenol ethers towards $AlCl_3$ gave the following reactivity sequence: isopropyl > ethyl > methyl. When 3,4-dimethoxybenzaldehyde is split, no alkylated material is formed by reaction with the methyl chloride which is also formed in the reaction. The corresponding ethyl and propyl ethers, however, undergo ring alkylation. It is therefore concluded that an S_N2 mechanism operates in the reaction of the methyl ethers, S_N1 being the main mechanism in the case of the other ethers[116].

Relatively efficient ether-cleaving reagents, besides aluminum halides, are the boron halides. Work has essentially been confined to preparative synthetic problems. Recent systematic work has mainly been concerned with the general applicability of the boron halides to ether cleavages. A summary has been given by Gerrard[117].

Diethyl and dimethyl ethers form complexes with BCl_3[118,119] which on heating result in cleavage of the ether. Alkoxyboron compounds are formed first according to reaction (47).

$$R_2O:BCl_3 \longrightarrow ROBCl_2 + RCl \qquad (47)$$

These react further with decomposition. For mixed dialkyl, diallyl and alkyl allyl ethers the overall equation is (48), where R^2 is the

$$R^1R^2O + BCl_3 \longrightarrow R^2Cl + R^1OBCl_2 \qquad (48)$$

stronger electron-donating group. The alkoxyboron compound formed may react further by addition of another ether molecule followed by disproportionation.

The reaction of alkyl aryl ethers with BCl_3 can be formulated as in equation (49). An excess of ether will cause disproportionation[34].

$$ArOR + BCl_3 \longrightarrow RCl + ArOBCl_2 \qquad (49)$$

Splitting of optically active ethers like ethyl $(+)$-1-methylheptyl ether results in inversion with some racemization. Ethyl $(+)$-1-phenylethyl ether yields racemic 1-chloro-1-phenylethane (α-phenylethyl chloride)[120]. Here an S_N1 mechanism is assumed. In the reaction of n-butyl s-butyl ether with hydrogen iodide cleavage yields n-butyl iodide and s-butyl alcohol, i.e. the mechanism is S_N2[26]. On the other hand the reaction with BCl_3 leads to s-butyl chloride and n-butyl alcohol. The rate-determining step is in this case the formation of a carbonium ion from the addition compound (reaction 50). The

$$R^1OR^2 + BCl_3 \rightleftharpoons \underset{\overset{|}{\ddot{B}Cl_3}}{R^1OR^2} \longrightarrow R^{2+} + (R^1OBCl_3)^- \longrightarrow R^2Cl + R^1OBCl_2 \quad (50)$$

stronger electron donor is R^2. This mechanistic description has been criticized, since anisole gives fast cleavage with BCl_3 and also since no rearranged alkyl halides are formed as should be the case if free carbonium ions are involved[2]. On the other hand, the carbonium ion type of reaction seems to be justified by stereochemical studies. A unique description is as yet unavailable.

Aliphatic ethers can easily be cleaved at room temperature with BF_3–etherate dissolved in acetic anhydride, in the presence of lithium halides. Acetoxycyclohexane and cyclohexene are obtained from methoxycyclohexane in the presence of LiBr[121]. Use has been made of BBr_3 and BCl_3 in dichloromethane to determine methoxy groups in mono- and polymethylated mono-, di- and polysaccharides[122].

B. Cyclic Ethers

Cyclic ethers are very reactive towards Lewis acids. Ethylene and propylene oxides give ring opening with $AlCl_3$[123], $TiCl_4$[124], $SnCl_4$[88], BF_3[125–127] and $FeCl_3$[128]. Addition of more ether leads in all these cases to polymerization as shown in Scheme 2. The cleavage occurs through an S_N2 mechanism.

$$BCl_3 + (CH_2)_nO \longrightarrow \overset{+}{C}H_2(CH_2)_{n-1}O\overset{-}{B}Cl_3 \longrightarrow Cl(CH_2)_nOBCl_2$$

$$\downarrow +(CH_2)_nO$$

$$\overset{+}{C}H_2(CH_2)_{n-1}O(CH_2)_nO\overset{-}{B}Cl_3 \longrightarrow Cl(CH_2)_nO(CH_2)_nOBCl_2$$

$$\downarrow +(CH_2)_nO$$

Polymeric products

SCHEME 2.

Using a molar ratio of 1:1 ethylene oxide reacts at $-80°$ according to equation (51) [125].

$$\underset{CH_2\text{———}CH_2}{\overset{O}{\triangle}} + BCl_3 \longrightarrow ClCH_2CH_2OBCl_2 \tag{51}$$

Propylene oxide yields 55–70% of **15a** (equation 52).

$$\underset{CH_3CH\text{———}CH_2}{\overset{O}{\triangle}} + BCl_3 — \begin{cases} \longrightarrow CH_3CHClCH_2OBCl_2 \quad \textbf{(15a)} \\ \\ \longrightarrow CH_3CH_2CHClOBCl_2 \quad \textbf{(15b)} \end{cases} \tag{52}$$

Epichlorohydrin yields higher products, which do not appear in the cases of ethylene and propylene oxides [126]. Epichlorohydrin reacts with BF_3–etherate, in the presence of alcohols, to yield α-chlorohydrin ethers. The reaction is first order in both the catalyst and the epichlorohydrin. The rate coefficients k_2 found in methanol and ethanol at $40°$ are $5\cdot34 \times 10^{-3}$ and $3\cdot44 \times 10^{-3}$ l/mole sec, respectively [129].

Mainly polymers are formed from trimethylene oxide. The stable 1:1 complex of tetrahydrofuran and BF_3 decomposes on heating to 1,4-dichlorobutane. When an excess of the ether is added the dimeric 4-(4′-chlorobutoxy)-1-butanol is formed [130].

C. Ring Opening and Rearrangement of Cyclic Ethers

When substituted oxiranes are attacked by Lewis acids the ring fission is often accompanied by rearrangement [3, 131].

The nature of the rearrangement is influenced by the direction of the fission and by the migration aptitude of the various substituents. The direction of the ring cleavage depends on the position of the substituents which assist the C—O bond breaking. The rearrangement can be generally described by reaction (53), where R^1 and R^2 represent the

$$\underset{R^2}{\overset{R^1}{\diagdown}}C\underset{R^4}{\overset{O}{\diagup}}\overset{R^3}{\diagup}C \longrightarrow R^1\underset{R^2}{\overset{R^3}{-}}C\overset{O}{\overset{\|}{-}}C-R^4 \tag{53}$$

stronger electron-donating groups, so that the carbon atom carrying these groups will be the one involved in the C—O bond cleavage.

Much attention has been given to the course of splitting and rearrangement in the reaction between BF_3 and the epoxy ketone. The ring opening can proceed in either of two directions with formation of different carbonium ions (reaction 54). The reaction of 1,1-disubsti-

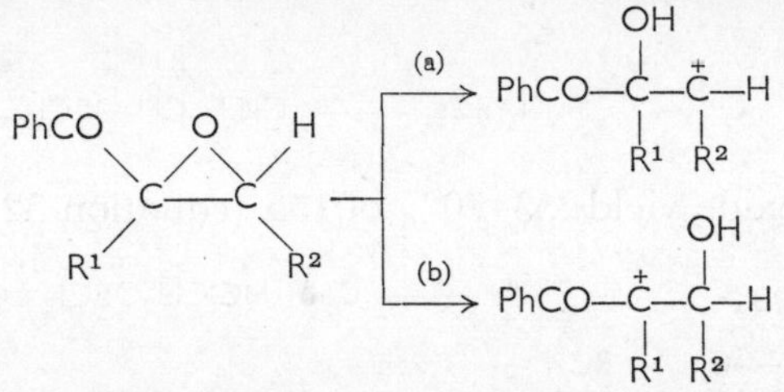

(54)

tuted oxiranes[132] (reaction 55) leads to the formation of that cation

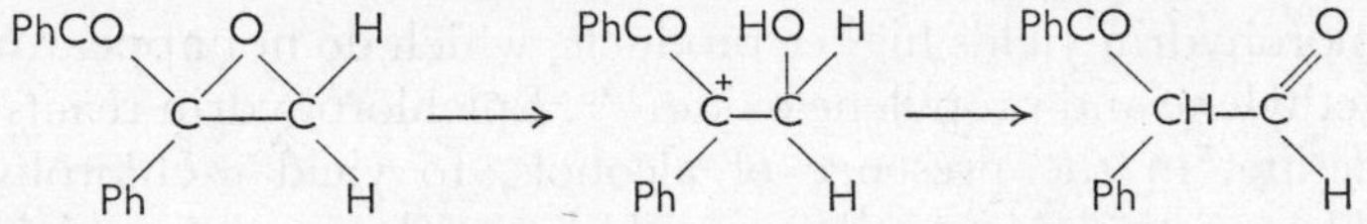

(55)

with a positive charge adjacent to the carbonyl group (b). This interpretation is based on the assumption that the carbonium ion formed via (b) is more stable than the primary carbonium ion. Steric evidence for simultaneous ring opening and migration is offered by the isomerization of the two diastereoisomers of α-phenylchalcone oxide[133]. The *cis* and *trans* forms yield different products (reactions 56 and 57).

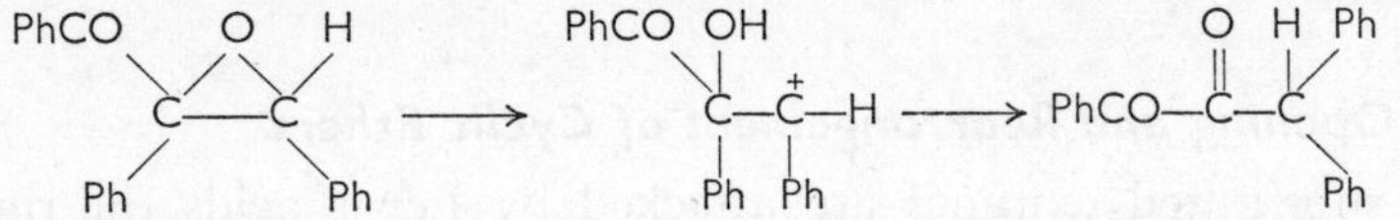

(56)

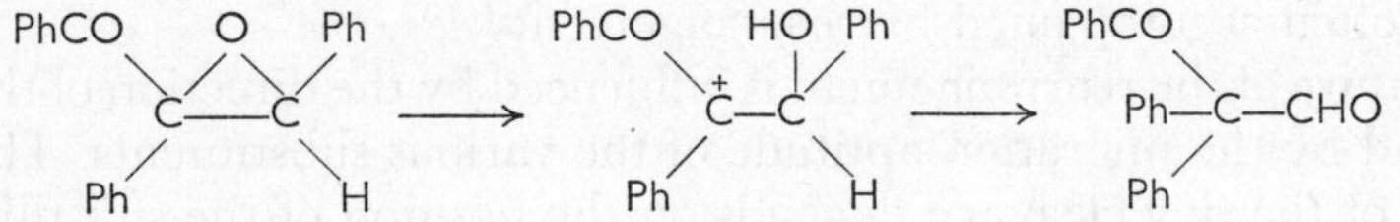

(57)

It must therefore be assumed that phenyl groups are equally capable of stabilizing both intermediate cations.

This condition is, however, not fulfilled by *cis*- and *trans*-ethylbenzalacetophenone oxide[134]. In this case formation of the intermediate cation according to reaction (56) is favored. This is followed by migration of the benzoyl group with subsequent formation of 1,2-diphenyl-1,3-pentanedione. This is taken as an indication for a nonconcerted process, in which the cation formation is the rate-determining step. Discrimination between a two-stage process and a concerted one is as yet impossible, since substituent effects and their steric influence must also be considered.

In a concerted rearrangement transition state **16a** is plausible; this is supported by experiments with p,p'-substituted *trans*-benzalacetophenone oxides[135]. The relative rates of rearrangement are shown in Table 17. The rates are first order with respect to the ether.

TABLE 17. Relative rates of rearrangement for some *trans*-benzalacetophenone oxides.

Substituent	Relative rate
Unsubstituted	1·00
4-Methyl	1·63
4-Methoxy	1·88
4-Chloro	0·72
4,4'-Dichloro	0·55

The reaction is accelerated by electron-donating substituents and retarded by electron-attracting groups. Generally the substituent effect can be considered to be small. Hence it can be concluded that a considerable part of the positive charge is carried by the group leaving the β position. This points to transition state **16a**.

(16a)   (16b)

Transition state **16b** is supported by experiments on the rearrangements of fluorohydrin and by the appearance of fluorohydrin as a by-product of the oxirane rearrangement. Nevertheless there is, as yet, no evidence for either the transition complex **16a** or the fluorohydrin complex **16b**.

With Lewis acids, triphenylethylene oxide rearranges to the corresponding aldehyde. Aluminum halides, unlike BF_3[136], increase the migration of hydrogen atoms (Table 18)[137].

TABLE 18. Rearrangement products of triphenylethylene oxide.

Lewis acid	%$Ph_2CHCOPh$	%Ph_3CCHO
BF_3–etherate	4–5	95–96
$AlCl_3$	24–28	72–76
$AlBr_3$	24–28	72–76

The dominating migration is still that of the phenyl group, even in the presence of BF_3, emphasizing the stronger tendency of the phenyl group for delocalization of a positive charge. This should also explain the rearrangement of stilbene oxide into diphenylacetaldehyde in the presence of $MgBr_2$ and BF_3–etherate[138].

Ring opening under the influence of aluminum halides can also be understood if complex formation of the intermediate chlorohydrin $(Ph_2CClCH(OH)Ph)$ is presumed; this subsequently undergoes rearrangement involving competitive migration between hydrogen and phenyl. According to Rerick and Eliel the formation of both ketones and aldehydes would then be anticipated, since in the reaction of *cis*-stilbene oxide with $MgBr_2$ phenyl migration takes place exclusively, while mainly hydrogen migration is observed in the case of *trans*-stilbene oxide, triphenylethylene oxide with its structure occupying an intermediate position between these two, should obviously be able to react in both directions (17).

$$
\begin{array}{ccc}
\text{Cl} & & \text{Cl} \\
& \diagdown \diagup & \\
& \text{Al} & \\
& \vdots & \\
\text{Cl} & & \text{O} \\
| & & | \\
\text{Ph—C} & \text{—} & \text{C—H} \\
| & & | \\
\text{Ph} & & \text{Ph}
\end{array}
$$

(17)

V. ORGANOMETALLIC COMPOUNDS

Ether cleavage with organometallic compounds usually results in β elimination accompanied, however, by an α',β elimination[139].

At room temperature ethane, ethylene and sodium ethylate are produced when ethylsodium reacts with diethyl ether (reaction 58)[140].

$$C_2H_5Na + (C_2H_5)_2O \longrightarrow C_2H_6 + CH_2{=}CH_2 + C_2H_5ONa \qquad (58)$$

Amylsodium cleaves 2-methoxyoctane[141]. Alkyl cholesteryl ethers yield cholesterol and the corresponding alkenes with amylsodium[142].

Alkyl phenyl ethers undergo metalation and cleavage[143]. The ease of splitting depends on the availability and reactivity of the hydrogen in the β position of the alkyl group. Metalation of cresyl methyl ether is limited by the adjacent oxygen atom. The cleavages of isopropyl 2,4,6-triisopropylphenyl ether and of dialkyl ethers by amylsodium demonstrate, however, that metalation is not always a prerequisite for cleavage. The first step in the reaction is considered to be a homolytic dissociation of the amylsodium; this is more probable than ion formation. The reaction then proceeds according to reaction (59).

$$RO\underset{Na\cdots C_5H_{11}}{\overset{CH_2CH_3}{\diagup}} \longrightarrow RONa + CH_2{=}CH_2 + C_5H_{12} \qquad (59)$$

β-Elimination seems to be the only possible explanation for the cleavage of aryl ethyl ethers with propylsodium (reaction 60)[144].

$$M^+B^- + RO\overset{H}{\underset{|}{\overset{|}{C}}}\overset{H}{\underset{|}{\overset{|}{C}}}{-} \longrightarrow [RO{-}\overset{H}{\underset{|}{C}}{-}\overset{\bar{}}{C}{-}]\,M^+ + BH \longrightarrow \overset{H}{\underset{|}{-C}}{=}C{-} + RO^-M^+ \qquad (60)$$

α Metalation may well account for the cases where an α position of the ether is activated by a phenyl group. The second step is presumably an intramolecular *cis* elimination. Evidence for this has been obtained by using deuterated benzyl ethers (reaction 61).

$$C_6H_5CD_2OCH_2CH_3 + C_3H_7Na \longrightarrow C_6H_5\overset{Na^+}{\bar{C}D}{-}O{-}CH_2CH_3 + C_3H_7D \qquad (61a)$$

$$C_6H_5{-}\overset{D}{\underset{H}{\overset{|}{C}}}{-}\overset{Na^+}{\underset{\overset{-}{CH_2}}{O}}{\underset{CH_2}{\cdots}} \longrightarrow C_6H_5{-}\overset{D}{\underset{|}{C}}HO^-Na^+ + CH_2{=}CH_2 \qquad (61b)$$

The fact that α elimination cannot possibly follow an α metalation is demonstrated by the example of 2-phenyltetrahydrofuran. The activated α position can be metalated, but a subsequent normal β elimination seems to be out of the question, since this would involve a proton transfer from the 1 to 3 position. From the reaction products, acetophenone and ethylene, it is obvious that the α metalation is followed by a 1,4-elimination with C—C bond fission. The primary attack on the α-hydrogen atom is also supported by the fact that unsubstituted tetrahydrofuran is unaffected by propylsodium (reaction 62).

Butyllithium is capable of cleaving alkyl ethers[145] and alkyl aryl ethers[146]. Allyl phenyl ethers are split by phenyllithium[1]. Alkyl phenyl ethers, on the other hand, seem to be stable to this reagent. 1,4-Dimethoxy-2,3,5-trimethylbenzene loses a methoxy group when

$$C_2H_4 + PhC \xrightarrow{H_2O} PhCOCH_3 + M^+OH^- \quad (62)$$

attacked by butyllithium at 27°. Apparently a reaction involving direct displacement takes place[147]. In this case nuclear magnetic resonance spectra have led to the conclusion that the methoxy group in the *ortho* position relative to the two methoxy groups is cleaved.

Vinyl ethers react with butyllithium to give acetylene and the corresponding alcohol[148]. Phenylvinyl tolyl ether yields cresol, phenylacetylene and *trans*-stilbene when reacted with phenyllithium[32].

Work on stereoisomeric ethers has shown that *cis* elimination is preferred to *trans* elimination[146]. As opposed to this, in the normal base-catalyzed reaction of stereoisomeric ethers, elimination of the *trans* substituents prevails. As far as the diastereoisomeric cyclohexyl methyl-2-phenyl ethers are concerned, the *trans* isomer reacts more rapidly than the *cis* isomer, yielding phenylcyclohexane. The transition state **18** seems likely.

(**18**)

The isomeric alcohols are formed when benzyl and benzhydryl ethers react with organolithium compounds[149]. An intramolecular nucleophilic substitution (S_Ni) has been postulated, which involves the formation of a carbanion intermediate (reaction 63)[150,82].

$$Ph-CH \quad R \longrightarrow PhCH-R \quad (63)$$

This step should occur with retention of configuration when an optically active group is shifted. Recent results, however, favor a description of a carbanionic cleavage–recombination mechanism[151]. According to this the migrating group is eliminated as a carbanion which forms a complex with the lithium. In the resulting transition state an aldehyde–organolithium ion pair is formed; e.g. carbinyl cyclopropyl ether reacts with methyllithium in tetrahydrofuran at room temperature to yield 94% of the corresponding alcohol, after 24 hours, with racemization through the carbanion.

Use has been made of the reactions of optically active alkyl benzyl ethers with butyllithium to study the stereochemical aspects of the mechanism[152, 153]. When the reaction was carried out in tetrahydrofuran considerable racemization was observed. It could be shown, using deuterated ethers, that racemization could not result from side-reactions. The coefficients, at $-56°$, for the reaction of α-metalated ethers are $k = 2.81 \times 10^{-3}$ min^{-1} for benzyl s-butyl ether and 4.36×10^{-3} min^{-1} for benzyl isopropyl ether. These results exclude an $S_N i$ mechanism almost completely. As racemic products are formed, only a two-step mechanism is conceivable, i.e. cleavage of the C—O bond and subsequent formation of the new C—C bond, the first step being rate determining. Racemization takes place during the rearrangement (reaction 64).

$$
\begin{array}{c}
\overset{Li^+}{\underset{H}{PhC}}-O-\overset{H}{\underset{CH_3}{C}} {\blacktriangleleft} C_2H_5 \longrightarrow
\left[
\begin{array}{c}
\overset{H}{\underset{}{Ph-C}}=O \quad Li^+ \\
H \\
\bar{C}-CH_3 \\
C_2H_5
\end{array}
\right]
\text{ or }
\left[
\begin{array}{c}
\overset{H}{\underset{}{Ph-C}}=O \quad Li^+ \\
C_2H_5 \\
\bar{C}-CH_3 \\
H
\end{array}
\right] \quad (64)
\end{array}
$$

(19)   (20)

The alcohol with retained configuration is formed from **19** and the inverted alcohol is formed from **20**. The observed solvent effects on the reaction indicate an ionic mechanism.

Nevertheless an $S_N i$ mechanism is suggested for tertiary-alkyl benzyl ethers[154]; e.g. α elimination is assumed for the reaction of benzyl phenyl ether with butyllithium (reaction 65)[155]. The further reaction

$$PhCH_2OPh \xrightarrow{C_4H_9Li} PhCHLiOPh \longrightarrow PhCH: + LiOPh \qquad (65)$$

of the carbene depends on the reaction conditions, e.g. in the presence of isobutene a substituted cyclopropane is formed together with some stilbene and polymeric material. α Elimination is also suggested by

Ziegler for the reactions of alkyl ethers with organolithium compounds where the corresponding alkenes are formed[145].

Normal products are obtained when oxirane rings are opened by organolithium compounds. The primary carbon atom is attacked in the case of propylene and styrene oxides[156]. The reaction between epichlorohydrin and phenyllithium is shown by reaction (66)[157]. In

$$CH_2ClCH\text{—}CH_2 \xrightarrow{\text{PhLi}} CH_2ClCH(OH)CH_2Ph \tag{66}$$

tetrahydrofuran the reaction with butyllithium follows a different course[158]: the addition of butyllithium results in the formation of α,β-unsaturated alcohols, and not the saturated ones. The proton in the chloromethyl group is attacked and the carbanion intermediate is transformed into the stable *trans*-alkoxide via a stereospecific ring opening reaction (67)[159].

$$ClCH_2\text{---}C\text{—}C\text{---}H \xrightarrow{C_4H_9Li} \left[\begin{array}{c} H \quad Cl \quad O \\ C\text{—}C\text{—}C\text{---}H \\ H \quad H \end{array} \right] Li^+$$

$$\begin{array}{c} H \quad CH_2OLi \\ C{=}C \\ ClH \quad H \end{array} \xrightarrow{H^+} ClCH{=}CHCH_2OH \tag{67}$$

Another way of cleaving cyclic ethers is by using a mixture of Lewis acids and bases, such as Ph_3CNa/Ph_3Al, which may give both nucleophilic and electrophilic attacks simultaneously. Under such conditions at 20° 90% of the tetrahydrofuran is cleaved after 24 hours. 70% yield is obtained when Ph_3CNa/Ph_3B is used[160].

VI. GRIGNARD REAGENTS

Most ethers, except those with strained ring systems, are unaffected by Grignard reagents at low temperatures. In order to describe the mechanism of the reaction between ethers and Grignard reagents both displacement and elimination reactions have been considered, because in reactions of alkyl aryl ethers alkanes and alkenes as well as phenols are formed. Amylmagnesium bromide reacts with phenetole at 160°[161]. Anisole, diphenyl ether, ethyl benzyl ether[162] and allyl phenyl ether[163] are also cleaved by Grignard reagents.

Oxiranes generally react with Grignard reagents to form alcohols and halohydrins.

Owing to the equilibrium of the solution, magnesium halides as well as alkyl- and arylmagnesiums are present. As has previously been shown for the reaction of ethers with metal halides, rearrangement of oxiranes may be caused by these compounds[164]. Epoxy ethers react with phenylmagnesium bromide with rearrangement to the respective alkoxy ketones, which further react with the Grignard reagent by a direct attack of diphenylmagnesium on the ketal carbon atom. It can be shown that the rearrangement with $MgBr_2$ proceeds more rapidly than the attack by diphenylmagnesium[165]. No such rearrangement occurs when diphenylmagnesium is used. The rate of migration of methyl groups is much smaller than that of phenyl or hydrogen, and hence dialkyl epoxy ethers react without the formation of any isomers (reaction 68)[166]. Propylene oxide reacts with phenylmagnesium

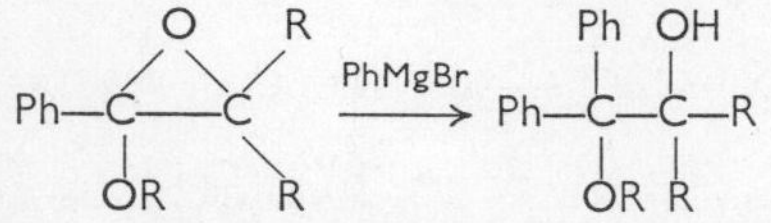

$$
\underset{\underset{OR}{|}}{\overset{\overset{O}{\diagup\diagdown}}{Ph-C}}\!-\!\underset{\underset{R}{|}}{\overset{\overset{R}{|}}{C}} \xrightarrow{PhMgBr} \underset{\underset{OR}{|}}{\overset{\overset{Ph}{|}}{Ph-C}}\!-\!\underset{\underset{R}{|}}{\overset{\overset{OH}{|}}{C}}\!-\!R \tag{68}
$$

bromide to yield a mixture of 1-phenyl-2-propanol and 1-bromo-2-propanol[167].

Oxetanes are cleaved by Grignard reagents in boiling benzene[168]. Tetrahydrofuran is cleaved with triphenylmagnesium bromide to yield 5,5,5-triphenyl-1-pentanol[169].

In the presence of catalytic amounts of $FeCl_3$ the reaction of propylene oxide and phenylmagnesium bromide[170] yields propylene and biphenyl as the main products, accompanied by minor amounts of propanol. Halohydrins are not formed. The mechanism shown in Scheme 3 is suggested.

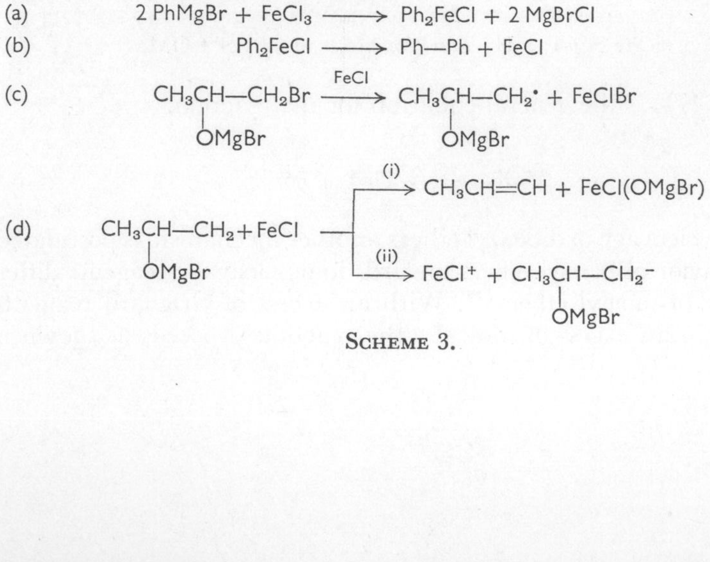

(a) $2\,PhMgBr + FeCl_3 \longrightarrow Ph_2FeCl + 2\,MgBrCl$

(b) $Ph_2FeCl \longrightarrow Ph\!-\!Ph + FeCl$

(c) $\underset{\underset{OMgBr}{|}}{CH_3CH\!-\!CH_2Br} \xrightarrow{FeCl} \underset{\underset{OMgBr}{|}}{CH_3CH\!-\!CH_2{}^{\bullet}} + FeClBr$

(d) $\underset{\underset{OMgBr}{|}}{CH_3CH\!-\!CH_2} + FeCl \longrightarrow$

 (i) $CH_3CH\!\!=\!\!CH + FeCl(OMgBr)$

 (ii) $FeCl^+ + \underset{\underset{OMgBr}{|}}{CH_3CH\!-\!CH_2{}^-}$

SCHEME 3.

Formation of the radical in (c) seems possible [171]. The alkene formation from this can result either through direct attack by FeCl (i) or by elimination from the carbanion formed in (ii) (reaction 69). Reaction (70) describes the alcohol formation.

$$CH_3CH-CH_2^- \longrightarrow CH_3CH{=}CH_2 + OMgBr^- \qquad (69)$$
$$\quad\;\; |$$
$$\quad OMgBr$$

$$CH_3CH-CH_2Br \xrightarrow{\text{FeCl}} CH_3CH-CH_2{}^{\bullet} \xrightarrow{\text{Solvent}} CH_3CHCH_3 \qquad (70)$$
$$\quad\;\; | \qquad\qquad\qquad\qquad | \qquad\qquad\qquad\qquad |$$
$$\quad OMgBr \qquad\qquad\qquad OMgBr \qquad\qquad\qquad OMgBr$$

The abnormal Grignard reaction has been used for cleavage of diaryl ethers in the presence of $CoCl_2$ [172]. It is supposed that in this case radicals are formed (Scheme 4) [173].

$$R^1MgX + CoCl_2 \longrightarrow R^1CoCl_2 + MgClX$$

$$R^1CoCl \longrightarrow {}^{\bullet}R^1 + {}^{\bullet}CoCl$$

$${}^{\bullet}CoCl + R^2X \longrightarrow {}^{\bullet}R^2 + CoClX$$

SCHEME 4.

The reaction of monosubstituted diphenyl ether with isopropyl-magnesium bromide must lead to a mixture of phenols if it is assumed that an aryloxy radical results from the fission of p-fluorophenyl phenyl ether. The fact that more than 50% of p-fluorophenol is obtained suggests a substituent-induced stabilization of the aryloxy radical. As far as can be concluded from the cleavage products, the stabilizing effect of the substituents decreases in the following series:

$$m\text{-Me} > p\text{-F} > H \quad \text{and} \quad m\text{-Me} > m\text{-CF}_3 > p\text{-OMe}$$

Equation (71) is the general equation for the reaction.

$$PhOPh \xrightarrow{\text{H}^{\bullet}} PhO^{\bullet} + PhH \qquad (71)$$

For the cleavage of dibenzyl ethers another mechanism is postulated. The behavior of benzyl ethers towards ionic-cleavage reagents differs from that of phenyl ethers [174]. With an excess of Grignard reagents, resulting in an excess of radicals, the reaction proceeds as shown in

Scheme 5. Hence, the radical disproportionates into benzaldehyde and

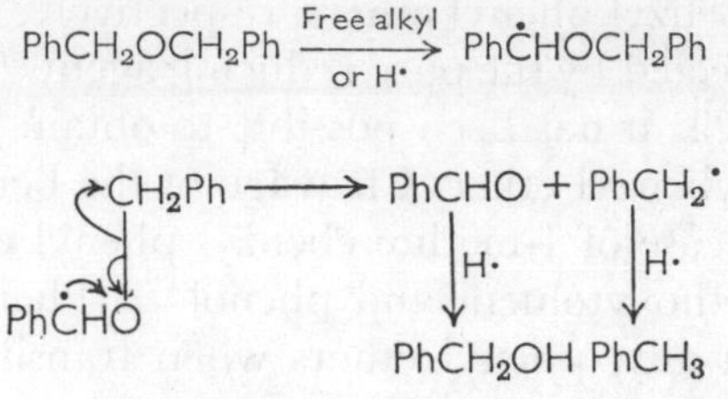

$$PhCH_2OCH_2Ph \xrightarrow[\text{or } H^\cdot]{\text{Free alkyl}} Ph\overset{\cdot}{C}HOCH_2Ph$$

SCHEME 5.

benzyl radical, both of which are further reduced to benzyl alcohol and toluene.

The effect of various substituents on radical stabilization may be estimated from the radicals obtained in the reaction; the following series were obtained:

(a) p-t-Bu > p-Me ~ p-Cl > p-OMe > H;

(b) m-Me ~ p-Me > m-Cl > p-OMe > H;

(c) p-Me > p-Ph > H.

Monosubstituted dibenzyl ethers cleave according to equation (72).

$$RC_6H_4CH_2OCH_2Ph \longrightarrow RC_6H_4CH_2OH + PhCH_3 \qquad (72)$$

Both electron-attracting and -donating substituents increase the stability compared to that of the unsubstituted radical. The explanation for this lies in the mesomeric and polar effects of the substituents[175].

VII. COMPLEX METAL HYDRIDES

The ether bond is generally stable to attack by $LiAlH_4$ and other complex hydrides[176]; as yet only a few examples dealing with cleavage of aryl and alkyl ethers by $LiAlH_4$ are available. β-Alkoxy- and β-aryloxypropionitriles are reduced by $LiAlH_4$[177]. A nitrile elimination was assumed for the mechanism (Scheme 6).

$$ROCH_2CH_2CN \xrightarrow{LiAlH_4} ROCH_2\overset{-}{C}HCN + AlH_3 + H_2$$

$$ROCH_2\overset{-}{C}HCN \longrightarrow RO^- + CH_2{=}CHCN$$

SCHEME 6.

Catalysts, however, turned out to be quite effective when used for this reaction. Transition metal halides significantly increase the activity

3+C.E.L.

of $LiAlH_4$. Thus the addition of $CoCl_2$ causes 25 and 10% cleavage of allyl phenyl and benzyl phenyl ethers, respectively, although they are known to be unaffected by the pure reducing agent[178]. With a mixture of $LiAlH_4$ and $AlCl_3$ it has been possible to obtain p-methoxytoluene from di-4-methoxybenzyl ether. Cleavage of the benzyl–oxygen bond takes place in the case of 4-methoxybenzyl phenyl ether, the reaction products being methoxytoluene and phenol[179]. Phenol and an alkene are obtained from allyl phenyl ethers when transition metal halides are used[180].

The reaction is subject to a strong solvent effect. The 18% yield obtained in ethyl ether rises through 59% in dioxane to 86% in tetrahydrofuran. The hydrogenolysis causes splitting of the alkyl–oxygen bond. No aryl–oxygen bond cleavage has been observed (reaction 73).

$$\underset{ArOCH_2\overset{\displaystyle R^1}{\underset{|}{C}}=\overset{\displaystyle R^2}{\underset{|}{C}}R^3}{} + LiAlH_4 \longrightarrow ArOH + CH_3\overset{\displaystyle R^1}{\underset{|}{C}}=\overset{\displaystyle R^2}{\underset{|}{C}}R^3 \qquad (73)$$

The effect of the various catalysts is shown in Table 19.

TABLE 19. Influence of catalysts on the yields of hydrogenolysis after 24 hours at 65°.

Catalyst	Mole catalyst/mole ether	% Reaction
None	—	12·4
$NiCl_2$	$41·6 \times 10^{-3}$	82·6
$CoCl_2$	$62·4 \times 10^{-3}$	44·0
$AlCl_3$	$40·4 \times 10^{-3}$	38·1
$FeCl_3$	$16·6 \times 10^{-3}$	22·4

When aryl vinyl ether or its chloro and methyl derivatives react with $LiAlH_4$ in the presence of $NiCl_2$ as catalyst, phenols and hydrocarbons are formed[181]. Bond cleavage takes place preferentially between the alkyl group and oxygen. The yield with $NiCl_2$ is 67% as opposed to 13% obtained in the uncatalyzed reaction. A 93% yield is obtained from phenyl vinyl ether at 0° in bis-(2-ethoxyethyl) ether solution, while only 38% cleavage occurs at 35° in ethyl ether. These results indicate the reversible formation of a complex between the ether and the solvent, and possibly also the hydride which is subsequently hydrogenated.

If a hydride attack occurs it takes place exclusively at the least substituted carbon atom in the reduction of oxiranes by $LiAlH_4$. A bimolecular S_N2-type displacement mechanism[3] is postulated for the normal reduction of oxiranes. Formation of the most highly substituted carbinol is favored (reaction 74). Thus from propylene oxide, **21** is

$$R^1R^2C\underset{\displaystyle O}{-\!\!-\!\!-}CHR^3 \xrightarrow{\text{LiAlH}_4} \begin{cases} \longrightarrow R^1R^2C(OH)CH_2R^3 \quad \textbf{(21)} \\ \\ \longrightarrow R^1R^2CHCH(OH)R^3 \quad \textbf{(22)} \end{cases} \qquad (74)$$

obtained exclusively (100%). This corresponds to the normal type of reaction which in the case of primary–secondary oxiranes results in the formation of secondary alcohols. Tertiary alcohols are formed from primary–tertiary and secondary–tertiary oxiranes[182]. With the more substituted oxiranes the yield decreases.

The substituent effect has been investigated in the case of *p*-chloro- and *p*-methylstilbene oxide[183]. Electron-donating substituents were found to assist an S_N2 attack by the hydride on the α-carbon atom, and electron-attracting substituents to favor attack on the β-carbon atom. The same has been found for *p*-substituted styrene oxides and LiBH$_4$[184]. *p*-Bromostyrene oxide reacts to an extent of 84% with the formation of the normal carbinol, and *p*-methoxystyrene oxide yields 95% of the abnormal carbinol.

Epoxy ethers yield products (**22**) (reaction 74, $R^1 = OCH_3$) with LiAlH$_4$[185]. This is reasonable, as the ether group facilitates a nucleophilic attack by forming a positive charge on the adjacent carbon atom. The hydride attack results in inversion. Reaction of LiBH$_4$ with the *trans*-epoxy ether (reaction 75) gives 43% of the *threo* form (**23**) and only 1% of the *meso* form (**24**)[186]. Besides these products, 9% of benzyl phenyl carbinol is formed. The stronger agent LiAlH$_4$ immediately leads to the carbinol (**25**).

(23)   (24)

PhCH$_2$CH(OH)Ph   (75)

(25)

Trimethylene oxide, like its 2-, 2,2- and 3,3- methyl-, ethyl- and phenyl-substituted products, reacts with LiAlH$_4$ to form the corresponding secondary propanols. Here, the normal directive effects are observed in the reactions of unsymmetrically substituted oxetanes, namely that cleavage takes place between the oxygen and the least-substituted carbon atom[187]. Even 2-phenyloxetane undergoes ring cleavage to yield 1-phenyl-1-propanol. Reduction with $LiBH_4$ gives the same result. The lack of the normal reaction product can be accounted for by the assumption that the oxetane ring has no tendency to form a polarized transition state; e.g. the abnormal product, 2-phenylethanol, is formed in the reaction of styrene oxide with $LiAlH_4$[184]. When $LiBH_4$ is used instead, 26% of the primary alcohol is obtained. In the reaction of 2-oxaspiro[2.3]hexane with $LiAlH_4$ the ether is cleaved (reaction 76)[46].

$$(76)$$

When mixed hydrides are used, for example when $AlCl_3$ is added to $LiAlH_4$, the results are necessarily different[188]. Lewis acids (AlX_3, AlH_3) are capable of an electrophilic attack[189], and hence effect rearrangements concurrently with the ring-opening reductions (reaction 77). The exclusive character of the formation of 26 is no longer

$$(77)$$

valid. Under these circumstances, in the reaction of propylene oxide with mixed hydrides, 16–19% of product 27 is formed.

Tracer studies on reaction (77) using deuterated $LiAlH_4$ have established that, in the presence of $AlCl_3$, hydride transfer occurs with the formation of a carbonyl intermediate. This has been demonstrated with styrene oxide and isobutylene oxide. Styrene oxide, for example, reacts with $LiAlH_4$ to yield 90–95% of 26 (R^1 = phenyl, R^2 = R^3 = H) but with a $LiAlH_4/AlCl_3$ mixture it forms 95–98% of 27.

The reactions of triphenylethylene oxide and β-diisobutylene oxide with mixed hydrides can be summarized as shown in Scheme 6.

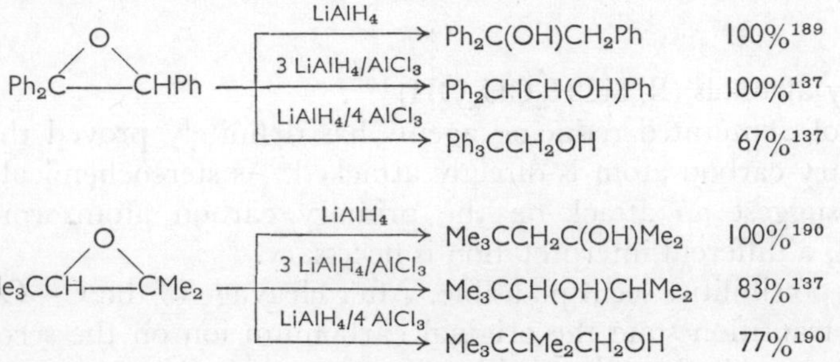

SCHEME 6.

The product composition therefore depends on the character of the reducing agents. With an excess of $LiAlH_4$, i.e. in the presence of AlH_3, direct electrophilic reductive ring cleavage of oxiranes gives mainly secondary alcohols. Whereas phenyl migration is caused by excess $AlCl_3$ with formation of aldehydes and primary alcohols, a t-butyl shift occurs in the intermediate chlorohydrin complex $(R_2CClCH(OH)R)$.

Addition of $AlCl_3$ to $LiAlH_4$ also brings about cleavage of tetra-hydrofuran in boiling n-butyl alcohol[191]. Change of the $AlCl_3$/$LiAlH_4$ ratio does not cause a change of yield. According to the equilibrium shown by equation (78) it is possible for a π complex to

$$AlCl_3 + 3\,LiAlH_4 \rightleftharpoons 4\,AlH_3 + 3\,LiCl \tag{78}$$

form, between AlH_3 and tetrahydrofuran, in which the C—O bond will be weakened; the reductive cleavage follows easily. The high yield is a direct consequence of the stability of this complex. Tetra-hydrofuran yields 100% n-butyl alcohol after 24 hours, while n-butyl ether cleaves to the extent of 5% in the same time.

The direction of the ring cleavage can therefore be completely reversed by using aluminum halides; carbonium ion formation and its subsequent rearrangement is consequently increased by the strong electrophile. Moreover, with para-substituted styrene oxides and $LiBH_4$, the steric accessibility to the carbon atom to be attacked is overshadowed by electronic factors even in the presence of Lewis acids[184]. Quite surprisingly, the reaction of $LiAlH_4$ with epoxysilanes (**28**) leads to uniformly high yields of the corresponding

$$R_3SiCH\overset{O}{\overbrace{}}CH_2$$

(**28**)

primary alcohols ($R_3SiCH_2CH_2OH$) [192].

Use of deuterated reducing agents has definitely proved that the secondary carbon atom is directly attacked. As stereochemical arguments suggest an attack on the primary carbon atom would be favored, a different interpretation is necessary.

Two possibilities seem plausible. After cleavage of the C—O bond in the transition state the original carbonium ion on the secondary carbon atom is far more stable than that with the charge on the primary carbon atom. Attack in transition state **29** is further facilitated by the adjacent electron-releasing silicon atom.

$$R_3Si\overset{\delta+}{\rightarrow}\overset{\overset{\overset{\delta-}{O}}{\vdots}}{C}\text{---}C$$

$$H_3AlH \quad H \quad H \quad H$$

(**29**)   (**30**)

On the other hand, formation of a three-centered transition state (**30**) is also likely. The second possibility seems to be acceptable since the yield of secondary alcohol diminishes from 13% when R = phenyl, to about 6% when R = p-$CH_3OC_6H_4$ and finally to 0% when R = C_2H_5.

No connection could be established between the various substituents and their electronic characteristics and the yields of secondary alcohols. This contradicts the assumption of a transition state like **29**. On the other hand, the increase in the yield of primary alcohol caused by electron-withdrawing substituents, as in the case of R = tri-p-fluoromethylphenyl, can be better understood on the basis of the three-centered transition state **30**. Further, the C—O bond is made more labile by electron-releasing groups increasing the effect of the silicon atom.

VIII. CLEAVAGE BY ALKALI METALS

Alkali metals are used in small pieces or in powder form for the ether-cleavage reaction; while alkyl ethers are mainly stable, aryl ethers yield the corresponding alkoxides and organometallic compounds. When benzyl phenyl ethers react with sodium the benzyl–oxygen bond is cleaved[193]. Benzhydryl methyl ether behaves similarly[194] and is cleaved with potassium at room temperature[195]. Rearrangements are also observed.

Toluene (23%) and 1-phenylethanol (15%) are obtained from reaction of benzyl methyl ether for 2 hours at $115°$[196]. The suggested mechanism involves ion-pair formation (reaction 79).

$$PhCH_2OCH_3 + 2\,Na \longrightarrow Ph\bar{C}H_2Na^+ + CH_3O^-Na^+ \tag{79}$$

Subsequent proton exchange with unreacted ether gives toluene (reaction 80). The alcohol is obtained through inner rearrangement

$$Ph\bar{C}H_2\overset{+}{Na} + PhCH_2OCH_3 \rightleftharpoons PhCH_3 + [Ph\bar{C}HOCH_3]Na^+ \tag{80}$$

(reaction 81). No rearrangement takes place in the reaction of alkyl

$$[Ph\bar{C}H\overset{O}{\diagup}\diagdown CH_3]\,Na^+ \longrightarrow [PhCH\overset{O^-}{\diagup}\!\!\!-\!\!\!-CH_3]Na^+ \tag{81}$$

benzyl ethers and lithium (reaction 82)[197]. R may be either methyl,

$$2\,Li^+ \left[\langle \bigcirc \rangle\!\!-\!\!CH_2OR \right]^{2-} \longrightarrow \left[\langle \bigcirc \rangle\!\!=\!\!CH_2 \right]^- Li^+ + LiOR \tag{82}$$

ethyl, phenyl or benzyl. 75 to 83% yields are obtained at -5 to $-15°$. Similarly the reaction between potassium and methyl α-phenylisopropyl ether proceeds without rearrangement. Phenylisopropylpotassium may be obtained preparatively by this reaction[198].

Electron spin resonance spectra have shown the appearance of ions in this reaction at room temperature and in inert solvents[199]. The reaction proceeds as shown by reaction (83).

$$PhOPh \overset{Na}{\rightleftharpoons} [{}^{\bullet}PhOPh]^- \overset{Na}{\rightleftharpoons} [Ph^{\bullet\bullet}OPh]^{2-} \longrightarrow (Ph^{\bullet\bullet})^- + PhO^- \tag{83}$$

$$\downarrow \text{Solvent}$$

$$[Ph^{\bullet}H]^- \qquad [Ph^{\bullet}Ph]^-$$

Cleavage of the aryl–oxygen bond follows the formation of the double negative ion. During cleavage the electron pair remains localized on the aryl and not on the aryloxy fragment. The aryl fragment then either abstracts a hydrogen atom from the solvent or combines with another fragment.

Better results and a smoother reaction can be achieved by addition of biphenyl in tetrahydrofuran instead of the free metal. A lithium–biphenyl adduct is formed (reaction 84). Here the electron transfer is

$$2\,\text{Li} + \langle\!\bigcirc\!-\!\bigcirc\!\rangle \;\rightleftharpoons\; \left[\langle\!-\!\bigcirc\!=\!\bigcirc\!-\!\rangle\right]^{2-} 2\text{Li}^+ \qquad (84)$$

carried out in a homogeneous phase which enables the use of milder conditions. Although anisole is not split by lithium alone[200], it is cleaved to 55–80% by the biphenyl adduct[201,202]. Diphenyl ether gives a 96% yield of phenol with the same reagent. The strong electron-attracting effect of the phenoxy groups makes the cleavage of phenyl ethers easier than that of methyl ethers (reaction 85).

$$2\text{Li}^+\left[\langle\!-\!\bigcirc\!=\!\bigcirc\!-\!\rangle\right]^{2-} + \langle\!\bigcirc\!\rangle\!-\!OCH_3 \longrightarrow \langle\!\bigcirc\!-\!\bigcirc\!\rangle +$$

$$2\text{Li}^+\left[\langle\!\bigcirc\!\rangle\!-\!OCH_3\right]^{2-} \longrightarrow \text{Products} \qquad (85)$$

Allyl phenyl ethers are easily cleaved, even by metallic lithium in tetrahydrofuran. The use of the biphenyl adduct results in rapid cleavage even below 0°[203]. The relatively fast reaction of allyl ethers to that of methyl ethers is explained by the fact that resonance stabilization of the two anionic fragments in the transition state is more pronounced in the case of the allyl ether (reactions 86).

$$2\text{Li}^+\left[\langle\!-\!\bigcirc\!-\!\rangle\!-\!O\!-\!CH_2CH\!=\!CH_2\right]^{2-} \xrightarrow{\text{Fast}} \text{Products} \qquad (86a)$$

$$2\text{Li}^+\left[\langle\!-\!\bigcirc\!-\!\rangle\!-\!O\!-\!CH_3\right]^{2-} \xrightarrow{\text{Slow}} \text{Products} \qquad (86b)$$

Lithium is made even more efficient by the addition of ethylene-diamine[204]. At 90–100°, up to 54% phenol together with methane is obtained from anisole.

1-Methoxy-2-naphthoic acid is reduced by lithium in liquid ammonia in the presence of ether as an additional solvent and of ethanol as a proton donor (reaction 87)[103,205].

Cleavage of alkyl phenyl ethers by sodium in liquid ammonia can follow either a one-electron mechanism, which in the case of anisole means the formation of a phenoxy ion and a methyl radical, or a two-electron mechanism in which the two fragments are ionic[206]. In an electron-rich environment the methyl carbanion, not the radical, is dominant. Ammonia will instantaneously react with the carbanion forming methane and an amide ion, according to the mechanism postulated by Birch[103]. Benzyl phenyl ether reacts according to the two-electron mechanism. The resulting toluene and 1,2-diphenyl-ethane are formed from the benzyl carbanion (reaction 88).

$$PhCH_2^- + PhOCH_2Ph \longrightarrow PhO^- + PhCH_2CH_2Ph \qquad (88)$$

The cleavage of phenyl phenylethyl ethers is considered to consist of a β elimination involving the amide ion formed in the solution and not the dissolved metal (reaction 89).

$$PhCH_2CH_2OPh + NH_2^- \longrightarrow [Ph\overset{\frown}{CH}-CH_2-\overset{\frown}{O}Ph] \longrightarrow PhO^- + NH_3 +$$

$$PhCH{=}CH_2 \quad (89)$$

The phenoxide ion elimination follows the deprotonation from the α-carbon atom. The styrene formed is further reduced to ethylbenzene. When heated for a long time tetrahydrofuran is split by lithium in the presence of biphenyl to yield n-butyl alcohol.

IX. ORGANOSILICON COMPOUNDS

Oxiranes are also split by chlorosilanes. Ethyl trichlorosilane cleaves ethylene oxide when carefully warmed in $ClCH_2CH_2OSi(CH_2CH_3)Cl_2$[207]. Propylene oxide is converted into $(CH_3)_3SiOCH_2CHClCH_3$ by trimethylchlorosilane[208].

3*

Steric factors reduce the efficiency of triphenylsilyllithium as cleavage reagent for alkyl phenyl ethers. Whereas the methyl ether reacts, the higher homologs remain intact[209]. An S_N2 mechanism is postulated (reaction 90).

$$(C_6H_5)_3Si^- + ROC_6H_5 \longrightarrow (C_6H_5)_3SiR + C_6H_5O^- \qquad (90)$$

Oxiranes form the corresponding carbinols. For ethylene oxide[210] the reaction can be formulated as in reaction (91). Propylene oxide,

styrene oxide, trimethylene oxide[211] and tetrahydrofuran[212] react in the same way. These reactions have previously been considered only from the purely preparative point of view.

X. FURTHER POSSIBILITIES OF ETHER CLEAVAGE

Recently radiolysis has been employed as a new method for cleavage of the ether bond. Thus diethyl ethers decompose when subjected to a dose of about 10^{20} ev/g of ^{60}Co gamma radiation. The main products identified were hydrogen, 2,3-diethoxybutane, ethanol, ethane and ethylene[213].

Free radicals can also cleave the ether bond. Alkyl benzyl ether is split by the t-butoxy radical; the attack is accompanied by hydrogen abstraction and formation of a radical on the benzyl α-carbon atom. This subsequently either decomposes to an aldehyde or undergoes recombination[214].

Ring opening of oxiranes is also caused by radicals[215]. t-Butoxy radicals extract α-hydrogen and epoxy radicals are formed, which are further converted into α-oxo radicals. Alternatively, a β-hydrogen may be extracted and an unsaturated alkoxy radical will result; e.g. propylene oxide reacts when heated with 1 mole per cent of t-butyl peroxide to yield allyl alcohol (reaction 92). 1,2-Butylene oxide give

2-butanone via α-hydrogen extraction as well as crotonaldehyde and crotyl alcohol via β-hydrogen extraction[216].

When stilbene oxide reacts with t-butoxy radicals[217] the dimer

$(C_6H_5\overset{|}{-}CHCOC_6H_5)_2$ is produced via the intermediate radical
$C_6H_5\overset{.}{C}HCOC_6H_5$.

In the presence of m-chlorobenzaldehyde ternary phosphines[218] such as t-butylphosphine oxide[219] have been used in opening oxirane rings. The latter reagent reacts with $trans$-stilbene oxide to yield desoxybenzoin and diphenylacetaldehyde.

XI. REFERENCES

1. A. Lüttringhaus and G. von Sääf, *Angew. Chem.*, **51**, 915 (1938).
2. R. L. Burwell, Jr., *Chem. Rev.*, **54**, 615 (1954).
3. R. E. Parker and N. S. Isaacs, *Chem. Rev.*, **59**, 737 (1959).
4. A. Skrabal and A. Zahorka, *Monatsh. Chem.*, **63**, 1 (1933).
5. F. A. Long and M. A. Paul, *Chem. Rev.*, **57**, 935 (1957).
6. E. Whalley, *Trans. Faraday Soc.*, **55**, 798 (1959).
7. L. L. Schaleger and F. A. Long in *Advances in Physical Organic Chemistry*, Vol. 1 (Ed. V. Gold), Academic Press, London, 1963, pp. 1–33.
8. J. Koskikallio and E. Whalley, *Can. J. Chem.*, **37**, 788 (1959).
9. E. Whalley in *Advances in Physical Organic Chemistry*, Vol. 2 (Ed. V. Gold), Academic Press, London, 1964, pp. 93–162.
10. J. Koskikallio and E. Whalley, *Trans. Faraday Soc.*, **55**, 815 (1959).
11. W. J. LeNoble and M. J. Duffy, *J. Phys. Chem.*, **68**, 619 (1964).
12. D. Jaques and J. A. Leisten, *J. Chem. Soc.*, 2683 (1964).
13. J. F. Bunnett, E. Bunzel and K. V. Nahabedian, *J. Am. Chem. Soc.*, **84**, 4136 (1962).
14. J. F. Bunnett and E. Bunzel, *J. Am. Chem. Soc.*, **83**, 1117 (1961).
15. J. F. Bunnett, *J. Am. Chem. Soc.*, **83**, 4956 (1961); **82**, 499 (1960).
16. L. Zucker and L. P. Hammett, *J. Am. Chem. Soc.*, **61**, 2791 (1939).
17. H. Kwart and A. L. Goodman, *J. Am. Chem. Soc.*, **82**, 1947 (1960).
18. W. M. Schubert and R. H. Quacchia, *J. Am. Chem. Soc.*, **85**, 1284 (1963).
19. J. K. Addy and R. E. Parker, *J. Chem. Soc.*, 915 (1963).
20. R. L. Burwell, Jr., and M. E. Fuller, *J. Am. Chem. Soc.*, **79**, 2332 (1957).
21. A. Butlerow, *Ann. Chem.*, **118**, 325 (1861).
22. S. Zeisel, *Monatsh. Chem.*, **6**, 989 (1885).
23. M. W. Anderson, J. L. Duncan, M. A. Herbrich and S. S. H. Zaidi, *Analyst*, **88**, 353 (1963).
24. H. J. Jacobsen, E. H. Larsen and S.-O. Lawesson, *Tetrahedron*, **19**, 1867 (1963).
25. S.-O. Lawesson and C. Frisell, *Arkiv. Kemi*, **17**, 393 (1961).
26. W. Lippert, *Ann. Chem.*, **276**, 148 (1893).
27. B. V. Tronov and L. V. Ladigina, *Chem. Ber.*, **B62**, 2844 (1929).
28. O. Diels and F. Bunzl, *Chem. Ber.*, **38**, 1486 (1905).
29. K. Kratzl and G. E. Mischke, *Monatsh. Chem.*, **94**, 753 (1963).
30. K. V. Sarkanen and C. W. Dence, *J. Org. Chem.*, **25**, 715 (1960)

31. C. A. Bunton, E. D. Hughes, C. K. Ingold, D. I. H. Jacobs, M. H. Jones, G. J. Minkoff and R. I. Reed, *J. Chem. Soc.*, 2628 (1950).
32. G. Wittig, W. Boll and K. H. Kruck, *Chem. Ber.*, **95**, 2514 (1962).
33. D. J. Pasto, *J. Am. Chem. Soc.*, **84**, 3777 (1962).
34. W. Gerrard and M. F. Lappert, *J. Chem. Soc.*, 1486 (1952).
35. C. A. Stewart and C. A. VanderWerf, *J. Am. Chem. Soc.*, **76**, 1259 (1954).
36. T. Cohen, M. Dughi, V. A. Notaro and G. Pinkus, *J. Org. Chem.*, **27**, 814 (1962).
37. F. N. Hayes and C. Gutberlet, *J. Am. Chem. Soc.*, **72**, 3321 (1950).
38. J. I. Jones, *J. Chem. Soc.*, 2735 (1957).
39. W. J. Hickinbottom and D. R. Hogg, *J. Chem. Soc.*, 4200 (1954).
40. C. L. Stevens and B. T. Gilles, *J. Am. Chem. Soc.*, **79**, 3448 (1957).
41. C. L. Stevens, R. L. McLean and A. J. Weinheimer, *J. Am. Chem. Soc.*, **80**, 2276 (1958).
42. C. L. Stevens and S. J. Dykstra, *J. Am. Chem. Soc.*, **75**, 5975 (1953).
43. T. B. Zalucky, L. Malspeis and G. Hite, *J. Org. Chem.*, **29**, 3143 (1964).
44. S. Searles, Jr., K. A. Pollart and F. Block, *J. Am. Chem. Soc.*, **79**, 952 (1957).
45. F. A. Long, J. G. Pritchard and F. E. Stafford, *J. Am. Chem. Soc.*, **79**, 2362 (1957).
46. S. Searles, Jr., and E. F. Lutz, *J. Am. Chem. Soc.*, **81**, 3674 (1959).
47. C. S. Rondestvedt, Jr., *J. Org. Chem.*, **26**, 3024 (1961).
48. S. Fried and R. D. Kleene, *J. Am. Chem. Soc.*, **63**, 2691 (1941).
49. W. Reppe, *Ann. Chem.*, **596**, 117 (1955).
50. K. Freudenberg, H. Wilk, H.-U. Lenck, L. Knof and T. H. Fung, *Ann. Chem.*, **630**, 1 (1960).
51. G. Wittig and L. Pohmer, *Chem. Ber.*, **89**, 1349 (1956).
52. E. Wenkert and T. Stevens, *J. Am. Chem. Soc.*, **78**, 5627 (1956).
53. E. Wolthius, B. Bossenbroek, G. DeWall, E. Geels and A. Leegwater, *J. Org. Chem.*, **28**, 148 (1963).
54. A. Skrabal and Z. Skrabal, *Z. Physik. Chem.*, **A181**, 449 (1938).
55. E. D. Hughes and C. K. Ingold, *J. Chem. Soc.*, 251 (1935).
56. R. L. Burwell, Jr., L. M. Elkin and L. G. Manor, *J. Am. Chem. Soc.*, **73**, 2428 (1951).
57. F. R. Mayo, W. B. Hardy and C. G. Schultz, *J. Am. Chem. Soc.*, **63**, 426 (1941).
58. A. Y. Drummond and A. M. Eastham, *J. Am. Chem. Soc.*, **79**, 3689 (1957).
59. W. Hoffmeister, *Chem. Ber.*, **3**, 347 (1870).
60. V. E. Stimson and E. J. Watson, *Chem. Ind. (London)*, 207 (1961).
61. H. Hart and H. S. Eleutario, *J. Am. Chem. Soc.*, **76**, 1379 (1954).
62. H. Hart and R. Elia, *J. Am. Chem. Soc.*, **83**, 985 (1961).
63. H. H. Wassermann and N. E. Aubry, *J. Am. Chem. Soc.*, **78**, 1726 (1956).
64. O. N. Witt and C. Schmidt, *Chem. Ber.*, **25**, 1913 (1892).
65. R. Daniels, R. T. Grady and L. Bauer, *J. Org. Chem.*, **27**, 4710 (1962).
66. R. Daniels, R. T. Grady and L. Bauer, *J. Am. Chem. Soc.*, **87**, 1531 (1965).
67. D. Jaques and J. A. Leisten, *J. Chem. Soc.*, 4963 (1961).
68. K. Okamoto, K. Takeuchi and M. Shingu, *Bull. Chem. Soc. Japan*, **37**, 276 (1964); *Chem. Abstr.*, **60**, 11863h (1964).
69. L. A. Kipriano and A. F. Rekasheva, *Dokl. Akad. Nauk SSSR*, **142**, 589 (1962).

70. D. M. Jones and N. F. Wood, *J. Chem. Soc.*, 5400 (1964).
71. T. H. Fife, *J. Am. Chem. Soc.*, **87**, 1084 (1965).
72. R. F. Brown and E. F. Claflin, *J. Am. Chem. Soc.*, **80**, 5960 (1958).
73. R. P. Ghaswalla and F. G. Donnan, *J. Chem. Soc.*, 1341 (1936).
74. J. G. Pritchard and F. A. Long, *J. Am. Chem. Soc.*, **78**, 2667, 6008 (1956).
75. J. H. Brewster, *J. Am. Chem. Soc.*, **78**, 4061 (1956).
76. F. A. Long and J. G. Pritchard, *J. Am. Chem. Soc.*, **78**, 2663 (1956).
77. H. Kwart and L. B. Weisfield, *J. Am. Chem. Soc.*, **80**, 4670 (1958).
78. G. David and S. D. Hamann, *Trans. Faraday Soc.*, **50**, 1188 (1954).
79. W. J. LeNoble, *J. Phys. Chem.*, **67**, 2451 (1963).
80. M. W. Miller, *J. Org. Chem.*, **28**, 1148 (1963).
81. J. K. Addy and R. E. Parker, *J. Chem. Soc.*, 644 (1965).
82. C. K. Ingold, *Structure and Mechanism in Organic Chemistry*, Cornell University Press, Ithaca, New York, 1953.
83. R. M. Laird and R. E. Parker, *J. Am. Chem. Soc.*, **83**, 4277 (1961).
84. J. Koskikallio and E. Whalley, *Can. J. Chem.*, **37**, 783 (1959).
85. F. Patat, *Chimia Aarau*, **18**, 233 (1964).
86. B. Wojtech and F. Patat, *Z. Physik. Chem.*, **25**, 39 (1960).
87. Y. Ishii, S. Sakai and T. Sugiyama, *Bull. Japan Petrol. Inst.*, **5**, 44 (1963).
88. D. J. Worsfold and A. M. Eastham, *J. Am. Chem. Soc.*, **79**, 897 (1957).
89. C. C. Price and M. Osgan, *J. Am. Chem. Soc.*, **78**, 4787 (1956).
90. R. Stoermer and B. Kahlert, *Chem. Ber.*, **34**, 1812 (1801).
91. G. K. Hughes and E. O. P. Thompson, *J. Proc. Roy. Soc. N.S. Wales*, **83**, 269 (1950); *Chem. Abstr.*, **46**, 928c (1952).
92. A. Klemenc, *Monatsh. Chem.*, **33**, 375 (1912).
93. Y. Ogata and M. Okano, *J. Am. Chem. Soc.*, **71**, 3211 (1949).
94. J. Gierer and I. Kunze, *Acta Chem. Scand.*, **15**, 803 (1961).
95. W. Mayer, R. Fikentscher, J. Schmidt, and O. Th. Schmidt, *Chem. Ber.*, **93**, 2761 (1960).
96. K. Tokoyama, *J. Pharm. Soc. Japan*, **76**, 897 (1956); *Chem. Abstr.*, 51, 2644 g (1957).
97. H. Salkowski, *Ann. Chem.*, **174**, 257 (1874).
98. E. Hertel and J. Dressel, *Z. Physik. Chem.*, **B29**, 178 (1935).
99. J. F. Bunnett and T. K. Brotherton, *Chem. Ind.* (*London*), 80 (1957).
100. D. J. Cram, C. A. Kingsbury and A. Langmann, *J. Am. Chem. Soc.*, **81**, 5785 (1959).
101. C. H. Hauser and S. W. Kantor, *J. Am. Chem. Soc.*, **73**, 1437 (1951).
102. D. Y. Curtin and S. Leskowitz, *J. Am. Chem. Soc.*, **73**, 2630 (1951).
103. A. C. Birch, *Quart. Rev.* (*London*), **4**, 69 (1950).
104. H. C. Chitwood and B. T. Freuer, *J. Am. Chem. Soc.*, **68**, 680 (1946).
105. R. M. Laird and R. E. Parker, *J. Chem. Soc.*, 6065 (1963).
106. N. S. Isaacs and R. E. Parker, *J. Chem. Soc.*, 3497 (1960).
107. F. Fischer and H. Ronsch, *Chem. Ber.*, **94**, 901 (1961).
108. D. R. Boyd and E. R. Marle, *J. Chem. Soc.*, **105**, 2117 (1914).
109. H. Meerwein, U. Eisenmenger and H. Matthiae, *Ann. Chem.*, **566**, 15 (1950).
110. F. Patat and B. Wojtech, *Makromol. Chem.*, **37**, 1 (1960).
111. F. Patat and E. Wittmann, *Z. Naturforsch.*, **189**, 169 (1963).
112. J. Itakura and F. Patat, *Makromol. Chem.*, **68**, 158 (1963).

113. F. Patat, *Pure Appl. Chem.*, **4**, 333 (1962).
114. C. Hartmann and L. Gattermann, *Chem. Ber.*, **25**, 3531 (1892).
115. W. Menzel and M. Froehlich, *Chem. Ber.*, **75**, 1055 (1942).
116. C. Szanty, *Acta Chim. Acad. Sci. Hung.*, **12**, 83 (1957).
117. W. Gerrard, *Chem. Rev.*, **58**, 1081 (1958).
118. H. Ramser and E. Wiberg, *Chem. Ber.*, **63**, 1136 (1930).
119. E. Wiberg and W. Sütterlin, *Z. Anorg. Allgem. Chem.*, **202**, 21 (1931).
120. W. Gerrard and M. F. Lappert, *J. Chem. Soc.*, 1020 (1951).
121. R. D. Youssefyeh and Y. Mazur, *Tetrahedron Letters*, 1287 (1962).
122. T. G. Bonner, E. J. Bourne and S. McNally, *J. Chem. Soc.*, 2929 (1960).
123. F. Schmidt, *U.S. Pat.*, 2,700,048 (1955); *Chem. Abstr.*, **49**, 15946a (1955).
124. M. S. Malinovskii, *J. Gen. Chem. USSR*, **10**, 1918 (1940); *Chem. Abstr.*, **35**, 4736 (1941).
125. J. D. Edwards, W. Gerrard and M. F. Lappert, *J. Chem. Soc.*, 1470 (1955).
126. J. D. Edwards, W. Gerrard and M. F. Lappert, *J. Chem. Soc.*, 348 (1957).
127. D. J. Worsfold and A. M. Eastham, *J. Am. Chem. Soc.*, **79**, 900 (1957).
128. A. B. Borkovec, *J. Org. Chem.*, **23**, 828 (1958).
129. S. Sekiguchi, I. Takase and K. Matsui, *Kogyo Kagaku Zasshi*, **66**, 1827 (1963); *Chem. Abstr.*, **60**, 14346h (1964).
130. W. Gerrard, M. J. Frazer and S. N. Mistry, *Chem. Ind. (London)*, 1263 (1958).
131. S. Winstein and R. B. Henderson in *Hetereocyclic Compounds*, Vol. I (Ed. R. C. Elderfield), John Wiley and Sons, New York, 1950, p. 1.
132. H. O. House, D. J. Reif and R. L. Wasson, *J. Am. Chem. Soc.* **79**, 2490 (1957).
133. H. O. House and D. J. Reif, *J. Am. Chem. Soc.*, **77**, 6525 (1955).
134. H. O. House and D. J. Reif, *J. Am. Chem. Soc.*, **79**, 6491 (1957).
135. H. O. House and B. D. Ryerson, *J. Am. Chem. Soc.*, **83**, 979 (1961).
136. A. C. Cope, P. A. Trumbull and E. R. Trumbull, *J. Am. Chem. Soc.*, **80**, 2844 (1958).
137. M. N. Rerick and E. L. Eliel, *J. Am. Chem. Soc.*, **84**, 2356 (1962).
138. H. O. House, *J. Am. Chem. Soc.*, **77**, 3070 (1955).
139. G. Wittig, *Experientia*, **14**, 389 (1958).
140. P. Schorigin, *Chem. Ber.*, **43**, 1931 (1910).
141. R. L. Letsinger, A. W. Schnizer and E. Bobko, *J. Am. Chem. Soc.*, **73**, 5708 (1951).
142. D. H. Gould, K. H. Schaaf and W. L. Rough, *J. Am. Chem. Soc.*, **73**, 1263 (1951).
143. A. A. Morton and A. E. Brachman, *J. Am. Chem. Soc.*, **76**, 2973 (1954).
144. R. L. Letsinger and D. F. Pollart, *J. Am. Chem. Soc.*, **78**, 6079 (1956).
145. K. Ziegler and H. G. Gellert, *Ann. Chem.*, **567**, 185 (1950).
146. R. L. Letsinger and E. Bobko, *J. Am. Chem. Soc.*, **75**, 2649 (1953).
147. K. A. Kun and H. G. Cassidy, *J. Org. Chem.*, **27**, 841 (1962).
148. K. E. Piotrovskii and M. P. Stotskaya, *Dokl. Akad. Nauk SSSR*, **135**, 868 (1960); *Chem. Abstr.*, **55**, 13300i (1961).
149. G. Wittig and L. Lohmann, *Ann. Chem.*, **550**, 160 (1949).
150. G. Wittig and E. Stahnecker, *Ann. Chem.*, **605**, 69 (1957).
151. P. T. Lansbury and V. A. Pattison, *J. Am. Chem. Soc.*, **84**, 4295 (1962).
152. V. Schöllkopf and D. Walter, *Ann. Chem.*, **654**, 27 (1962).

153. V. Schöllkopf and W. Fabian, *Ann. Chem.*, **642**, 1 (1961).
154. P. T. Lansbury and V. A. Pattison, *J. Org. Chem.*, **27**, 1933 (1962).
155. V. Schöllkopf and M. Eisert, *Angew. Chem.*, **72**, 349 (1960).
156. S. J. Cristol, J. R. Douglass and S. J. Meek, *J. Am. Chem. Soc.*, **73**, 816 (1951).
157. H. Gilman, B. Hofferth and J. B. Honeycutt, *J. Am. Chem. Soc.*, **74**, 1594 (1952).
158. D. F. Hoeg and D. L. Lusk, *J. Am. Chem. Soc.*, **86**, 816 (1964).
159. D. F. Hoeg, J. F. Forrette and D. L. Lusk, *Tetrahedron Letters*, 2059 (1964).
160. G. Wittig and G. Kolb, *Chem. Ber.*, **93**, 1469 (1960).
161. V. Grignard, *Compt. Rend.*, **151**, 322 (1910).
162. E. Späth, *Monatsh. Chem.*, **35**, 319 (1914).
163. A. Lüttringhaus, G. von Sääf and K. Hauschild, *Chem. Ber.*, **71**, 1673 (1938).
164. N. G. Gaylord and E. J. Becker, *Chem. Rev.*, **49**, 413 (1951).
165. C. L. Stevens, M. L. Weiner, and C. T. Lenk, *J. Am. Chem. Soc.*, **76**, 2698 (1954).
166. C. L. Stevens and W. Holland, *J. Org. Chem.*, **23**, 781 (1958).
167. R. C. Huston and H. E. Tiefenthal, *J. Org. Chem.*, **16**, 673 (1951).
168. S. Searles, Jr., *J. Am. Chem. Soc.*, **73**, 124 (1951).
169. F. R. Jensen and R. L. Bedard, *J. Org. Chem.*, **24**, 874 (1959).
170. M. S. Kharasch, L. Biritz, W. Nudenberg, A. Bhattacharaya and N. C. Yang, *J. Am. Chem. Soc.*, **83**, 3229 (1961).
171. M. S. Kharasch, R. D. Mulley and W. Nudenberg, *J. Org. Chem.*, **19**, 1477 (1954).
172. R. L. Huang, *J. Chem. Soc.*, 3725 (1958).
173. R. O. C. Norman and W. A. Waters, *J. Chem. Soc.*, 950 (1957).
174. R. L. Huang and S. S. Si-Hoe, *J. Chem. Soc.*, 3988 (1957).
175. R. L. Huang and S. Singh, *J. Chem. Soc.*, 3183 (1959).
176. N. G. Gaylord, *Reduction with Complex Metal Hydrides*, Interscience Publishers, New York, 1956.
177. L. M. Soffer and E. W. Parotta, *J. Am. Chem. Soc.*, **76**, 3580 (1954).
178. P. Karrer and O. Ruttner, *Helv. Chim. Acta*, **33**, 812 (1950).
179. B. R. Brown and G. A. Somerfield, *Proc. Chem. Soc.*, 7 (1958).
180. V. L. Tweedie and M. Cuscurida, *J. Am. Chem. Soc.*, **79**. 5463 (1957).
181. V. L. Tweedie and B. G. Barron, *J. Org. Chem.*, **25**, 2023 (1960).
182. W. G. Brown in *Organic Reactions*, Vol. 6 (Ed. R. Adams), John Wiley and Sons, New York, 1951, p. 476.
183. A. Feldstein and C. A. VanderWerf, *J. Am. Chem. Soc.*, **76**, 1626 (1954).
184. R. Fuchs and C. A. VanderWerf, *J. Am. Chem. Soc.*, **76**, 1631 (1954).
185. C. L. Stevens and T. H. Coffield, *J. Am. Chem. Soc.*, **80**, 1919 (1958).
186. C. L. Stevens and T. H. Coffield, *J. Org. Chem.*, **23**, 336 (1958).
187. S. Searles, Jr., K. A. Pollart and E. F. Lutz, *J. Am. Chem. Soc.*, **79**, 948 (1957).
188. H. Kwart and T. Takeshita, *J. Org. Chem.*, **28**, 670 (1963).
189. E. L. Eliel and D. W. Delmonte, *J. Am. Chem. Soc.*, **80**, 1744 (1958).
190. E. L. Eliel and M. N. Rerick, *J. Am. Chem. Soc.*, **82**, 1362 (1960).
191. W. J. Bailey and F. Marktscheffel, *J. Org. Chem.*, **25**, 1797 (1960).
192. J. J. Eisch and J. T. Trainor, *J. Org. Chem.*, **28**, 2870 (1963).
193. P. Schorigin, *Chem. Ber.*, **57**, 1627 (1924).

194. W. Schlenk and E. Bergmann, *Ann. Chem.*, **464**, 1 (1928).
195. K. Ziegler and F. Thielmann, *Chem. Ber.*, **56**, 1740 (1923).
196. D. R. Moore, *J. Org. Chem.*, **26**, 3596 (1961).
197. H. Gilman, H. A. McNinch and D. Wittenberg, *J. Org. Chem.*, **23**, 2044 (1958).
198. K. Ziegler and H. Dislich, *Chem. Ber.*, **90**, 1107 (1957).
199. D. H. Eagle, Jr., *J. Org. Chem.*, **28**, 1703 (1963).
200. H. Gilman and J. J. Dietrich, *J. Am. Chem. Soc.*, **80**, 380 (1958).
201. J. J. Eisch, *J. Org. Chem.*, **28**, 707 (1963).
202. J. J. Eisch and W. C. Kaska, *Chem. Ind. (London)*, 470 (1961).
203. J. J. Eisch and A. M. Jacobs, *J. Org. Chem.*, **28**, 2145 (1963).
204. L. Reggel, R. A. Friedel and I. Wender, *J. Org. Chem.*, **22**, 891 (1957).
205. E. L. Eliel and T. E. Hoover, *J. Org. Chem.*, **24**, 938 (1959).
206. C. D. Hurd and G. L. Oliver, *J. Am. Chem. Soc.*, **81**, 2795 (1959).
207. M. F. Shostakovskii and S. P. Lavrov, *Dokl. Akad. Nauk SSSR*, **124**, 128 (1957); *Chem. Abstr.*, **52**, 1056i (1958).
208. S. Kohoma, *Nippon Kagaku Zasshi*, **81**, 1602 (1960); *Chem. Abstr.*, **56**, 2467e (1962).
209. H. Gilman and W. J. Trepka, *J. Organomet. Chem.*, **1**, 222 (1964).
210. H. Gilman, D. Aoki and D. W. Wittenberg, *J. Am. Chem. Soc.*, **81**, 1107 (1959).
211. D. W. Wittenberg, D. Aoki and H. Gilman, *J. Am. Chem. Soc.*, **80**, 5933 (1958).
212. D. W. Wittenberg and H. Gilman, *J. Am. Chem. Soc.*, **80**, 2677 (1958).
213. M. K. M. Ng and G. R. Freeman, *J. Am. Chem. Soc.*, **87**, 1635 (1965).
214. H. G. Ang, R. L. Huang and H. G. Sim, *J. Chem. Soc.*, 4841 (1963).
215. C. Sabatino and R. J. Gritter, *J. Org. Chem.*, **28**, 3437 (1963).
216. T. J. Wallace and R. J. Gritter, *Tetrahedron*, **19**, 657 (1963).
217. R. L. Huang and H. H. Lee, *J. Chem. Soc.*, 2500 (1964).
218. A. J. Speziale and D. E. Bissing, *J. Am. Chem. Soc.*, **85**, 1888 (1963).
219. D. E. Bissing and A. J. Speziale, *J. Am. Chem. Soc.*, **87**, 1405 (1965).

CHAPTER **3**

Directive and activating effects of alkoxy and aryloxy groups in aromatic and aliphatic reactions

G. Kohnstam and D. L. H. Williams

University of Durham, England

I. INTRODUCTION

The effect of methoxy substituents on chemical equilibria, rates of reaction, and isomer proportions in aromatic substitution has been extensively studied by many workers, often because the introduction of this group provides useful information about reaction mechanisms and structure–reactivity relations. Other alkoxy groups have received less attention, but this is not as great a disadvantage as might appear at first sight since different alkoxy derivatives usually show closely similar reactivities even when their rates of reaction are vastly greater than those of the parent compound, as for example in the halogenation of benzene (section VI.B.2). In the absence of complicating features (e.g. steric factors and neighbouring-group effects) the reactivity of an alkoxy compound can therefore be predicted reasonably reliably from data for the methoxy derivative. Greater differences in kinetic behaviour are observed when alkoxy and phenoxy substituents are compared, and further modifications can be expected when substituents are introduced into the aromatic nucleus. Substituted phenoxy groups have, however, been studied on only a few occasions.

It is clearly not possible to discuss all the reactions which have been investigated but it is hoped that the examples quoted will indicate the general behaviour of the substituents.

The systematic IUPAC nomenclature has not been employed invariably throughout this chapter as it was felt that a clear picture would often emerge more readily by describing compounds as o-, m-, and p-derivatives. This applies particularly to discussions of the reactivities of substituted anisoles relative to the reactivity of anisole itself.

A. The Polar Effects of Substituents

The introduction of a substituent alters the rates of reactions (or chemical equilibria) by causing different changes in the stabilities (free energies) of the initial and transition states (or final states); the polar character of the substituent is usually an important factor in determining the magnitude of these changes. Alkoxy and aryloxy groups show electron attraction by the general inductive effect $(-I)$, but they can also release electrons by the conjugative effect $(+T)$. The magnitude of both effects is intermediate between those shown by secondary amino and fluoro groups, as shown by the following sequence:

$$-I \text{ effect} \qquad F > RO \text{ (ArO)} > R_2N$$

$$+T \text{ effect} \qquad R_2N > RO(ArO) > F.$$

Both modes of electron displacement can be subdivided into a permanent polarization and a polarizability effect; the latter depends on the electric field acting on the substituent (i.e. on the polar nature of other groups present) and may therefore support or oppose the permanent polarization. It is, however, convenient to neglect this subdivision in the present discussion though it must be borne in mind that the magnitudes of the $-I$ and $+T$ effects may vary considerably from one system to another; this applies particularly to conjugative electron release.

These polar effects are well established and are therefore only outlined below. Further details can be obtained by reference to standard works[1].

1. The inductive effect

The $-I$ effect of alkoxy and aryloxy groups arises from the different electronegativities of oxygen and carbon. The electrical centre of gravity of the C—O valency electrons is therefore displaced towards the oxygen atom and the resulting dipole induces partial positive charges over the rest of the molecule (1). The transmission of this type

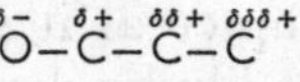

$$\overset{\delta-}{R}O-\overset{\delta+}{C}-\overset{\delta\delta+}{C}-\overset{\delta\delta\delta+}{C}$$
(1)

of electron displacement along a saturated chain is heavily damped so that the influence of a $-I$ group on a reaction rate (or equilibrium) can be expected to decrease rapidly with increasing distance from the reaction centre. Inductive effects can also be relayed to another site in the molecule by electrostatic interaction through the space between groups. This can be of importance in ring systems [2, 3] but the magnitude of any such transmission again decreases with increasing separation. In addition inductive electron displacements may be relayed conjuga-

(2)

tively in suitable systems (e.g. 2), but any such effect will be obscured in alkoxy compounds by the accompanying electron release $(+T)$.

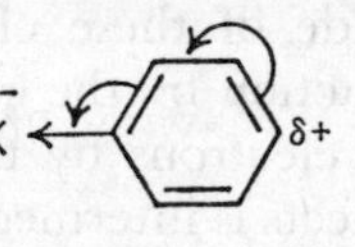

2. The conjugative effect

The $+T$ effect of alkoxy and aryloxy groups arises from the tendency of the unshared electrons to increase the covalency of the oxygen atom. The resulting electron displacement can be relayed to other sites in the molecule by conjugation, as illustrated for anisole (3);

(3)

these displacements will occur to that extent which leads to the minimum energy for the system. As the unshared electrons are relatively easily polarized, the presence of electron-attracting or other highly polarizable centres at other sites in the molecule will enhance conjugative electron release, so that the electron displacements will be more marked in *p*-nitroanisole (**4**) than in **3**. On this view, an increase

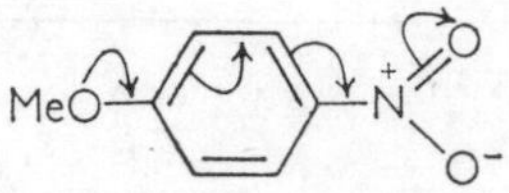

(4)

in $+ T$ electron release is associated with an enhanced stability of the system. Alternatively, the situation can be described by regarding anisole as a resonance hybrid in which the valence-bond forms (**5**) contribute significantly to the final structure, but not as much as **6** contributes to the final structure of *p*-nitroanisole.

(5)

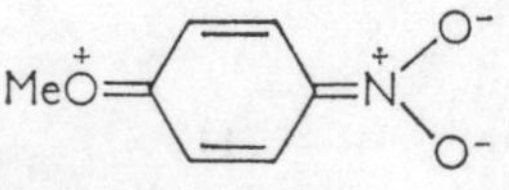

(6)

Obviously, the full operation of the $+ T$ effect and its efficient relay to other parts of the molecule requires a planar system. If the coplanarity of the various groups involved is destroyed (e.g. by the introduction of bulky *ortho* substituents in aromatic compounds) a reduction of $+ T$ electron release by alkoxy and aryloxy groups can be expected. The general problem of steric inhibition of resonance has been reviewed [4, 5], and all the considerations put forward in this and the preceding subsection are fully supported by physical properties such as dipole moments [6, 7], conjugation energies [7, 8], electrical polarizability [9], and light absorption [7, 10, 11]. For example the effect of other groups on the $+ T$ release by a methoxy group is particularly well illustrated by the extinction coefficients of substituted anisoles in the neighbourhood of 2800 Å[10]; some of the results are given in Table 1. The elec-

TABLE 1. Extinction coefficients of substituted anisoles[10].

Compound		$\lambda_{max.}$(Å)	ϵ
MeO—⬡	(7)	2700	1400
MeO—⬡—NO$_2$	(8)	3050	13000
MeO—⬡—⬡	(9)	2596	27000
MeO—⬡ (Me, Me)	(10)	2650	600
MeO—⬡—NO$_2$ (Me, Me)	(11)	2763	3000
MeO—⬡—NO$_2$ (Me, Me)	(12)	2886	9500

tronic transitions involved correspond qualitatively to electron displacements along the axis of the system, and the large increase in the extinction coefficient of anisole (7) on the introduction of a p-nitro or p-phenyl group (8 and 9) clearly demonstrates the enhancement of the

$+ T$ effect of the methoxy group by these substituents. Similarly, the small extinction coefficients of the dimethyl derivatives (**10, 11,** and **12**) relative to the compounds from which they are derived (**7** and **8**) are fully consistent with the steric inhibition of conjugation expected from the loss of coplanarity in the resonating system. This type of behaviour is also exemplified by the fact that the dipole moment is reduced from 4·76 in *p*-nitroanisole to 3·69 in *p*-nitroethoxydurene (**13**) [6b].

(**13**)

B. General Considerations

The present considerations of the $-I$ and $+T$ effects of alkoxy and aryloxy groups are supported by a vast amount of chemical information. Some of the evidence is discussed later in this chapter, but the effects are now so well established that it is convenient to reverse the procedure and to consider the experimental observations in terms of the electron displacements which can occur in the systems under consideration.

In general the introduction of alkoxy and aryloxy groups does not cause radical changes in reactivity by the operation of the $-I$ effect, especially when the substituent is at some distance from the reaction centre. The resulting electron displacement is greater for a phenoxy than for a methoxy group since phenyl itself, unlike methyl, attracts electrons. Although the efficient transmission of the $+T$ effect to another site in the molecule requires a fully conjugated system, the consequences of the $-I$ effect are often obscured by the much greater capacity for electron release $(+T)$ even when this requirement is not met. This applies particularly to the *p*-alkoxy phenyl group which tends to act as an overall donor of electrons under these conditions, relative to the phenyl. Apparently *p*-$ROC_6H_4CH_2CH_2X$ (say) involves a significant contribution from the valence-bond structure **14**; this

(**14**)

seems to be sufficient to reverse the consequences of the $-I$ effect of the alkoxy group and to allow the inductive transmission of the negative charge to the reaction centre (X).

On the other hand, the m-alkoxyphenyl group almost invariably behaves as an overall electron-attracting group but, nevertheless, does not always withdraw electrons from a reaction centre as strongly as would have been expected if no $+T$ effect had been operating (cf. reference 11). This second-order relay of $+T$ electron release can arise from electrostatic interaction through space between the reaction centre and the negative charge resulting from a contribution of the valence-bond structure 15, but this relay appears to be less effective

$$RO^+ \quad \text{---} \text{CH}_2\text{---}\text{CH}_2\text{---}X$$

(15)

than in 14 although both 14 and 15 can be expected to be of similar importance in determining the structure of the respective molecules.

The efficient relay of the $+T$ effect to another site in a molecule requires a fully conjugated system but there is evidence that this transmission also becomes damped with increasing distance (see section IV.C.2). Nevertheless, the accelerating effect of the p-methoxy group can be very large, as it is very sensitive to the electron demand at a reaction centre to which it is conjugated; for example the approximately 1000-fold acceleration of the protodesilylation of phenyltrimethylsilane[12] is increased to a factor of about 10^{10} in the molecular bromination of benzene[13,14]. The available evidence suggests that these large accelerations arise essentially from a reduction in the activation energy on the introduction of a p-methoxy group; in some cases the accompanying change in the entropy of activation even tends to retard the reaction[15]. As a result, the increase in reaction rate caused by alkoxy and aryloxy substitution can depend markedly on the temperature; for example the ratio $k_{p'\text{-MeO}}/k_H$ for the hydrolysis of p-nitrodiphenylmethyl chloride in 85% aqueous acetone decreases from 5×10^5 at $0°$ to 5×10^4 at $50°$[16].

All the available chemical evidence suggests that the magnitude of the $+T$ effect decreases in the order: HO > MeO > PhO. The behaviour of the phenoxy group is not unexpected since conjugative electron release will be hindered by the electron-attracting phenyl group, and the apparently anomalous position of the hydroxy group has been interpreted in terms of hyperconjugation of the H—O linkage[17] and the greater solvation stabilization of $H—\overset{+}{O}=$ relative to $Me—\overset{+}{O}=$[12].

II. STRUCTURE–REACTIVITY RELATIONS

The vast amount of information which is now available about the effect of substituents on reaction rates and equilibria has stimulated many attempts to correlate structure with reactivity. The resulting relations (linear free energy or structure–reactivity relations) have been based on empirical or semiempirical considerations but their theoretical implications have often been examined and discussed. While these relations have been successfully employed in the recognition of the main reaction types and in the discussion of the mechanistic details operating in some reactions, the correlations are usually not quantitative within the limits of the experimental error of the actual determinations, and the stage has not yet been reached when the various parameters can be predicted from purely theoretical considerations. A detailed discussion is beyond the scope of this chapter and, in any case, several excellent reviews have been published during the last few years[18-23]. The present section is therefore limited to an outline of the main features which are relevant to the discussion of alkoxy and aryloxy substituents.

A. The Hammett Equation

Most of the present relations between the rate or equilibrium constant of a substituted derivative (k_X) and that of its parent compound (k_H) are of the same form as the original Hammett equation[24] (equation 1) although a variety of different sets of substituent constants (σ)

$$\log (k_X/k_H) = \sigma\rho \tag{1}$$

have been proposed for different types of reaction. Positive values of the reaction constant (ρ) show that electron-attracting substituents (positive σ) facilitate the reaction under consideration, and vice versa. It seems reasonable to consider that the value of σ reflects the magnitude of the electron displacement caused by the substituent at the site of substitution, and that ρ is a measure of the sensitivity of the stability of the transition state (or final state) to changes in the electron densities, relative to the initial state. As a result ρ is not solely controlled by the electron demand at the reaction centre but also depends on the structure of the system which governs, among other factors, the efficiency of the transmission to the reaction centre of electron displacements initiated by the substituent.

It was originally assumed that equation (1) would only apply to systems where the introduction of substituents does not alter the standard entropy change ($\Delta S°$ or $\Delta S^{\ddagger}$) of the process since σ must be independent of the temperature. However, this condition is also met by the isokinetic relation (2) which was found to apply to many re-

$$\Delta H_X - \Delta H_H = \alpha(\Delta S_X - \Delta S_H) \tag{2}$$

action series[25]. On the other hand, a large number of processes show the linear relation between $\log k_X$ and σ required by equation (1) although a similar relation does not hold for $\Delta H^{\ddagger}$ and $\Delta S^{\ddagger}$, and it is noteworthy that p-methoxy and p-phenoxy substituents decrease $\Delta S^{\ddagger}$ for the S_N1 hydrolysis of diphenylmethyl chloride by about 4 cal/deg at 50°, while many other substituents leave $\Delta S^{\ddagger}$ virtually unaltered[15]. Similarly, specific interactions between the solvent and the substituent which do not occur in the standard series employed for establishing σ may well invalidate equation (1) when such interactions do not occur on the same relative scale with all substituents. Again, alkoxy and aryloxy groups can be expected to be particularly favourable to the operation of such specific solvation effects since the interaction between the medium and the positive charge on the oxygen atom (see structures 5) may differ greatly from one solvent to another (see also reference 26). The general question of entropy and solvation effects has been discussed by Ritchie and Sager[23], and these effects probably represent one of the factors which prevent equation (1) from being a completely precise relation for some reactions.

Equation (1) must inevitably fail to correlate substituent effects if the polar requirements of the system are altered by some substitutions; i.e. if substituents alter the reaction mechanism or the kinetic importance of the individual steps in a multistage process. This situation is easily recognized when both electron-attracting and electron-releasing groups accelerate the reaction, as in the reactions of benzyl halides with relatively strong nucleophiles[27, 28]; several other examples have been given by Grunwald and Leffler[19].

I. The substituent constants σ and σ^-

The original Hammett substituent constants (σ) were obtained by taking ρ as unity for the ionization of benzoic acids in water; they gave good correlations for a large number of reactions[24]. Values of σ are now available* for a number of alkoxy and phenoxy groups[29,30], and a selection is given in Table 2.

It was, however, recognized from the beginning[24] that 'exalted' σ values were required for substituents capable of $-T$ electron attraction when they were conjugated to an electron-releasing reaction centre, as in the ionization of *para*-substituted phenols and anilinium ions. The resulting substituent constants (σ^-)[31] have also been found to give good correlations in nucleophilic aromatic substitution for most substituents[20,32] but the methoxy group appears to be highly anomalous, different reactions often requiring different values of σ^-. Thus the ionization of phenols leads to $\sigma^- = -0\cdot11$, the ionization of anilinium ions to $\sigma^- = -0\cdot25$, and nucleophilic aromatic substitution to $\sigma^- \approx -0\cdot60$[20]. It seems reasonable to expect that the $+T$ effect of the methoxy group will be suppressed to some extent when this group is conjugated to an electron-releasing reaction centre. As a result σ^- should be less negative than σ, but it can be seen that even this requirement is not always met, since $\sigma = -0\cdot27$ (see Table 2).

2. The substituent constant σ^+

Reactions in which substituents capable of $+T$ electron release are conjugated to an electron-demanding reaction centre have been found to give poor correlations with σ; alkoxy and aryloxy groups clearly belong to this class. Electrophilic substituent constants (σ^+) were initially obtained from the S_N1 hydrolysis of *para*-substituted 2-phenyl-2-propyl chlorides (16) where the polar requirements of the transition

(16)

state are unambiguous[33], and have given good correlations for a wide variety of electrophilic aromatic substitution reactions[21,34] as well as

* In the subsequent pages of this chapter σ denotes the Hammett substituent constants obtained from the ionization of benzoic acids. Other substituent constants will be identified by the conventional subscripts or superscripts.

for numerous other processes (see reference 23). As expected, σ^+ is more negative than σ for p-methoxy and p-phenoxy groups (see Table 2).

Several authors have seriously questioned the concept of the three distinct sets, σ, σ^-, and σ^+, for *para* substituents* and have argued that a continuous range of substituent constants, corresponding to a range of conjugation and polarization, is to be expected for substituents which can conjugate directly with the reaction centre. This prediction has been confirmed by two different sets of workers who found such a continuous range within the limiting values of σ^- and σ^+ for methoxy, phenoxy, and other polarizable substituents in various cases where conjugation can occur[35, 36]. On the other hand, Brown and Stock have provided strong evidence for the application of σ^+ to a variety of electrophilic aromatic substitution reactions having widely differing reaction constants (ρ)[21, 34], and therefore consider that a revision is required of the notion that resonance stabilizations in anisole will necessarily alter as the electrophilic properties of the reagent are modified. Their general conclusion about the validity of σ^+ in these reactions is, however, weakened by a number of inconsistencies[37].

It has already been pointed out that the accelerating effect of the methoxy group can be very large (section I.B). Under these conditions the determination of the ratio $k_{p\text{-MeO}}/k_H$ often requires comparisons of several different derivatives in different solvents or at widely different temperatures, and may therefore be subject to inaccuracies which could obscure small changes in the substituent constant. Evidence that the changes expected for the substituent constants of methoxy and phenoxy groups with increasing electron demand in a conjugated system do occur has been obtained for the effect of substituents (X) in the S_N1 hydrolysis of diphenylmethyl chlorides (**17** where Y = MeO, H, NO$_2$) in 85% aqueous acetone[38]. The resulting substituent constant for the methoxy group (Y = H) is more negative than σ^+ and suggests

(17)

* For *meta* substituents, $\sigma = \sigma^- = \sigma^+$.

that σ^+ derived from the hydrolysis of 2-phenyl-2-propyl chlorides[33] may require revision since the ratio k_X/k_H has the same value in both these systems for most of the substituents studied. The discrepancy may arise from inaccuracies in the solvent correction[39] when σ^+ was calculated and it is noteworthy that the methoxy group, the most accelerating substituent studied in many electrophilic substitution reactions[34], requires a different substituent constant in the hydrolysis of alkyl aryl halides if the results obtained with **17** are reliable.

Many other reactions which give a better correlation with σ^+ than with σ for a variety of substituents nevertheless appear to require substituent constants for methoxy substituents which differ significantly from σ^+. Ritchie and Sager have drawn attention to the surprising feature that reaction centres may be sufficiently electron-deficient to require direct conjugation with electron donors without causing a large value of ρ for the reaction[23]. It must also be stressed that although the conjugation effect might be expected to increase with increasing ρ[40], this prediction is contrary to much of the available evidence which shows little relation, if any, between these two factors[34, 35, 41, 42].

3. Other substituent constants

It is now generally agreed that conjugation with the substituent can occur in the benzoic acids (see section III.C) and that the values of σ are therefore not free from direct conjugation effects. In attempts to overcome this difficulty new scales of 'normal' substituent constants have been proposed by Wepster and his coworkers[35] (σ^n) and by Taft[36, 43] (σ°) from results for systems in which the substituent is insulated from the reaction centre; in general these two scales differ little from each other. It has, however, been argued that the values of σ^n do not entirely eliminate the polar effect of the substituent on the resonance interaction of the reaction centre with the benzene ring, and a further scale (σ_G) which is held not to suffer from this disadvantage has been established from a study of the saponification of ethyl phenyl acetates[44]. Table 2 shows that σ^n, σ°, and σ_G are negative for the p-methoxy group, presumably because some of the positive charge created in the resonance stabilization of the aromatic nucleus is transmitted inductively to the site of the reaction (see section I.B).

Comparison of σ^n (or σ°) with the substituent constant ($\sigma_{obs.}$) required by processes in which the substituent is conjugated to the reaction centre provides information about the additional resonance stabilization of the transition state (or final state) relative to the initial state. Wepster and his coworkers have, however, pointed out[35] that erroneous conclusions would result by merely considering the 'exaltation' of the substituent constant $(\sigma_{obs.} - \sigma^n)$ and that the magnitude of this stabilization is given by equation (3). This expression has been

$$\Delta F_X - \Delta F_H = -2 \cdot 303RT\rho(\sigma_{obs.} - \sigma^n) \tag{3}$$

applied to a number of systems containing p-methoxy substituents, and values of $\Delta F_X - \Delta F_H$ have been found to be -5 kcal or less in some cases[35].

The first successful attempt to correlate aliphatic reactivities by equation (1) was based on a study of 4-substituted bicyclo[2.2.2]octane-1-carboxylic acids[3] where the substituents exert their effect by the transmission of the inductive effect through space. The work led to a scale of aliphatic polar substituent constants $(\sigma_I(al.))$. This scale has been extended by Taft and his coworkers to other substituents, including methoxy and phenoxy groups in the course of their general study of the separation of substituent effects in aliphatic systems into polar (inductive), resonance (conjugative), and steric contributions. Details of this work can be obtained from Taft's review[45] and from other discussions of structure–reactivity relationships[19, 20, 23].

Striking success has also been achieved by Taft and his coworkers in separating the polar and resonance effects of substituents in aromatic reactivities[43, 46]; the assumptions made in this treatment have been examined critically by Wells[20] and by Ritchie and Sager[23]. The polar (inductive) substituent constants $(\sigma_I(ar.))$ were usually the same as $\sigma_I(al.)$, but this does not apply to phenoxy groups (see Table 2). On the other hand, no common scale independent of the nature of the reaction could be found for the resonance (conjugative) contribution (σ_R) and while such a scale appeared to apply to some *meta* substituents, the methoxy group could not be included unless only reactions with a small electron demand were considered. A precise scale for these effects (σ_R°) could, however, be defined for systems in which direct conjugation with the reaction centre is prohibited, and σ_R° was interpreted as indicating the ability of the substituent to undergo conjugation with the benzene ring. This scale is related to σ° by equation (4).

$$\sigma^\circ = \sigma_I(ar.) + \sigma_R^\circ \tag{4}$$

It is noteworthy that the chemical shifts arising from ^{19}F in the nuclear magnetic resonance spectra of *meta*-substituted fluorobenzenes are correlated extremely well by $\sigma_I(ar.)$ [36], and that the differences of these chemical shifts for the corresponding m- and p-fluorobenzenes give excellent correlations with σ_R° [36,47].

Steric effects may operate when *ortho* substituents are examined, and values of 0·99 and 0·90 have been assigned to the steric substituent constants (E_S) of methoxy and phenoxy groups in *ortho*-substituted benzoates[45].

TABLE 2. Mean values of substituent constants.

	CF$_3$O		PhO		MeO	
	meta	*para*	*meta*	*para*	*meta*	*para*
σ	0·47	0·28	0·25	−0·32	0·12	−0·27
σ^-	—	—	—	—	—	−0·2
σ^+	—	—	—	−0·5	0·05	−0·78
σ^n	—	—	—	—	—	−0·11
σ°	0·48	0·42	—	—	0·13	−0·12
σ_G	—	—	—	—	—	−0·05
σ_I(al.)	—	—	0·38	—	0·25	—
σ_I(ar.)	0·55	(0·55)^a	0·48	(0·48)^a	0·28	∼ (0·28)^a
σ_R°	−0·13	−0·18	−0·31	—	−0·41	−0·43

^{a} It is assumed that σ_I(ar.) has the same value for *meta* and *para* substituents.

4. Comparison of different substituent constants

Ritchie and Sager have collected the mean values of the various substituent constants for many groups[23]. Their values for perfluoromethoxy, phenoxy, and methoxy groups are given in Table 2 and require only a few additional comments; values for other alkoxy groups are not shown but they are very similar to those for the methoxy group.

The positive values of σ_I(al.) and σ_I(ar.) and the negative values of σ_R° are fully consistent with the $-I$ and $+T$ effects shown by these groups; so is the fact that *meta* substituents always show more positive values than the corresponding *para* substituents. The decrease in the values of the substituent constants almost invariably follows the sequence: CF$_3$O > PhO > MeO, as expected from the decrease of the $-I$ effect of the organic groups in the order: CF$_3$ > Ph > Me; the σ value for the p-phenoxy group is, however, anomalous.

In general the values of σ, σ^n, σ°, and σ_G for a given substituent are very similar[23] but this does not apply to the present groups. It is also noteworthy that $\sigma_{\text{I}}(\text{ar.})$, $\sigma_{\text{R}}^{\circ}$, and σ° do not bear the relation required by equation (4). Virtually all the difficulties in the application of linear free-energy relations, such as equation (1), have arisen when polarizable groups were considered and it may well be that even the present diversity of scales of substituent constants is not sufficient to account for all the reactions involving the highly polarizable alkoxy and aryloxy groups.

B. Other Structure–Reactivity Relations

Several authors have attempted to attack the problem of variable conjugative effects by adding further parameters to equation (1). Tsuno and Yakawa[48] obtained good correlations for a number of electron-demanding reactions with equation (5), where the resonance parameter (r) depends only on the nature of the reaction and is taken

$$\log (k_{\text{X}}/k_{\text{H}}) = \rho[\sigma + r(\sigma^+ - \sigma)] \tag{5}$$

as unity for the hydrolysis of 2-phenyl-2-propyl chlorides. This equation has been employed successfully by other workers and it has been found that r is not related to ρ in the sense that one must increase with the other[42, 49a,b,c], a conclusion which renders any interpretation of r difficult. Another three-parameter equation proposed for electrophilic aromatic substitution[41] suffers from the disadvantage of requiring increased conjugation effects as ρ increases (see section II.A.2). In a different attempt to take the conjugation effect into account Hine[50] allowed different ρ values for meta and para reactivities, and incorporated a separate resonance term in the expression for para reactivities. This treatment resulted in a further scale of resonance substituent constants but sufficient data are not available to test the general validity of the approach, although excellent correlations were obtained in some cases.

It is of course inevitable that the introduction of a further disposable parameter in equation (1) should improve the correlation of substituent effects in related reactions, but some pessimism must be expressed about the possibility of obtaining precise results when polarizable substituents are considered. Even equation (6) which contains four

$$\log (k_{\text{X}}/k_{\text{H}}) = \rho'\sigma' + \rho''\sigma'' \tag{6}$$

disposable parameters, and corresponds to the operation of two completely independent interaction mechanisms[51] with the ratio ρ'/ρ''

remaining constant, does not give internally consistent results for the S_N1 hydrolysis of the three highly similar reaction series based on 17[38].

For this reason, and because of the uncertainty in the choice of the scale of substituent constants, the subsequent discussion of the effects of alkoxy and phenoxy substituents on chemical reactions is not based solely on structure–reactivity relations.

III. EQUILIBRIA

Changes in equilibrium constants arising from the introduction of alkoxy and aryloxy groups are discussed below in terms of the alterations in the stabilities of the initial and final states caused by these substituents. The overall polar effect resulting from the two opposing electron displacements $(-I \text{ and } +T)$ is often small but its direction can be established, if necessary, by the use of unambiguously electron-attracting or -releasing groups (e.g. nitro and methyl). This supporting evidence has usually been omitted for reasons of space.

A. Ionization Constants of Carboxylic Acids and their Derivatives

No direct conjugation is possible between a substituent and the carboxylate group in acetic acid and its derivatives. Changes in the acid dissociation constant can therefore only arise from the operation of the inductive effect, or from the inductive transmission of conjugative electron displacements in other parts of the molecule. Since 18 repels electrons more strongly than 19, electron-attracting substituents

(18)   (19)

should stabilize 18 more than 19; they should therefore increase the dissociation constant (K), and vice versa.

Table 3 shows the effect of alkoxy and phenoxy groups on the ionization constants (K_X/K_H) of some carboxylic acids in which no direct conjugation can occur. It can be seen that a phenoxy group increases the strength of acetic acid more than an ethoxy group, as expected from the differences in the $-I$ effects (see section II.A.3); other alkoxy groups, which are not shown, have similar effects to the ethoxy group. In compounds 20–23 the o- and p-methoxy groups act as overall

4+c.e.l.

TABLE 3. Values of the ratio K_X/K_H for carboxylic acids and their derivatives in aqueous solution[a].

Carboxylic acid		Substituent (X)			Ref.
		EtO		PhO	
XCH_2CO_2H		12·7		38·6	52
		o-MeO	m-MeO	p-MeO	
$XC_6H_4CH_2CO_2H$	(20)	—	—	0·89	53
$XC_6H_4CH_2CH_2CO_2H$	(21)	0·72	1·01	0·93	53
$XC_6H_4OCH_2CO_2H$	(22)	0·87	1·07	0·91	52
$XC_6H_4NHCH_2CO_2H$	(23)	—	1·02	0·78	54

[a] The figures refer to the equilibrium $RCO_2H \rightleftharpoons RCO_2^- + H^+$.

electron-releasing groups but the m-methoxy group shows electron attraction. This kind of behaviour is fairly general even when the substituents are not directly conjugated with the reaction centre, and has already been discussed (section I.B); in any case the effects are obviously small. The conjugative effect will be relayed to the carboxylate group in 20 and 21, but such a relay to the oxygen atom of phenoxyacetic acid (22) or to the nitrogen atom in the phenylamino derivative (23) would be sufficient to modify the electron attraction of the phenoxy or phenylamino group in the observed direction.

It is noteworthy that the introduction of an o-methoxy group decreases acid strengths a little more than the introduction of a p-methoxy group. This could arise from the fact that 24 makes a greater contribution to the structure of the anisyl residue than 25, but the opposite

(24)   (25)

conclusion has already been proposed in connection with electrophilic aromatic substitution (see section VI.B.1) and a solvation effect could equally well be responsible (see section III.C). A similar result is observed for o- and p-methyl groups in 22[52], but not in 21[53]. The ratio K_X/K_H has the same value for p-methoxy and p-methyl groups in 22 and 23, suggesting approximately the same overall electron release by both groups.

B. Oxygen and Nitrogen Bases

The effect of methoxy substituents on the dissociation constants (K_X/K_H) of phenol and the conjugate acids of some nitrogen bases is shown in Table 4. Electron release towards the reaction centre of the amines and anilines stabilizes the acid (**26**) more than the base (**27**),

and should therefore give a decrease in K. Similar considerations apply to phenol, although it would be more correct to consider that here the result is a consequence of the greater destabilization of the base relative to the acid. Since a p-methoxy group generally acts as an overall donor of electrons its introduction should decrease K and the electron-attracting m-methoxy group should increase K.

TABLE 4. Values of the ratio K_X/K_H for phenol and conjugate acids of nitrogen bases.

Acid		Substituent (X)			
		o-MeO	m-MeO	p-MeO	Ref.
XC_6H_4OH	(**28**)	1·00	2·19	0·60	52
$XC_6H_4NH_3{}^+$	(**29**)[a]	1·35	2·63	0·21	53
$XC_6H_4NMe_2H^+$	(**30**)	0·052	—	0·112	53
$XC_6H_4CH_2NH_3{}^+$	(**31**)	0·42	1·51	0·73	53
$XC_6H_4NH_2{}^+CH_2CO_2H$	(**32**)[b]	—	2·93	0·19	54
$XC_6H_4NH_2{}^+CH_2CO_2H$	(**32**)[c]	—	2·51	0·15	54
$XC_5H_4NH^+$	(**33**)	132	1·86	0·051	55

[a] The values for the ethoxy substituent are very similar to those for the methoxy substituent.
[b] For $-NH_2{}^+CH_2CO_2H \rightleftharpoons -NH_2{}^+CH_2CO_2{}^-$.
[c] For $-NH_2{}^+CH_2CO_2H \rightleftharpoons -NHCH_2CO_2H + H^+$.

These predictions are fully confirmed by the figures in Table 4*. The acid-weakening effect of the p-methoxy group is least in benzylamine (**31**) where the substituent is furthest removed from the reaction centre, and greatest in pyridine (**33**) where direct conjugation can be

* The equilibria involving phenylaminoacetic acid (**32**) can be expected to be controlled by the changes in the electron density of the nitrogen atom which is closer to the substituent than the carboxylate group.

expected to provide additional stabilization of the acid by a contribution from structure **34**. Conjugation in this compound may also account

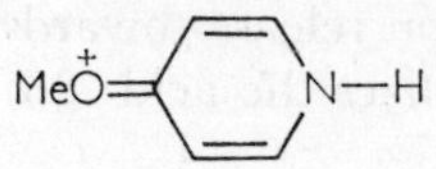

(34)

for the fact that the ratio K_X/K_H for the *m*-methoxy group is less than might have been expected from the proximity of this group to the reaction centre. Thus, the suggested contribution[55] from structure **35**

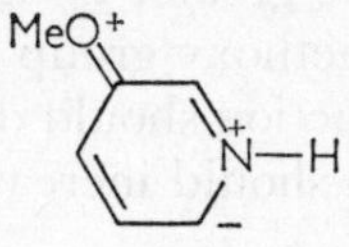

(35)

would presumably stabilize the acid by electrostatic interaction of the positive and negative charges. Similarly, the analogue of **35** has also been proposed to account for the acid-weakening effect of 6-alkoxy substituents in 4-chloroquinolines[56a] (**36**) where the acid strengthen-

(36)

ing expected from the operation of the $-I$ effect is apparently less than in *m*-methoxypyridine, probably because of the greater distance between the substituent and the reaction centre.

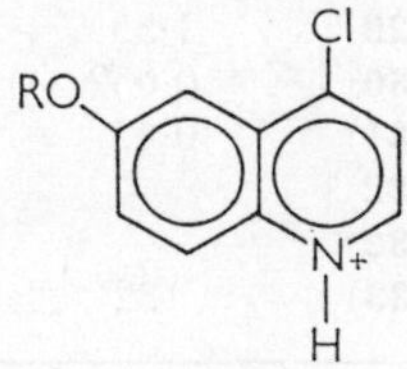

The values of the ratio K_X/K_H for the *o*-methoxy substituent are less easily explained. The small effect of the substituent in phenol (**28**) and aniline (**29**) could arise from a virtual cancellation of the opposing $-I$ and $+T$ electron displacements*, and electrostatic interaction

---

* The consequences of a $-I$ effect can be expected to be more marked for *ortho* than for *para* substituents.

between the charges in structures **37** and **38** would also tend to increase

K. However, this interpretation is not supported by the figures for di-methylaniline (**30**) and benzylamine (**31**) where $K_{o\text{-OMe}} \simeq \frac{1}{2} K_{p\text{-OMe}}$, and it is difficult to see why $+ T$ electron release should be much more important in these compounds than in **28** and **29**. Hydrogen bonding between the methoxy group and N—H or C—H has been postulated on a number of previous occasions to account for abnormal acidities[20]. The six-membered cyclic hydrogen-bonded structures **39** and **40** could

well stabilize the acid forms of **30** and **31,** but an explanation of the results in these terms requires the further assumption of a much smaller stabilization of the conjugate bases by similar interactions. No reason can be advanced for the high acidity of o-methoxypyridine (**33**).

C. Ionization Constants of Conjugated Acids

Direct conjugation effects are likely to operate in the ionization of substituted benzoic acids. Structure **41** will make some contribution to the stability of the acid but this contribution will probably not be large since the molecule contains a hydroxyl group which can release

electrons more efficiently by the $+ T$ effect than the alkoxy group, and which is also nearer to the electron-demanding centre. As a result the valence-bond form **42*** can be expected to have a smaller energy than structure **41** and should therefore be of greater importance in the neutral acid. Conjugation with the substituent, as in **43**, is unlikely to have any significant effect on the stability of the carboxylate ion in view of the much lower energies of the two equivalent structures corresponding to **44**. As a result, *p*-alkoxy and *p*-methoxy groups should

(43)   (44)

stabilize the acid relative to the base and hence reduce K, but it is unlikely that this effect will be large. Acid strengthening arising from the inductive electron attraction $(-I)$ is swamped even in insulated systems, and can therefore be neglected.

An increase in K should, however, occur on introducing the groups in the *meta* position since there is now no direct conjugation, and the *ortho* substituents will tend to turn the carboxylate group out of the plane of the ring, reducing the possibility of resonance. As the $-I$ effect will remain unaltered *o*-alkoxy and *o*-phenoxy groups could easily strengthen the acid and it could even be envisaged that the loss of coplanarity in the derivative is sufficiently serious to prevent any stabilization of the acid by a contribution from structure **41a**; this would result in a further enhancement of the acidity.

(41a)

Considerations similar to those advanced when discussing the benzoic acids (**45**) should also apply to the cinnamic acids (**46**), and Table 5 shows that both sets of methoxy derivatives behave in the expected manner. The effect of the same substitution on K is always less in **46** than in **45**, probably because of the less-crowded situation near

* A contribution from structure **42** has already been proposed[56b] to account for the resonance energy of the carboxylic group (approximately 24 kcal.[8]).

Table 5. Values of the ratio K_X/K_H for conjugated carboxylic acids in water.

Substituent	Acid	
	$XC_6H_4CO_2H^{53}$ (45)	trans-$XC_6H_4CH{=}CHCO_2H^{53}$ (46)
o-MeO	1·285	0·945
m-MeO	1·303	1·153
p-MeO	0·539[a]	0·792
o-PhO	4·736	—
m-PhO	1·786	—
p-PhO	0·478	—

[a] Data for other p-alkoxy derivatives are available[29]; they show little difference from the methoxy derivatives.

the site of substitution (*ortho* derivatives) and the greater distance required for the relay of the electron displacements initiated by the substituent. It is noteworthy that this damping of the transmission of polar effects also appears to apply to the conjugative electron release which is primarily responsible for the acid weakening caused by the *p*-methoxy group (see also section IV.C.2).

Comparison of methoxy and phenoxy substituents in 45 reveals the expected difference in the steric inhibition of resonance by *ortho* groups of different sizes and the greater $-I$ effect of phenoxy groups (*meta* derivatives). However, the strengths of the *para*-substituted acids suggest that the phenoxy group acts as a slightly better electron donor than the methoxy group, contrary to expectation (section I) and most of the other available evidence. A more recent examination[29] of the acidities of 45 does not alter this observation which is also reflected in the σ values of the two groups, and it may well be that the apparent discrepancy arises from solvation effects. These are discussed briefly in the succeeding paragraph.

Table 6. Values of the ratio K_X/K_H for benzoic acids in various solvents.

Solvent	Substituent			Ref.
	o-MeO	m-MeO	p-MeO	
Water	1·285	1·303	0·539	53
25% aq. ethanol	0·912	1·253	0·506	53
10% aq. acetone	0·877	1·390	0·438	57
25% aq. acetone	0·942	1·466	0·621	57

Values of the ratio K_X/K_H for the ionization of methoxybenzoic acids in a number of slightly different solvents are given in Table 6. It is difficult to rationalize these observations when some solvent changes alter the ratio K_X/K_H for all three substituents in the same direction while others do not. Solvation effects of this type are generally accepted as a disturbing feature affecting the quantitative discussion of substituent effects, and it must be stressed that they are not taken into account in linear free-energy relations (equation 1) or in the more qualitative approach based on the consideration of inductive and conjugative effects.

Several workers have discussed the simultaneous effect of several substituents $(X, Y, \ldots)$ in terms of the additivity principle (equation 7), which assumes that the alteration in the standard free-energy

$$\Delta F_{X,Y} \ldots - \Delta F_H = (\Delta F_X - \Delta F_H) + (\Delta F_Y - \Delta F_H) + \ldots \quad (7)$$

change $(\Delta F_{X,Y} \ldots - \Delta F_H)$ is an additive property of the individual substituents. The application of this principle has been shown to be valid for the ionization of 3,4-dimethoxy- and 3,4,5-trimethoxybenzoic acid[58,59], and also for benzoic acids containing one methoxy group and other substituents; equation (7)[58] was only invalid for derivatives containing 2,3- and 2,6-substituents. Further discussion of the additivity principle will be found in section VI.

D. Positively Charged Acids

Stewart and his coworkers have determined the effect of many substituents on the strengths of the conjugate acids of benzaldehyde (47), acetophenone (48), benzoic acid (45), and benzamide (49)[26,60]; their results for methoxy and nitro substituents are shown in Table 7. The strongly electron-demanding reaction centre in the acids derived from

TABLE 7. Values of log (K_X/K_H) for the ionization of positively charged conjugate acids of some bases[26,60].

Base		Substituent		
		m-MeO	p-MeO	p-NO$_2$
XC_6H_4CHO	(47)	—	−1·56	+1·35
$XC_6H_4COCH_3$	(48)	+0·55	−1·34	+1·80
$XC_6H_4CO_2H$	(45)	+0·19	−0·58	+0·73
$XC_6H_4CONH_2$	(49)	—	−0·36	+1·07

47 and 48 ensures a significant stabilization by $+T$ substituents via structure 50, but this will be obscured to some extent by a similar though smaller stabilization of the bases via structure 51. The values of

(50)   (51)

the ratio K_X/K_H for these two compounds correlated well with σ^+ for most substituents, as expected when direct conjugation can occur; a similar correlation for 45 was taken to indicate a symmetrical protonated form (52) rather than 53. Conversely, the results for

(52)   (53)

benzamide (49) gave better agreement with σ, and it was therefore concluded that both protons in the acid were associated with the nitrogen atom since then direct conjugation with the substituent is not possible.

The stabilization of the acid forms of 47 and 48 by a p-methoxy group was, however, less than would have been predicted from the σ^+ plot through all the substituents studied. Attractive interactions between the oxygen atom and the solvent were therefore postulated[26], but the absence of a similar effect in 49 was not consistent with this explanation[60a]. The results can, however, be interpreted in more qualitative terms by permitting a variable capacity for $+T$ electron release by the alkoxy group in a fully conjugated system. Such a variation is readily indicated by comparing the value of log (K_X/K_H) for the p-methoxy substituent with that for the p-nitro substituent which shows virtually no response to an increase in electron demand.

One of the interesting features of these systems is the relatively small stabilization (less than four-fold in 45) of a positively charged centre by a methoxy group which is conjugated to it. This is not an isolated example and the general phenomenon has already attracted comment[23].

E. Miscellaneous Equilibria

Two examples will suffice to illustrate further the wide variations in the effect of alkoxy groups on equilibrium constants.

4*

Baker's values[11] for the methoxy substituent in the cyanohydrin equilibrium of substituted benzaldehydes are given below. Substituents capable of $+T$ electron release will stabilize the aldehyde (47) by direct conjugation with the carbonyl oxygen atom, as in 50, and the cyanohydrin (54) is stabilized by electron-attracting groups.

$$XC_6H_4\overset{OH}{\underset{CN}{\overset{|}{\underset{|}{C}}}H} \quad \rightleftharpoons \quad XC_6H_4CHO + HCN$$

(54)   (47)

X	m-MeO	p-MeO
K_X/K_H	0·97	9·75

The small effect of the m-methoxy group on K, and comparison with the effects of m-methylthio and m-methylseleno groups, led to the conclusion that some of the $+T$ electron release of the methoxy group could be transmitted to a reaction site by a second-order effect when the substituent was in the *meta* position[11]. Comparison with other substituents[61] showed that this system does not follow the requirements of linear free-energy relations, but that K increases with increasing electron attraction and with increasing electron release from its minimum at the m-bromo compound.

The effect of the methoxy group on the equilibrium between arylmethyl carbinols (ROH) and their carbonium ions (R^+) in strongly acid solutions[62] are given in Table 8. The substituents should stabilize

TABLE 8. Values of log (K_X/K_H) for
$$ROH + H^+ \rightleftharpoons R^+ + H_2O\,[62].$$

	R in ROH	
Substituents	Ar_3C	Ar_2CH
4-MeO	3·20	5·4
4,4'-(MeO)$_2$	5·39	7·5
4,4',4''-(MeO)$_3$	7·45	—

R^+ significantly via structures such as 55, and should have virtually no

$$MeO\overset{+}{=}\!\!\left\langle\!\!\!=\!\!\!\right\rangle\!\!=\!\!\overset{|}{\underset{|}{C}}$$

(55)

effect on the stability of the carbinol where no appreciable electron demand exists at the reaction centre. The large values of K_X/K_H fully confirm these predictions.

The successive introduction of 4-methoxy groups results in successively smaller increases in the value of log (K_X/K_H) and the stabilizing effect is clearly greater when R = Ar$_2$CH than when R = Ar$_3$C, probably because stabilization by a larger number of structures such as **56** and **57** reduces the stabilization resulting from **54**. These observa-

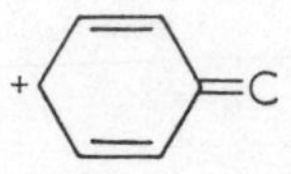

(56) 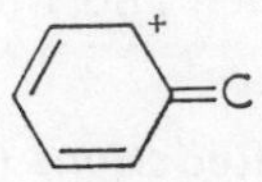   (57)

tions parallel the results for the rates of ionization of arylmethyl halides in quite different solvents (see section IV.C.2). The large stabilization of the positively charged reaction centre in the present systems is in contrast to the very much smaller stabilization of such a centre in the ionization of protonated benzoic acid in a similar solvent. Resonance stabilization of the neutral species is likely to be small in both systems and no explanation of this difference has yet been proposed.

IV. NUCLEOPHILIC ALIPHATIC SUBSTITUTION

It is generally accepted that nucleophilic substitution at a saturated carbon atom can occur by one of two general mechanisms[63–66].

A. The Unimolecular Mechanism ($S_N I$)

The unimolecular process (S_N1) in its simplest form involves only the heterolysis of the bond linking the departing group (A) to the substrate in the rate-determining step with no participation by the nucleophile (B), as shown in **58**; the product is formed by the subsequent

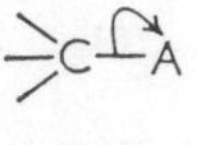

(58)

rapid reaction of the resulting carbonium ion with B. The rate-determining heterolysis is unambiguously favoured by electron release towards the central carbon atom, and alkoxy and phenoxy substituents should therefore substantially accelerate the process if the structure of the system permits direct conjugation with the electron-deficient reaction centre. This conclusion is unaltered by the recognition of the fact[64-67] that reactions of this type often proceed via intermediate ion pairs which may undergo further rapid reactions.

The nature of the nucleophile is immaterial in reaction by this general mechanism, and all the examples have therefore been drawn from the field of solvolytic reactions (see section IV.C) which have been widely studied and which show many interesting features.

B. Bimolecular Reactions (S_N2)

Covalent participation by the nucleophile (B) in the rate-determining step is an essential feature of reaction by the alternative bimolecular mechanism (S_N2). Bond fission and bond formation occur simultaneously as shown in **59**, and the polar requirements of the transition

$$B \overset{\curvearrowright}{} \underset{|}{C} \overset{\curvearrowleft}{-} A$$

(59)

state are now ambiguous since electron donation by substituents to the reaction centre will favour the heterolysis of the C—A linkage but will, at the same time, hinder the formation of the new bond with B[63].

A discussion of the effect of electron displacements on the rates of these reactions involves the relative importance of the bond-breaking and bond-forming processes in the transition state which can be regarded[68] as the resonance hybrid of structures **60–62**. The reaction must be considered bimolecular as long as the contribution of structure **61** is not negligibly small, but it will be recognized that an electron-

$$B \quad \overset{\diagdown}{\underset{\diagup}{C}}{-}A \qquad\qquad B^+{-}\overset{\diagup}{\underset{\diagdown}{C}} \quad A^- \qquad\qquad B \quad \overset{\diagup}{\underset{|}{C^+}}\diagdown A^-$$

(60)   (61)   (62)

releasing substituent may strongly accelerate the reaction (as in S_N1 reactions) by stabilizing a transition state in which structure **62** makes a large contribution (bond-breaking predominant), while it will accelerate less and may even retard the reaction if structure **61** is the main contributor (bond-making predominant); this could apply particularly when the nucleophile (B) carries a negative charge. A wide range of kinetic effects can therefore be expected in bimolecular reactions on the introduction of alkoxy and phenoxy groups even when these groups can stabilize **62** by direct conjugation.

1. Variations in the nucleophile

For a given substrate it seems reasonable to assume that bond formation (i.e. structure **61**) becomes progressively more important as the nucleophilic power of B increases. This behaviour is shown in the bimolecular reactions of p-methoxy- and p-phenoxybenzyl chloride with anions in aqueous acetone (see Table 9) [69]. The p-methoxy group is a

TABLE 9. Reactions of p-methoxy- and p-phenoxy-benzyl chloride with anions in aqueous acetone [69].

Anion	k_{MeO}/k_{PhO}
NO_3^-	139[a]
$PhSO_3^-$	125
Cl^-	87
F^-	86
Br^-	15.5
N_3^-	4.9

[a] The larger values are subject to an error of approximately ±10%; the smaller values are more accurate.

better electron donor by the $+T$ effect than the p-phenoxy group and the decrease of k_{MeO}/k_{PhO} on passing down Table 9 is consistent with a diminishing electron demand at the reaction centre; i.e. an increasing importance of **61**. Alternatively, the results could merely be held to indicate a decrease in the reaction constant ρ with increasing nucleophilic strength.

2. Variations in substrate structure

It must be stressed that the methoxy and phenoxy derivatives need not necessarily react with the same anion by precisely the same mechanism, and there is indeed much evidence to support the view that the structure of S_N2 transition states can be radically altered by the introduction of substituents. Thus, the attack of nucleophiles on benzyl and β-phenylethyl halides is usually accelerated by p-methoxy and p-nitro groups (see Table 10), which is consistent with transition states

TABLE 10. The effect of p-methoxy and p-nitro substituents on reactions of organic halides.

Reaction		k_{MeO}/k_H	k_{NO_2}/k_H	Ref.
$PhCH_2Br + MeO^-$	(63)	17·40	2·57	28b
$PhCH_2Br + PhS^-$	(64)	4·56	6·94	28
$PhCH_2Br + MeOC_6H_4S^-$	(65)	4·42	11·30	28a
$PhCH_2Cl + Me_3N$	(66)	3·07	0·98	70
$PhCH_2Br + Br^-$	(67)	6·16	11·24	27
$PhCH_2CH_2Cl + I^-$	(68)	1·41	5·12	71

in which the importance of bond formation is appreciably increased by the p-nitro group (stabilization of **61**) while p-methoxy results in a much greater significance of the bond-breaking process (stabilization by **62**).

The accelerations caused by the p-methoxy group in the reactions of benzyl halides with relatively strong nucleophiles (reactions **63–67**) are very much less than in solvolysis (see section IV.C.2), and a little larger than in reaction (**68**) where the substituent is at a greater distance from the reaction centre and insulated with respect to direct conjugation. Changes in the electron density at the site of reaction should therefore be less when a p-methoxy group is introduced into β-phenylethyl chloride than into a benzyl halide; this could be held to account for the smaller value of k_{MeO}/k_H. Such a hypothesis is, however, not entirely supported by the values of k_{NO_2}/k_H and appears to be contradicted by the observation that the rates of reactions of primary alkyl halides with iodide ions can be altered between three- and nine-fold on the introduction of ω-alkoxy or ω-phenoxy groups[72]. In these systems changes in the electron density at the reaction centre arising from substitution can only occur by transmission of the inductive effect through a saturated chain, and should therefore be small. Neighbouring-group participation (see section IV.D.1) is very unlikely, and these anomalies probably arise, at least partly, from a comparison of reactions with different nucleophiles in different solvents when relatively minor changes may well be reflected to a disproportionate extent in the small values of k_{MeO}/k_H.

The introduction of a p-methoxy group in the thiophenolate ion accelerates the reaction with benzyl halides[28a] as electron-releasing substituents will increase the nucleophilic power of an anion. The effect of changes in the strength of the nucleophile on k_{MeO}/k_H is shown more strikingly by a comparison of reactions **63** and **64** (see Table 10); the results refer to the same solvent and complement those given in Table 9 since PhS$^-$ is a much stronger nucleophile than MeO$^-$. Although the value of k_{MeO}/k_H is usually not large for S_N2 reactions involving reasonably efficient nucleophiles, it has been estimated that the bimolecular reaction between EtO$^-$ and methyl chloride is accelerated by at least a factor of 10^5 on the introduction of a methoxy group into the chloride[73]. This has been explained in terms of a substantial contribution to the transition state by the relatively stable structure **69** (a particularly stable form of **62**); no similar structure of corresponding importance can be written for methyl chloride.

$$EtO^- \qquad \overset{\displaystyle MeO^+}{\underset{\displaystyle CH_2}{\|}} \qquad Cl^-$$

(69)

C. Solvolytic Reactions

The media employed in studies of solvolysis are always very much weaker nucleophiles than the reagents discussed in section IV.B, and the rates should therefore be more sensitive to the introduction of a methoxy group. This conclusion is, however, only strictly relevant to very few reactions since methoxy derivatives invariably undergo solvolysis by an S_N1 mechanism when the substituent is conjugated to the reaction centre. They should therefore show much larger rates than the parent compounds irrespective of any considerations of the nucleophilic strength of the solvent. Benzyl toluene-p-sulphonate, -chloride, and -bromide react at least partly by an S_N2 mechanism in aqueous solvents[16,74] and in formic acid[75]; the same mechanism can therefore be expected to operate in the solvolysis of their m-methoxy derivatives. Although many different departing groups (A) have been studied (e.g. Cl, Br, TsO*, p-NO$_2$C$_6$H$_4$CO$_2$), there are reasons[76] to believe that the nature of A has very little effect, if any, on the acceleration of S_N1 reactions resulting from the introduction of a methoxy group. This greatly simplifies the discussion of the available information.

* TsO = toluene-p-sulphonate.

I. Alkyl systems

The introduction of 1-alkoxy substituents in n-alkyl halides can be expected to cause an enormous acceleration of solvolysis by mechanism S_N1 since structure **70** should make a substantial contribution to

$$R^1\overset{+}{O}\!\!=\!\!CH_2$$
$$(\mathbf{70})$$

the transition state. No such acceleration should, however, be observed if the alkoxy group is placed at a position further removed from the reaction centre as no conjugation can occur and the substituent can only affect the rate by the highly inefficient transmission of its $-I$ effect*. The results in Table 11 fully confirm these predictions, especially since methyl chloride (**71**) and 2-methoxyethyl chloride (**73**) will undergo S_N2 solvolysis so that k (rel.) for the other compounds underestimates the relative rates for reaction by mechanism S_N1.

TABLE 11. Relative rates for the solvolysis of XCH_2Cl[73, 77].

Substituent (X)		k (rel.)
H	(**71**)	1
MeO	(**72**)	10^{13}
MeOCH$_2$	(**73**)	1
EtO	(**74**)	3×10^{13}
EtOCH$_2$O$_{(1)}$	(**75**)	3×10^{11}
CH$_2$ClO	(**76**)	10^9

The effects shown in Table 11 parallel those in the chlorination of ethers[78] but they are larger in the present systems where the substituent is closer to the site of reaction. As a result, a significant difference is found between methoxy- (**72**) and ethoxymethyl chloride (**74**), which is consistent with a greater capacity for electron release towards oxygen atom in **74**. Similarly, compounds **75** and **76** reflect the influence of inductive electron attraction (by ethoxy and chloro groups) on the $+T$ electron release of $O_{(1)}$, these effects being again greater than in other systems.

Further evidence of the huge acceleration on introducing an alkoxy

* The 4- and 5-substituents can, however, accelerate solvolysis by neighbouring-group participation (see section IV.D.1).

group at the reaction centre is provided by the acid-catalyzed hydroly-sis of diethyl acetal (77) which occurs approximately 10^{11} times more

$$EtO-CH\begin{matrix} Me \\ \\ OEt \end{matrix} \qquad\qquad EtO-CH\begin{matrix} Me \\ \\ H \end{matrix}$$

$$\text{(77)} \qquad\qquad\qquad \text{(78)}$$

rapidly than the corresponding reaction of diethyl ether (78), probably via the rate-determining unimolecular heterolysis of the conjugate acid (78b)[79].

$$EtO\overset{\frown}{-}CHMe\overset{\overset{+}{\frown}}{-}OHEt \longrightarrow EtO\overset{+}{=}CHMe + EtOH$$

$$\text{(78b)}$$

2. Alkylaryl systems

The kinetic effect of methoxy and phenoxy groups on the solvolysis of arylmethyl compounds has often been studied. Some of the avail-able results are given in Table 12 and show all the features expected

TABLE 12. Relative rates ($\log k_X/k_H$) for the hydrolysis of aralkyl systems.

Parent compound	Conditions	Substituent		
		p-PhO	p-MeO	m-MeO[a]
$PhCH_2Cl$	(79a), 70% aq. acetone, 0°	2·78[80]	4·40[80]	−0·18[81]
$PhCH_2OTs$	(80), 85% aq. acetone, 0°	3·06[82]	5·04[82]	−0·22[83]
$PhCH_2Br$	(81), formic acid, 80·17°	—	5·72[75]	—
$PhCHBr=CH_2$	(82), 80% aq. ethanol, 0°	—	5·28[84]	—
$PhCHClC_6H_4NO_2$	(84a), 85% aq. acetone, 0°	3·67[38]	5·72[38]	—
$PhCMe_2Cl$	(83), 90% aq. acetone, 25°	—	3·53[39]	−0·21[39]
Ph_2CHCl	(84b), 85% aq. acetone, 0°	2·84[38]	4·59[38]	—
$PhCHClC_6H_4OMe$	(84c), 85% aq. acetone, 0°	1·40[38]	2·40[38]	—
Ph_3CCl	(85), 60% ethanolic ether, 25°	—	1·95[85]	—

[a] The reaction conditions for the m-methoxy compounds are not always those stated for the *para* compounds.

for a system in which a $-I$, $+T$ substituent can conjugate with an electron-demanding reaction centre. Thus, the p-methoxy group in-creases the rate by factors of between 10^2 and 5×10^5, the p-phenoxy group shows a smaller though still very appreciable acceleration, and the m-methoxy group retards solvolysis by approximately 30%. The introduction of the o-methoxy group into benzyl chloride (**79a**) also enhances the rate (approximately 100-fold)[81], but the effect is much less than for a p-methoxy group, consistent with the assumption of some steric inhibition of resonance in the *ortho* compound. No direct conjugation with the reaction centre can occur in β-phenylethyl chloride and it is therefore not surprising that the p-methoxy group now only accelerates solvolysis three-fold[81]. Other β-phenylethyl systems are discussed in section IV.D under neighbouring-group effects.

The results in Table 12 for the benzyl systems (**79a–81**) underestimate the effect of the substituents on reaction by mechanism S_N1 since the parent compounds undergo partly S_N2 solvolysis. In the other compounds listed the sensitivity of the S_N1 rate to the introduction of a p-methoxy or p-phenoxy group follows the sequence: **82,84a** > **83*,84b** > **84c,85**. This also represents the converse of the order in which the transition states in the reactions of the parent compounds can be stabilized by resonance. This effect has already been discussed in connection with equilibrium studies on arylmethyl cations (see section III.E) and also accounts for the results in Table 13 where

TABLE 13. The effect of increased conjugation on the acceleration of solvolysis by a p-methoxy substituent.

Compound		Log (k_{MeO}/k_H)	Ref.
XCH_2Cl		~ 13	73
p-$XC_6H_4CH_2Cl$	(**79a**)	4·40	80
p-$XC_6H_4C_6H_4CH_2Cl$	(**79b**)	1·04	80
XCH_2Cl	(**72**)	~ 13	73
p-$XC_6H_4CHPhCl$	(**84b**)	4·59	38
p-$XC_6H_4C_6H_4CHPhCl$	(**84d**)	1·01	38

acceleration by a methoxy group can be seen to become progressively less as the conjugated system is lengthened, thus providing an

---

* The discrepancy between the results for **83** and **84b** (see Table 12) arises partly from the fact that the two reactions were studied at different temperatures. Moreover, the p-methoxy derivative of **83** was studied in a solvent different from that employed for the parent compound and the method of interpolation adopted[39] may have caused some error. It is noteworthy, in this connection, that relative rates (k_X/k_H) are generally insensitive to changes in the nature and composition of hydroxylic solvents[86].

explanation of the damping of the transmission of $+T$ electron release through conjugated carbon chains.

The striking decrease of k_{MeO}/k_H on passing from phenyl to diphenyl systems (see Table 13) has also been observed in electrophilic aromatic substitution (see section VI) and has often attracted comment in connection with other reactions. While it has been suggested that the lack of coplanarity between the two benzene rings in diphenyl prevents efficient resonance[87], recent results show that any non-coplanarity in this system does not seriously alter the transmission of conjugative effects[88]. Some of this evidence is considered in section VI.B.2.

A substantial resonance stabilization of the transition state in the reaction of the parent compound could also be responsible for the relatively small effect of methoxy substituents on the rate of S_N1 hydrolysis of 9-chloro-9-phenylfluorene (86) where, in effect, three phenyl groups are attached to the reaction centre. The results[89] show that the similar accelerations caused by 3-methoxy in the fluorene system and by p-methoxy in the phenyl ring of 86 do not differ greatly from that observed in the solvolysis of triphenylmethyl chloride (Table 12); the introduction of 2- or m-methoxy groups retards the reaction:

Substituent	3-MeO	p-MeO	2-MeO	m-MeO
k_{MeO}/k_H	100	150	0·56	0·82

This clear demonstration of the analogy between the 2- and 3-positions in fluorene and the *meta* and *para* positions in phenylmethyl compounds also shows that any electron displacements of the type shown in 87 do not significantly stabilize the transition state in the solvolysis of the 2-methoxy derivative of 86[89].

(86)   (87)

Variations in the structure of the alkoxy substituent have a small but noticeable effect on the rate of solvolysis of p-$XC_6H_4CH_2Cl$[90]:

X	MeO	EtO	i-PrO	t-BuO
k(rel.)	1·00	1·60	2·79	0·70

The reactivity sequence MeO < EtO < i-PrO is consistent with the order of electron release by the alkyl groups towards the oxygen atom, and the relatively low rate for the t-butoxy derivative was considered to arise from a steric effect. The extinction coefficients parallel the observed rates.

It would have been expected that the solvolysis of p-MeOC$_6$H$_4$CH$_2$Cl (**79a**) is retarded by the introduction of a m-methoxy group which should withdraw electrons from the reaction centre, but the 3,4-dimethoxy compound reacts three times more rapidly than **79a** under the same conditions[90]. Smith has suggested[91] an explanation of this observation in terms of the stabilization of structure **88** by electro-

(88)

static interaction between the unshared electrons of the 3-methoxy group and the positive charge on the 4-methoxy group; structure **88** contributes to the transition state of S_N1 solvolysis, but not to the initial state.

The introduction of other substituents in p-MeOC$_6$H$_4$CH$_2$Cl (**79a**) may disturb coplanarity between oxygen and the benzene ring, and should therefore reduce the accelerating effect of the p-methoxy group in solvolysis. This is strikingly demonstrated by two examples[92] shown in Table 14.

An electron-releasing methyl group in the 3-position (**89**) increases the rate of solvolysis of **79a**, probably by a second-order effect which may well be large enough to obscure the consequences of a slight change in the position of the methoxy group resulting from steric effects. There can, however, be no doubt that a further methyl group adjacent to the methoxy group (**90**) causes serious steric inhibition of resonance between the methoxy group and the reaction centre in the transition state. It is noteworthy that the deceleration of solvolysis of **90**, relative to **79a** and **89**, arises mainly from a decrease in the entropy of activation. This observation argues against the general validity of the view[93], proposed for ester hydrolysis, that steric hindrance to solvation in the transition state is an important factor in the retarding effect of the o-methoxy group (relative to the p-methoxy group) since the entropy should increase as solvation is reduced[15].

TABLE 14. Steric effects in the solvolysis of substituted $4\text{-ROC}_6\text{H}_4\text{CH}_2\text{Cl}$[92].

(a)

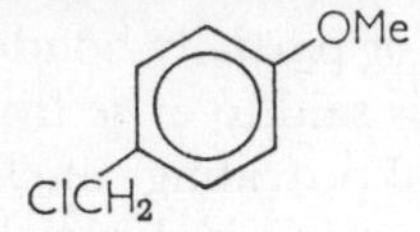

(79)   k(rel) 1·00

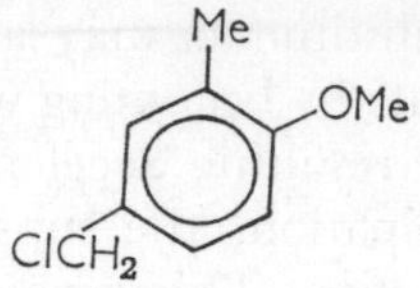

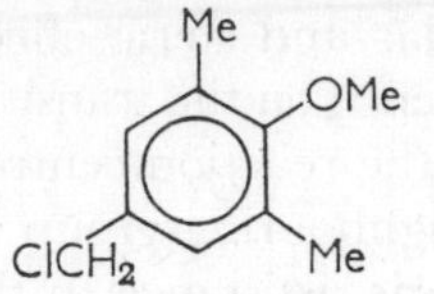

(89)   4·55

(90)   0·31

(b)

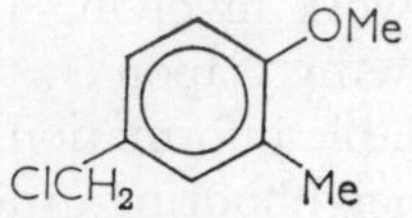

(89)   k(rel) 1·00

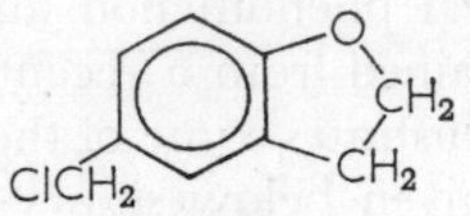

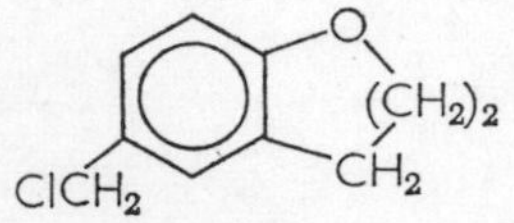

(91)   10·20

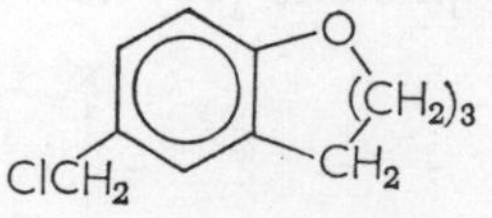

(92)   2·34

(93)   0·06

Alterations in rate resulting from ring closure involving the oxygen atom are shown in Table 14(b). The formation of the five-membered ring (91) actually accelerates solvolysis relative to 89, probably by constraining the system into the optimum configuration for conjugation[90]. Increases in the size of the ring (92 and 93) progressively force the oxygen further out of the plane of the aromatic nucleus, resulting in the expected decrease in rate which is particularly marked for 93. Similar trends have been observed for the bromination[92] of the analogous compounds 94 and 95, where substitution occurs mainly in the

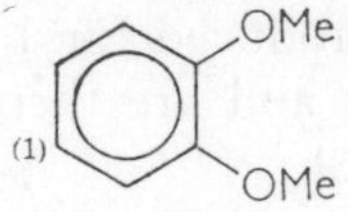

(94)

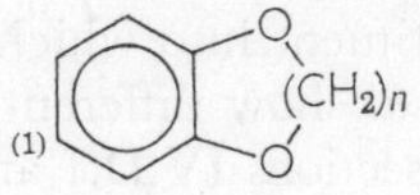

(95)

1-position, and for acid-catalyzed deuterium exchange of their $[1\text{-}^2\text{H}]$ derivatives[94].

D. Neighbouring-group Participation

Apart from affecting rates of chemical reactions by the operation of polar and steric effects, substituents may also exert a stabilizing influence on the transition state by becoming wholly or partially bonded to the reaction centre. The resulting acceleration is said to arise from neighbouring-group participation, the substituent providing anchimeric assistance to the reaction. This type of behaviour is shown by alkoxy derivatives in nucleophilic aliphatic substitution and many examples have been described, mainly by Winstein and his coworkers. Full details of the general phenomenon and of work involving the alkoxy group can be obtained from a recent review by Capon[95]; the present discussion only illustrates some of the available information.

The simple example given below shows that neighbouring-group participation can be recognized by an unexpected acceleration on the introduction of a substituent (X) since the S_N1 solvolysis of the toluene-p-sulphonate (96) now involves a contribution to the transition state

from structure 97. Moreover, the product (98) expected from the reaction of 96 may well be accompanied by 99 since the solvent can

attack the intermediate carbonium ion, or ion pair, at the α- or β-carbon atom if 97 makes a reasonably large contribution to the structure of this intermediate.

The alkoxy group can either provide anchimeric assistance itself (alkoxy participation) or may modify the neighbouring-group effect of a phenyl substituent into which it is introduced (aryl participation). These two cases show different features and are therefore discussed separately, in sections IV.D.1 and IV.D.2.

1. Alkoxy participation

Alkoxy groups provide anchimeric assistance by permitting the co-ordination of the unshared electrons of the oxygen atom with an electron-deficient reaction centre in the molecule, but this naturally requires that the distance between the substituent and the site of reaction should not be too great. In saturated systems the neighbouring group participation appears to be confined to 2-, 4-, and 5-alkoxy groups which can form (or partly form) three-, five-, and six-membered cyclic oxonium ions, as indicated in structures **100–102**; the effects are

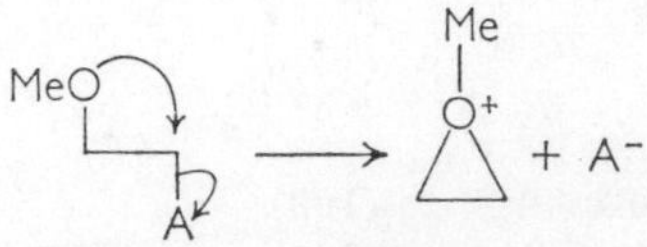

(**100**)

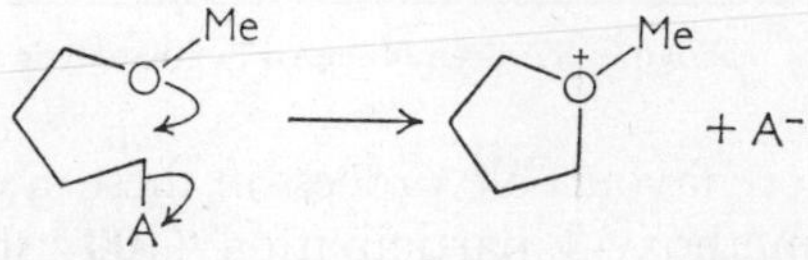

(**101**)

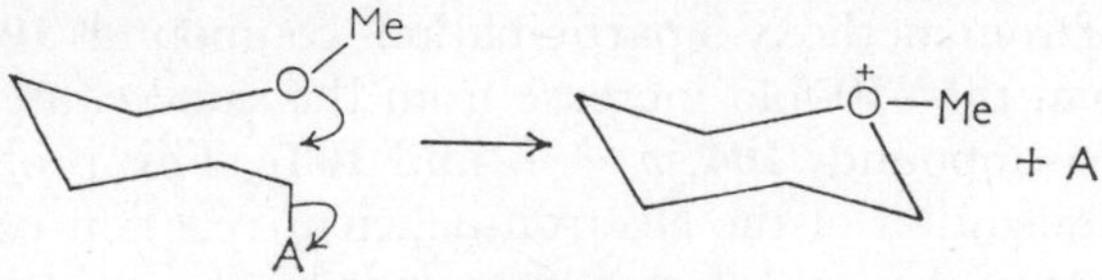

(**102**)

called alkoxy-3, alkoxy-5, and alkoxy-6 participation, respectively. Usually, but not invariably, the resulting acceleration is of a similar order to that arising from the polar effect of the p-methoxy group in the S_N1 solvolysis of triphenylmethyl halides (see Table 12).

The acetolysis of primary alkyl p-bromobenzenesulphonates (**103**) is usually retarded or, at best, accelerated by only 10–20% on the introduction of a ω-methoxy group, as expected from the operation of the $-I$ effect. Table 15(a), however, shows that the 4-methoxybutyl and 5-methoxypentyl compounds (**104**, $n = 4$ and 5) react very much more rapidly than the other members of the series, indicating the operation of anchimeric assistance in the two reactive compounds. Winstein and his coworkers have suggested[96] that the two rapid reactions proceed through the cyclic oxonium ions **101** and **102**, respectively, and the results show that methoxy-5 participation (**101**) is

TABLE 15. The acetolysis of methoxy alkyl p-bromobenzenesulphonates (ROBs)[96].

ROBs		k (rel.)	
(a)[a] Me(CH$_2$)$_3$OBs (103a)		1·00	
MeO(CH$_2$)$_n$OBs (104):	$n = 2$	0·28	
	$n = 3$	0·63	
	$n = 4$	657	
	$n = 5$	123	
	$n = 6$	1·16	
(b) Me(CH$_2$)$_4$OBs (103)		1·00	—
MeCH$_2$CHMeOBs (105)		140	1·00
MeO(CH$_2$)$_3$CHMeOBs (106)		4140	29·6
MeOCHMe(CH$_2$)$_3$OBs (107)		4110	29·4

[a] A similar trend of reactivities has been observed in ethanolysis and formolysis.

energetically the more favourable process in these systems. There is no evidence for any methoxy-3 participation (100) since 104 ($n = 2$) actually reacts more slowly than 103.

Secondary alkyl sulphonates (Table 15 (b)) only show a 30-fold increase in rate from methoxy-5 participation (compounds 106 and 105), much less than the 650-fold increase from the same cause in the primary series (compounds 104, $n = 4$, and 103). This probably arises from the stabilization of the electron-deficient reaction centre in the transition state of the secondary compounds by the electron-releasing 1-methyl substituent so that there is now less need for assistance from the methoxy group*; the stabilizing effect of the 1-methyl group is demonstrated by the 140-fold difference between the rates of 103a and 105. It is also noteworthy that 107 with a secondary methoxy group appears to be more favourable to methoxy-5 participation than 104 ($n = 4$) with a primary methoxy group; this is similar to the accelerating effect of alkyl substituents in other ring-closure reactions[95].

* In valence-bond language the presence of the 1-methyl group stabilizes structure 108 in the transition states of 105 and 106 by inductive and hyper-

$$Me—\overset{/}{\underset{\backslash}{C^+}}$$

(108)

conjugative electron release so that the contribution of 101 to the transition state of 106 is less than its contribution to the transition state of 104 ($n = 4$).

The hypothesis that a reaction involving methoxy-5 participation occurs via the cyclic oxonium ion (**101**) requires that **106** and **107** have the same intermediate in solvolysis and should therefore yield the same products; this is observed[96]. Similarly, methoxy-3 participation (**100**) is indicated for secondary methoxy compounds by the fact that **109**, **110**, and **111** all form methoxyacetates of retained configuration in the

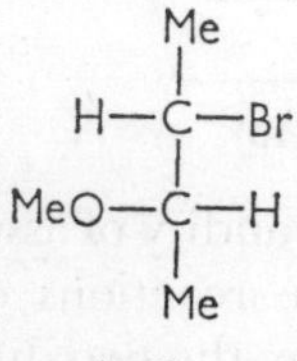

(**109**) 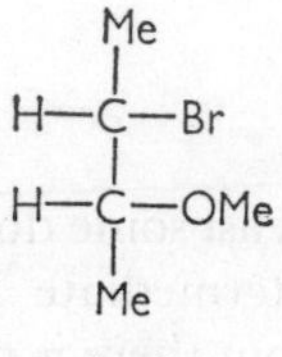   (**110**) 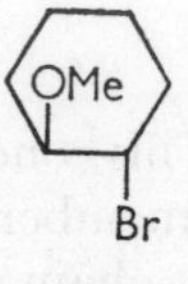   (**111**)

reaction with silver acetate in acetic acid[97]. Similarly, a tertiary methoxy group can provide considerable anchimeric assistance by methoxy-3 participation. Thus the acetolysis of **112** is about 1500 times

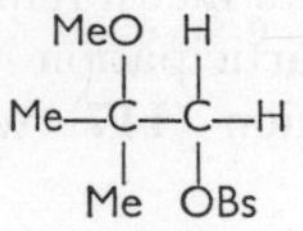

(**112**)

more rapid than the rate calculated for the unassisted reaction, and the products of hydrolysis are also consistent with a substantial participation by the neighbouring group[98].

Assistance by the methoxy group in cyclohexyl systems has been studied by Noyce and his coworkers[99]. The acetolysis of *trans*-3-methoxycyclohexyltoluene-*p*-sulphonate (**113**) occurs at the rate expected in the absence of methoxy-4 participation; there can, of course,

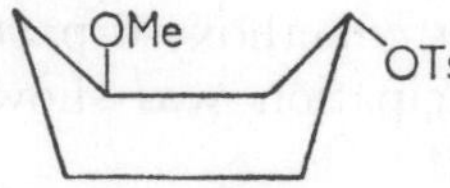

(**113**)

be no question of any such participation for the *cis* compound. However, the *trans*-4-methoxy compound (**114**) reacts 5·6 times more rapidly than estimated for the reaction in the absence of assistance, clear indication of methoxy-5 participation. A thorough study of the

products formed in the reaction of the [1-³H] derivative showed that
solvolysis cannot occur entirely via the intermediate cyclic oxonium
ion (**115**) though structure **115** clearly contributes to the transition

(**114**)   (**115**)

state. This conclusion must cast some doubt on the validity of assuming
a five-membered cyclic intermediate (**101**) in the reactions of the
straight-chain compounds, but there is no reason why the two different
systems should undergo solvolysis via precisely the same paths. Obviously, further work is needed on this problem.

Evidence exists for the direct participation of the methoxy group
attached to a benzene ring, as in **116**. Unfortunately, the conclusions
which can be drawn from rate measurements are complicated by the
fact that methoxy-(n + 4) participation (**116**) may occur side by side
with aryl-(n + 2) participation (**117**) which will be aided by the

(**116**)   (**117**)

presence of the o-methoxy group. Thus, although the solvolysis products of 2-(o-methoxy phenyl)-2-methylpropyl toluene-p-sulphonate
(**118**) show the occurrence of o-methoxy-5 participation, no estimate
can be made of the acceleration resulting from this assistance since the
rate is only about one-tenth of that for the *para* isomer[96,100]. There is,
however, no doubt about o-methoxy-6 participation in the 3-propyl
system (**119**). Aryl participation was shown to be unimportant in

(**118**)   (**119**)

acetolysis and formolysis (from work on the *p*-methoxy compounds) and the acceleration provided by the *o*-methoxy group from anchimeric assistance was found to be approximately 20-fold for **119** (R = H), and greater for **119** (R = Me)[96].

2. Aryl participation

Phenyl groups have been shown to be capable of providing anchimeric assistance on many occasions. Thus, the acetolysis of neophyl *p*-bromobenzenesulphonate (**120**) proceeds about 80 times faster than that of the isobutyl compound[101], clear evidence of aryl$_{(1)}$-3 participation from a contribution of structures such as **121** to the transition state.

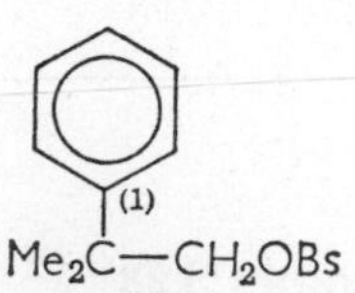

Me$_2$C—CH$_2$OBs

(**120**)

Me$_2$C—CH$_2$

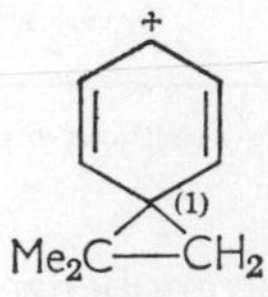

(**121**)

The introduction into the benzene ring of substituents which can release electrons towards the aryl$_{(1)}$ position should obviously assist aryl$_{(1)}$-3 participation, and it has been found that the kinetic effect of such substituents correlates well with σ^+; $\rho = -2.96$[101]. The acceleration resulting from *p*-methoxy substituents is about 250-fold, similar to that resulting from direct conjugation with the reaction centre in the S_N1 ethanolysis of triphenylmethyl chloride (Table 12) though it must be stressed that any comparison of the two reactions is rendered difficult since they refer to entirely different solvents.

As in alkoxy participation, the anchimeric assistance is greatly reduced when a secondary alkyl sulphonate is employed. Thus the replacement of H$_{(1)}$ in 1-methylpropyl toluene-*p*-sulphonate (**122**) by a

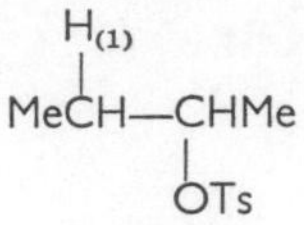

H$_{(1)}$
|
MeCH—CHMe
|
OTs

(**122**)

p-methoxyphenyl group accelerates acetolysis approximately 45-fold[102], compared with the factor of 2×10^4 for the same alteration of isobutyl toluene-*p*-sulphonate[101].

The effect of increasing the distance between the aromatic ring and the reaction centre on the accelerating effect of the methoxy group in $aryl_{(1)}$ participation is illustrated in Table 16 for the acetolysis of some

TABLE 16. The effect of methoxy substitution in the aromatic ring on the acetolysis of $Ph(CH_2)_nOBs$ [103]

		k (rel.)		
		H	4-MeO	2,4-(MeO)$_2$
$Ph(CH_2)_nOBs$ (123):	$n = 2$	1·00	81	1590
	$n = 3$	1·00	1·07	3·69^a
	$n = 4$	1·00	1·31	4·32
	$n = 5$	1·00	—	1·05

^{a} The reaction involves o-methoxy-6 participation.

ω-phenylalkyl p-bromobenzenesulphonates (123) [103]. It can be seen that the methoxy group accelerates in the following order: $n = 2 \gg n = 4 > n = 3 \sim n = 5$, suggesting that $aryl_{(1)}$-3 participation occurs most readily, followed by $aryl_{(1)}$-5 participation where the effect is already small, and that $aryl_{(1)}$-4 and $aryl_{(1)}$-6 participation are not important.

An interesting example of acceleration of an electron-demanding reaction by the m-methoxy group occurs in the formolysis of 4-(3,5-dimethoxyphenyl)butyl p-bromobenzenesulphonate (124) which occurs about 6 times more rapidly than the reaction of the 4-phenylbutyl compound [104]. These results have been attributed to assistance from the 2-position of the aromatic ring ($aryl_{(2)}$-6 participation) which will

(124)   (125)

result in a contribution from structures like 125 to the transition state; these structures will of course be stabilized by the 3- and 5-methoxy groups. The reaction products are consistent with this scheme.

V. REACTIONS AT THE CARBONYL GROUP

Most studies of the effect of alkoxy groups on reactivity at carbonyl carbon atoms have involved the solvolysis of carboxylic esters. The results illustrate the general features of these reactions and are therefore discussed in some detail, together with a few other examples.

A. The Solvolysis of Carboxylic Esters

The solvolysis of a carboxylic ester (**126**) is usually catalyzed by bases and by hydrogen ions, and may either involve rupture of the R^1—O

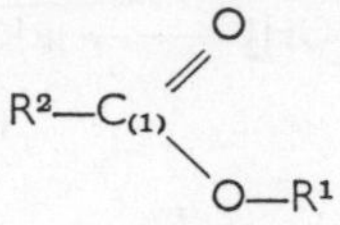

$$R^2—C_{(1)} \overset{O}{\nwarrow} \quad O—R^1$$

(**126**)

linkage (alkyl–oxygen fission, AL) or fission of the $C_{(1)}$—O bond (acyl–oxygen fission, AC). Acyl–oxygen fission is the more common process, and both the acid- and base-catalyzed process often occur by bimolecular mechanisms.

The rate-determining step in base-catalyzed bimolecular hydrolysis by acyl–oxygen fission ($B_{AC}2$) is illustrated below and it can be seen that the polar requirements of the activation process are ambiguous, as in S_N2 reactions (see section III.B). Electron-releasing substituents in

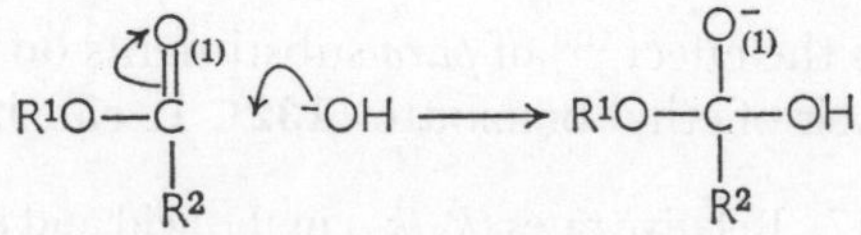

$$R^1O—\overset{O_{(1)}}{\underset{R^2}{C}} \quad \overset{\frown}{}OH \longrightarrow R^1O—\overset{O^-_{(1)}}{\underset{R^2}{C}}—OH$$

(**127**)

R^1 and R^2 will facilitate electron accession to $O_{(1)}$ but will, at the same time, tend to hinder bond formation with the hydroxide ion. However, such substituents in R^2 may also stabilize the ester by a contribution from structure **128** if they are conjugated to the reaction centre, although it seems very likely that this contribution will not be large since the energy of **128** will be considerably larger than that of structure **129**

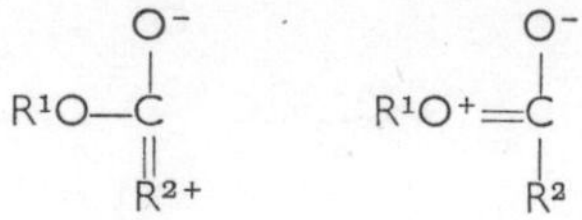

$$R^1O—\overset{O^-}{\underset{R^{2+}}{C}} \qquad R^1O^+{=}\overset{O^-}{\underset{R^2}{C}}$$

(**128**)   (**129**)

which is of much greater importance in the ester (see also section III.C).

It can therefore be concluded that the effects of polar substituents on the rate of $B_{AC}2$ reactions will probably be small, that they will be greater for substitution in R^2 than for substitution in R^1, and that electron-releasing groups are likely to retard hydrolysis.

In the corresponding acid-catalyzed process ($A_{AC}2$) the protonated ester (**130**) is in rapid equilibrium with its conjugate base and reacts

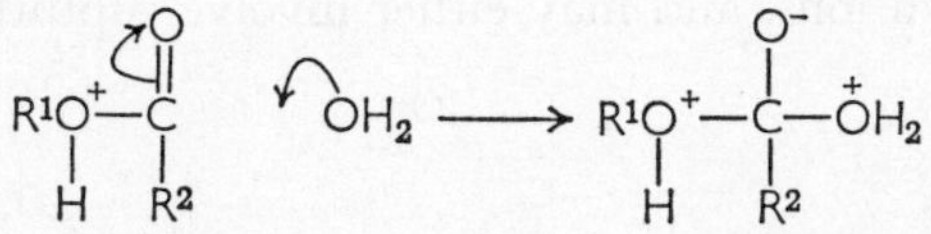

$$R^1O^+\!\!-\!\overset{\displaystyle O}{\underset{\displaystyle R^2}{\overset{|}{\underset{|}{C}}}}\quad \curvearrowleft OH_2 \longrightarrow R^1O^+\!\!-\!\overset{\displaystyle O^-}{\underset{\displaystyle R^2}{\overset{|}{\underset{|}{C}}}}\!\!-\!\overset{+}{O}H_2$$

$$\text{(130)} \qquad\qquad \text{(131)}$$

with the solvent in the rate-determining step, as shown above for water. The polar requirements of this process are again ambiguous, but the proportion of the ester present as **130** will obviously be increased by electron-releasing substituents, particularly when they are introduced in R^1, so that they can be expected to retard the reaction by this mechanism less than they retard $B_{AC}2$ hydrolysis.

Further details about mechanisms of ester hydrolysis relevant to the present discussion can be obtained by reference to standard works[105].

I. Alkoxy substituents in R^2

Table 17 shows the effect[106] of *para* substituents on the rates of $B_{AC}2$ and $A_{AC}2$ hydrolysis of ethyl benzoate (**132**). It can be seen that both

TABLE 17. Relative rates (k_X/k_H) in the acid and alkaline hydrolysis of ethyl p-benzoates[106].

Substituent	Base catalyzed ($B_{AC}2$)	Acid catalyzed ($A_{AC}2$)
NO$_2$	103	1·04
Me	0·45	0·97
MeO	0·21	0·92

$$p\text{-}XC_6H_4C\overset{\displaystyle O}{\underset{\displaystyle OEt}{\diagup}}$$

(132)

processes are accelerated by electron-attracting groups $(X = NO_2)$ and retarded by electron donation $(X = Me)$. The p-methoxy group behaves as an overall electron-releasing group, as in other reactions, but it is now apparently a better donor than the methyl group, even though it is not conjugated to the reaction centre. The substituent effects are very small in the acid-catalyzed process, probably because the retarding effect of electron release on the activation step is largely cancelled by the accompanying increase in the proportion of the protonated ester (**130**).

Further work on the alkaline hydrolysis of ethyl benzoate with a variety of p-alkoxy substituents (R=Me, Et, i-Pr, CH_2=$CHCH_2$, $PhCH_2$) gave relative rates which did not vary by more than 10% from the mean[107]; the smallest value of the ratio k_X/k_H in this series was obtained for the isopropoxy group and the largest for benzyloxy, as expected from the inductive effect of the alkyl group. This study also showed an accelerating effect by the m-methoxy group ($k_X/k_H = 1.33$); this is fully consistent with the well established behaviour of this group as an overall attractor of electrons. Multiple substitution in the aromatic ring showed that the methoxy group affected the value of k_X/k_H in the manner predicted from the additivity principle (equation 7) irrespective of the nature of the other substituent, provided no interaction could occur between adjacent groups. For example the 3,5-dimethoxy compound gave the value of k_X/k_H required by equation (7) but the 3,4,5-trimethoxy derivative did not, in contradiction to observations on the dissociation constant of the corresponding benzoic acid[59].

Some results for the alkaline hydrolysis of aryl-substituted ethyl cinnamates[108] are given in Table 18. As expected, the effect of the

TABLE 18. Relative rates (k_X/k_H)
for the alkaline hydrolysis of
substituted ethyl cinnamates[108].

Substituent	k_X/k_H
o-MeO	0.37
m-MeO	1.12
p-MeO	0.38
2,3-$(MeO)_2$	0.83[a]
2,4-$(MeO)_2$	0.14
3,4-$(MeO)_2$	0.49[a]
2,3,4-$(MeO)_3$	0.38[a]

[a] These values are greater than those calculated from the additivity principle.

methoxy group on the rate is less than in the benzoates since the substituent is now further removed from the reaction centre; the behaviour of the *o*-methoxy group is very similar to that of the *p*-methoxy
group, as in the ionization of the cinnamic acids (see section III.C).
The additivity principle was thoroughly tested for a large number of
derivatives and was found to be invalid when substituents occupied
adjacent positions in the aromatic ring. Thus, the 2,3- and 3,4-
dimethoxy, and the 2,3,4-trimethoxy compound gave rates greater
than those calculated from equation (7), consistent with reduced conjugation as coplanarity is disturbed. An enhancement of electron
donation by the 4-methoxy group in the presence of the 3-methoxy
group (see section IV.C.2) does not appear to occur in this system.

The introduction of a methoxy group into ethyl phenyl acetate (**133**)

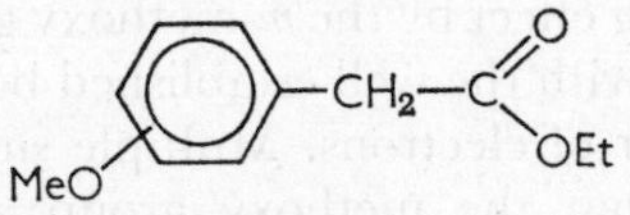

(**133**)

affects the rate of alkaline hydrolysis in a manner similar to that found
in cinnamates for *meta* and *para* substitution, but the *o*-methoxy group
is now clearly subject to a substantial steric effect[109]:

Substituent	*o*-MeO	*m*-MeO	*p*-MeO
k_X/k_H	0·16	1·12	0·88

Observations of the effect of solvent changes on k_X/k_H led to the conclusion that the *ortho* effect arose, at least partly, from steric hindrance
to solvation in the transition state.

On the other hand, no steric effect for the *o*-methoxy group was
observed in the acid hydrolysis of ethyl isophthalates (**134**), the results

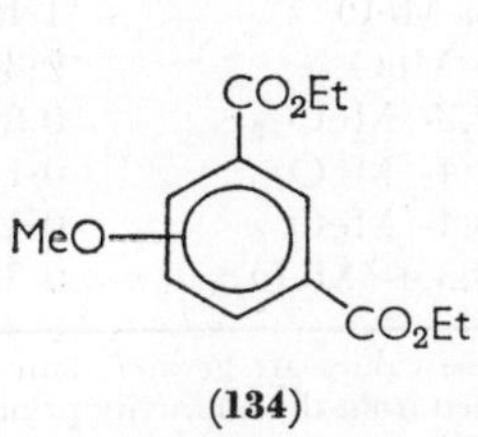

(**134**)

showing the 'normal' retardation by *ortho* and *para* substituents and an enhanced rate for the *meta* derivative[110]:

Substituent	2-MeO	4-MeO	5-MeO
k_X/k_H	0·75	0·81	1·17

No explanation can be provided for this discrepancy.

2. Alkoxy substituents in R^1

In general the introduction of substituents in R^1 which is joined to the alkyl-oxygen atom (see **130**) affects the rates of $B_{AC}2$ and $A_{AC}2$ hydrolysis in a manner similar to that shown by substitution in R^2. Polar effects are relayed less efficiently to the reaction centre which is now further removed from the site of substitution, but acid hydrolysis will be a little more sensitive to the nature of the substituent in view of the closer proximity of the alkyl-oxygen atom.

However, substantial changes in the structure of R^1 in the direction of stabilizing the carbonium ion R^{1+} may well alter the mechanism of neutral or alkaline hydrolysis from $B_{AC}2$ to $B_{AL}1$ (**135**) which involves

$$R^1\!\!-\!\!O\!\!-\!\!\overset{\displaystyle O}{\underset{\displaystyle R^2}{C}} \longrightarrow R^{1+} + {}^-O\!\!-\!\!\overset{\displaystyle O}{\underset{\displaystyle R^2}{C}} \qquad\qquad (135)$$

the heterolysis of the R—O linkage and is indistinguishable from the unimolecular mechanism of nucleophilic substitution (S_N1). Diphenylmethyl *p*-nitrobenzoate reacts by this mechanism with aqueous solvents, and the introduction of a *p*-methoxy group should therefore cause the approximately 2×10^4-fold acceleration of solvolysis found for the same substitution in diphenylmethyl chloride (see Table 12); this has been observed[76].

The introduction of a *p*-methoxy group into other benzyl, 1-phenylethyl, and diphenylmethyl esters also increases the rate of neutral or alkaline hydrolysis[105b]. The products of the reactions of the derivatives require $B_{AL}1$ hydrolysis even when the parent compounds show a much smaller tendency to follow this mechanism. The effect of an *o*-methoxy substituent on the rate is similar to that of a *p*-methoxy substituent but a little smaller, while a *m*-methoxy substituent does not accelerate hydrolysis and does not increase the tendency of the compound to react by mechanism $B_{AL}1$[105b]. All these observations are fully consistent with the expected response of the substituents to an electron-demanding situation.

Similarly, in acid hydrolysis, the conjugation of a methoxy substituent in R^1 with the site of attachment of R^1 to the alkyl–oxygen atom should cause the replacement of mechanism $A_{AC}2$ by unimolecular alkyl–oxygen fission ($A_{AL}1$ (**136**)) since the transition state in the

$$R^1{-}\overset{\overset{\displaystyle H}{|}}{O}{}^+{-}\overset{\overset{\displaystyle O}{\diagup\!\!\!\diagup}}{C}\diagdown_{R^2} \longrightarrow R^{1+} + \overset{\overset{\displaystyle H}{|}}{O}{-}\overset{\overset{\displaystyle O}{\diagup\!\!\!\diagup}}{C}\diagdown_{R^2} \tag{136}$$

heterolysis of $R^1{-}O$ will be stabilized by resonance. Thus, the acid hydrolysis of alkoxymethyl acetates and formates[111] is very much faster than that of the methyl compounds, and the rates are proportional to Hammett's acidity function (λ_0). This is fully consistent with the interpretation that the operation of mechanism $A_{AL}1$ is favoured in the alkoxymethyl esters since the relatively stable structure **70** makes a substantial contribution to the transition state. Similarly the large acceleration of the acid hydrolysis of benzoic anhydride by a p-methoxy group is accompanied by a mechanistic change which results in hydrolysis of the methoxy derivative entirely by an $A1$ mechanism[112], consistent with a process involving conjugation of a methoxy group with an electron-demanding reaction centre, as in **137**.

(**137**)

Although not strictly relevant to this section, it is also noteworthy that 2,4,6-trimethoxybenzyl alcohol rapidly forms the acetate in acetic acid[105b], presumably by an $A_{AL}1$ reaction which would be favoured by the presence of three powerfully electron-donating groups. The corresponding reaction of benzyl alcohol is immeasurably slow under similar conditions.

B. Other Reactions

I. The solvolysis of benzoyl chlorides

The enrichment of the ^{18}O content of benzoyl chloride during its hydrolysis in $H_2{}^{18}O$ suggests that the rate-determining step involves the reversible formation of an intermediate (**138**) similar to that

$$
\begin{array}{c}
O^{-}_{(1)} \\
| \\
Ph-C-Cl \\
| \\
H_2O^{+}
\end{array}
$$

(**138**)

formed in the $B_{AC}2$ hydrolysis of esters[113]. Alternatively the reaction can be regarded as involving an extreme form of mechanism S_N2 in which only bond formation is required in the activation process, though electron displacement to $O_{(1)}$ must of course occur. By analogy with ester hydrolysis, acceleration can therefore be expected on the introduction of electron-attracting substituents into the aromatic ring and retardation by electron donors. This has been observed for a large number of substituents[114,115].

The results for methoxy substitution on the rate of ethanolysis[114] show the small acceleration by the *m*-methoxy group and the small retardation by the *p*-methoxy group which is usually observed in ester hydrolysis. The approximately 30-fold increase in rate with the *o*-methoxy group is uncommon but presumably arises from steric inhibition of conjugation between the aryl ring and the carbonyl group in the initial state, as already invoked for the acid-strengthening effect of the *o*-methoxy group in benzoic acid (section III.C).

Hudson and his coworkers[115] found that retardation by a *p*-methoxy group in ethanolic solvents and 5% aqueous acetone was replaced by a progressively increasing acceleration as the ionizing power of the solvent was raised (a 30-fold rate enhancement was observed in 50% aqueous acetone) until the solvolysis of the methoxy derivative became too fast to measure (in moist formic acid). From this and other evidence they concluded that the mechanism changed in the direction of an S_N1 reaction with increasing ionizing power, and it seems very likely that the more rapid reactions of the *p*-methoxy compound proceed entirely by this mechanism. These experiments represent one of the most clear demonstrations of the way in which the accelerating effect of the methoxy group can be altered by changing the reaction conditions.

2. Carbonyl methylene condensations

The base-catalyzed reaction of malononitrile with benzaldehydes in ethanol is considered[116a] to proceed via a rate-determining step in which the carbanion (**139**) adds on to the carbonyl group to form an intermediate (**140**) which undergoes further reaction. The electron

$$(CN)_2CH^- + \overset{\overset{\textstyle O}{\|}}{\underset{\underset{\textstyle H}{|}}{C}}-C_6H_4X \longrightarrow H-\overset{\overset{\textstyle CN}{|}}{\underset{\underset{\textstyle CN}{|}}{C}}-\overset{\overset{\textstyle O^-}{|}}{\underset{\underset{\textstyle H}{|}}{C}}-C_6H_4X$$

(**139**)   (**140**)

displacements which occur on activation parallel those in the $B_{AC}2$ hydrolysis of esters, as do all additions to the carbonyl group, but no structural analogue of **129** exists in this system and resonance stabilization of the initial state by a p-methoxy group could therefore play a significant part. In agreement with this conclusion the ten-fold decrease in rate on the introduction of this substituent[116a] is about twice that observed in the $B_{AC}2$ hydrolysis of ethyl benzoate (Table 17), though a bigger difference might perhaps have been expected.

The reaction is also of interest as it was found to give a much better correlation with σ^+ than with σ, in spite of the small value of ρ ($+1\cdot45$), an observation which confirms that conjugation between the substituent and the carbonyl group must play an important part in the activation process. At the same time it is noteworthy that $k_{MeO}/k_H = \frac{1}{2}k_H/k_{NO_2}$, while the σ^+ scale requires that the two ratios should be equal. The results could therefore be interpreted as further evidence for the variable capacity of the methoxy group for conjugative electron release.

Many other additions to carbonyl groups in which the initial state is stabilized relative to the transition state by conjugative electron release show the expected retardation by p-methoxy and slight acceleration by m-methoxy groups, although the effects are often remarkably small (e.g. reference 116b).

VI. ELECTROPHILIC AROMATIC SUBSTITUTION

Electrophilic substitution in aromatic systems has been widely studied. Early efforts in this field concentrated on the nitration of hydrocarbons and their derivatives but the work was soon extended to include other reactions such as halogenation, sulphonation, acylation, and mercuration. More recently the replacement of the isotopes of hydrogen and the rupture of carbon–metalloid and carbon–metal bonds have attracted much attention, usually for reaction with hydrogen ions though other electrophiles (e.g. bromine) have also been studied. Comparisons of the reactivities of anisole and benzene have been particularly popular for the assessment of the effect of a polar substituent on the rates since the accelerating effect of a methoxy group varies widely from one reaction to another (see Table 20).

No attempt at a comprehensive discussion of electrophilic aromatic substitution is possible in this section; details can be obtained from some of the excellent reviews which have been published [21, 117].

A. General Considerations

I. Mechanisms

It seems very likely that the replacement of a group B attached to an aromatic system by an electrophilic reagent A proceeds via the rate-determining formation of an intermediate (**141**) which decomposes rapidly to yield the products. This view is supported by ample evidence for the replacement of hydrogen or its isotopes (cf. reference 21) and also satisfies the facts in many other substitutions [118]. Structures like **142** and **143** can therefore be expected to contribute to the transition

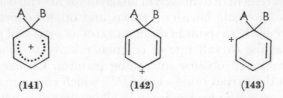

(141)   (142)   (143)

state. The considerable capacity of alkoxy and aryloxy groups for electron release when conjugated to an electron-demanding reaction centre will stabilize the analogues of structures **142** and **143** when these groups are in the *ortho* and *para* position with respect to the site of reaction, and their introduction should therefore accelerate the reaction. Thus, *ortho* and *para* substitution should occur more rapidly in alkoxybenzene and aryloxybenzene than substitution at one of the six equivalent sites in benzene. No similar stabilization of the transition state for *meta* substitution is possible and the well-known behaviour of the *m*-alkoxy group as an overall electron attractor with respect to an electron-deficient reaction centre in other reactions suggests that *meta* substitution in anisole (say) should be retarded relative to the corresponding reaction in benzene. Similarly, m-ROC_6H_4B should react more slowly than C_6H_5B.

It must, however, be stressed that not all electrophilic substitutions necessarily occur in this manner. Thus, the very large rate of rupture of C—Sn and C—Pb linkages has led to arguments for a rate-determining step involving nucleophilic attack at the metal atom[119], and four- and six-centre transition states have been postulated for some reactions[120]; such a mechanism is regarded as particularly attractive[21] for mercuridesilylation (144). Under these conditions the effect of alkoxy

(144)

substituents on the rate is likely to differ from that predicted for the operation of the more common mechanism.

2. Partial rate factors

The replacement of hydrogen in alkoxybenzenes can occur at several sites in the molecule but steric effects and other factors (see section VI.B.1) are likely to result in different rates for *ortho* and *para* substitution so that the overall rate of reaction relative to that of benzene (k_X/k_H) could well obscure interesting features. Clearer information arises from the partial rate factors (f^{RO}) which compare the reactivity of the *ortho*, *meta*, and *para* positions in alkoxybenzenes with that of one of the possible reaction sites in benzene; under kinetically controlled conditions these parameters are easily obtained from the ratio k_X/k_H and the isomer proportions via equations 8 to 10. Values of f_m^{RO} are

$$f_o^{RO} = \frac{6k_X}{2k_H} \frac{\% \; ortho}{100} \tag{8}$$

$$f_m^{RO} = \frac{6k_X}{2k_H} \frac{\% \; meta}{100} \tag{9}$$

$$f_p^{RO} = \frac{6k_X}{k_H} \frac{\% \; para}{100} \tag{10}$$

always small and have to be obtained indirectly from results for poly-substituted compounds by the additivity principle (equation 7). For example each of the available reaction sites in p-methoxyanisole (**145**)

$$\text{MeO}-\!\!\!\left\langle\!\!\!\bigcirc\!\!\!\right\rangle\!\!\!-\text{OMe}$$

(**145**)

can be considered to be subject to the activating (or deactivating) influence of one o- and one m-methoxy group so that the overall rate of reaction relative to benzene is given by equation (11), whence f_m^{MeO} can be obtained if f_o^{MeO} is known from the corresponding reaction of anisole.

$$\frac{k(p\text{-MeOC}_6\text{H}_4\text{OMe})}{k_{\text{H}}} = \frac{4 f_o^{\text{MeO}} f_m^{\text{MeO}}}{6} \tag{11}$$

The validity of this procedure clearly depends on whether the additivity principle applies with sufficient accuracy (see section VI.C).

No similar difficulty applies when a group other than hydrogen is replaced; the partial rate factor for the substitution of B in $\text{ROC}_6\text{H}_4\text{B}$ is identical with the rate relative to that of the parent compound (PhB). Partial rate factors for such reactions are, however, often quoted in preference to relative rates since this facilitates comparison with substitution in alkoxybenzenes.

3. Selectivity

It has already been pointed out that the effect of substituents on the rates of electrophilic substitution reactions is often correlated satisfactorily by the Hammett relation (equation 1) if the substituent constants σ^+ are employed (section II.A.2). While this does not apply to the methoxy group in nitration by NO_2^+ [37], $\log f_p^{\text{MeO}}$ shows the required proportionality with the reaction constant (ρ) over a range of other reactions which involves a 10^6-fold variation of f_p^{MeO} [21, 34]. These results lead to a substituent constant of $-0\cdot74$ for the methoxy group, in good agreement with the value of $-0\cdot78$ obtained from the hydrolysis of 2-phenyl-2-propyl chlorides [33] (see, however, section II.A.2).

An equivalent approach [21, 34] discusses the reactions of monosubstituted benzenes in terms of the selectivity of the electrophilic reagent. The selectivity factor (S_f) is defined by equation (12) and is often found to be directly proportional to $\log f_p^{\text{MeO}}$ or the corresponding term

$$S_f = \log \left(f_p^{\text{Me}} / f_m^{\text{Me}} \right) \tag{12}$$

for other substituents. The same reactions also give reasonably good correlations with σ^+ so that the reaction constant (ρ) represents a direct measure of the selectivity (S_f). Values of f^{MeO} for these systems can therefore be calculated to a reasonable degree of approximation either from S_f (selectivity relation) or from ρ (extended selectivity relation). A highly selective reagent (or a reaction with a high selectivity) will result in large values of f_p^{MeO} and f_o^{MeO}, and vice versa, but calculations of f_o^{MeO} are usually less reliable than those of f_p^{MeO} since steric effects may well operate in *ortho* substitution.

B. Monosubstituted Compounds

I. Orientational effects of methoxy and phenoxy groups

It has already been pointed out that alkoxy and aryloxy groups should deactivate the *meta* position in electrophilic substitution (section VI.A.2). No detectable amounts of the *meta* isomer should therefore appear in the products of the reactions of anisole and diphenyl ether, as generally observed*. The proportions of *ortho* and *para* isomers are summarized in Table 19 for a number of reactions which have been arranged in the order of decreasing selectivity. These isomer proportions represent a measure of the relative reactivities at the sites *ortho* and *para* to the methoxy and phenoxy groups, and can also be calculated from the partial rate factors†. Values for the 'displacement' processes in Table 19 (reactions 4, 5, 10, and 11) were obtained in this manner in order to permit a wider range for the comparison, but it will be recognized that the figures are hypothetical since these reactions all yield the same product (anisole or diphenyl ether).

The results in Table 19 show a tendency for the reactivity at the *ortho* position to increase with decreasing selectivity though there are a number of exceptions. Steric effects may be responsible for the 'abnormally' small amounts of *ortho* isomer in mercuration (reaction 9) and in the desilylation of the phenoxy compound (reaction 10), and could conceivably be considered to account for the different degrees of *ortho* substitution in molecular bromination and chlorination (reactions 1 and 2). The bromination is, however, kinetically more complex than

---

* 1–2% of *m*-nitroanisole have been claimed for the nitration of anisole[121], but subsequent workers were unable to detect any *meta* isomer under similar conditions[122] or for the reaction of anisole with acyl nitrates[123].

† When $f_m = 0$, as in the present reactions, equations (8) and (10) show that:

$$\% \; ortho = \frac{200f_o}{2f_o + f_p}, \quad \% \; para = \frac{100f_p}{2f_o + f_p}$$

TABLE 19. Isomer proportions (%) for substitution in methoxy and phenoxy derivatives.

| | MeO | | PhO | | |
Reaction	*ortho*	*para*	*ortho*	*para*	Ref.
1. Bromination $(ROPh, Br_2)$	2	98	0	100	13, 14
2. Chlorination $(ROPh, Cl_2)$	21	79	—	—	124
3. Acetylation $(ROPh, MeCOCl)$	0	100	—	—	125
4. Detritiation (ROC_6H_4T, H^+)	—	—	30	70	126
5. Dedeuteration $(ROC_6H_4D, H^+)^a$	46	54	—	—	127
6. Nitration $(ROPh, AcONO_2)^b$	72	28	50	50	123, 128
7. Chlorination $(ROPh, Cl^+)$	35	65	—	—	129
8. Nitration $(ROPh, NO_2{}^+)$	44	56	—	—	122
9. Mercuration $(ROPh, Hg(OAc)_2)$	14	86	—	—	130
10. Desilylation $(ROC_6H_4SiMe_3, H^+)$	31	69	16	84	12, 131
11. Degermylation $(ROC_6H_4GeMe_3, H^+)$	43	57	—	—	132

[a] The *ortho/para* ratio for this reaction has been shown to depend on the temperature[133].

[b] The figures for methoxy and phenoxy groups were not obtained under the same conditions.

chlorination[14a], and the two reactions may not proceed by the same mechanism. It must also be stressed that steric effects are often sufficiently small to have little effect on the reactivity at the *ortho* position (see section VI.B.3).

Two equivalent sites are available for *ortho* substitution but the proportion of the *para* isomer is always greater than 50% for the reactions listed in Table 19 (except for reaction 6). Although steric factors could be thought to be responsible, an examination of the available data for a variety of substituents has led to the conclusion that this '*ortho* effect' is primarily electronic in origin[134,135] possibly because an electron-releasing substituent (X) can be expected to stabilize the p-phenonium ion (**146a**) more than the o-phenonium ion (**146b**)[135]. The

(146a)   (146b)

results for methoxy and phenoxy groups support this conclusion, but the irregular variation of the isomer ratios as the selectivity is altered (see Table 19) suggests that steric effects or other factors may also be important in at least some of the reactions.

5*

The unusually large fraction of *ortho* substitution in the reaction with acyl nitrates (reaction 6) has also been observed with other alkoxy derivatives[136a] and the reaction with nitronium tetrafluoroborate[136b], in contrast to nitration with mixtures of nitric and sulphuric acids (reaction 8). Mercuration leads to *ortho–para* ratios in excess of unity when the reagent is mercuric perchlorate[136c], but not when the acetate is employed (reaction 9), and abnormally large values have also been reported for alkylation with isopropyl compounds in nitromethane or perchloric acid while *t*-butyl compounds show the more usual preponderance of *para* substitution under the same conditions[136c]. Several sets of workers have suggested that these abnormal proportions may arise from the fact that a part of the reaction proceeds via an initial attack on the oxygen atom of the alkoxy group, followed by intramolecular rearrangement which would favour *ortho* substitution[123,136]. The rate of such a process, however, often appears to be much more sensitive to the reaction conditions than the normal substitution; the reasons for this are not always clear.

The introduction of methoxy groups into naphthalene (**147**) results

(**147**)

in nitration exclusively at those positions which can be activated by conjugation with the substituents[137]. The partial rate factors depend markedly on the reaction conditions but the isomer proportions always follow the same general sequence:

1-MeO	$2\text{-NO}_2 > 4\text{-NO}_2 \gg 5\text{-NO}_2$
2-MeO	$6\text{-NO}_2 > 1\text{-NO}_2 > 8\text{-NO}_2.$

The preponderance of 2-nitration in the 1-methoxy compound can be compared with the abnormal *ortho–para* ratios discussed in the preceding paragraph. However, the corresponding 1-substitution is not the most favourable process in the reaction of the 2-methoxy compound, probably[137] because of steric effects caused by the presence of the 2-methoxy group and the 8-hydrogen atom. It is also noteworthy that both methoxy derivatives show the least reactivity at the positions which require the relay of the $+T$ effect over the greatest distance for their activation.

2. Reactivities of methoxy and phenoxy derivatives

Table 20 shows the overall rates $(k/k_{\rm H})$ for some reactions of methoxy and phenoxy derivatives relative to the rates for the parent compounds, and the corresponding partial rate factors for *meta* and *para* substitution; $f_o^{\rm MeO}$ can be readily deduced from the results or from those quoted in Table 19.

The reactions in Table 20 have again been arranged in the order of decreasing selectivity and it can be seen that $f_p^{\rm MeO}$ is abnormally small for nitration by NO_2^+ (reaction 8), a conclusion which has already been mentioned in connection with the failure of the σ^+ correlation (section VI.A.3). It is one of the striking features of electrophilic aromatic substitution that the reactivities of compounds containing the highly polarizable methoxy group are so often predicted fairly well by selectivity relations, in contrast to other electron-demanding reactions like solvolysis, but an occasional exception need not be surprising.

In bromodeboronation (reaction 13), $f_p^{\rm MeO}$ is considerably larger than expected from the selectivity, i.e. from the partial rate factors of other substituents, and it has been suggested that a side-reaction may be responsible[21]. Bromine is a highly selective reagent in the replacement of hydrogen, and the powerful activating effect of a suitably placed methoxy group can occasionally bring about this substitution in preference to, or side by side with, the 'normal' reaction. Thus, the reaction of bromine with *p*-methoxyphenyltrimethylsilane[141] does not break the C—Si linkage but produces the bromo derivative (**148**), and

MeO—⟨⟩—SiMe₃
Br

(**148**)

m-methoxyphenylboronic acid (**149**) forms the dibromo compound (**150**) before the final product (**151**) in reaction (13)[142]. A similar sequence would account for the high reactivity of the *p*-methoxy compound.

TABLE 20. Relative rates and partial rate factors for methoxy and phenoxy derivatives.

Reaction[a]	k_{MeO}/k_H	f_p^{MeO}	f_m^{MeO}	k_{PhO}/k_H	f_p^{PhO}	Ref.
1. Bromination ($ROPh, Br_2$)	1.8×10^9	1.1×10^{10}	2.0^b	1.7×10^7	1.0×10^8	13, 14
2. Chlorination ($ROPh, Cl_2$)	9.7×10^6	4.6×10^7	—	—	—	124
3. Acetylation ($ROPh, MeCOCl$)	2.9×10^5	1.8×10^6	—	—	—	125
4. Detritiation (ROC_6H_4T, H^+)	—	—	—	—	3.1×10^4	126
5. Dedeuteration (ROC_6H_4D, H^+)	8.3×10^4	5.5×10^4	0.25	—	—	127
12. Diphenylmethylation ($ROPh, Ph_2CH^+$)	—	—	—	1.6×10^2	2.3×10^2	138
6. Nitration ($ROPh, AcONO_2$)	70	$2.5 \times 10^{2\ c}$	—	—	—	128
8. Nitration ($ROPh, NO_2^+$)	—	1.5×10^6	—	—	—	122
13. Deboronation ($ROC_6H_4B(OH)_2, Br_2$)	—	2.2×10^4	—	—	—	139
14. Deboronation ($ROC_6H_4B(OH)_2, H^+$)	4.5×10^2	2.3×10^3	1.2^b	65	3.8×10^2	140
9. Mercuration ($ROPh, Hg(OAc)_2$)	—	1.5×10^3	0.25	—	89	130
10. Desilylation ($ROC_6H_4SiMe_3, H^+$)	—	5.4×10^2	0.58	—	38	12, 131
11. Degermylation ($ROC_6H_4GeMe_3, H^+$)	—	63	0.85	—	—	132
15. Destannylation ($ROC_6H_4SnR^1_3, H^+$)	—	21	—	—	—	49b
16. Deplumbylation ($ROC_6H_4PbR^1_3, H^+$)	—	—	—	—	—	49a

[a] Reactions having the same number as those in Table 19 refer to the same process.
[b] Calculated from reactions of polysubstituted compounds by the additivity principle.
[c] Calculated assuming 60% *para* substitution.

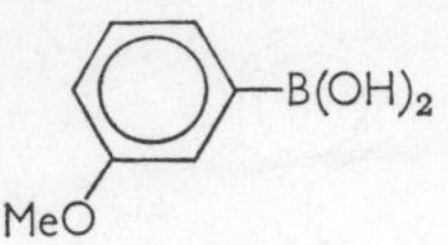

MeO—⟨C₆H₃⟩—B(OH)₂

(149)

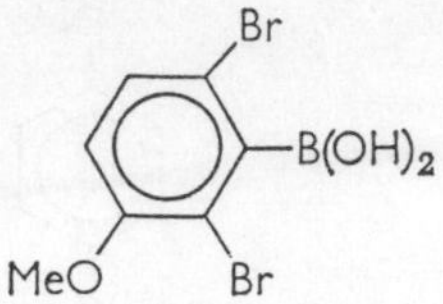

MeO—⟨C₆H₂(Br)⟩—B(OH)₂   Br

(150)

MeO—⟨C₆H₂(Br)⟩—Br   Br

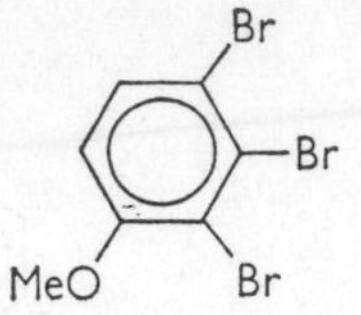

(151)

As expected the *p*-phenoxy group accelerates electrophilic substitution less than the *p*-methoxy, and *m*-methoxy group retards all the reactions in which its effect can be measured directly (see Table 20). On the other hand f_m^{MeO} calculated from results for *p*-methoxyanisole (see section VI.A.2) suggests some activation by this substituent (reactions 1 and 9). This conclusion could be erroneous as the additivity principle does not always predict rates with good precision, but the possibility of a stabilizing contribution from structure **152** to the transition state has also been considered[143].

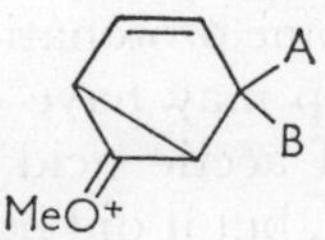

MeO⁺

(152)

It is noteworthy that f_m^{MeO} tends to increase on passing down Table 20, as expected from the decreasing selectivity. This observation could, however, be fortuitous since reaction (15) may not occur by the same mechanism as reactions (1) to (14) (see section VI.A.1).

The accelerating effect of the methoxy group on protodesilylation in diphenyl and on protodetritiation in diphenyl and fluorene[89] is compared below with its effect on the reactions of benzene derivatives. It can be seen that the relative rates are greatly decreased as the conjugated system is lengthened, as in S_N1 solvolysis and probably for the same reason (see section IV.C.2). The similarity of $k_{\text{MeO}}/k_{\text{H}}$ for the detritiation of **156** and **157** suggests very strongly that steric inhibition of conjugation arising from any non-coplanarity in the diphenyl

MeO—⟨C₆H₄⟩—SiMe₃

$k_{\text{MeO}}/k_{\text{H}}$ 1500

(153)

MeO—⟨C₆H₄⟩—⟨C₆H₄⟩—SiMe₃

3·15

(154)

$$k_{\text{MeO}}/k_{\text{H}} > 10^4 \text{(est.)} \qquad 3\cdot3 \qquad 3\cdot0$$

$$(155) \qquad\qquad\qquad (156) \qquad\qquad (157)$$

system (156) is negligibly small since the fluorene system (157) is generally regarded as coplanar.

The original results showed the unexpected feature of greater acceleration by the methyl than by the methoxy group in both 156 and 157. These reactions were carried out in a strongly acidic medium (trifluoroacetic acid) and some protonation of the weakly basic oxygen atom in the methoxy group may have occurred. A reduction in the acidity by the addition of acetic acid[89] gave the expected order: $k_{\text{MeO}} > k_{\text{Me}}$ for 156 and 157, but it did not significantly affect the large difference between these compounds and the tritiated benzene (155).

3. Changes in the nature of the alkoxy group

Results considered in previous sections have shown that changes in the alkyl group (R) only alter the accelerating effect of the alkoxy group by relatively small amounts, even in strongly electron-demanding situations. The reasons for this behaviour have already been discussed.

Some of the relevant information for electrophilic substitution is summarized in Table 21 and it can be seen that the orientating effect of the alkoxy group in chlorination is virtually independent of the nature of alkyl group, as expected for substituents of similar reactivity. The values of $k_{\text{RO}}/k_{\text{MeO}}$ for halogenation are the means of the numerous results obtained by Jones and his coworkers for a variety of reactions of alkoxybenzenes and their substituted derivatives (158). Except for isopropoxy groups (see footnote c, Table 21), the nature of the reaction or the substrate had virtually no effect on the value of $k_{\text{RO}}/k_{\text{MeO}}$, suggesting that any steric effects in the ortho-substituted compounds (158) were the same for all alkoxy groups. In most of the compounds studied

TABLE 21. The effect of changes in the alkoxy group on orientation and reactivity in halogenation[78,124,144] and dedeuteration[133].

	Halogenation		Dedeuteration
	$RO-\langle\bigcirc\rangle-Y$ with X below		$RO-\langle\bigcirc\rangle-^2H$
	(158)		**(159)**
Alkyl group	% para[a]	k_{RO}/k_{MeO}[b]	k_{RO}/k_{MeO}
i-Pr	79	4·40[c]	2·60
n-Oct	—	2·18	—
n-Pr	—	2·15	1·37
Et	80	1·99	1·36
Me	79	1·00	1·00
$MeC_6H_4CH_2$	73[d]	0·95	—
$PhCH_2$	—	0·68	—
$HO_2CCH_2CH_2$	—	0·48	—
$NO_2C_6H_4CH_2$	—	0·14	—
HO_2CCH_2	—	0·08	—

[a] These results refer to the molecular chlorination of compounds with X=H, Y=H; no detectable amounts of the *meta* product were found.[124]

[b] These results represent the mean values for a variety of reactions (molecular chlorination, molecular bromination and bromination with HOBr) of compounds in which a wide variety of substituents X and Y (including H) were employed.

[c] This value varied up to 30% depending on the nature of the *ortho* substituent (X).

[d] For $R=EtC_6H_4CH_2$.

steric effects were clearly absent since the actual rates agreed, within the limits of the experimental error, with those predicted from the additivity principle. Results for the halogenation of naphthyl ethers are also available[145], and the results show the same trends as those for **158** though the values of k_{RO}/k_{MeO} are not always precisely the same in the two systems.

The effects of changes in the alkoxy group on the rate of halogenation (Table 21) are qualitatively consistent with what would have been predicted from the electron-attracting or -releasing properties of the alkyl group (R). Thus, the powerfully electron-attracting carboxylate group (R = HO_2CCH_2) reduces the rate by a factor of twelve relative to the methoxy group but it will be recognized that this change is small when compared with the acceleration of these reactions on replacing hydrogen by an alkoxy group ($k_{MeO}/k_H \sim 10^7$–10^9).

Changes in the alkyl group alter the rates of dedeuteration in the same direction as for halogenation (see Table 21) though the effects are now smaller, as expected for a reaction of lower selectivity (see Table 20); the same order of reactivities for alkoxy groups can be obtained from the orientation of the products of nitration of phenyl compounds containing two different alkoxy substituents (see section VI.C.1).

C. Polysubstituted Compounds

I. Several alkoxy substituents

Partial rate factors for the bromination of anisole and its methoxy derivatives[14b] are shown below. The enhanced reactivity at the 4-position of o-methoxyanisole (160) relative to anisole (7) is a little

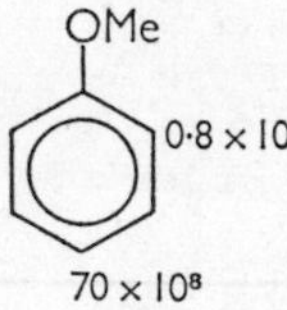

OMe
0.8×10^8
70×10^8
(7)

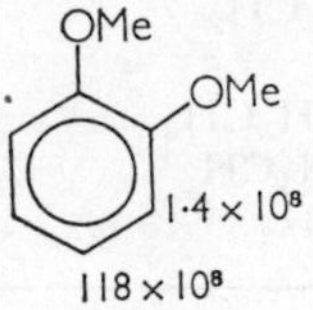

OMe
OMe
1.4×10^8
118×10^8
(160)

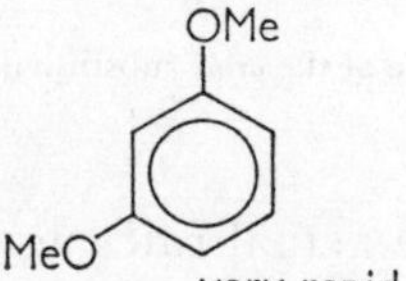

OMe
MeO
very rapid
(161)

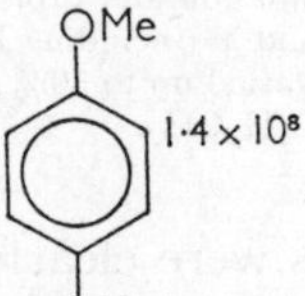

OMe
1.4×10^8
OMe
(145)

surprising but similar results are obtained for deuterium exchange[94a] and diphenylmethylation[138] (see Table 22). Additional activation in an electron-demanding reaction of a site *para* to the methoxy group by the introduction of a further methoxy group in the *meta* position has also been observed in solvolysis (see section IV.C.2); the explanation in terms of a stabilizing electrostatic interaction between the two adjacent methoxy groups in the transition state[91] could also apply to the present reactions.

The high reactivity at the 4-position of m-methoxyanisole (161) is not unexpected since this site is activated by electron displacements from one *p*- and one *o*-methoxy group. All the available sites of substitution are equivalent in *p*-methoxyanisole (**145**) but it is interesting that the partial rate factor is slightly larger than in the *ortho* position of anisole. In terms of the additivity principle this result requires activation by a *m*-methoxy group (see section VI.A.3).

Overall rates for bromination, diphenylmethylation, and deuterium exchange are given in Table 22, and it can be seen that all three reactions follow the same general pattern.

TABLE 22. Overall rates of electrophilic substitution in methoxy anisoles.

		k/k_{MeOPh}		
Substrate		Bromination[14b]	Diphenyl-methylation[138]	Deuterium exchange
C_6H_6		$8\cdot3 \times 10^{-10}$	$1\cdot2 \times 10^{-5}$	$1\cdot8 \times 10^{-5a}$
MeOPh	(**7**)	$1\cdot0$	$1\cdot0$	$1\cdot0$
o-MeOC$_6$H$_4$OMe	(**160**)	$3\cdot3^b$	$1\cdot1$	$3\cdot0^c$
m-MeOC$_6$H$_4$OMe	(**161**)	$>10^4$	97	—
p-MeOC$_6$H$_4$OMe	(**145**)	$0\cdot075$	$0\cdot3$	—

[a] Reference 127.
[b] A similar value has been reported for slightly different reaction conditions[94b].
[c] Reference 94a.

Rates of deuterium exchange[94a] and bromination[94b] in the cyclic compounds (**95**) related to *o*-methoxyanisole vary in a similar manner with the size of the heteroring as the rates of hydrolysis[92] of the cyclic ethers (**162**) discussed in section IV.C.2. It has been suggested that

(**95**)   (**162**)

optimum acceleration of electrophilic substitution occurs when the plane defined by each oxygen atom and the carbon atoms to which it is bound coincides with the plane of the quinonoid ring, or alternatively that the most favoured disposition of the bonds between oxygen and carbon in the heteroring is the *trans/trans* form since electrostatic interaction between the two oxygen atoms will then exert the greatest stabilizing effect on the transition state[94].

A conformational explanation has also been proposed[146] to account for the observation that the detritiation of [4,6-^{3}H]-1,2,3-trimethoxybenzene occurs 60 times more slowly than calculated from the additivity principle. Steric inhibition of resonance was considered unlikely as the 1- and 3-methoxy groups can easily lie in the plane of the ring but they would then shield the 4- and 6-positions from the approaching reagent if they were in the *trans/trans* form.

Some of the earliest information about the activating effects of different alkoxy groups was provided by the nitration of *o*- and *p*-alkoxyanisoles (**163** and **164**)[147]. The acceleration of *para* substitution

(163)   **(164)**

by alkoxy relative to methoxy groups is given by the ratio of the 4- and 5-nitro products in the reaction of **163**; similarly, the ratio of the 2- and 3-products for **164** gives the relative effect of alkoxy groups on *ortho* substitution. The results are shown in Table 23 and it can be seen that k_{RO}/k_{MeO} follows the same pattern as in reactions of compounds containing a single alkoxy substituent (see Table 21). It is also noteworthy

TABLE 23. Relative rates of nitration (k_{RO}/k_{MeO}) in alkoxy anisoles[147].

Alkyl group	*ortho* Substitution	*para* Substitution
Me	1·00	1·00
Et	1·64	1·35
n-Pr	1·80	1·28
iso-Pr	—	1·50
n-Bu	1·86	1·23

that similar experiments on *p*-phenoxyanisole[148] first revealed the difference between the activating effects of methoxy and phenoxy groups.

In diphenyl and related compounds a powerful electron-releasing group like methoxy usually directs substitution into its own ring.

Consequently 4,4′-dimethoxydiphenyl (**165a**) yields the symmetrical 3,3′-disubstituted product (**165b**) on nitration[149].

(165a)   (165b)

2. Alkoxy group in the presence of other substituents

The orientation of electrophilic attack on a polysubstituted hydrocarbon (e.g. **166**) can usually be predicted from the electron-attracting

(166)

and -releasing powers of the substituents, relative to each other, and the partial rate factors can often be calculated with reasonable precision from the additivity principle[21,150]. Most of the quantitative work in this field does not include alkoxy groups, but the extensive studies of Jones and his coworkers on the halogenation of ethers (see section VI.B.3) have shown the wide range of the validity of the additivity principle for overall rates of reaction in these compounds.

(167)   (168)

Thus the halogenation of o- and p-anisidine (**167** and **168**) occurs mainly at the indicated positions[151], as expected from the greater capacity of the amino group for electron release, and the nitration[152] of *o*-fluoroanisole (**169**) shows the isomer proportion which would

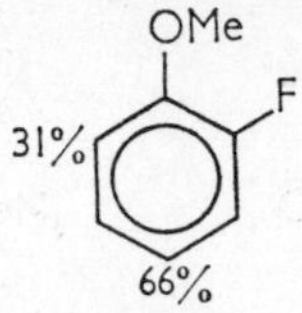

(**169**)

have been predicted from the nitration of anisole. Difficulties inevitably arise when a substituent of approximately the same activating power as the alkoxy group is present. A dominance in the directing power of ethoxy over acylamino is indicated in the halogenation[151] of

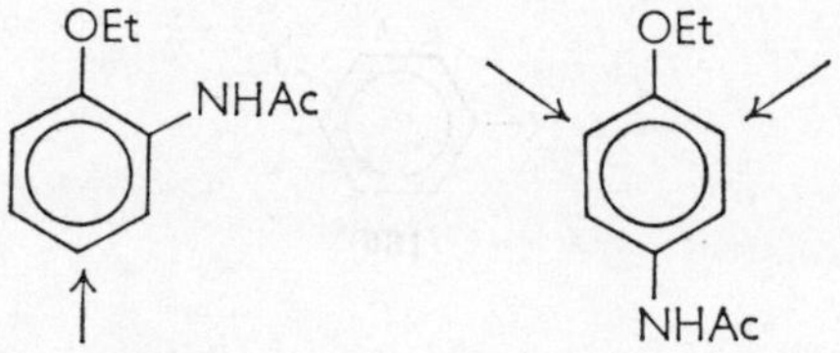

(**170**)   (**171**)

o- and *p*-ethoxyacetanilide (**170** and **171**) but the converse applies in the nitration[153] of the *o*-methoxy compound (**172**); the relatively poor

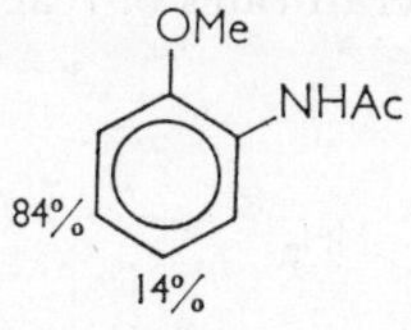

(**172**)

activating effect of the methoxy group in nitration (see section VI.B.2) may be responsible for this observation.

The additivity principle will obviously not apply when significant steric effects are operating, but it has been pointed out[150] that alterations in the electron distribution resulting from conjugative interaction between substituents may also limit the validity of this principle. Thus, halogenation of *m*-nitroanisole (**173**) occurs mainly in the 2- and not at 4-position as would have been expected, probably because the electron-withdrawing nitro group favours structures such as **174** where

(**173**)   (**174**)

conjugative electron release from the methoxy group can only occur in the indicated direction[151]. Similarly, 1,4-methoxy-2-nitrobenzene (**175**) shows mainly 3-halogenation instead of the expected 5- and 6-substitution, an observation which can be explained by the limitations imposed by structure **176** on the electron displacements[151].

(**175**)   (**176**)

Steric inhibition of conjugation with the aromatic system should obviously decrease the activating effect of the alkoxy group in electrophilic substitution. This is particularly well illustrated by the effect of *o*-methyl groups on the bromination of anisole[92]. The introduction of the 2-methyl group (**177**) increases the overall rate, presumably because of its electron-releasing properties, but the large decrease in rate on going to the 2,6-dimethyl compound (**178**) strongly suggests

	(7)	(177)	(178)
k/k_{MeOPh}	1·0	6·3	0·39

that steric factors now prevent full conjugation of the methoxy group
with the phenyl ring. The results parallel those for the S_N1 solvolysis of
the corresponding 4-chloromethyl compounds[92], and illustrate again
the similarity of the activating effect of alkoxy groups in different
types of electron-demanding reactions.

Similar considerations account for the observation[154] that the
bromination of methoxydurene (**179**) occurs only $1\cdot6 \times 10^5$ as rapidly
as the reaction with durene, while the methoxy group accelerates the
para bromination of benzene by a factor of 10^{10} (see Table 20). It is
noteworthy that this polymethylbenzene approach suggests deactivation by the *m*-methoxy group since methoxymesitylene (**180**) under-

(179)   (180)

goes bromination at about one-fifth of the rate observed with mesityl-
ene[154]. While this conclusion agrees with other direct determinations
of f_m^{MeO} (see section IV.B.2) it must be stressed that full conjugation
with the aromatic ring cannot occur in **180**. This could conceivably
prevent a stabilizing contribution from structure (**152**) which has been
postulated in order to explain the small activating effect of the *m*-
methoxy group deduced for halogenation and mercuration from results
for dimethoxy compounds via the additivity principle (see section
VI.C.1). On the other hand, the additivity principle may not be
sufficiently precise to permit such conclusions, especially as all the
direct determination of f_m^{MeO} lead to values less than unity.

VII. MISCELLANEOUS REACTIONS

A. Nucleophilic Aromatic Substitution

Although nucleophilic aromatic substitution has been studied by
several workers, relatively little information relates to the effect of
alkoxy substituents on the rate; general reviews are available[155,156].

An interesting example of an aromatic S_N1 reaction arises in the decomposition of diazonium ions[156] where the rate-determining step can

be represented by **181** and **182**. As expected, electron-attracting substituents retard the reaction but, surprisingly, electron-releasing groups

(181)   (182)

in the *para* position show a similar effect. Hughes has suggested[157] that resonance stabilization of the initial state by a contribution from structure **183** might be responsible; such a contribution would not

(183)   (184)

help the attainment of the transition state which requires the electron displacement shown in **184a**. The retarding effect of the *p*-methoxy group is quite substantial but the *m*-methoxy group actually facilitates the reaction (see below). Presumably this group has little effect on the initial state and stabilizes the strongly electron-demanding transition state by second-order relay of conjugative electron release (see **184b**).

Substituent (in **181**)	H	*p*-MeO	*m*-MeO
k (rel.)	1·0	$1·5 \times 10^{-4}$	4·6

Many of the nucleophilic aromatic substitution reactions which have been studied involve the attack of a base (B) on a carbon–halogen bond; they occur by a bimolecular mechanism. There is ample evidence that bond-breaking is of little importance in the rate-determining step, and structures like **185** can therefore be expected to

(184a)   (184b)   (185)

contribute significantly to the transition state, which will be stabilized by the presence of electron-attracting substituents in the aromatic ring.

The reactions will, in fact, not proceed at measurable rates in the absence of such groups (e.g. nitro) unless very strong bases are employed as the reagent (see below).

The reactions of 1-bromo-2-nitrobenzene (**186**) with piperidine[158] and of 1-chloro-2,6-dinitrobenzene (**187**) with methoxide ions[32] are

(**186**)   (**187**)

retarded by 4-alkoxy substituents as expected. The rates for the reaction of **186** (see below) suggest that the ethoxy group is a better donor of electrons than the methoxy group, in agreement with conclusions drawn from other reactions; considerably better electron-releasing groups (e.g. hydroxyl) retard the reaction more than the methoxy group. The effect of a 4-alkoxy group on the rates probably arises from the $+T$ electron release towards the site of reaction, a process which will destabilize the transition state.

4-Substituent (in **186**)	H	MeO	EtO
k (rel.)	1·0	0·018	0·015

A further retarding effect in these reactions can be envisaged when the alkoxy group can conjugate directly with the activating nitro

(**188**)   (**189**)   (**190**)

group. Thus, in 1-chloro-2,4-dinitro-5-methoxybenzene (**188**) contributions from structures **189** and **190** will stabilize the initial state relative to the transition state in nucleophilic displacement of Cl*.

* This conclusion can be expressed in an equivalent form by stating that structures **189** and **190** deactivate the activating nitro group[158].

Retardation from this cause may, however, not be substantial since **188** reacts with methoxide ions at about a quarter of the rate observed with 1-chloro-2,4-dinitrobenzene[159] but the effect may be largely obscured by the acceleration resulting from the presence of the electron-withdrawing *m*-methoxy group.

Although some of the reactions give fairly good correlations with the Hammett substituent constants (σ)[158] others do not and a new scale of substituent constants has been proposed for these reactions[32]. It has already been pointed out that the resulting substituent constant for the methoxy group differs significantly from σ^- (see section II.A.1).

When the methoxy substituent is insulated from the aromatic ring, only its inductive effect can be relayed to the reaction centre. The expected acceleration has been observed in the reaction of 1-chloro-2-nitro-4-X-benzene with methoxide ions[160]; a change of the substituent (X) from a methyl to a methyl methoxy group increases the rate by a factor of 6·2.

The reaction of bromoanisoles with potassium amide in liquid ammonia[161] represents an interesting example of a process in which the orientation of the products is controlled by the $-I$ effect of the methoxy group directly attached to an aromatic ring*. The reactions proceed via a benzyne intermediate (**194** and **195**); proton removal from the bromoanisole is rate-determining. Thus *o*-bromoanisole (**191**) reacts via the intermediate **194** which only forms *m*-anisidine (**196**), possibly because of steric hindrance to attack by NH_2^- at the *ortho* position. At first sight, the reaction of the *m*-bromo compound (**192**) could be thought to occur via either **194** or **195** but the formation of **194** is favoured since the acidity of the aromatic hydrogens is controlled by the $-I$ effect of the methoxy group and will therefore be greatest for the least separation. In agreement with this prediction **192** yields the same product (**196**) as **191** while the *p*-bromo compound (which can only form the intermediate **195**) produces roughly equal amounts of *m*- and *p*-anisidines (**196** and **197**).

The rates of reaction of substituted pentafluorobenzenes (**198**) with methoxide ions follow the same sequence as the proportions of the *meta* isomers produced[162a], namely, X = H > Me > MeO > O$^-$. Pentafluoroanisole (**198** where X = MeO) gives 50% *para*, 35% *meta*, and 15% *ortho* products[162a] while its chlorinated analogue, pentachloroanisole, shows 70% *meta* substitution and very little reaction at the *para* position[162b]. These results have been interpreted in terms of

* Strictly, this reaction is not a nucleophilic aromatic substitution but it has been included in this section for convenience.

the effect of the substituent on the stabilities of the initial and transition states [162c].

B. Electrophilic Reactions in Non-aromatic Systems

No new features arise when the effect of alkoxy groups on rates of electrophilic aliphatic substitution is considered. The process should be accelerated by substituents which promote additional electron displacements towards the reaction centre, as observed in the iodo demercuration[163] of *para*-substituted benzylmercurihalides (**199**) where

$$p\text{-}XC_6H_4CH_2HgHal + I_2 \longrightarrow p\text{-}XC_6H_4CH_2I + HgIHal$$
(**199**)

k_{MeO}/k_H has a value of about eleven. The conjugative electron release of the methoxy group into the aromatic ring is relayed inductively to the site of reaction, as in many other electron-demanding processes. Abnormally, a *p*-nitro group also shows an accelerating effect but this has been ascribed to a change of reaction mechanism.

Similarly, electron-releasing substituents (X) should facilitate the hydration of phenylacetylenes (**200**) to give the corresponding acetophenones (**201**) since the reaction proceeds via the rate-determining

$$XC_6H_4C\equiv CH + H_2O \longrightarrow XC_6H_4COCH_3$$
(**200**)   (**201**)

addition of a proton (**202**). The results[164] show the expected acceleration by a *p*-methoxy group and retardation by *m*-methoxy, but *o*-

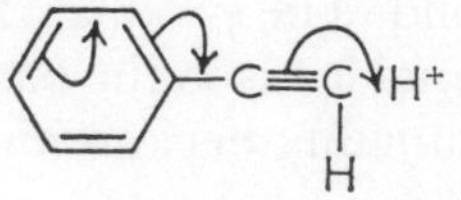

(**202**)

methoxy also retards the reaction although appreciable steric effects would not have been anticipated:

X (in **200**)	*p*-MeO	*m*-MeO	*o*-MeO
k_X/k_H	950	0·52	0·52

The addition of trifluoro acetic acid to 5-methoxy-1-hexene also involves a rate-determining protonation (**203**). The substituent should

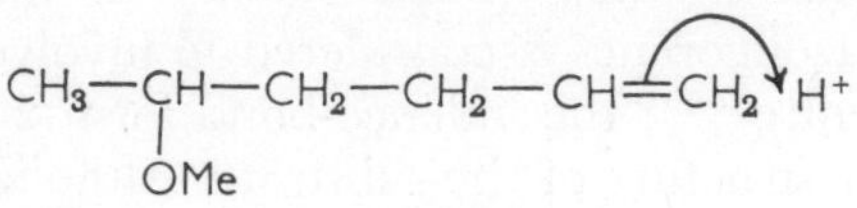

(**203**)

retard the reaction by the operation of the $-I$ effect, but the observed relative rate $(k_{MeO}/k_H \sim 0.3)$ has been considered to be larger than expected and anchimeric assistance by the methoxy group has therefore been postulated[165], with a contribution from structure **204** to the

(204)

transition state. Although a large decrease in rate resulting from a $-I$ effect would not be anticipated when the methoxy group is so far removed from the reaction centre, the argument for neighbouring-group participation is strengthened by the fact that 5-methoxy-1-pentene and 6-methoxy-1-hexene react at the same rate[165]. The effect of a non-participating substituent should decrease with increasing distance and the results have been considered to suggest that a favourable methoxy-5 participation partially counteracts the inductive rate depression.

A 4-alkoxy group in 1-cyclohexene (**205a**) induces stereospecific addition at the double bond. The product (**205b**) of the reaction with mercuric acetate in methanol leads to the *trans*-1,4-dialkoxy compound (**205c**) on reduction, presumably because the Lewis base group (RO)

(205a)   (205b)   (205c)

at the 4-position assists the formation of the intermediate organo-mercury complex in which the mercuric salt is held at the same side as the Lewis base group[166a].

The rate-determining step (**206a**→**206b**) in the acid-catalyzed hydrolysis of 9-diazofluorenes is considered to involve proton transfer to the reaction centre[166b]; the valence-bond form **206a** is one of the contributors to the structure of the substrate. Although the behaviour of 2- and 4-substituents in fluorene generally parallels that of the *meta*

(206a)   (206b)

groups in the phenylmethyl systems, the reaction is accelerated by the introduction of 2-alkoxy groups and only retarded very slightly by 4-methoxy[166c,d]:

Substituent	H	2-MeO	2-EtO	4-MeO
k (rel.)	1·00	1·57	1·73	0·97

Direct conjugation of the substituent with the reaction centre (as in **87**) would not facilitate hydrolysis but structures such as **207a** and **207b**

(207a)   (207b)

could help to localize a negative charge at the reaction centre, as opposed to other positions in the cyclopentadiene ring (cf. reference 166c). This corresponds to a stabilization of the transition state by a second-order relay of conjugative electron donation. On this inter-pretation, the results are consistent with the different capacities of ethyl and methyl groups for electron release (cf. section VI.B.3) and with the different stabilities of *o*- and *p*-phenonium ions (section VI.B.1, see also reference 166d).

C. Reactions Involving Radicals

The attack of radicals on anisole usually occurs at the *ortho* and *para* positions[167]. Similarly, the piperidino radical (**208**) derived from the chloramine (**209**) shows no reaction with benzene or with derivatives containing electron-attracting substituents, but it attacks anisole and *m*-methoxyanisole at those sites to which electrons can be supplied (*ortho* and *para* to the methoxy group)[168]. The polar requirements of

(208)   **(209)**

homolytic aromatic substitution are, however, ambiguous since methoxy and nitro substitution in benzene both facilitate the reaction with phenyl radicals, by factors of 2·5 and 4·0, respectively[169].

No such ambiguity arises in the side-chain halogenation of substituted toluenes (**210**) which is accelerated by electron-releasing

(210)

substituents and retarded by electron-attracting groups. The introduction of a *p*-methoxy group increases the rate of reaction with bromine, *N*-bromosuccinimide, and its tetramethyl and tetrafluoro derivatives about 10-fold[170]. All these reactions show virtually the same selectivity and gave good correlations with σ^+ for a variety of substituents. Similarly, photobromination with $BrCCl_3$ showed the acceleration by *p*-methoxy ($k/k_H = 14\cdot2$) and the retardation by *m*-methoxy ($k/k_H = 0\cdot87$) expected in an electron-demanding reaction[171], and analogous results were observed for the effect of the phenoxy group on the rates of chlorination with chlorine radicals[172]:

Substituent	H	*p*-PhO	*m*-PhO
k (rel.)	1·00	2·50	0·86

A polar transition state involving proton abstraction by $Cl_3C\cdot$ and stabilized by electron-releasing substituents in the aromatic ring was postulated for the photobromination[171] in view of the good correlation of the results with σ^+.

A greater facility for electron release in radical reactions than would have been expected from studies of heterolytic processes has been noted for m-methoxy in the decomposition of benzoyl peroxides and its initiation of polymerization[43]; the enhancement corresponds to a stabilization of approximately 0·3 kcal/mole. More impressively, the radical (211) formed by the polarographic oxidation of m-anisidine is subject to an additional stabilization of 1·1 kcal, probably because of contributions from structures such as 212. The radical formed from p-anisidine shows the stabilization expected when the methoxy group is conjugated to an electron-deficient site.

(211)   (212)

The *ortho* Claisen rearrangement of allyl phenyl ethers (213) to form o-allylhydroxybenzenes (214) is also facilitated by electron release towards the reaction centre. *para* substituents give a fairly good correlation with σ^+ but the accelerating effect of p-methoxy is greater than the

(213)   (214)

retardation caused by p-nitro, and ρ is numerically small $(-0·61)$[173,174]. As expected, p-ethoxy facilitates reaction a little more than p-methoxy but the effect of m-methoxy is actually greater than that of the *para* substituent[174]:

X	p-EtO	p-MeO	m-MeO	p-NO$_2$
k_X/k_H	3·15	3·01	3·24	0·59

The observations can be explained[175] in terms of homolytic fission of the O—C linkage in the initial step to produce the two radicals (215). These radicals will be stabilized by contributions from structures like 216 and 217, and it can be seen that p-methoxy facilitates the initial bond-fission (via 216) but has little effect on the product-forming step which requires a contribution from 217. A m-methoxy substituent in 213 is, however, in the *para* position with respect to product formation and can therefore facilitate this step by a contribution from structure **218**.

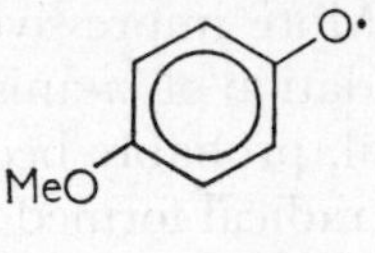

(215) 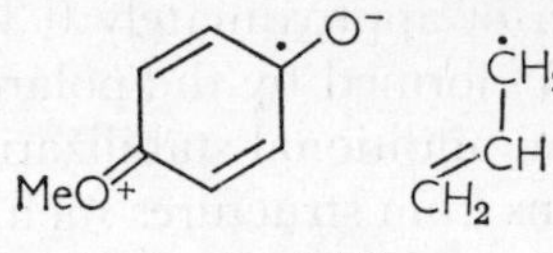   (216)

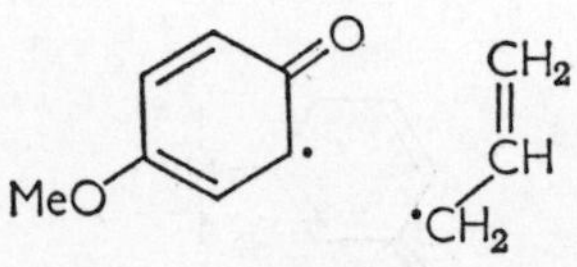

(217) 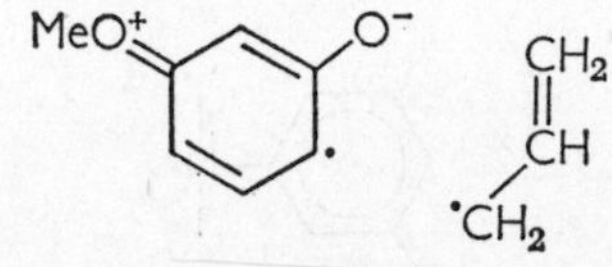   (218)

The similar rearrangement of substituted cinnamyl-*p*-tolyl ethers (**219**) also shows a reasonably good correlation with σ^+ for the *para*

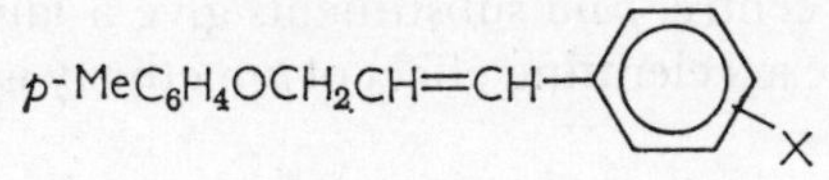

$$p\text{-MeC}_6\text{H}_4\text{OCH}_2\text{CH}=\text{CH}-\text{X}$$

(219)

substituents ($k_{p\text{-MeO}}/k_\text{H} \approx 2\cdot8$) but *m*-methoxy has virtually no effect on the rate[176]. The accelerating effect of *p*-methoxy could arise from a contribution of structure **220** to the transition state of the initial bond-

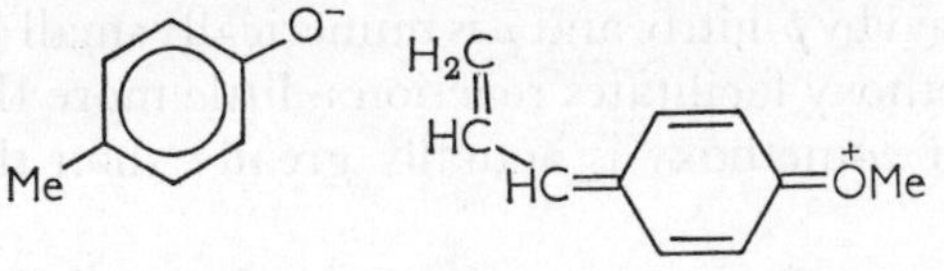

(220)

breaking step. No similar contribution arises for the *m*-methoxy derivative which is presumably too far removed from the reaction centre to affect the rate by its $-I$ effect.

VIII. REFERENCES

1. (a) C. K. Ingold, *Structure and Mechanism in Organic Chemistry*, G. Bell and Sons, London, 1953, pp. 60–92; (b) E. S. Gould, *Mechanism and Structure in Organic Chemistry*, H. Holt and Co., New York, 1959, pp. 199–220.

2. F. H. Westheimer, *J. Am. Chem. Soc.*, **61**, 1977 (1939).
3. J. D. Roberts and W. T. Moreland, *J. Am. Chem. Soc.*, **75**, 2167 (1953).
4. B. M. Wepster in *Progress in Stereochemistry*, Vol. 2 (Ed. W. Klyne and P. B. D. de la Mare), Butterworths, London, 1958, p. 99.
5. For a more elementary treatment, see ref. 1(b), pp. 236–239.
6. (a) J. W. Smith, *Electric Dipole Moments*, Butterworths, London, 1955, pp. 200–219; (b) C. E. Ingham and G. C. Hampson, *J. Chem. Soc.*, 981 (1939).
7. L. A. Wiles, *Chem. Rev.*, **56**, 329 (1956).
8. Reference 1(a), p. 116.
9. Reference 1(a), p. 128.
10. A. Burawoy and J. T. Chamberlain, *J. Chem. Soc.*, 2310 (1952).
11. J. W. Baker, G. F. C. Barnett, and W. T. Tweed, *J. Chem. Soc.*, 2831 (1952).
12. C. Eaborn, *J. Chem. Soc.*, 4858 (1956).
13. H. C. Brown and L. M. Stock, *J. Am. Chem. Soc.*, **80**, 1942 (1960).
14. (a) P. W. Robertson, P. B. D. de la Mare, and W. T. G. Johnston, *J. Chem. Soc.*, 276 (1943); (b) P. B. D. de la Mare and C. A. Vernon, *J. Chem. Soc.*, 1764 (1951).
15. G. Kohnstam in *The Transition State*, Chem. Soc. Special Publ., No. 16, 179 (1962).
16. J. R. Fox and G. Kohnstam, unpublished results.
17. (a) P. W. Robertson, P. B. D. de la Mare, and B. E. Swedlund, *J. Chem. Soc.*, 782 (1953); (b) P. B. D. de la Mare, O. M. H. el Dusouqui, J. G. Tillett and M. Zeltner, *J. Chem. Soc.*, 5306 (1964).
18. R. W. Taft, N. C. Deno, and P. S. Skell in *Annual Review of Physical Chemistry*, Vol. 9 (Ed. H. Eyring), Annual Reviews, Palo Alto, 1958, pp. 287–300.
19. J. E. Leffler and E. Grunwald, *Rates and Equilibria of Organic Reactions*, John Wiley and Sons, London, 1963, Chap. 7, pp. 171–262.
20. P. R. Wells, *Chem. Rev.*, **63**, 171 (1963).
21. L. M. Stock and H. C. Brown in *Advances in Physical Organic Chemistry*, Vol. 1 (Ed. V. Gold), Academic Press, London, 1963, pp. 35–154.
22. S. Ehrenson in *Progress in Physical Organic Chemistry*, Vol. 2 (Ed. S. Cohen, A. Streitwieser, and R. W. Taft), Interscience, New York, 1964, pp. 195–251.
23. C. D. Ritchie and W. F. Sager in *Progress in Physical Organic Chemistry*, Vol. 2 (Ed. S. Cohen, A. Streitwieser, and R. W. Taft), Interscience, New York, 1964, pp. 323–400.
24. L. P. Hammett, *Physical Organic Chemistry*, McGraw-Hill Book Co., New York, 1940, pp. 184–193; H. H. Jaffé, *Chem. Rev.*, **53**, 191 (1953).
25. J. E. Leffler, *J. Org. Chem.*, **20**, 1202 (1955).
26. R. Stewart and K. Yates, *J. Am. Chem. Soc.*, **80**, 6355 (1958); R. Stewart and K. Yates, *J. Am. Chem. Soc.*, **82**, 4059 (1960).
27. S. Sugden and J. B. Willis, *J. Chem. Soc.*, 1360 (1951).
28. (a) R. F. Hudson and G. Klopman, *J. Chem. Soc.*, 1062 (1962); (b) *Helv. Chim. Acta.*, **44**, 1914 (1961).
29. D. H. McDaniel and H. C. Brown, *J. Org. Chem.*, **23**, 420 (1958).
30. W. A. Sheppard, *J. Am. Chem. Soc.*, **83**, 4860 (1961).
31. A. I. Biggs and R. A. Robinson, *J. Chem. Soc.*, 388 (1961).
32. J. Miller, *Australian J. Chem.*, **9**, 61 (1956); *J. Am. Chem. Soc.*, **79**, 93 (1957).

33. H. C. Brown and Y. Okamoto, *J. Am. Chem. Soc.*, **79**, 1913 (1957); **80**, 4979 (1958).
34. H. C. Brown and L. M. Stock, *J. Am. Chem. Soc.*, **84**, 3298 (1962), and references there cited.
35. H. van Bekkum, P. E. Verkade, and B. M. Wepster, *Rec. Trav. Chim.*, **78**, 815 (1959).
36. R. W. Taft, *J. Phys. Chem.*, **64**, 1805 (1960).
37. P. B. D. de la Mare and J. H. Ridd, *Aromatic Substitution*, Butterworths, London, 1959, pp. 239–240.
38. J. R. Fox and G. Kohnstam, *Proc. Chem. Soc.*, 115 (1964).
39. H. C. Brown and Y. Okamoto, *J. Am. Chem. Soc.*, **79**, 1909 (1957).
40. J. R. Knowles, R. O. C. Norman, and G. K. Radda, *J. Chem. Soc.*, 4885 (1960).
41. H. C. Brown and L. M. Stock, *J. Am. Chem. Soc.*, **84**, 1668 (1962).
42. R. W. Bott and C. Eaborn, *J. Chem. Soc.*, 2139 (1963).
43. R. W. Taft and I. C. Lewis, *J. Am. Chem. Soc.*, **81**, 5343 (1959).
44. R. O. C. Norman, G. K. Radda, D. A. Brimacombe, P. O. Ralph, and E. M. Smith, *J. Chem. Soc.*, 3247 (1961).
45. R. W. Taft in *Steric Effects in Organic Chemistry* (Ed. M. S. Newman), John Wiley and Sons, New York, 1956, pp. 556–675.
46. R. W. Taft and I. C. Lewis, *J. Am. Chem. Soc.*, **80**, 2436 (1958); R. W. Taft, S. Ehrenson, I. C. Lewis, and R. E. Glick, *J. Am. Chem. Soc.*, **81**, 5352 (1959); R. W. Taft, S. Ehrenson, I. Fox, I. C. Lewis, and R. E. Glick, *J. Am. Chem. Soc.*, **82**, 756 (1960).
47. R. W. Taft, E. Price, I. R. Fox, K. K. Anderson, and G. T. Davis, *J. Am. Chem. Soc.*, **85**, 3146 (1963).
48. Y. Tsuno and Y. Yukawa, *Bull. Chem. Soc. Japan*, **32**, 971 (1959).
49. (a) C. Eaborn and K. C. Pande, *J. Chem. Soc.*, 3715 (1961); 5082 (1961); (b) C. Eaborn and J. A. Waters, *J. Chem. Soc.*, 542 (1961); (c) T. Inukai, *Bull. Chem. Soc., Japan*, **35**, 400 (1962).
50. J. Hine, *J. Am. Chem. Soc.*, **82**, 4877 (1960).
51. Reference 19, p. 192.
52. G. Kortüm, W. Vogel, and K. Andrussow, *Dissociation Constants of Organic Acids in Aqueous Solutions*, Butterworths, London, 1961.
53. J. F. J. Dippy, *Chem. Rev.*, **25**, 151 (1939).
54. A. Bryson, N. R. Davies, and E. P. Serjeant, *J. Am. Chem. Soc.*, **85**, 1933 (1963).
55. F. Basolo and R. K. Murmann, *J. Am. Chem. Soc.*, **77**, 3484 (1955).
56. (a) E. Bacuicchi and G. Illuminati, *Gazz. Chim. Ital.*, **87**, 981 (1957); (b) J. Hine, *Physical Organic Chemistry*, McGraw-Hill Book Co., New York, 1962, p. 59.
57. J. F. C. Dippy, S. R. C. Hughes, and B. C. Kitchiner, *J. Chem. Soc.*, 1275 (1964).
58. J. Shorter and F. J. Stubbs, *J. Chem. Soc.*, 1180 (1949).
59. R. K. Chaturverdi and S. S. Katiyar, *J. Sci. Ind. Res. (India)*, **21B**, 47 (1962).
60. (a) R. Stewart and K. Yates, *Can. J. Chem.*, **37**, 664 (1959); (b) H. S. Chang, J. T. Edwards, R. Stewart, and K. Yates, *Can. J. Chem.*, **38**, 1518 (1960).

61. J. W. Baker and H. B. Hopkins, *J. Chem. Soc.*, 1089 (1949).
62. N. C. Deno and A. Schriesheim, *J. Am. Chem. Soc.*, **77**, 3051 (1955).
63. Reference 1(a), pp. 306–418.
64. Reference 1(b), pp. 250–313.
65. C. A. Bunton, *Nucleophilic Substitution at a Saturated Carbon Atom*, Elsevier, London, 1963.
66. E. R. Thornton, *Solvolysis Mechanisms*, Ronald Press, New York, 1964.
67. B. Appel, R. Baker, A. Diaz, and S. Winstein in *Organic Reaction Mechanisms*, Chem. Soc. Special Publ., No. 19, 1965, pp. 109–130, and references there cited.
68. E. Grunwald and S. Winstein, *J. Am. Chem. Soc.*, **70**, 846 (1948).
69. G. Kohnstam, A. Queen, and T. Ribar, *Chem. Ind. (London)*, 1287 (1962).
70. C. G. Swain and W. P. Langsdorf, *J. Am. Chem. Soc.*, **73**, 2813 (1951).
71. G. Baddeley and G. M. Bennett, *J. Chem. Soc.*, 1819 (1935).
72. W. R. Kirner, *J. Am. Chem. Soc.*, **48**, 2745 (1926); F. B. Tutwiler and R. L. McKee, *J. Am. Chem. Soc.*, **76**, 6342 (1954).
73. P. Ballinger, P. B. D. de la Mare, G. Kohnstam, and B. M. Presst, *J. Chem. Soc.*, 3641 (1955).
74. (a) G. R. Cowie, J. R. Fox, H. J. M. Fitches, K. A. Hooton, D. M. Hunt, G. Kohnstam, and B. Shillaker, *Proc. Chem. Soc.*, 222 (1962); (b) G. Kohnstam, and D. Tidy, *Chem. Ind. (London)*, 1193 (1962); (c) G. R. Cowie, H. J. M. Fitches, and G. Kohnstam, *J. Chem. Soc.*, 1585 (1963).
75. J. R. Fox and G. Kohnstam, *Chem. Comm.*, 249 (1965).
76. J. R. Fox and G. Kohnstam, *J. Chem. Soc.*, 1593 (1963).
77. P. Salomaa, *Annales Universitatis Turkuensis*, A XIV (1953).
78. A. Bradfield and B. Jones, *Trans. Faraday Soc.*, **37**, 726 (1941).
79. Reference 1(a), p. 334.
80. From the results summarized in reference 74(a).
81. G. Favini and M. Simonetta, *J. Chem. Soc.*, 1840 (1954).
82. From the results summarized in reference 74(b).
83. G. S. Hammond and J. K. Kochi., *J. Am. Chem. Soc.*, **75**, 3445 (1953).
84. Calculated from C. A. Grob and G. Cseh, *Helv. Chim. Acta*, **47**, 194 (1964).
85. G. E. K. Branch and A. C. Nixon, *J. Am. Chem. Soc.*, **58**, 492 (1936).
86. H. C. Brown, T. Inukai, and Y. Okamoto, *J. Am. Chem. Soc.*, **80**, 4964, 1958.
87. H. C. Brown, T. Inukai, and Y. Okamoto, *J. Am. Chem. Soc.*, **80**, 4964 (1958).
88. P. B. D. de la Mare, E. A. Johnson, and J. S. Lomas, *J. Chem. Soc.*, 5317 (1964); R. Baker, R. W. Bott, C. Eaborn, and P. M. Greasley, *J. Chem. Soc.*, 627 (1964).
89. C. Eaborn, R. C. Goldsworthy, and M. N. Lilly, *J. Chem. Soc.*, 3036, 3641 (1959); J. A. Parry and K. D. Warren, *J. Chem. Soc.*, 4049 (1965).
90. G. Baddeley and N. H. P. Smith, *Nature*, **164**, 1014 (1949).
91. N. H. P. Smith in *Steric Effects in Conjugated Systems*, Butterworths, London, 1958, p. 113.
92. G. Baddeley, N. H. P. Smith, and M. A. Vickers, *J. Chem. Soc.*, 2455 (1956).
93. J. G. Watkinson, W. Watson, and B. L. Yates, *J. Chem. Soc.*, 5437 (1963).
94. (a) W. G. Brown, K. E. Wilzbach, and W. H. Urry, *Can. J. Res.*, **27B**, 398 (1949); (b) G. Baddeley, G. Holt, N. H. P. Smith, and F. A. Whittaker, *Nature*, **168**, 386 (1951).

95. B. Capon, *Quart. Rev.*, **18**, 45 (1964).
96. S. Winstein, E. Allred, R. Heck, and R. Glick, *Tetrahedron*, **3**, 1 (1958).
97. S. Winstein and R. B. Henderson, *J. Am. Chem. Soc.*, **65**, 2196 (1943).
98. S. Winstein, C. R. Lindegren, and L. L. Ingraham, *J. Am. Chem. Soc.*, **75**, 155 (1953).
99. D. S. Noyce, B. R. Thomas, and B. N. Bastian, *J. Am. Chem. Soc.*, **82**, 855 (1960); D. S. Noyce and B. N. Bastian, *J. Am. Chem. Soc.*, **82**, 1246 (1960).
100. R. Heck, J. Corse, E. Grunwald, and S. Winstein, *J. Am. Chem. Soc.*, **79**, 3278 (1957).
101. R. Heck and S. Winstein, *J. Am. Chem. Soc.*, **79**, 3432 (1957).
102. S. Winstein, M. Brown, K. C. Schreiber, and A. H. Schlesinger, *J. Am. Chem. Soc.*, **74**, 1140 (1952).
103. R. Heck and S. Winstein, *J. Am. Chem. Soc.*, **79**, 3105 (1957).
104. R. Heck and S. Winstein, *J. Am. Chem. Soc.*, **79**, 3114 (1957).
105. For example: (a) reference 1(a), pp. 752–782; (b) A. G. Davies and J. Kenyon, *Quart. Rev.*, **9**, 203 (1955).
106. C. K. Ingold and W. S. Nathan, *J. Chem. Soc.*, 222 (1936); C. N. Hinshelwood, and E. W. Timm, *J. Chem. Soc.*, 862 (1938).
107. B. Jones and J. Robinson, *J. Chem. Soc.*, 3845 (1955).
108. B. Jones and J. G. Watkinson, *J. Chem. Soc.*, 4064 (1958).
109. J. G. Watkinson, W. Watson, and B. L. Yates, *J. Chem. Soc.*, 5437 (1963).
110. C. A. Burkhard and R. E. Burnett, *J. Am. Chem. Soc.*, **80**, 341 (1958).
111. P. Salomaa, *Acta Chem. Scand.*, **11**, 125, 132, 141, 239 (1957).
112. J. Koskikallio, *Acta Chem. Scand.*, **18**, 2248 (1964).
113. C. A. Bunton, T. A. Lewis, and D. R. Llewellyn, *Chem. Ind.* (*London*), 1154 (1954); C. A. Bunton and D. R. Llewellyn, *Chem. Ind.* (*London*), 180 (1956).
114. J. F. Norris, E. V. Fasce, and C. J. Staud, *J. Am. Chem. Soc.*, **57**, 1415 (1935).
115. D. A. Brown and R. F. Hudson, *J. Chem. Soc.*, 883, 3352 (1953); E. W. Grunden and R. F. Hudson, *J. Chem. Soc.*, 501 (1956).
116. (a) S. Patai and Y. Israeli, *J. Chem. Soc.*, 2025 (1960); (b) J. D. Dickinson and C. Eaborn, *J. Chem. Soc.*, 3036, 3641 (1959); J. A. Parry and K. D. Warren, *J. Chem. Soc.*, 4049 (1965).
117. For example: reference 1(a), pp. 221–305; P. B. D. de la Mare and J. H. Ridd, *Aromatic Substitution*, Butterworths, London, 1959; R. O. C. Norman and R. Taylor, *Electrophilic Substitution in Benzenoid Systems*, Elsevier, London, 1965.
118. C. Eaborn, *Organosilicon Compounds*, Butterworths, London, 1960, pp. 146–157.
119. C. Eaborn and K. C. Pande, *J. Chem. Soc.*, 1566 (1960).
120. R. E. Dessy and Y. E. Lee, *J. Am. Chem. Soc.*, **82**, 689 (1960).
121. P. H. Griffiths, W. A. Walkey, and H. B. Watson, *J. Chem. Soc.*, 631 (1934).
122. C. A. Bunton, G. J. Minkoff, and R. I. Reed, *J. Chem. Soc.*, 1416 (1947).
123. K. Halvarson and L. Melander, *Arkiv. Kemi*, **11**, 77 (1957).
124. B. Jones and E. N. Richardson, *J. Chem. Soc.*, 3939 (1956).
125. H. C. Brown and G. Marino, *J. Am. Chem. Soc.*, **84**, 1658 (1962).
126. R. Baker and C. Eaborn, *J. Chem. Soc.*, 5077 (1961).
127. D. P. N. Satchell, *J. Chem. Soc.*, 3911 (1956).
128. M. J. S. Dewar and D. S. Urch, *J. Chem. Soc.*, 3079 (1958).

129. D. R. Harvey and R. O. C. Norman, *J. Chem. Soc.*, 3604 (1961).
130. H. C. Brown and M. Dubek, *J. Am. Chem. Soc.*, **82**, 1939 (1960).
131. C. Eaborn and J. A. Sperry, *J. Chem. Soc.*, 4921 (1961).
132. C. Eaborn and K. C. Pande, *J. Chem. Soc.*, 297 (1961).
133. J. T. Day and W. M. Lauer, *J. Am. Chem. Soc.*, **77**, 1904 (1955).
134. Reference 37, p. 82.
135. R. O. C. Norman and G. K. Radda, *J. Chem. Soc.*, 3610 (1961).
136. (a) R. O. C. Norman and G. K. Radda, *J. Chem. Soc.*, 3030 (1961);
     (b) P. Kovacic and J. J. Miller, *J. Org. Chem.*, **30**, 2871 (1965); (c) P.
     Kovacic and J. J. Miller, *J. Org. Chem.*, **30**, 1581 (1965); (d) reference 37,
     p. 76.
137. P. G. E. Alcorn and P. R. Wells, *Australian J. Chem.*, **18**, 1391 (1965).
138. D. Bethell, V. Gold, and T. Riley, *J. Chem. Soc.*, 3134 (1959).
139. H. G. Kuivila and A. R. Hendrickson, *J. Am. Chem. Soc.*, **74**, 5068 (1952).
140. H. G. Kuivila and K. V. Nahabedian, *J. Am. Chem. Soc.*, **83**, 2167 (1961).
141. C. Eaborn and D. E. Webster, *J. Chem. Soc.*, 179 (1960).
142. H. G. Kuivila, L. D. Benjamin, C. J. Murphy, A. D. Price, and J. H.
     Polevy, *J. Org. Chem.*, **27**, 825 (1962).
143. Reference 37, p. 141.
144. A. Bradfield, G. I. Davies, and E. Long, *J. Chem. Soc.*, 1389 (1949);
     S. J. Branch and B. Jones, *J. Chem. Soc.*, 2921 (1955).
145. B. Jones and J. P. Sleight, *J. Chem. Soc.*, 1775 (1954).
146. D. P. N. Satchell, *J. Chem. Soc.*, 463 (1959).
147. J. Allan and R. Robinson, *J. Chem. Soc.*, 376 (1926); J. C. Smith, *J. Chem. Soc.*, 251 (1931).
148. T. R. Lea and R. Robinson, *J. Chem. Soc.*, 411 (1926).
149. J. van Alphen, *Rec. Trav. Chim.*, **49**, 769 (1930).
150. Reference 37, pp. 88–92.
151. Reference 37, pp. 132–134.
152. E. L. Holmes and C. K. Ingold, *J. Chem. Soc.*, 1328 (1926).
153. C. K. Ingold and E. H. Ingold, *J. Chem. Soc.*, 1310 (1926).
154. G. Illuminati, *J. Am. Chem. Soc.*, **80**, 4945 (1958).
155. Reference 1(a), pp. 797–815.
156. J. F. Bunnett and R. E. Zahler, *Chem. Rev.*, **49**, 273 (1951).
157. E. D. Hughes, private communication quoted in reference 156.
158. E. Berliner and L. C. Monack, *J. Am. Chem. Soc.*, **74**, 1574 (1952).
159. M. Liveris, P. G. Lutz, and J. Miller, *J. Am. Chem. Soc.*, **78**, 3375 (1956).
160. D. T. Downing, R. L. Heppolette, and J. Miller, *Chem. Ind. (London)*, 1260
     (1953).
161. J. D. Roberts, C. W. Vaughan, L. A. Carlsmith, and D. A. Semenov,
     J. Am. Chem. Soc., **78**, 611 (1956).
162. (a) J. Burdon, W. B. Hollyhead, and J. C. Tatlow, *J. Chem. Soc.*, 5152
     (1965); (b) L. S. Kokrina, G. G. Yakokron, and N. N. Vorozhtsov, *Zh.
     Obshch. Khim.*, **35**, 137, 142 (1965); (c) J. Burdon, *Tetrahedron*, **21**, 3373
     (1965).
163. I. P. Beletskaya, T. P. Fetirova, and O. A. Reutov, *Dolk. Akad. Nauk.
     SSSR*, **155**, 1095 (1964).
164. R. W. Bott, C. Eaborn, and D. R. M. Walton, *J. Chem. Soc.*, 384 (1965).
165. P. E. Petersen and G. Allen, *J. Am. Chem. Soc.*, **85**, 3608 (1963).

166. (a) H. B. Henbest and B. Nichols, *J. Chem. Soc.*, 227 (1959); (b) K. D. Warren, *J. Chem. Soc.*, 2561 (1961); (c) K. D. Warren, *J. Chem. Soc.*, 598 (1963); (d) K. D. Warren and J. R. Yandle, *J. Chem. Soc.*, 4221 (1965).
167. G. H. Williams, *Homolytic Aromatic Substitution*, Pergamon Press, Oxford, 1960, p. 47.
168. F. Minisci and R. Galli, *Tetrahedron Letters*, **8**, 433 (1965).
169. Reference 166, p. 57.
170. R. E. Pearson and J. C. Martin, *J. Am. Chem. Soc.*, **85**, 3142 (1963).
171. E. S. Huyser, *J. Am. Chem. Soc.*, **82**, 394 (1960).
172. G. A. Russell and R. C. Williamson, *J. Am. Chem. Soc.*, **86**, 2357 (1964).
173. W. N. White, D. Gwynn, R. Schlitt, C. Girard, and W. Fife, *J. Am. Chem. Soc.*, **80**, 3271 (1958).
174. H. L. Goering and R. R. Jacobson, *J. Am. Chem. Soc.*, **80**, 3277 (1958).
175. W. N. White, C. D. Slater, and W. K. Fife, *J. Org. Chem.*, **26**, 627 (1961).
176. W. N. White and W. K. Fife, *J. Am. Chem. Soc.*, **83**, 3846 (1961).

CHAPTER **4**

The pyrolysis of ethers

K. J. Laidler

University of Ottawa, Canada

and

D. J. McKenney

University of Windsor, Canada

I. INTRODUCTION

Studies of the pyrolysis of organic ethers have been largely confined to the smaller molecules. Kineticists have conducted much research over the years in attempts to elucidate the nature of the elementary processes that occur in organic pyrolyses. The investigations of the thermal decompositions of simple hydrocarbons, simple aldehydes and ketones, as well as such ethers as dimethyl and diethyl ether, have yielded much information about the nature of free-radical reactions. The over-all kinetics of gas-phase pyrolyses are usually simple to study experimentally, but the problem of investigating the elementary processes which occur in such systems has been exceedingly difficult and challenging.

167

This review will be mainly concerned with the simple ethers (since the bulk of the research is in this area) and with some work on higher ethers where data are available. The pyrolyses of epoxy compounds are not included since these could be considered in a class by themselves, at least insofar as the mechanisms of their thermal decompositions are concerned.

It was assumed for a long time that the pyrolyses of organic compounds were totally molecular in nature. When the presence of free radicals in these decompositions was confirmed by the mirror technique, explaining the observed simple kinetic laws presented a baffling problem. In 1934 Rice and Herzfeld[1] showed, however, that most of the experimental data for such decompositions, including the fact that they are frequently of simple orders, could be explained in terms of complex free-radical mechanisms.

The view that part of the decomposition was molecular was originally taken by Hinshelwood and his students. This idea came about as a result of their work on the inhibition of organic pyrolyses. Inhibitors such as nitric oxide and certain olefins, added in very small quantities, decreased the rate to a fraction of the rate in the absence of inhibitor, and the residual reaction was thought to be purely molecular. Evidence has accumulated since that time, however, to indicate that even the inhibited decompositions are also mainly free-radical processes. The evidence for these conflicting conclusions is reviewed by Stubbs and Hinshelwood[2] and by Wojciechowski and Laidler[3]. More recent work provides further support for free-radical inhibited decompositions[4]. Investigations of inhibited pyrolyses are of interest in themselves, and often they provide clues to the nature of certain elementary reactions which occur in the uninhibited decompositions. This is also sometimes true of certain effects observed when other additives such as accelerating agents (H_2S, CH_3SH, HCl, etc.) are investigated. For these reasons a review of ether pyrolyses must necessarily include at least a brief discussion of the effects of additives. The present review, however, will deal mainly with the uninhibited decompositions, work on the effects of additives being dealt with only insofar as it throws light on the pyrolyses of the pure compounds.

II. DIMETHYL ETHER

Dimethyl ether undergoes pyrolysis at a convenient rate in the temperature range 500–550°, and the process has been studied in great detail by many workers. A thorough review of this reaction based on investigations carried out prior to 1953 is given by Steacie[5]. The formation of the main products can be represented by equation (1).

$$CH_3OCH_3 \longrightarrow CH_4 + CH_2O \longrightarrow CH_4 + CO + H_2 \qquad (1)$$

The concentration of formaldehyde builds up in the system and goes through a maximum when the reaction is about half complete.

More recently Benson[6] discussed earlier work on the decomposition and concluded that the overall order was three-halves with respect to ether, and not first order as had previously been thought. Benson and Jain[7] confirmed this experimentally and obtained a rate coefficient given by (2). They found that added inert gas had very little effect.

$$k = 1\cdot3 \times 10^{15}\, e^{-55,\,600/RT}\, cc^{\frac{1}{2}}/mole^{\frac{1}{2}}\, sec \qquad (2)$$

The decomposition mechanism postulated by Benson and Jain[7] consisted of first-order initiation, and termination involving two β radicals. A β radical is one which is involved in second-order propagation reactions, and examples are hydrogen and methyl radicals. The μ radicals, on the other hand, undergo first-order propagation reactions. These definitions were first suggested by Goldfinger and coworkers[8], who pointed out that the overall order of a free-radical reaction depends on the orders of the initial and termination processes. Their general conclusions have been summarized by Laidler, Sagert and Wojciechowski[9] and are shown in Table 1. Benson and Jain[7] suggested that the decomposition of the methoxymethyl radical was in its pressure-dependent second-order region. Also, Anderson and Benson[10]

TABLE 1. Overall orders of reaction for various types of initiation and termination reactions[a].

First-order initiation		Second-order initiation		Overall order
Simple termination	Third-body termination	Simple termination	Third-body termination	
		$\beta\beta$		2
$\beta\beta$		$\beta\mu$	$\beta\beta M$	$\frac{3}{2}$
$\beta\mu$	$\beta\beta M$	$\mu\mu$	$\beta\mu M$	1
$\mu\mu$	$\beta\mu M$		$\mu\mu M$	$\frac{1}{2}$
	$\mu\mu M$			0

[a] M represents a third body; $\beta\beta M$, for example, means that the termination reaction between two β radicals is in its third-order region, where the rate is proportional to the concentration of the third body.

6*

found $CH_3OC_2H_5$ and $CH_3OCH_2CH_2OCH_3$ in the products of the decomposition, though in much smaller quantities than predicted.

Imai and Toyama[11] pyrolyzed dimethyl ether in the temperature range of 360–440°. Their overall rate coefficient (equation 3) agreed

$$k = 1 \cdot 45 \times 10^{15} \, e^{-54, \, 500/RT} \, cc^{\frac{1}{2}}/mole^{\frac{1}{2}} \, sec \qquad (3)$$

well with that obtained by Benson and Jain[7]. McKenney and Laidler's[12] study of the uninhibited thermal decomposition of dimethyl ether in the temperature range of 500–550° and the pressure range of approximately 100–700 mm Hg yielded an overall rate coefficient given by (4). The value for the activation energy is in good agreement

$$k = 2 \cdot 98 \times 10^{14} \, e^{-54, \, 900/RT} \, cc^{\frac{1}{2}}/mole^{\frac{1}{2}} \, sec \qquad (4)$$

with the values obtained by previous workers, as quoted above. The frequency factor, however, is significantly lower than those obtained previously. This may be due to the different method used by McKenney and Laidler[12] in conditioning the reaction vessel. These workers also showed by isotope-mixing studies that the decomposition occurs almost entirely by a free-radical chain process.

A considerable number of mechanisms have been suggested for the decomposition of dimethyl ether. Rice and Herzfeld[1] proposed Scheme 1. In the terminology of Laidler, Sagert and Wojciechowski[9]

$$CH_3OCH_3 \longrightarrow CH_3 + CH_3O \qquad (5)$$

$$CH_3 + CH_3OCH_3 \longrightarrow CH_4 + CH_2OCH_3 \qquad (6)$$

$$CH_2OCH_3 \longrightarrow CH_2O + CH_3 \qquad (7)$$

$$CH_3O \longrightarrow CH_2O + H \qquad (8)$$

$$H + CH_3OCH_3 \longrightarrow H_2 + CH_2OCH_3 \qquad (9)$$

$$CH_3 + CH_3 \longrightarrow C_2H_6 \qquad (10)$$

SCHEME 1.

this mechanism is of the $^1\beta\beta_{\frac{3}{2}}$ type; initiation is first order and there is simple termination of the $\beta\beta$ type. The corresponding rate equation is given by (11). As matters stand at the present time, this may well be

$$-\frac{d\,[CH_3OCH_3]}{dt} = k_6 \left(\frac{k_5}{k_{10}}\right)^{\frac{1}{2}} [CH_3OCH_3]^{\frac{3}{2}} \qquad (11)$$

the correct mechanism. The scheme agrees with experiment in predicting no inert-gas effect. Benson and Jain[7], however, rejected this mechanism on the grounds that the overall frequency factor and activation energy could not be obtained by introducing the appropriate values for k_5, k_6 and k_{10}. The most reliable values for E_5, E_6 and E_{10}, however, would seem to be 87, 9·5 and 0 kcal, respectively, and these lead to an activation energy of 53·0 kcal, which is in satisfactory agreement with McKenney and Laidler's activation energy of 54·9 kcal. Satisfactory agreement can also be obtained for the frequency factor, so that it does not appear that Benson and Jain's criticism is valid. Benson and Jain[7] alternatively proposed that the chain-ending step is reaction (12), instead of (10); all other steps are the same, but they

$$CH_3 + CH_2OCH_3 \longrightarrow CH_3CH_2OCH_3 \tag{12}$$

regarded reaction (7) as being in its second-order region; it may be represented as (7a). The simplified Benson–Jain mechanism is given by

$$M + CH_2OCH_3 \longrightarrow CH_2O + CH_3 + M \tag{7a}$$

Scheme 2. Reaction (13) was also considered to occur, but to a lesser

$$CH_3OCH_3 \longrightarrow CH_3 + CH_3O \quad \text{(first order)} \tag{5}$$

$$CH_3 + CH_3OCH_3 \longrightarrow CH_4 + CH_2OCH_3 \tag{6}$$

$$M + CH_2OCH_3 \longrightarrow CH_2O + CH_3 + M \quad \text{(second order)} \tag{7a}$$

$$CH_3O \longrightarrow CH_2O + H \tag{8}$$

$$H + CH_3OCH_3 \longrightarrow H_2 + CH_2OCH_3 \tag{9}$$

$$CH_3 + CH_2OCH_3 \longrightarrow CH_3CH_2OCH_3 \quad \text{(second order)} \tag{12}$$

SCHEME 2.

$$2\,CH_2OCH_3 \longrightarrow CH_3OCH_2CH_2OCH_3 \tag{13}$$

extent than (12). This scheme is of the $^1\beta\beta_{\frac{3}{2}}$ type, and the rate law it leads to is given by equation (14). It predicts a positive inert-gas

$$v = \left(\frac{k_5 k_6 k_{7a}}{k_{12}}\right)^{\frac{1}{2}} [\text{CH}_3\text{OCH}_3]^{\frac{3}{2}} \tag{14}$$

effect, since the rate of (7a) is increased by addition of inert gas, and this is in disagreement with the fact that inert gases have little effect on the overall rate.

It may be noted that three-halves-order overall kinetics are also obtained if the orders of reactions (5) and (7a) are reversed, i.e. if the reactions are (5a) and (7). Initiation is now second order and the

$$M + CH_3OCH_3 \longrightarrow CH_3 + CH_3O + M \qquad (5a)$$

$$CH_2OCH_3 \longrightarrow CH_2O + CH_3 \qquad (7)$$

methoxymethyl radical is a μ radical; this again gives rise to three-halves-order kinetics ($^2\beta\mu_{\frac{3}{2}}$), and predicts a positive inert-gas effect, in disagreement with experiment.

Anderson and Benson's[10] analytical investigations of the trace termination products of the pyrolysis failed to establish unequivocally which of the possible termination reactions is the most important. This information is vital to the understanding of the nature of the initiation process and the propagation reaction[3]. In an effort to resolve this difficulty Anderson and Benson[13] studied the hydrogen chloride catalyzed pyrolysis of dimethyl ether. Gaseous hydrogen chloride (3–16 mole %) increased the rate of decomposition about ten-fold. The accelerated rate was independent of hydrogen chloride and was three-halves order with respect to ether. The products were the same as in the uncatalyzed decomposition. Anderson and Benson[13] argued that if step (6) were replaced by a process which removed methyl radicals much faster than reaction (6), then reaction (7a) would become the slow step, whose rate would increase as the methoxymethyl radical concentration increases. If all the methyl radicals were converted into methoxymethyl radicals the maximum rate increase would be by a factor of two. If the acceleration were greater than two-fold, then reaction (6) must be slower than reaction (7a).

Since the observed acceleration, presumably owing to replacement of reaction (6) by (15) followed by (16), was approximately ten-fold

$$CH_3 + HCl \longrightarrow CH_4 + Cl \qquad (15)$$

$$Cl + CH_3OCH_3 \longrightarrow HCl + CH_2OCH_3 \qquad (16)$$

they suggested that reaction (6) was much slower than the reaction (7a). Thus Anderson and Benson[13] conclude that the methoxymethyl radical cannot be the important chain breaker as in the scheme of Benson and Jain[7]. To support this argument Anderson and Benson[13] assumed that since the results of the hydrogen sulfide catalyzed decomposition of dimethyl ether as studied by Imai and Toyama[11] were somewhat similar, the same argument also applied here.

These observations and conclusions led Anderson and Benson[13] to reject reactions (12) and (13) as significant terminators and to suggest new termination processes. They postulated that for the main part the reactions (17) and (18) were the principal chain-breaking steps.

$$CH_3 + CHO \longrightarrow CH_4 + CO \tag{17}$$

$$CHO + CHO \longrightarrow H_2 + CO \tag{18}$$

McKenney and Laidler[12] disputed Benson and Jain's[7] suggestion that the decomposition of the ether radical (methoxymethyl) is in its second-order region. Benson and Jain's main reason for preferring the $^1\beta\beta_{\frac{3}{2}}$ scheme was that the apparent first-order frequency factor for reaction (7), as calculated by Trotman-Dickenson[14] from the results of Marcus, Darwent and Steacie[15a], was $\sim 10^{10}$ sec^{-1}; this is much too low to be a true frequency factor for a unimolecular dissociation which involves no change of multiplicity. An apparent way out of the difficulty is to suggest that the reaction is really in its second-order region. McKenney and Laidler[12] expressed doubts as to the reliability of the experimental data from which the value of $\sim 10^{10}$ sec^{-1} was calculated. In fact recent data from Anderson and Benson's[13] study of the hydrogen chloride catalyzed decomposition of dimethyl ether lead to a much higher value for the frequency factor for this reaction. According to these workers $k_6/k_7 \approx 0 \cdot 1$, which leads to an estimate of $\sim 10^{15}$ sec^{-1} for A_7. This value is fairly typical of a unimolecular decomposition in its first-order region. Anderson and Benson[13], however, still prefer to consider reaction (7) to be second order. Other arguments against this idea have been put forward by McKenney and Laidler[12].

Recently Loucks and Laidler[15b] have investigated the thermal decomposition of the methoxymethyl radical and have found that the decomposition is pressure dependent over the pressure range 3–600 mm at temperatures of 200–300°. The order of the decomposition varies from about four-thirds at the higher pressure to about three-halves at the lower pressures. The extrapolated first-order rate coefficient for the methoxymethyl radical decomposition is given by equation (18a). For

$$k = 1 \cdot 0 \times 10^{13} e^{-25,500/RT} \text{ sec}^{-1} \tag{18a}$$

pressures used by Benson and Jain[7] (35–400 mm), Anderson and Benson[10] (50–400 mm), and McKenney and Laidler[12] (100–700 mm), the decomposition of the methoxymethyl radical would therefore not be second order. This work suggests that reaction schemes based on a first-order decomposition of the methoxymethyl radical more accurately describe the overall reaction, although they are invalid to the extent of the increased order of the decomposition of the methoxymethyl radical. The matter is clearly somewhat more complicated than originally envisaged.

Important information concerning the order of the initiation process came about as a result of the study of the hydrogen sulfide catalyzed decomposition of dimethyl ether[16]. This reaction was first investigated by Imai and Toyama[11]. Ether containing as much as 67% of hydrogen sulfide was decomposed over the temperature range of 360–440°. Imai and Toyama observed an acceleration, the rates increasing to a plateau with the addition of hydrogen sulfide and remaining constant over a range of concentrations. They suggested that the catalytic effect of hydrogen sulfide is essentially due to the fast reaction of methyl radicals with hydrogen sulfide, with the production of mercapto (SH) radicals which in turn abstract hydrogen atoms readily from the substrate. These reactions are suggested to be faster than the reaction between methyl radicals and the substrate. The mechanism suggested for the reaction in the presence of sufficient hydrogen sulfide to ensure 'limiting' acceleration is shown by Scheme 3. The rate equation to

$$CH_3OCH_3 \longrightarrow CH_3 + CH_3O \qquad (5)$$

$$CH_3O + H_2S \longrightarrow CH_3OH + HS \qquad (19)$$

$$CH_3 + H_2S \longrightarrow CH_4 + HS \qquad (20)$$

$$CH_3OCH_3 + HS \longrightarrow H_2S + CH_2OCH_3 \qquad (21)$$

$$CH_3OCH_2 \longrightarrow CH_2O + CH_3 \qquad (7)$$

$$HS + HS \longrightarrow Products \qquad (22)$$

SCHEME 3.

which this mechanism leads is given by (23) and a three-halves-order

$$-\frac{d\,[CH_3OCH_3]}{dt} = \frac{d\,[CH_4]}{dt} = k_{21} \left(\frac{k_5}{k_{22}}\right)^{\frac{1}{2}} [CH_3OCH_3]^{\frac{3}{2}} \qquad (23)$$

dependence on ether concentration was obtained experimentally. They obtained an overall rate coefficient given by (24). It is to be noted that

$$k = 1 \cdot 82 \times 10^{15}\,e^{-51,\,800/RT}\,cc^{\frac{1}{2}}/mole^{\frac{1}{2}}\,sec \qquad (24)$$

if reaction (22) is a combination reaction it would have to be, for such

small radicals, in its third-order region; if the process is a disproportionation reaction, however, leading to hydrogen sulfide and sulfur,
it may remain second order down to indefinitely low pressures.

McKenney and Laidler[16] extended the experimental study of this
reaction to much higher concentrations of hydrogen sulfide (up to
99% hydrogen sulfide) and to higher temperatures (480–530°). Their
results, illustrated in Figure 1, agreed with those of Imai and Toyama[11]

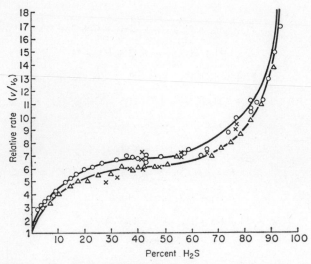

FIGURE 1. The H_2S-catalyzed decomposition of dimethyl ether.

at lower concentrations of hydrogen sulfide. The rate coefficient for the
reaction in the 'plateau' region is given by (25). At concentrations of

$$k = 1 \cdot 06 \times 10^{14}\, e^{-53,200/RT}\ cc^{\frac{1}{2}}/mole^{\frac{1}{2}}\ sec \qquad (25)$$

hydrogen sulfide greater than 75%, however (beyond the range studied
by Imai and Toyama[11]), the rate increased further with added hydrogen sulfide. In this region the reaction was found to be first order in
ether, and one-half order in hydrogen sulfide concentration. The rate
coefficient for the reaction accelerated by very high percentages of
hydrogen sulfide is given by equation (26).

$$k = 4 \cdot 98 \times 10^{14}\, e^{-52,500/RT}\ cc^{\frac{1}{2}}/mole^{\frac{1}{2}}\ sec \qquad (26)$$

To explain these observations it was necessary to modify the mechanism postulated by Imai and Toyama[11]. Their mechanism does not

predict the dependence on hydrogen sulfide and the additional acceleration observed at very high concentrations of hydrogen sulfide. The rate expression should involve two terms: one predicting three-halves-order behavior with respect to dimethyl ether and no dependence on hydrogen sulfide, the second predicting dependence with respect to both hydrogen sulfide and dimethyl ether.

McKenney and Laidler[16] therefore suggested the mechanism given in Scheme 4, where M represents a third body. Application of the

$$M + CH_3OCH_3 \longrightarrow CH_3 + CH_3O + M \qquad (5a)$$

$$M + H_2S \longrightarrow H + HS + M \qquad (27)$$

$$H + CH_3OCH_3 \longrightarrow H_2 + CH_2OCH_3 \qquad (9)$$

$$HS + CH_3OCH_3 \longrightarrow H_2S + CH_2OCH_3 \qquad (21)$$

$$CH_2OCH_3 \longrightarrow CH_2O + CH_3 \qquad (7)$$

$$CH_3 + H_2S \longrightarrow CH_4 + HS \qquad (20)$$

$$M + CH_3O \longrightarrow CH_2O + H + M \qquad (8a)$$

$$HS + HS \rightleftharpoons H_2S + S \qquad (28)$$

$$M + HS + HS \longrightarrow H_2S_2 + M \qquad (22a)$$

SCHEME 4.

steady-state treatment leads to the simplified rate expression given by equation (29).

$$-\frac{d\,[CH_3OCH_3]}{dt} = k_{21} \left(\frac{2k_{27}}{k_{22a}}\right)^{\frac{1}{2}} [H_2S]^{\frac{1}{2}} [CH_3OCH_3]$$
$$+ k_{21} \left(\frac{2k_{5a}}{k_{22a}}\right)^{\frac{1}{2}} [CH_3OCH_3]^{\frac{3}{2}} \qquad (29)$$

Reaction (27) is unimportant until large relative quantities of hydrogen sulfide are used. With reactions (27) and (9) omitted, the mechanism is essentially the same as that postulated by Imai and Toyama[11]. The rate in the 'plateau' region is therefore given by (30).

$$v = k_{21} \left(\frac{2k_{5a}}{k_{22a}}\right)^{\frac{1}{2}} [CH_3OCH_3]^{\frac{3}{2}} \qquad (30)$$

Substitution of the appropriate values in Table 2 yields (31), which can

$$k_{21} \left(\frac{2k_{5a}}{k_{22a}}\right)^{\frac{1}{2}} = 1 \cdot 0 \times 10^{14} \, e^{-52,800/RT} \, cc^{\frac{1}{2}}/mole^{\frac{1}{2}} \, sec \qquad (31)$$

TABLE 2. Kinetic parameters for the decomposition of dimethyl ether.

Reaction	Frequency factor (appropriate cc, mole, sec units)	Activation energy (kcal/mole)	Ref.
(5a)	1×10^{18}	$74 \cdot 0$ (estimated)	12
(6)	3×10^{11}	$9 \cdot 5$	17
(7)	$7 \times 10^{10 \, a}$	$19 \cdot 0$	14, 15a
(10a)	7×10^{14}	$-13 \cdot 5$ (estimated)	12
(27)	1×10^{18}	$81 \cdot 0$ (estimated)	16
(21)	1×10^{12}	$13 \cdot 0$ (assumed)	16
(20)	$2 \cdot 5 \times 10^{11}$	$2 \cdot 6$	18
(22a)	1×10^{14}	$-5 \cdot 6$ (estimated)	16

[a] As mentioned in the text, Anderson and Benson's[13] data suggest that the frequency factor A_7 should be approximately 10^{15}/sec.

be compared to the experimental value of $1 \cdot 06 \times 10^{14} \, e^{-53,200/RT} \, cc^{\frac{1}{2}}/mole^{\frac{1}{2}}$ sec.

In the region of high percentages of hydrogen sulfide the rate is given by (32). Experimentally the reaction is one-half order with respect to hydrogen sulfide and first order with respect to dimethyl ether

$$v = k_{21} \left(\frac{2k_{27}}{k_{22a}}\right)^{\frac{1}{2}} [H_2S]^{\frac{1}{2}}[CH_3OCH_3] \qquad (32)$$

in this region, in agreement with this rate expression. The calculated rate coefficient given by (33) is in fair agreement with the experi-

$$k_{21} \left(\frac{2k_{27}}{k_{22a}}\right)^{\frac{1}{2}} = 1 \cdot 0 \times 10^{14} \, e^{-56,300/RT} \, cc^{\frac{1}{2}}/mole^{\frac{1}{2}} \, sec \qquad (33)$$

mental value of $4 \cdot 98 \times 10^{14} \, e^{-52,500/RT} \, cc^{\frac{1}{2}}/mole^{\frac{1}{2}}$ sec.

A very important conclusion arises from this study with regard to the order of the initiation reaction, in which the ether molecule dissociates into methyl and methoxy radicals. Consideration of the steady-state equations shows that the only apparent way to obtain the correct pressure dependence in both hydrogen sulfide and dimethyl ether is by having the initiation in its low-pressure second-order region.

This evidence appears to exclude Benson and Jain's $^1\beta\beta_{\frac{3}{2}}$ mechanism for the pyrolysis of the pure ether. It is consistent with a mechanism in which the chain-ending step involves the recombination of two β radicals, in the low pressure region ($^2\beta\beta M_{\frac{3}{2}}$), and also with a $^2\beta\mu_{\frac{3}{2}}$ mechanism. These are the only two possibilities if initiation is second order. The $^2\beta\mu_{\frac{3}{2}}$ mechanism would predict a substantial positive inert-gas effect since inert gases will increase the rate of initiation but will have no effect on the rate of termination. Experimentally there is only a very slight effect of inert gases[6]. This is predicted by a $^2\beta\beta M_{\frac{3}{2}}$ mechanism, since both initiation and termination are affected by the addition of an inert gas, and the two effects will approximately cancel.

To decide on the most important termination step, McKenney and Laidler[12] calculated approximate rates of the following possible reactions. (Reactions (17) and (18) suggested by Anderson and Benson[13] lead to three-halves-order kinetics only if the initiation is first order.)

$$CH_3 + CH_3 + M \longrightarrow C_2H_6 + M \tag{10a}$$

$$CH_3 + CH_2OCH_3 + M \longrightarrow CH_3CH_2OCH_3 + M \tag{12a}$$

$$2\,CH_2OCH_3 + M \longrightarrow CH_3OCH_2CH_2OCH_3 + M \tag{13a}$$

$$CH_3 + CHO + M \longrightarrow CH_3CHO + M \tag{34}$$

The calculations indicated that reaction (10a) is the most important termination step, but the other reactions cannot be excluded entirely. Initially the concentration of formyl radicals must be much less than that of methyl radicals, so that reaction (34) must be unimportant. As decomposition proceeds, however, reaction (34) may become an increasingly important termination step.

These considerations lead therefore to the simplified Scheme 5.

$$M + CH_3OCH_3 \longrightarrow CH_3 + CH_3O + M \tag{5a}$$

$$CH_3 + CH_3OCH_3 \longrightarrow CH_4 + CH_2OCH_3 \tag{6}$$

$$CH_2OCH_3 \longrightarrow CH_2O + CH_3 \tag{7}$$

$$M + CH_3O \longrightarrow CH_2O + H + M \tag{8a}$$

$$H + CH_3OCH_3 \longrightarrow H_2 + CH_2OCH_3 \tag{9}$$

$$CH_3 + CH_3 + M \longrightarrow C_2H_6 + M \tag{10a}$$

Scheme 5.

Application of the steady-state treatment to this mechanism leads to equation (35) for the overall rate. Substitution of the appropriate

$$-\frac{d\,[CH_3OCH_3]}{dt} = k_6 \left(\frac{2k_{5a}}{k_{10a}}\right)^{\frac{1}{2}} [CH_3OCH_3]^{\frac{3}{2}} \tag{35}$$

values from Table 2 leads to equation (36). This is in fair agreement

$$k_6 \left(\frac{2k_{5a}}{k_{10a}}\right)^{\frac{1}{2}} = 1\cdot6 \times 10^{13}\,e^{-53,300/RT}\,cc^{\frac{1}{2}}/mole^{\frac{1}{2}}\,sec \tag{36}$$

with the experimental value of $2\cdot98 \times 10^{14}\,e^{-54,900/RT}\,cc^{\frac{1}{2}}/mole^{\frac{1}{2}}\,sec$ considering the long extrapolation required to calculate the low-pressure rate coefficients for the initiation and termination steps.

Additional evidence relating to the order of the methyl radical combination is discussed in section V.

III. DIETHYL ETHER

The pyrolysis of diethyl ether can be represented by the stoichiometric equations (37) and (38). At the usual pyrolytic temperatures ($\sim 600°$)

$$C_2H_5OC_2H_5 \longrightarrow C_2H_5OH + C_2H_4 \tag{37}$$
$$C_2H_5OC_2H_5 \longrightarrow CH_3CHO + C_2H_6 \tag{38}$$

the acetaldehyde and ethane decompose further into methane, carbon monoxide, ethylene and hydrogen. The decomposition of diethyl ether has been studied by many workers (see Steacie[5]), most recently by Freeman[19,20], Freeman, Danby and Hinshelwood[21], Danby and Freeman[22], Long and Skirrow[23] and Laidler and McKenney[24]. Danby and Freeman[22] have carried out a thorough analytical study of the pyrolysis at $525°$. In the pressure region of about 400–1600 mm the reaction was found to be three-halves order, but below 400 mm the order decreased. The free-radical mechanism postulated by Freeman[20] can be written as Scheme 6. After some approximations the steady-

$$C_2H_5OC_2H_5 \longrightarrow C_2H_5 + C_2H_5O \tag{39}$$
$$C_2H_5 + C_2H_5OC_2H_5 \longrightarrow C_2H_6 + C_2H_4OC_2H_5 \tag{40}$$
$$C_2H_4OC_2H_5 \longrightarrow C_2H_5 + CH_3CHO \tag{41}$$
$$C_2H_5O \longrightarrow CH_3 + HCHO \tag{42}$$
$$C_2H_5 \longrightarrow H + C_2H_4 \tag{43}$$
$$H + C_2H_5OC_2H_5 \longrightarrow H_2 + C_2H_4OC_2H_5 \tag{44}$$
$$C_2H_5 + C_2H_4OC_2H_5 \longrightarrow Products \tag{45}$$
$$H + C_2H_4OC_2H_5 \longrightarrow Products \tag{46}$$

SCHEME 6.

state treatment led to a rate expression predicting first-order dependence on ether. In order to explain the three-halves-order behavior at high pressures it was assumed that the rate for the initiation reaction eventually takes the form of equation (47), where A, B and C are con-

$$k = \frac{A[M]}{1 + B[M]} + C[M] \tag{47}$$

stants, and M represents the ether molecule. When this is substituted into the rate expression, the mechanism predicts three-halves-order dependence at high pressures of ether. This assumption is based on an empirical relationship derived by Jach and Hinshelwood[25] to explain the shapes of the rate–pressure curves for the decomposition of paraffins in the presence of inert gases. Some of their experimental data have been shown to be of questionable validity[26], and the form of the rate coefficient (k) in equation (47) is therefore probably erroneous. This would invalidate the mechanism suggested by Freeman[20]. Danby and Freeman[22] found that the ethanol formation was not inhibited by nitric oxide, and from this they concluded that the process giving rise to ethanol and ethylene is a molecular one. Laidler and McKenney[24,27] arrived at the same conclusion. The reaction leading to acetaldehyde and ethane, on the other hand, is concluded to be almost entirely a free-radical chain process.

The uninhibited thermal decomposition of diethyl ether was studied from 560 to 620°, and at pressures ranging from 15 to 370 mm Hg, by Laidler and McKenney[24]. They also investigated the reaction inhibited by nitric oxide, in the temperature range of 560–640°, and at pressures between 10 and 360 mm Hg[27]. Some of Laidler and McKenney's[24] data for the uninhibited decomposition of diethyl ether are shown in Figure 2, which shows double logarithmic plots of rate against ether pressure. All of the lines have slopes between 1·2 and 1·3. Freeman[20] working at 525° has shown that the order becomes 1·5 at high pressure. This increase in order has also been demonstrated by Fletcher and Rollefson[28] at 521°. Laidler and McKenney[24] therefore suggest that the overall rate expression involves at least two terms, each corresponding to a different order. The mechanism suggested leads to a somewhat complex rate expression (as will be discussed later) but the behavior predicted is closely represented by an equation of the form (48), where M represents ether. The rate constants k_m and k_r

$$v = (k_m + k_r)\,[M] + k'[M]^{\frac{3}{2}} \tag{48}$$

relate to molecular and free-radical reactions, respectively.

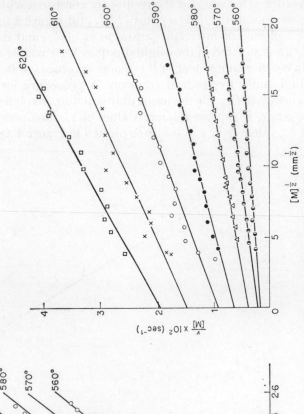

FIGURE 3. Plots made to verify equation (48) for the uninhibited decomposition of diethyl ether.

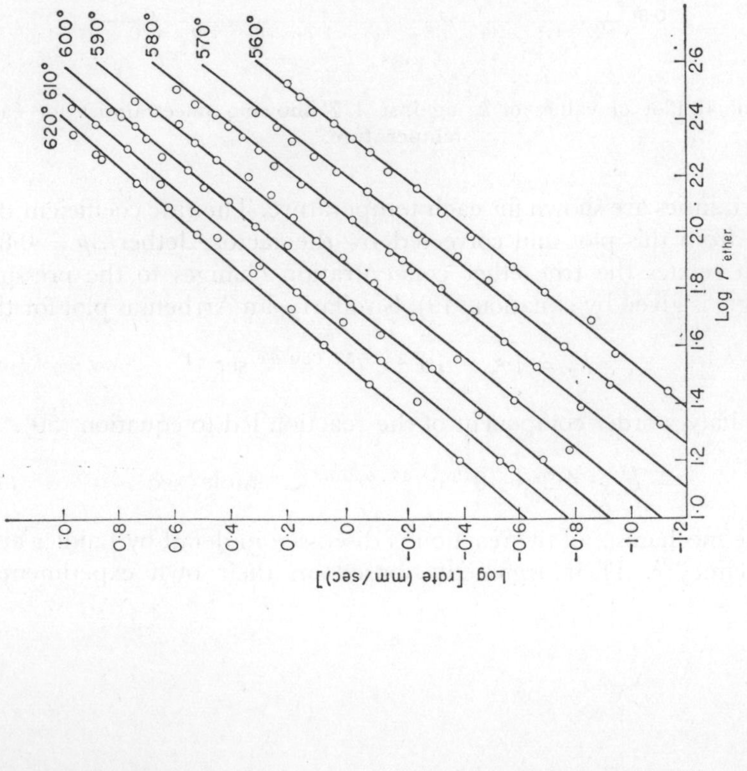

FIGURE 2. The uninhibited decomposition of diethyl ether.

In order to see whether the results are consistent with this equation, plots were made of $v/[M]$ against $[M]^{\frac{1}{2}}$, and Figure 3 shows the results of such plots. The intercepts (equal to $k_m + k_r$) and the slopes (equal to k') are tabulated in the original paper[24]. As will be discussed later, the first-order component of the reaction consists of both a molecular reaction and a free-radical reaction. A procedure for obtaining the rate coefficients k_m for the molecular reaction, involving inhibition by nitric oxide, is explained later. Values of k_r, obtained by subtracting these k_m values from $k_m + k_r$, are plotted in Figure 4 against $1/T$. The

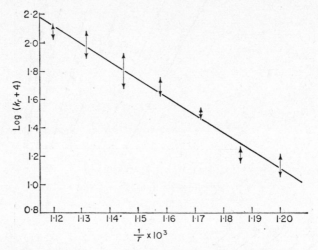

FIGURE 4. Plot of values of k_r against $1/T$ showing uncertainties for each temperature.

uncertainties are shown for each temperature. The rate coefficient derived from this plot and corrected by the factor $\Delta ether/\Delta p = 0.84$, which relates the true ether concentration changes to the pressure change, is given by equation (49). Similarly, an Arrhenius plot for the

$$k_r = 1.4 \times 10^{12}\,e^{-57,600/RT}\,\sec^{-1} \qquad (49)$$

three-halves-order component of the reaction led to equation (50).

$$k' = 4.8 \times 10^{12}\,e^{-47,400/RT}\,cc^{\frac{1}{2}}/mole^{\frac{1}{2}}\,\sec \qquad (50)$$

The mechanism of the reaction is discussed in detail by Laidler and McKenney[24]. Their arguments, based on their own experimental kinetic data and the analytical work of Freeman and coworkers[19-22], led to the simplified reaction Scheme 7. Reaction (39m) is a molecular

$$C_2H_5OC_2H_5 \longrightarrow C_2H_5OH + C_2H_4 \tag{39m}$$

$$C_2H_5OC_2H_5 \longrightarrow C_2H_5O + C_2H_5 \tag{39}$$

$$C_2H_5 + C_2H_5OC_2H_5 \longrightarrow C_2H_6 + CH_2CH_2OC_2H_5 \tag{51}$$

$$C_2H_5 + C_2H_5OC_2H_5 \longrightarrow C_2H_6 + CH_3CHOC_2H_5 \tag{52}$$

$$C_2H_5O \longrightarrow CH_3 + CH_2O \tag{42}$$

$$CH_3 + C_2H_5OC_2H_5 \longrightarrow CH_4 + CH_2CH_2OC_2H_5 \tag{53}$$

$$CH_3 + C_2H_5OC_2H_5 \longrightarrow CH_4 + CH_3CHOC_2H_5 \tag{54}$$

$$CH_2CH_2OC_2H_5 + C_2H_5OC_2H_5 \longrightarrow CH_3CHOC_2H_5 + C_2H_5OC_2H_5 \tag{55}$$

$$CH_2CH_2OC_2H_5 \longrightarrow C_2H_4 + C_2H_5O \tag{56}$$

$$CH_3CHOC_2H_5 \longrightarrow CH_3CHO + C_2H_5 \tag{41}$$

$$C_2H_5 + CH_2CH_2OC_2H_5 \longrightarrow C_4H_9OC_2H_5 \tag{57}$$

Scheme 7.

reaction perhaps proceeding through a four-center transition complex (1)[19]. Reaction (39), leading to an ethoxy and ethyl radical, is

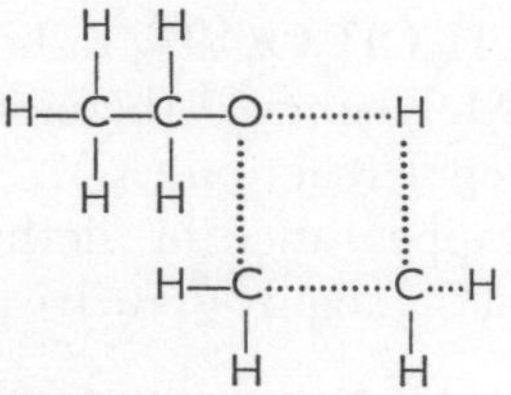

(1)

considered to be a unimolecular reaction in its first-order region. The alternative reaction (58) leads to exactly the same products under

$$C_2H_5OC_2H_5 \longrightarrow CH_3 + CH_2OCH_2CH_3 \tag{58}$$

pyrolytic conditions, and it has consequently not been possible to distinguish between the two possibilities.

Abstraction of a hydrogen atom from the ether molecule leads to either $CH_2CH_2OC_2H_5$ or $CH_3CHOC_2H_5$. The analytical and kinetic data summarized by Laidler and McKenney[24] clearly showed that the $CH_2CH_2OC_2H_5$ radical is less reactive than the $CH_3CHOC_2H_5$

radical. The former radical decomposes to yield C_2H_5O and C_2H_4 (reaction 56). The ethoxy radical could possibly abstract a hydrogen atom to form ethanol, but thermochemical evidence[24, 29] suggests that the breakdown of the ethoxy radical by reaction (42) is strongly favored. Hence most of the ethanol is produced by a molecular reaction (39m), in agreement with Danby and Freeman's[22] conclusion.

Because of its relative stability the $CH_2CH_2OC_2H_5$ radical can probably abstract a hydrogen atom to form $CH_3CHOC_2H_5$. This corresponds to the transfer reaction (55). Hence $CH_2CH_2OC_2H_5$ is both a β and a μ radical. Alternatively, the $CH_2CH_2OCH_2CH_3$ radical may isomerize into $CH_3CHOCH_2CH_3$ via a five-membered cyclic intermediate (2).

(2)

The recombination of $CH_2CH_2OC_2H_5$ radicals is unlikely for steric reasons and Laidler and McKenney[24] therefore assume that the predominant chain-ending step is reaction (57).

The overall rate of disappearance of diethyl ether is given, after some approximations, from the steady-state treatment by equation (59).

$$v = k_{39m}[M] + (k_{51} + k_{52}) \left\{ \frac{(k_{53} + k_{54})k_{39}k_{55}[M] + k_{39}k_{54}k_{56}}{(k_{53} + k_{54})k_{51}k_{57}} \right\}^{\frac{1}{2}} [M] \tag{59}$$

At high concentrations of ether the limiting rate expression is given by equation (60), whereas at low concentrations the kinetics are first-

$$v_{\text{high}} = (k_{51} + k_{52}) \left(\frac{k_{39}k_{55}}{k_{51}k_{57}} \right)^{\frac{1}{2}} [M]^{\frac{3}{2}} \tag{60}$$

order, the rate expression being equation (61). The experimental

$$v_{\text{low}} = k_{39m}[M] + (k_{51} + k_{52}) \left\{ \frac{k_{39}k_{54}k_{56}}{(k_{53} + k_{54})k_{51}k_{57}} \right\}^{\frac{1}{2}} [M] \tag{61}$$

three-halves- and first-order rate coefficients, being extrapolated values, can be approximately identified with the rate coefficients in these equations. Substitution of known and estimated activation energies for elementary reactions from reference 24 yields activation energies in good agreement with the experimental values.

A thorough investigation of the thermal decomposition of diethyl ether maximally inhibited by nitric oxide was made by Laidler and

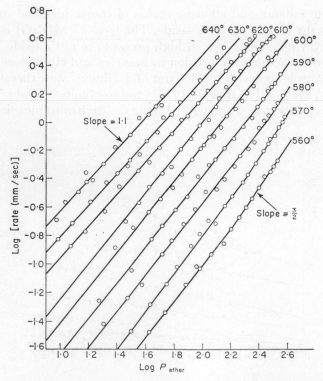

FIGURE 5. Plot for the thermal decomposition of diethyl ether maximally inhibited by NO showing the variation in the order with respect to ether.

McKenney[27]. The results were particularly interesting and useful in this case since they allowed the determination of the value of the rate coefficient for the molecular reaction (39m). About 7 mm of nitric oxide gave the maximal inhibition and as the nitric oxide pressure was increased beyond about 40 mm the rate increased linearly. Figure 5 shows double logarithmic plots of initial rate against diethyl ether pressure for the reaction maximally inhibited by nitric oxide. These plots show that the order with respect to ether varies between one at high temperatures and low pressures to three-halves at low temperatures and high pressures. Laidler and McKenney[27] proposed a chain mechanism in which nitric oxide is involved in both initiation and termination. Their scheme led to an expression of the form given in equation (62). The term $k_m[M]$ corresponds to the molecular reaction

$$v = k_m[M] + k''[M]^{\frac{3}{2}} + k'''[M][NO] \tag{62}$$

leading to ethanol and ethylene and is of course identical to the reaction in the absence of nitric oxide. The term $k'''[M][NO]$ is responsible for the increase in rate at high pressures of nitric oxide. From a study of the reaction in this region by Staveley and Hinshelwood[30] the value of k''' was obtained. Laidler and McKenney[27] were therefore able to plot $v/[M] - k'''[NO]$ against $[M]^{\frac{1}{2}}$ and so obtain k_m and k'' at temperatures between 560 and 640° (Figure 6). Arrhenius plots led to the

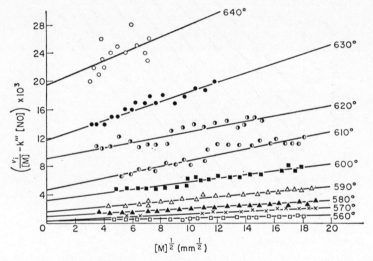

FIGURE 6. Plots to determine k_m and k'' at temperatures between 560 and 640°.

values given in (63) and (64). The frequency factor of $2 \cdot 75 \times 10^{18} \text{ sec}^{-1}$

$$k_m = 2 \cdot 75 \times 10^{18} e^{-83,800/RT} \text{ sec}^{-1} \tag{63}$$

$$k'' = 5 \cdot 5 \times 10^{15} e^{-62,000/RT} \text{ cc}^{\frac{1}{2}}/\text{mole}^{\frac{1}{2}} \text{ sec} \tag{64}$$

for the molecular reaction is rather high (as compared with vibrational frequencies) but is in line with the values for a large number of other unimolecular decompositions[31].

IV. OTHER ETHERS

Steacie summarized briefly the work done prior to 1953 on the ethers listed in Table 3. In every case the overall mechanism is uncertain. Later work is equally fragmentary, with a few exceptions.

TABLE 3. Ethers studied prior to 1953[a].

Ether	Free radicals present	Inhibited by nitric oxide
Methyl ethyl	Yes	Yes
Ethyl propyl	Yes	Yes
Dipropyl	Yes	Yes
Methyl butyl	Yes	Yes
Vinyl ethyl	Yes (above 537°)	No
Divinyl	Yes	—
Vinyl allyl	No	No
Diphenyl	Yes	—
Dibenzyl	Yes	—
Dioxane	Yes	Yes
Tetrahydrofuran	Yes	No
Dioxolane	Yes	Yes
2,2'-Dichlorodiethyl	(Probably)	—
Phenyl methyl	Yes	—

[a] Brief summaries are given by Steacie[5].

Thomas[32] investigated the thermal decomposition of 1-chloroethyl methyl ether (reaction 65) over the temperature range of 180–250°

$$CH_3CHClOCH_3 \longrightarrow CH_2{=}CHOCH_3 + HCl \qquad (65)$$

and the pressure range of 33–420 mm Hg. The reaction appears to be typical of the pyrolysis of alkyl chlorides and there is no evidence of a C—C or C—O bond split. The decomposition is homogeneous and first order. The measured rate coefficient for this reaction is given by (66). After 35–40% decomposition there is an appreciable decrease in

$$k_{36} = 2{\cdot}90 \times 10^{11}\, e^{-33,300/RT}\ sec^{-1} \qquad (66)$$

the first-order rate, and this is attributed to the reversal of the reaction. The decomposition is not inhibited by cyclohexene.

Recently Stimson and Watson[33, 34] pyrolyzed *t*-butyl methyl ether in the presence of hydrogen bromide. Between 258 and 371° the major part of the reaction is the homogeneous decomposition into iso-butene and methanol (reaction 67). The presence of methyl bromide

$$t\text{-}C_4H_9OCH_3 + HBr \longrightarrow i\text{-}C_4H_8 + CH_3OH + HBr \qquad (67)$$

is suggested to be due to a subsequent reaction (probably hetero-geneous) between the methanol and hydrogen bromide (reaction 68).

$$CH_3OH + HBr \longrightarrow CH_3Br + H_2O \qquad (68)$$

Trace products in the decomposition included isobutane and per-manent gases. No attempt is made to write a detailed mechanism, though Stimson and Watson[33] suggest that the isobutane is probably formed by free-radical reactions such as those shown in Scheme 8. The

$$t\text{-}C_4H_9OCH_3 \longrightarrow t\text{-}C_4H_9 + CH_3O \qquad (69)$$

$$t\text{-}C_4H_9 + t\text{-}C_4H_9OCH_3 \longrightarrow i\text{-}C_4H_{10} + t\text{-}C_4H_9OCH_2 \qquad (70)$$

$$t\text{-}C_4H_9OCH_2 \longrightarrow t\text{-}C_4H_9 + \text{Other products} \qquad (71)$$

SCHEME 8.

rate of disappearance of t-butyl methyl ether is given by (72) and (73).

$$v = k[t\text{-}C_4H_9OCH_3][HBr] \qquad (72)$$

$$k = 6 \cdot 7 \times 10^{11} e^{-25,600/RT} \text{ cc/mole sec} \qquad (73)$$

Elkobaisi and Hickinbottom[35] thermally decomposed a series of aromatic ethers. The mechanisms are undoubtedly complicated as is evident from the variety of products. The pyrolyses were carried out by heating the ether (alone or in a suitable solvent) at 250–270° for periods ranging from 10 to 17 days in sealed tubes. Generally not all of the products could be identified.

Benzyl phenyl ether yielded such major products as o- and p-benzylphenols and 2,4-dibenzylphenol with some phenol, toluene and 9-phenylxanthen. Diphenylmethyl phenyl ether formed tetraphenyl-ethane, phenol and some diphenylmethane. o- and p-tolyl, 2,4-di-methylphenyl and 2,6-dimethylphenyl benzyl ethers also produced toluene and the corresponding xanthen.

Elkobaisi and Hickinbottom[35] concluded that the reactions proceed by a free-radical mechanism. Thus in the presence of the solvent quinoline, benzyl phenyl ether produces benzyl and phenoxy radicals, since both benzyl and phenoxy substituted quinolines were found in the products. Similarly benzyl 2,4,6-trimethylphenyl ether when heated alone or in quinoline produced 1,2-diphenylethane as one of the products. They therefore concluded that free benzyl radicals were produced.

A similar complex and little understood mechanism probably occurs in the gas-phase pyrolysis of 2,2′-dibenzoyloxydiethyl ether. This ether was decomposed between 450 and 500° by Iengar and Ritchie[36]. By means of chemical and infrared spectroscopic analytical methods the following products were identified: carbon monoxide, carbon dioxide, acetaldehyde, methane, benzoic acid and anhydride, benzene, vinyl benzoate, styrene, acetophenone, ethylene dibenzoate, vinyl ether, acetylene and traces of ethylene. The major products can be accounted for by Scheme 9. Iengar and Ritchie[36] stress that free-radical mechanisms undoubtedly operate in at least some stages.

$$BzOCH_2CH_2OCH_2CH_2OBz \longrightarrow [BzOCH_2CH_2OCH{=}CH_2] + BzOH \qquad (74)$$

$$[BzOCH_2CH_2OCH{=}CH_2] \begin{cases} \longrightarrow BzOCH{=}CH_2 + MeCHO \\[4pt] \longrightarrow \dfrac{1}{2}\begin{matrix} CH_2OBz \\ | \\ CH_2OBz \end{matrix} + \dfrac{1}{2}\begin{matrix} CH_2OCH{=}CH_2 \\ | \\ CH_2OCHCH_3 \end{matrix} \\[12pt] \longrightarrow BzOH + CH_2{=}CHOCH{=}CH_2 \end{cases} \qquad (75)$$

$$\begin{matrix} CH_2OCH{=}CH_2 \\ | \\ CH_2OCH{=}CH_2 \end{matrix} \longrightarrow MeCHO + CH_2{=}CHOCH{=}CH_2 \qquad (76)$$

$$CH_2{=}CHOCH{=}CH_2 \longrightarrow MeCHO + CH{\equiv}CH \qquad (77)$$

SCHEME 9.

Vinyl ethers have been studied in somewhat more detail. Blades[37], using a conventional flow system with toluene as carrier gas, thermally decomposed isopropyl vinyl ether. In the temperature range of 447–521° the reaction proceeds molecularly yielding propylene and acetaldehyde. Above 570° there appears to be a minor free-radical reaction occurring as well. A rate coefficient of $3.8 \times 10^{12}\, e^{-43,560/RT}$ sec^{-1} corresponding to the reaction (78) was measured. A similar reaction was presumed to occur in the pyrolysis of isobutyl vinyl ether[37].

$$CH_2{=}CHOCH(CH_3)_2 \longrightarrow CH_3CH{=}CH_2 + CH_3CHO \qquad (78)$$

Here the major products are acetaldehyde and isobutene. Small quantities of propylene, propionaldehyde and fairly large quantities of permanent gases (CO, H_2 and CH_4) were produced. Blades[37] suggests a cyclic activated complex (3).

(3)

Molera and coworkers[38-40], in a series of papers, described experiments on the thermal decomposition of isobutyl vinyl and n-butyl vinyl ethers. Pressure–time curves were obtained over a range of temperature (322–378·5°) and of pressure (~ 50 to ~ 300 mm Hg). The analytical results indicated the following products from the pyrolysis of isobutyl vinyl ether: methane, carbon monoxide, ethylene, propylene, isobutylene, acetic acid and polymers. Corresponding products are presumably obtained from the pyrolysis of n-butyl vinyl ether. Additions of toluene, inert gases and nitric oxide do not inhibit the major part of the decomposition, but it appears that both inert gases and nitric oxide inhibit the polymerization process.

Molera and coworkers[38-40] conclude that the reaction proceeds mainly by a molecular rearrangement through a hexagonal activated complex. (This is in agreement with Blades's[37] suggestion.) A secondary free-radical chain reaction is believed to be responsible for the formation of the polymer, and the free radicals also induce the decomposition of the primary products.

De Puy and coworkers[41, 42] include vinyl ethers among the examples of compounds which undergo pyrolytic *cis* eliminations. Thus they form olefins through a cyclic nonchain process by the general reaction (79)*. *s*-Butyl vinyl ether was pyrolyzed at 450° and the ole-

$$\underset{\substack{| \quad | \\ H \quad OCH=CH_2}}{R_2C-CR_2} \longrightarrow R_2C{=}CR_2 + CH_3CHO \qquad (79)$$

fins formed consisted of 47% 1-butene, 37% *trans*-2-butene and 16% *cis*-2-butene. *t*-Amyl vinyl ether under the same conditions yielded 66% 2-methyl-1-butene and 34% 2-methyl-2-butene. Analyses were carried out by vapor-phase chromatography.

---

* The activated complex is probably a six-membered ring, though De Puy and colleagues[41, 42] do not suggest this.

Molera and Ariza[43] thermally decomposed allyl ether in the gas phase between 359 and 390° and over a pressure range of 20–100 mm Hg pressure. The activation energy was found to be 42·3 kcal/mole. Allyl ethyl ether was also decomposed between 393 and 430° and over a pressure range of 30–150 mm Hg. Here the energy of activation was 48·5 kcal/mole. In each case the products were analyzed by infrared spectroscopy. They suggest that, as in the case of the vinyl ethers, the reaction proceeds mainly by rearrangement through a hexagonal-ring activated complex.

$$CH_2{=}CHO\overset{*}{C}H_2CH{=}CH_2 \rightarrow \left[\begin{array}{c} H_2C\cdots CH \\ H_2C \qquad\quad O \\ HC\cdots \overset{*}{C}H_2 \end{array} \right] \longrightarrow \begin{array}{c} H_2C{-}CH \\ H_2C \qquad O \\ CH{=}\overset{*}{C}H_2 \end{array} \qquad (80)$$

Pocker[44] provided convincing evidence in support of the hexagonal ring activated complex suggestion. He carried out the rearrangement of allyl vinyl ether labelled with ^{14}C. The reaction was homogeneous (provided the vessel was well seasoned) and first-order at temperatures of about 200° and pressures between 150 and 400 mm. The rate coefficient showed a fall-off at pressures below 1 mm Hg. The reaction can be written as (80). The products consisted of 97%

$$\overset{*}{C}H_2{=}CHCH_2CH_2CHO$$

This reaction can be considered as an example of a Claisen-type[45,46] rearrangement. More common examples of this type of reaction involve the thermal rearrangement of allyl aryl ethers. Much research has been done on the Claisen rearrangement of many different allyl aryl ethers in recent years by many workers (see references 45 and 46 and papers cited therein), and a thorough discussion of this aspect is beyond the scope of this review. As an example, the rearrangement of allyl phenyl ether proceeds through a cyclic activated complex and an intermediate dienone (reaction 80a)[47].

$$(80a)$$

TABLE 4. Pyrolysis of allyl ethers: products and relative rates[a].

Ether	Temp. (°C)	Olefin	Ketone	Rel. rate at 430°
(1) 1-Methylallyl diphenylmethyl	540	trans-But-2-ene[b] (82%) cis-But-2-ene (12%)	Benzophenone (92%)	3·6 ± 0·8
(2) Allyl fluorenyl	400	Propene (90%)	Fluorenone (83%)	3·10 ± 0·27
(3) But-2-enyl-diphenyl-methyl	530	But-1-ene[b] (94%) Buta-1,3-diene (6%)	Benzophenone (91%)	1·14 ± 0·11
(4) Allyl diphenylmethyl	540	Propene (91%)	Benzophenone (92%)	1·00
(5) Allyl benzyl	500	Propene (97%)	Benzaldehyde (82%)	0·81 ± 0·03
(6) Allyl-4-methoxy benzyl	450	Propene (79%)	p-Methoxybenzaldehyde (93%)	0·72 ± 0·08
(7) Allyl 4-nitrobenzyl	430	Propene (34%)	p-Nitrobenzaldehyde (33%)	0·64 ± 0·09
(8) 3-Cyclohexenyl diphenylmethyl	510	Cyclohexene (87%)	Benzophenone (88%)	0·41 ± 0·06
(9) Allyl phenethyl	600	Propene (94%)	Phenylacetaldehyde (82%)	0·28 ± 0·02
(10) Allyl 2-methylallyl	390	Propene[b] (55%) Isobutene (45%)	—	≈ 0·4
(11) 1-Cyclohexenyl-methyl diphenyl-methyl	500	Methylenecyclohexane[c] (70%)	Benzophenone (82%)	—

[a] From Cookson and Wallis[48].
[b] Yields refer to C_3 and C_4 hydrocarbons. There were also traces of fragment hydrocarbons, e.g. C_2H_4.
[c] Corrected for 33% of unchanged ether.

Recently Cookson and Wallis[48] pyrolyzed eleven different ethers at relatively high temperatures. In every case the products were those expected from a cyclic molecular elimination. The results are shown in Table 4.

Wallace and Gritter[49] suggest that butyl radicals abstract the hydrogen atom in the α position to the oxygen atom in cyclic ethers. These radicals induced the reaction of four-, five- and six-membered cyclic ethers with 1-octene, e.g. Scheme 10. Apparently a transfer of

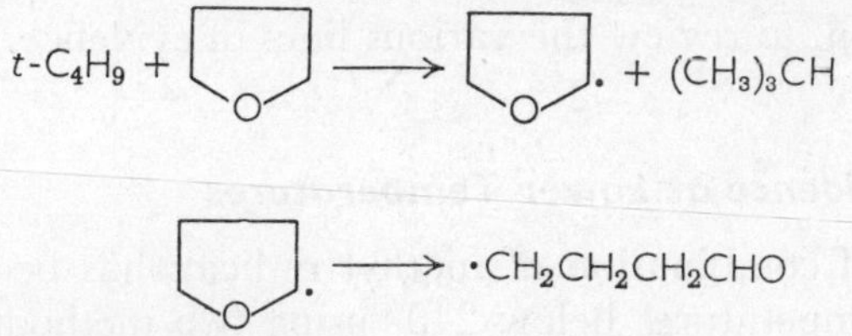

$$t\text{-}C_4H_9 + \underset{O}{\square} \longrightarrow \underset{O}{\square} \cdot + (CH_3)_3CH \tag{81}$$

$$\underset{O}{\square} \cdot \longrightarrow \cdot CH_2CH_2CH_2CHO \tag{82}$$

$$CH_2CH_2CH_2CHO \longrightarrow CH_3CH_2CH_2CO \cdot \tag{83}$$

$$CH_3CH_2CH_2CO \cdot + 1\text{-Octene} \longrightarrow \text{Addition radical, which abstracts H} \tag{84}$$

SCHEME 10.

a hydrogen atom occurs intramolecularly, to give aldehyde radicals before addition to 1-octene.

V. THE KINETICS OF THE COMBINATION OF METHYL RADICALS WITH SPECIAL REFERENCE TO PYROLYSIS MECHANISMS*

It has been seen in the discussion of the dimethyl ether pyrolysis that the order of methyl radical combination (reaction 85) is a matter

$$2\,CH_3 \longrightarrow C_2H_6 \tag{85}$$

of considerable importance. The results on dimethyl ether somewhat point to the conclusion that the reaction is in its low-pressure, third-order region (reaction 86). A similar conclusion is suggested by the

$$2\,CH_3 + M \longrightarrow C_2H_6 + M \tag{86}$$

* This section was written by M. H. Back, M. Eusuf and K. J. Laidler, Dept. of Chemistry, University of Ottawa. The present address of M. Eusuf is East Regional Laboratories, Pakistan Council of Scientific and Industrial Research, Dhanmondi, East Pakistan.

results for the acetaldehyde pyrolysis, as indicated below. The most recent work on the ethane pyrolysis, on the other hand, leads to the conclusion that under pyrolysis conditions the reverse decomposition of ethane (reaction 87) is closer to its high-pressure, first-order region,

$$C_2H_6 \longrightarrow 2 CH_3 \tag{87}$$

and this would require that the radical-recombination reaction is almost in its second-order region.

In view of these discrepancies it has been thought expedient, in the present section, to review the various lines of evidence.

A. Direct Evidence at Lower Temperatures

The rate of combination of methyl radicals has been determined directly at temperatures below 240° using two methods, namely, the photochemical rotating-sector technique[50] and the measurement of the rate of combination relative to that of reaction with nitric oxide[51,52]. The measurement of the combination rate coefficient was extended to low pressures (0·2 mm) by the measurement of the rate of combination relative to abstraction from acetone in the photolysis of acetone[53]. Clear indication of the pressure-dependence of the combination rate coefficient was obtained at pressures below 10 mm of acetone at a temperature of 247°. At 0·2 mm the second-order rate coefficient had fallen by a factor of almost four. There was quantitative agreement for this effect between results obtained by the rotating-sector technique and using steady illumination.

Direct measurements of the combination rate have also been made at 1000° using a mass spectrometer coupled to a fast flow system[54]. The carrier gas was helium and the range of pressures was 3–15 mm. Under these conditions the rate coefficient varied linearly with the carrier gas pressure and a negative activation energy of 1·5 kcal/mole was observed. This is smaller than that calculated by Gill and Laidler[55] for the purely third-order combination. Either the temperature dependence is much smaller than predicted, or the rate was not purely third order; the latter is possible despite the apparent linear dependence on pressure since the range of pressure was not large. However, a surface reaction may have caused error in either of these measurements. Nevertheless, the *second-order* combination rate coefficient is undoubtedly to some extent pressure-dependent in this region of temperature and pressure.

The variation with temperature of the rate coefficient in its pressure-dependent region is of great importance in the development of the theory of unimolecular reactions, and an exact interpolation of the combination rate coefficient between the high- and low-temperature regions would be very useful. However, between these regions the results relating to the combination of methyl radicals are sometimes obtained by indirect kinetic evidence and are somewhat conflicting. Laidler and Wojciechowski[56] have estimated that at 600° the combination will be largely in its third-order region at pressures below 2000 mm, but this is admittedly subject to considerable uncertainty.

Brinton[57] has studied the photolysis of acetone at temperatures up to 475° and pressures from 25–100 mm. At temperatures above 300° the ratio $v_{CH_4}/v_{C_2H_6}{}^{\frac{1}{2}}[A]$ was found to vary with light intensity and acetone concentration, showing that reactions (88) and (89) were not sufficient

$$CH_3 + CH_3COCH_3 \xrightarrow{k_1} CH_4 + CH_2COCH_3 \qquad (88)$$

$$CH_3 + CH_3 \xrightarrow{k_2} C_2H_6 \qquad (89)$$

to represent the production of methane and ethane. To explain this the additional reaction (90) was proposed. Inclusion of this reaction in the

$$CH_3 + CH_3COCH_3 \xrightarrow{k_3} C_2H_6 + CO + CH_3 \qquad (90)$$

kinetic scheme leads to equation (91) where k_2 is the second-order

$$\frac{v_{CH_4}}{v_{C_2H_6}{}^{\frac{1}{2}}[CH_3COCH_3]} = \frac{k_1[CH_3]}{(k_2[CH_3]^2 + k_3][CH_3COCH_3])^{\frac{1}{2}}} \qquad (91)$$

coefficient for reaction (89). Extrapolation of the results to low acetone concentrations allows $k_1/k_2{}^{\frac{1}{2}}$ to be obtained, and a plot of the logarithm of this against $1/T$ shows a marked upward curvature at temperatures between 400 and 435°. This behavior is most likely to be due to a deviation from second-order kinetics at the higher temperatures, the second-order coefficient being less than it would be if the behavior were truly second order. In agreement with this point of view it is found that the activation energy corresponding to $k_1/k_2{}^{\frac{1}{2}}$ increases from 10·0 kcal at the lower temperatures (where it is equal to E_1) to 14·6 kcal at 435°; the change corresponds to a negative activation energy of $-9·8$ kcal for reaction (89), which is consistent with the value of $-11·7$ estimated by Gill and Laidler[55] on the basis of a theoretical treatment of the reaction in its third-order region. The results of Brinton therefore suggest that this reaction is close to third order at the highest temperature (435°), but in view of the complexities of the system other explanations are possible.

Danby, Buchanan and Henderson[58] studied the photolysis of acetaldehyde in the temperature range 212–340° and the pressure

$$CH_3CHO + h\nu \longrightarrow CH_3 + CHO \qquad (92)$$

$$CH_3 + CH_3CHO \xrightarrow{k_1} CH_4 + CH_3CO \qquad (93)$$

$$CH_3CO \longrightarrow CH_3 + CO \qquad (94)$$

$$2\,CH_3 \xrightarrow{k_2} C_2H_6 \qquad (95)$$

SCHEME 11.

range 19–317 mm. The mechanism is given by Scheme 11. The steady-state treatment leads to the expression given by (96). The results do

$$\frac{v_{CH_4}}{v_{C_2H_6}^{\frac{1}{2}}} = \frac{k_1[CH_3CHO]}{k_2^{\frac{1}{2}}} \qquad (96)$$

not reveal any divergence from this relationship of the kind that gives a clear indication that the methyl radical combination is in its pressure-dependent region; at these lower temperatures the combination is therefore close to second order.

Dodd[59] has measured the combination rate coefficient directly by using the rotating-sector technique on the photolysis of acetaldehyde, at temperatures from 150 to 450° and pressures from 200 to 400 mm. A plot of $\log\,[k_{termination}/k_{propagation}]$, derived from an analysis of the half-lives, against $1/T$, showed no curvature over the temperature range investigated, but the slope corresponded to an activation energy of 10·7 kcal/mole. Since the activation energy for reaction (93) is in fact 7·5 kcal/mole[60], the value of 10·7 suggests a negative activation energy of about 3·2 kcal for the radical-combination reaction, and therefore that the behavior is somewhat in the pressure-dependent region. The results are, however, not sufficiently precise for this conclusion to be a firm one.

The evidence from the above three sources is not completely clear, but is consistent with the view that the combination rate coefficient is somewhat pressure-dependent at pressures below 100 mm and at temperatures above 400° and perhaps lower. Additional evidence is provided by results on the pyrolyses of acetaldehyde and ethane, and is discussed in the next two sections.

B. Pyrolysis of Acetaldehyde

An important result obtained by Bril and coworkers[61], and confirmed in more detail by Eusuf and Laidler[62], is that the rate of the acetaldehyde decomposition is strongly decreased by addition of inert gases in the temperature range 480–525°. Such a result can only be explained if the inert gases aid the chain-ending step. The main chain carriers are methyl and acetyl radicals, with the former in excess, so that the main chain-ending step is the methyl-radical combination. It therefore seems that inert gases have a strong effect on the rate of this reaction, which must therefore be in its pressure-dependent region.

Trenwith[63] has studied the rate of hydrogen production in the acetaldehyde decomposition, and has found that it is proportional to the square of the acetaldehyde concentration. The main source of hydrogen is almost certainly hydrogen atoms, which produce molecular hydrogen by reaction (97), so that the hydrogen atoms must be produced by a second-order initiation process.

$$H + CH_3CHO \longrightarrow CH_3CO + H_2 \tag{97}$$

The same conclusion is to be drawn from the result[62] that the initial rate of ethane formation is proportional to the square of the acetaldehyde concentration. In the steady state the rate of production of methyl radicals is equal to the rate of their disappearance; it follows that the initiation reaction is second order in acetaldehyde.

Since the decomposition is three-halves order in acetaldehyde concentration the chain-ending steps may be $\beta\mu$ or $\beta\beta M$, in the terminology of Goldfinger, Letort and Niclause[8] (cf. Table 1), and in the acetaldehyde system are reactions (98) and (99), respectively. Of these

$$CH_3 + CH_3CO \longrightarrow CH_3COCH_3 \quad \beta\mu \tag{98}$$

$$CH_3 + CH_3 + M \longrightarrow C_2H_6 + M \quad \beta\beta M \tag{99}$$

two possibilities the first predicts no inert-gas effect, and hence the second must be the main termination step. It should be pointed out that the acetyl radical is here described as a μ radical (one that undergoes a unimolecular propagating reaction) whereas in fact its decomposition may be in its pressure-dependent region. If so its termination would have to be at least partly third order to give a proper overall order, and this would be surprising. It seems unlikely therefore that acetyl radicals are involved in the main chain-ending step.

The kinetics of the reaction and the effect on the rate of additions of foreign gases both therefore lead to the conclusion that in the temperature range 480–525° and at pressures from 30 to 579 mm Hg the combination of methyl radicals is a third-order reaction.

C. Pyrolysis of Ethane

$$C_2H_6 \xrightarrow{k_1} 2\,CH_3 \tag{100}$$

$$CH_3 + C_2H_6 \xrightarrow{k_2} CH_4 + C_2H_5 \tag{101}$$

$$C_2H_5 \xrightarrow{k_3} C_2H_4 + H \tag{102}$$

$$H + C_2H_6 \xrightarrow{k_4} H_2 + C_2H_5 \tag{103}$$

$$2\,C_2H_5 \xrightarrow{k_5} C_4H_{10} \text{ (or } C_2H_4 + C_2H_6) \tag{104}$$

$$H + C_2H_5 \xrightarrow{k_6} C_2H_6 \tag{105}$$

SCHEME 12.

The decomposition of ethane follows first-order kinetics and the chain carriers are hydrogen atoms and ethyl radicals. The mechanisms proposed include the reactions in Scheme 12. This mechanism leads to first-order kinetics only if termination is by reaction (105). There is good evidence, however, that under the conditions of temperature and pressure of most of the experimental work the concentration of ethyl radicals is greater than that of hydrogen atoms and termination should occur by reaction (104). Küchler and Theile[64] suggested that the initiation was a second-order process, and termination by reaction (104) would then lead to first-order kinetics. Laidler and Wojciechowski[56] showed by extrapolation of the pressure-dependence of the methyl radical combination observed at 250° that reaction (100) would indeed be expected to be second order at 600° and at the pressures used in the experiments. In the terminology of Laidler, Sagert and Wojciechowski[9] this mechanism is of the $^2\mu\mu_1$ type: second-order initiation, termination by μ radicals, first-order kinetics. The overall order, activation energy and the effect of inert gases on the rate were readily explained by these reactions. At higher temperatures and lower pressures it was predicted that the concentration of hydrogen atoms would exceed that of ethyl radicals so that the main chain-ending step would be reaction (105). Termination would thus be $\beta\mu$ and the overall order would be three-halves. Such a transition to three-halves order was indeed found[56] at approximately the predicted pressure. If the ethane dissociation is second order it follows that under the same conditions the methyl radical combination is third order.

More recently, however, several investigations of the initial rate of formation of methane[65-67] have shown that this rate is first order with respect to ethane, indicating that the initiation step is a first-order process. This result has been reconciled with the other evidence in various ways. Davis and Williamson[65], whose experiments were carried out in a flow system at high temperatures (676–775°), found that the rate of formation of methane was slightly pressure-dependent. They favored the combination of ethyl radicals as the chain-ending step, and suggested that the pressure sensitivity of both the initiation step and the decomposition of the ethyl radical combined to give first-order kinetics, which were, in any case, only roughly obeyed under their conditions. Quinn[66] made this suggestion more specific by proposing that when the overall rate and the rate of production of methane were exactly first order, as he found under his conditions, the rate coefficient for decomposition of the ethyl radical should be approximately proportional to the square root of the pressure. Evidence from a previous study of the pyrolysis of n-butane supported this view[73]. Gordon[67], on the other hand, found a considerable surface dependence of the rate and suggested that one of the termination reactions was heterogeneous.

Further results on the measurement of the rates of production of methane and butane from 550 to 720°[68] have confirmed the mechanism proposed by Quinn. The rate of production of methane was first order, but a fall-off in the first-order rate coefficients was observed at pressures below about 100 mm, over the whole range of temperatures. The rate of production of butane showed that this was the main termination product, but at high temperatures and low pressures there was probably some termination by reaction (105). The measurement of butane allowed the order of the ethyl radical decomposition to be determined directly (equation 106). Plots of $\log [v_{H_2}/v_{C_4H_{10}}^{\frac{1}{2}}]$ against

$$\frac{v_{H_2}}{v_{C_4H_{10}}^{\frac{1}{2}}} = \frac{k_3}{k_5^{\frac{1}{2}}} \tag{106}$$

$\log [C_2H_6]$ showed that k_3 was pressure-dependent. The rate of decomposition of the ethyl radical could be expressed empirically as shown by equation (107), where x was found to vary from 0·35 at high

$$-\frac{d\,[C_2H_5]}{dt} = k_3[C_2H_5]M^x \tag{107}$$

pressures and low temperatures, to 0·80 at low pressures and high temperatures. The activation energy for k_3 was about 31 kcal/mole and did not vary significantly in the range of temperature and pressure used.

The order of the decomposition, determined from the rate of production of hydrogen, was unity at high pressures but was observed to increase at low pressures and high temperatures. This change in order was shown to be the result of the changing order of the initiation reaction, combined with the changing order of the decomposition of the ethyl radical. The rate of decomposition is given by equation (108) and

$$v = k_3 \left(\frac{2k_1}{k_5}\right)^{\frac{1}{2}}[C_2H_6]^{\frac{1}{2}} \tag{108}$$

the overall order thus depends on the orders of k_3 and k_1.

There are, however, several results on the ethane pyrolysis and related reactions which are not explained by Quinn's mechanism. In an earlier investigation Danby, Spall, Stubbs and Hinshelwood[69] also studied the rate of methane production in the ethane pyrolysis, and also noted that it was first order in ethane. They obtained the significant result that the methane production was not inhibited by nitric oxide. This appears to eliminate the possibility that the main source of methane is abstraction by methyl radicals, since nitric oxide will reduce markedly the concentration of methyl radicals. Danby and coworkers concluded that methane production occurred by reaction (109). This

$$C_2H_6 \longrightarrow CH_4 + CH_2 \tag{109}$$

reaction might be first order, and the split into methyl radicals second order, if different numbers of normal modes are involved in the formation of the activated complex in each case. This question of the mode of initiation has not yet been satisfactorily settled.

It was also observed by Küchler and Theile[64] that inert gases have hardly any effect on the rate of the decomposition of ethane maximally inhibited by nitric oxide, in contrast to their accelerating effect on the uninhibited reaction. Quinn's mechanism for the uninhibited reaction explains this result in terms of the effect of inert gases on the breakdown of the ethyl radical. The rate of the maximally inhibited reaction must, however, according to any mechanism be proportional to the rate of this breakdown. The fact that there is little inert-gas effect therefore requires that the ethyl radical decomposition is in its first-order region, and this in turn leads to the result that the ethane dissociation into methyl radicals must, in order for the overall kinetics to be explained, be second order.

The small inert-gas effect on the maximally-inhibited ethane pyrolysis is readily explained in terms of the Laidler–Wojciechowski mechanism (Scheme 13)[70].

$$C_2H_6 + NO \underset{k_{-1}}{\overset{k_1}{\rightleftharpoons}} C_2H_5 + HNO \tag{110}$$

$$HNO \underset{k_{-2}}{\overset{k_2}{\rightleftharpoons}} H + NO \tag{111}$$

$$H + C_2H_6 \overset{k_3}{\longrightarrow} H_2 + C_2H_5 \tag{112}$$

$$C_2H_5 \overset{k_4}{\longrightarrow} C_2H_4 + H \tag{113}$$

SCHEME 13.

The overall rate is given by equation (114), where K is the equilibrium

$$v = (k_3 k_4 K)^{\frac{1}{2}}[C_2H_6] \tag{114}$$

constant for $C_2H_6 \rightleftharpoons C_2H_5 + H$. Inert gases have no effect on k_3 and K, and they have none on k_4 provided that the reaction is in its first-order region.

D. Decomposition of the Ethyl Radical

The order of the decomposition of the ethyl radical under pyrolysis conditions is intimately related to that of the methyl radical combination. Information on this question may be obtained from the kinetics of the thermal decomposition of other compounds in which the ethyl radical has an important role.

In the decomposition of propionaldehyde the major source of ethylene is the decomposition of the ethyl radical. However, at temperatures of 520–560° the experiments of Laidler and Eusuf[71] showed that the rate of production of ethylene was not increased by the addition of an equal pressure of carbon dioxide. This appears to suggest that the decomposition of the ethyl radical is not pressure-dependent at these temperatures.

In a study of the mercury-photosensitized reaction of ethane at high

7*

temperatures Bywater and Steacie[72] measured the activation energy for the decomposition of the ethyl radical at temperatures from 400 to 500° and at 400 mm. They obtained a value of 39·5 kcal/mole, which suggests that the rate coefficient for decomposition was first order in this region. The evidence from both these systems seems incompatible with the results from the ethane decomposition.

On the other hand, a study of the pyrolysis of n-butane[73] has been interpreted to indicate the pressure-dependence of the ethyl radical decomposition. The mechanism which has been postulated is as shown by Scheme 14[73, 26]. The expression shown in equation (123) can be

$$C_4H_{10} \xrightarrow{k_1} 2 C_2H_5 \tag{115}$$

$$C_2H_5 + C_4H_{10} \xrightarrow{k_2} C_2H_6 + C_4H_9 \tag{116}$$

$$C_4H_9 \xrightarrow{k_3} CH_3 + C_3H_6 \tag{117}$$

$$C_4H_9 \xrightarrow{k_4} C_2H_5 + C_2H_4 \tag{118}$$

$$CH_3 + C_4H_{10} \xrightarrow{k_5} CH_4 + C_4H_9 \tag{119}$$

$$C_2H_5 \xrightarrow{k_6} C_2H_4 + H \tag{120}$$

$$H + C_4H_{10} \xrightarrow{k_7} H_2 + C_4H_9 \tag{121}$$

$$2 C_2H_5 \xrightarrow{k_8} C_4H_{10} \text{ (or } C_2H_6 + C_2H_4) \tag{122}$$

SCHEME 14.

$$\frac{v_{C_2H_4} - v_{C_2H_6}}{v_{C_2H_6}} [C_4H_{10}] = \frac{2k_6}{k_2} \tag{123}$$

obtained on the basis of this mechanism. The ratio on the left-hand side was found to decrease as the concentration of butane was reduced, and this was attributed by Purnell and Quinn[73] to the pressure-dependence of k_6. Furthermore, additions of inert gas were found to increase the ethylene yield at the expense of ethane, and the activation energy for decomposition of the ethyl radical was in good agreement with that found in the ethane pyrolysis at higher temperatures.

E. Conclusion

The situation with regard to the order of the methyl radical combination under the usual pyrolysis conditions, and the related one of the order of the ethyl radical decomposition, is still by no means clear. The main difficulty undoubtedly arises from the different conditions employed in different experiments. Surface effects in the ethane and butane pyrolyses may play a more important role than has been realized, and complications due to them might be responsible for the fact that some of the experiments in those systems have tended to support the view that the methyl radical combination is second order and the ethyl radical decomposition is of intermediate order. The aldehyde decompositions, which support the alternative view (third-order kinetics for $CH_3 + CH_3$ and first-order for $C_2H_5 \rightarrow C_2H_4' + H$), appear to be less complicated by surface effects. It is evident from what has been said that the situation is somewhat borderline, and evidence such as that given in this review must be considered carefully in order for reliable overall mechanisms to be formulated for these systems.

VI. REFERENCES

1. F. O. Rice and K. F. Herzfeld, *J. Am. Chem. Soc.*, **56**, 284 (1934).
2. F. J. Stubbs and C. N. Hinshelwood, *Discussion Faraday Soc.*, **10**, 129 (1951); C. N. Hinshelwood, *Chem. Soc. (London), Spec. Publ.*, **9**, 49 (1957).
3. B. W. Wojciechowski and K. J. Laidler, *Can. J. Chem.*, **38**, 1027 (1960).
4. M. Eusuf and K. J. Laidler, *Can. J. Chem.*, **42**, 1861 (1964), and earlier papers cited.
5. E. W. R. Steacie, *Atomic and Free Radical Reactions*, Vol. 1, Reinhold Publishing Corp., New York, 1954, pp. 196–198.
6. S. W. Benson, *J. Chem. Phys.*, **25**, 27 (1956); S. W. Benson, *The Foundations of Chemical Kinetics*, McGraw-Hill Book Co., New York, 1960, pp. 386–392.
7. S. W. Benson and D. V. S. Jain, *J. Chem. Phys.*, **31**, 1008 (1959).
8. P. Goldfinger, M. Letort, and M. Niclause, *Volume commemoratif Victor Henri: Contribution à l'Etude de la Structure moléculaire*, Desoeur, Liège, 1948, p. 283.
9. K. J. Laidler, N. H. Sagert, and B. W. Wojciechowski, *Proc. Roy. Soc., Ser. A*, **270**, 242 (1962).
10. K. H. Anderson and S. W. Benson, *J. Chem. Phys.*, **36**, 2320 (1962).
11. N. Imai and O. Toyama, *Bull. Chem. Soc. Japan*, **34**, 328 (1961).
12. D. J. McKenney and K. J. Laidler, *Can. J. Chem.*, **41**, 1984, 1993 (1963).
13. K. H. Anderson and S. W. Benson, *J. Chem. Phys.*, **39**, 1677 (1963).
14. A. F. Trotman-Dickenson, *J. Chem. Phys.*, **19**, 261 (1951).
15. (a) R. A. Marcus, B. de B. Darwent and E. W. R. Steacie, *J. Chem. Phys.*, **16**, 987 (1948); (b). L. M. Loucks and K. J. Laidler, to be published.
16. D. J. McKenney and K. J. Laidler, *Can. J. Chem.*, **41**, 2009 (1963).
17. A. F. Trotman-Dickenson and E. W. R. Steacie, *J. Chem. Phys.*, **19**, 329 (1951).
18. N. Imai and O. Toyama, *Bull. Chem. Soc., Japan*, **33**, 652 (1960).
19. G. R. Freeman, *D. Phil. Thesis*, University of Oxford (1957).

20. G. R. Freeman, *Proc. Roy. Soc. (London)*, *Ser. A*, **245**, 49 (1958).
21. G. R. Freeman, C. J. Danby, and C. N. Hinshelwood, *Proc. Roy. Soc. (London)*, *Ser. A*, **245**, 28 (1958).
22. C. J. Danby and G. R. Freeman, *Proc. Roy. Soc. (London)*, *Ser. A*, **245**, 40 (1958).
23. J. Long and G. Skirrow, *Trans. Faraday Soc.*, **58**, 1403 (1962).
24. K. J. Laidler and D. J. McKenney, *Proc. Roy. Soc. (London)*, *Ser. A*, **278**, 505 (1964).
25. J. Jach and C. N. Hinshelwood, *Proc. Roy. Soc. (London)*, *Ser. A*, **231**, 145 (1955).
26. N. H. Sagert and K. J. Laidler, *Can. J. Chem.*, **41**, 838 (1963).
27. K. J. Laidler and D. J. McKenney, *Proc. Roy. Soc. (London)*, *Ser. A*, **278**, 517 (1964).
28. C. J. M. Fletcher and G. K. Rollefson, *J. Am. Chem. Soc.*, **58**, 2129 (1936).
29. R. E. Rebbert and K. J. Laidler, *J. Chem. Phys.*, **20**, 574 (1952).
30. L. A. K. Staveley and C. N. Hinshelwood, *Proc. Roy. Soc. (London)*, *Ser. A*, **154**, 335 (1936).
31. C. Steel and K. J. Laidler, *J. Chem. Phys.*, **34**, 1827 (1961).
32. P. J. Thomas, *J. Chem. Soc.*, 136 (1961).
33. V. R. Stimson and E. J. Watson, *J. Chem. Soc.*, 524 (1963).
34. V. R. Stimson and E. J. Watson, *Chem. Ind. (London)*, 207 (1961).
35. F. M. Elkobaisi and W. J. Hickinbottom, *J. Chem. Soc.*, 1286 (1960); *J. Chem. Soc.*, 1873 (1959).
36. H. V. R. Iengar and P. D. Ritchie, *J. Chem. Soc.*, 3563 (1956).
37. A. T. Blades, *Can. J. Chem.*, **31**, 418 (1953).
38. M. J. Molera and J. A. López Quirós, *Anales Real Soc. Españ. Fis. Quim (Madrid)*, **54B**, 137 (1958); *Chem. Abstr.*, 52, 17089h (1958).
39. M. J. Molera and J. A. López Quirós, *Anales Real Soc. Españ. Fis. Quim (Madrid)*, **54B**, 127 (1958); *Chem. Abstr.*, 54, 10471b (1960).
40. J. A. López Quirós and M. J. Molera, *Anales Real Soc. Españ. Fis. Quim (Madrid)*, **50B**, 851 (1954); *Chem. Abstr.*, **49**, 7344c (1955).
41. C. H. De Puy, C. A. Bishop, and C. N. Goeders, *J. Am. Chem. Soc.*, **83**, 2151 (1961).
42. C. H. De Puy and R. W. King, *Chem. Revs.*, **60**, 431 (1960).
43. M. J. Molera and E. Ariza, *Anales Real Soc. Españ. Fis. Quim (Madrid)*, **56B**, 851 (1960); *Chem. Abstr.*, **55**, 12269 i (1961).
44. Y. Pocker, *Proc. Chem. Soc. (London)*, 141 (1961).
45. E. S. Gould, *Mechanism and Structure in Organic Chemistry*, Henry Holt and Co., New York (1959), pp. 644–649.
46. D. S. Tarbell in *Organic Reactions*, Vol. 2 (Ed. R. Adams, W. E. Bachmann, L. F. Fieser, J. R. Johnson and H. R. Snyder), John Wiley and Sons, New York, 1944, pp. 1–48.
47. S. Marcinkiewicz, J. Green and P. Mamalis, *Tetrahedron*, **14**, 208 (1961).
48. R. C. Cookson and S. R. Wallis, *Proc. Chem. Soc. (London)*, 58 (1963).
49. T. J. Wallace and R. J. Gritter, *J. Org. Chem.*, **27**, 3067 (1962); **26**, 5256 (1961).
50. G. B. Kistiakowsky and E. K. Roberts, *J. Chem. Phys.*, **21**, 1637 (1953).
51. D. M. Miller and E. W. R. Steacie, *J. Chem. Phys.*, **19**, 73 (1951).
52. R. W. Durham and E. W. R. Steacie, *J. Chem. Phys.*, **20**, 682 (1952).

53. R. E. Dodd and E. W. R. Steacie, *Proc. Roy. Soc. (London), Ser. A*, **223**, 283 (1954).
54. K. W. Ingold, I. H. S. Henderson and F. P. Lossing, *J. Chem. Phys.*, **21**, 2239 (1953).
55. E. K. Gill and K. J. Laidler, *Proc. Roy. Soc. (London), Ser. A*, **250**, 121 (1959).
56. K. J. Laidler and B. W. Wojciechowski, *Proc. Roy. Soc. (London), Ser. A*, **260**, 91 (1961).
57. R. K. Brinton, *J. Am. Chem. Soc.*, **83**, 1541 (1961).
58. C. J. Danby, A. S. Buchanan and I. H. S. Henderson, *J. Chem. Soc.*, 1426 (1951).
59. R. E. Dodd, *Trans. Faraday Soc.*, **47**, 56 (1951).
60. D. H. Volman and R. K. Brinton, *J. Chem. Phys.*, **20**, 1764 (1952).
61. K. Bril, P. Goldfinger, M. Letort, H. Mattys and M. Niclause, *Bull. Soc. Chim. Belges*, **59**, 263 (1950).
62. M. Eusuf and K. J. Laidler, *Can. J. Chem.*, **42**, 1851 (1964).
63. A. B. Trenwith, *J. Chem. Soc.*, 4426 (1963).
64. L. Küchler and H. Theile, *Z. Physik. Chem.*, **B42**, 359 (1939).
65. H. G. Davis and K. D. Williamson, *Fifth World Petroleum Congress, 1959*, Section IV.
66. C. P. Quinn, *Proc. Roy. Soc. (London)*, **A275**, 190 (1963).
67. A. S. Gordon, *Symp. on Kinetics of Pyrolytic Reactions*, Chemical Institute of Canada, Ottawa, September 1964.
68. M. C. Lin and M. H. Back, to be published.
69. C. J. Danby, B. C. Spall, F. J. Stubbs and C. N. Hinshelwood, *Proc. Roy. Soc. (London), Ser. A*, **218**, 450 (1953).
70. K. J. Laidler and B. W. Wojciechowski, *Proc. Roy. Soc. (London), Ser. A*, **260**, 103 (1961).
71. K. J. Laidler and M. Eusuf, *Can. J Chem.*, **43**, 268 (1965).
72. S. Bywater and E. W. R. Steacie, *J. Chem. Phys.*, **19**, 326 (1951).
73. P. H. Purnell and C. P. Quinn, *Proc. Roy. Soc. (London), Ser. A*, **270**, 267 (1962).

CHAPTER **5**

Biological formations and reactions

KURT WALLENFELS and HANS DIEKMANN*

Department of Biochemistry, University of Freiburg, Germany

---

* Present address: Department of Microbiology, University of Tübingen.

I. THE OCCURRENCE OF THE C—O—C GROUPING IN NATURAL PRODUCTS

The ether functions which are found in natural products may be classified as follows:

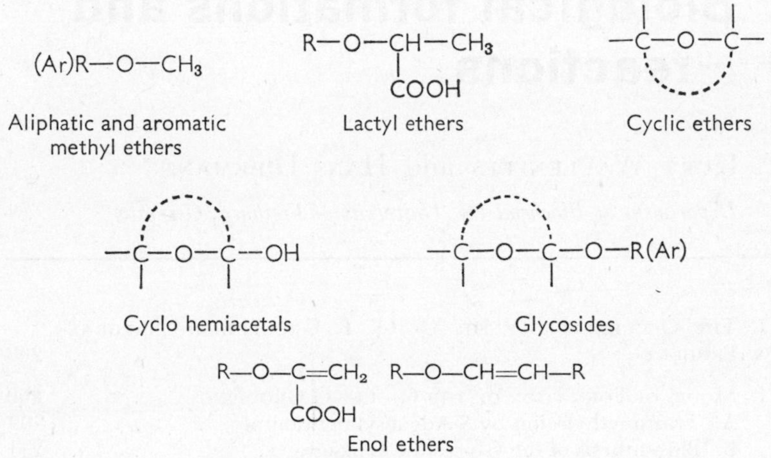

(Ar)R—O—CH$_3$ R—O—CH—CH$_3$ —C—O—C—
                                    |
                                 COOH

Aliphatic and aromatic   Lactyl ethers   Cyclic ethers
methyl ethers

—C—O—C—OH   —C—O—C—O—R(Ar)

Cyclo hemiacetals   Glycosides

R—O—C=CH$_2$ R—O—CH=CH—R
        |
     COOH
        Enol ethers

There are compounds with analogous structures which contain sulfur, and in a few cases selenium or tellurium, instead of oxygen.

The C—O—C grouping appears in polymeric carbohydrates such as cellulose, starch, glycogen[1], dextrans[2], inulin[3], and pectin[4]; in mucopolysaccharides[5] such as chitin, hyaluronic acid, chondroitin sulfate, heparin, blood group substances[6], and the constituents of capsuls[7] and cell walls[8]; in lignin[9]; in mono- and oligosaccharides[10,11]; in heterosides[12] such as flavonoid and digitalis glycosides; in methylated sugars[13], cyclitols[14], and phenols[15,16]; in plasmalogenes[17] and α-glyceryl ethers[18]; in numerous heterocyclic compounds[19] such as the anthocyanines and flavones; and many others.

The corresponding sulfur compounds are the thioethers[20] such as methionine, thioglycosides[21], and many sulfur heterocyclic compounds. The list would be even more impressive if many other compounds were included which, though occurring in small amounts only, possess a pronounced biological activity.

The following survey aims to point out several main routes for the biosynthesis and the metabolism of the ether function in natural products, and to account for our present knowledge of the mechanism of these reactions.

II. MODES OF FORMATION OF THE C—O—C GROUPING

A. Transmethylation by S-Adenosylmethionine

Methionine (1) is the methyl group donor in the biological methylation[22,23] of alcoholic and phenolic hydroxyl groups. Prior to the methylation reaction this essential amino acid is transformed to S-adenosylmethionine ('active methionine' 2) (reaction 1)[24,25], in

$$HOOCCH(NH_2)CH_2CH_2SCH_3 + ATP + H_2O \longrightarrow$$

(1)

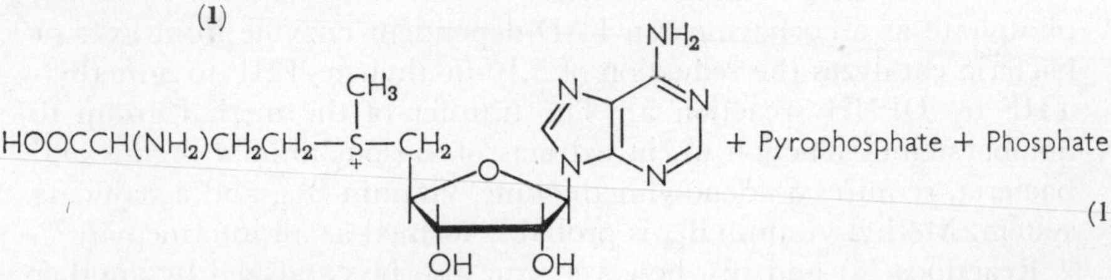

$$+ \text{ Pyrophosphate } + \text{ Phosphate}$$

(1)

(2)

this energy-rich compound the bonds between the sulfonium atom and its substituents are weakened; consequently the methyl group can be transferred with greater ease. It may also be remembered that, in the nonenzymatic methylation in dimethylsulfoxide, the trimethylsulfoxonium salt is considered to be the methylating agent[26].

In the reactions catalyzed by the methyl transferases (transmethylases)[23,27] S-adenosylhomocysteine (3) is liberated, while the methyl group is transferred to the acceptor (reaction 2). Another enzyme cleaves 3 into adenosine and homocysteine (reaction 3). This reaction

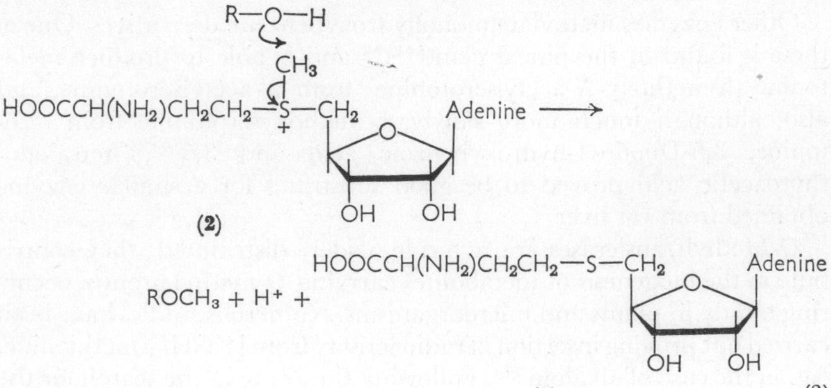

(2)

$$ROCH_3 + H^+ +$$

(3)

(2)

$$3 \rightleftharpoons \text{Adenosine} + \text{Homocysteine}$$

(3)

is reversible[28]. The *de novo* biosynthesis of a methyl group[22,29] from serine* and the transfer to homocysteine are shown in reactions (4) to (6), where THF = tetrahydrofolic acid.

$$\text{Serine} + \text{THF} \longrightarrow 5,10\text{-Methylene-THF} \qquad (4)$$

$$5,10\text{-Methylene-THF} \longrightarrow 5\text{-Methyl-THF} \qquad (5)$$

$$5\text{-Methyl-THF} + \text{Homocysteine} \longrightarrow \text{THF} + \mathbf{1} \qquad (6)$$

The serine transhydroxymethylase (reaction 4) requires pyridoxal phosphate as a coenzyme. An FAD-dependent enzyme from liver or bacteria catalyzes the reduction of 5,10-methylene-THF to 5-methyl-THF by DPNH (reaction 5). The transfer of the methyl group to homocysteine (reaction 6), in extracts of various animal organs and bacteria, requires S-adenosylmethionine, vitamin B_{12}, and a reducing system. Methyl-vitamin B_{12} is probably formed as an intermediate[30].

Reactions (5) and (6), however, can also be catalyzed by another enzyme system (obtained from microorganisms) which is not co-bamide-dependent. In this case the cofactor will be 5,10-methylene-tetrahydropteroyl triglutamate and not 5,10-methylene-THF[31].

O-Methyltransferases, whose substrates are catechine and pyrogallol derivatives, are mostly found in liver and kidney, but they are also found in other organs of mammals[32,33]; and also in amaryllidaceae[34], in cambial tissue of apple[35], in pampas grass[36], in triticum and petunias[37], in *Streptomyces rimosus*[38], and in *Lentilus lepideus*[39].

An enzyme with similar specificity, which converts guanidinoethyl phosphate into the phosphoric acid methyl ether (opheline), was found in *Ophelia neglecta* S[40].

Other enzymes methylate monohydroxybenzene derivatives. One of these is found in the pineal gland[41,42] and is able to produce mela-tonine (5-methoxy-N-acetylserotonine) from N-acetylserotonine, and also, although much more slowly, 5-methoxyserotonine from sero-tonine. 3,5-Diiodo-4-hydroxybenzoic acid and 3,5,3',5'-tetraiodo-thyroacetic acid proved to be good substrates for a similar enzyme obtained from rat liver[43].

O-Methyltransferases are, as a rule, widely distributed; they contri-bute to the biogenesis of metabolites carrying O-methyl groups, occur-ring mostly in plants and microorganisms. Numerous studies have been carried out proving insertion of radioactivity from $[^{14}CH_3]$-methionine, e.g. in the case of alkaloids[44]. Following this route in the search for the

---

* The methyl group of methionine may originate from different C_1 sources, but the β-carbon atom of serine is probably the most important among them.

enzyme, one should bear in mind that C- and N-methyl groups may also originate from radioactive methionine.

In the reaction catalyzed by O-methyltransferases the $(-)$-S-adenosyl-L-methionine alone is active[45]. The absolute configuration around the sulfonium atom is not known. Some of these enzymes studied need magnesium ions for activity. The reaction is initiated by a nucleophilic attack of the acceptor on the methyl group of 2 (reaction 2). The carbonyl oxygen of methionine is the nucleophile which attacks, in the presence of a different enzyme from yeast, the $C_{(4)}$ atom of the same molecule (reaction 7)[46].

The presence of ethionine[47] or selenium *in vivo* and *in vitro* yields the corresponding analogs which can be substituted for 2 in the enzyme reactions[48]. It is not known whether these compounds, i.e. S-adenosylethionine or selenoadenosylmethionine, have any significance under physiological conditions[49,50].

B. Biosynthesis of the Glycosidic Linkage

The cleavage and transfer of glycosidic linkages by glycosidases and phosphorylases were discovered quite early and attracted much attention because of the wide distribution and great importance of the materials containing glycosidic bonds.

Synthesis of polysaccharides is also possible with these enzymes. Glucanes are formed from glucose-1-phosphate in this way, with the aid of polysaccharide phosphorylase; and dextranes and levanes can also be synthesized from sucrose (see section III.B). Similarly, the synthesis of disaccharides from glucose-1-phosphate and a suitable acceptor is catalyzed by disaccharide phosphorylases (see section III.C). It is now assumed that the physiological significance of the phosphorylases consists of the degradation of di- and polysaccharides. Likewise, a glycoside transfer by glycosidases cannot be regarded as a synthesis of a *new* glycosidic bond. How then does the synthesis of the enormous quantity of low and high molecular weight compounds with glycosidic linkages occur in nature?

About 1950 new types of compounds were discovered in yeast[51] and in penicillin-treated *Staphylococcus aureus*[52]. These compounds were found to be uridine diphosphate glucose (UDPG) (6)[53] and uridine diphosphate-*N*-acetylmuramic acid (7)[54], respectively. It was shown

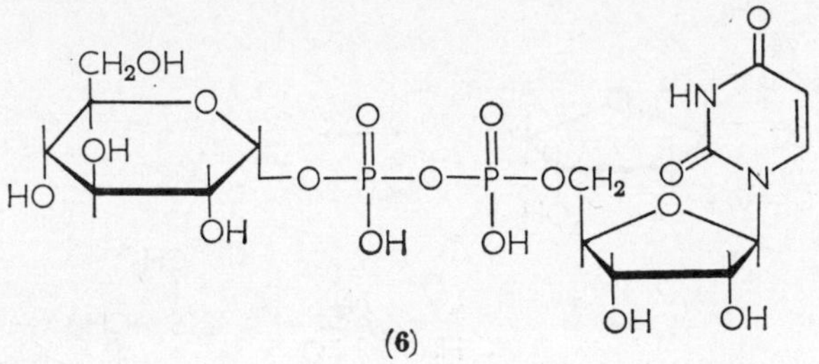

(6)

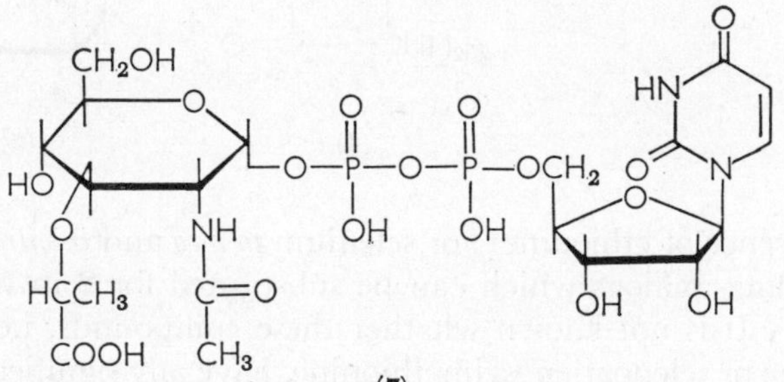

(7)

that compounds of this type, designated as sugar nucleotides[55], are the glycoside donors in the biosynthesis of oligo- and polysaccharides[56]. Besides uridine, guanosine, adenosine, cytidine, deoxyuridine, and deoxythymidine may also form the nucleoside moiety[57]. It should be mentioned that the mutual conversion of sugars through oxidation, reduction, epimerization, and decarboxylation is very often achieved when they are bound to nucleoside phosphates[58].

At the present time about fifty sugar nucleotides are known[59]. Their biosynthesis takes place according to reaction (8).

$$\text{Nucleoside triphosphate} + \alpha\text{-D-Sugar-1-phosphate} \underset{\text{[Pyrophosphorylase]}}{\rightleftharpoons}$$

$$\text{Sugar nucleotide} + \text{Pyrophosphate} \quad (8)$$

In all the cases studied up to now, the sugar nucleotide structure is similar to that of UDPG: the purine or pyrimidine is combined with a D-ribose or D-deoxyribose by a β-glycosidic linkage, while the pyrophosphate bridge is held by an α-glycosidic bond at the anomeric carbon atom of the sugar.

In the presence of an acceptor, which has to contain at least one hydroxyl (or amino) group and a suitable enzyme, the sugar moiety (e.g. glucose in reaction (9)) will be transferred to the acceptor ROH.

$$(9)$$

Table 1 presents the sugar nucleotides and the acceptors, as well as the products of their reactions. Enzymes are known for all these reactions[82, 83], many of them in the form of partly purified preparations, but none yet in crystalline form. Many other similar reactions and their enzymes have yet to be discovered, leaving many interesting and important problems to be solved. One of these, for example, is the question whether the saccharides responsible for the serological specificity, which are found in erythrocytes[84] and in the cell walls of bacteria[85, 86], are formed by stepwise additions of oligosaccharide residues to the macromolecular framework, or whether the oligosaccharide chain grows in the form of a nucleoside diphosphate derivative and is subsequently transferred in a single step. It has recently been shown[80, 87, 88] that the second alternative is in principle possible.

I. Specificity

Many enzymes are not absolutely specific for the sugar nucleotides mentioned in Table 1. Thus the glycogen-synthesizing enzyme from rat muscle also reacts, though much more slowly, with ADP–glucose and with TDP–glucose[89]. On the other hand, the cellulose-synthesizing enzyme reacts with no other sugar nucleotide but GDP–glucose (UDP–, ADP–, TDP–, and CDP–glucose have been tested as possible substrates)[71].

The specificity of the glycoside-synthesizing enzymes towards an acceptor varies. It is very high when the acceptor is a sugar phosphate,

TABLE 1. Enzymatic glycoside syntheses with sugar nucleotides.

Sugar nucleotide	Acceptor	Product	Ref.
UDP–xylose	β-1,4-Xylooligosaccharides	One xylose unit added to β-1,4-xylooligosaccharides	60
UDP–glucose	Phage DNS	Glucosylated DNS	61
UDP–glucose	Glucose-6-phosphate	Trehalosephosphate	62
UDP–glucose	Fructose	Sucrose	63
UDP–glucose	Fructose-6-phosphate	Sucrosephosphate	64
UDP–galactose	Glucose-1-phosphate	Lactose-1-phosphate	65
UDP–galactose	N-Acetylglucosamine	Lactosamine	66
UDP–glucuronic acid	Phenols	Glucuronides	67
UDP–glucose	Hydroquinone	Arbutin	68
UDP–glucose	Phenyl-β-glucoside	Phenyl-β-gentiobioside	69
TDP–rhamnose	3-Quercetin-D-glucoside	3-Quercetin-O-L-rhamnosyl-6-D-glucoside	70
GDP–glucose		Cellulose	71
UDP–glucose		Glycogen	72, 73
ADP–glucose		Starch	74
UDP–glucose		Callose	75
GDP–mannose		Mannan	76
UDP–N-acetyl-glucosamine		Chitin	77
CMP–neuraminic acid		Colominic acid	78
UDP–N-acetylglucos-amine + UDP-glucuronic acid		Hyaluronic acid	79
UDP–N-acetylglucos-amine + UDP-muramic acid		Cell-wall building units (Staphylococcus aureus)	80
UDP–glucose + UDP-glucuronic acid		Capsule substance (Pneumococci Type III)	81

but in all other cases a great number of compounds may successfully function as acceptors, e.g. the sucrose-synthesizing enzyme transfers to fructose, xylulose, rhamnulose, and sorbose[90]. Besides its reaction with hydroquinone, the arbutine-synthesizing enzyme reacts with resorcinol, pyrocatechol, phloroglucinol, pyrogallol, and other polyhydric phenols[68]. The glucuronide-synthesizing enzyme transfers the glucuronic acid moiety to hydroxyl and amino groups in compounds widely varying in structure[91,92].

Dextrins or polysaccharides are needed as acceptors in the syntheses of polysaccharides. These reactions are practically irreversible. Several equilibrium constants have been determined for the synthesis of disaccharides. These are given in Table 2.

TABLE 2. Equilibrium constants for disaccharide syntheses with sugar nucleotides[62-64].

Product	$K = \dfrac{[ROX]\ [UDP]}{[UDPX]\ [ROH]}$	pH[a]	Temp. (°c)
Trehalosephosphate	40		
Sucrose	5	7·4	37
Sucrose phosphate	3250	7·5	38

[a] The equilibrium constant is pH dependent, as the proton which is formally conveyed from the acceptor to the terminal phosphate group of the UDP is partly dissociated.

2. Structure

Little is known about the protein part of the sugar nucleotide-dependent transglycosylases. The glycogen synthetase from muscle has been most closely studied. The activities of this enzyme and of phosphorylase are inhibited by glucose and phloridzin to approximately the same extent[93]. The amino acid sequence at the active site of glycogen synthetase has been recently elucidated[94]:

$$\left.\begin{matrix} Arg \\ Lys \end{matrix}\right\} Glu—Ile—\overset{\overset{\textstyle P}{\textstyle |}}{Ser}—Val—Arg$$

This sequence is, as far as is known at present, identical in the vicinity of the serine phosphate to that in phosphorylase (see section III.C). Further studies may show whether similarity of amino acid sequence also exists in cases of other enzymes capable of synthesizing glycoside linkages from phosphorylated sugars. Such correspondence between function and structure is already known in hydrolases.

3. Mechanism

During the transfer, the configuration around the anomeric carbon atom of the donor can either be retained or inverted (reaction 10). It was questioned whether exchange of the nucleotide moiety, in the presence of glycogen synthetase, will occur between UDPG and ^{14}C-labeled UDP. No labeled UDPG was found, and it was therefore concluded that no glycosyl–enzyme linkage has been formed under the conditions of the experiment[95]. Comparison of various transfer enzymes showed many similarities, with respect to stereochemistry,

$$
\begin{array}{ll}
& \text{Example} \\
\text{NDP} + \alpha\text{-Glycosides} & \text{Trehalose phosphate} \\
& \text{Sucrose} \\
& \text{Glycogen} \\
\text{NDP–O} + \text{ROH} & \\
& \text{Lactose} \\
\text{NDP} + \beta\text{-Glycosides} & \text{Phenyl-}\beta\text{-glycoside} \\
& \text{Cellulose}
\end{array}
\tag{10}
$$

specificity, pH dependence, etc.; a general reaction mechanism has been proposed[96–99]. Examples will be discussed in connection with the glycosidases (section III.B) and phosphorylases (section III.C).

These considerations also very probably apply to the sugar nucleotide-dependent transglycosylases. The great resemblance, together with the peculiarities in the reaction of these enzymes, may be illustrated by the following example of four enzymes with specificity for sucrose (reactions 11 to 14).

$$
\text{Sucrose} + (\text{Glucose})_n \xrightarrow{\text{Dextransucrase}} \text{Dextran} + \text{Fructose} \tag{11}
$$

$$
\text{Sucrose} + \text{Water} \xrightarrow{\text{Glucosido invertase}} \text{Glucose} + \text{Fructose} \tag{12a}
$$

$$
\text{Sucrose} + \text{Glucose} \xrightarrow{\text{Glucosido invertase}} \text{Maltose} + \text{Fructose} \tag{12b}
$$

$$
\text{Sucrose} + \text{Phosphate} \xrightarrow{\text{Sucrose phosphorylase}} \alpha\text{-Glucose-1-phosphate} + \text{Fructose} \tag{13}
$$

$$
\text{Sucrose} + \text{UDP} \xrightarrow{\text{Sucrose synthethase}} \text{UDPG} + \text{Fructose} \tag{14}
$$

4. Regulation[58]

As in the case of polysaccharide phosphorylase from muscle, two different forms of glycogen synthetase have been found, one of which can be activated by glucose-6-phosphate[100]. With the aid of a kinase in the presence of ATP and magnesium ions it is possible to transform the glucose-6-phosphate dependent form into the independent one, the enzyme protein obviously being phosphorylated in the process[101]. The independent form, again in analogy to phosphorylase, can be transformed to the dependent enzyme with the aid of adrenaline or calcium ions[102, 103].

Experimental evidence is also available regarding the participation of insulin in the regulation of glycogen synthetase[104]. The regulation reactions complement each other as follows: in the case of glucose requirement through the same mechanism the glycogen degradation is enhanced by activation of the phosphorylase, and the glycogen synthesis is retarded through inactivation of the synthetase, and vice versa.

C. Biogenesis of Cyclic Ethers

The oxygen heterocyclic compounds existing in nature are so numerous, and the variety in structure so great, that it is impossible to describe their biogenesis by a simple scheme[105].

From the great variety of processes, the biogenesis of the $C_6C_3C_6$ compounds (chalcones, flavones, and anthocyanines) has been selected. This group of chroman derivatives occurs widely[106, 107], and has been extensively studied in the last few years[108].

Starting with cinnamic acid (9) (or one of its derivatives) and three acetate (or malonate) molecules (8), the formation of a chalcone (11) can be assumed to take place via a poly-β-keto intermediate (10). The chalcone is in equilibrium with the cyclic flavanone (12). *In vivo* the reaction 11⇌12 is probably enzyme-catalyzed. The oxygen atoms of ring A in 11 come from acetate (or malonate) carboxyl groups[109]. The compounds 11 and 12 are the precursors of the aurones, anthocyanines, flavones, catecholes, and isoflavones. Glycosidation is presumably the last step in the biosynthesis of the naturally occurring glycosides of these groups.

A peculiarity of the biogenesis of the isoflavones is a phenyl migration after formation of the $C_6C_3C_6$ compound[110,111]. In this process a chalcone, or a substance in rapid equilibrium with it, must be an intermediate[112].

The routes of biogenesis have been elucidated by means of tracer studies in *in vivo* experiments. Cell-free extracts have been used only in a few cases, and the corresponding enzymes have not been characterized.

D. Biogenesis of Enol Ethers

In the study of the biosynthesis of aromatic amino acids, two compounds with an enol ether structure have been observed. These are intermediates in the metabolic route from 5-phosphoshikimic acid (**13**) to prephenic acid; they are 5-phosphoshikimate-3-enolpyruvate[113] (**15**) and chorisminic acid[114] (**16**). The formation of **15** has been studied with extracts from *Escherichia coli* (reaction 16). The reaction mechanism presented is hypothetical[113].

$$(13) \qquad (14)$$

$$(16)$$

$$(15) \qquad (16)$$

Muramic acid also is apparently formed by pyruvyl transfer[115,116] and subsequent reduction[117].

The enol ethers of plasmalogenes, on the other hand, are probably synthesized through hemiacetal formation from long-chain aldehydes with the α-hydroxy group of glycerine. This is followed by the elimination of water. The biogenesis of plasmalogenes and the problem of its relation to α-glyceryl ethers has been studied by means of compounds labeled with isotopic carbon ^{14}C [118–120].

E. Biogenesis of Thioethers

The naturally occurring compounds containing the C—S—C group are of the same type as the analogous oxygen compounds. Some alkyl thioethers may be mentioned: dialkyl sulfides (such as dimethyl sulfide (18)), dimethyl propiothetin (17), and methionine (1). An enzyme from kidney methylates thiopurines and thiopyrimidines by methyl transfer from S-adenosyl methionine (2) [121].

Belonging to the group of O,S-acetals are the mustard-oil glycosides (e.g. glucotropeolin (20)); sulfur heterocycles are biotin (21) and thiamine (22) [122].

Dimethyl propiothetin (17) which was first found in algae is the source of dimethyl sulfide (18) produced by several algae and molds (reaction 17) [123].

$$(CH_3)_2\overset{+}{S}CH_2CH_2COOH \longrightarrow (CH_3)_2S + CH_2{=}CHCOOH + H^+ \qquad (17)$$
$$\qquad (17) \qquad\qquad\qquad (18) \qquad\qquad (19)$$

An enzyme which catalyzes this reaction has been detected [124]. A widely distributed enzyme which has been purified from horse [125] and rat [126] liver is capable of transferring the methyl group of 17 to homocysteine, thus producing methionine.

Certain molds which were cultivated on sterile media containing sodium selenate or potassium tellurite, produced dimethyl selenide [127] and dimethyl telluride [128], respectively. Presumably a selenium or tellurium analog of 17 occurs as an intermediate.

An account has been given of a series of S-substituted cysteine derivatives occurring in plants [129]. Possible ways for the biogenesis of mustard-oil glucosides were discussed [21]. Recently it has been shown that L-phenylalanine, with the exception of its carboxyl group, is entirely incorporated by *Tropaeolum majus* L into glucotropaeolin (20) [130]. Biotin (21) is formed in biosynthesis from pimelic acid, carbamyl phosphate, and cysteine [131,132]. Also the sulfur atom in the thiazole part of thiamine (22) probably originates from cysteine [133]. Similarly it is assumed that the thiazolidine and the dihydrothiazine rings of antibiotics like penicillin and cephalosporine C are formed through cyclization and subsequent oxidation of peptides containing cysteine[134].

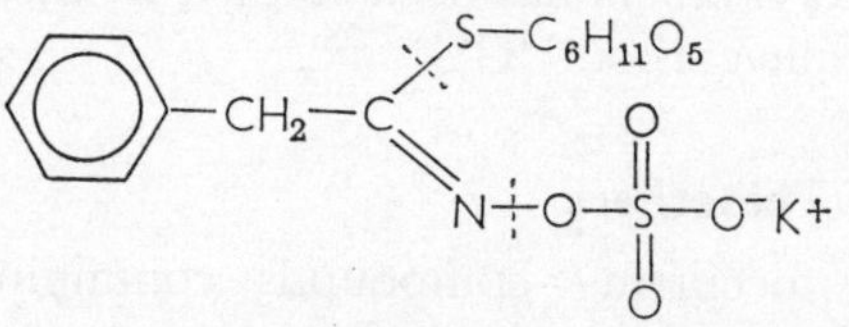

(20)

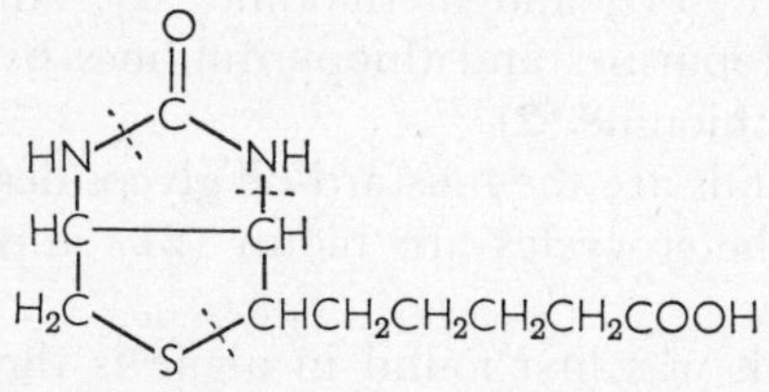

(21)

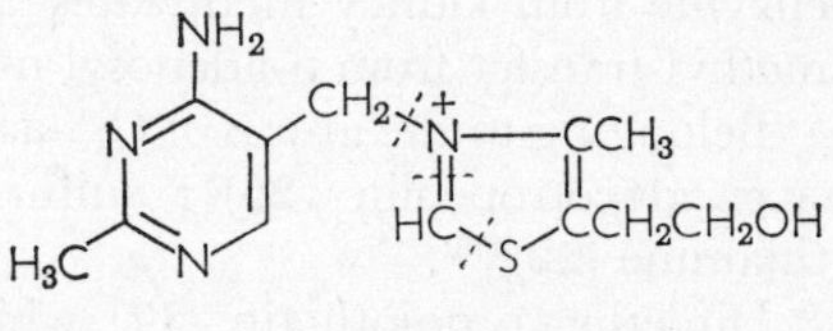

(22)

III. REACTIONS OF THE C—O—C GROUPING

A. Dealkylation

Enzymes, capable of cleaving O-methyl bonds in phenolic ethers, have been observed in liver microsomes of higher animals (rabbits, rats, mice, chickens, pigs, cattle, and sheep)[135, 136] and in microorganisms (reaction 18)[137].

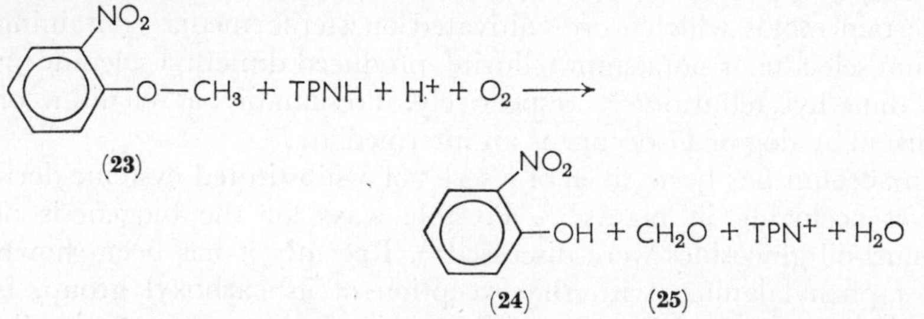

(23)

(24)   (25)   (18)

They are related to the hydroxylases and reach their maximum activity only when both TPNH *and* DPNH are present[138]. Nothing is known as yet about the intermediates. The only established fact is that the methyl carbon atom is liberated in the form of formaldehyde (25).

Among the substrates which have been tested are *o*-nitroanisole (**23**), codeine, 4,4'-dimethoxydiethylstilbestrol, ferreirine, and a series of methylated isoflavones, among them biochanine A[136].

An *S*-demethylating activity is also found in liver microsomes. This, however, contrary to the *O*-demethylase, is unaffected by certain inhibitors such as the diethylaminoethanol ester of diphenylpropylacetic acid[139]. From demethylation of methionine, homocysteine and formaldehyde are obtained[140], and from the cleavage of the enol ether group of choline lysoplasmalogen an aldehyde[141] is produced besides the α-glycerophosphorylcholine, by an enzyme obtained from rat liver. Little is known about the degradation of the α-glyceryl ethers[142,143].

B. Hydrolysis and Transfer of O- and S-Glycosides

The great number of natural products containing glycosidic bonds has been referred to in section I. As each of these is synthesized by a specific enzyme, the number of the glycoside-cleaving enzymes is as large. The glycosidases belong to the category of the longest known and best studied enzymes. Nevertheless, it is still impossible at present to describe a common reaction mechanism or even to explain fully the function of all these enzymes, which differ both in their structure and mode of action. Thus we have to restrain our description to several special characteristics of these enzymes. Among these are the specificity towards the glycon, aglycon and acceptor, the transglycosidation, the groups on the enzyme-protein which are essential for the catalytic activity, the question whether the bond cleaved is the one between the glycoside-oxygen and the glycon or the aglycon, and the configuration of the reaction products. Finally, several attempts for the interpretation of the reaction mechanism will be described.

I. Specificity

The specificity of the glycosidases is rigorous only in regard to the configuration of the glycosidic carbon atom. The features which will determine, to a different degree in various enzymes, whether a potential substrate will be affected are the following: the structure of the glycons and that of the glycosidic monomers; the site of linkage on the aglycon; the chain-length of the substrate; the chain lengths of the sequences.

Other points of interest regarding the enzyme activity are: whether the substrate is attached at the inner part of the chain (*endo*), or at the chain-end (*exo*), and whether a branch or a bond near a branching point is cleaved.

α-Amylases[144] cleave at random the α-1,4-linkages of amylose, amylopectin, glycogen, and low molecular weight α-1,4-oligosaccharides with *n* greater than two. The decomposition products of amylose are maltose and maltotriose. Since the α-1,6-branches in amylopectin and glycogen are not attacked, in the course of the decomposition by α-amylase, maltose, maltotriose, and so called 'grenz dextrins' such as 6³-α-glycosyl maltotriose and 6³-α-maltosylmaltotriose remain[145]. At higher enzyme concentration, formation of glucose was also reported.

β-Amylases[146] split maltose units off the nonreducing ends of amylose, amylopectin, glycogen, and linear oligosaccharides, so that maltose, maltotriose, and 'grenz dextrins' are produced. The latter may have a high molecular weight, in contrast to those produced by α-amylase.

Dextranases[147] hydrolyze α-1,6-glucosidic linkages in sequences as they occur in dextrans; but not, however, at branched sites and not when isolated. The attack with enzymes from microorganisms proceeds in a random manner and mainly isomaltose is formed, together with some isomaltotriose and glucose. On the other hand, enzymes produced from the organs of mammals attack the chain terminals and glucose is obtained[148].

Cellulases[149] hydrolyze cellulose, carboxymethylcellulose, and lower oligosaccharides (also cellobiose)[150]. In the case of very short chains the attack on the nonreducing ends predominates; it becomes random with longer chains[151].

Pectinases[147,152] cleave, according to their origin, pectin or pectic acid. Both a stepwise and a random degradation of methylated α-1,4-galacturonic acid polymers has been observed[153].

Lysozymes (muramidases)[154,155] hydrolyze cell walls of bacteria and chitin. Probably a β-1,4-glucosamine bond is involved in the cleavage, although α- or β-*N*-acetylglucosaminides do not act as substrates[156].

Hyaluronidases[157] break down hyaluronic acid, chondroitin, and chondroitin sulfate. The enzymes extracted from testes and snake venom function as *endo*hexosaminidases. The end-products are tetra- and hexasaccharides, etc., which are formed by transfer[158]. When hyaluronic acid is cleaved by enzymes obtained from bacteria, an unsaturated disaccharide, 2-acetamido-2-desoxy-3-*O*-(β-D-gluco-4-ene-pyranosyluronic acid)-D-glucose, is produced[159]. The enzyme from leaches acts on the other hand as an endoglucurunidase and cleaves hyaluronic acid only[160]. The product is a tetrasaccharide with D-glucuronic acid at the reducing end.

Glucamylases[161] are enzymes which split single glucose units from the nonreducing end of α-1,4-oligo- and polysaccharides. These enzymes are abundant in many microorganisms.

Cyclodextrinase (cyclodextringlycosyltransferase)[162,163] obtained from *Bacillus macerans* breaks down amylose and amylopectin and produces from the fragments the so-called Schardinger dextrins.

Amylo-1,4 → 1,6-transglucosidases (*'branching enzymes'* or *'Q-enzymes'*)[161,163] cleave a certain part of a linear α-1,4-glucosidic chain (which, however, must have a minimal length), and transfer this to a primary hydroxyl group of another amylose chain, thus producing a new α-1,6 branching. Maltose can act as an acceptor only in exceptional cases[164].

Debranching enzymes[149] have a specificity for α-1,6-glucosidic bonds at branching sites. Depending on their origin they attack a large variety of substrates as shown by the data of Table 3[161,165].

The glycosidases which attack oligo- and heterosaccharides possess a high specificity for the sugar at the nonreducing end, and are named and divided into groups according to this specificity. In those groups, further subdivision may again be made according to their specificity towards the aglycon and especially towards the acceptors.

Substrates for these enzymes may be synthesized in almost unlimited variations with differing substitutions. It is hence possible to define, with the help of these materials, the enzyme specificity in the most detailed manner. For example more than forty potential substrates have been tested with β-galactosidase from *Escherichia coli* ML 309[174].

(X denoting various substituents)

Among the *α-1,4-glucosidases* (maltases)[175] the best studied are those extracted from *Saccharomyces cerevisiae*[176] and *Saccharomyces italicus Y* 1225[177]. Their specificity is very distinct for the glycon part but less so regarding the aglycon. According to their origin, the

TABLE 3. Enzymes with specificity for α-1,6-glucosidic linkages.

Enzyme	Source	Substrate	Products	Materials not affected	Ref.
Amylo-1,6-glucosidase	Muscle	Phosphorylase–limit dextrin	Glucose + dextrin	Glycogen, amylo-pectin	166
R-Enzyme	Potatoes, beans, malt	Amylopectin and its limit dextrins	Linear amylo-saccharides	Glycogen, isomaltose, panose, glycogen and β-amylase limit dextrins	167
Pullulanase	Aerobacter aerogenes	Pullulan, glycogen, glycogen and β-amylase limit dextrins, 6^3-α-maltosylmaltotriose	Maltotriose, dextrins	Isomaltose, panose	168, 169
Isoamylase	Yeast	Glycogen, amylopectin, limit dextrin, isomaltose	Linear amylo-saccharides	—	170
Limit dextrinase	Malt, molds	α-Amylase limit dextrin, isomaltose, panose	Glucose, maltose, maltotriose	Amylopectin, glycogen (?)	171, 172
Oligo-1,6-glucosidase	Intestine	α-Amylase limit dextrin, isomaltose, panose	Glucose, maltose, maltotriose	Phosphorylase limit dextrins	173

enzymes behave differently in the transfer reactions[165,178,179]. In some cases α-1,4-linked sugars (maltotriose and maltotetrose) are produced exclusively. In other cases α-1,6 linkages are formed by the transfer, as with the previously mentioned amylo-1,4 → 1,6-trans-glucosidases. The enzymes from *Aspergillus oryzae*[178,180], *Cladophora rupestris*[181], *Tetrahymena pyriformis*[182], and brewer's yeast[183,184] transfer both to the $C_{(4)}$ atom and to the $C_{(6)}$ atom of the acceptors (glucose and maltose).

The specificities of *glucosido invertase*[185], *trehalase*[186], *α-mannosidase*[187], *α-galactosidase*[188], *α-fucosidase*[189], and *neuraminidase*[190] are characterized by their names. An enzyme from *Patella vulgata*[191] hydrolyzes both α-glucuronides and α-galacturonides, hence it is nonspecific in regard to the configuration of the $C_{(4)}$ hydroxyl of the glycon. The transfer action of *α-galactosidases* was thoroughly investigated[192].

The *β-glucosidase* of almonds[193] which is the main component of emulsin similarly splits β-galactosides. But the β-glucosidase obtained from *Rhodotorula minute*[194] is specific concerning the $C_{(4)}$-hydroxyl and its configuration, but nonspecific regarding the substitution at the $C_{(2)}$ atom (mannose is strongly bound by the enzyme).

The *β-galactosidase* from *Escherichia coli*[195] responds to the methylation of any of the hydroxyl groups at the $C_{(2)}$, $C_{(3)}$, $C_{(4)}$, or $C_{(6)}$ atoms, with complete loss or considerable reduction of its activity against such substrates. Yet the CH_2OH group at the $C_{(5)}$ atom may be replaced by a hydrogen or methyl group with at least partial retention of the cleaving power. Phenyl β-D-galactofuranoside is not hydrolyzed[196]. In the case of the thiogalactosides it has been observed that the alkyl-substituted derivatives are not hydrolyzed at all, and that nitrophenyl derivatives are cleaved to an appreciable extent only in the presence of very high enzyme concentrations[197]. The relative rates of cleavage of the isomers 1,6-, 1,4-, 1,3-, and 1,2-β-D-galactosidoglucose are[198] 13·9:10·7:4·3:1. The same sequence with β-galactosidase from calf intestine[199] gives the ratios 1:56:61:65. In the transfer reaction where phenyl-β-D-galactoside is the substrate mainly 1,6- and 1,4-linkages are formed with glucose as the acceptor, and 1,6- and 1,3-bonds are produced with galactose as acceptor[200]. When the incubation periods are very short, and especially with *o*-nitrophenyl-β-D-fucoside or *o*-nitrophenyl-α-L-arabinoside as substrates, the transfer is almost exclusively directed to galactose and not to water (i.e. hydrolysis). Presumably, the most important biological function of the transfer action of β-galactosidase is the role which it plays in induced enzyme synthesis[201].

The substrate-specificity in the hydrolysis with the two above-mentioned enzymes can be presented in a simplified way as follows:

Substrate specificity of

β-Glucosidase from almonds   β-Galactosidase from *E. coli*

(X = H, CH₃, CH₂OH, CH₂Halogen)   (X = H, CH₃, CH₂OH)

Other enzymes capable of splitting the *β-O*-glycosidic linkage are the *β-N-acetylglucosaminidase*[187, 202], *β-glucuronidase*[203], *β-fructofuranosidase* (invertase)[204], *β-mannosidase*[187], and *β-fucosidase*[205]. An enzyme abundant in animals, plants, and microorganisms, namely *β-thioglucosidase*[206, 207], cleaves a great number of *β-O-* and *β-S*-glycosides, especially heterosides.

Sucrose is the substrate for three other enzymes which synthesize polysaccharides of high molecular weight via transfer reactions. *Levansucrase*[208] transfers the fructosyl fragment; the resulting polymer (levan) contains predominantly β-2,6-linkages with a smaller number of β-2,1-bonds. No levan is produced in cases where the fructose part of the sucrose is substituted at $C_{(1)}$, $C_{(3)}$, or $C_{(6)}$[209]. The same enzyme can also transfer the fructose moiety from β-fructofuranosides to the hydroxyl group of the anomeric carbon-atom of another sugar; for this the $C_{(2)}$ and $C_{(3)}$ atoms of the acceptor must have the configuration of D- or L-threose, but variations on the $C_{(4)}$, $C_{(5)}$, or $C_{(6)}$ atoms, on the other hand, do not affect the activity of the acceptor[210]. *Dextransucrase*[211] transfers the glucoside part of sucrose to α-1,6-linkages, with some formation of branches in α-1,3- and α-1,4-bonds. This enzyme also exhibits interesting specificity towards acceptors[212].

By the action of *amylosucrase*[213] fructose is liberated, and a glucosyl polymer with α-1,4-linkages is formed.

Finally, oligosaccharide syntheses by glycosidases in concentrated monosaccharide solutions should be mentioned[200, 214, 215].

2. Structure

Of the previously mentioned enzymes, twelve have so far been obtained in crystalline form: these are α-amylase from human saliva[216] and pancreas[217], from swine[218] and rat[219] pancreas, barley malt[220], *Aspergillus candidus*[221], *Aspergillus oryzae*[222], *Bacillus coagulans*[223], *Bacillus subtilis*[224], *Pseudomonas saccharophila*[225], and *Bacillus stearothermophilus*[226]; β-amylase from potatoes[227], barley[228], wheat[229], and soybeans[230]; cellulase from *Irpex lacteus*[231]; xylanase from *Bacillus*[232]; β-galactosidase from *Escherichia coli* K 12[233], ML 308[234], and ML 309[235]; glucamylase from *Aspergillus niger*[236]; β-glucuronidase from calf liver[237] and *Helix pomatia*[238]; limit dextrinase from *Aspergillus oryzae*[171]; lysozyme from egg-white[239], papaya-latex[240], *Bacillus subtilis*[241], and rabbit spleen[242]; maltase from *Aspergillus oryzae*[243]; neuraminidase from *Vibrio cholerae*[244,245] and trehalase from *Neurospora crassa*[246].

The molecular weights of these enzymes vary between wide limits: 20,000 is the order of magnitude found for lysozymes[247] and neuraminidase[244]; 50,000 was found for α-amylases[144]. For β-amylase from potatoes[248] the determined molecular weight is 152,000, and for β-galactosidase from *E. coli*[249], 518,000. Dissociation into smaller units was characteristic of β-galactosidase under denaturing conditions[250]. The pH for optimal activity, and the isoelectric point for many of the glycosidases, lies in the range of five to seven. Many of these enzymes contain, even in the purified state, carbohydrates which are probably covalently bonded (cf. α-amylase[251]). The amino acid composition has been determined for various α-amylases[144], β-galactosidases from *E. coli*[252], and for several lysozymes[154]. End-group analyses were performed for α-amylases[253], β-galactosidase[252], and lysozyme[154]. The amino acid sequence has been elucidated in the case of the last enzyme[155]. Little is known about the functional groups, but evidence exists for many enzymes, that the presence of both a basic and an acidic group is essential for the catalytic function, e.g. a primary amino and a carboxyl group in the α-amylases[144], or an imidazol and a sulfhydryl group in the β-galactosidase[195]. α-Amylases need calcium ions, probably in order to stabilize the enzymatically active chain conformations. β-Galactosidase is activated by alkali-metal, magnesium, or manganese ions[254].

3. Mechanism[96–99]

Regarding the reaction mechanisms it was shown for a series of glycosidases that the bond cleaved is that between the $C_{(1)}$ atom of the glycon and the glycosidic oxygen. This has been proved for α-amylase[255], β-amylase[256], α-glucosidase[257], β-glucosidase[258], β-galactosidase[259], β-glucuronidase[260], and β-fructofuranosidase[261] in experiments where enzyme and substrate were incubated together in the presence of $H_2{}^{18}O$, or in some cases by use of a labeled substrate.

The problem of the configuration of the $C_{(1)}$ atom of the sugar which is released during hydrolysis or transfer has attracted much effort. Two enzymes are known (β-amylase[262] and *Rhizopus delemar-glucamylase*[263]) which cause inversion, i.e. the sugars released are β-maltose and β-glucose, respectively. In all other cases tested (α-amylase[262], amylosucrase[213,264], dextransucrase, dextrandextrinase[265], Q enzyme[266]; transglucosidase from *Aspergillus oryzae*[267], α-glucosidase, β-glucosidase[268], and β-galactosidase[269]), the configuration of the anomeric carbon atom is retained.

The reaction catalyzed by glycosidases can be presented as reaction (19). If AOH = H_2O, the reaction is a hydrolysis, if AOH is an

$$\text{Glycosyl—O—R} + \text{AO*H} \rightleftharpoons \text{Glycosyl—O*—A} + \text{ROH} \qquad (19)$$

alcohol or a sugar, a transfer results. Considering the polarity of the $C_{(1)}$—O bond, a nucleophilic substitution on the glycosyl $C_{(1)}$ atom seems likely. An S_N1 reaction, as has been shown to occur in the acid-catalyzed hydrolysis of glycosides[270], is also conceivable in the enzyme-catalyzed reaction. In the intermediate the $C_{(1)}$ atom of the glycon would be positively charged; the configuration of the products must be explained by consideration of additional factors like the geometry of the sites of bonding in the substrate and in AOH[255]. However, for most glycosidases, an S_N2 mechanism seems more likely, especially when considering all the known facts and evidence obtained about other transfer enzymes. Inversion at the $C_{(1)}$ carbon is then explained by a single step bimolecular nucleophilic substitution ('single displacement'), e.g. reaction (20) of an α-glucoside.

Retention of configuration at the $C_{(1)}$ atom, on the other hand, is explained by a two-stage S_N2 reaction ('double displacement'), where the postulated intermediate consists of a glycosyl–enzyme compound. Since the enzyme probably contains both a nucleophilic (N:) and an electrophilic (H—X) function, the following description can be deduced; it is again exemplified by an α-glycoside reaction (reaction 21).

$$\text{(21)}$$

C. Phosphorolysis of O-Glycosides

The distinction between phosphorylases and glycosidases is more justifiable from the practical point of view than from any fundamental one. The same reaction equation applies to both cases, with AOH being either phosphoric acid or a phosphate. In the phosphorolytic cleavage of a glycoside the bond energy of the glycosidic linkage is preserved in the phosphoric acid ester group, as it is in the case of transfer of a glycosidic fragment to another acceptor. Since water may act as an acceptor in the reaction of glycosidases, and is present in high concentration in all cases, all glycosidic linkages are finally hydrolyzed by glycosidases unless limited by specificity factors. On the other hand, water acts as a very poor substrate, if at all, in phosphorylase reactions[271]. Hence the latter remain reversible as long as no other enzyme attacks the substrate or the products, for example by hydrolysis of the phosphoric acid ester. Thus the phosphorylases capable of splitting O-glycosidic linkages will be surveyed, stressing the same points as with the glycosidases (see introduction to section III.B).

I. Specificity

The widely distributed polysaccharide phosphorylase[272] degrades polysaccharides with α-1,4-glucosidic linkages, such as glycogen and starch. Phosphate may be substituted by arsenate[273]. In the synthesis reaction only α-D-glucose-1-phosphate was found to be active of all tested sugar-1-phosphates[274]. Acting as acceptors, for the glucosyl group (also called 'starters' in this connection), are maltotriose and higher homologs (up to polysaccharides), and also oligo- and polysaccharides with α-1,6-linkages.

The disaccharide phosphorylases abundant in microorganisms[275], sucrose[276,277], maltose[278], and cellobiose phosphorylases[279], cleave only the natural disaccharides specified in the enzyme names. They are specific for each monosaccharide phosphate (α-D-glucose-1-phosphate or β-D-glucose-1-phosphate), but relatively nonspecific for the acceptor in the synthesis. With these enzymes, phosphate may be substituted by arsenate.

The equilibrium constants for the polysaccharide phosphorylase[280] are 1·25 (pH 7·3 at 30°), for saccharose phosphorylase[281] 0·5 (pH 6·6 at 30°) and for maltose and cellobiose phosphorylase[282] 4·4 (pH 7·0 at 37°).

2. Structure

The polysaccharide phosphorylases from rabbit[283] and crab muscles[284] have been crystallized. The 'phosphorylase a' from rabbit muscle[285] has a molecular weight of 495,000, contains four phosphoserin groups and binds four pyridoxal-5'-phosphate molecules. By the action of a specific phosphatase ('PR enzyme')[286] it is transformed into 'phosphorylase b', the molecular weight of which is 242,000 and which contains no serine-bound phosphate. A specific kinase changes phosphorylase b, through phosphorylation with ATP, into phosphorylase a again[287]. Phosphorylase b and also phosphorylase b' (obtained from phosphorylase a by the action of trypsin[288]) need AMP for activation.

In contrast the phosphorylase obtained from potatoes[289] contains no phosphoserine groups, and needs no AMP for activation, but uses pyridoxal phosphate. This is obviously linked to an ε-amino group of a lysine residue[290]. The inhibition by —SH reagents[291,292] and the amino acid sequence in the vicinity of the serine phosphate function of muscle phosphorylase have been studied[288]:

$$\begin{array}{c} \text{P} \\ | \\ \text{Lys—Gln—Ile—Ser—Val—Arg} \end{array}$$

Phosphorylases, like glycosidases, split the bond between the glycon $C_{(1)}$ atom and the glycosidic oxygen[293]. The configuration at the anomeric carbon atom is retained in the reaction of polysaccharide[294] and sucrose phosphorylases[276], but is inverted in the reaction of maltose[278] and cellobiose phosphorylase[295].

Of these four phosphorylases, sucrose phosphorylase is the only one to exhibit the following interesting features: incubation of the enzyme with glucose-1-phosphate and ^{32}P-phosphate[296], or with sucrose and ^{14}C-fructose[297], results in isotopic exchange. In addition the enzyme catalyzes the arsenolysis of sucrose even in the absence of an acceptor.

3. Mechanism

From these data it is clear that for polysaccharide phosphorylase neither a 'single displacement' (since the configuration at $C_{(1)}$ is retained), nor a 'double displacement' (since no isotope exchange takes place) is accepted. The simplest interpretation would be a substitution mechanism, in which the approaching and the leaving nucleophilic groups will do so from the *same* side, involving a 'front-side attack'[96].

The most probable mechanism for the sucrose phosphorylase is a double exchange in which an intermediate glycosyl–enzyme complex is formed. A 'single displacement' mechanism, of the kind described for glycosidases, satisfactorily accounts for the reactions of maltose and cellobiose phosphorylases.

4. Regulation[298, 299]

As explained for the regulation of glycogen synthetase (section II.B), two mechanisms were suggested for the activation of the kinase which is responsible for the transformation shown by reaction (22),

$$\text{Phosphorylase } b \longrightarrow \text{Phosphorylase } a \qquad (22)$$

namely, through cyclic 3',5'-AMP, the formation of which is accelerated by adrenaline, together with a protein, or by calcium ions, together with another protein.

D. Enzyme-catalyzed Mutarotation

It is generally assumed that the mutarotation of sugars proceeds through an open-chain intermediate[316]. An enzyme, aldose 1-epimerase (mutarotase), accelerates this reaction[301, 302]. Little is known about the physiological function of this enzyme. In the general acid–base-catalyzed mutarotation in $H_2{}^{18}O$ no exchange of ^{18}O takes place at the hydroxyl group of the $C_{(1)}$ of the aldose[315]. Therefore it is necessary to conclude that the open-chain form of the sugar is an intermediate of the mutarotation reaction (see, for example, glucose in reaction (23)). Similarly, it can be assumed that the open-chain form (27) is also an intermediate in the enzyme-catalyzed reaction. In this case one of the physiological functions of the enzyme could be to catalyze the opening of the cyclic hemiacetal, if in some further reactions only the carbonyl form could be used as a substrate. Another insight into the mechanism of the enzymic mutarotation of sugars was possible by the experiments with $H_2^{18}O$ as a solvent. No exchange of ^{18}O occurred at the anomeric carbon atom[300]. Thus one may conclude that, in the enzyme-catalyzed mutarotation, ring opening of the hemiacetal must indeed occur, but that neither hydration of the open-chain

α-D-Glucopyranose   D-Glucose   β-D-Glucopyranose

(26)   (27)   (28)

form nor Schiff base formation takes place. Polarographic measurements have recently shown, however, that in the mutarotation reaction, catalyzed by aldose 1-epimerase from *E. coli*, formation of a reducible open-chain form is not accelerated[303]. Therefore it is concluded that the reaction proceeds as shown by reaction (24). The nature of the

α-D-Aldose + Enzyme $\rightleftharpoons$ D-Aldose–Enzyme $\rightleftharpoons$ β-D-Aldose + Enzyme   (24)

enzyme–substrate complex is still unknown. As a matter of fact, aldose 1-epimerase from *E. coli* is inhibited by 10^{-6} M *p*-CMB. Thus S—H groups may participate in the catalysis. In this case it is possible that the intermediate has the structure of a thiol hemiacetal[303]. A thiol hemiacetal–enzyme complex has yet to be isolated.

Aldose 1-epimerase is found in *Penicillium notatum*[300,306], in various mutants of *E. coli*[304], and in many animal organs[305]. The highest activities are observed in kidneys and crystalline lenses of mammals. The purification of this enzyme from *P. notatum*[306], hog kidney[307], and *E. coli* K 12[308] has been described.

All the enzymes mentioned have a high specificity for glucose and galactose. Sugars with other configurations of the hydroxyl groups at $C_{(2)}$ or $C_{(3)}$ are very slowly anomerized, if at all. The polarimetric analysis of the mutarotation of D-ribose shows that the reaction consists of at least two steps; because the rotation values reach a maximum and decrease with time. Only one of these steps is accelerated by the enzyme of *E. coli*[303]. Glucose-6-phosphate isomerase from yeast catalyzes the mutarotation of α-D-glucopyranose-6-phosphate to a higher extent than that of α-D-glucose[309]. It should be noted that the general acid–base-catalyzed mutarotation of sugar phosphates is faster by two powers of ten than that of the free sugars. Since inorganic phosphate is known to catalyze the mutarotation[310], one might describe the above catalysis as an 'intramolecular' one.

The aldose 1-epimerase is inhibited competitively by many mono- and some disaccharides, as well as by a few glycosides. In animal organs both the ability for active transport of sugars and the glucose consumption are often parallel to the aldose 1-epimerase activity. Since the inhibitory constants for phlorizin are almost the same in relation to active sugar transport and aldose 1-epimerase activity in hog kidney cortex, it is concluded that aldose 1-epimerase participates in the control of sugar transport and consumption[305]. The interdependence between the occurrence of aldose 1-epimerase and cataractogenic sugars in the lens has also been discussed[311].

Some enzymes exhibit a high specificity for the configuration of the anomeric carbon atom as, for example, the glucose dehydrogenase from liver[312], the glucose oxidase from *P. notatum*[302], the galactose dehydrogenase from *Pseudomonas saccharophila*[269], and the glucose 6-phosphate dehydrogenase from yeast[309]. All these enzymes are highly β specific. On the other hand, the galactokinase from yeast is α specific[313]. The glucose-phosphate isomerase from yeast has a greater affinity to the open-chain form than to the cyclic hemiacetal form of its substrate, and the hexokinase from yeast phosphorylates both α- and β-glucose[309].

The main significance of aldose 1-epimerase may be its ability to catalyze the reversible transformation of the free or phosphorylated sugars to their anomers. This would mean that the enzyme is a controlling factor in the hexose or hexose phosphate metabolism.

It may be pointed out that the catalytic effect of the most purified preparations of aldose 1-epimerase from *E. coli* is higher by about nine powers of ten, compared with multifunctional ions, e.g. phosphate[303]. One should keep this also in mind in discussions of catalysis mechanisms of so-called enzyme models, e.g. '2-hydroxypyridine'[314].

IV. REFERENCES

1. J. S. Brimacombe and M. Stacey in *Comparative Biochemistry*, Vol. 4 (Ed. M. Florkin and H. S. Mason), Academic Press, New York, 1962, p. 27.
2. M. Stacey and S. A. Barker, *Polysaccharides of Microorganisms*, Clarendon Press, Oxford, 1960.

3. G. Neumüller in *Handbuch der Pflanzenphysiologie*, Vol. 6 (Ed. W. Ruhland), Springer-Verlag, Berlin, 1958, p. 252.
4. F. A. Henglein in *Handbuch der Pflanzenphysiologie*, Vol. 6 (Ed. W. Ruhland), Springer-Verlag, Berlin, 1958, p. 405.
5. J. S. Brimacombe and J. M. Webber, *Mucopolysaccharides*, Elsevier Publishing Co., Amsterdam, 1964.
6. M. J. How, J. S. Brimacombe, and M. Stacey in *Advances in Carbohydrate Chemistry*, Vol. 19 (Ed. M. L. Wolfrom and R. S. Tipson), Academic Press, New York, 1964, p. 303.
7. M. R. J. Salton, *The Bacterial Cell Wall*, Elsevier Publishing Co., Amsterdam, 1964.
8. E. Kabat, *Blood Group Substances*, Academic Press, New York, 1956.
9. F. F. Nord and W. J. Schubert in *Comparative Biochemistry*, Vol. 4 (Ed. M. Florkin and H. S. Mason), Academic Press, New York, 1962, p. 5.
10. F. Shafizadeh and M. L. Wolfrom in *Handbuch der Pflanzenphysiologie*, Vol. 6 (Ed. W. Ruhland), Springer-Verlag, Berlin, 1958, pp. 10, 63.
11. D. J. Bell in *Comparative Biochemistry*, Vol. 3 (Ed. M. Florkin and H. S. Mason), Academic Press, New York, 1962, p. 288.
12. A. Stoll and E. Jucker in *Handbuch der Pflanzenphysiologie*, Vol. 6 (Ed. W. Ruhland), Springer-Verlag, Berlin, 1958, p. 534.
13. T. Reichstein in *Fourth International Congress of Biochemistry*, Vol. 1, Pergamon Press, Oxford, 1958, p. 124.
14. T. Posternak, *Les Cyclitols, Chimie, Biochimie, Biologie*, Hermann, Paris, 1962.
15. P. Schwarze in *Handbuch der Pflanzenphysiologie*, Vol. 10 (Ed. W. Ruhland), Springer-Verlag, Berlin, 1958, p. 507.
16. T. A. Geissman in *Comprehensive Biochemistry*, Vol. 9 (Ed. M. Florkin and E. H. Stotz), Elsevier Publishing Co., Amsterdam, 1963, p. 215.
17. M. M. Rapport and W. T. Norton, *Ann. Rev. Biochem.*, **31**, 103 (1962).
18. D. J. Hanahan and G. A. Thompson, Jr., *Ann. Rev. Biochem.*, **32**, 215 (1963).
19. I. M. Dean, *Naturally Occurring Oxygen Ring Compounds*, Butterworths, London, 1963.
20. F. Challenger, *Aspects of the Organic Chemistry of Sulphur*, Butterworths, London, 1959.
21. A. Kjaer in *Fortschritte der Chemie organischer Naturstoffe*, Vol. 18 (Ed. L. Zechmeister), Springer-Verlag, Vienna, 1960, p. 122.
22. D. M. Greenberg in *Advances in Enzymology*, Vol. 25 (Ed. F. F. Nord), Interscience Publishers, New York, 1963, p. 395.
23. S. H. Mudd and G. L. Cantoni in *Comprehensive Biochemistry*, Vol. 15 (Ed. M. Florkin and E. H. Stotz), Elsevier Publishing Co., Amsterdam, 1964, p. 1.
24. G. L. Cantoni in *Comparative Biochemistry*, Vol. 1 (Ed. M. Florkin and H. S. Mason), Academic Press, New York, 1960, p. 181.
25. G. L. Cantoni, *J. Biol. Chem.*, **204**, 403 (1953).
26. R. Kuhn and H. Trischmann, *Ann. Chem.*, **611**, 117 (1958).
27. Reference 23, p. 31.
28. G. de la Haba and G. L. Cantoni, *J. Biol. Chem.*, **234**, 603 (1959).
29. H. Weissbach and H. Dickerman, *Physiol. Rev.*, **45**, 80 (1965).
30. J. R. Guest, S. Friedman, and D. D. Woods, *Nature*, **195**, 340 (1962).

31. J. R. Guest, C. W. Helleiner, M. J. Cross, and D. D. Woods, *Biochem. J.*, **76**, 396 (1960).
32. J. Axelrod and R. Tomchick, *J. Biol. Chem.*, **233**, 702 (1958).
33. M. S. Masri, A. N. Booth, and F. DeEds, *Biochim. Biophys. Acta*, **65**, 495 (1962).
34. J. D. Mann, H. M. Fales, and S. H. Mudd, *J. Biol. Chem.*, **238**, 3820 (1964).
35. B. J. Finkle and M. S. Masri, *Biochim. Biophys. Acta*, **78**, 747 (1963).
36. B. J. Finkle and M. S. Masri, *Biochim. Biophys. Acta*, **85**, 167 (1964).
37. D. Hess, *Z. Naturforsch.*, **19b**, 447 (1964).
38. S. Gatenbeck and V. Brunsberg, *Acta Chem. Scand.*, **18**, 2061 (1964).
39. H. Shimazono, *Arch. Biochem. Biophys.*, **83**, 206 (1959).
40. N. V. Thoai, Y. Robin, and C. Audit, *Biochim. Biophys. Acta*, **93**, 264 (1964).
41. J. Axelrod and H. Weissbach, *Science*, **131**, 1312 (1960).
42. J. Axelrod, R. J. Wurtman, and S. H. Snyder, *J. Biol. Chem.*, **240**, 949 (1965).
43. K. Tomita, C. J. M. Cha, and H. A. Lardy, *J. Biol. Chem.*, **239**, 1202 (1964).
44. E. Leete in *Biogenesis of Natural Compounds* (Ed. P. Bernfeld), Pergamon Press, Oxford, 1963, p. 739.
45. G. de la Haba, G. A. Jamieson, S. H. Mudd, and H. H. Richards, *J. Am. Chem. Soc.*, **81**, 3975 (1959).
46. S. H. Mudd, *J. Biol. Chem.*, **234**, 87, 1784 (1959).
47. S. H. Mudd and G. L. Cantoni, *J. Biol. Chem.*, **231**, 481 (1958).
48. L. W. Parks, *J. Biol. Chem.*, **232**, 169 (1958).
49. J. A. Stekol in *Advances in Enzymology*, Vol. 25 (Ed. F. F. Nord), Interscience Publishers, New York, 1963, p. 369.
50. M. L. Scott in *Mineral Metabolism*, Vol. 2B (Ed. C. L. Comar and F. Bronner), Academic Press, New York, 1962, p. 543.
51. C. E. Cardini, A. C. Paladini, R. Caputto, and L. F. Leloir, *Nature*, **165**, 191 (1950).
52. J. T. Park and M. J. Johnson, *J. Biol. Chem.*, **179**, 585 (1949).
53. R. Caputto, L. F. Leloir, C. E. Cardini, and A. C. Paladini, *J. Biol. Chem.*, **184**, 333 (1950).
54. J. T. Park, *J. Biol. Chem.*, **194**, 877, 885, 897 (1952).
55. W. Z. Hassid, E. F. Neufeld, and D. S. Feingold, *Proc. Nat. Acad. Sci. U.S.*, **45**, 905 (1959).
56. L. F. Leloir and C. E. Cardini in *The Enzymes*, Vol. 2 (Ed. P. D. Boyer, H. Lardy, and K. Myrbäck), Academic Press, New York, 1960, p. 39.
57. E. Cabib, *Ann. Rev. Biochem.*, **32**, 321 (1963).
58. L. F. Leloir, *Proceedings of the Plenary Sessions*, Sixth International Congress of Biochemistry, New York, 1964, p. 15.
59. V. Ginsburg in *Advances in Enzymology*, Vol. 26 (Ed. F. F. Nord), Interscience Publishers, New York, 1964, p. 35.
60. D. S. Feingold, E. F. Neufeld, and W. Z. Hassid, *J. Biol. Chem.*, **234**, 488 (1959).
61. S. B. Zimmerman, S. R. Kornberg, and A. Kornberg, *J. Biol. Chem.*, **237**, 512 (1962).
62. E. Cabib and L. F. Leloir, *J. Biol. Chem.*, **231**, 259 (1958).
63. C. E. Cardini, L. F. Leloir, and J. Chiriboga, *J. Biol. Chem.*, **214**, 149 (1955).
64. J. Mendicino, *J. Biol. Chem.*, **235**, 3347 (1960).

65. J. E. Gander, W. E. Petersen, and P. D. Boyer, *Arch. Biochem. Biophys.*, **69**, 85 (1957).
66. W. M. Watkins and W. Z. Hassid, *J. Biol. Chem.*, **237**, 1432 (1962).
67. G. J. Dutton, *Biochem. J.*, **64**, 693 (1956); **71**, 141 (1960).
68. T. Yamaha and C. E. Cardini, *Arch. Biochem. Biophys.*, **86**, 127 (1960).
69. G. A. Barber, *Biochemistry*, **1**, 463 (1962).
70. G. A. Barber and E. F. Neufeld, *Biochem. Biophys. Res. Comm.*, **6**, 44 (1961).
71. A. D. Elbein, G. A. Barber, and W. Z. Hassid, *J. Am. Chem. Soc.*, **86**, 309 (1964).
72. L. F. Leloir and S. H. Goldemberg, *J. Biol. Chem.*, **235**, 919 (1960).
73. I. D. Algranati and E. Cabib, *J. Biol. Chem.*, **237**, 1007 (1962).
74. E. Recondo and L. F. Leloir, *Biochem. Biophys. Res. Comm.*, **6**, 85 (1961).
75. D. S. Feingold, E. F. Neufeld, and W. Z. Hassid, *J. Biol. Chem.*, **233**, 783 (1958).
76. E. Cabib and L. F. Leloir, *J. Biol. Chem.*, **206**, 779 (1954).
77. L. Glaser and D. H. Brown, *J. Biol. Chem.*, **228**, 729 (1957).
78. D. Aminoff, F. Dodyk, and S. Roseman, *J. Biol. Chem.*, **238**, PC 1177 (1963).
79. A. Markowitz, J. A. Cifonelli, and A. Dorfman, *J. Biol. Chem.*, **234**, 2343 (1959).
80. E. Ito and M. Saito, *Biochim. Biophys. Acta*, **78**, 237 (1962).
81. E. E. B. Smith, G. T. Mills, and H. P. Bernheimer, *J. Biol. Chem.*, **236**, 2179 (1961).
82. Number 14, 16, 17, 18 in *Methods in Enzymology*, Vol. 5 (Ed. S. P. Colowick and N. O. Kaplan), Academic Press, New York, 1962.
83. K. Wallenfels and H. Diekmann in *Handbuch der physiologisch- und patho-logisch-chemischen Analyse*, Vol. 6B (Ed. K. Lang and E. Lennartz), Springer-Verlag, Berlin, 1966, p. 292.
84. W. T. J. Morgan, *Proc. Roy. Soc. (London), Ser. B.*, **151**, 308 (1960).
85. H. Nikaido, *Proc. Natl. Acad. Sci. U.S.*, **48**, 1337, 1542 (1962).
86. M. J. Osborne, S. M. Rosen, L. Rothfield, and B. L. Horecker, *Proc. Natl. Acad. Sci. U.S.*, **48**, 1831 (1962).
87. A. N. Chatterjee and J. T. Park, *Proc. Natl. Acad. Sci.*, **51**, 9 (1964).
88. P. M. Meadow, J. S. Anderson, and J. L. Strominger, *Biochem. Biophys. Res. Comm.*, **14**, 382 (1964).
89. S. H. Goldemberg, *Biochim. Biophys. Acta*, **56**, 357 (1962).
90. R. C. Bean and W. Z. Hassid, *J. Am. Chem. Soc.*, **77**, 5737 (1955).
91. J. L. Strominger, E. S. Maxwell, J. Axelrod, and H. M. Kalckar, *J. Biol. Chem.*, **224**, 79 (1957).
92. R. Schmid, L. Hammaker, and J. Axelrod, *Arch. Biochem. Biophys.*, **70**, 285 (1957).
93. L. F. Leloir, J. M. Olavarrià, S. H. Goldemberg, and H. Carminatti, *Arch. Biochem. Biophys.*, **81**, 508 (1959).
94. J. Larner and F. Sanger, *J. Mol. Biol.*, **11**, 491 (1965).
95. R. Kornfeld and D. H. Brown, *J. Biol. Chem.*, **237**, 1772 (1962).
96. D. E. Koshland, Jr. in *The Mechanism of Enzyme Action* (Ed. W. D. McElroy and B. Glass), John Hopkins Press, Baltimore, 1954, p. 608.
97. D. E. Koshland, Jr. in *The Enzymes*, Vol. 1 (Ed. P. D. Boyer, H. Lardy, and K. Myrbäck), Academic Press, New York, 1959, p. 305.

98. H. M. Kalckar in *The Mechanism of Enzyme Action* (Ed. W. D. McElroy and B. Glass), Johns Hopkins Press, Baltimore, 1954, p. 675.
99. M. A. Jermyn, *Reviews of Pure and Applied Chemistry*, **11**, 92 (1961).
100. M. Rosell-Perez and J. Larner, *Biochemistry*, **1**, 769 (1962); **3**, 75 (1964).
101. D. L. Friedman and J. Larner, *Biochim. Biophys. Acta*, **64**, 185 (1962).
102. E. Belocopitow, *Arch. Biochem. Biophys.*, **93**, 458 (1961).
103. M. M. Appleman, E. Belocopitow, and H. N. Torres, *Biochem. Biophys. Res. Comm.*, **14**, 550 (1964).
104. C. Villar-Palasi and J. Larner, *Arch. Biochem.*, **94**, 436 (1961).
105. See reference 19, p. 586.
106. J. B. Harborne and N. W. Simmonds in *Biochemistry of Phenolic Compounds* (Ed. J. B. Harborne), Academic Press, New York, 1964, p. 77.
107. T. Swain and E. C. Bate-Smith in *Comparative Biochemistry*, Vol. 3 (Ed. M. Florkin and E. H. Stotz), Elsevier, Amsterdam, 1962, p. 755.
108. H. Grisebach in *Chemistry and Biochemistry of Plant Pigments* (Ed. T. W. Goodwin), Academic Press, New York, 1965, p. 279.
109. S. Gatenbeck and K. Mosbach, *Acta Chem. Scand.*, **13**, 1561 (1959).
110. H. Grisebach, *Z. Naturforsch.*, **14b**, 802 (1959).
111. H. Grisebach and N. Doerr, *Z. Naturforsch.*, **15b**, 284 (1960).
112. H. Grisebach and G. Brandner, *Biochim. Biophys. Acta*, **60**, 51 (1962).
113. J. G. Levin and D. B. Sprinson, *J. Biol. Chem.*, **239**, 1142 (1964).
114. F. Gibson and L. M. Jackman, *Nature*, **198**, 388 (1963).
115. J. L. Strominger, *Biochim. Biophys. Acta*, **30**, 645 (1958).
116. M. R. J. Salton, *J. Gen. Microbiol.*, **29**, 15 (1962).
117. M. H. Richmond and H. R. Perkins, *Biochem. J.*, **76**, 1P (1960).
118. D. Gambal and K. J. Monty, *Federation Proc.*, **18**, 232 (1959).
119. R. W. Keenan, J. B. Brown, and B. H. Marks, *Biochim. Biophys. Acta*, **51**, 226 (1961).
120. G. A. Thompson, Jr., *J. Biol. Chem.*, **240**, 1912 (1965).
121. C. N. Remy, *J. Biol. Chem.*, **238**, 1078 (1963).
122. F. Challenger and M. I. Simpson, *J. Chem. Soc.*, 1591 (1948).
123. F. Challenger, *Aspects of the Organic Chemistry of Sulfur*, Butterworth, London, 1959, p. 32.
124. G. L. Cantoni, *Third International Congress of Biochemistry*, Brussels, 1955, p. 236.
125. G. A. Maw, *Biochem. J.*, **70**, 168 (1958).
126. J. Durell, D. G. Anderson, and G. L. Cantoni, *Biochim. Biophys. Acta*, **26**, 270 (1957).
127. F. Challenger and H. E. North, *J. Chem. Soc.*, 68 (1934).
128. M. L. Bird, F. Challenger, P. T. Charlton, and J. D. Smith, *Biochem. J.*, **43**, 78 (1948).
129. L. Fowden, *Ann. Rev. Biochem.*, **33**, 173 (1964).
130. E. W. Underhill and M. D. Chisholm, *Biochem. Biophys. Res. Comm.*, **14**, 425 (1964).
131. M. A. Eisenberg, *Biochem. Biophys. Res. Comm.*, **8**, 437 (1962).
132. A. Lezius, E. Ringelmann, and F. Lynen, *Biochem. Z.*, **336**, 510 (1963).
133. G. W. E. Plaut, *Ann. Rev. Biochem.*, **30**, 409 (1961).
134. E. P. Abraham in *Comprehensive Biochemistry*, Vol. 11 (Ed. M. Florkin and E. H. Stotz), Elsevier, Amsterdam, 1963, p. 181.

135. J. Axelrod in *Proc. First Intern. Pharmacol. Congress*, Stockholm, 1961, p. 107.
136. A. Nilsson, *Arkiv. Kemi*, **21**, 97 (1963).
137. A. Shimazono and F. F. Nord, *Arch. Biochem. Biophys.*, **78**, 263 (1958).
138. A. Nilsson and B. C. Johnson, *Arch. Biochem. Biophys.*, **101**, 494 (1963).
139. P. Mazel, J. F. Henderson, and J. Axelrod, *J. Pharmacol. Expt. Therap.*, 143, 1 (1964).
140. Y. Tomita, *Japan J. Bacteriol.*, **7**, 297 (1952).
141. H. R. Warner and W. E. M. Lands, *J. Biol. Chem.*, **236**, 2404 (1961).
142. R. Blomstrand, *Proc. Soc. Exp. Biol. Med.*, **102**, 662 (1959).
143. R. Blomstrand and E. H. Ahrens, Jr., *Proc. Soc. Exp. Biol. Med.*, **100**, 802 (1959).
144. E. H. Fischer and E. A. Stein in *The Enzymes*, Vol. 4 (Ed. P. D. Boyer, H. Lardy, and K. Myrbäck), Academic Press, New York, 1960, p. 313.
145. G. J. Walker and W. J. Whelan, *Biochem. J.*, **76**, 257 (1960).
146. D. French in *The Enzymes*, Vol. 4 (Ed. P. D. Boyer, H. Lardy, and K. Myrbäck), Academic Press, New York, 1960, p. 345.
147. E. H. Fischer and E. A. Stein in *The Enzymes*, Vol. 4 (Ed. P. D. Boyer, H. Lardy, and K. Myrbäck), Academic Press, New York, 1960, p. 301.
148. E. L. Rosenfeld, *Biokhimiya*, **21**, 84 (1956); **23**, 635 (1958).
149. J. Larner in *The Enzymes*, Vol. 4 (Ed. P. D. Boyer, H. Hardy, and and K. Myrbäck), Academic Press, New York, 1960, p. 371.
150. D. R. Whitacker, *Arch. Biochem. Biophys.*, **53**, 439 (1954).
151. D. R. Whitacker, *Canad. J. Biochem. Physiol.*, **35**, 733 (1957).
152. H. Deuel and E. Stutz in *Advances in Enzymology*, Vol. 20 (Ed. F. F. Nord), Interscience Publishers, New York, 1958, p. 341.
153. A. L. Demain and H. J. Phaff, *Wallerstein Lab. Commun.*, **20**, 119 (1957).
154. P. Jollès in *The Enzymes*, Vol. 4 (Ed. P. D. Boyer, H. Lardy, and K. Myrbäck), Academic Press, New York, 1960, p. 431.
155. P. Jollès, *Angew. Chem.*, **76**, 20 (1964).
156. L. R. Berger and R. S. Weiser, *Biochm. Biophys. Acta*, **26**, 517 (1957).
157. K. Meyer, P. Hoffman, and A. Linker in *The Enzymes*, Vol. 4 (Ed. P. D. Boyer, H. Lardy, and K. Myrbäck), Academic Press, New York, 1960, p. 447.
158. B. Weissmann, K. Meyer, P. Sampson, and A. Linker, *J. Biol. Chem.* **208**, 417 (1954).
159. K. Meyer, A. Linker, P. Hoffman, and E. D. Korn in *Proc. of International Symposium of Enzyme Chemistry* (Ed. K. Ichahara), Academic Press, New York, 1958, p. 132.
160. A. Linker, K. Meyer, and P. Hoffman, *J. Biol. Chem.*, **235**, 924 (1960).
161. J. R. Turvey in *Handbuch der physiologisch- und pathologisch-chemischen Analyse*, Vol. 6B (Ed. K. Lang and E. Lennartz), Springer-Verlag, Berlin, in press.
162. D. French in *Advances in Carbohydrate Chemistry*, Vol. 12 (Ed. M. L. Wolfrom and R. S. Tipson), Academic Press, New York, 1957, p. 189.
163. W. Z. Hassid and E. F. Neufeld in *The Enzymes*, Vol. 6 (Ed. P. D. Boyer, H. Lardy, and K. Myrbäck), Academic Press, New York, 1960, p. 278.
164. J. Larner and D. N. Uwah, *J. Am. Chem. Soc.*, **68**, 3647 (1956).
165. K. Wallenfels and H. Diekmann in *Handbuch der physiologisch- und patholo-gisch-chemischen Analyse*, Vol. 6B (Ed. K. Lang and E. Lennartz), Springer-Verlag, Berlin, 1966, p. 1156.

166. G. T. Cori and J. Larner, *J. Biol. Chem.*, **188**, 17 (1951).
167. S. Peat, W. J. Whelan, and G. J. Thomas, *J. Chem. Soc.*, 4546 (1952).
168. H. Bender and K. Wallenfels, *Biochem. Z.*, **334**, 79 (1961).
169. M. Abdullah, B. J. Catley, E. Y. C. Lee, J. Robyt, K. Wallenfels, and W. J. Whelan, *Cereal Chem.*, in press.
170. G. Terui and H. Okada, *Technology reports of the Osaka University*, **9**, 237 (1959).
171. L. A. Underkofler and K. Roy, *Cereal Chem.*, **28**, 18 (1951).
172. I. C. McWilliam and G. Harris, *Arch. Biochem.*, **84**, 442 (1959).
173. J. Larner and C. M. McNickel, *J. Biol. Chem.*, **215**, 723 (1955).
174. K. Wallenfels, J. Lehmann, and O. P. Malhotra, *Biochem. Z.*, **333**, 209 (1960).
175. A. Gottschalk in *The Enzymes*, Vol. 1/1 (Ed. J. B. Sumner and K. Myrbäck), Academic Press, New York, 1951, p. 556.
176. A. W. Philips, *Arch. Biochem.*, **80**, 346 (1959).
177. H. Halvorson and L. Ellias, *Biochem. Biophys. Acta*, **30**, 28 (1958).
178. K. Wallenfels in *Biologie und Wirkung der Fermente*, Springer-Verlag, Berlin, 1953, p. 160.
179. D. J. Manners, *Bull. Soc. Chim. Biol.*, **42**, 1789 (1960).
180. J. H. Pazur and D. French, *J. Biol. Chem.*, **196**, 265 (1952).
181. W. A. M. Duncan and D. J. Manners, *Biochem. J.*, **69**, 343 (1958).
182. A. R. Archibald and D. J. Manners, *Biochem. J.*, **73**, 292 (1959).
183. Z. H. Gunja and D. J. Manners, *J. Inst. Brewing*, **66**, 409 (1960).
184. S. Chiba, S. Sugawara, T. Shimomura, and Y. Nakamura, *Bull. Agr. Chem. Soc. Japan*, **26**, 787 (1962).
185. K. Myrbäck in *The Enzymes*, Vol. 4 (Ed. P. D. Boyer, H. Lardy, and K. Myrbäck), Academic Press, New York, 1960, p. 394.
186. Reference 175, p. 580.
187. J. Conchie, J. Findlay and G. A. Levvy, *Biochem. J.*, **71**, 318 (1959).
188. K. Wallenfels and O. P. Malhotra in *Advances in Carbohydrate Chemistry*, Vol. 16 (Ed. M. L. Wolfrom and R. S. Tipson), Academic Press, New York, 1961, p. 290.
189. G. A. Levvy, *Nature*, **186**, 472 (1960).
190. A. Gottschalk in *The Enzymes*, Vol. 4 (Ed. P. D. Boyer, H. Lardy, and K. Myrbäck), Academic Press, New York, 1960, p. 461.
191. C. A. Marsh and G. A. Levvy, *Biochem. J.*, **68**, 610 (1958).
192. J. E. Courtois, F. Petek, and To Dong, *Bull. Soc. Chim. Biol.*, **44**, 11 (1962); **45**, 95 (1963).
193. H. Bauman and W. Pigman in *The Carbohydrates* (Ed. W. Pigman), Academic Press, New York, 1957, p. 587.
194. J. H. Duerksen and H. Halvorson, *J. Biol. Chem.*, **233**, 1113 (1958).
195. K. Wallenfels and O. P. Malhotra in *The Enzymes*, Vol. 4 (Ed. P. D. Boyer, H. Lardy, and K. Myrbäck), Academic Press, New York, 1960, p. 409.
196. M. L. Zarnitz, *Dissertation*, Universität Freiburg, 1958.
197. B. Müller-Hill, *Dissertation*, Universität Freiburg, 1962 (see reference 188).
198. D. Beck and K. Wallenfels, *Ann. Chem.*, **655**, 173 (1962).
199. K. Wallenfels and J. Fischer, *Z. Physiol. Chem.*, **321**, 223 (1960).
200. D. Beck, *Dissertation*, Universität Freiburg, 1962.

240   K. Wallenfels and H. Diekmann

201. B. Müller-Hill, H. V. Rickenberg, and K. Wallenfels, *J. Mol. Biol.*, **10**, 303 (1964).
202. J. W. Wollen, P. G. Walker, and R. Heyworth, *Biochem. J.*, **79**, 294 (1961).
203. G. A. Levvy and C. A. Marsh in *The Enzymes*, Vol. 4 (Ed. P. D. Boyer, H. Lardy, and K. Myrbäck), Academic Press, New York, 1960, p. 397.
204. Reference 185, p. 379.
205. G. A. Levvy and A. McAllan, *Biochem. J.*, **87**, 206 (1963).
206. E. T. Reese, R. C. Clapp, and M. Mandels, *Arch. Biochem.*, **75**, 228 (1958).
207. I. Goodman, I. R. Fouts, E. Bresnick, R. Menegas, and G. H. Hitchings, *Science*, **130**, 450 (1959).
208. S. Hestrin, S. Avineri-Shapiro, and M. Ashner, *Biochem. J.*, **37**, 450 (1943).
209. S. Hestrin, D. S. Feingold, and G. Avigad, *Biochem. J.*, **64**, 340 (1956).
210. S. Hestrin, and G. Avigad, *Biochem. J.*, **69**, 388 (1958).
211. E. J. Hehre, *J. Biol. Chem.*, **163**, 221 (1946).
212. S. A. Barker, E. J. Bourne, P. M. Grant, and M. Stacey, *J. Chem. Soc.*, 601 (1958).
213. E. J. Hehre and D. M. Hamilton, *J. Biol. Chem.*, **166**, 777 (1946).
214. E. Bourquelot, H. Hèrissey, and J. Coire, *C.R. Hebd. Seances Acad. Sci.*, **157**, 732 (1913).
215. J. Lehmann, *Dissertation*, Universitat Freiburg, 1959.
216. K. H. Meyer, E. H. Fischer, A. Staub, and P. Bernfeld, *Helv. Chim. Acta*, **31**, 2158 (1948).
217. E. H. Fisher, F. Duckert, and P. Bernfeld, *Helv. Chim. Acta*, **33**, 1060 (1950).
218. E. H. Fischer and P. Bernfeld, *Helv. Chim. Acta*, **31**, 1831 (1948).
219. N. G. Heatley, *Nature*, **181**, 1069 (1958).
220. S. Schwimmer and A. K. Balls, *J. Biol. Chem.*, **179**, 1063 (1949).
221. K. I. Takaoka, H. Fuwa, and Z. Nikuni, *Mem. Inst. Sci. Ind. Res. Osaka Univ.*, **10**, 199 (1952).
222. E. H. Fischer and R. de Montmollin, *Helv. Chim. Acta*, **34**, 1987 (1951).
223. L. L. Campbell, *J. Am. Chem. Soc.*, **76**, 5256 (1954).
224. J. Fellig, E. A. Stein, and E. H. Fischer, *Helv. Cheim. Acta*, **40**, 529 (1957).
225. A. Markowitz, H. P. Klein, and E. H. Fischer, *Biochim. Biophys. Acta*, **19**, 267 (1956).
226. G. B. Manning and L. L. Campbell, *J. Biol. Chem.*, **236**, 2952 (1961).
227. A. K. Balls, M. K. Walden, and R. R. Thompson, *J. Biol. Chem.*, **173**, 9 (1948).
228. K. H. Meyer, E. H. Fischer, and A. Piquet, *Helv. Chim. Acta*, **34**, 316 (1951).
229. K. H. Meyer, P. F. Spahr, and E. H. Fischer, *Helv. Chim. Acta*, **36**, 1924 (1953).
230. J. Fukumoto and Y. Tsujisaka, *Kagaku To Kogyo* (*Osaka*), **29**, 124 (1955).
231. K. Nisizawa, *J. Biochem.* (*Tokyo*), **42**, 825 (1955).
232. M. Inaoka and H. Soda, *Nature*, **178**, 202 (1956).
233. K. Wallenfels and Mitarbeiter. Unpublished results.
234. A. S. L. Hu, R. G. Wolfe, and F. J. Reithel, *Arch. Biochem.*, **81**, 500 (1959).
235. K. Wallenfels, M. L. Zarnitz, G. Laule, H. Bender, and M. Keser, *Biochem. Z.*, **331**, 459 (1959).
236. Y. Tsujisaka, J. Fukumoto, and T. Yamamoto, *Nature*, **181**, 770 (1958).
237. R. Bonnichsen, *Acta Chem. Scand.*, **18**, 1302 (1964).
238. A. Alfsen and M. F. Jayle, *Bull. Soc. Chim. Biol.*, **40**, 2143 (1959).

239. E. P. Abraham and R. Robinson, *Nature*, **140**, 24 (1937).
240. E. L. Smith, J. R. Kimmel, D. M. Brown, and E. O. P. Thompson, *J. Biol. Chem.*, **215**, 67 (1955).
241. Y. Satomura, S. Okada, and J. Fukumoto, *Nippon Nogeikagaku Kaishi*, **31**, 281 (1957).
242. G. Jollès and C. Fromageot, *Biochim. Biophys. Acta*, **14**, 219 (1954).
243. S. Sugawara, Y. Nakamura, and T. Shimomura, *Bull. Agr. Chem. Soc. Japan*, **23**, 156 (1959).
244. G. Schramm and E. Mohr, *Nature*, **183**, 1677 (1959).
245. G. L. Ada and E. L. French, *Nature*, **183**, 1740 (1959).
246. E. P. Hill and A. S. Sussman, *Arch. Biochem.*, **102**, 389 (1962).
247. J. C. Lewis, N. S. Snell, D. J. Hirschmann, and H. Fraenkel-Conrat, *J. Biol. Chem.*, **186**, 23 (1950).
248. S. Englard and T. P. Singer, *J. Biol. Chem.*, **187**, 213 (1950).
249. H. Sund and K. Weber, *Biochem. Z.*, **337**, 24 (1963).
250. K. Wallenfels, H. Sund, and K. Weber, *Biochem. Z.*, **338**, 714 (1963).
251. A. Tsugita and S. Akabori, *J. Biochem.* (*Tokyo*), **46**, 695 (1959).
252. K. Wallenfels and A. Arens, *Biochem. Z.*, **332**, 247 (1960); K. Wallenfels, C. Steffer, C. Gölker, *Biochem. Z.*, 342, 495 (1965).
253. S. Akabori and T. Ikenaka, *J. Biochem.* (*Tokyo*), **42**, 603 (1955).
254. K. Wallenfels, O. P. Malhotra, and D. Dabich, *Biochem. Z.*, **333**, 377 (1960).
255. F. C. Mayer and J. Larner, *J. Am. Chem. Soc.*, **81**, 188 (1959).
256. M. Halpern and J. Leibowitz, *Biochim. Biophys. Acta*, **36**, 29 (1959).
257. C. A. Bunton, T. A. Lewis, D. R. Llewellyn, H. Tristram, and C. A. Vernon, *Nature*, **174**, 560 (1954).
258. S. S. Springhorn and D. E. Koshland, *Am. Chem. Soc. Meet. Abstr.*, 1955, p. 37C.
259. K. Wallenfels, O. P. Malhotra, H. Dahm, and H. Moll, unpublished results.
260. F. Eisenberg, *Federation Proc.*, **18**, 221 (1959).
261. D. E. Koshland and S. S. Stein, *J. Biol. Chem.*, **208**, 139 (1954).
262. R. Kuhn, *Ann. Chem.*, **443**, 1 (1925).
263. S. Ono, K. Hiromi, and Z.-J. Hamanzu, *J. Biochem.* (*Tokyo*), **57**, 34 (1965).
264. E. J. Hehre and D. M. Hamilton, *J. Biol. Chem.*, **177**, 267 (1949).
265. W. Z. Hassid and H. A. Barker, *J. Biol. Chem.*, **134**, 163 (1940).
266. K. Myrbäck and K. Ahlborg, *Biochem. Z.*, **311**, 213 (1940).
267. D. French, *Science*, **113**, 352 (1951).
268. E. F. Armstrong, *J. Chem. Soc.*, **83**, 1305 (1903).
269. K. Wallenfels and G. Kurz, *Biochem. Z.*, **335**, 559 (1962).
270. W. G. Overend, C. W. Rees, and J. S. Sequeira, *J. Chem. Soc.*, 3429 (1962).
271. M. Cohn in *The Enzymes*, Vol. 5 (Ed. P. D. Boyer, H. Lardy, and K. Myrbäck), Academic Press, New York, 1961, p. 179.
272. D. H. Brown and C. F. Cori in *The Enzymes*, Vol. 5 (Ed. P. D. Boyer, H. Lardy, and K. Myrbäck), Academic Press, New York, 1961, p. 207.
273. J. Katz and W. Z. Hassid, *Arch. Biochem. Biophys.*, **30**, 272 (1951).
274. Reference 272, p. 218.
275. M. Doudoroff in *The Enzymes*, Vol. 5 (Ed. P. D. Boyer, H. Lardy, and K. Myrbäck), Academic Press, New York, 1961, p. 229.
276. M. Doudoroff, N. Kaplan, and W. Z. Hassid, *J. Biol. Chem.*, **148**, 67 (1943).
277. R. Weimberg and M. Doudoroff, *J. Bacteriol.*, **68**, 381 (1954).

278. C. Fitting and M. Doudoroff, *J. Biol. Chem.*, **199**, 153 (1952).
279. W. A. Ayers, *J. Bacteriol.*, **76**, 515 (1958).
280. S. Hestrin, *J. Biol. Chem.*, **179**, 943 (1949).
281. M. Doudoroff, *J. Biol. Chem.*, **151**, 351 (1943).
282. Reference 271, p. 192.
283. A. A. Green and G. T. Cori, *J. Biol. Chem.*, **151**, 21 (1943).
284. R. W. Cowgill, *J. Biol. Chem.*, **234**, 3146 (1959).
285. P. J. Keller and G. T. Cori, *Biochim. Biophys. Acta*, **12**, 235 (1953).
286. E. G. Krebs and E. H. Fischer, *Biochim. Biophys. Acta*, **20**, 150 (1956).
287. E. G. Krebs, A. B. Kent, and E. H. Fischer, *J. Biol. Chem.*, **231**, 73 (1958).
288. E. H. Fischer, D. Graves, E. S. Crittenden, and E. G. Krebs, *J. Biol. Chem.*, **234**, 1698 (1959).
289. Y. P. Lee, *Biochim. Biophys. Acta*, **43**, 18 (1960).
290. E. H. Fischer, A. B. Kent, E. R. Snyder, and E. G. Krebs, *J. Am. Chem. Soc.*, **80**, 2906 (1958).
291. N. B. Madsen, *J. Biol. Chem.*, **223**, 1067 (1956).
292. N. B. Madsen and F. R. N. Gurd, *J. Biol. Chem.*, **223**, 1075 (1956).
293. M. Cohn, *J. Biol. Chem.*, **180**, 771 (1949).
294. M. L. Wolfrom, C. S. Smith, and A. E. Brown, *J. Am. Chem. Soc.*, **65**, 255 (1943).
295. W. A. Ayers, *J. Biol. Chem.*, **234**, 2819 (1959).
296. M. Doudoroff, H. A. Barker, and W. Z. Hassid, *J. Biol. Chem.*, **168**, 725 (1947).
297. H. Wolochow, E. W. Putman, M. Doudoroff, W. Z. Hassid, and H. A. Barker, *J. Biol. Chem.*, **180**, 1237 (1949).
298. E. W. Sutherland and T. W. Rall, *Pharmacol. Rev.*, **12**, 265 (1960).
299. E. G. Krebs and E. H. Fischer in *Advances in Enzymology*, Vol. 24 (Ed. F. F. Nord), Interscience Publishers, New York, 1962, p. 263.
300. R. Bentley and D. S. Bhate, *J. Biol. Chem.*, **235**, 1225 (1960).
301. R. Bentley and A. Neuberger, *Biochem. J.*, **45**, 584 (1949).
302. D. Keilin and E. F. Hartree, *Biochem. J.*, **50**, 331 (1952).
303. K. Wallenfels, F. Hucho, and K. Herrmann, *Biochem. Z.*, **343**, 307 (1965).
304. K. Wallenfels, K. Herrmann, and G. Kurz, *Sixth International Congress of Biochemistry, Abstracts*, New York, 1964, p. 324.
305. A. S. Keston, *Science*, **120**, 355 (1954).
306. R. Bentley and D. S. Bhate, *J. Biol. Chem.*, **235**, 1219 (1960).
307. L. K. Li, *Arch. Biochem.*, **110**, 156 (1965).
308. K. Wallenfels and K. Herrmann in *Methods in Enzymology*, Vol. 8 (Ed. S. P. Colowick and N. O. Kaplan), Academic Press, New York, in press; *Biochem. Z.*, 343, 294 (1965).
309. M. Salas, E. Vinuela, and A. Sols, *J. Biol. Chem.*, **240**, 561 (1965).
310. A. M. Chase, S. L. Lapedes, and H. C. von Meier, *J. Cellular Comp. Physiol.*, **61**, 187 (1963).
311. A. S. Keston, *Arch. Biochem. Biophys.* **102**, 306 (1963).
312. H. J. Strecker and S. J. Korkes, *J. Biol. Chem.*, **196**, 769 (1952).
313. M. R. Heinrich, *J. Biol. Chem.*, **239**, 50 (1964).
314. C. G. Swain and J. F. Brown, *J. Am. Chem. Soc.*, **74**, 2534 (1952).
315. D. Rittenberg and C. Graff, *J. Am. Chem. Soc.*, **80**, 3370 (1958).
316. W. G. Overend, A. R. Peacocke, and J. B. Smith, *J. Chem. Soc.*, 3487 (1961).

CHAPTER 6

Basicity and complexing ability of ethers

SCOTT SEARLES, Jr.

Department of Chemistry, University of Missouri, U.S.A.

and

MILTON TAMRES

Department of Chemistry, University of Michigan, U.S.A.

I. INTRODUCTION

Ethers can form coordination complexes with a wide variety of Brönsted and Lewis acids by employing the unshared pairs of electrons on the oxygen atom, just as in the cases of water, alcohols and sulfides. This coordination ability is, in fact, central to much of the chemistry of ethers. Most of their reactions proceed through such coordinated intermediates, and they may also serve a role in synthesis of ethers under acidic conditions. Coordination ability has certainly been recognized as of prime importance in the solvent properties of ethers, for they can participate in relatively weak as well as strong interactions.

The scope of the coordination chemistry of ethers is thus very broad. Since space does not permit us in the span of this chapter to give an exhaustive review of the subject or a complete compilation of data, this treatment will be limited to the presentation of the broad categories of ether complexes, as well as an outline of the general concepts of basicity that apply to ether complexation and the methods of measuring the strength and composition of the complexes. The literature has been surveyed through early 1965, and emphasis will be placed on recent developments. A brief general survey of the subject was published by Arnett[1] in 1963, and reviews of several special phases are available; these will be cited in appropriate sections.

The addition compounds of ethers can be classified in three categories: (a) ionized oxonium salts, in which a hydrogen, metal or alkyl cation has been transferred completely to the ether oxygen atom, (b) nonionized coordination complexes, having a coordinate covalent bond between the oxygen atom and an atom of a Lewis base, and (c) weakly bonded complexes due to charge transfer, including hydrogen bonding.

In all of these categories, only one of the two unshared pairs of electrons on the ether oxygen atom appears to be available for co-ordination. The lack of coordination with a second electron-acceptor molecule may be due in part to steric factors and in part to the decrease in availability of an unshared pair of electrons when the other pair is coordinated. Coordination of ethers with triethylaluminum and triethylgallium has been observed to cause an increase in the electronegativity of the oxygen atom, as shown by changes in the nuclear magnetic resonance spectra[2].

Since oxygen is a relatively small atom, being in the second period of elements in the periodic table, the oxygen atom in ethers presents a field of high electron density, making it relatively difficult to polarize the oxygen atom. This situation has recently led to the classification of ethers as 'hard bases'[3,4]. Such bases generally interact more strongly with 'hard acids', such as H^+, Li^+, Mg^{2+} and BF_3, than do soft bases, such as the corresponding sulfides.

II. CONCEPTS AND MEASUREMENT OF INTERACTION

A. Types of Interaction

Association occurs when the total attractive forces are greater than the repulsive forces, the magnitude of the difference being reflected in the strength of association. Both strong and weak complexation with ethers depends in large measure on the polar nature of the ether. This is true also in the case of 1,4-dioxane, which has a small dipole moment, greater than zero because of the existence of the boat as well as the chair form. More important than the total dipole moment, however, are the local dipoles within the molecule, which serve as the sites for association.

The types of forces operative in the interaction of ethers with electron acceptors are:

1. ion–dipole, such as

$$\left[Li^+ \cdots O^{\delta-} \underset{R}{\overset{R^{\delta+}}{<}} \right]$$

which is of particular importance in the solvation of many salts,

2. dipole–dipole, such as

$$\begin{array}{c}R\\\diagdown\\\overset{\delta+}{R}\diagup\end{array}\overset{\delta-}{O}\cdots\overset{\delta+}{H}\cdots\overset{\delta-}{Cl}$$

which is exemplified by hydrogen bonding,

3. dipole–induced dipole, shown in halogen–ether complexes

$$\begin{array}{c}R\\\diagdown\\\overset{\delta+}{R}\diagup\end{array}\overset{\delta-}{O}\cdots\overset{\delta+}{I}\cdots\overset{\delta-}{I}$$

Actually, in all cases, the ether induces a polarization in the species with which it complexes. The effect would be small in the case of the less easily polarized Li^+ ion and greater for HCl. In turn, the ether is itself polarized by the interacting species. Thus, superimposed on the forces above are those due to induced dipole–induced dipole.

In the case of crystalline complexes, there would be a small contribution from *London dispersion forces*, which might be considered qualitatively as resulting from the synchronized motions of the electrons among the molecules. The location of an electron in a molecule at a given instant gives rise to an 'instantaneous dipole', which induces a dipole in its neighbor, and the effect continues through the crystal.

B. The Stronger Complexes

'Strong complexation' of ethers generally involves interaction with Brönsted or Lewis acids with formation of a coordinate covalent bond. The strength of these 'strong complexes' varies, however, over a wide range, and it is naturally of interest to establish criteria for comparing the strengths of interactions.

The strength of interaction has frequently been correlated with the heat of formation of the complex involved. This criterion, however, cannot be applied with certainty, because part of the observed effect may be associated with alteration of the donor or acceptor molecule on complex formation. The heat of reaction in forming an adduct cannot be equated with the energy of the bond formed. The former is smaller by the amount of energy required to alter the geometry of the donor and acceptor species from the free to the complexed state. This correlation is more likely to be valid for a homologous series of donors with a common acceptor, as the energies of structure alteration will tend to be similar with such a series.

In many cases, strong complexes can be treated in terms of the Brönsted–Lowry concept of acids and bases, or more generally by the Lewis theory. The equilibrium constant for the reaction can be measured, and this often provides a useful criterion for comparison of the strength of complexing of a series of acceptor molecules with a common donor or a series of donors with a common acceptor molecule. Such equilibrium constants are, of course, highly temperature-dependent, and their relative values may vary with temperature; indeed, a case is reported of reversal of apparent donor ability of tetrahydrofuran and tetrahydropyran towards o-cresol between 5 and 20°[5].

A related approach is to measure the equilibrium constant of a Lewis acid between two donor molecules, such as reaction (1), or of two

$$Et_2O \cdot BF_3 + Me_2O \rightleftharpoons Et_2O + Me_2O \cdot BF_3 \qquad (1)$$

Lewis acids and one donor molecule. The concentrations in the equilibrium mixture can be determined spectrally, using infrared[6] or nuclear magnetic resonance spectra[7], and the results give a measure of the relative strength of the two complex species involved in the equilibrium.

Direct spectral correlations have received attention from several workers recently. The B—H symmetric and asymmetric stretching frequencies in ether– and amine–borane adducts were found to correlate closely with the heats of complex formation[8]. It has recently been proposed that the change in the C—H stretching frequencies in ethyl ether after complexation with boron trifluoride is due to the bonding of one of the unshared pairs of electrons[9], and a correlation with complex strength may be established when more data are obtained.

A number of nuclear magnetic resonance spectral correlations have been studied on a limited number of compounds. The ^{19}F chemical shift in boron trifluoride ethyl etherate, methyl etherate and ethyl methyl etherate was found by Craig and Richards[10] to correlate well with their stabilities, as measured by other methods. This is reasonable, since complexation should increase the electron density on the boron atom and hence the shielding of the fluorine atoms[2]. The electron density on the oxygen atom of an ether molecule should be correspondingly reduced on complexation, and the change in chemical shift of O-methyl protons in methyl ether and ethyl methyl ether complexes of boron trifluoride has been found to be in the order expected from the stability of these complexes[11]. The change of the internal differences between the methyl and methylene protons of ethyl groups was also

found to correlate with ethyl ether and ethyl methyl ether–boron trifluoride, but this method would probably not be valid generally[10,11].

C. The Weaker Complexes

As the interactions become weaker, it becomes increasingly more
difficult to get isolable complexes. Some of the less stable complexes
have been prepared at low temperatures and studied by x-ray diffraction, e.g. the ethyl ether–bromodichloromethane complex at $-130°$ [12].
Others have been detected by constructing phase diagrams from cryo-
scopic studies, e.g. the dinitrogen tetroxide adducts of tetrahydrofuran
and tetrahydropyran[13].

Most of the weak complexes, however, have been studied by other
methods, and many methods have been devised because of the importance and interest attached to their interactions. Many of the
ether complexes to which charge-transfer theory has been applied fall
into the class of weak complexes.

Weak interactions are of particular value in the study of relative
intrinsic electron-donor abilities of ethers, because they perturb the
ground state of the ether molecule only slightly. Hence the extent of
interaction is a measure of the ground-state electron-donor ability,
which in turn depends on the hybridization of the oxygen atom. In
strong interactions, there is a change in hybridization as the coordination number of the oxygen atom increases from two to three. The
energies required for these hybridization changes may not always be
comparable, as may be the case for cyclic ethers, where the ring size
might well affect ease of rehybridization.

The Brönsted–Lowry and Lewis definitions of acids and bases are
not applicable to weak interactions where, as a result of polarization,
there is only a small shift of electronic charge from donor (D) to
acceptor (A). Mulliken[14] has extended the concept of donors and
acceptors to include all cases of interaction, strong and weak, in forming complexes of any molecular ratio. The most widely studied cases
have been complexes of $1:1$ composition. In the Mulliken theory[14,15],
the wave function of the ground state, ψ_N, of a complex formed between
one molecule of D and one of A may be approximated as a combination of two extreme forms: (a) $\psi_{0(D, A)}$, called a 'no-bond' wave
function, where the electrons remain in the occupied levels of the
donor, and (b) $\psi_{1(D^+ A^-)}$, called a 'dative-bond' wave function, where
an electron from an occupied level (usually the highest filled level) of
the donor is transferred to an unoccupied level (usually the lowest un-

filled level) of the acceptor. This may be written as shown in equation
(2), where a and b are a measure of the magnitude of the contribution

$$\psi_N = a\psi_{0(D, A)} + b\psi_{1(D^+ A^-)} \tag{2}$$

of states ψ_0 and ψ_1 to the ground state; for weak complexes $a^2 \gg b^2$.
The greater the shift of negative charge from donor to acceptor, the
greater will be the relative magnitude of b. The ratio $b^2/(a^2 + b^2)$ is
a measure of the polarity of the complex.

The wave function of the excited state of the complex is given by
equation (3), where, for weak complexes, $a^{*2} \gg b^{*2}$. The transfer of

$$\psi_E = a^*\psi_{1(D^+ A^-)} - b^*\psi_{0(D, A)} \tag{3}$$

an electron from donor to acceptor upon absorption of energy of the
proper frequency ($\psi_N \xrightarrow{h\nu} \psi_E$) gives rise to a spectral band characteristic
of the complex, called a 'charge-transfer' (or CT) band. The com-
plexes are termed 'charge-transfer' (or CT) complexes, although
recently the terminology 'donor–acceptor complexes' is becoming
widely used.

Ethers are classified as n donors, i.e. donors which use lone-pair
electrons in complexation. The CT spectrum arises from an excitation
of one of the lone-pair electrons (reaction 4).

$$\text{R}:\overset{..}{\underset{\overset{|}{\text{R}}}{\text{O}}}: + \overset{..}{\text{A}}: \rightleftharpoons \text{R}:\overset{..}{\underset{\overset{|}{\text{R}}}{\text{O}}}:\cdots\overset{..}{\text{A}}: \xrightarrow{h\nu} \text{R}:\overset{..}{\underset{\overset{|}{\text{R}}}{\text{O}}}\cdot^+\cdots\overset{..}{\text{A}}:^- \tag{4}$$

For aryl ethers, there are two possible bonding sites, the oxygen
atom (n donor) and the aromatic ring (π donor) (**1** and **2**). For the

n donor	π donor
(**1**)	(**2**)

purposes of this chapter, the latter will be considered as a substituted
benzene and will not be of concern here. Specific examples of charge-
transfer complexes will be presented later.

D. Stoichiometry and Base Strengths of Ethers

The interactions involving complexation with ethers naturally result in modification of the chemical and physical properties of both interacting species, and give rise to new properties attributable to the complex. These changes may be correlated with the stoichiometry and base strength of the complex.

In the general reaction of donor (D) and acceptor (A) to form a complex (C) (reaction 5), the modification in properties results in a

$$D + A \rightleftharpoons C \tag{5}$$

deviation from ideal behavior. Positive or negative deviations may be obtained, depending on the physical property measured.

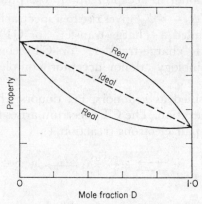

FIGURE 1. Types of variations of properties of an interacting system.

It is useful to plot just the difference in physical property from ideality as a function of composition, as in the example shown in Figure 2. In the absence of steric complications, the magnitude of the difference is a measure of the electron-donor ability. Use of a common acceptor for a series of ethers will give relative basicities of ethers. Furthermore, if the property measured is a simple function of composition, the position of the maximum establishes the composition of the complex (method of continuous variation), which in Figure 2 is 1:1.

It is of interest to note in this figure that the strength of interaction measured decreased with increased temperature. This is a general phenomenon for complexes, since increased thermal motion opposes the formation of the complex.

It must be borne in mind that the heats observed in such weak interactions do not represent heats of formation per mole of complex, since only a small fraction of the molecules are in complexed form. It is necessary to determine the degree of association before determining the actual molar heat of formation of the complex. It is not necessary to do this to establish relative basicities for a series of ethers, since in the absence of changing steric effects, the degree of association parallels the strength of interaction.

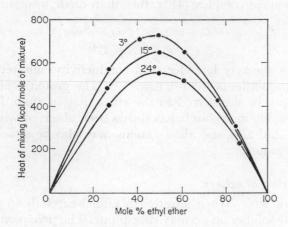

FIGURE 2. Heats of mixing for ethyl ether and chloroform. Data from McLeod and Wilson[16].

Among other physical properties that have been studied to detect complexation with ethers are solubility[17,18], parachor[19], vapor pressure[20], osmotic pressure[21], free surface energy[22], diffusivity and viscosity[23], second virial coefficient[24], ultrasonic sound velocities[25], refractive index[26] and dipole moments[27]. A number of these measurements enable determination of the composition of the complex, but not the equilibrium concentration. The common method of determining association constants is spectroscopy.

III. CLASSIFICATION OF COMPLEXES

A. Oxonium Salts

With Lewis acids of the type H—Y or R—Y, a strong interaction with an ether can dissociate the acid, resulting in the transfer of a cation to form an oxonium salt. Such a reaction is observed with several strong mineral acids, such as pure nitric acid (reaction 6), giving the corresponding dialkyloxonium nitrates (**3**). This type of interaction depends not only on the strength of the acid, but also on the nature of the

$$R_2O + HNO_3 \rightleftarrows R_2OH^+NO_3^- \qquad (6)$$
$$(\mathbf{3})$$

anion and of the medium. Thus, addition of an equimolecular amount of hydrogen chloride to ethyl ether (reaction 7) gives merely a weak hydrogen-bonded complex (**4**), rather than diethyloxonium chloride,

$$Et_2O + HCl \rightleftarrows Et_2O\cdots HCl \qquad (7)$$
$$(\mathbf{4})$$

as shown by the very low electrical conductivity, infrared spectrum and other properties of the mixture[28, 29]. The proton is not the only ion which can be transferred to the ether oxygen atom, forming an oxonium ion, for analogous behavior has been observed with Group I metal ions, and acyl and alkyl cations may also be attached to the ether oxygen atom.

I. Protonation of ethers

a. By nitric acid.   When an ether is added carefully to pure nitric acid, a white solid or an oil may precipitate. The precipitate has been isolated in the cases of ethyl ether, n-butyl ether and 1,4-dioxane, and was found to contain one molecule of nitric acid per ether molecule[30, 31]. The isolation of the ethyl ether and tetrahydrofuran adducts was rendered difficult by their tendency to decompose explosively after isolation. The ether nitrates are considered to have essentially the ionic structure **3** because of the presence in their infrared spectra of a band at about 1400 cm^{-1}, characteristic of the nitrate ion, and the shift of the typical C—O—C vibration to lower wave numbers[31].

The extraction of butyl ether from benzene by aqueous nitric acid[32] seems attributable to protonation of the ether to form the oxonium salt, which must be quite soluble in water. The dissociation constant of butyl ether nitrate in water, $K = [Bu_2O \cdot HNO_3]/[HNO_3][Bu_2O]$, was determined by Fomin and Maslova[32] to be 8.8×10^{-4} corresponding to a pK_a of -3.05 for n-butyl ether in water. Deviations from this relation in dilute acid solutions were attributed to hydration of the ether–acid complex.

b. By sulfuric acid and halogenosulfuric acids.   Sulfuric acid reacts with aliphatic ethers to give low-melting crystalline compounds of both

1:1 and 1:2 composition (reaction 8). A number of these have been

$$R_2O + H_2SO_4 \longrightarrow H_2SO_4 \cdot R_2O \text{ and } H_2SO_4 \cdot 2R_2O \tag{8}$$

isolated[33] and additional evidence for these two types of oxonium sulfate salts from ethyl ether has been obtained from heat capacity data[34]. The 1:1 complex was found to be the higher-melting and presumably more stable form in each case.

The oxonium salt structure for the 1:1 ethyl ether–sulfuric acid complex is shown by the initial van't Hoff i factor of 2·0 for the freezing-point lowering of sulfuric acid by ethyl ether[35,36]. Other n-alkyl ethers give similar results, which are attributable to complete or nearly complete protonation of the ether oxygen atom, giving the oxonium and bisulfate ions (reaction 9)[36,37]. Negatively substituted ethers are some-

$$R_2O + H_2SO_4 \rightleftharpoons R_2OH^+ + HSO_4^- \tag{9}$$

what less strong bases, e.g. 2,2'-dichloroethyl ether with an initial i factor of 1. An initial i factor of 2·24 observed for isopropyl ether is probably due to the diisopropyloxonium ion formed being less stable than di-n-alkyloxonium ions. In all cases, the i factor increases with time to a value of about 4, probably due to fission of the oxonium ion in the sulfuric acid[36]. The observation of Jacques and Leisten that the rate of ether cleavage in concentrated sulfuric acid is unimolecular in ether, with the rate proportional to the sulfur trioxide concentration of the acid, led them to propose that the active reagent is the free sulfur trioxide present, which adds to the protonated ether to give a new oxonium ion (5), which subsequently undergoes fission (reaction 10)[36].

$$R_2OH^+ + SO_3 \rightleftharpoons [R_2OSO_3H]^+ \longrightarrow R^+ + ROSO_3H \tag{10}$$
$$(5)$$

Chlorosulfonic acid is reported to give a complex with ethyl ether which is a useful sulfonating agent for secondary alcohols[38].

Aromatic ethers are only sparingly soluble in sulfuric acid, and the low i factors show them to be weak bases in this solvent[36]. It has been proposed that protonation occurs on the oxygen, because anisole and dimethylaniline show similar ultraviolet spectral changes when protonated by sulfuric acid[39]; but nuclear magnetic resonance studies on anisole in fluorosulfuric acid and in HF plus BF_3 showed clearly that protonation is on the aromatic ring (reaction 11), primarily at the *para*-carbon atom, as in **6**[40, 41]. The resulting oxonium ion is thus more

$$C_6H_5{-}O{-}CH_3 + H^+ \longrightarrow \quad \text{(6)} \quad \tag{11}$$

like a carbonyl oxonium ion than an aliphatic ether oxonium ion and is exceptionally labile to displacement processes on the aliphatic carbon atom, like trialkyloxonium ions (section III.A.5). Similar carbon protonation appears to occur with conjugated enol ethers in acetic acid solution, to give similar, very labile carbonyl oxonium ion intermediates[42].

Ring protonation of aryl ethers is probably quite general, having been demonstrated for 1,3-dimethoxybenzene[41] and 1,3,5-trimethoxybenzene[43], but 5,5-dimethylhomochroman (**7**) may be an exception. Marked steric inhibition of resonance in this compound, no doubt

(7)

imposed by the noncoplanarity of the seven-membered oxygen-containing ring, has been indicated by its ultraviolet spectrum[44, 45], and it is a stronger base than anisole by 4·60 pK units[39, 46]. Since steric inhibition of resonance in aromatic amines has a much smaller effect on basicity (there is a difference of only 2·73 pK units between N,N-dimethylaniline and benzoquinuclidine, both of which apparently protonate on nitrogen[47]), it seems reasonable that oxygen protonation may occur with **7**.

c. By complex halogen acids. In the presence of a metal halide, which is able to form complex halide anions, hydrogen halides react with ethers to give protonated oxonium salts. These are commonly etherates of the complex halogen acids, HMX_n, where X represents a halogen atom and M the metal atom. Many such etherates have been reported.

The simplest types have the formula $HMX_n \cdot R_2O$, with X as chlorine, M as antimony(v), iron(III) or aluminum and the ether as methyl, ethyl, isopropyl or phenyl ether, or tetrahydrofuran, anisole or phenetole[48–50]. These etherates are crystalline compounds of white or yellow color, which melt with decomposition at moderate temperatures. The high electrical conductivity observed for them in liquid sulfur dioxide solution led Klages to formulate them as oxonium salts, $R_2OH^+MCl_n^-$, and they are named as such, e.g. dimethyloxonium hexachloroantimonate for the case where R is methyl and M is antimony.

Similar complex etherates are obtained when the metal atom is tin(IV), but the stoichiometry is necessarily different, due to the presence of two protons and two ether molecules per tin atom, which is hexacoordinated in the complex anion, e.g. $H_2SnCl_6 \cdot 2Et_2O$[50]. It has been reported recently that the complex acid from stannic chloride and acetic acid forms an ethyl etherate of structure, Et_2OH^+ $[SnCl_4OAc \cdot HOAc]^-$, where apparently the coordinated acetate anions tie up one proton per molecule too firmly to allow the ether to coordinate with it[51].

The simple complex acid etherates are generally prepared by introduction of hydrogen halide into the appropriate metal etherates (section III.B.3, 4 and 5) dissolved or suspended in a solvent such as methylene chloride or liquid sulfur dioxide (reaction 12). The oxonium

$$SbCl_5 + Me_2O \longrightarrow Me_2O \cdot SbCl_5 \xrightarrow{HCl} Me_2OH^+SbCl_6^- \qquad (12)$$

salt either precipitates as formed, or is obtained by removal of the solvent and may be recrystallized from ethylene chloride, liquid sulfur dioxide or other solvents. These products are obtained in high yield and purity. The same method can be used for making monoalkyloxonium salts from alcohols instead of ethers[50].

The reaction of hydrogen halide with metal halide etherate, which is used in the preparations described above, is generally reversible, and there is a tendency for these complex acid etherates to decompose on standing, reforming the hydrogen halide and metal halide etherate. Klages and his collaborators[50] have determined the equilibrium pressure for many of these etherates at various temperatures; particularly high were the equilibrium pressures of dimethyloxonium tetrachloroaluminate and tetrachloroferrate, reflecting the lower stability of these complex acid etherates.

A second molecule of ether reacts readily with each of the simple etherates described above, to form a new compound with an ether to acid proton ratio of 1:2. These compounds, which typically have the molecular formula $HMX_n \cdot 2R_2O$, have much lower vapor pressure and correspondingly greater stability than those of the simpler formula[48,50]. These etherates are low-melting crystalline solids or viscous oily liquids, usually intensely colored. They are insoluble in nonpolar solvents such as benzene, but readily soluble in moderately polar solvents, such as nitrobenzene, chloroform or liquid sulfur dioxide, forming electrically conducting solutions[50,52a,52b]. Some of these compounds, such as $HGaCl_4 \cdot 2Et_2O$[52a], are moderately soluble in ether, while others, such as $HAlBr_4 \cdot 2Et_2O$[52a,53], are not appreciably ether soluble, reflecting the importance of the size of the anion. All of these compounds, however, react vigorously with water, and the beryllium complex acid etherates, $HBeCl_3 \cdot 2Et_2O$ and $HBeCl_2Br \cdot 2Et_2O$, are reported to fume in air with loss of hydrogen halide[54].

In view of the properties and elemental analyses obtained for these compounds, they are considered to possess ionic structures, composed of the complex anion and a large cation consisting of the dialkyloxonium ion hydrogen bonded to a second ether molecule[50]. For example the compound $HAlClBr_3 \cdot 2Et_2O$ would have the structure 8 and would be named diethyloxonium chlorotribromoaluminate

(8)

ethyl etherate. Galinos[53] has proposed that the proton serves as a 'hydrogen bridge' between the two ether molecules and is situated midway between them, but there is no evidence as yet on the exact position of the proton relative to the two oxygen atoms.

It is interesting that it is possible to exchange the ether in these complex acid etherates by treatment with another ether. Klages[50] reported that the reaction of n-butyl ether with dimethyloxonium hexachloroantimonate methyl etherate in ethylene chloride at 75° gave the corresponding dibutyloxonium hexachloroantimonate, identified by conversion into tributyloxonium hexachloroantimonate by reaction with diazoacetic ester (section III.A.3). The ether exchange in the complex acid etherate may have proceeded actually by the oxonium ion serving as a Brönsted acid towards the uncomplexed n-butyl ether, with the expected equilibrium displaced in this case by volatilization of methyl ether at the reaction temperature used (reactions 13 and 14).

$$[Me_2OH \cdot OMe_2]^+ + Bu_2O \rightleftharpoons [Me_2OH \cdot OBu_2]^+ + Me_2O \uparrow \qquad (13)$$

$$[Me_2OH \cdot OBu_2]^+ + Bu_2O \rightleftharpoons [Bu_2OH \cdot OBu_2]^+ + Me_2O \uparrow \qquad (14)$$

There seems to have been no attempt to investigate the possibility of mixed etherates, $[R_2{}^1O—H\cdots OR_2{}^2]^+MX_n{}^-$, ammonium etherates, sulfide etherates or the like, but a recently reported etherated ammonium salt of vanadium hexacarbonyl hydride, of the formula $NH_4V(CO)_6OEt_2$ [54b], may be of this general type, as $[NH_4\cdots OEt_2]^+$ $[V(CO)_6]^-$, although there is as yet no information on the structure of this compound.

Complex halogen acid dietherates can often be prepared in high yield and excellent purity by the very simple procedure of dissolving the metal involved in an ether solution of the hydrogen halide[51, 55], or by the equally simple method of directly bringing the anhydrous metal halide and hydrogen halide into reaction in the anhydrous ether[51, 56–58]. The latter method has been termed 'etherohydrohalogenosis' by Galinos[53]. These procedures have been used for making a large number of complex acid etherates, but in some cases a ratio of ether to acid proton different from 2:1 has been observed, viz. $HMBr_4 \cdot 5Et_2O$ with M = Mn or Fe[58] and $H_2CdX_4 \cdot 3Et_2O$ with X = Cl or Br[55]. These complexes are no doubt of the same general type, differing from the usual cases in the degree of solvation by ether; those with more ether molecules than usual may have some entering the coordination sphere of the metal atom.

Complex halogen acid etherates are important in the extraction of various metals which form them. In the ether extraction of ferric iron from hydrochloric acid solutions, which has been an analytical procedure for over seventy-five years, the species in the ether phase has been shown to be $HFeCl_4$ complexed with ether[59, 60] and the analogous extraction of gallium(III) involves the analogous $HGaCl_4$–ether complex[61], the solubility of which in ether was noted above. This type of extraction of such metals is quite general for ethers, as well as for other mildly basic organic solvents, such as ketones and esters[62]. The extraction of cobalt(II) from perchloric acid–thiocyanate solutions[63], of plutonium(IV) from nitric acid solutions[64] and of polonium(IV) from hydrochloric and nitric acid solutions[65] provides additional examples of this application of complex acid etherates.

d. By perchloric acid. Although only carbonization was observed on mixing dioxane with pure perchloric acid, even at $-80°$, a crystalline molecular addition compound was isolated by mixing 1,4-dioxane with 70% perchloric acid and immediately cooling to $0°$ to cause precipitation of the etherate[66]. It was found to be stable in a dry atmosphere, although it liquefied in moist air, and it was given the formula $HClO_4 \cdot C_4H_8O_2 \cdot H_2O$, although the analysis actually corresponded approximately to $HClO_4 \cdot 2C_4H_8O_2 \cdot H_2O$. The physical properties and analysis suggest the structure **9** by analogy with the complex

(**9**)

halogen acid etherates. The relative basicities of dioxane and of ethyl ether have been determined by titration with perchloric acid in glacial acetic acid[67–69].

e. By hydrogen halides. The nature of the hydrogen halide–ether complexes has aroused a great deal of interest, because of the different results obtained under different conditions. The solubility of hydrogen halides is greatly dependent upon the temperature, as well as the structure of the ether, and the properties of the complexes are much affected by the amount of hydrogen halide present. Thus, the electrical conductivity of methyl ether–hydrogen chloride is very low in compositions containing less than a 1:1 ratio of hydrogen chloride to ether, but increases approximately ten-fold as the amount of hydrogen chloride is increased beyond the 1:1 ratio until maximum conductance is observed at about a 5:1 ratio[70]. The Raman spectrum of this system changes greatly with the hydrogen chloride–ether ratio, and has been interpreted by Vidale and Taylor as due to three complexes, having 1:1, 3:1 and 4:1 ratios of hydrogen chloride to ether[71]. The isotope effect with deuterium chloride showed that the first of these was a hydrogen-bonded complex and that the other two were oxonium salts. The structures of these must be **10** and **11** with the additional hydrogen chloride molecules solvating the chloride and the resulting decreased basicity of the anion permitting separation of the dimethyl-oxonium ion (reaction 15).

$$Me_2O + HCl \longrightarrow Me_2O\cdots HCl \xrightarrow{2\,HCl} Me_2OH^+Cl(HCl)_2^- \xrightarrow{HCl}$$
$$(\mathbf{10})$$

$$Me_2OH^+Cl(HCl)_3^- \quad (15)$$
$$(\mathbf{11})$$

Similar oxonium salt formation with excess hydrogen halide has been observed in the case of hydrogen fluoride also. Ethers dissolve with ease in anhydrous hydrogen fluoride to give solutions which are highly conducting when there is a large molar excess of hydrogen fluoride, but which have very low conductances even when the acid to ether ratio is less than 5:1. Apparently the amount of acid required to solvate the halide ion sufficiently to permit ionization is much greater for hydrogen fluoride than hydrogen chloride. In a study of the effect of concentration on the conductance of ethyl ether–hydrogen fluoride solutions, Quarterman and his collaborators[72] showed that maximum conductance was observed at 5·6% ether, corresponding to a 70:1 molar ratio of hydrogen fluoride to ether. Dunken and coworkers have recently reported that mixing equimolar amounts of hydrogen fluoride and ethyl ether in octane solutions gave complex formation, as shown by the heat evolution of about 18·7 kcal/mole[73,74]. This is a somewhat higher heat of mixing than observed with hydrogen chloride and ethyl ether under the same conditions (10·5 kcal/mole) and indicates formation of a stronger hydrogen-bonded complex. Further hydrogen fluoride was absorbed by the ether, however (as much as 10 moles of hydrogen fluoride per mole of ether), with further enthalpy changes and with the separation of the complex from the octane solution as a heavy second layer, indicating the formation of an oxonium salt under these conditions (reaction 16).

$$R_2O + HF \longrightarrow R_2O\cdots HF \xrightarrow{\; n\,HF \;} R_2OH^+F(HF)_n^- \qquad (16)$$

Hydrogen bromide forms a 1:1 complex with methyl ether which melts and boils at a considerably higher temperature ($-13°$ and $5°$, respectively)[75] than the corresponding hydrogen chloride complex, and the Raman spectrum showed[71] that it was not a hydrogen-bonded species but was similar to the oxonium salts (10 and 11). In the condensed phase, hydrogen bromide has a greater apparent ability to form an oxonium salt structure, $Me_2OH^+Br^-$, of the 1:1 complex. 1,8-Cineole, a terpene ether (12), is reported to form a well-defined

(12)

salt readily with hydrobromic acid[76]. This relatively stable compound melted at 56–57° and gave an elemental analysis in agreement with the 1:1 adduct, $C_{10}H_{18}OH^+Br^-$.

The ease of cleavage of ethers with hydrogen iodide[77] is attributable to similar oxonium salt formation, with the anion being a strong nucleophile which attacks an α-carbon atom in the cation. Burwell[78] has presented arguments for all ether cleavages proceeding by way of oxonium salt intermediates, which may, of course, exist in equilibrium with hydrogen-bonded complexes.

f. Basicity constants. Attempts have been made to determine basicity constants of ethers by several groups with widely different results. The most extensive study was made by Arnett and Wu[79,80] using the relation between pK_a, the acidity function H_0 of concentrated sulfuric acid solutions and the distribution coefficient of an ether between such solutions and cyclohexane[81]. The distribution coefficient was determined by gas chromatography. The results indicated the general basicity of aliphatic ethers to be much lower than that of water, varying widely with structure over the pK_a range of $-5\cdot4$ to $-2\cdot0$[80,82]. The pK_a for ethyl ether was found to be $-3\cdot61$.

The much lower pK_a value of $-6\cdot2$ has been reported for ethyl ether by Edward and his colleagues, who determined the concentration of protonated and unprotonated species in sulfuric acid solutions by intensities of nuclear magnetic resonance absorptions[83a], and a similar value is indicated by the conductance of formic acid solutions[83b]. The validity of the nuclear magnetic resonance method was indicated by agreement of pK_a values obtained by it for the conjugate acids of propionamide and propionic acid with those by the Hammett indicator method. These workers pointed out that Arnett and Wu's extraction would probably have included hydrogen-bonded complexes, such as $Et_2O \cdots H_3O^+$, with the simple diethyloxonium ion. It may be noted that with concentrated sulfuric acid the precision was much limited by difficulties with the H_0 scale, due to the lack of overlap of the different indicator scales used[80,83a].

Lemaire and Lucas[67] determined the pK_a of 1,4-dioxane in glacial acetic acid to be -4, by means of titration with perchloric acid and the use of indicators. The basicity of ethyl ether has been estimated as $-4\cdot13$ by a similar method[68,69]. The basicity of n-butyl ether was lower, so that it was beyond the range accessible by this method[67].

A different approach has been reported recently by Giles and Wells[84], who observed that the addition of 5% of dioxane, acetone or an alcohol to dilute aqueous hydrochloric acid solutions has a significant effect on the apparent acidity of the solution, as shown by indicators. With the ionic strength of the solution maintained at $1\cdot0$ to minimize activity variations, the results could be correlated with variations in the basicity of the organic solvent present. The resulting order of basicity observed was dioxane > acetone > alcohols > water, and the basicity constant of dioxane, $K'_b = [C_4H_8O_2H^+]/[C_4H_8O_2][H_3O^+]$, was evaluated as 0.70 at $25°$, corresponding to a pK_a of 1.58. This is in marked contrast to the value of -3.16 obtained by Arnett and Wu for dioxane[82].

Wells has expressed the view that this great difference in the basicity of ethers relative to water determined by the two methods is largely explicable in terms of the difference in the protonic species present in the solutions[85]. In dilute aqueous solution, there is substantial evidence for the proton being present as $(H_2O)_4H^+$, while in moderately concentrated sulfuric acid solutions it is present as a lower hydrate, such as $(H_2O)_2H^+$[86], which is less acidic, due to the proton affinities of the oxygen atom of the water being less satisfied by internal hydrogen bonding. The differences in the solvating ability of dilute, aqueous and concentrated acid solutions is no doubt another factor. There is similar difficulty in interpreting relative basicities of organic compounds by comparing the extent of reaction of hydrogen chloride in each as pure solvent, as has been done in some cases[87]. The fact that dioxane reacts with hydrogen chloride to a lesser extent than does water could be attributed to the poorer solvating ability of dioxane for the ionic species[84].

There have been two additional, independent determinations of the pK_a values of ethers. The determination of pK_a for n-butyl ether as -3.05 by Fomin and Maslova[32], mentioned in section III.A.1.a, from the distribution of nitric acid between n-butyl ether and water, is much higher than Arnett and Wu's value of -5.40[80]. On the other hand, a very much lower basicity for ethyl ether may be inferred from the ionization in anhydrous hydrogen fluoride. Quarterman and his collaborators[72] observed that ionization of ethyl ether in anhydrous hydrogen fluoride was 50% in 0.36 M solutions (and extrapolation of the data gives 51% ionization at infinite dilution). This result would correspond to a pK_a for ethyl ether approximately equal to the H_0 of anhydrous hydrogen fluoride, which is -10.2[88].

For the moment, therefore, it would appear reasonable that the pK_a values of ethers are not entirely settled and may have to be defined in terms of the solvent used. Nevertheless, Arnett and Wu's pK_a values for ethers[80] are very interesting in showing combined effects of steric and electronic factors on the basicity of ethers in sulfuric acid solutions. It was observed that methyl and t-butyl ethyl ethers were more basic than methyl isopropyl ether, which was more basic in turn than di-n-alkyl ethers with four carbon atoms or less. Increased length of an n-alkyl group, however, was associated with much lower basicity; presumably, this decrease in basicity is due to decreased solvation, whereas the effect of increasing the degree of substitution of the alkyl group is presumably an electronic effect. Phenyl ethers were found to have basicity constants about one thousand times smaller than aliphatic ethers[46].

A marked effect of ring size was observed among saturated cyclic ethers, the basicity of the simple five- and seven-membered cyclic ethers being greater than that of the six-membered one[82]. The reasons for such effect of ring size has been more fully studied by other techniques and is further discussed in section IV.D. Dioxane was noted to be less basic than other cyclic ethers, no doubt due to the mutual negative inductive effect of each oxygen atom, but nevertheless it was more basic than any acyclic di-n-alkyl ether. Some typical pK_a values for ethers are given in Table 4 (end of section III.C). For a recent and more extensive compilation of pK_a data for ethers, the reader is referred to a recent review by Arnett[89].

2. Solvation of metal ions by ethers

It would seem reasonable that cations other than the proton could coordinate with ethers, by analogy with the familiar hydration of cations. It has been established in a number of cases that this type of interaction does indeed occur, but most of the metallic salt etherates fit the category of molecular complexes better than that of oxonium salts, and are treated in section III.B. Ether-solvated cations would, of course, be most expected with small ions, such as lithium and sodium, which do not tend to form complex anions.

One of the most striking cases of metallooxonium ion formation is that with lithium perchlorate, which is soluble in ether to the extent of 44 mole per cent at 25°[90]. The electrical conductance of ethereal lithium perchlorate solutions indicates the presence of ether-solvated lithium ions, and vapor pressure studies by Ekelin and Sillen[91] showed that the ether to lithium molecular ratio was between one and two. Although these complexes and the anion may form ion clusters, these are sufficiently loose to allow conductance to take place by single-ion transport, and introduction of other ionizing species appears to lead to ion quadruplets. A remarkable importance of the latter phenomenon was observed by Winstein and coworkers[92], who found an increase in the rates of ionization of alkyl tosylates and cyclohexadienyl p-nitrobenzoate of 10^5 to 10^6 in ether upon addition of 0·1 M lithium perchlorate.

Lithium perchlorate is soluble in other ethers, but the degree of solubility does not parallel the relative basicities of ethers as measured by other methods (Table 4). Thus, it is nearly as soluble in propylene oxide as in ethyl ether, and about one third as soluble in n-butyl ether and tetrahydrofuran as in ethyl ether. The solubility in anisole and dioxane was very low[93]. The low solubility of lithium perchlorate hydrate in ethyl ether (0.2%) indicates the importance of direct attachment of the ether to the lithium ions for solubility.

Lithium aluminum hydride forms stable monoetherates with ethyl ether and with tetrahydrofuran, and an unstable dietherate with ethyl ether[94]. By analogy, these may be considered to involve ionic structures with ether-coordinated lithium ions. The reported stable monoetherates of lithium borohydride with ethyl ether and with tetrahydrofuran, and a less stable dietherate with the latter[95] are undoubtedly similar. Likewise, lithium tris(diphenylamino)aluminum hydride has been obtained as a monoetherate[96]. Lithium indium hydride, however, is reported by Nordwig to form tri- and penta-etherates, and lithium trihalogenoindium hydrides, to form tetra- and hexaetherates[97], suggesting that ether coordination with the complex indium anion, as well as with the lithium cation, may occur. A phenyllithium–phenyltungsten–ether complex, analyzing as $WPh_4 \cdot 2LiPh \cdot 3Et_2O$[98], may be an ionic complex salt, Li_2WPh_6, with one to two ether molecules coordinated with each lithium ion. Lithium iodide has been isolated as a crystalline dietherate by Talalaeva and associates[99], and the etherated 'double salts', $MeLi \cdot LiI \cdot 2Et_2O$, $MeLi \cdot LiBr \cdot 3Et_2O$, etc., isolated from the reactions of lithium metal with methyl iodide and bromide in ethyl ether[99], are likely to be complex salts, possessing ether-solvated lithium ions, such as $(Li \cdot 2Et_2O)^+ (MeLiBr)^-$.

There is definite evidence for ether coordination with the sodium ion, also. The substituted sodium borohydride salts, $NaBH_3SCN$, NaB_2H_6CN and $NaBH_3NMe_2$, were isolated by Aftandilian and colleagues[100] as etherates with dioxane, the first two involving two molecules of dioxane per sodium atom and the last one-half molecule of dioxane (and one ether oxygen atom) per sodium atom. Sodium tridecahydrodecaborate has been isolated as a monoetherate with ethyl ether, $NaB_{10}H_{13} \cdot Et_2O$, and a dietherate with methyl ether[101,102].

The conductance of sodium tetraethylaluminum in toluene was found by Day and coworkers[103] to be enhanced approximately tenfold by addition of ethyl ether in an equimolecular amount; further addition of ether had no further marked effect, indicating that the ether had caused dissociation of the ion pairs by forming the sodium monoetherate ion, which is less prone to associate with the anion (reaction 17)[103]. The effect of temperature on the conductance also

$$(Na^+AlEt_4^-) + Et_2O \longrightarrow (NaOEt_2)^+ + AlEt_4^- \qquad (17)$$

was revealing: increased conductance with temperature was observed for the salt in pure toluene, as is to be expected from the tendency for thermal dissociation of ion pairs, whereas the conductance decreased with increasing temperature of ether solutions, indicating thermal dissociation of the sodium ion–ether complex.

The monoethyl etherate of sodium tetraethylboron has been isolated as a crystalline solid, but the ether molecule is not held very firmly, as it is lost by volatilization *in vacuo* at 120° [104]. Sodium triethylboron hydride and sodium phenyltriethylboron appear to form similar ethyl etherates (being readily prepared in ether and very soluble in it) from which the ether can be readily removed by volatilization.

Polyethers such as diethylene glycol dimethyl ether ('diglyme') appear to complex much more strongly and more extensively with sodium ion than does ethyl ether. Zook and Russo[105], who formulate this complexation as in 13, observed that the sodium enolates of n-butyrophenone and diphenylacetophenone are much more soluble in the dimethyl ethers of ethylene glycol and diethylene glycol than in ethyl ether, and that these solutions show a high degree of electrical conductivity, in contrast to the lack of conductivity reported for solutions of sodium enolates in ethyl ether[106]. The much greater rate of alkylation of these enolates with ethyl bromide in these glycol ether solvents than in ethyl ether also indicates a much higher degree of ionization.

These observations, of course, correlate with the greater solvation of sodium ions by di- and polyethers, leading Zook and Russo[105] to formulate the products as enolate salts, such as 13 + 14, tetraco-

(13)   (14)

ordination of the sodium ion being assumed from the fact that it has been observed in some known complexes of the sodium ion[107,108].

Similar solvation effects of ethers have been observed in the addition of sodium to naphthalene (reaction 18), which has been found to take

$$
\text{[naphthalene]} + \text{Na} \xrightarrow{\text{R}_2\text{O}} \left[\text{[naphthalene]} \cdot \right]^{-} \text{Na}^{+} \tag{18}
$$

place better in methyl ether[109] and in tetrahydrofuran[110] than in ethyl ether, as to be expected from the greater basicity of the first two ethers shown towards many other Lewis acids. The reaction takes place particularly readily, however, in 1,2-dimethoxyethane, again indicating the increased stability of coordination when a chelate ring can be formed. Similar ease of reaction is observed in 1,2-diethoxyethane and in the dimethyl and diethyl ethers of diethylene glycol[111,112].

The green, ethereal solutions of sodium naphthalene show electrical conductance, leading Coates to state that they consist of solvated metal cations and hydrocarbon anions[110,113]. Recent electron spin resonance evidence on the rate of reaction of naphthalene with the naphthalene radical anions confirms such an ionic structure for the glycol ether solutions, but indicates that the ethyl ether solutions contained the sodium naphthalene principally in the form of ion pairs[114].

Eargle's observation of similar structural effects in aliphatic ethers used as solvents for alkali metal cleavage of aromatic ethers, is very interesting (reaction 19)[115]. The rate of this cleavage reaction de-

$$
\text{Ar}_2\text{O} + 2\,\text{M} \longrightarrow \text{ArOM} + \text{ArM} \tag{19}
$$

pended strongly on the nature of the ether solvent in the approximate order: 1,2-dimethoxyethane > tetrahydrofuran > tetrahydropyran > 2-methyltetrahydropyran.

Such an order suggests that the solvation of alkali metal cations formed is a rate-determining factor here. Wilkinson and his students have observed similar structural effects of ethers in the dissolving of sodium and potassium to give blue ethereal solutions of the metals[116]. The ability of an ether to stabilize the metal cations by solvation appears to control the rate of solution of metals, forming solvated cations and electrons[112].

It has long been recognized that α-arylalkylsodium compounds, such as tritylsodium, are dissociated into ions in ether solutions, as shown

9*

by the electrical conductivity of such solutions[113,117]. Such dissociation is actually rather slight[113], and the observed decrease in apparent ionization of tritylsodium with decrease in concentration indicates that the ionization occurring is into sodium cations and ditritylsodium anions, $(Ph_3C)_2Na^-$ [106]. The probable ether solvation of the sodium ions is generally acknowledged but has not been specifically investigated. The situation is probably similar to that recently observed for the equimolar mixture of phenylsodium and phenyllithium in ether, which Wittig and collaborators found to be in the form of the complex salt, $Na^+(Ph_2Li)^-$ [118], which was isolated as a monoetherate. It seems reasonable that the ether molecule was associated with the sodium atom, although this was not proved.

Recently, the formation of sodium salts of 6-methylazulene and guiazulene were reported by Hafner and colleagues[119], who obtained them by reaction of the hydrocarbons with sodium N-methylanilide in ethyl ether solution, and isolated them as monoetherates (reaction 20). The properties of these compounds suggested an ionic structure, with the ether molecule, of course, coordinated with the sodium ion.

$$\qquad\qquad\qquad\qquad\qquad\qquad\qquad\qquad\qquad\qquad\qquad\qquad (20)$$

The high solubility of $KFeCl_4$ in ethyl ether[120] probably may be viewed as indicative of ether solvation of the potassium ion.

Organolithium compounds are also well known to coordinate with ether, but often this may be molecular association, as in Grignard reagents (section III.B.2), rather than lithium ion solvation. Fluorenyllithium, however, has been found to form complexes with tetrahydrofuran and 1,2-dimethoxyethane, which appear to be ionic. Dixon and coworkers concluded from ^1H and ^7Li nuclear magnetic resonance studies on these complexes that the lithium ion and ether are both located directly above the plane of the aromatic anion, with the lithium thus being present as a solvated ion[121].

3. Trialkyloxonium salts

An aliphatic ether may act as a Lewis base towards an alkyl halide in the presence of a third substance which can react with the halide ion. This general reaction was discovered by Meerwein and coworkers[122,123] and may be illustrated by the direct reaction of ethyl fluoride with methyl ether–boron trifluoride, which takes place slowly at room temperature to form the crystalline dimethylethyloxonium tetrafluoroborate (reaction 21)[122]. The use of the preformed ether–boron trifluoride complex is convenient and provides the correct stoichiometry.

$$EtF + Me_2O:BF_3 \longrightarrow Me_2OEt^+BF_4^- \tag{21}$$

Trimethyloxonium and methyldiethyloxonium tetrafluoroborate have also been made in the same way, but the method is not of preparative value, as the slowness of the reaction causes the isolated yields of oxonium salts to be low even after days or weeks of reaction. The synthesis of triethyloxonium hexachloroantimonate from ethyl chloride and ethyl ether–antimony pentachloride was very similar, but no oxonium salts were obtained from the addition of ethyl or methyl chloride to the etherates of aluminum chloride, ferric chloride, boron trichloride or stannic chloride. These can be made, however, by other methods.

Trialkyloxonium salts are extraordinarily strong alkylating agents, effective for a large variety of substances, including phenols, carboxylic acids, acetoacetic and malonic esters, dialkyl sulfides, pyridine, ammonia and other amines, nitrites, amides, ketones and lactones[122,124]. The oxygen alkylation of amides by triethyloxonium tetrafluoroborate, sometimes called 'Meerwein's reagent', is synthetically useful in the hydrolysis of amides, since the resulting imino esters are easily hydrolyzed, and an application of this method has been employed recently in the synthesis of anhydroaureomycine[125].

Alkylation of other ethers is also possible and may occur in the case of the reaction of n-propyl fluoride with dimethyl ether–boron trifluoride, which gives trimethyloxonium tetrafluoroborate, instead of the expected dimethylpropyloxonium salt (reaction 22). This type of

$$PrF + 2Me_2O:BF_3 \longrightarrow Me_3O^+BF_4^- (+ MePrO:BF_3 \ ?) \tag{22}$$

ether alkylation has been studied in detail in the case of tetrahydrofuran, which can be polymerized by treatment with several trialkyloxonium salts, such as triethyloxonium tetrafluoroborate, hexachloroantimonate, tetrachloroaluminate and tetrachloroferrate (reaction 23)[126].

$$Et_3O^+BF_4^- + (CH_2)_4O \longrightarrow [Et-O(CH_2)_4]^+BF_4^- + Et_2O$$

$$\downarrow$$

$$EtO(CH_2)_3CH_2^+BF_4^- \xrightarrow{(CH_2)_4O} Polymer \tag{23}$$

A similar type of cross alkylation involving ethers apparently occurs in the reaction of metal halide–ether adducts with epichlorohydrin in a solution of the same ether. Thus, addition of epichlorohydrin to a solution of ethyl ether–boron trifluoride adduct in ethyl ether rapidly gives a high yield of crystalline triethyloxonium tetrafluoroborate (reaction 24), and a great variety of other trialkyloxonium salts have been

$$3\ ClCH_2\text{—}CH\text{—}CH_2 + 4\ Et_2O : BF_3 + 2\ Et_2O \longrightarrow$$
$$\underset{O}{\diagdown\diagup}$$

$$3\ Et_3O^+BF_4^- + B(\text{—}O\text{—}\underset{CH_2Cl}{\overset{|}{CH}}CH_2OEt)_3 \quad (24)$$

prepared by this method, such as trimethyl- and tripropyloxonium tetrafluoroborates, trimethyloxonium hexachloroantimonate and triethyloxonium tetrachloroaluminate and tetrachloroferrate. The convenience and ease of this method makes it of synthetic value.

Another very convenient method for preparing trialkyloxonium salts has been developed by Meerwein and coworkers, and consists of the reaction of silver fluoroborate with an alkyl bromide and the corresponding ether[127]. Triethyloxonium fluoroborate was prepared in 90% yield from ethyl bromide, ethyl ether and silver fluoroborate in ethylene chloride solution (reaction 25). The silver fluoroborate is

$$EtBr + Et_2O + AgBF_4 \longrightarrow Et_3O^+BF_4^- + AgBr \quad (25)$$

prepared conveniently from silver oxide and the ether–boron trifluoride adduct.

Klages and his collaborators have extensively developed a method of preparing trialkyloxonium salts by reaction of diazoalkanes with etherates of complex halogen acids[48–50]. This is, of course, basically similar to Meerwein's method, as reaction of diazoalkanes with strong acids is known to give carbonium ion intermediates. Methyldiethyloxonium hexachloroantimonate was obtained in 83% yield by reaction of diethyloxonium hexachloroantimonate (section III.A.1.c) with diazomethane in ethylene chloride solution, and a series of trialkyloxonium fluoroborates, chloroaluminates, hexachlorostannates and hexachloroantimonates, including even the aromatic example, phenyldimethyloxonium hexachloroantimonate. The latter was prepared also by diazomethane alkylation of phenyloxonium hexachloroantimonate (reaction 26).

$$[Ph\text{—}\underset{H}{\overset{|}{O}}\text{—}Me]^+SbCl_6^- + CH_2N_2 \longrightarrow [Ph\text{—}OMe_2]^+SbCl_6^- + N_2 \quad (26)$$

Reaction of diazoacetic ester with dialkyloxonium hexachloroanti-monates generally gave the simple trialkyloxonium salt (reaction 27),

$$2\ Pr_2O + SbCl_5 + HCl \longrightarrow [Pr_2OH \cdot OPr_2]^+ SbCl_6^- \xrightarrow{N_2CH_2CO_2Et} Pr_3O^+ SbCl_6^- \quad (27)$$

due to the presence of coordinated ether in the dialkyloxonium salt, but in the cases of diisopropyl- and diisoamyloxonium hexachloro-antimonates the expected ester salts, $[R_2OCH_2CO_2Et]^+ SbCl_6^-$ (R = i-Pr or i-Am), were obtained in low yields[49].

Anion exchange can be achieved with trialkyloxonium salts by means of simple double decomposition reactions. In this way, chloro-aurate, chloroplatinate, trichloromercurate, triiodomercurate, tetra-iodobismuthate, heptachlorodibismuthate and the dihydrogenferri-cyanide salts have been prepared from the more easily obtained fluoroborates and chloroantimonate salts[123]. Most of these were not very stable, due to dissociation of the complex anion to give a nucleo-philic anion, which, of course, is rapidly alkylated by the oxonium salt. It was demonstrated that the more nucleophilic the anion, the less stable is the oxonium salt[78,122].

4. Dialkylacyloxonium salts

The acylation of ethers by acyl halides in the presence of an appro-priate metallic halide, giving a dialkylacyloxonium salt, has been demonstrated by Klages and his collaborators[128]. For example di-ethylacetyloxonium hexachloroantimonate was obtained in good yield as a crystalline solid from the reaction of acetyl chloride, ethyl ether and antimony pentachloride in methylene chloride solution at low temperature (reaction 28). Its ionic nature was shown by its electrical conductivity in liquid sulfur dioxide.

$$CH_3COCl + Et_2O + SbCl_5 \longrightarrow [CH_3CO \cdot OEt_2]^+ SbCl_6^- \quad (28)$$

Such salts are probably intermediates in the well-known cleavage of ethers with acid halides in the presence of zinc chloride or other metallic salts capable of forming complex anions[129,130]. A recently re-ported method of cleaving ethers, by treatment with an acid anhydride in the presence of boron trifluoride etherate and a lithium halide, has also been postulated as involving an acyldialkyloxonium salt, but the role of the lithium halide was not clarified[131].

B. Nonionized Coordination Complexes

Many salts and other compounds which can act as Lewis acids react with ethers to form nonionic addition compounds. Certain types of

these, particularly those involving boron, have been extensively
studied, with many conclusions being apparently applicable to the
whole class.

The bonding of these compounds with ethers is considered to be
essentially of a dipolar nature, involving coordinate covalence of the
ether oxygen atom to the metal atom, as in structure (15). Such a

$$R—O:ZX_n$$
$$|$$
$$R$$

(15)

structure is supported by the electron-diffraction study reported by
Bauer and coworkers of methyl ether–boron trifluoride showing a new
B—O bond, 1·5 Å in length, in addition to the original C—O and
B—F bonds[132]. The coordinate complex structure is also in accord
with numerous properties observed for boron fluoride–ether adducts,
including nuclear magnetic resonance[9-11] and Raman spectra[133],
their low vapor pressures[134], the occurrence of rapid displacement reactions[6], and the easy dissociation into the original components often
observed.

The position of the equilibrium between the adduct and the Lewis

$$R_2O:ZX_n \rightleftharpoons R_2O + ZX_n \tag{29}$$

acid and base varies greatly (reaction 29), with borane etherates being
highly dissociated and trialkylaluminum etherates so stable that it is
difficult to remove the ether. The reader is referred to the excellent
reviews of the chemistry of coordination compounds of Group III
elements by Stone[135], Martin[136,137], Martin and Canon[138], Greenwood and Martin[139] and Greenwood and Wade[140], for many of the
concepts involved apply to nonionized coordination complexes in
general.

I. Coordination compounds of alkali metals

The most conspicuous examples of this type are the organolithium
compounds, since salts and other organometallic compounds of this
group tend to form ionic complexes[141] (section III.A.2). The evidence
for complexation of organolithium compounds with ethers is quite
varied and includes Talalaeva and coworkers' isolation of a solid 1:1
adduct of ethyl ether with methyllithium, $MeLi \cdot Et_2O$, by cooling and
concentrating an ether solution prepared from methyl chloride[99] and
lithium. When methyl bromide or iodide was used for the preparation,

ternary complexes containing lithium halide were obtained, such as $MeLi \cdot LiBr \cdot 3Et_2O$.

A marked effect of ether observed on the chemical properties of butyllithium may be attributed to complex formation. Thus, Hauser and his students[141] found that butyllithium reacted with mesityl-acetonitrile in ether solution to form butane and the lithium salt of the nitrile, whereas in benzene the reaction proceeded by addition to give the expected imine. This result was interpreted as indicative of an ionic structure for the ether complex, consisting of an ether-solvated lithium cation and the butyl anion.

Welch[142] drew a similar conclusion from the great enhancement of the rate of polymerization of styrene by butyllithium when small amounts of ethers were added, since the polymerization appeared to be subject to anionic catalysis. The kinetic effects of the ethers present indicated complexes of type $BuLi \cdot 2R_2O$, with the very large association constants of 3×10^6, $1 \cdot 5 \times 10^5$ and $2 \cdot 0 \times 10^3$ for the tetrahydrofuran, 2,5-dimethyltetrahydrofuran and ethyl ether complexes, respectively.

The conclusion that ionic reactions of the complexes point to an ionic structure is not necessarily certain, since the effect of the ether on the reaction transition states may be of the greatest importance in these reactions. There is significant physical evidence for their co-valent nature. Nikitin, Rodionov and their collaborators[143,144] have observed that the infrared absorption bands of various alkyllithium and aryllithium compounds in hydrocarbon solvents become displaced to lower frequencies by approximately 100 cm^{-1} in the presence of most ethers. This effect would indicate an association of the ether oxygen atom with the lithium atom, resulting in a weakening but not breaking of the carbon–lithium bond. The larger ethers, such as n-butyl ether and isoamyl ether, had relatively little effect on the infrared absorption, suggesting that the solvation was much affected by steric hindrance.

From determinations of the molecular weight by freezing-point

(16)

depression in cyclohexane, Eastham and coworkers[145] concluded that the stoichiometry of butyllithium ethyl ether was that of a hemi-etherate, $(BuLi)_2 \cdot Et_2O$. The nuclear magnetic resonance spectrum of the complex in hexane solvent seemed best interpreted in terms of a solvated cyclic dimer (16).

2. Coordination compounds of alkaline earth elements

a. Salts. Several etherates of beryllium and magnesium halides have been recognized and are of importance in the solubility of these salts in ethers. A series of dietherates of beryllium chloride and bromide with methyl ether, ethyl ether, tetrahydrofuran and tetrahydropyran have been prepared by Turova and associates, using the reaction of beryllium with the corresponding halogen or halogen acid in the ether as solvent, or by addition of the ether to the anhydrous salt[146-150]. Such etherates may generally be crystallized and isolated as solids with well-defined melting points, although the dietherate of beryllium chloride with n-butyl ether was an apparently uncrystallizable oil[149]. Dioxane formed 1:1 addition compounds with beryllium chloride and iodide, which appeared to be of a linear polymeric structure,

$$\left[X_2Be \cdot O \bigcirc O \right]_n$$

Various etherates of magnesium bromide and iodide have been prepared by similar methods, as well as by reaction of magnesium with the corresponding mercuric halide in ether solution[151-153]. With ethyl ether, magnesium iodide forms a tetraetherate, which is stable in ether solution below 8°, a trietherate which is stable below 17° and a dietherate which has been isolated and is variously reported at 23° and at 48–50°[151]. Di- and trietherates of magnesium bromide with ethyl ether have been reported[151,154]. Magnesium chloride and fluoride, on the other hand, do not appear to form etherates and are very nearly insoluble in ether[151].

A higher etherate of a beryllium salt has been observed in only one instance, that of $BeBr_2 \cdot 3Et_2O$; this was found to be the stable etherate in ether solutions of beryllium bromide below $-4°$[148,155]. A report of beryllium chloride trietherate[147,156] was later found to be incorrect[155].

The ether molecules in beryllium salt dietherates are relatively loosely bound, as they lose their ether on heating at moderate temperatures[157].

The ether in beryllium and magnesium halide etherates can be displaced by another ether by dissolving or heating in the latter as solvent. Thus, tetrahydropyran and 1,2-dimethoxyethane displaced ethyl ether from $BeCl_2 \cdot 2Et_2O$,[149] and tetrahydrofuran and dioxane displaced ethyl ether from $MgI_2 \cdot 2Et_2O$[152,153].

Dioxanates of the bromides and iodides of calcium, strontium and barium have been prepared as reticulate polymeric compounds[149]. The possible polymeric structure of simple etherates, such as $MgBr_2 \cdot 2Et_2O$, has been considered; vapor-pressure studies indicate that association to dimers probably occurs, with the monomeric form, however, predominant[158,159].

b. Organometallic compounds. An excellent general review of the chemistry of this class of compounds up to 1960 has been provided by Coates[110b]. Although the general importance of the coordination of ethers with these compounds in general is well recognized, the nature of such coordination has been studied mainly with Grignard reagents.

It is well accepted that coordinated ether is an integral part of a Grignard reagent. Kharasch and Reinmuth[160] have reviewed the evidence on ether coordination with Grignard reagents up to 1950. Recently Bryce-Smith[161] has reported the preparation of unsolvated organomagnesium halides, which had properties quite different from those of Grignard reagents, and the effect of varying the solvating ether has received considerable study. With weakly basic ethers, such as anisole, formation of Grignard reagents was much slower than with ethyl and n-butyl ethers, while the more basic tetrahydrofuran is observed to greatly facilitate the formation of vinyl Grignard reagents, though not that of alkyl Grignard reagents[162]. Based on such effects, Kirrmann, Hamelin and Hayes[162-164] have proposed the following order of basicity of ethers towards organomagnesium halides:

PhOMe, PhOEt < i-Pr$_2$O < n-Bu$_2$O < Et$_2$O < (CH$_2$)$_4$O < 1,4-dioxane

The exact nature of the complexation is, of course, affected by the question of the possible dimerization of the Grignard reagent, which has been a matter of discussion for many years[165-167]. The etherated, unsymmetrical dimer structure (**18**) has been widely accepted[167-169], but Ashby and Smith[170] have recently cast new light on the problem with new determinations of molecular weights and a reexamination of previous data. It now appears that the principal species are solvated monomer and symmetrical dimer (**17**), although alkyl exchange may

(**17**)   (**18**)

also occur to give dialkylmagnesium and magnesium halide[170,171].
The equilibrium between the monomeric and dimeric forms is
governed to a large extent by the nature of the halogen and of the
solvating ether present[170,172]. The alkylmagnesium chlorides are dimeric in ethyl ether solutions over a wide concentration range, but
with alkylmagnesium bromides and iodides both forms are present in
comparable amounts in ethyl ether[170]. The effect of the ether has
been shown by the observation that ethylmagnesium chloride is
monomeric in tetrahydrofuran, even at concentrations as high as
2 M[171]. Apparently the greater basicity of tetrahydrofuran enables it
to compete more successfully than ethyl ether with the halide ions for
complexing with the magnesium ions.

An x-ray crystallographic study of solid phenylmagnesium bromide
dietherate recently reported by Stucky and Rundle[159] showed that the
unit structure of this compound contained two ether oxygen atoms, a
bromine atom and a phenyl group coordinated at tetrahedral angles
with the magnesium atom, and studies on the molecular weight of this
Grignard reagent in ethyl ether indicated that it consisted of loosely
associated ether-solvated monomers[173].

3. Coordination compounds of Group III elements

Many compounds of boron, aluminum, gallium, thallium and indium react with ethers, as well as other Lewis bases, to form addition
compounds. Their stoichiometry is usually 1 Group III atom:1 ether
oxygen atom, but exceptions have been observed occasionally. Among
these exceptions are certain dioxanates, such as $BF_3 \cdot C_4H_8O_2$,[139,174]
and $AlCl_3 \cdot 2Me_2O$,[175] where complexation of the ether oxygen atoms
is incomplete, and some weak addition compounds containing more
than an equivalent amount of boron trifluoride, such as $2BF_3 \cdot Et_2O$[176]
and $3BF_3 \cdot Et_2O$[177]. The latter are generally unstable with respect
to the 1:1 complexes but may be observed at low temperatures.
Shchegoleva[176] has proposed an ionic structure for ether complexes
containing excess boron trifluoride, $R_2O-BF_2^+BF_4^-$.

In view of the excellent reviews available on this subject[135-140] attention will be limited to recent developments and the structural effects on donor abilities of ethers. No attempt will be made to review the extensive literature on the applications of these etherates to catalysis of numerous reactions.

a. Boron trifluoride etherates. The interaction of ethers with boron trifluoride to form molecular addition compounds is almost general. The few ethers which appear not to give complexes with boron trifluoride are those which have markedly electron-withdrawing groups or considerable steric hindrance, such as ethyl 2-octyl ether[178], phenyl ether[179] or benzyl ether[180].

Boron trifluoride etherates are generally isolable as quite stable liquids which can be crystallized at somewhat below ambient temperatures and can be distilled in many cases without decomposition. Distillation generally involves dissociation of the adduct (reaction 30),

$$R_2O : BF_3 \rightleftharpoons R_2O + BF_3 \tag{30}$$

followed by recombination on condensation[139]. In the case of anisole–boron trifluoride, it is possible to heat the complex at a temperature of 155–170° with the anisole returned by reflux and the boron trifluoride swept out with a dry nitrogen stream, thus, achieving a complete thermal dissociation of the complex, and a convenient laboratory source of boron trifluoride[181].

The dissociation constants of such etherates provide a measure of the strengths of these complexes, as do also the heats of dissociation or association. These data indicate an order of stability for simple aliphatic ether–boron trifluoride complexes, decreasing with increasing α substitution[182,183]:

$$Me_2O : BF_3 > Et_2O : BF_3 > i\text{-}Pr_2O : BF_3$$

Thus, the order of stability in this series seems to follow the order of steric strain in the complex, rather than the inductive effects of the alkyl groups. When the steric hindrance is reduced by a cyclic structure for the ether, as in tetrahydrofuran and tetrahydropyran, the stability of the complexes is much greater[184]. Three- and four-membered cyclic ethers are prone to undergo polymerization when treated with boron trifluoride at temperatures high enough to study vapor pressures, but phase-data evidence indicates that ethylene oxide does form a 1:1 complex at −80° [177,185].

Exchange of boron trifluoride between ethers occurs with ease and at rates comparable to those for proton acid–base reactions (reaction

31). Determination of equilibrium constants for such exchange pro-

$$Me_2O + Et_2O : BF_3 \rightleftharpoons Me_2O : BF_3 + Et_2O \qquad (31)$$

cesses has been used to determine the relative stability of etherates. This has been done by estimating the composition by infrared spectral measurements[6] and by nuclear magnetic resonance studies, using ^{19}F resonance[186,190]. The equilibrium constant for the exchange reaction between methyl ether and boron trifluoride–ethyl ether, as formulated above, was $2 \cdot 5$[187] while that for the analogous exchange with anisole was less than 5×10^{-3}[188]. The results from the infrared spectral measurements were similar and somewhat more extensive, giving the following order for the relative basicities of ethers towards boron trifluoride:

$$(CH_2)_4O > (CH_2)_5O > Me_2O > MeOEt > Et_2O > Pr_2O > i\text{-}Pr_2O > PhOMe$$

The most basic ether in the series, tetrahydrofuran, was comparable in basicity to methanol and ethanol, while the least basic ether in the series, anisole, complexed more strongly with boron trifluoride than ethyl sulfide[185,189].

An intensive study has been made of the use of such exchange reactions to attain a separation of the boron isotopes, making use of the higher volatility of the $^{10}BF_3$ adduct[191-199]. A discussion of this work is beyond the scope of this chapter, but it is of general interest that the activation energies for boron trifluoride–etherate exchange reactions were observed to be less than the heat of dissociation of the complexes, indicating a displacement mechanism for the exchange reaction[187,188,190].

b. Etherates of other boron compounds. With trifluoromethylboron difluoride, methyl ether forms a solid 1:1 addition compound of low volatility. The addition compound of anisole with this Lewis acid is rather unstable[200].

Generally, boron trichloride complexes with ethers, exceptions being phenyl ether[201] and bis(chloromethyl) ether[178], but the complexes are often very unstable with respect to an ether cleavage (reaction 32).

$$R_2O + BCl_3 \rightleftharpoons R_2O : BCl_3 \longrightarrow RCl + ROBCl_2 \qquad (32)$$

By working at a low temperature, such as $-80°$, Gerrard and coworkers were able to observe formation of complexes of boron trichloride with methyl, ethyl, allyl and allyl methallyl ethers, and also with anisole[178,202,203]; some ethers proved to be sufficiently unreactive with respect to cleavage, to make possible the isolation of pure 1:1

adducts with boron trichloride. Such adducts were prepared from methyl chloromethyl ether, methyl 2-chloroethyl ether, ethyl 2-chloroethyl ether, bis-(2-chloroethyl) ether, n-butyl ether, tetrahydrofuran and tetrahydropyran[178,204,205].

The cleavage of ethers by phenylboron dichloride has been postulated by Gerrard and coworkers to involve intermediate formation of a 1:1 complex, but no ether complexes of this reagent have been isolated[206]. Graham and Stone observed that trimethylboron was too weak a Lewis acid to form any complex with methyl ether even at $-78°$[207].

Diborane is a very weak Lewis acid for ethers[208a]. No association with ethyl ether was detectable even at $-78°$[208b], but with tetrahydrofuran the complex, $(CH_2)_4O:BH_3$, was observed at $-78°$, although not at room temperature[209]. Tetraborane is cleaved by ethers to form ether–B_3H_7 complexes (reaction 33)[209]. The latter may be formed also

$$2 R_2O + 2 B_4H_{10} \longrightarrow 2 R_2O \cdot B_3H_7 + B_2H_6 \tag{33}$$

by reaction of the diammoniate of tetraborane with acids in ether solution[210].

Etherates of monochloroborane and dichloroborane have been reported by Brown and Tierney. These were formed by the reaction of boron trichloride with diborane or sodium borohydride in ether solution, the ether being ethyl ether, methyl ether, tetrahydrofuran, tetrahydropyran or diglyme[211]. These etherates were obtained as white, low-melting solids and have been patented as reagents for hydrogenation of various carbonyl compounds[212].

c. *Etherates of aluminum, gallium and indium compounds.* It is well known that aluminum chloride generally complexes with ethers[140]. Bercaw and Garrett have pointed out that, due to the dimeric nature of aluminum chloride, the complexation with ethers generally involves two equilibria; the first involving cleavage of just one Al—Cl—Al bond giving $R_2O \cdot AlCl_3 \cdot AlCl_3$ complexes, and the second involving complete rupture of the dimeric chloride to give $R_2O:AlCl_3$[213]. The first equilibrium apparently can be observed separately with dioxane, but most ethers give complexes with monomeric aluminum chloride, which may be isolated or studied by physical means[213-215].

Several alkylaluminum chlorides have been isolated recently in the form of etherates, which were stable, distillable liquids. These include the ethyl, n-propyl and n-butyl etherates of ethylaluminum dichloride and diethylaluminum chloride, and the ethyl etherate of di-n-butyl-aluminum chloride[216,217].

The ether complexes of trialkylaluminums generally are very stable, distillable liquids, even in the cases of weakly basic ethers, such as anisole and phenetole [218, 219]. The ethyl etherate of optically active tris-(S-2-methylbutyl)aluminum was stable at room temperature for months and at 110° for at least an hour [220]. Complexation of these aluminum compounds is not greatly affected by steric hindrance, as tri-t-butylaluminum was found to form a relatively stable etherate with ethyl ether [221]. The heats of complexation of triethylaluminum with a series of ethers led to an order of base strength of ethers quite similar to that observed with boron trifluoride [222]:

$$(CH_2)_4O > Alk_2O, \text{ 1,4-dioxane} > MeOPh, Ph_2O > \text{dibenzofuran}$$

Triphenylaluminum forms 1:1 complexes with ethyl ether, n-butyl ether, ethyl vinyl ether, tetrahydrofuran and anisole, but not with phenyl ether [216, 223, 224]. Trivinylaluminum has been isolated in the form of its ethyl ether and tetrahydrofuran adducts [225], and diethylaluminum diphenylphosphide was observed to form a crystalline ethyl etherate [226]. Aluminum hydride is reported to react with ethyl ether and tetrahydrofuran to form addition compounds with stoichiometry of 1:1 [227, 228], approximately 2:1 [229] or 1:2 [227, 230], depending on the manner of formation of the complex.

Gallium trichloride and tribromide form stable 1:1 adducts with methyl ether and ethyl ether [175], and phase studies showed the existence of a less stable dietherate, $GaCl_3 \cdot 2Et_2O$ [140, 231]. Gallium hydride has been found to form a 1:1 adduct with ethyl ether which is stable below 35° [232].

Fairbrother and collaborators reported recently that indium trichloride, tribromide and triiodide complex with ethers generally, with the interesting feature that the formation of 1:2 complexes greatly predominates over 1:1 complexes here [233].

4. Ether complexes of heavy metal compounds

Compounds of heavy metal atoms which have a tendency for additional coordinate covalent bond formation, frequently complex with ethers to form nonionized addition compounds. For example auric chloride monoetherate, $Cl_3Au \cdot OEt_2$, and mercuric chloride dioxanate, $Cl_2Hg \cdot C_4H_8O_2$, readily form by the interaction of ethyl ether or dioxane with the designated salt [234a]. Although ether complexation is basically similar to aquation and ammonia complexation, it is not always parallel, and some compounds which are susceptible to the latter, such as cupric bromide, cadmium bromide and nickel bromide, apparently do not form etherates, even when prepared from the elements in ether solution[154].

Ether-complexed salts of zinc and cadmium have been long known and may be illustrated by adducts of cineole with zinc and cadmium iodide, which have the general structure, $MI_2 \cdot 2$cineole[234b, 235]. The monoetherates and hemietherates of a series of arylzinc halides have been isolated as crystalline solids from the reaction of diarylzinc compounds with zinc halide salts in ether solution[236], and Thiele[237] has recently reported that dimethylzinc forms monoetherates with methyl ether, ethylene oxide and oxetane, and dietherates with tetrahydrofuran and tetrahydropyran. The compositions were determined by elemental analyses of the distilled etherates, but molecular-weight determinations in benzene and cyclohexane solutions indicated that considerable dissociation occurred in solution. From the degree of dissociation thus observed, it appeared that the electron-donor abilities of the cyclic ethers studied increased in order of increasing ring size: ethylene oxide < oxetane < tetrahydrofuran < tetrahydropyran. Thiele explained this unusual order of ring-size effects as being due to the nature of the unshared electron orbitals in the ethers, tetrahedral (sp^3) orbitals being more favorable for bonding than orbitals with more s character, which would be expected to an increasing degree with decreasing ring size.

Addition of ethers to stannic chloride gives generally strong complexes of structure, $SnCl_4 \cdot 2R_2O$, while germanium and silicon tetrachlorides do not complex appreciably with ethers, as reported by Sisler and his students[238, 239]. A study of the stability of complexes of several cyclic ethers with stannic chloride by Ciaffi and Zenchelsky[240] showed the following apparent order of basicity: tetrahydrofuran > tetrahydropyran > 4-methyltetrahydrofuran > 2-methyltetrahydrofuran > 2,5-dimethyltetrahydrofuran. This order was interpreted as being due mainly to a combination of I-strain and F-strain factors.

Both titanium tetrachloride and zirconium tetrachloride form solid dietherates with ethyl ether[241, 242], and apparently similar adducts are formed with other ethers, including tetrahydrofuran, tetrahydropyran and dioxane with titanium tetrachloride[243] and phenyl ether and bis-(2-chloroethyl) ether with zirconium tetrachloride[244, 245]. The complex of titanium tetrachloride with anisole seemingly had 1:1 stoichiometry, however, and 1:1 complexes with tetrahydrofuran and tetrahydropyran could be prepared by use of excess titanium tetrachloride[243]. While the above titanium complexes were all of yellow to orange color, the tetrahydrofuran complex of methyltitanium trichloride, $MeTiCl_3 \cdot 2C_4H_8O$, was dark red in color[246]. A mono-etherate of titanium oxychloride, $TiOCl_2 \cdot 2Et_2O$, is reported to be a yellow solid. Dietherates of titanium tetrabromide with tetrahydro-furan, tetrahydropyran and dioxane were successfully prepared as red solids, low temperatures being required for the preparation to mini-mize cleavage of the ether function[247].

A series of ether complexes of niobium and tantalum pentachlorides and pentafluorides has recently been isolated by Fairbrother and collaborators[248,249]. These complexes were liquids or low-melting solids of the general formula, $MX_5 \cdot R_2O$, where R was methyl, ethyl or n-propyl. Dietherates also were formed from niobium and tanta-lum pentafluorides with methyl ether at low temperature, but these lost one molecule of ether on being warmed to $-9°$.

Chromium tribromide and triphenylchromium both form octahedral trietherates with tetrahydrofuran[250]. This ether complexation gives important stability to triphenylchromium; when the tetrahydrofuran is removed by reduced pressure, warming or adding ethyl ether, the chromium–phenyl σ bond collapses to form a π-complexed dibenzene-chromium 'sandwich compound'. This type of behavior cannot occur when chelatable ether oxygen atoms are attached at an *ortho* position of each phenyl group, as in tris-(o-anisyl)chromium, which was re-cently isolated by Hein and Tille[251] as a reddish-brown crystalline solid.

There are a few reports of ether complexation of molybdenum and tungsten compounds, including the dietherates of molybdic oxide hydrochloride[252] and tungsten pentachloride[253] with ethyl ether. Molybdenum tribromide is reported not to form an ethyl etherate[154].

The extraction of uranyl nitrate from aqueous solution by ethers has received considerable attention, ethyl ether being more effective for this extraction than isopropyl, n-butyl or isoamyl ethers[62,254]. It has been determined that the ether-complexed species, $UO_2(NO_3)_2 \cdot 3H_2O \cdot Et_2O$ and $UO_2(NO_3)_2 \cdot 2H_2O \cdot 2Et_2O$, are formed on addition of ether[255,256]. Infrared spectral data show that ether molecules also associate with the hydrated water molecules by hydrogen bonding[257].

The solubility of cobalt nitrate in ethers, such as ethyl ether, tetra-hydrofuran and 1,2-diethoxyethane, appears to be somewhat similar to that of uranyl nitrate; and from heats of solution data and other evidence Katzin concluded that ether molecules and anions co-ordinate with the cobalt atom to form tetracovalent species, $Co(NO_3)_2(R_2O)_2$[64,258].

In the absence of water, ferric chloride reacted with dioxane to form a dioxanate complex having the empirical formula, $FeCl_3 \cdot C_4H_8O_2$, while in the presence of water ternary complexes containing water and additional dioxane were obtained[259]. Under reduced pressure, however, the water and part of the dioxane could be removed from the latter with formation of the dioxanate obtained in the absence of water, thus showing the iron–dioxane bond to be stronger than the iron–water bond. An etherated, bridged cationic structure, $[Fe_2Cl_4(C_4H_8O_2)_2]^{2+}2\ Cl^-$, was proposed for the stable complex, while the ternary complexes seemed to be solvated monoferric species, such as $[FeCl_2(C_4H_8O_2)_2H_2O]^+Cl^-$. The polymerization of epoxides in the presence of catalytic amounts of ferric chloride or other metallic halide is considered to involve similar complexation as a first step[260–262].

It is of interest that manganese bromide and iodide form relatively stable, isolable monoetherates with ethyl ether[154,263].

5. Other nonionic coordination complexes of ethers

Several oxides and halides of nonmetals not previously covered have been shown to act as Lewis acids towards ethers, forming addition compounds with them. Among these is sulfur trioxide, which when passed into ethyl ether caused separation of a heavy layer having the composition, $2Et_2O \cdot SO_3$[264]. Further addition of sulfur trioxide was reported to give the complexes $Et_2O \cdot SO_3$ and $Et_2O \cdot 2SO_3$.

Similar results were obtained with selenium trioxide by Schmidt and coworkers[265]. Evaporation of a saturated solution of selenium trioxide in ether or dioxane gave a solid material which was found to be $SeO_3 \cdot Et_2O$ or $SeO_3 \cdot C_4H_8O_2$, respectively.

Molecular addition compounds of dinitrogen tetroxide with a series of ethers have been described by Sisler and his collaborators[13,266–268]. Thermal-phase studies on N_2O_4–ether systems showed the formation of compounds containing one molecule of dinitrogen tetroxide to two molecules of ethyl, n-propyl, n-butyl and isopropyl ethers and of oxetane, tetrahydropyran, tetrahydrofuran, 2-methyltetrahydrofuran and 2,5-dimethyltetrahydrofuran. The melting points of these complexes were in the range of -20 to $-78°$, but the 1:1 complexes of dinitrogen tetroxide with 1,3- and 1,4-dioxane were much higher, being 2 and 45°, respectively, apparently due to a more stable crystal structure for such addition compounds, which are of a polymeric nature[269].

Magnetic and Raman spectral studies on representative ether–dinitrogen tetroxide addition compounds showed that the N_2O_4 units were not dissociated into radicals or ions[13]. The best structure for the addition compounds appears to be one in which each nitrogen atom is coordinated with an ether oxygen atom. Three instances were observed where only one ether oxygen atom was associated with the N_2O_4 unit, the 1:1 adducts with oxetane and tetrahydrofuran and a 2:1 adduct with 1,2-diethoxyethane, and it was concluded that this stoichiometry was a consequence of the relatively high basicity of these ethers towards this Lewis acid. It is not known whether these are of the same structural type or if the ether oxygen atom can become coordinated with both nitrogen atoms of the N_2O_4 unit.

The following approximate order of electron donor ability of ethers towards dinitrogen tetroxide can be deduced from the melting-point data and the sharpness of the phase curves at the melting points: 1,4-dioxane > 1,3-dioxane > 1,3,5-trioxane > oxetane > tetrahydrofuran > tetrahydropyran > ethyl ether > n-propyl, n-butyl and isopropyl ethers > t-butyl ether, bis-(2-chloroethyl) ether and perfluorotetrahydrofuran. The last three ethers formed no detectable compounds at all with dinitrogen tetroxide, showing the effects of steric and inductive factors in this interaction[13, 266, 268].

Phosphorus pentafluoride was found by Muetterties and co-workers[270a] to form addition compounds with ethyl ether, tetrahydrofuran and 2-methyltetrahydrofuran. The complexes with the two cyclic ethers were relatively stable, decomposing only at about 116° in the case of tetrahydrofuran, but the ethyl ether complex was largely dissociated at 25°. The tetrahydrofuran complex was useful in bringing about polymerization of tetrahydrofuran[270b].

Antimony pentachloride has been found to form a 1:1 adduct with ethyl ether[271]. An antimony(v) oxychloride–ethyl etherate has been reported recently by Dehnicke[272], with an analysis which would be in agreement with the trietherate of a pentameric oxychloride structure (**19**).

$$\text{Cl}_4\text{Sb}-\text{O}(-\overset{\overset{\displaystyle O}{\|}}{\underset{\underset{\displaystyle \text{Cl}}{}}{\text{Sb}}}-\text{O}-)_3\text{SbCl}_4$$
$$\overset{\nwarrow}{\text{OEt}_2}$$

(**19**)

C. Weakly Bonded Complexes

For the reaction of donor and acceptor molecules (equation 5), the equilibrium constant (neglecting activity coefficients) is given by equation (34), where D_0 and A_0 are the initial concentrations of donor

$$K = \frac{[C]}{[D_0 - C][A_0 - C]} \tag{34}$$

and acceptor, and C is the equilibrium concentration of the complex. Spectroscopy is often used to determine C, the intensity of the absorption band being related to the concentration of the complex. By measuring the temperature dependence of the intensity, the thermodynamic properties (ΔG_T, ΔH and ΔS) can be evaluated, and these can be compared for a series of ethers complexed with a common acceptor to establish the sequence of relative basicities. Spectroscopic studies have the added advantage of giving information on relative basicities in still another way, i.e. the position of the spectral band is an indication of the strength of donor–acceptor interaction. Correlation of spectral and thermodynamic data is generally good whenever comparison is made for a *homologous* series of donors with a given acceptor.

These features apply to studies in all regions of the electromagnetic spectrum. In the ultraviolet and visible regions, complex formation results in perturbed electronic bands or gives rise to charge-transfer bands. Many ether–halogen complexes have been studied in this way, and will be discussed below in terms of charge-transfer theory. In addition, infrared (vibrational frequency shifts) and radio wave (nuclear magnetic resonance) spectral studies have been applied to many hydrogen-bonded complexes with ethers, and these too will be discussed.

I. Halogen complexes

Ethers have long been classified as 'brown' solvents for iodine because they shift the iodine color from violet to brown. This color change is due to a shift of the iodine band towards shorter wavelengths ('blue shift') and is indicative of complex formation of the type **20**. The

$$R_2\ddot{O}{:}{\cdots}\overset{\delta^+ \; \delta^-}{I{-}I}$$

(20)

shift is attributed to a 'solvent-cage' effect[273], i.e. a more polar ground state will induce greater polarization of the solvent molecules, and will stabilize the ground state relative to the excited state because of the increase in solvation energy. The magnitude of the polarization of the iodine depends on the strength of the interaction; hence, the shift serves as a measure of the strength of the complex. The band maxima for aliphatic ether–iodine complexes in n-heptane lie in the range 452–462 mμ[274], for sulfide–iodine in the range 436–446 mμ[275], and for triethylamine–iodine at 414 mμ[276], which are in agreement with the thermodynamic results that the ethers are the weakest n donors towards iodine.

Further evidence for the mutual polarization is the apparent dipole moment of iodine in ether solvents. The value in diethyl ether has been reported as 0·7 D[277] which probably is low[278], and in 1,4-dioxane a range of values has been given: 0·95 D[279], 1·3 D[280] and 3·0 D[281].

For the ether–iodine complex an intense new band appears in the ultraviolet region where neither component absorbs by itself. This is the charge-transfer (CT) band mentioned earlier[14,282,283]. For weak complexes, such as the ether–iodine, the energy involved in the transfer of an electron from donor to acceptor is approximated by expression (35), where W_E and W_N are the energies of the excited state

$$h\nu = W_E - W_N \approx I_p - E_a - e^2/r \tag{35}$$

and ground state, respectively, I_p is the ionization potential of the donor, E_a is the electron affinity of the acceptor and e^2/r is the coulombic attraction of the oppositely charged species at a distance r (approximated by the sum of the van der Waals' radii). In a homologous series of donors interacting with the same acceptor, E_a and e^2/r may be considered as remaining essentially constant, with the result that a lower I_p shifts the band to shorter frequency, or longer wavelength (i.e. 'red shift'). Empirical correlations of I_p and $h\nu$[284–286] permit ν to be estimated if I_p is known or, conversely, estimating I_p if ν is measured, but some caution is required in the case of stronger complexes[276,287,288].

Referring to equation (2) (section II.C), for weak complexes the coefficient b is small. From theory[289], the polarity of the complex, which is a measure of its strength, may be approximated as expression (36) where ΔH is the heat of formation of the complex and $\nu_{max.}$

$$\frac{b^2}{a^2 + b^2} \approx \frac{b^2}{a^2} \approx \frac{\Delta H}{h\nu_{max.}} \tag{36}$$

is the frequency of the CT band maximum.

The spectral data for a series of ether–iodine complexes for both the visible and ultraviolet regions are summarized in Table 1. Included also are the thermodynamic data. Good agreement is found in the relative basicities from both the spectral and thermodynamic results.

TABLE 1. Relative donor abilities of ethers in iodine complexation in n-heptane.

Ether[a]	Vis. Band		U.v. band		$-\Delta H°$ ± 0.2 kcal/ mole	$-\Delta G°$ $\pm 0.02^c$ kcal/ mole	$-\Delta S°$ (e.u.)	b^2/a^{2f}
	λ_{max} (mμ)	$a_c{}^b$	λ_{max} (mμ)	$a_c{}^b$				
Oxetane	452	800	248	6800	6·4	1·93	15·0	0·056
2-Methyltetrahydro-furan	454	850	252	3400	6·2	1·84	14·6	0·055
Tetrahydrofuran	455	950	249	5350	5·3	1·70^d	11·6	0·046
Tetrahydropyran	456	930	253	6200	4·9	1·66	10·7	0·043
Propylene oxide	460	970	232	10950	3·8	1·10	9·0	0·031
Ethyl ether	462	950	252	5650	4·2	1·12	10·3	0·037
1,4-Dioxane[e]	452	990	264	4440	3·5	1·3	7·3	0·032

[a] Data from references 274 and 278, except where indicated.
[b] Molar absorbency index in l/mole cm.
[c] Equilibrium constant employed in mole fraction units.
[d] Error limits ± 0.05.
[e] Data from J. A. A. Ketelaar, C. Van de Stolpe and H. R. Gersmann, *Rec. Trav. Chim.*, **70**, 499 (1951); J. A. A. Ketelaar, C. Van de Stolpe, A. Goudsmit and W. Dzcubas, *Rec. Trav. Chim.*, **71**, 1104 (1952); reference 285. The data for dioxane are for n-hexane solutions.
[f] Ratio of squares of wave function coefficients (equation 2, section II.C), $b^2/a^2 \approx \Delta H°/h\nu$.

The heats of reaction determined spectroscopically compare favorably with those determined by calorimetry, e.g. -4.4 kcal/mole for ethyl ether–iodine and -3.25 kcal/mole for dioxane–iodine[290]. Somewhat higher values for the heat of reaction and equilibrium constant of the latter complex were found from solubility studies[291] and may be due to activity factors from working in a different concentration range[292]. It has been reported that the solvent has a pronounced effect on the properties of the complex. A study of ethyl ether–iodine in the vapor phase, while giving about the same heat of reaction as in n-heptane solution, gave a much higher equilibrium constant, a much lower molar absorbency index and a blue shift in the position of the CT band[293].

Other complexes which have been studied spectroscopically and thermodynamically are iodine with n-butyl[294], isopropyl[285] and methyl butyl ether[291]; sulfur dioxide with ethyl and n-butyl ether[295]; cyanogen iodide with ethyl ether, dioxane, propylene oxide and tetrahydrofuran[296, 297a] and tetracyanoethylene with tetrahydrofuran, tetrahydropyran and 1,4-dioxane[297b].

When pyridine is added to a solution of iodine and a saturated ether, a complex of the formula, 1 pyridine: 1 iodine: 1 ether, is formed[298]. If an electron-attracting group is present, such as phenyl in anisole, no complex is formed. Since a complex is formed with vinyl ether, it is presumed that complexation occurs through the olefinic group and not the ether oxygen. Similarly, iodine complexation with methoxy-substituted benzenes and biphenyls has been attributed to interaction with the π electrons of the aromatic ring[295].

Direct evidence for the formation of charge-transfer complexes has been obtained by Hassel and coworkers[299] from x-ray diffraction studies. The 1:1 adducts of 1,4-dioxane with the halogens (iodine, bromine and chlorine) are all isomorphous, with a halogen molecule linking together two dioxane molecules in a linear arrangement, O—X—X—O. Chains of alternating molecules also are formed in the 1:1 adducts of 1,4-dioxane with sulfuric acid and with dinitrogen tetroxide, by hydrogen–oxygen association in the former[299] and nitrogen–oxygen association in the latter[269]. Crystalline adducts of 1,4-dioxane with oxalyl chloride and oxalyl bromide also have been studied[299]. It should be kept in mind, however, that the orientation of an isolated donor–acceptor species in the vapor phase or in solution is not necessarily the same as that found in the crystal, although a similarity might be suggested.

2. Hydrogen bonding with ethers

Probably the interaction of ethers that has been most widely studied to determine their donor properties is hydrogen bonding. The effects on physical properties and the methods of study are amply covered in Pimentel and McClellan's book, *The Hydrogen Bond*[300], which gives a critical survey of the literature to 1957. This section will emphasize the subsequent developments.

The interaction of an ether with a Brönsted–Lowry acid leads to the equilibria in reaction (37). The stronger the interaction, the more the

$$R^1-\overset{\vert}{\underset{R^2}{\ddot{O}}}: + H-Y \rightleftharpoons R^1-\overset{\vert}{\underset{R^2}{\ddot{O}}}:\cdots H-Y \rightleftharpoons R^1-\overset{\vert}{\underset{R^2}{\ddot{O}}}:H^+ + Y^- \qquad (37)$$

(Hydrogen-bonded complex)

equilibria are shifted towards the formation of the oxonium salt. For the weaker interactions, heats of hydrogen-bond formation have been reported which range from a few tenths to several kilocalories per mole, depending on the nature of R^1, R^2 and Y; however, the actual strength of the hydrogen bond is greater than the measured value because the net heat change is the difference between the energy released in the O·····H association and that required to stretch the H—Y bond.

Hydrogen-bonding interactions frequently are studied by spectroscopic methods. The association of an ether with HY perturbs the electronic energy levels of each species and causes a shift in the electronic spectrum, much like the shift in the iodine spectrum. But, to date, no case has been reported of a CT band for hydrogen bonding to ethers. The weakening of the H—Y bond can be measured by the shift in vibrational stretching frequency to longer wavelengths or shift in bending frequency to shorter wavelengths. A new band due to O—H would appear in the case of oxonium salt formation. Association changes the electron environment around the hydrogen, which can be measured by nuclear magnetic resonance. In the hydrogen-bonding interaction there is a migration of charge from donor to acceptor, and it is not surprising, therefore, that charge-transfer theory has been applied to the hydrogen bond [301, 302].

a. *Ultraviolet and visible studies.* The ultraviolet bands of phenol and of aniline are shifted to longer wavelength in ethyl ether solution than in cyclohexane [303, 304]. The shift is greater for phenol, indicating that it is a better Lewis acid than aniline. Similar 'red' shifts have been reported for o-, m- and p-nitrophenol and m- and p-nitroaniline in the presence of ethyl ether [305], and 1- and 2-naphthols in ethyl ether and in tetrahydrofuran [306]. Solution of benzoic acid in ether, on the other hand, causes a spectral shift towards the 'blue', as observed by Ito [307].

These spectral shifts may be explained on the basis of the relative hydrogen-bonding abilities of the ground and excited states of the aromatic hydrogen donors. The electronically excited states of phenol and aniline are better hydrogen donors than the ground states, because of the positive charge on the oxygen and nitrogen atoms in the excited states. Thus hydrogen bonding to ethers stabilizes the excited states more than the ground states, with a consequent decrease in the excitation energy. The excited state of benzoic acid, however, is characterized by an enhanced negative charge on the carboxyl group, with a consequent decrease in hydrogen-donor ability. Here hydrogen bonding to ethers stabilizes the ground state more than the excited state, increasing the excitation energy.

The total absorption intensity of aniline in n-hexane does not seem to vary with temperature, but in ethyl ether there is an increase with decrease in temperature due to greater hydrogen-bond formation [308]. Absorption spectra of Schiff bases having an o-hydroxyl group in the aldehyde ring show a long wavelength band at 400–450 mμ in dioxane and in ethyl ether which is not present in hydrocarbon solvents [309].

b. Infrared studies. Infrared studies have been the most widely used of the spectroscopic methods, and often have been correlated with other types of measurements. Among the weaker hydrogen bonds measured in the infrared are those formed by acetylenes and substituted acetylenes in ethyl ether[310, 311] with a reported heat of formation in the range 1–1·5 kcal/mole. A large number of ethynyl compounds in ethyl ether were studied by Brand, Eglinton and Morman[312]. They determined the association constant of the ether with benzoylacetylene ($K_x = 2·0$ at 29°) and with phenylacetylene ($K_x = 1·1$ at 29°). For the latter compound, combination of the spectrometric with thermochemical data gave $\Delta H = 1·4$ kcal/mole and $\Delta S = -4·5$ e.u. Increased solubility and increased retention time in gas–liquid chromatography were further evidence for the formation of hydrogen bonds.

Chloroform forms rather comparable hydrogen bonds with ethers. Infrared data for chloroform-d in ethyl ether give an association constant at room temperature of $0·80 \pm 0·15$ l/mole[313]. With dioxane, there is thermochemical evidence for a 1:1 and a 2:1 complex[314] with a molecule of chloroform associated with each oxygen atom (at 50° $K_{x_1} = 1·11$ and $K_{x_2} = 1·24$). The heat of reaction is about 0·5 kcal/mole for the 1:1 complex. Heats of mixing of chloroform with a number of saturated cyclic and acyclic ethers have been used to compare relative donor strengths. Searles and Tamres[315] report a heat of mixing of chloroform with ethyl ether as 650 cal/mole at 3°, which agrees with that of 670 cal/mole at 0° obtained by Lacher, McKinley and Park[316]. These are slightly lower than the value determined by McLeod and Wilson[16] (Figure 2, section II.D), perhaps due to volatilization of the ether, which would have a cooling effect.

Recently, a solid complex of ethyl ether–bromodichloromethane was prepared at −130°, and x-ray analysis showed that the crystal contains C—H·····O bonds[317].

Alcohol interaction with ethers is a more complicated system to study because the self-association of alcohol may make uncertain the exact nature of the complex. This problem is minimized by working with dilute solutions of the alcohol in the ether. For infrared studies, a favorable hydrogen-bonding system for determining relative basicities of ethers is R_2O·····D—OCH_3 because the O—D band (at 2689 cm^{-1} in CCl_4) is in an optically clear spectral region (as are C—D bands in, say, chloroform-d), and is shifted appreciably on complexation. Gordy and Stanford[318] measured the O—D shifts of CH_3OD in a large number of electron donors, including many ethers, and found general correlation with basicity as determined by other methods, e.g. K_b, solubility in $CHCl_2F$ and heat of mixing with $CHCl_3$. The same technique was used by Searles and Tamres[315] to study ring-size effects in ethers (Table 2). A systematic study of inductive effects was made by Ginzburg, Petrow and Schatenstein[319] (Table 3).

TABLE 2. Hydrogen bonding of cyclic ethers[a].

Ether	O—D shift[b] of CH_3OD (cm^{-1})	Heat of mixing with $CHCl_3$ of 1 : 1 solution (cal/mole)	
		25°	3°
Epichlorohydrin	80	190	—
Styrene oxide	85	215	—
Propylene oxide	99	443	461
Cyclohexene oxide	99	566	—
Oxetane	120	703	760
2,2-Dimethyloxetane	125	—	915
2.2-Diethyloxetane	125	847	—
Tetrahydrofuran	117	677	750
2,2-Dimethyltetrahydrofuran	120	720	—
Tetrahydropyran	115	600	640
Cineole	125	835	—

[a] Data from reference 315.
[b] Reference solvent is CCl_4 in which the O—D band is at 2689 cm^{-1}.

A few studies of alcohol–ether systems show that hydrogen bonding persists in the vapor phase. From infrared data for the methanol–ethyl ether complex, a dissociation energy of $4\cdot7 \pm 0\cdot7$ kcal/mole is reported[320], which may be high since for trifluoroethanol–tetrahydrofuran the dissociation energy is reported only as $2\cdot3 \pm 0\cdot3$ kcal/mole[321]. Undoubtedly, hydrogen bonding plays an important role in the formation of azeotropes, as in the case of methyl alcohol–tetrahydrofuran[322].

Gramstad studied the interaction of phenols with ethers[323]. Since phenols are stronger acceptors than alcohols, larger O—H shifts are observed. Gramstad found a linear correlation between the frequency shift and equilibrium constant of the complex. The spectral and thermodynamic data of Powell and West[324] for phenol–ethyl ether in CCl_4, obtained by measuring the first overtone of the O—H stretching fundamental in the near infrared, are in good agreement with Gramstad's results. The interaction of pentachlorophenol with tetrahydropyran in CCl_4 gives a larger O—H shift but smaller equilibrium

TABLE 3. O—D shifts of CH_3OD in ethers[a].

Ether	$\Delta\nu^b$ (cm^{-1})	Ether	$\Delta\nu$ (cm^{-1})
$CH_3OCH_2OCH_3$	84	$(CH_2)_4O$	115
$CH_3OCH(CH_3)OCH_3$	90		
$CH_3O(CH_2)OCH_3$	93		
$CH_3O(CH_2)_2OC_2H_5$	95		
$CH_3O(CH_2)_2OC_3H_7$	97		
$CH_3O(CH_2)_2OC_4H_9$	95		
$CH_3O(CH_2)_2OC_5H_{11}$	98		
$CH_3OCH_2CH(CH_3)OCH_3$	96		
$CH_3O(CH_2)_3OCH_3$	100		
$CH_3O(CH_2)_4OCH_3$	104		
$CH_3O(CH_2)_5OCH_3$	104		
$C_2H_5O(CH_2)_2OC_2H_5$	98		
$C_4H_9O(CH_2)_2OC_4H_9$	100		
$C_2H_5O(CH_2)_3OC_2H_5$	106		
$C_2H_5O(CH_2)_4OC_2H_5$	106		
$C_2H_5OC_2H_5$	106		
$C_2H_5O(CH_2)_2OCH_3$	95		
$CH_3O(CH_2)_2O(CH_2)_2OCH_3$	90		
$C_2H_5O(CH_2)_2OC_2H_5$	98		
$C_2H_5O(CH_2)_2O(CH_2)_2OC_2H_5$	98		

Structures in right column (with $\Delta\nu$ values):

- 2,3-bis(ethoxy)... CH—OEt / $(CH_2)_2$ / CH—OEt ring with O : 92
- O / $(CH_2)_2$ ... CH_2 / O : 76
- O / $(CH_2)_2$ ... $CHCH_3$ / O : 88
- $(CH_2)_5O$: 112
- $(CH_2)_2$ ring: O...O with $(CH_2)_2$: 100
- $(CH_2)_3$ / O...O / CH_2 : 85

[a] Data from reference 319.

[b] Reference solvent is CCl_4, in which the O—D band is at 2689 cm^{-1}.

constant (K_c) than phenol. Gramstad considered that pentachloro-phenol does not enter into hydrogen bonding as strongly as phenol, probably because of the lower K_c value. However, the larger O—H shift would indicate that the lower K_c might be due perhaps to a steric effect; it would be expected that chlorine substitution in phenol would make the molecule more acidic.

Further comparison of alcohol and phenol interactions with ethers in CCl_4 have been made by Henry[325], whose results are in about the same range as those of Gramstad. The data show good correlation between frequency shift ($\Delta\nu$) and pK_a.

The study of phenol interactions also has been made to determine the basicity sequence for a series of vinyl and aryl ethers[326].

Interactions of secondary amines with tetrahydrofuran in hydrocarbon solvents were studied both in the infrared and ultraviolet regions[327]. The association constants and molar absorbancy indexes in both regions were evaluated using the same equations which have been applied to charge-transfer spectra. The principles are equally applicable. The results for diphenylamine–tetrahydrofuran in 2,2,4-trimethylpentane were: (a) i.r., $\Delta\nu = 95$ cm^{-1} and $K_c^{22°} = 1\cdot53 \pm 0\cdot15$ l/mole, (b) u.v., $K_c^{30°} = 1\cdot43 \pm 0\cdot1$ l/mole; and for di-o-tolyl-amine–tetrahydrofuran in the same solvent: (a) i.r., $\Delta\nu = 68$ cm^{-1} and $K_c^{22°} = 0\cdot44 \pm 0\cdot02$, (b) u.v., $K_c^{28°} = 0\cdot9 \pm 0\cdot3$ l/mole. The smaller value for both K_c and $\Delta\nu$ for the di-o-tolylamine case indicates that steric hindrance weakens the hydrogen bond.

Perfluoro fatty acids react with ethers to give stable addition compounds, e.g. $3CF_3CO_2H \cdot 2(C_2H_5)_2O$, $2C_3F_7CO_2H \cdot (C_2H_5)_2O$ and $3C_3F_7CO_2H \cdot 2$dioxane[328]. Acetic and n-butyric acids seem comparatively inert towards these ethers, but polyethers interact with polycarboxylic acids to give insoluble polymers, presumably due to the effect of multiple hydrogen-bond formation[329].

The hydrogen halides are, of course, strong acids, and their interaction with ethers is quite marked. Band broadening has been correlated with strength of interaction[300] and the H—X bands of the hydrogen halides and of HNO_3 in ethers are quite broad. Millen and coworkers[330–333] have shown that Fermi resonance from the interaction of adjacent vibrational levels is not the main cause of the broadening, but rather it is due to the presence, near the strong peak of the H—X stretch, ν_3 (**21**), of two equispaced subsidiary peaks which are assigned to the sum and difference between ν_3 and the stretch of the hydrogen bond, ν_1 (**22**).

$$\overset{\nu_3}{R_2O\cdots\overset{\leftarrow}{H}\text{---}\vec{X}} \qquad \overset{\nu_1}{\overset{\leftarrow}{R_2O}\cdots\overset{\rightarrow}{H\text{---}X}}$$
$$\textbf{(21)} \qquad\qquad\qquad \textbf{(22)}$$

It was mentioned earlier (section III.A.1.e) that the heat of reaction of ethers in n-octane solution is larger with HF than with HCl[73]. A similar sequence has been observed from infrared studies of these hydrogen halides with ethyl ether both in CCl_4[334] and in the gas phase[335]. A study of the interaction of $(CH_3)_2O$ and HCl in the gas phase gave an internal energy of molecular association of $-4\cdot1$ kcal/mole[24].

TABLE 4. Basicity measurements of some ethers.

Measurement	$(CH_2)_4O$	$(CH_2)_5O$	1,4-Dioxane	Et_2O	$i\text{-}Pr_2O$	$n\text{-}Pr_2O$	$n\text{-}Bu_2O$	Ref.
N.m.r, $\Delta\delta$ (p.p.m.) in CHCl$_3$	0·900; 0·80		0·587; 0·64	0·76; 0·78	0·713; 0·86	0·632	0·502	339; 338
in CHBr$_3$	0·785		0·520	0·639	0·639	0·514	0·452	339
in H$_2$O	2·89		1·93	2·11				340
Δv (cm^{-1}) C—D in CDCl$_3$	19·6		15·7	20·0	25·3	20·9	21·6	339
O—D in CH$_3$OD	117; 115; 112	115; 112	111; 100	96; 106; 95	110; 130; 123	117	101	315, 341; 315, 318, 319, 341; 318, 340, 344
O—H in H$_2$O	301		153	148	308		292	341
O—H in PhOH	283	290		288; 271	287	282	286	184, 346, 323, 342; 184, 323
$-\Delta H$ (kcal/mole) with PhOH	5·55			5·31			6·00	342
with BF$_3$	16·80	15·42		11·93				184
with I$_2$	5·3	4·9	3·5	4·2				274
$-\Delta H_{\text{mix}}$ at 25° with CHCl$_3$, (cal/mole)	677	600	453	597	678		412	315
$-pK_a{}^a$ at 20°	2·08	2·79	3·22	3·59	4·30	4·40	5·40	80, 82
Solubility of HCl at 10° (moles HCl/mole ether)	1·38		1·046	0·892	0·978	0·930	0·890	28
Henry's law constant^b for HCl	2100	2600	7500	4000	5200	5200	5200	343

^{a} See discussion, section III.A.1.f. ^{b} At infinite dilution.

c. *Nuclear magnetic resonance studies.* A number of nuclear magnetic resonance studies have been made involving hydrogen bonding to ethers, with the magnitude of the proton shift serving as a measure of relative basicity. The shift for phenol in ethyl ether is larger than that in dioxane; and even larger shifts in these ethers are obtained with *o*-chlorophenol, in accord with the expected trend in acceptor properties[336]. Other acceptor molecules studied include water[337] and the haloforms[338,339]. Correlation of relative basicities from nuclear magnetic resonance and infrared data for the same acceptors is fairly good, as shown in Table 4. Comparison is made also with basicity measurements using a wide variety of methods involving different acceptors. An extensive tabulation of data on the interaction of ethers may be found in the review by Arnett[1].

IV. FACTORS AFFECTING THE STRENGTH OF COMPLEXES

While the relative basicities of different ethers towards various acids are generally quite similar, it is apparent in Table 4 that a number of reversals occur which are beyond the range attributable to experimental error. This points to the necessity of specifying a basicity sequence in terms of the reference acid involved and possibly other conditions of the measurement.

Several factors contribute to the strength of interaction in complex formation. These are by no means unique to ethers, but examples will be selected to illustrate their application to ethers.

A. Inductive Effects

The electron-donor ability of ethers is markedly decreased by the presence of electron-withdrawing substituents. Perfluorinated ethers show no reaction with dinitrogen tetroxide[266] or with cyanogen iodide[294] and cooling rather than heating is observed on mixing with chloroform[316]. Cyclopropyl ethyl ether shows much less solubility in water than ethyl ether[345], and bis(chloromethyl) ether is reported to form no complex with boron trichloride[178].

On the other hand, increasing the positive inductive effect of the alkyl groups on the oxygen atom by α branching or increase in chain length[346] tends to increase the donor ability of the ethers, unless offset by other factors, such as steric hindrance. The influence of the inductive effect may be seen in the hydrogen bonding of various dialkyl ethers towards methanol-d_1, chloroform and phenol[315,347,348]. Likewise, the hydrogen-bonding ability of 1,2-dialkoxyethanes is reported to be enhanced by increase in the size of the alkyl groups (Table 3)[319].

B. Conjugation

The interaction of a lone pair of electrons on an ether oxygen atom with an adjacent π orbital diminishes the ability of the ether to co-ordinate with an acceptor molecule. The very low solubility of vinyl ethers in water can be ascribed to this effect causing diminished hydrogen bonding with water[345], and vinyl ethers also bind less strongly to phenol than do saturated ethers[326]. Aromatic ethers appear to be poorer donors than saturated ethers in all interactions where relative stability of complexes has been studied. The anisole–phenol interaction is reported to give two infrared absorption bands, one attributed to a hydrogen bond with nonbonding electrons on the ether oxygen atom and the other to association with the aromatic π orbital. It is estimated that 75–80% of the association is with the oxygen atom[349].

C. Steric Effects

The presence of bulky groups on either the ether or the acceptor molecule may inhibit the close approach of the latter, resulting in weaker bonding than otherwise would occur. There are numerous examples of this effect. For example the stability of the addition compounds of boron trifluoride with dialkyl ethers followed the steric order: $Me_2O > Et_2O > i\text{-}Pr_2O$, rather than the inductive order, and the same was true for the complexes of these ethers with dinitrogen tetroxide[13].

With acceptor molecules having large central atoms, steric factors would be expected to be of less importance: in the case of triethylaluminum, the heats of complex formation with various dialkyl ethers are practically the same[222], indicating that the differences in inductive and steric effects are about balanced with this Lewis acid.

Even with hydrogen bonding, steric effects may be observed, at least in special cases. In a study of the interaction of ethers with a variety of *ortho*-substituted phenols, Bellamy and his collaborators observed much weaker association in the case of 2,6-di-*t*-butylphenol[350, 351]. Another example may be in the association of n-butyl ether with chloroform, where the heat of mixing is significantly lower than that for ethyl ether and chloroform; this effect may be caused by steric hindrance to the approach of the chloroform molecule by the ends of the butyl groups[315].

D. Ring-size Effects

The ring size of cyclic ethers has a considerable effect on their donor abilities, the magnitude of this effect depending greatly on the Lewis acid involved.

Several factors that may be involved in complex formation are, of course, affected by change in ring size: (a) a decrease in the $\widehat{COC}$ angle, associated with a decrease in ring size, results in less steric hindrance for interaction at the oxygen atom; (b) changes in hybridization of the orbitals of the oxygen atom, due to changes in its valence angle, result in considerable variation in the electron density on the oxygen atom with ring size and in the strength of a coordinate covalent bond that might be formed with an acceptor molecule; and (c) changes in nonbonded repulsions between the electrons on the oxygen atom and those on the adjacent carbon atoms are to be expected with changes in ring size.

The only case where a systematic increase of donor abilities of cyclic ethers has been reported is that of dimethylzinc[237]. The relative donor abilities, however, were estimated in a rather indirect manner and should receive further study. The ratio of ether to dimethylzinc observed when the complexes were slowly distilled through a fractionating column was taken as a measure of basicity of the ether. This ratio increased with increasing ring size of the cyclic ether: 0·8 for ethylene oxide, 1·2 for oxetane, 1·6 for tetrahydrofuran and 2·0 for tetrahydropyran. The same order was observed in the boiling points of the complexes on rapid distillation (47, 81, 82·5 and 93·5°), though the stoichiometry of the complexes was different. Thiele proposed that the coordination bonding strength of the oxygen atom must increase as the $\widehat{COC}$ bond angle increases to the tetrahedral value, because the p character of the oxygen orbitals used should increase until sp^3 hybridization is reached with the six-membered ring[237].

Tetrahydrofuran is, however, a stronger complexing agent than tetrahydropyran in other interactions reported, including the relatively strong interactions with boron trifluoride[184] and stannic chloride[240]. The order with these two may well be due to predominance of the steric factor, since it was observed that the degree of interaction was decreased by α-methyl substitution[240,352]. The fact that tetrahydrofuran is a better electron donor than acyclic ethers in numerous interactions is also in accord with its lower steric requirements, but there is another possible explanation, based on the effect of bond angles on the electron density on the oxygen atom.

Iodine complexation of cyclic ethers[274] and their hydrogen bonding with methanol and with chloroform[315] are of interest, because the weakness of these interactions and their low steric requirements* would tend to minimize both the orbital overlap and steric factors. The ring-size effect observed in these interactions follows the order: 4- > 5- > 6- ≫ 3-membered ring. This is the same order as the variation of electron density on the oxygen atom with ring size, as deduced from nuclear magnetic resonance studies on the shielding of α protons in cyclic ethers[353, 354]. The net electronic effect is not a simple function of orbital hybridization; studies of ^{13}C—H nuclear magnetic resonance coupling constants suggest a decrease in s character with increasing ring size[354].

It is, of course, possible that part of the differences in the apparent donor ability of the four-, five- and six-membered rings may be ascribable to steric effects, since they would favor the same order. This view was taken recently by West and his students[355a], who were able to observe no significant difference in the enthalpies of hydrogen bonding of oxetane, tetrahydrofuran and tetrahydropyran with phenol, since the data for each interaction were approximately within the error limit for the determinations. This approach, however, is subject to rather high error limits, relative to the differences in the interactions studied, and necessarily includes the assumption that enthalpy changes at other sites in the reacting species are essentially constant for the series. Hydrogen-bonding studies based on comparison of vibrational frequency shifts in the acceptor molecule are more sensitive and are concerned only with the hydrogen-bonding interaction. Frequency shifts as well as complete thermodynamic data for the association of phenol with cyclic ethers have been reported by Lippert and Prigge[355b], and the results are in accord with the donor ability sequence found with methanol and with chloroform[315]. The several studies serve to emphasize that the ring-size effect on donor ability is largest between the three- and four-membered rings, and is much less for the four-, five- and six-membered rings.

Bellon[356] has interpreted the difference in the equilibrium constants for the association of phenols with tetrahydrofuran and tetrahydropyran in terms of a solvent cage model, involving the relative sizes of the ether molecules.

---

* Although the iodine molecule is relatively large, only one atom of it complexes directly with the ether oxygen atom and the distance for this interaction is probably longer than a hydrogen bond (cf. Hassel and Rømming, reference 299).

The observation of Sisler and coworkers[266,268] that the strength of complexing of cyclic ethers with dinitrogen tetroxide was in the order: oxetane > tetrahydrofuran > tetrahydropyran, appears to be satisfactorily explained by the effect of ring size on electron distribution. The alternative explanation based on steric factors would not be consistent with lack of appreciable steric effect associated with α-methyl and α,α'-dimethyl substitution in tetrahydrofuran[267,268].

The only study of the effect of seven-membered ring size on the donor properties of an ether is that of Arnett and Wu[82] who determined, by means of their extraction method, pK_a values for hexamethylene oxide, tetrahydropyran and tetrahydrofuran of $-2\cdot02$, $-2\cdot79$ and $-2\cdot08$, respectively. Because of the similarity of the basicities of the five- and seven-membered rings, Arnett and Wu proposed that ring-size effects may be due to the variation of nonbonded repulsions with ring size, considering that the repulsion between lone pairs of electrons on the oxygen atom and the electrons in the adjacent C—H bonds acts as a driving force favoring complexation.

E. Solvation

It is well known that differences in solvation energies often far outweigh any other factor in determining the extent of many donor–acceptor interactions, but this factor has not received much attention with complexation of ethers.

An interesting example of the role of solvation may be seen in the determinations of relative basicity of 7-oxabicyclo[2.2.1]heptane (**23**)

(**23**)

in different solvents. The $\widehat{COC}$ angle in this compound is comparable to that in oxetane. It was found from pK_a measurements in aqueous sulfuric acid that this bridged ether was less basic than tetrahydrofuran and of about the same basicity as tetrahydropyran[82]. This result could well be due to the hydrocarbon 'cage' preventing solvent stabilization of the oxonium ion in the aqueous medium. Hydrogen-bonding and iodine-complexation studies in n-heptane showed that this ether was a better donor than tetrahydrofuran[357], in

10*

298 S. Searles, Jr., and M. Tamres

accord with the concept that the relation between electron density and valency angle at the ether oxygen atom is an important factor in donor ability.

F. Chelation

Although the presence of an α-alkoxy group in an ether is base weakening in many interactions, such as protonation[82], hydrogen bonding[319] and aluminum chloride[213] addition, it is greatly base strengthening in association with acceptor species which coordinate readily with two or more ether molecules. As proposed by Zook and Russo[105], this effect is undoubtedly due to the chelation possible with diethers and triethers with such species. It has been clearly observed with sodium ions[105,115,116] and probably with dinitrogen tetroxide[267] and beryllium and magnesium compounds[149,162], and it may be involved in the common use of dioxane for making ether complexes of heavy metal compounds.

V. REFERENCES

1. E. M. Arnett in *Progress in Physical Organic Chemistry*, Vol. 1, Interscience Publishers, New York, 1963, pp. 223–403.
2. S. Brownstein, B. C. Smith, G. Ehrlich and A. W. Laubengayer, *J. Am. Chem. Soc.*, **81**, 3826 (1959).
3. R. G. Pearson, *J. Am. Chem. Soc.*, **85**, 3533 (1963).
4. *Chem. Eng. News*, **43**, 90 (1965).
5. C. Quivoron and J. Néel, *Compt. Rend.*, **259**, 1845 (1964).
6. H. E. Wirth and P. I. Slick, *J. Phys. Chem.*, **66**, 2277 (1962).
7. A. C. Rutenberg, A. A. Palko and J. S. Drury, *J. Am. Chem. Soc.*, **85**, 2702 (1963); *J. Phys. Chem.*, **68**, 976 (1964).
8. B. Rice, R. J. Galiano and W. J. Lehmann, *J. Phys. Chem.*, **61**, 1222 (1957).
9. E. Taillander and M. Taillander, *Compt. Rend.*, **257**, 1522 (1963).
10. R. A. Craig and R. E. Richards, *Trans. Faraday Soc.*, **59**, 1962 (1963).
11. T. D. Coyle and F. G. A. Stone, *J. Am. Chem. Soc.*, **83**, 4138 (1962).
12. P. Anderson and T. Thurmann-Moe, *Acta Chem. Scand.*, **18**, 433 (1964).
13. B. Rubin, H. H. Sisler and H. Shechter, *J. Am. Chem. Soc.*, **74**, 877 (1952).
14. R. S. Mulliken, *J. Am. Chem. Soc.*, **74**, 811 (1952) and later papers.
15. S. P. McGlynn, *Chem. Rev.*, **58**, 1113 (1958).
16. D. B. McLeod and F. S. Wilson, *Trans. Faraday Soc.*, **31**, 596 (1935).
17. M. J. Copely, G. F. Zellhoefer and C. S. Marvel, *J. Am. Chem. Soc.*, **61**, 3550 (1939).
18. L. Ehrenberg and I. Fischer, *Acta Chem. Scand.*, **2**, 657 (1948).
19. W. V. Bhagwat, S. N. Kaveeshwar and P. H. Trivedi, *J. Indian Chem. Soc.*, **30**, 574 (1953).
20. J. Kohoutek, *Collection Czech. Chem. Commun.*, **25**, 288 (1960).

21. V. Kello, *Collection Czech. Chem. Commun.*, **12**, 510 (1947).
22. F. Kunze, *Monatsh. Chem.*, **78**, 362 (1948).
23. D. K. Anderson and A. L. Babb, *J. Phys. Chem.*, **65**, 1281 (1961).
24. K. P. Lawley and L. E. Sutton, *Trans. Faraday Soc.*, **59**, 2680 (1963).
25. A. E. Lutskii and V. N. Solonko, *Zh. Fiz. Khim.*, **38**, 415 (1964).
26. D. Papousek, E. Dvorakova and F. Sevcik, *Chem. Listy*, **51**, 1605 (1957); *Chem. Abstr.*, **52**, 4541 (1958).
27. O. A. Osipov, *Uch. Zap. Rostovsk. na Donu Gos. Univ.*, **41**, 3 (1958); *Chem. Abstr.*, **55**, 22973 (1961).
28. W. Gerrard and E. D. Macklen, *Chem. Rev.*, **59**, 1105 (1959).
29. K. Wickert, *Naturwissenschaften*, **26**, 500 (1938).
30. D. McIntosh, *J. Am. Chem. Soc.*, **27**, 1013 (1905).
31. W. Hofman, L. Stefaniak and T. Urbanski, *J. Chem. Soc.*, 2343 (1962).
32. V. V. Fomin and R. N. Maslova, *Russ. J. Inorg. Chem. (Eng. Transl.)*, **6**, 243 (1961).
33. A. K. Seleznev, *Zh. Prikl. Khim.*, **32**, 2363 (1959).
34. R. K. Kadyrov, *Uzbeksk. Khim. Zh.*, **44** (1961); *Chem. Abstr.*, **56**, 9508 (1961).
35. A. Hantzsch, *Z. Physik. Chem. (Leipzig)*, **65**, 41 (1908).
36. D. Jacques and J. A. Leisten, *J. Chem. Soc.*, 4963 (1961).
37. R. J. Gillespie and J. A. Leisten, *Quart. Rev. (London)*, **8**, 40 (1954).
38. I. K. Getmanskii, *U.S.S.R. Pat.*, 154,360 (1963); *Chem. Abstr.*, **60**, 6747 (1964).
39. E. M. Arnett and C. Y. Wu, *J. Am. Chem. Soc.*, **82**, 5660 (1960).
40. T. Birchall and R. J. Gillespie, *Can. J. Chem.*, **42**, 502 (1964).
41. C. MacLean and E. L. Mackor, *Discussions Faraday Soc.*, **34**, 165 (1962).
42. N. A. J. Rogers and A. Sattar, *Tetrahedron Letters*, 1311 (1964).
43. A. J. Kresge and Y. Chiang, *Proc. Chem. Soc.*, 81 (1961).
44. G. Baddely, N. Smith and M. Vickers, *J. Chem. Soc.*, 2455 (1956).
45. H. Hart and C. Wagner, *Proc. Chem. Soc.*, 284 (1958).
46. E. M. Arnett and C. Y. Wu, *Chem. Ind. (London)*, 1488 (1959).
47. J. Hine, *Physical Organic Chemistry*, 2nd ed., McGraw-Hill Book Co., New York, 1962, p. 63.
48. F. Klages and H. Meuresch, *Chem. Ber.*, **85**, 863 (1952).
49. F. Klages and H. Meuresch, *Chem. Ber.*, **86**, 1322 (1953).
50. F. Klages, H. Meuresch and W. Steppich, *Ann. Chem.*, **592**, 81 (1955).
51. M. N. Usanovich and E. I. Kalabanovskaya, *Izv. Vysshikh Uchebn. Zavedenii Khim. i Khim. Tekhnol.*, **3**, 991 (1960); *Chem. Abstr.*, **55**, 12012 (1961).
52. (a) E. Wiberg, M. Schmidt and A. G. Galinos, *Angew. Chem.*, **66**, 443 (1954) (2 papers); (b) *Angew. Chem.*, **66**, 444 (1954) (2 papers).
53. A. G. Galinos, *J. Am. Chem. Soc.*, **82**, 8032 (1960).
54. (a) J. A. Miliotis, A. G. Galinos and J. M. Tsangaris, *Bull. Soc. Chim. France*, 1413 (1961); (b) W. Hieber, J. Peterhans and E. Winter, *Chem. Ber.*, **94**, 2572 (1961).
55. A. G. Galinos, *Angew. Chem.*, **69**, 507 (1957).
56. H. Funk, W. Weiss and K. P. Roethe, *Z. Anorg. Allgem. Chem.*, **301**, 271 (1959).
57. K. I. Askitopoulos, A. G. Galinos and I. M. Tsangaris, *Prakt. Akad. Athēnōn*, **32**, 388 (1958); *Chem. Abstr.*, **54**, 3040 (1960).

58. C. J. Askitopoulos and A. G. Galinos, *Prakt. Akad. Athēnōn*, **32**, 395 (1959), *Chem. Abstr.*, **54**, 147 (1960).
59. S. Kato and R. Ishii, *Sci. Papers Inst. Phys. Chem. Res.* (*Tokyo*), **36**, 82 (1934).
60. J. Axelrod and E. H. Swift, *J. Am. Chem. Soc.*, **62**, 33 (1940).
61. N. H. Nachtrieb and R. E. Fryzell, *J. Am. Chem. Soc.*, **71**, 4035 (1949).
62. L. I. Katzin, *J. Inorg. Nucl. Chem.*, **4**, 187 (1957).
63. C. H. Brubaker, Jr., and C. E. Johnson, *J. Inorg. Nucl. Chem.*, **9**, 184 (1959).
64. V. A. Khalkin, P. N. Palei and A. A. Nemodruck, *Radiokhimiya*, **5**, 215 (1963); *Chem. Abstr.*, **60**, 576 (1964).
65. I. E. Stauk and N. I. Ampelogova, *Radiokhimiya*, **3**, 261 (1961); *Chem. Abstr.*, **56**, 998 (1962).
66. C. Smeets, *Natuurw. Tijdschr.* (*Ghent*), **19**, 12 (1937); *Chem. Abstr.*, **31**, 1815 (1937).
67. H. Lemaire and H. J. Lucas, *J. Am. Chem. Soc.*, **73**, 5198 (1951).
68. T. Higuchi, C. H. Barnstein, H. Ghassemi and W. E. Perez, *Anal. Chem.*, **34**, 400 (1962).
69. E. M. Arnett in *Progress in Physical Organic Chemistry*, Vol. I, Interscience Publishers, New York, 1963, p. 290.
70. O. Maass and D. McIntosh, *J. Am. Chem. Soc.*, **35**, 535 (1913).
71. G. L. Vidale and R. C. Taylor, *J. Am. Chem. Soc.*, **78**, 294 (1956).
72. L. M. Quarterman, H. H. Hyman and J. J. Katz, *J. Phys. Chem.*, **65**, 90 (1961).
73. H. Dunken, H. Fischer and W. Zahlten, *Z. Chem.*, **1**, 345 (1961).
74. H. Dunken, W. Zahlten and R. Schlegelmilch, *Z. Chem.*, **4**, 37 (1964).
75. A. T. Gladeshev and Y. A. Syrkin, *Compt. Rend. Acad. Sci. U.R.S.S.*, **20**, 145 (1938); *Chem. Abstr.*, **33**, 1578 (1939).
76. J. L. Simonsen and L. N. Owen, *The Terpenes*, 2nd ed., Vol. I, Cambridge University Press, Cambridge, 1947, p. 430.
77. H. Stone and H. Schechter, *J. Org. Chem.*, **14**, 491 (1950).
78. R. L. Burwell, Jr., *Chem. Rev.*, **54**, 615 (1954).
79. E. M. Arnett and C. Y. Wu, *J. Am. Chem. Soc.*, **82**, 4999 (1960).
80. E. M. Arnett and C. Y. Wu, *J. Am. Chem. Soc.*, **84**, 1680 (1962).
81. E. M. Arnett, C. Y. Wu, J. N. Anderson and R. D. Bushnick, *J. Am. Chem. Soc.*, **84**, 1674 (1962).
82. E. M. Arnett and C. Y. Wu, *J. Am. Chem. Soc.*, **84**, 1684 (1962).
83. (a) J. T. Edward, J. B. Leane and I. C. Wang, *Can. J. Chem.*, **40**, 1521 (1962); (b) J. T. Edward, personal communication.
84. G. D. Giles and C. F. Wells, *Nature*, **201**, 606 (1964).
85. C. F. Wells, personal communication; *Discussions Faraday Soc.*, in press.
86. R. P. Bell, *The Proton in Chemistry*, Cornell University Press, Ithaca, 1959, pp. 83–84.
87. E. A. Braude, *J. Chem. Soc.*, 1971 (1948).
88. H. H. Hyman, M. Kilpatrick and J. J. Katz, *J. Am. Chem. Soc.*, **79**, 3668 (1957).
89. E. M. Arnett in *Progress in Physical Organic Chemistry*, Vol. I, Interscience Publishers, New York, 1963, pp. 356–365.
90. H. H. Willard and G. F. Smith, *J. Am. Chem. Soc.*, **45**, 286 (1923).
91. K. Ekelin and L. G. Sillen, *Acta Chem. Scand.*, **7**, 987 (1953).
92. S. Winstein, E. C. Friedrich and S. Smith, *J. Am. Chem. Soc.*, **86**, 305 (1964).

93. M. M. Markowitz, W. N. Hawley, D. A. Boryta and R. F. Harris, *J. Chem. Eng. Data*, **6**, 325 (1961).

94. E. Wiberg and W. Gosele, *Z. Naturforsch.*, **11B**, 487 (1956).

95. E. Wiberg, H. Noth and R. Usón Lacal, *Z. Naturforsch.*, **11B**, 490 (1956).

96. P. Longi, G. Mazzanti and F. Bernardini, *Gazz. Chim. Ital.*, **90**, 180 (1960).

97. A. Nordwig, *Naturwissenschaften*, **47**, 407 (1960).

98. B. Sarry and M. Dettke, *Angew. Chem.*, **75**, 1022 (1963).

99. T. V. Talalaeva, A. N. Rodionov and K. A. Kocheshkov, *Dokl. Akad, Nauk SSSR*, **140**, 867 (1961); *Chem. Abstr.*, **56**, 5989 (1962).

100. V. D. Aftandilian, H. C. Miller and E. I. Muetterties, *J. Am. Chem. Soc.*, **83**, 2471 (1961).

101. H. G. Normant, *Acta Cryst.*, 695 (1959).

102. H. G. Normant, *U.S. Dept. Com. Office Tech. Serv. PB Report*, **148**, 373 (1959); *Chem. Abstr.*, **56**, 11170 (1962).

103. M. C. Day, H. M. Barnes and A. J. Cox, *J. Phys. Chem.*, **68**, 2595 (1964).

104. J. B. Honeycutt, Jr., and J. M. Riddle, *J. Am. Chem. Soc.*, **83**, 364 (1961).

105. H. D. Zook and T. J. Russo, *J. Am. Chem. Soc.*, **82**, 1258 (1960).

106. D. G. Hill, J. Burkus, S. M. Luck and C. R. Hauser, *J. Am. Chem. Soc.*, **81**, 2787 (1959).

107. N. V. Sidgwick and F. M. Brewer, *J. Chem. Soc.*, 2379 (1925).

108. O. L. Brady and M. D. Porter, *J. Chem. Soc.*, 840 (1933).

109. N. D. Scott, J. F. Walker and V. L. Hansley, *J. Am. Chem. Soc.*, **58**, 2442 (1936).

110. G. E. Coates, *Organo-Metallic Compounds*, 2nd ed., Methuen and Co., London, 1960; (a) pp. 30–34, (b) pp. 43–63.

111. A. I. Shatenshtein, E. S. Petrov, M. I. Belousova, K. G. Yanova and E. A. Yakovleva, *Dokl. Akad. Nauk. S.S.S.R.*, **151**, 353 (1963); *Chem. Abstr.*, **59**, 8769 (1963).

112. E. S. Petrov, E. A. Yakovleva and A. I. Shatenshtein, *Zh. Obshch. Khim.*, **33**, 107 (1963); *Chem. Abstr.*, **59**, 416 (1963).

113. N. B. Keevil and H. E. Bent, *J. Am. Chem. Soc.*, **60**, 193 (1938).

114. A. C. Aten, J. Dieleman and G. J. Hoijtink, *Discussions Faraday Soc.*, **29**, 182 (1960).

115. D. H. Eargle, Jr., *J. Org. Chem.*, **28**, 1703 (1963).

116. J. L. Down, J. Lewis, B. Moore and G. Wilkinson, *Proc. Chem. Soc.*, 209 (1957).

117. W. Schlenk and E. Marcus, *Chem. Ber.*, **47**, 1664 (1914).

118. G. Wittig, R. Ludwig and R. Polster, *Chem. Ber.*, **88**, 294 (1955).

119. K. Hafner, H. Pelster and H. Patzett, *Ann. Chem.*, **650**, 80 (1961).

120. H. L. Friedman, *J. Am. Chem. Soc.*, **74**, 5 (1952).

121. J. A. Dixon, P. A. Gwinnen and D. C. Lini, *J. Am. Chem. Soc.*, **87**, 1379 (1965).

122. H. Meerwein, G. Hinz, P. Hofmann, E. Kroning and E. Pfeif, *J. Prakt. Chem.*, **147**, 257 (1937).

123. H. Meerwein, E. Battenberg, H. Gold, E. Pfeil and G. Willfang, *J. Prakt. Chem.*, **154**, 83 (1939).

124. H. Meerwein, K. Bodenbenner, P. Borner, F. Kunert and K. Wunderlich, *Ann. Chem.*, **632**, 38 (1960).

125. H. Muxfeldt, paper presented at Nineteenth National Organic Chemistry Symposium, Tempe, Arizona, June 15, 1965.
126. H. Meerwein, D. Delfs and H. Morschel, *Angew. Chem.*, **72**, 927 (1960).
127. H. Meerwein, V. Hederich and K. Wunderlich, *Arch. Pharm.*, **291**, 541 (1958).
128. F. Klages, E. Muhlbauer and G. Lukasdzyk, *Chem. Ber.*, **94**, 1464 (1961).
129. L. M. Smorgonskii, *Zh. Obshch. Khim.*, **17**, 416 (1947); *Chem. Abstr.*, **42**, 858 (1948).
130. V. L. Guyer and R. E. Dunbar, *Proc. N. Dakota Acad. Sci.*, **11**, 26 (1957); *Chem. Abstr.*, **52**, 634 (1958).
131. R. D. Youssefyeh and Y. Mazur, *Tetrahedron Letters*, 1287 (1962).
132. S. H. Bauer, G. R. Finlay and A. W. Laubengayer, *J. Am. Chem. Soc.*, **65**, 889 (1943); **67**, 339 (1945).
133. F. V. Dunderman and S. H. Bauer, *J. Phys. Chem.*, **50**, 32 (1946).
134. D. E. McLaughlin and M. Tamres, *J. Am. Chem. Soc.*, **82**, 5618 (1960).
135. F. G. A. Stone, *Chem. Rev.*, **58**, 101 (1958).
136. D. R. Martin, *Chem. Rev.*, **34**, 461 (1944).
137. D. R. Martin, *Chem. Rev.*, **42**, 581 (1948).
138. D. R. Martin and J. M. Canon in *Friedel–Crafts and Related Reactions*, Vol. I (Ed. G. A. Olah), Interscience Publishers, London, 1963, Chap. 6.
139. N. N. Greenwood and R. L. Martin, *Quart. Rev. (London)*, **8**, 1 (1954).
140. N. N. Greenwood and K. Wade in *Friedel–Crafts and Related Reactions*, Vol. I (Ed. G. A. Olah), Interscience Publishers, London, 1963, Chap. 7.
141. W. I. Sullivan, F. W. Swamer, W. J. Humphlett and C. R. Hauser, *J. Org. Chem.* **26**, 2306 (1961).
142. F. J. Welch, *J. Am. Chem. Soc.*, **82**, 6000 (1960).
143. V. N. Nikitin, G. V. Rakova and N. V. Mikhalova, *Dokl. Akad. Nauk S.S.S.R.*, **124**, 873 (1959); *Chem. Abstr.*, **55**, 8040 (1961).
144. A. N. Radionov, T. V. Talaeva, D. N. Shigorin and K. A. Kocheskov, *Dokl. Akad. Nauk.*, *SSSR*, **136**, 369 (1961); *Chem. Abstr.*, **55**, 16458 (1961).
145. Z. K. Cheema, G. W. Gibson and J. F. Eastham, *J. Am. Chem. Soc.*, **85**, 3517 (1963).
146. N. Y. Turova, A. V. Novoselova and K. N. Semenenko, *Zh. Neorgan. Khim.*, **4**, 1215 (1959).
147. N. Y. Turova, A. V. Novoselova and K. N. Semenenko, *Zh. Neorgan. Khim.*, **5**, 117 (1960).
148. N. Y. Turova, A. V. Novoselova and K. N. Semenenko, *Zh. Neorgan. Khim.*, **5**, 941 (1960).
149. N. Y. Turova, A. V. Novoselova and K. N. Semenenko, *Zh. Neorgan. Khim.*, **5**, 1705 (1960).
150. N. Y. Turova and A. V. Novoselova, *Zh. Neorgan. Khim.*, **8**, 575 (1963).
151. B. K. Lewis, *Ph.D. Thesis*, University of Oklahoma, 1959; *Dissertation Abstr.*, **20**, 2544 (1960).
152. V. I. Esafov, *Zh. Obshch. Khim.*, **28**, 1212 (1958).
153. V. I. Esafov and G. I. Yakahina, *Zh. Obshch. Khim.*, **30**, 3572 (1960).
154. J. R. Masaquer and A. Bustelo, *Anales Real Soc. Españ. Fis. Quim. (Madrid)*, **55B**, 823 (1959).
155. N. Y. Turova, A. V. Novoselova and K. N. Semenenko, *Zh. Neorgan. Khim.*, **7**, 113 (1962).

156. N. S. Sitdykova, N. Y. Turova, K. N. Semenenko and A. V. Novoselova, *Zh. Neorgan. Khim.*, **6**, 2512 (1961).
157. N. Y. Turova, N. S. Sitdykova, A. V. Novoselova and K. N. Semenenko, *Zh. Neorgan. Khim.*, **8**, 528 (1963).
158. A. D. Vreugdenhil and C. Blomberg, *Rec. Trav. Chim.*, **83**, 453, 461 (1963).
159. G. Stucky and R. Rundle, *J. Am. Chem. Soc.*, **86**, 4825 (1964).
160. M. S. Kharasch and O. Reinmuth, *Grignard Reactions of Nonmetallic Substances*, Prentice-Hall, New York, 1954, pp. 99–112.
161. D. Bryce-Smith, *Bull. Soc. Chim. France*, 1418 (1963).
162. R. Hamelin, *Bull. Soc. Chim. France*, 684 (1961).
163. A. Kirrman, R. Hamelin and S. Hayes, *Bull. Soc. Chim. France*, 1395 (1963).
164. R. Hamelin and S. Hayes, *Bull. Soc. Chim. France*, 692 (1961).
165. P. Jolibois, *Compt. Rend.*, **155**, 353 (1912).
166. W. Schlenk and W. Schlenk, Jr., *Chem. Ber.*, **62**, 920 (1929).
167. R. E. Dessy, G. S. Handler, J. A. Wotiz and C. A. Hollingsworth, *J. Am. Chem. Soc.*, **79**, 3476 (1957).
168. J. Miller, G. Grigorion and H. S. Mosher, *J. Am. Chem. Soc.*, **83**, 3966 (1961).
169. N. M. Bikales and E. I. Backer, *Can. J. Chem.*, **41**, 1329 (1962).
170. E. C. Ashby and M. B. Smith, *J. Am. Chem. Soc.*, **86**, 4363 (1964).
171. E. C. Ashby and W. E. Becker, *J. Am. Chem. Soc.*, **85**, 118 (1963).
172. M. Andrac, F. Gaudemar, M. Gaudemar, B. Gross, L. Miginiac, P. Miginiac and C. Prevost, *Bull. Soc. Chim. France*, 1385 (1963).
173. W. Slough and A. H. Ubbelhodde, *J. Chem. Soc.*, 108 (1955).
174. A. K. Holliday and J. Sowler, *J. Chem. Soc.*, 11 (1952).
175. R. E. Van Dyke and H. E. Crawford, *J. Am. Chem. Soc.*, **72**, 2829 (1950).
176. T. A. Shchegoleva, V. D. Sheludyakov and B. M. Mikhailov, *Dokl. Akad. Nauk SSSR*, **152**, 888 (1963); *Chem. Abstr.*, **60**, 6455 (1964).
177. H. E. Wirth, M. J. Jackson and H. W. Griffiths, *J. Phys. Chem.*, **62**, 871 (1958).
178. J. D. Edwards, W. Gerrard and M. F. Lappert, *J. Chem. Soc.*, 377 (1957).
179. H. Bowlus and J. A. Niewland, *J. Am. Chem. Soc.*, **53**, 3835 (1931).
180. G. A. Olah and M. W. Meyer in *Friedel–Crafts and Related Reactions*, Vol. I (Ed. G. A. Olah), Interscience Publishers, London, 1963, pp. 695–710.
181. I. Penczek and S. Penczek, *Przemysl Chem.*, **42**, 221 (1963); *Chem. Abstr.*, **60**. 6051 (1964).
182. H. C. Brown and R. M. Adams, *J. Am. Chem. Soc.*, **64**, 2557 (1942).
183. M. Tamres and S. Searles, unpublished observations; S. Kambara and M. Hatana, *J. Chem. Soc. Japan, Ind. Chem. Sect.*, **59**, 77 (1956).
184. D. E. McLaughlin, M. Tamres and S. Searles, *J. Am. Chem. Soc.*, **82**, 5621 (1960).
185. J. Grimley and A. K. Holliday, *J. Chem. Soc.*, 1215 (1954).
186. P. Diehl and R. A. Ogg, *Nature*, **180**, 1114 (1957).
187. A. C. Rutenberg, A. A. Palko and J. S. Drury, *J. Am. Chem. Soc.*, **85**, 2702 (1963).
188. A. C. Rutenberg, A. A. Palko and J. S. Drury, *J. Phys. Chem.*, **68**, 976 (1964).
189. A. A. Palko and J. S. Drury, *J. Chem. Phys.*, **40**, 278 (1964).
190. A. C. Rutenberg and A. A. Palko, *J. Phys. Chem.*, **69**, 527 (1965).

191. I. Kirshenbaum, N. Sabi and P. W. Shutz, *U.S. At. Energy Comm.*, **A-2120** (1944); *Chem. Abstr.*, **55**, 18374 (1961).

192. D. A. McCauley, *U.S. At. Energy Comm.*, **A-2357** (1945); *Chem. Abstr.*, **55**, 18374 (1961).

193. K. O. Hambrock, *U.S. At. Energy Comm.*, **HEC-80** (1957); *Chem. Abstr.*, **55**, 18374 (1961).

194. G. M. Panchenkov, A. V. Makarov and L. I. Pechalin, *Zh. Fiz. Khim.*, **34**, 2489 (1960).

195. A. V. Makarov and G. M. Panchenkov, *Zh. Fiz. Khim.*, **35**, 2147 (1961).

196. G. M. Panchenkov, A. V. Makarov and L. I. Pechalin, *Zh. Fiz. Khim.*, **35**, 2110 (1961).

197. S. C. Saxena, A. R. Gupta, R. P. Poncha and M. R. Ghate, *J. Sci. Ind. Res. (India)*, **20D**, 393 (1961); *Chem. Abstr.*, **56**, 11134 (1962).

198. P. Kulicke, G. Ketzschmann and G. Schmidt, *Kernenergie*, **5**, 267 (1962); *Chem. Abstr.*, **60**, 15379 (1964).

199. A. V. Makarov and G. M. Panchenkov, *Vestn. Mosk. Univ. Ser. II, Khim.*, **18**, 58 (1963); *Chem. Abstr.*, **59**, 180 (1963).

200. T. D. Parsons, E. D. Baker, A. B. Burg and G. L. Juvinall, *J. Am. Chem. Soc.*, **83**, 250 (1961).

201. A. A. Palko, *J. Inorg. Nucl. Chem.*, **27**, 287 (1965); A. A. Palko and J. S. Drury, *J. Chem. Phys.*, **35**, 103 (1961).

202. W. Gerrard, M. F. Lappert and H. B. Silver, *J. Chem. Soc.*, 3285 (1956).

203. W. Gerrard and M. F. Lappert, *J. Chem. Soc.*, 1486 (1952).

204. J. D. Edwards, W. Gerrard and M. F. Lappert, *J. Chem. Soc.*, 1470 (1955).

205. J. D. Edwards, W. Gerrard and M. F. Lappert, *J. Chem. Soc.*, 348 (1957).

206. S. H. Dandegaonker, W. Gerrard and M. F. Lappert, *J. Chem. Soc.*, 2893 (1957).

207. W. A. G. Graham and F. G. A. Stone, *J. Inorg. Nucl. Chem.*, **3**, 164 (1956).

208. (a) H. E. Wirth, F. E. Massoth and D. X. Gilbert, *J. Phys. Chem.*, **62**, 870 (1958); (b) G. E. MacWood and L. J. Paridon, *J. Phys. Chem.*, **63**, 1302 (1959).

209. T. D. Coyle, H. D. Kaesz and F. G. A. Stone, *J. Am. Chem. Soc.*, **81**, 2989 (1959).

210. L. J. Edwards, W. V. Hough and M. D. Ford, *Congr. Intern. Chim. Pure Appl.*, *16e, Paris 1957, Mem. Sect. Chim. Minerale*, 475–481 (1958); *Chem. Abstr.*, **54**, 15062 (1960).

211. H. C. Brown and P. A. Tierney, *J. Inorg. Nucl. Chem.*, **9**, 51 (1959).

212. Purdue Research Foundation, *Brit. Pat.*, 873,267 (1961); *Chem. Abstr.*, **57**, 11104 (1962).

213. J. R. Bercaw and A. B. Garrett, *J. Am. Chem. Soc.*, **78**, 1841 (1956).

214. O. K. Kudra and N. I. Ternovaya, *Ukr. Khim. Zh.*, **27**, 612 (1961); *Chem. Abstr.*, **56**, 9488 (1962).

215. G. Geiseler and W. Knothe, *E. Ger. Pat.* 17,611 (1959); *Chem. Abstr.*, **55**, 1445 (1961).

216. J. F. Nobis, *U.S. Pat.* 2,960,516 (1960); *Chem. Abstr.*, **55**, 9346 (1961).

217. F. Gallais and P. de Loth, *Compt. Rend.*, **259**, 785 (1964).

218. G. Geiseler and W. Knothe, *Ger. Pat.* 1,044,959 (1958); *Chem. Abstr.*, **55**, 2485 (1961).

219. E. B. Baker and H. H. Sisler, *J. Am. Chem. Soc.*, **75**, 4828 (1953).

220. P. Pino, L. Lardici and G. P. Lorenzi, *Ann. Chim.* (*Rome*), **48**, 1426 (1958).
221. I. Paul and T. D. Smith, *J. Chem. Soc.*, 2770 (1964).
222. E. Bonitz, *Chem. Ber.*, **88**, 742 (1955).
223. T. Mole, *Australian J. Chem.*, **16**, 794, 801, 807 (1963).
224. G. Costa and R. Calcinari, *Gazz. Chim. Ital.*, **89**, 1415 (1959).
225. B. Bartocha, A. J. Bilbo, D. E. Bublitz and M. Y. Gray, *Z. Naturforsch.*, **16B**, 357 (1961).
226. K. Issleib and H. J. Deylig, *Z. Naturforsch*, **17B**, 198 (1962).
227. E. Wiberg, *Agnew. Chem.*, **65**, 16 (1953).
228. R. Dautel and W. Zeil, *Z. Electrochem.*, **64**, 1234 (1960).
229. I. McClure and T. D. Smith, *J. Inorg. Nuclear Chem.*, **19**, 170 (1961).
230. E. Wiberg and W. Gosele, *Z. Naturforsch.*, **11B**, 485 (1956).
231. N. N. Greenwood and P. G. Perkins, *Chem. Soc.* (*London*) *Spec. Publ.*, **13**, 193 (1959).
232. E. Wiberg and M. Schmidt, *Z. Naturforsch.*, **6B**, 172 (1951).
233. F. Fairbrother, N. Flitcroft and H. Prophet, *J. Less-Common Metals*, **2**, 49 (1960).
234. (a) H. Funk and H. Kohler, *Z. Anorg. Allgem. Chem.*, **294**, 233 (1958); (b) R. H. Pickard and J. Kenyon, *J. Chem. Soc.*, **91**, 896 (1907).
235. V. A. Plotnikov and N. N. Gratsionskii, *Bull. Acad. Sci. USSR, Div. Chem. Sci.*, **101** (1947); *Chem. Abstr.*, **42**, 4480 (1948).
236. N. I. Sheverdina, L. V. Abramova and K. A. Kocheshkov, *Dokl. Akad. Nauk SSSR*, **134**, 853 (1960); *Chem. Abstr.*, **55**, 12330 (1961).
237. K. H. Thiele, *Z. Anorg. Allgem. Chem.*, **319**, 183 (1962).
238. H. H. Sisler, W. J. Wilson, B. J. Griffins, H. H. Batey, B. Pfahler and R. Mattair, *J. Am. Chem. Soc.*, **70**, 3818 (1948).
239. H. H. Sisler, H. H. Batey, B. Pfahler and R. Mattair, *J. Am. Chem. Soc.* **70**, 3821 (1948).
240. F. J. Ciaffi and S. T. Zenchelsky, *J. Phys. Chem.*, **67**, 357 (1963).
241. D. Schwartz and R. Reski, *J. Inorg. Nucl. Chem.*, **27**, 747 (1965).
242. O. A. Osipov and Y. B. Uletnik, *Zh. Obshch. Khim.*, **31**, 2451 (1961).
243. P. M. Hamilton, R. McBeth, W. Bekebrede and H. H. Sisler, *J. Am. Chem. Soc.*, **75**, 2881 (1953).
244. J. L. Ernst and R. M. Thomas, *U.S. Pat.*, 2,682,531 (June 29, 1954); *Chem. Abstr.*, **48**, 12450 (1954).
245. Esso Research and Eng. Co., *Ger. Pat.*, 948,088 (1956); *Chem. Abstr.*, **53**, 12730 (1959).
246. G. A. Razuvaev and L. M. Bobinova, *Dokl. Akad. Nauk. S.S.S.R.*, **152**, 1363 (1963); *Chem. Abstr.*, **60**, 1784 (1964).
247. R. F. Rolsten and H. H. Sisler, *J. Am. Chem. Soc.*, **79**, 1068 (1957).
248. D. B. Copely, F. Fairbrother and A. Thompson, *J. Chem. Soc.*, 315 (1964).
249. F. Fairbrother, K. H. Grundy and A. Thompson, *J. Chem. Soc.*, 765 (1965).
250. H. H. Zeiss, *Bull. Soc. Chim. France*, 1500 (1963).
251. F. Hein and D. Tille, *Monatsber. Deut. Akad. Wiss. Berlin*, **4**, 414 (1962).
252. J. Bye and M. J. Weill, *Bull. Soc. Chim. France*, 1130 (1960).
253. H. Funk and H. Schauer, *Z. Anorg. Allgem. Chem.*, **306**, 203 (1960).
254. V. M. Vdovenko and E. A. Smirnova, *Radiokhimiya*, **1**, 43 (1959); *Chem. Abstr.*, **53**, 21059 (1959).
255. L. I. Katzin and J. C. Sullivan, *J. Phys.* (*and Colloid*) *Chem.*, **55**, 346 (1951).

256. V. M. Vdovenko, I. G. Suglobova, D. N. Suglobov and Y. V. Datyuk, *Radiokhimiya*, **5**, 739 (1963); *Chem. Abstr.*, **60**, 11433 (1964).
257. V. M. Vdovenko, D. N. Suglobov and E. A. Smirnova, *Radiokhimiya*, **2**, 296 (1960); *Chem. Abstr.*, **55**, 4145 (1961).
258. L. I. Katzin and J. R. Ferraro, *J. Am. Chem. Soc.*, **74**, 6040 (1952).
259. P. A. McCusker, T. J. Lane and M. S. Kennard, *J. Am. Chem. Soc.*, **81**, 2974 (1959).
260. E. J. Corey, *Tetrahedron Letters*, 1 (1959).
261. R. Robinson, *Tetrahedron*, **5**, 96 (1959).
262. R. D. Colclaugh, G. Gee, W. C. E. Higginson, J. B. Jackson and M. Litt, *J. Polymer Sci.*, **34**, 171 (1959).
263. A. Z. Chkhenkeli, *Svobshcheniya Akad. Nauk. Gruzin SSR*, **19**, 37 (1957); *Chem. Abstr.*, **52**, 16848 (1958).
264. R. C. Paul and S. P. Narula, *J. Sci. Ind. Res. (India)*, **20B**, 184 (1961); *Chem. Abstr.*, **55**, 20912 (1961).
265. M. Schmidt, P. Bornmann and I. Wilhelm, *Angew. Chem.*, **75**, 1024 (1963).
266. J. G. Whanger and H. H. Sisler, *J. Am. Chem. Soc.*, **75**, 5188 (1953).
267. H. W. Ling and H. H. Sisler, *J. Am. Chem. Soc.*, **75**, 5191 (1953).
268. H. H. Sisler and P. E. Perkins, *J. Am. Chem. Soc.*, **78**, 1135 (1956).
269. P. Groth and O. Hassel, *Proc. Chem. Soc.*, 379 (1962).
270. (a) E. L. Muetterties, T. A. Bither, M. W. Farlow and D. D. Coffman, *J. Inorg. Nucl. Chem.*, **16**, 52 (1960); (b) E. L. Muetterties, *U.S. Pat.*, 2,856,370 (1958); *Chem. Abstr.*, **53**, 2683 (1959).
271. J. R. Masagauer, *Anales Real Soc. Españ. Fis. Quim. (Madrid)*, **53B**, 518 (1957).
272. K. Dehnicke, *Z. Anorg. Allgem. Chem.*, **312**, 237 (1961).
273. N. S. Bayliss and E. G. McRae, *J. Phys. Chem.*, **58**, 1002 (1954).
274. Sr. M. Brandon, M. Tamres and S. Searles, Jr., *J. Am. Chem. Soc.*, **82**, 2129 (1960).
275. M. Tamres and S. Searles, Jr., *J. Phys. Chem.*, **66**, 1099 (1962).
276. S. Nagakura, *J. Am. Chem. Soc.*, **80**, 520 (1958).
277. K. Higasi, *J. Sci. Res. Inst. (Tokyo)*, **24**, 57 (1934).
278. M. Tamres and Sr. M. Brandon, *J. Am. Chem. Soc.*, **82**, 2134 (1960).
279. Y. K. Syrkin and K. M. Amisimora, *Dokl. Akad. Nauk SSSR*, **59**, 1457 (1948).
280. F. Fairbrother, *Nature*, **160**, 87 (1947); *J. Chem. Soc.*, 1051 (1948).
281. G. Kortüm and H. Walz, *Z. Elektrochem.*, **57**, 73 (1953).
282. G. Briegleb, *Elektronen-donator Acceptor-Komplexe*, Springer-Verlag, Berlin, 1961.
283. L. J. Andrews and R. M. Keefer, *Molecular Complexes in Organic Chemistry*, Holden-Day, San Francisco, 1964.
284. S. H. Hastings, J. L. Franklin, J. Schiller and F. A. Matsen, *J. Am. Chem. Soc.*, **75**, 2900 (1953).
285. C. Van de Stolpe, *Ph.D. Thesis*, University of Amsterdam, 1953.
286. H. McConnell, J. S. Ham and J. R. Platt, *J. Chem. Phys.*, **21**, 66 (1953).
287. G. Briegleb and J. Czekalla, *Z. Elektrochem.*, **63**, 6 (1959).
288. J. Collin, *Z. Elektrochem.*, **64**, 936 (1960).
289. J. A. A. Ketelaar, *J. Phys. Radium.*, **15**, 197 (1954).
290. K. Hartley and H. A. Skinner, *Trans. Faraday Soc.*, **46**, 621 (1950).

291. G. Kortüm and M. Kortüm-Seiler, *Z. Naturforsch.*, **5a**, 544 (1950).
292. P. A. D. deMaine, *J. Mol. Spectry.*, **7**, 83 (1961).
293. F. T. Lang and R. L. Strong, *J. Am. Chem. Soc.*, **87**, 2345 (1965).
294. L. J. Andrews and R. M. Keefer, *J. Am. Chem. Soc.*, **75**, 3561 (1953).
295. P. A. D. deMaine, *J. Chem. Phys.*, **26**, 1036, 1189 (1957).
296. R. N. Hazeldine, *J. Chem. Soc.*, 4145 (1954).
297. (a) D. L. Glusker and H. W. Thompson, *J. Chem. Soc.*, 471 (1955);
     (b) R. Vars, L. A. Tripp and L. W. Pickett, *J. Phys. Chem.*, **66**, 1754 (1962).
298. D. D. Eley and J. Saunders, *J. Chem. Soc.*, 1672 (1954).
299. O. Hassel and C. R. Rømming, *Quart. Rev. (London)*, **16**, 1 (1962).
300. G. C. Pimentel and A. L. McClellan, *The Hydrogen Bond*, W. H. Freeman and Co., San Francisco, 1960.
301. M. R. Basila, E. L. Saier and L. R. Cousins, *J. Am. Chem. Soc.*, **87**, 1665 (1965).
302. (a) S. Nagakura, *J. Chim. Phys.*, 217 (1964); (b) P. G. Puranik and N. Kumar, *Proc. Indian Acad. Sci., Sect. A.*, **58**, 29, 327 (1963); (c) H. Tsubomura, *J. Chem. Phys.*, **24**, 927 (1956) (d) K. Szczepaniak, *8th European Cong. Mol. Spectry.*, Copenhagen, Denmark, Aug. 14–20, 1965, abstracts from paper 323.
303. J. C. Dearden and W. F. Forbes, *Can. J. Chem.*, **38**, 898 (1960).
304. M. Ito, *J. Mol. Spectry.*, **4**, 125 (1960).
305. K. Semba, *Bull. Chem. Soc. Japan*, **34**, 723 (1961).
306. D. Papousek, J. Krusina and J. Kucirek, *Collection Czech. Chem. Commun.*, **24**, 2967 (1959).
307. M. Ito, *J. Mol. Spectry.*, **4**, 144 (1960).
308. M. Ito, *J. Mol. Spectry.*, **4**, 106 (1960).
309. J. Hires and P. Nagy, *Szegedi Pedagog. Foiskola Evkonyve, Masodik Resz*, 183 (1960).
310. J. Jacob, *Compt. Rend.*, **250**, 1624 (1960).
311. E. A. Gastilorich, D. N. Shigoren, E. P. Gracheva and M. F. Shostakovskii, *Dokl. Akad. Nauk SSSR*, **129**, 1085 (1959).
312. J. C. D. Brand, G. Eglinton and J. F. Morman, *J. Chem. Soc.*, 2526 (1960).
313. R. C. Lord, B. Nolin and H. D. Stidham, *J. Am. Chem. Soc.*, **77**, 1365 (1955).
314. M. L. McGlashan and R. P. Rastogi, *Trans. Faraday Soc.*, **54**, 496 (1958).
315. S. Searles and M. Tamres, *J. Am. Chem. Soc.*, **73**, 3704 (1951).
316. J. R. Lacher, J. J. McKinley and J. D. Park, *J. Am. Chem. Soc.*, **70**, 2598 (1948).
317. R. Anderson and T. Thurmann-Moe, *Acta. Chem. Scand.*, **18**, 433 (1964).
318. W. Gordy and S. C. Stanford, *J. Chem. Phys.*, **9**, 204 (1941).
319. J. M. Ginzburg, E. S. Petrow and A. I. Schatenstein, *Zh. Obshch. Khim.*, **34**, 2294 (1964).
320. R. G. Inskeep, F. E. Dickson and J. M. Kelliker, *J. Mol. Spectry.*, **4**, 477 (1960).
321. H. E. Hallam and D. Jones, *8th European Cong. Mol. Spectry.*, Copenhagen, Denmark, Aug. 14–20, 1965, paper 86.
322. D. Papousek and L. Pago, *Collection Czech. Chem. Commun.*, **24**, 2666 (1959).
323. T. Gramstad, *Spectrochim. Acta*, **19**, 497 (1963).
324. D. L. Powell and R. West, *Spectrochim. Acta*, **20**, 983 (1964).

325. L. Henry, *Hydrogen Bonding* (Ed. D. Hadzi), Pergamon Press, Oxford, 1959, p. 163.
326. K. Maksyutin, V. L. Frolov, A. V. Kalabina and V. A. Sheveleya, *Zh. Fiz. Khim.*, **38**, 2604 (1964).
327. H. Hartig and W. W. Brandt, *J. Phys. Chem.*, **69**, 335 (1965).
328. M. Hauptschein and A. V. Grosse, *J. Am. Chem. Soc.*, **73**, 5139 (1951).
329. K. L. Smith, E. A. Winslow and D. E. Peterson, *Ind. Eng. Chem.*, **51**, 1361 (1959).
330. J. Arnold, J. E. Bertie and D. J. Millen, *Proc. Chem. Soc.*, 121 (1961).
331. D. J. Millen and O. A. Samsonov, *Chem. Ind. (London)*, 1694 (1963).
332. J. E. Bertie and D. J. Millen, *J. Chem. Soc.*, 497, 514 (1965).
333. J. Arnold and D. J. Millen, *J. Chem. Soc.*, 503 (1965).
334. I. M. Aref'ev and V. I. Malyshev, *Opt. i Spectroskopiya*, **13**, 206 (1962).
335. J. Lascombe, University of Bordeaux, private communication.
336. T. Gränather and P. Diehl, *Arch. Sci. (Geneva)*, **12**; *Fasc. Spec.*, 238 (1959).
337. G. Mavel, *J. Phys. Radium*, **20**, 834 (1959).
338. M. Martin, *Ann. Phys.*, **7**, 35 (1962).
339. W. G. Paterson and D. M. Cameron, *Can. J. Chem.*, **41**, 198 (1963).
340. G. Mavel, Doctoral Thesis, Paris, 1960.
341. L. J. Bellamy, H. E. Hallam and R. L. Williams, *Trans. Faraday Soc.*, **54**, 1120 (1958).
342. R. West, C. S. Kraihanzel, D. L. Powell and K. R. Bright, *Sixth Report on Research*, Petroleum Research Fund, 463-A1, 78 (1961).
343. W. Strohmeier and A. Echte, *Z. Elektrochem.*, **61**, 549 (1957).
344. J. L. Down, J. Lewis, B. Moore and G. Wilkinson, *J. Chem. Soc.*, 3767 (1959).
345. I. Fischer and L. Ehrenberg, *Acta Chem. Scand.*, **2**, 669 (1958).
346. C. K. Ingold, *Structure and Mechanism in Organic Chemistry*, Cornell University Press, Ithaca, 1953, p. 70.
347. C. H. Van Dyke and A. G. MacDiarmid, *J. Phys. Chem.*, **67**, 1930 (1963).
348. R. West, L. S. Whatley and K. J. Lake, *J. Am. Chem. Soc.*, **83**, 761 (1961).
349. B. B. Wayland and R. S. Drago, *J. Am. Chem. Soc.*, **86**, 5240 (1964).
350. L. J. Bellamy and R. L. Williams, *Proc. Roy. Soc.*, *Ser. A*, **254**, 119 (1960).
351. L. J. Bellamy, G. Eglinton and J. F. Morman, *J. Chem. Soc.*, 4762 (1961).
352. D. E. McLaughlin, M. Tamres, S. Searles and S. Nukina, *J. Inorg. Nucl. Chem.*, **17**, 112 (1961).
353. H. S. Gutowsky, R. L. Rutledge, M. Tamres and S. Searles, *J. Am. Chem. Soc.*, **76**, 4242 (1954).
354. E. Lippert and H. Prigge, *Ber. Bunsenges. Physik. Chem.*, **67**, 415, 554 (1963).
355. (a) R. West, D. L. Powell, M. K. Lee and S. Whatley, *J. Am. Chem. Soc.*, **86**, 3227 (1964); (b) E. Lippert and H. Prigge, *Ann. Chem.*, **659**, 81 (1962).
356. L. Bellon, *Trav. Inst. Sci. Cherifien, Ser. Sci. Phys.*, **6** (1960).
357. M. Tamres, S. Searles and J. M. Goodenow, *J. Am. Chem. Soc.*, **86**, 3934 (1964).

CHAPTER **7**

Acetals and hemiacetals

Ernst Schmitz and Inge Eichhorn

German Academy of Sciences, Berlin-Adlershof, G.D.R.

I. INTRODUCTION

Hemiacetals (**1**) are addition products formed from one molecule of a hydroxy and one molecule of a carbonyl compound. The hydroxy compound is usually an alcohol, and rarely a phenol. The carbonyl compound may be either an aldehyde or a ketone. In the latter case the designation hemiketal is also used (reaction 1). Acetals (**2**) are

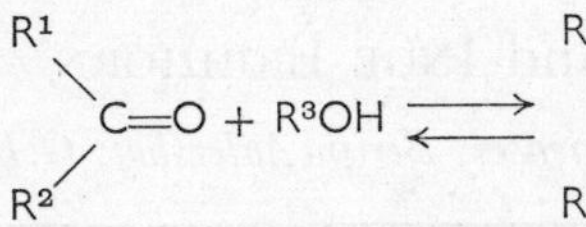

$$R^1 \diagdown C{=}O + R^3OH \rightleftharpoons R^1 \diagup R^2 \diagdown C \diagup OH \diagdown OR^3 \tag{1}$$

(**1**)

etherification products of hemiacetals. Formally, they result from elimination of one molecule of water from a carbonyl compound and two molecules of an alcohol (reaction 2).

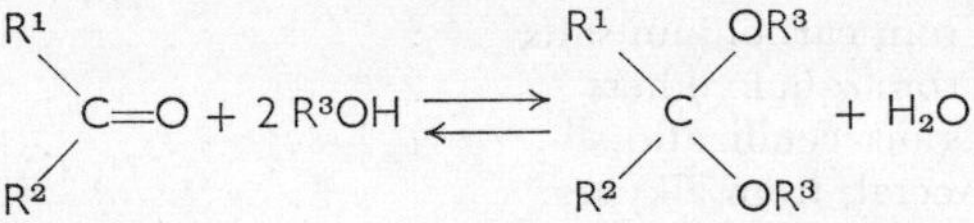

$$R^1 \diagdown C{=}O + 2\,R^3OH \rightleftharpoons R^1 \diagup R^2 \diagdown C \diagup OR^3 \diagdown OR^3 + H_2O \tag{2}$$

(**2**)

The compounds derived from ketones are usually called ketals, sometimes also ketone acetals. The designation acetal is used, however, not only for the products derived from aldehydes, but as a general term for the whole field.

The great variety of the acetals is due to the fact that they may contain both the oxygens in one ring (**3**), one oxygen in one ring (**4**) or both oxygens in two rings (**5**).

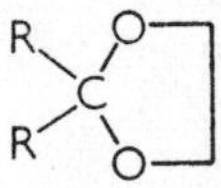

(**3**) 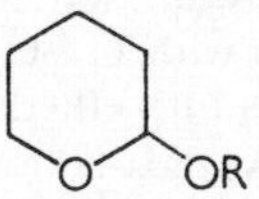   (**4**) 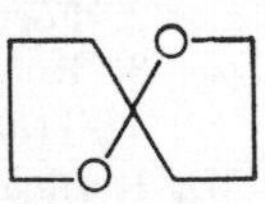   (**5**)

The acetal group plays an important role in glycosides and in the side-chain of steroids; the methylenedioxy group appears in many alkaloids. Simple acetals do not seem to occur in nature.

II. HEMIACETALS

The addition products of alcohols and carbonyl compounds can be isolated in rare cases. A whole series of hemiacetals of chloral, which can be crystallized or distilled, have been described[1]. The ethyl hemiacetal of chloral (6) decomposes rapidly into its components

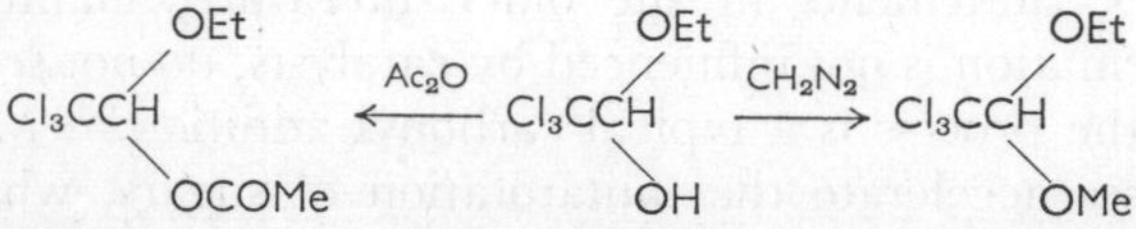

$$
\begin{array}{ccccc}
\text{OEt} & & \text{OEt} & & \text{OEt} \\
| & \xleftarrow{\text{Ac}_2\text{O}} & | & \xrightarrow{\text{CH}_2\text{N}_2} & | \\
\text{Cl}_3\text{CCH} & & \text{Cl}_3\text{CCH} & & \text{Cl}_3\text{CCH} \\
| & & | & & | \\
\text{OCOMe} & & \text{OH} & & \text{OMe}
\end{array}
\qquad (3)
$$

$$(6)$$

at 160°, but only slowly at its boiling point (115°). The hydroxyl group of 6 can be acylated by acetic anhydride and methylated by diazomethane (equation 3)[2].

Additional examples are the ethyl hemiacetal of glyoxylic acid ethyl ester (7)[3], the methyl hemiacetal of cyclopropanone (8)[4] and the hemiacetal of the heterocyclic aldehyde (9)[5]. The examples 7, 8 and 9 show that hemiacetals are stable in those cases in which the

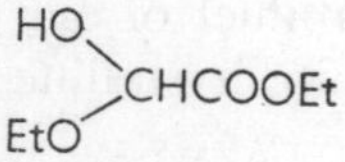

(7)

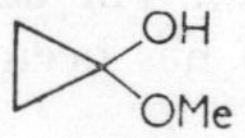

(8)

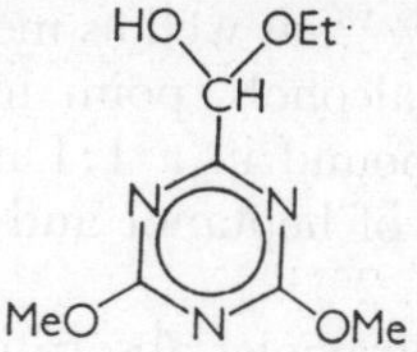

(9)

parent carbonyl group is strongly electron deficient. The relative stability of certain isolated hemiacetals (e.g. 10, 11 and 12) is due to their cyclic structure[6-8].

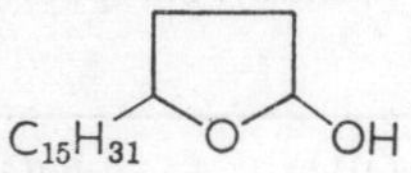

(10)

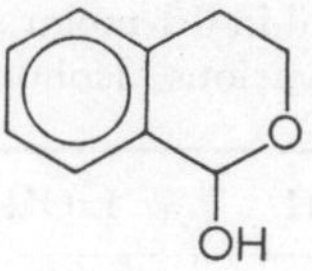

(11)

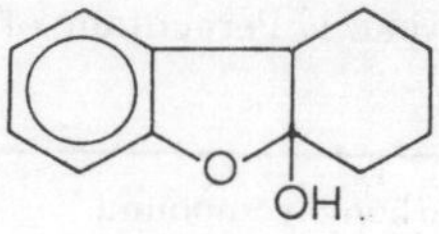

(12)

While the isolation of a stable hemiacetal is limited to special cases, an equilibrium between a carbonyl compound, alcohol and hemiacetal is evident in all cases. In alcoholic solutions, as a rule, aldehydes form hemiacetals to a considerable extent, while ketones form hemiacetals to only a very small degree[9, 10]. In the absence of acids or bases hemiacetal formation proceeds very slowly. A mixture of propionaldehyde and propyl alcohol contained, after 95 minutes at 25°, 83% of the hemiacetal, which is very nearly equal to the equilibrium concentration (87·6%)[9]. Statements in the older literature, claiming that hemiacetal formation is not influenced by catalysts, do not seem to be correct since the process is a typical carbonyl addition[11]. Moreover, acids and bases accelerate the mutarotation of sugars, which is in principle the same type of reaction[12].

More accurate studies, in particular on the catalytic influence of bases, are missing. Attempts to study the acid-catalyzed hemiacetal formation[13] were occasionally inaccurate, since formation of the acetal intervened[14].

The possibility of hemiacetal formation during various reactions, such as acetalization, should be postulated. Several independent physical methods showed that hemiacetal formation indeed occurs to quite an appreciable extent. Measurements of the heat of reaction[9], deviations from additivity of the refractive index and of the density[15, 16], as well as melting-point diagrams[17] in mixtures of aldehydes and alcohols, point to the formation of considerable quantities of a compound in a 1:1 molar ratio. The addition product of one mole each of heptanol and heptanal has been isolated in crystalline form (m.p. 2°)[18].

Ultraviolet absorption was extensively used to determine the hemiacetal formation. The absorption of the carbonyl group, in the region of 300 mμ, disappears as a result of the addition of alcohol. Systematic studies were made by Herold in 1932[10]. Even at that early date the dependence of the equilibrium position on steric hindrance was established. Some results are shown in Table 1.

TABLE 1. Percentage of hemiacetal in 0·1 molar solution of carbonyl compounds in various alcohols.

Carbonyl compound	MeOH	EtOH	i-PrOH	t-BuOH
Acetaldehyde	97	91	71	12
Propionaldehyde	95	87	58	
Isobutyraldehyde	90	81	42	
Bromoacetone	47	22	16	

It is apparent that in methanol simple aliphatic aldehydes exist almost completely in the form of the hemiacetal. Branching in aldehydes somewhat decreases the amount of the hemiacetal while branching in the alcohol component decreases it to a considerable extent, e.g. acetaldehyde in t-butyl alcohol gives only 12% of the hemiacetal. The formation of hemiketals is similarly influenced by the alcohol.

Quantitative data on the promotion of the hemiacetal formation by halogen substitution were obtained by Cantacuzène[19]. Measurements of ultraviolet absorption have shown that the formation of hemiacetal from acetaldehyde and ethyl alcohol is strongly increased by successive chlorine substitution in the aldehyde; however, the final increase on passing from dichloroacetaldehyde to chloral is very small. Chlorine substitution in the alcohol decreases the amount of hemiacetal formed. Equilibrium between the components in cyclohexane solution is usually attained after approximately one hour, but with chloral the equilibrium was attained very much more slowly.

Attempts were made quite early to determine the equilibrium position in intramolecular hemiacetal formation. These experiments served as models for the investigation of the oxo–cyclo tautomerism of carbohydrates. Helferich[20] deduced the presence of the cyclic hemiacetals such as 14 from measurements of the molar refraction of γ-hydroxybutyraldehyde, γ-hydroxyvaleraldehyde (13) and δ-hydroxycaproaldehyde. Reactions of the aldehyde group with solutions of silver salts in ammonia and with fuchsine sulfurous acid occurred only on heating.

The 2-hydroxy-5-methyltetrahydrofuran (14) reacts with methanolic HCl to form an ether, and with acetic anhydride to form an acetyl derivative (equation 4).

$$\text{HOCHCH}_2\text{CH}_2\text{CHO} \longrightarrow \quad\quad \xrightarrow{(\text{CH}_3\text{CO})_2\text{O}} \quad\quad \quad\quad (4)$$

(13)   (14)

Hydroxy ketones have much less tendency to form intramolecular hemiacetals. Infrared and Raman spectra show[21] that the γ-acetylpropyl alcohol contains only traces of the cyclic isomer. More precise determinations of the equilibrium position were carried out with the help of ultraviolet spectroscopy[22]. The percentage of cyclic hemiacetal present was determined by comparing the ultraviolet spectra of ω-hydroxy aldehydes and ω-methoxy aldehydes in dioxane–water.

While five-membered (**15**) and six-membered (**16**) rings are favored in the equilibrium, the higher homologs appear as the

open-chain hydroxy aldehydes. This dependence of the equilibrium position on ring size is in accordance with the fact known from sugar chemistry, that the pyranoid structure prevails over the furanoid one and that the cyclic forms with larger rings are not important.

III. PREPARATION OF ACETALS

A. Acid-catalyzed Acetal Formation

The acid-catalyzed reaction between a carbonyl group and an alcohol to form an acetal is an equilibrium reaction. As a rule, the acetal formation is not complete. Some numerical values are given in Table 2[24].

TABLE 2. Acetal percentages at equilibrium in 1:5 aldehyde–alcohol mixtures.

Aldehyde	EtOH	Cyclohexanol	i-PrOH	t-BuOH
Acetaldehyde	78	56	43	23
Isobutyraldehyde	71		23	
Trimethylacetaldehyde	56	16	11	
Benzaldehyde	39	23	13	

Comparison with Table 1 shows that substitution has the same effect on acetal formation as on hemiacetal formation. Branching of the alkyl group either in the aldehyde or in the alcohol decreases the tendency to form acetals. The presence of an electron-attracting group favors acetal formation. The equilibrium constant for the acetalization with ethanol is 0·0744 for acetaldehyde and 0·1121 for bromoacetaldehyde[25]. Acetal formation is adversely influenced by stabilization of the carbonyl double bond by conjugation. This is shown by the tabulated value for benzaldehyde and the equilibrium constants for acrolein (0·00455)[25] and crotonaldehyde (0·00063)[25].

The forcing conditions which have to be employed with ketones for the removal of water justify the assumption that the equilibria with these ketones are less favorable than for benzaldehyde; the trend is the same as in the equilibria for the formation of hemiacetals.

Djerassi and coworkers[26] carried out very instructive qualitative experiments on the equilibrium of the ketal formation. Optical rotatory dispersion* was used to follow the decrease of the concentration of the ketone. The ketal formation is very strongly affected by steric and conformational factors. The degree of ketal formation of 3-methyl-cyclohexanone (17) with methanol, ethanol and isopropyl alcohol was 93, 33 and 0%, respectively. The relatively high values for ketalization result from an extremely high ratio of alcohol to ketone (approximately 1000:1). The maximum amount of ketal was obtained with six-membered cyclic ketones. Ketal formation was smaller with 3-methylcyclopentanone (24%) and 3-methylcycloheptanone (21%). The presence of an α-methyl group in 17 decreases the amount of ketal formation to 25%, a *gem*-dimethyl group in the α position decreases the formation to 0%. The ketal formation of an oxo steroid, such as 18, amounted only to 1%, because of the branching of the adjacent carbon atom. In the 3-oxo steroid (19), where there is no steric

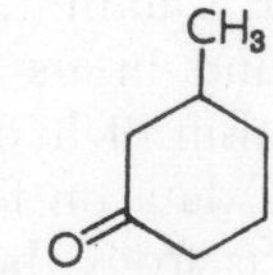

(17) 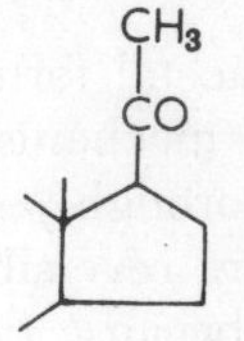   (18) 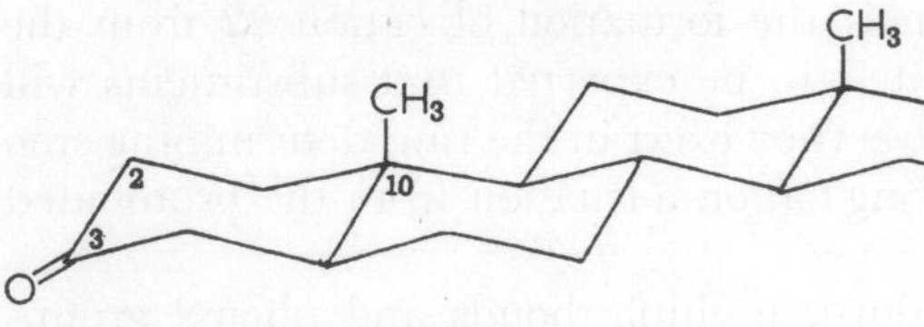   (19) 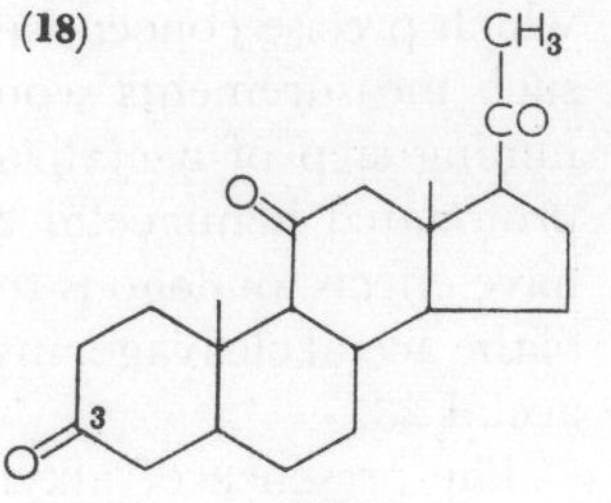   (20)

---

* Since the work was carried out in presence of acid, ketal was formed and not a hemiketal as the authors assumed (cf. reference 14).

hindrance of the carbonyl group, 81% ketalization was found. With a 2-oxo steroid the yield was only 12%, because the ketal formation leads to a 1,3-diaxial interference with the methyl group at $C_{(10)}$. Appreciable differences in ketal-forming ability of carbonyl groups in different positions on the steroid skeleton indicate the possibility of selective ketalization. Oliveto and coworkers[27a] observed partial formation of a dimethyl ketal at the $C_{(3)}$ atom of the triketone (**20**). Janot and coworkers[27b] achieved selective ketalization at $C_{(3)}$ of a steroid and obtained a dimethyl ketal, while the carbonyl group at $C_{(20)}$ was unaffected.

The mechanism of acetal formation is at present undisputed (equation 5). Although acetal cleavage was thoroughly examined,

(5)

kinetic data on acetal formation are poor. Qualitative conformation for the reaction mechanism may be found in its being the exact reverse of the thoroughly studied mechanism of hydrolysis; all steps of the reaction are reversible. The lack of data on formation rates is understandable, because the reaction starts from the hemiacetal for which precise concentration measurements are difficult. The result of such measurements would be very interesting. Since the rate-determining step of acetalization is the formation of cation **22** from the protonated hemiacetal **21**, it is to be expected that substituents will have effects analogous to those they exert in the rate-determining step of the acetal cleavage, involving cation formation from the protonated acetal **23**.

The presence of alkyl groups, multiple bonds and phenyl groups should enhance the reaction rate, while electron-attracting substituents should decrease it. The rate of formation would then change corresponding to different substituents in precisely the opposite way to the equilibrium constant for acetals or hemiacetals. Adkins and Adams[28] found that ethanol reacts forty times faster with benzaldehyde than with acetaldehyde to yield the corresponding acetal. Ketones, for which the equilibrium is least favorable, could be expected to have the highest rate of formation; good hemiacetal precursors such as chloral should have the slowest rate of acetal formation.

This regularity is in extreme cases evident from data in the preparative literature; in order to compensate for the low reaction rate the amount of acid must be increased. In the typical case of chloral the acetalization takes place only under drastic conditions. In order to obtain a cyclic acetal[29] with glycol, chloral had to be heated with three times the quantity (by weight) of concentrated sulfuric acid. Trifluoroacetaldehyde forms a stable hemiacetal, which could not be made to react with alcohol and acid to form an acetal[30]. On the other hand ketones, in spite of unfavorable equilibria, yield ketals quite readily. This is evident from the fact that the reaction proceeds very rapidly in the presence of weak acids like ammonium or calcium chloride[31].

The opposing effects of substituents on the concentration of hemiacetals and on the rate of its reaction to form an acetal, lead to a weakening of the overall effect of substituents. It should be reemphasized that, contrary to a widespread belief, 'poor' acetal-precursors (like ketones) have high rate coefficients while 'good' ones (such as chlorinated carbonyl compounds) react particularly slowly.

The following influences of the alcoholic component are evident from the mechanism of acetal formation (equation 5). The concentration of the hemiacetal, from which the acetal formation starts, is decreased by branching in the alcohol component (see section II). The equilibrium in the protonation step of the hemiacetal should depend somewhat (but not strongly) on the structure. The rate of acetalization will be influenced by the alkoxy group of the hemiacetal, but will be independent of the entering alcohol molecule, since reaction with the latter takes place after the rate-determining cation formation. The rate coefficients with methanol, ethanol, isopropyl alcohol and t-butyl alcohol were found to have the relative magnitudes of 1·02, 2·37, 5·52 and 11·30, respectively[23].

The equilibrium of acetal formation does depend on the structure of the alcohol (Table 2). Acetalization through ring formation is quite favored. For example the pentaerythritol acetal of formaldehyde hydrolyzes ten thousand times more slowly than formaldehyde diethyl acetal[32]. Postulating similar rates of formation it follows that the six-membered ring acetal has an equilibrium constant greater by a factor of about 10^4. Therefore it is possible to obtain cyclic acetals even in water solution[33]. The rates of acetal hydrolysis for methyl, ethyl and isopropyl acetals were found to be roughly in the ratio $1:10:100$[34]. Again assuming that the rate coefficient of the acetal formation depends only partially on the alcoholic component, this explains the shift of the equilibrium favoring successively less of the acetal when passing from methyl to ethyl to isopropyl alcohol. Ketones are more influenced by space requirements of the components which they add; on the other hand, the ketal formation starts from the unfavorable equilibrium of hemiketals. This explains why ketals of secondary alcohols were not synthesized until recently. The first successful synthesis was in 1960[35]. Ketals of tertiary alcohols are not known.

The equilibrium being essentially unfavorable for the formation of acetals, the main problem in their preparation is to shift the equilibrium by reducing the concentration of water. Thus it is mainly a thermodynamic problem; only in the case of carbonyl compounds with a very electron-poor carbonyl group, such as chloral, does the problem become a kinetic one.

In favorable cases it is sufficient to keep the concentration of water low by the addition of a large excess of alcohol. Acetals of aliphatic[36] and some aromatic aldehydes[37, 38] may be obtained by reaction with a large excess of alcohol containing approximately 1% HCl. Another method is the removal of water by azeotropic distillation[39], with some inert solvent added if necessary[40].

In cases with very unfavorable equilibrium of acetalization it is necessary to remove the water completely by adding a compound which reacts readily with water. Suitable compounds are esters of sulfurous[41] and silicic[42] acids, acetone ketal[43] and orthoformates[44]. Practically all carbonyl compounds yield acetals in the presence of orthoformates.

The linear dependence of the reaction rate on the acidity function H_0 of the solution, which was established[45] for acetal hydrolysis, is probably also valid for acetal formation. The anion of the acid present is not important. The choice of a certain acid is mainly governed by the solubility of the latter. p-Toluenesulfonic acid is frequently used[46]. In the cases where milder conditions are required oxalic[47] or adipic[48] acids are used; since these are weak acids, the exact measure of acidity required is easier to achieve. Mild conditions are desired when side-reactions may be caused by acids. In the steroid series it is possible to avoid the danger of shifting the double bond to the Δ^5-position[49] during ketalization of $\varDelta^4$-3-ketones by using weak adipic acid as the catalyst[48]. With p-toluenesulfonic acid mixtures of $\varDelta^4$- and $\varDelta^5$-ketals resulted.

B. Other Acetal Formations via the Alkoxy Carbonium Ion

I. From carbonium salts

The mechanism of acetal formation as described above (equation 5), implying the formation of an alkoxy carbonium ion (**22**), is supported by the fact that many other reactions in which alkoxy carbonium ions are formed yield acetals if alcohols are present.

The work of Meerwein and coworkers[50] provides the most instructive examples. The alkoxy carbonium ions are formed as salts of complex anions, and treatment with sodium alcoholate yields acetals (equation 6). The formation of acetals from pyrylium salts is well known[51]. A newer example[52] is shown in equation (7).

$$\text{(6)}$$

$$\text{(7)}$$

2. From α-halo ethers

α-Halo ethers have a pronounced tendency to dissociate[53]. In alcohols, in the presence of acid-neutralizing agents if needed, they yield acetals (equation 8). Clearly, the method is useful only if the

$$RO\text{—}CH_2Cl \longrightarrow RO\overset{+}{\cdots}CH_2 \xrightarrow{ROH} ROCH_2OR \qquad \text{(8)}$$

α-halo ether cannot be obtained from the carbonyl compound and alcohol, while the α-halo ether can be obtained by halogenation of the corresponding ether. For example Reppe and coworkers[54] chlorinated tetrahydrofuran and obtained with methanol a 2-methoxy compound (equation 9).

$$\text{(9)}$$

γ-Bromocrotonaldehyde diethyl acetal was obtained by 1,4-addition of bromine to 1-ethoxybutadiene and subsequent treatment of the resulting compound with sodium ethoxide (equation 10)[55]. The above

$$CH_2=CH-CH=CHOEt \xrightarrow{Br_2} BrCH_2-CH=CH-CH\begin{smallmatrix}Br\\ \\OEt\end{smallmatrix} \xrightarrow{-OEt}$$

$$BrCH_2-CH=CH-CH\begin{smallmatrix}OEt\\ \\OEt\end{smallmatrix} \quad \text{(10)}$$

procedure is advantageous in the preparation of phenol acetals; many side-reactions which occur in acid solution between phenols and aldehydes are avoided by this method. For example Kröhnke and coworkers[56] obtained phenol acetals from α-keto aldehydes (equation 11).

$$C_6H_5COCH\begin{smallmatrix}Br\\ \\OC_6H_4NO_2\text{-}p\end{smallmatrix} \xrightarrow{p\text{-}NO_2C_6H_4O^-} C_6H_5COCH\begin{smallmatrix}OC_6H_4NO_2\text{-}p\\ \\OC_6H_4NO_2\text{-}p\end{smallmatrix} \quad \text{(11)}$$

α-Halo ethers are very frequently used for the introduction of an acetal linkage in carbohydrate chemistry[57,58].

3. Transacetalization

An alkoxy exchange occurs in a mixture of acetal and alcohol in the presence of acids (equation 12). This reaction was already known in

$$\begin{smallmatrix}R^1\\ \\R^1\end{smallmatrix}C\begin{smallmatrix}OR^2\\ \\OR^2\end{smallmatrix} + R^3OH \xrightarrow{H^+} \begin{smallmatrix}R^1\\ \\R^1\end{smallmatrix}C\begin{smallmatrix}OR^2\\ \\OR^3\end{smallmatrix} + R^2OH \quad \text{(12)}$$

the last century[59], but a thorough examination has only been made in recent years. A kinetic study[60] showed that the reaction is of first order both for the acid and for the acetal, and that it is independent of the alcohol concentration, as required for a rate-determining cation formation followed by rapid alcohol addition (equation 13). A study of the

$$CH_3-\overset{\displaystyle OEt}{\underset{\displaystyle \overset{+}{O}Et}{\underset{\displaystyle H}{CH}}} \quad \rightleftarrows \quad CH_3CH\overset{+}{\cdots}OEt \quad \rightleftarrows \quad CH_3-\overset{\displaystyle OEt}{\underset{\displaystyle OMe}{CH}} \qquad (13)$$

equilibrium position showed that dimethyl acetal and methyl ethyl acetal are energetically equivalent $(K = 1.01)$. Diethyl acetal is energetically less favored than methyl ethyl acetal $(K = 4.54)$. This fact is not surprising, since diethyl acetals hydrolyze much faster than the corresponding methyl acetals[34].

In a mixture of two symmetric ketals of the same ketone an equilibrium mixture is formed with the mixed ketal (equation 14)[61]. The

$$\overset{\displaystyle CH_3}{\underset{\displaystyle CH_3}{\diagup}}C\overset{\displaystyle OMe}{\underset{\displaystyle OMe}{\diagdown}} \quad + \quad \overset{\displaystyle CH_3}{\underset{\displaystyle CH_3}{\diagup}}C\overset{\displaystyle OCH_2CH=CH_2}{\underset{\displaystyle OCH_2CH=CH_2}{\diagdown}} \quad \overset{H^+}{\longrightarrow} \quad \overset{\displaystyle CH_3}{\underset{\displaystyle CH_3}{\diagup}}C\overset{\displaystyle OMe}{\underset{\displaystyle OCH_2CH=CH_2}{\diagdown}} \qquad (14)$$

mixture of dimethoxypropane and dipropoxycyclohexane contains at equilibrium all six possible ketals[61].

The use of transacetalization for preparative purposes is mainly a problem of distillation. The addition of an inert solvent, such as benzene, which gives an azeotropic mixture with the alcohol to be removed is useful. Asymmetric ketals were obtained in yields up to 30–50% by Lorette and Howard[61] from ketal and one mole of higher alcohol. The synthesis of symmetric ketals is even simpler, since here only the lowest-boiling alcohol has to be completely removed from the equilibrium mixture. Acetone dibutyl ketal was obtained in 82% yield from dimethyl ketal and acetone diallyl ketal in 75% yield[61]. By careful control of conditions transacetalization can be carried out without causing transesterification[62] when an ester group is present in the molecule. Ketals of secondary alcohols may also be synthesized by alkoxy exchange[61]. It is also possible to form the starting ketal in the reaction mixture itself[61].

Transacetalization is also important for synthesis of cyclic acetals. Side-reactions occurring with aldehydes can be prevented by using an acetal. The transacetalization of halogenated acetals with glycol was used by McElvain and Curry (equation 15)[29]. Acetals of glycerine were successfully synthesized by Piantadosi and coworkers[63].

$$ClCH_2-CH\underset{OMe}{\overset{OMe}{<}} \xrightarrow{HOCH_2-CH_2OH} ClCH_2-CH\left[\underset{O-}{\overset{O-}{<}}\right] \tag{15}$$

4. Acetals from alkynes

Under conditions similar to those necessary for the hydration of alkynes to form carbonyl compounds, ketals and acetals are formed

$$R-C\equiv CH + 2\ EtOH \xrightarrow{BF_3/HgO} \underset{CH_3}{\overset{R}{>}}C\underset{OEt}{\overset{OEt}{<}} \tag{16}$$

with alcohols (equation 16). A boron trifluoride–mercuric oxide catalyst[64,65] is used as a rule.

5. Addition of alcohols to α,β-unsaturated ethers

The proton addition to α,β-unsaturated ethers yields an alkoxy carbonium ion (**22**), which in the presence of alcohol forms an acetal (equation 17).

$$CH_2=CHOR^1 \xrightarrow{H^+} CH_3-CH\overset{+}{\cdots}OR^1 \xrightarrow{R^2OH} CH_3CH\underset{OR^1}{\overset{OR^2}{<}} \tag{17}$$

$$(22)$$

Reppe added alcohols to vinyl ethers in the presence of acids; vinyl ethers are easy to obtain on an industrial scale from acetylene and alcohols. Phenols may be added as well[66]. Both symmetric and asymmetric acetals were obtained.

The addition of alcohols to dihydropyrane (equation 18) discovered by Paul[67] was used to provide a reversible protecting group for an alcohol.

$$\tag{18}$$

Positive halogen sources may lead, by addition to a vinyl ether, to an alkoxy carbonium ion and further to the formation of acetal (equation 19) [68].

$$CH_2{=}CHOR^1 \xrightarrow{\text{t-BuOCl}} ClCH_2{-}CH{\cdots}{\overset{+}{O}}R^1 \xrightarrow{R^2OH} ClCH_2{-}CH \overset{\displaystyle OR^2}{\underset{\displaystyle OR^1}{\diagup}} \quad (19)$$

The base-catalyzed addition of an alcohol to the carbon–carbon double bond proceeds through a carbanionic mechanism. It is successful only in the presence of substituents (e.g. —SO$_2$R, —CO—) which stabilize the carbanion, as in equation (20) [69].

$$\overset{EtO}{\underset{CH_3}{\diagup}}C{=}CHCOOEt \xrightarrow{EtO^-} \overset{EtO}{\underset{EtO}{\diagup}}\overset{\bar{C}HCOOEt}{\underset{CH_3}{C}} \xrightarrow{H^+} \overset{EtO}{\underset{EtO}{\diagup}}\overset{CH_2{-}COOEt}{\underset{CH_3}{C}} \quad (20)$$

C. Acetalization in Basic Media

While the acetal syntheses described above proceed via alkoxy carbonium ions, acetal syntheses are also known in which the anion of the hemiacetal is alkylated. Schmitz [70] alkylated aldehydes which tend to form a hemiacetal with dimethyl sulfate and sodium hydroxide (equation 21). For example the three nitrobenzaldehydes were converted into dimethyl acetals in yields of about 85%.

$$p{-}NO_2C_6H_4\overset{OMe}{\underset{O^-}{\overset{|}{CH}}} \underset{Me{-}OSO_2OMe}{\Big\downarrow} \longrightarrow p{-}NO_2C_6H_4\overset{OMe}{\underset{OMe}{\overset{|}{CH}}} \quad (21)$$

Kuhn and Trisch [71] methylated benzil, ninhidrine and phenanthrenequinone to the corresponding monoketals with methyl iodide and barium oxide in dimethylformamide. This reaction was also limited to electron-poor carbonyl groups.

Especially useful is the procedure with polyhalogenated carbonyl compounds, which build hemiacetals easily and which cannot be acetalized in acid media. Simmons and Wiley [30] obtained, for example, the mixed ketal from the ethyl hemiacetal of tetrafluorodichloroacetone (**24**) with dimethyl sulfate and potassium carbonate (equation 22).

$$
\underset{(\mathbf{24})}{\underset{ClF_2C}{\overset{ClF_2C}{\diagdown}}C\underset{OEt}{\overset{OH}{\diagup}}} \xrightarrow{(MeO)_2SO_2, K_2CO_3} \underset{ClF_2C}{\overset{ClF_2C}{\diagdown}}C\underset{OEt}{\overset{OMe}{\diagup}} \tag{22}
$$

A special case of acetal formation in basic media is the well-known action of alcoholates on α-halocarbonyl compounds[72,73]. According to equation (23) the reaction proceeds through addition of a methoxy group to the carbonyl group followed by intramolecular alkylation to yield the alkoxy epoxide (**25**).

$$
R-CO-CH_2Cl \xrightarrow{MeO^-} \underset{MeO}{\overset{R}{\diagdown}}C\underset{O^-}{\overset{CH_2Cl}{\diagup}} \longrightarrow \underset{MeO}{\overset{R}{\diagdown}}\underset{(\mathbf{25})}{\overset{CH_2}{C\underset{O}{\diagup}}} \tag{23}
$$

The formation of larger rings was observed in rare cases only. Rieche and Schmitz obtained 1-ethoxy isochroman (equation 24) from 2-β-bromoethylbenzaldehyde (**26**) in ethanol in the presence of pyridine[74].

$$
\text{(26)} \xrightarrow[\text{Pyridine}]{\text{EtOH}} \tag{24}
$$

D. Syntheses of Acetals from Orthoesters

Acetals can be obtained by nucleophilic substitution of one of the alkoxy groups of orthoesters. In almost all cases described orthoformates were used.

Acetals are obtained, for example, from Grignard reagents and orthoformates (equation 25)[75]. The Reformatsky reaction leads, according to equation (26), to acetals[76].

$$HC(OEt)_3 + RMgI \longrightarrow R-CH \begin{array}{c} OEt \\ \diagdown \\ \diagup \\ OEt \end{array} \qquad (25)$$

$$HC(OEt)_3 + Zn + BrCH_2COOR \longrightarrow \begin{array}{c} EtO \\ \diagdown \\ \diagup \\ EtO \end{array} CHCH_2COOR \qquad (26)$$

Addition of orthoesters to vinyl ethers in the presence of Friedel–Crafts catalysts was achieved even at low temperatures, and acetals of dicarbonyl compounds were obtained (equation 27)[77]. Ketene and

$$HC(OMe)_3 + CH_2=CHOMe \xrightarrow{BF_3} \begin{array}{c} MeO \\ \diagdown \\ \diagup \\ MeO \end{array} CH-CH_2-CH \begin{array}{c} OMe \\ \diagdown \\ \diagup \\ OMe \end{array} \qquad (27)$$

orthoformate give, in the presence of zinc chloride, 3,3-diethoxy-propionic acid ethyl ester (equation 28)[78].

$$HC(OEt)_3 + H_2C=C=O \xrightarrow{ZnCl_2} \begin{array}{c} EtO \\ \diagdown \\ \diagup \\ EtO \end{array} CHCH_2COOEt \qquad (28)$$

Even alkynes add to orthoformates, in the presence of catalysts like zinc chloride, to form alkynyl-substituted acetals (equation 29)[79].

$$HC(OEt)_3 + C_6H_5C{\equiv}CH \xrightarrow{ZnCl_2} C_6H_5C{\equiv}CCH \begin{array}{c} OEt \\ \diagdown \\ \diagup \\ OEt \end{array} \qquad (29)$$

Diisobutylaluminum hydride hydrogenates ethyl orthobenzoate to the acetal (equation 30)[80].

$$C_6H_5C(OEt)_3 + (i\text{-Bu})_2AlH \longrightarrow C_6H_5CH \begin{array}{c} OEt \\ \diagdown \\ \diagup \\ OEt \end{array} \qquad (30)$$

Propionaldehyde diethyl acetal is formed in 94% yield from ortho-formate, carbon monoxide and hydrogen in the presence of dicobalt-octacarbonyl at 100° under pressure[81].

E. Further Methods

The exchange of halogen for an alkoxy group in *gem*-dihalo compounds (equation 31) is of interest only in cases where no elimination is possible[82]. An example is the preparation of benzophenone ketal[83].

$$R_2^1CCl_2 + 2 NaOR^2 \longrightarrow R_2^1C\begin{array}{c} OR^2 \\ \diagdown \\ OR^2 \end{array} \tag{31}$$

Acetals of benzaldehyde and benzophenone may be obtained in good yields by electrolysis of α-methoxyphenyl- and α-methoxydiphenylacetic acid in methanol or ethanol (equation 32)[84].

$$(C_6H_5)_2C\begin{array}{c} COOH \\ \diagup \\ \diagdown \\ OMe \end{array} \longrightarrow (C_6H_5)_2C\begin{array}{c} OMe \\ \diagup \\ \diagdown \\ OMe \end{array} \tag{32}$$

Simple quinone acetals were also obtained recently by electrolysis. For example quinone tetramethyl ketal (**27**) resulted from electrolysis of hydroquinone dimethyl ether in methanolic potassium hydroxide[85]. The synthesis of compounds containing the quinone ketal configuration was previously known only in some complicated cases, e.g. from *o*-quinones and aliphatic diazo compounds[86] or from tocopherol by oxidation in alcohol[87].

The addition products of alcoholates and alkyl picrates, described by Meisenheimer[88], were believed to be acetals (**28**).

The 1,4-addition of vinyl ethers to α,β-unsaturated carbonyl compounds leads to acetals as well; an example is **29**[89]. The formation of

(**27**)   (**28**)   (**29**)

α-amidinoketo acetals (equation 33) was observed on decomposition of the azide **30** followed by treatment with methanol[90]. It was proposed to use this reaction as a preparative method.

(33)

IV. PROPERTIES OF ACETALS

Acetals of low molecular weight formed from aliphatic components are colorless liquids with flower-like or fruit-like smells. Higher substituted cyclic acetals often give a peppermint–camphor-like smell. Some acetals are used in the perfume industry[91]. Acetals are also used as solvents.

The acetal group is of technical importance in some polymers[92], for instance in polyvinyl acetals[91]. The use of vinyl ketals as monomers in polymerization[93] was considered.

The chemical analysis of acetals is based almost in all cases on their hydrolysis to the carbonyl compound and alcohol, followed by the analytical determination of the latter[94].

Acetals and hemiacetals do not absorb in the customarily used ultraviolet region, and this fact was used to determine the equilibrium position of hemiacetal formation[10]. The disappearance of the optical rotatory dispersion of the carbonyl group during acetal formation was also used for concentration measurements[26].

The infrared spectra of acetals show several strong bands in the unspecific, single-bond region (1050–1200 cm^{-1}), in which ethers and alcohols also absorb[95]. The complete assignment of the bands of 1,3-dioxolans[96] made possible a partial assignment of the spectral bands of 3,4-O-isopropylidene ketals of sugar alcohols. Brügel and Oster[97] pointed out a band at 2820–2830 cm^{-1}, which was observed to recur in the spectra of fifteen open-chain acetals.

Detailed examinations of infrared and Raman spectra of formaldehyde dimethyl acetal and its deuterated derivatives were recently described by Nukada[98]. Most of the bands could be assigned.

Nuclear magnetic resonance spectra showed a shift in the τ value of acetone (7·90) on transition to dimethyl ketal (8·825)[99]. τ values of acetalic methoxy protons wcrc measured for sugar derivatives[100]. The protons of equatorial methoxy groups of 1-methoxypyranoses absorb at $\tau = 6\cdot68$–$6\cdot70$, those in the axial position at 6·84–6·88. The single peak of the methoxy proton of ketal **31** ($\tau = 6\cdot85$) at 100°, splits at

(31)

$-5°$ into two signals, at $\tau = 6\cdot50$ and $\tau = 7\cdot22$. The nonplanar conformation of the seven-membered ring becomes at the low temperature stable enough to make the different chemical environment of the two methoxy groups observable[101].

The chemical shift of the methylene group of formaldehyde acetals was examined by many authors. Nukada and coworkers[102] found values for five aliphatic acetals of formaldehyde in the region of $\tau = 5\cdot18$–$5\cdot59$. The value found for 1,3-dioxane was $5\cdot18$[103]. Extensive material was compiled by Crabb[104] in connection with a study on the ring size of cyclic formaldehyde acetal groups in delphinium alkaloids. He found τ values between 4·89 and 5·42. The coupling constants were 0–2 cycles/sec for five-membered rings and about 6 cycles/sec for six-membered rings.

Data on ^{17}O nuclear magnetic resonance of acetals are also available[105].

Examination of the behavior of acetals in a mass spectrometer was made on sugar derivatives. The derivative **32** of glucopyranose tetraacetate eliminates the methoxy group preferentially in consequence of the cation-stabilizing ability of the ring oxygen[106]. The 2,2-dimethyl-1,3-dioxolan group (**33**) is useful in mass spectroscopy for the same reason, since the elimination of a methyl group is favored. The resulting cation **34** is again resonance stabilized[107]. The tendency of the

(32)   (33)   (34)

ketal group to cleave next to the original carbonyl group (equation 34) was retained also with ketals of 3-oxo steroids[108]. In some twenty

$$(34)$$

ketals which were examined further fragmentation was found to be quite independent of additional substituents in the A ring.

V. REACTIONS OF ACETALS

A. Acetals as Protective Groups

One of the characteristics of acetals is the sharp contrast between their practically unlimited stability in basic media and their extraordinary reactivity in acid media. An alkoxy group is a leaving group only if it is protonated or coordinated with a Lewis acid. The acetals are therefore resistant to bases and nucleophilic agents.

Aldehydes and alcohols are very sensitive to oxidizing agents in alkaline media. Aldehydes may be either attacked by an appropriate oxidizing agent at the carbonyl group, losing a hydrogen atom subsequently, or they may add a hydroxyl ion, in which case the hydrogen becomes available as a hydride. In the deprotonated form alcohols are particularly susceptible to electrophilic attacks. The same holds for deprotonated ketones. By conversion into an acetal, aldehydes, ketones and alcohols lose practically all their sensitivity to two-electron oxidation. In the absence of protons and Lewis acids acetals are as unreactive as ethers. After subjecting acetals to the most drastic conditions in alkaline media without destroying the acetal group, it is possible to render them extremely reactive by changing the environment. A ketal which is stable towards strong alkali at 200° can be cleaved in a fraction of a second at room temperature by a 1N acid. Acetalization is therefore a nearly ideal way of protecting alcohols, aldehydes and ketones.

A few examples will illustrate the drastic conditions under which acetals are stable.

Acetal groups are not affected by heating with diluted sodium hydroxide, as in the saponification of an ester group in the same

11*

molecule[109]. The acetal group of **35** was not affected by boiling for 20 hours with 25% potassium hydroxide; these conditions resulted in the cleavage of the amido group[110].

In the synthesis of ribo–oligo nucleotides it is possible to protect the 2'-hydroxy group by acetalization with dihydropyran. Alkaline ester cleavage can subsequently be carried out[111]. During conversion of the cyano group of **36** into the methyl group, the ketal group was resistant

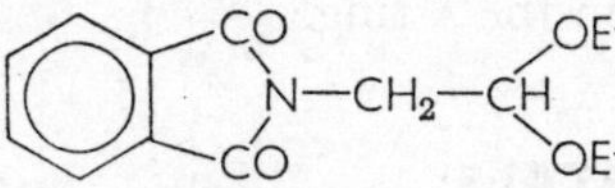

(35)

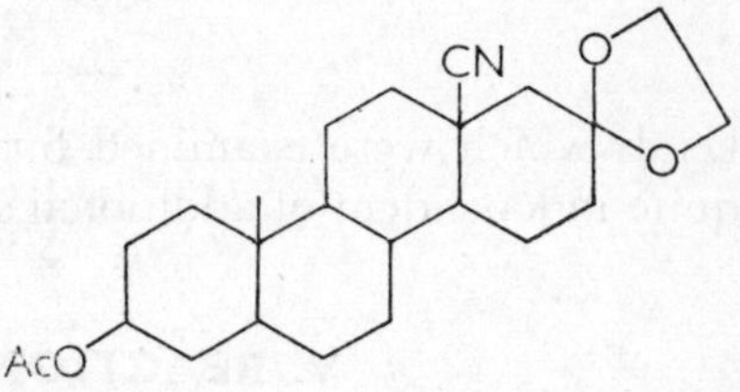

(36)

to lithium aluminum hydride reduction as well as to subsequent Wolff–Kishner reaction of the aldehyde hydrazone with potassium hydroxide in triethylene glycol at 210–220° [112].

By heating acetals of α-halo aldehydes in aqueous or ethanolic alkali it is possible to substitute a hydroxyl group for the halogen[113]. The halogen may also be exchanged for an alkoxy group. The acetal group of **37** is not affected, although the reaction is carried out at 140° [114].

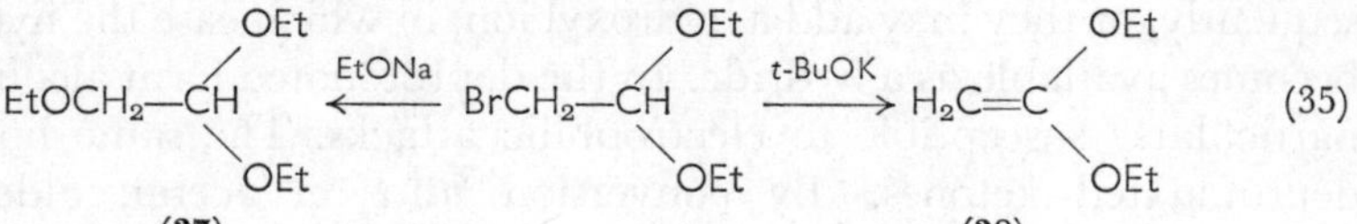

$$\underset{(37)}{\overset{\text{OEt}}{\underset{\text{OEt}}{\text{EtOCH}_2\!-\!\text{CH}}}} \xleftarrow{\text{EtONa}} \underset{(38)}{\overset{\text{OEt}}{\underset{\text{OEt}}{\text{BrCH}_2\!-\!\text{CH}}}} \xrightarrow{\text{t-BuOK}} \underset{(38)}{\overset{\text{OEt}}{\underset{\text{OEt}}{\text{H}_2\text{C}\!=\!\text{C}}}} \tag{35}$$

The acetal group also stays intact during the elimination of hydrogen bromide by potassium *t*-butoxide when ketene acetals (**38**) are obtained (equation 35)[115]. A four-membered ring, containing sulfur (**40**), results from the dibromoketal **39** on treatment with sodium sulfide at 150° [116]. The compound **41** can be metalated by butyllithium.[117]

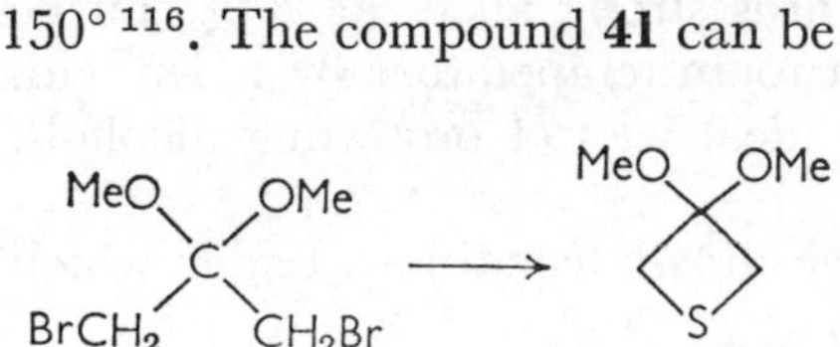

(39)

(40)

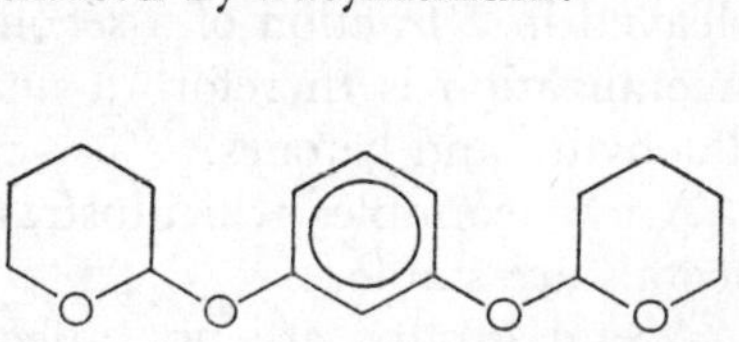

(41)

Acetal groups in alkaline media are resistant to the strongest reducing agents. For example the reduction of an azide to an amine or the debenzylation of a benzyl thioether with sodium in liquid ammonia can be carried out without affecting the acetal groups present[118]. Catalytic hydrogenation of a nitro group under hydrogen pressure of 115 atm[119], reduction of a nitrile group with lithium aluminum hydride in boiling tetrahydrofuran[120] and an ester reduction with lithium aluminum hydride[121] were carried out without attacking the acetal groups present.

Acetal groups also serve as protective groups during oxidation, even with very strong oxidants. The secondary alcohol group in **42** was oxidized to a keto group by a chromium trioxide–pyridine complex[122].

(**42**)   (**43**)

In one of the stages in the synthesis of ascorbic acid, the primary alcohol group of compound **43** was oxidized to a carboxyl group by potassium permanganate in alkaline solution[123].

Some examples from the recent literature indicate the limits of the stability of acetals. Schmidt and Grafen[124] were able to hydrogenate the acetal group in **44** to an ether (equation 36) by catalytic hydrogenation under very drastic conditions (190°, 200 atm hydrogen pressure, 8 hours).

$$(MeO)_2CHCHOH(CH_2)_4COOEt \longrightarrow MeOCH_2CHOH(CH_2)_4COOEt \quad (36)$$

(**44**)

References to further cases of hydrogenation of acetals to ethers or even to hydrocarbons were given by Howard and Brown[125]. Acetals are attacked under very drastic conditions by Grignard reagents. The

action of methylmagnesium iodide on cyclic ketals for 16 hours at 75°
yields glycol monoethers (equation 37a) [126].

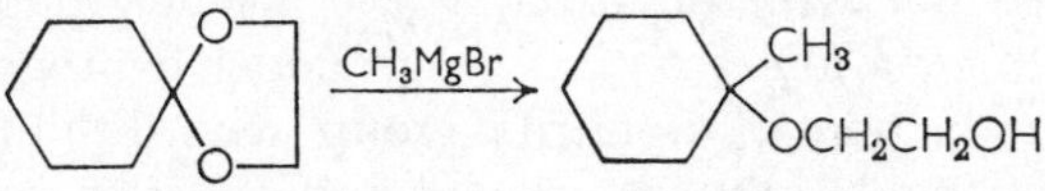

$$
\text{(37a)}
$$

A drastic electrophilic attack on an acetal may be successful.
1,3-Dioxolane (**45**) with p-chlorophenyldiazonium chloride yields the
hydroxy compound **46**[127] and with ozone it forms glycol carbonate
(**47**) (reaction 37b) [128].

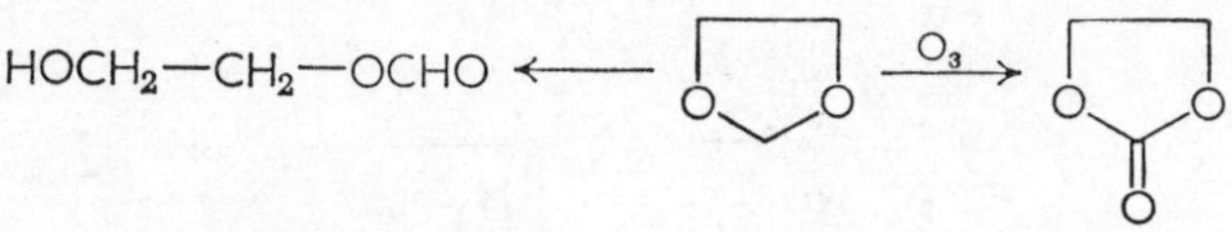

$$
\text{HOCH}_2\text{—CH}_2\text{—OCHO} \longleftarrow \qquad \xrightarrow{\text{O}_3} \qquad \text{(37b)}
$$

$$
\textbf{(46)} \qquad\qquad\qquad \textbf{(45)} \qquad\qquad \textbf{(47)}
$$

B. Hydrolysis of Acetals

Acetal formation is reversible, and all acetals can be cleaved to
their constituent carbonyl compounds and alcohols in the presence of
water and acid. In preponderantly aqueous solutions, because of the
unfavorable position of the equilibrium, there remains practically no
acetal in the mixture.

At present it is known that no alkyl–oxygen cleavage occurs during
acetal hydrolysis[129]. The mechanism of acetal hydrolysis is not con-
troversial. It is the reverse of the acetal formation (equation 3) going
through protonation and cation formation (equation 38). The reaction
is specifically proton[130] catalyzed, with the rate-determining step
being the formation of cation **22** from the conjugated acid of the acetal.

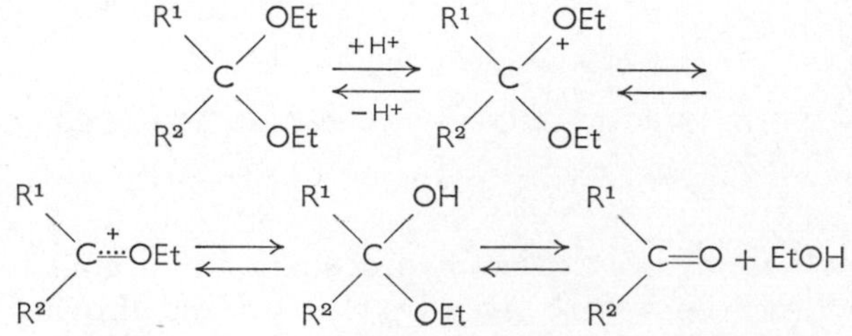

$$
\text{(38)}
$$

$$
\textbf{(22)}
$$

Since the acid concentration remains constant during the acetal hydrolysis, the overall reaction appears to be first order with the rate coefficient being proportional to the hydrogen ion concentration in weakly acid solutions. In stronger acids dependence on H_0 is observed[45].

The relatively fast cleavage of acetals is made possible by the ability of cation formation on carbon, facilitated by the neighboring oxygen. The stability of these cations is also demonstrated by the fact that acetal cleavage is not accompanied by skeletal rearrangements. The hydrolysis of the ketal of camphor exclusively yields camphor[131].

The influence of substituents present on the carbonyl carbon is large. Already Skrabal and Zlatewa[32] have found that the rates of hydrolysis of pentaerythritol acetals of formaldehyde, acetaldehyde and acetone are in the ratio $1:6000:10000000$. The extent and direction of substituent effects correspond to a typical S_N1 reaction.

Kreevoy and Taft[132] investigated the influence of substituents in the carbonyl component. The results are shown in Table 3.

TABLE 3. Hydrolysis of diethyl acetals of some carbonyl compounds in dioxane–water $(1:1)$ at 25°.

Carbonyl compound	Hydrolysis of acetals		
	$k(\text{sec}^{-1})^a$	$\log k/k_0{}^b$	$t_{\frac{1}{2}}$ (sec)^c
Acetone	750 $(=k_0)$	0·000	0·001
Acetaldehyde	0·248	− 3·482	2·8
Formaldehyde	0·0000413	− 7·26	16,800
Chloroacetaldehyde	0·0000103	− 7·863	67,300
Crotonaldehyde	298	− 0·4	0·002
Benzaldehyde	7·07	− 2·026	0·1

^{a} Rate coefficients k at pH = 0.
^{b} Logarithms of the ratio of the rate coefficients, with acetone diethyl ketal as reference.
^{c} Half-lives.

The following rules can be deduced from the observed facts: the rate is not influenced sterically; the possibility of resonance-stabilization drastically enhances the cation formation and hence the hydrolysis, e.g. an α,β-double bond increases the rate by a factor of 10^3 (acetaldehyde–crotonaldehyde); polar and hyperconjugation effects, which influence the reaction independently, are both very important. The polar effects fit the Taft equation[132,133]. The hyperconjugation effects of the hydrogen atoms bound to the carbon atom adjacent to the carbonyl group are additive. Each hydrogen atom in that position accelerates the hydrolysis of the acetal by a factor of $10^{0.54}$.

The transition from dimethyl acetals to diethyl and diisopropyl acetals accelerates the hydrolysis by approximately one order of magnitude in each case: for the acetals of formaldehyde in 1N acid the rate coefficients[34] are 25.5×10^{-6}, 217×10^{-6} and 1205×10^{-6} sec^{-1}, respectively.

The cleavage of cyclic acetals is markedly slower than that of open-chain ones. Formaldehyde pentaerythritol acetal hydrolyses are slower by a factor of 10^4 than formaldehyde diethyl acetal[32]. The reasons for the slower hydrolysis of cyclic acetals are possibly of stereoelectronic character. A smooth hydrolysis demands parallel orientation of the C—O bond to be cleaved with the assisting lone pair of electrons of the unprotonated oxygen. An extremely slow hydrolysis of rigid acetalic systems was occasionally observed[134,135].

The quantitative data may be supplemented by some qualitative observations. Even slower than the hydrolysis of acetals studied by Kreevoy and Taft is the cleavage of α-carbonyl acetals[136]. The cleavage of polyhalogenated acetals and ketals is still slower and they are frequently stable towards strong mineral acids even above $100°$[30,137].

In acetal cleavage for preparative purposes it should be considered that the products may undergo secondary reactions under the influence of the acid present or that other groups in the molecule may also react. Most 'tricks' for the careful hydrolysis of acetals consist of not using either a higher temperature, a longer reaction time or a stronger acid than is strictly necessary.

The knowledge of the rates of hydrolysis, which are very often quite different for various acetal groups, makes partial cleavages possible. Cleavages of ketals were accomplished without destroying an acetal group present[138]. An alkyl-substituted ketal was cleaved while a chloro-substituted ketal group was not attacked[139]. An α,β-unsaturated ketal could be selectively hydrolyzed in the presence of a saturated one[48].

C. Additional Reactions of Acetals via α-Alkoxy Carbonium Ions

Most reactions of acetals are formulated via α-alkoxy carbonium ions (22). This formulation is justified since most of the reactions discussed in the present section are subject to the same influences of substituents as is the hydrolysis of acetals. Additional support for the assumption of cationic intermediates is given by the recent work of Meerwein and coworkers; they succeeded in synthesizing stable α-alkoxy carbonium ions, such as **48** and **49**. The salts were formed from acetals with boron trifluoride or antimony pentachloride[50].

$$\left(\begin{array}{c} C_6H_5 \\ \diagdown \\ C\text{····}OMe \\ \diagup \\ C_6H_5 \end{array}\right)^{+} \; [SbCl_6]^{-} \qquad\qquad \left(\begin{array}{c} C_6H_5 \\ \diagdown \\ C\text{····}OMe \\ \diagup \\ H \end{array}\right)^{+} \; [SbCl_6]^{-}$$

$$\textbf{(48)} \qquad\qquad\qquad\qquad \textbf{(49)}$$

I. Exchange of alkoxy groups with preservation of geminal groups on carbon

The exchange of an alkoxy group in acetals for some other functional group is not limited to the transacetalization. Acyl groups, halogens or sulfur-containing groups may be substituted for the alcohol. For example Exner obtained a dioxazole derivative (**50**) by treating benzophenone ketal with benzohydroxamic acid under acid catalysis (equation 39)[140]. Rieche and Bischoff[141] described the exchange

$$\begin{array}{c} C_6H_5 \quad OEt \\ \diagup \\ C \\ \diagdown \\ C_6H_5 \quad OEt \end{array} + C_6H_5\text{—}CO\text{—}NHOH \longrightarrow \begin{array}{c} C_6H_5 \quad O\text{—}N \\ \diagup \qquad\qquad \| \\ C \qquad\qquad C \\ \diagdown \qquad\qquad \diagdown \\ C_6H_5 \quad O\text{——}C_6H_5 \end{array} \qquad (39)$$

$$\textbf{(50)}$$

of alkoxy by peroxide groups. Propionaldehyde diethyl acetal and enanthaldehyde diethyl acetal exchanged an ethoxy group on heating to 80° for 8 to 12 hours with *t*-butylhydroperoxide (equation 40).

$$\begin{array}{c} OEt \\ | \\ C_6H_{13}\text{—}CH \\ | \\ OEt \end{array} \xrightarrow{\text{t-BuOOH}} \begin{array}{c} OEt \\ | \\ C_6H_{13}\text{—}CH \\ | \\ OO(t\text{-Bu}) \end{array} \qquad (40)$$

Exchange also took place with hydrogen peroxide (equation 41)[142].

$$\begin{array}{c} OEt \\ | \\ CH_3\text{—}CH \\ | \\ OEt \end{array} \xrightarrow[80°]{\text{H}_2\text{O}_2} \begin{array}{c} OEt \\ | \\ CH_3\text{—}CH \\ | \\ OOH \end{array} \qquad (41)$$

Reactions of acetals with peracetic acid under acid catalysis give good yields of esters[143]. The reaction is particularly smooth if the alkoxy exchange is facilitated by appropriate substituents, such as phenyl; this leads to the postulation of an α-alkoxy perester intermediate (equation 42).

$$
\underset{\overset{|}{OEt}}{\overset{\overset{|}{OEt}}{C_2H_5-CH}} \xrightarrow{CH_3COOOH} \underset{\overset{|}{H}\quad\overset{|}{OOCOCH_3}}{\overset{\overset{|}{C_2H_5}\quad\overset{|}{OEt}}{C}} \longrightarrow C_2H_5COOEt \qquad (42)
$$

Cyclic acetals are more resistant to alkoxyl cleavage, and under the influence of peracids may undergo epoxidation at an α,β-double bond[144].

The exchange of an alkoxyl group for an acyloxy group (discovered by Claisen) takes place, for example, on heating acetaldehyde diethyl acetal to 150° with acetic anhydride (equation 43)[145]. It was

$$
\underset{\overset{|}{OEt}}{\overset{\overset{|}{OEt}}{R^1-CH}} \xrightarrow{(R^2CO)_2O} \underset{\overset{|}{OCOR^2}}{\overset{\overset{|}{OEt}}{R^1-CH}} \qquad (43)
$$

found later that the reaction also takes place under much milder conditions if acid catalysts are present[146].

It is assumed that acylation is an intermediate step in the well known[147] conversion of acetals into α-halo ethers, using acid chlorides. Hünig[148] formulates the reaction through the reversible addition of the acid chloride (equation 44). The adduct **51** decomposes into the ester and cation. The formation of the ester according to equation (44)

$$
\underset{\overset{|}{OR^1}}{\overset{\overset{|}{OR^1}}{H_2C}} + R^2COCl \rightleftarrows \underset{\overset{|}{R^2CO}}{\overset{\overset{\overset{|}{OR^1}}{H_2C}}{\overset{+}{OR^1}}} \longrightarrow
$$

$$
\textbf{(51)}
$$

$$
H_2\overset{+}{C}\text{---}OR^1 + R^2COOR^1 \xrightarrow{Cl^-} \underset{\overset{|}{Cl}}{\overset{\overset{|}{OR^1}}{H_2C}} \qquad (44)
$$

was used to characterize the alcoholic components of acetals[149]; 3,5-dinitrobenzoyl chloride with acetals yields the 3,5-dinitrobenzoates of the corresponding alcohols.

Mercaptans displace alcohols from most acetals, even from the relatively stable glycol acetals. Acetaldehyde glycol acetal was converted in 64% yield into the mercaptal on heating with thiophenol at 120–130° for several hours (equation 45)[150].

$$
CH_3-CH \underset{O-CH_2}{\overset{O-CH_2}{|}} + 2\ C_6H_5SH \longrightarrow CH_3-CH \underset{SC_6H_5}{\overset{SC_6H_5}{}} \tag{45}
$$

2. Formation of α,β-unsaturated ethers from acetals

When no other reactions are possible α-alkoxy carbonium ions lose a proton and form an α,β-unsaturated ether (equation 46). With increasing temperature the equilibrium shifts to the side of the elimination product.

$$
\underset{R^2CH_2}{\overset{R^1}{}} \!\!\!\! C \!\!\!\! \underset{OR^3}{\overset{OR^3}{}} \longrightarrow \underset{R^2CH_2}{\overset{R^1}{}} \!\!\!\! \overset{+}{C} \cdots OR^3 \xrightarrow{-H^+} R^2CH = \underset{OR^3}{\overset{R^1}{}} \tag{46}
$$

Data on the dependence between the formation of unsaturated ethers and structure are in good agreement with the assumption that the tendency for cation formation is decisive for elimination: ketals are more prone to elimination than acetals, and ketals of secondary alcohols more than ketals of primary alcohols. In the case of ketals of secondary alcohols an equilibrium of ketal, alcohol and unsaturated ether is detectable in the presence of acids even at room temperature[125]. Ketals of primary alcohols may be preparatively converted into α,β-unsaturated ethers by fractional distillation in the presence of p-toluenesulfonic acid[151]. Alcohol and ether are continuously removed from the mixture and their recombination does not occur in the absence of acid. For example ketals of methyl ketones with six to eight carbon atoms formed the unsaturated ethers in yields of 80–90%.

Acetals of aldehydes do not react under the same conditions. All preparative procedures to obtain vinyl ethers from acetals therefore use higher temperatures, almost always in gaseous phase and in the presence of catalysts. For example copper sulfate-active charcoal catalyst was used at 260–330° under reduced pressure[152]. Other authors used platinum on asbestos at 280–290°[153] or kaolin on asbestos at 340–350°[154].

Catalytic procedures also make possible the formation of dialkoxy ethylenes from trialkoxy ethanes (equation 47)[155].

$$\text{EtOCH}_2-\overset{\displaystyle OEt}{\underset{\displaystyle OEt}{\overset{|}{\underset{|}{CH}}}} \xrightarrow[190°]{\text{Al}_2\text{O}_3} \text{EtOCH}=\text{CHOEt} \qquad (47)$$

3. Reactions of acetals with C—C bond formation

Acetals easily form the α-alkoxy carbonium ion, which is an electrophilic entity, while the vinyl ether resulting from the deprotonation of the latter is a nucleophile. In a series of reactions in which C—C bond formation between nucleophilic and electrophilic components occurs, one or both reactants may be derived from acetals in the manner described above.

One example is the formation of β-alkoxy acetals on heating acetals with Lewis acid (equation 48). Paul and Tchelitcheff[156] obtained 1,1,3-triethoxybutane (52) by heating acetaldehyde diethyl acetal with boron trifluoride for one hour to 100°. The yield was only 10%. Similar results were obtained with butyraldehyde acetals.

$$2\ \text{CH}_3-\overset{\displaystyle OEt}{\underset{\displaystyle OEt}{\overset{|}{\underset{|}{CH}}}} \xrightarrow{\text{BF}_3} \underset{\displaystyle EtO}{\overset{\displaystyle CH_3}{\overset{\diagdown}{\diagup}}}CH-CH_2-\overset{\displaystyle OEt}{\underset{\displaystyle OEt}{\overset{|}{\underset{|}{CH}}}} \qquad (48)$$

$$(52)$$

The reaction of acetals with vinyl ethers is much easier. In the presence of boron trifluoride the addition to β-alkoxy acetals (53) occurs already under very mild conditions[157]. Hoaglin and Hirsch[158] proved that the reaction proceeds via an alkoxy carbonium ion (54) which adds to the vinyl ether (reaction 49).

$$\text{R}-\overset{\displaystyle OEt}{\underset{\displaystyle OEt}{\overset{|}{\underset{|}{CH}}}} \xrightarrow{\text{BF}_3} \text{R}-\overset{+}{CH}\text{····OEt} \xrightarrow{\text{CH}_2=\text{CHOEt}} \underset{\displaystyle EtO}{\overset{\displaystyle R}{\overset{\diagdown}{\diagup}}}CH-CH_2-\overset{\displaystyle OEt}{\underset{\displaystyle OEt}{\overset{|}{\underset{|}{CH}}}} \qquad (49)$$

$$(54) \qquad\qquad\qquad (53)$$

Yields of 60–70% were obtained from acetals of acetaldehyde or butyraldehyde with vinyl ethers derived from simple aldehydes[158]. The resulting alkoxy acetals (53) are easily cleaved to aldehydes, which by elimination of alcohol yield α,β-unsaturated aldehydes.

This reaction is in effect an aldol condensation, but with obvious advantages: instead of four unsaturated aldehydes expected from aldolization of two different aldehydes, acetal and vinyl ether yield a single one.

The exchange of an aldehyde entity between vinyl ethers and acetals is quite unimportant under mild reaction conditions. On the other hand both starting materials should contain the same alkoxy group since alkoxy exchange is possible[158]. The addition product (**53**) is still an acetal and the addition of another molecule of vinyl ether is possible[158]. In one very important application of this reaction, in the synthesis of polyenes, this further addition is not very significant. The starting material in this case is usually an α,β-unsaturated acetal (**55**) which reacts under milder conditions than the acetal **56**, obtained by

$$R^1CH{=}CH{-}CH\begin{smallmatrix}OR^2\\ \\OR^2\end{smallmatrix} \qquad R^1CH{=}CH{-}CH{-}CH_2{-}CH\begin{smallmatrix}OR^2\\ \\OR^2\end{smallmatrix}$$

$$\text{(55)} \qquad\qquad\qquad \text{(56)}$$

addition. The reaction was used in the synthesis of vitamin A[159] and later in the technical synthesis of carotene[160].

The α-alkoxy carbonium ion attacks other electron-rich groups as well, forming C—C bonds. In the presence of boron trifluoride acetals add to ketene (equation 50)[78].

$$CH_2\begin{smallmatrix}OMe\\ \\OMe\end{smallmatrix} + CH_2{=}C{=}O \longrightarrow MeOCH_2CH_2COOMe \qquad (50)$$

$$\text{(57)}$$

Acetals of formaldehyde, acetaldehyde, benzaldehyde and phenyl-acetaldehyde were used in the reaction and formed esters of the corresponding β-alkoxy carboxylic acids (**57**) in 30–80% yield.

Schönberg and Praefcke recently observed that acetals react with diazoacetic ester in the presence of Lewis acids (equation 51)[161]. The α-alkoxy carbonium ion obviously adds to the diazoacetic ester to form **58**, which then gives a stable α,β-dialkoxycarboxylic ester (**59**)

$$CH_3{-}\overset{+}{CH}{\cdots}OEt + \overset{+}{N}{\equiv}N{-}\overset{-}{CH}{-}COOEt \longrightarrow$$

$$CH_3{-}CH{-}CH{-}COOEt \longrightarrow CH_3{-}CH{-}CH{-}COOEt \quad (51)$$
$$\underset{OEt}{|}\ \underset{\overset{N{\equiv}N}{+}}{|} \qquad\qquad \underset{OEt}{|}\ \underset{OEt}{|}$$

$$\text{(58)} \qquad\qquad\qquad \text{(59)}$$

by elimination of nitrogen. Benzaldehyde diethyl acetal reacted in 79% yield.

In some recently described condensations of steroids the nucleophilic component originated from acetals. An acetyl group in position two was introduced to cholestan-3-one ethylene ketal (**60**) under the

$$\text{(60)} \qquad \xrightarrow[\text{BF}_3]{\text{Ac}_2\text{O}} \qquad \qquad \text{(52)}$$

influence of acetic anhydride and boron trifluoride (equation 52)[162], probably through attack on the enol ether formed as an intermediate. Vilsmeier's reagent leads to the corresponding formyl compounds[163].

4. Transition of acetals into ethers

The resistance of acetals to reduction disappears if the oxygen becomes positively charged, either by addition of a proton or a Lewis acid. Thus acetals react easily with lithium aluminum hydride in the presence of aluminum chloride and yield ethers (equation 53). Acetals of benzaldehyde, acetophenone, acetone and cyclohexanone were hydrogenated to ethers in yields of 70–90%[164].

$$\underset{\text{CH}_3}{\overset{\text{C}_6\text{H}_5}{\diagdown}} \text{C} \underset{\text{OEt}}{\overset{\text{OEt}}{\diagup}} \quad \xrightarrow[\text{AlCl}_3]{\text{LiAlH}_4} \quad \text{C}_6\text{H}_5 - \underset{\text{CH}_3}{\overset{\text{OEt}}{\text{CH}}} \qquad \text{(53)}$$

In the presence of a trace of concentrated hydrochloric acid ketals can be catalytically hydrogenated[125]. The hydrogenation of ketals of secondary alcohols is particularly easy. Benzaldehyde diethyl acetal may be reduced to benzyl ethyl ether with decaborane[165] (equation 54).

$$\text{C}_6\text{H}_5 - \underset{\text{OEt}}{\overset{\text{OEt}}{\text{CH}}} \quad + \text{ B}_{10}\text{H}_{14} \quad \longrightarrow \quad \text{C}_6\text{H}_5\text{CH}_2\text{OEt} \qquad \text{(54)}$$

Acetals may also be reduced with diisobutylaluminum hydride. At reaction temperatures of 70–80° acetals of propionaldehyde, isobutyraldehyde and acetophenone formed the corresponding ethers in yields of 80–90% (equation 55) [80].

$$
\underset{(55)}{C_2H_5CH\begin{smallmatrix}OEt\\OEt\end{smallmatrix} \quad + \text{(i-Bu)}_2AlH \longrightarrow C_2H_5CHOEt}
$$

Under much more drastic conditions, certain acetals are able to undergo reduction by hydride ions originated in the same molecule. Rondestvedt and Mantell[166] passed 1,3-dioxanes, substituted at $C_{(2)}$, and with the $C_{(5)}$ position blocked by two alkyl groups (61), at temperatures of 350–400° over pumice or weakly acid catalysts. A detailed examination, in particular of the influence of substituents at $C_{(2)}$, pointed to cation formation at the $C_{(2)}$ atom, followed by intramolecular hydride shift. β-Alkoxy aldehydes (62) were obtained in good yields (equation 56).

(61)   (62)   (56)

Rieche and Schmitz[167] observed ether formation from a hemiacetal-type compound on heating with sulfuric acid. 1-Hydroxyisochroman (11) formed ether and lactone under the influence of 30% sulfuric acid (equation 57). The alkoxy carbonium ion was thus able to remove a hydride ion from another molecule.

(11)   (57)

D. Radical Reactions of Acetals

Acetals are relatively susceptible to radical attack on the C—H bond. The formation of radical 63, by loss of hydrogen, occurs selectively on autooxidation. A competing attack on the neighboring methylene group occurs on bromination, while competing attack on the α positions of the alkoxyl groups takes place with alkyl radicals. Various reactions are known in which good yields of derivatives of the radical **63** are formed (reaction 58).

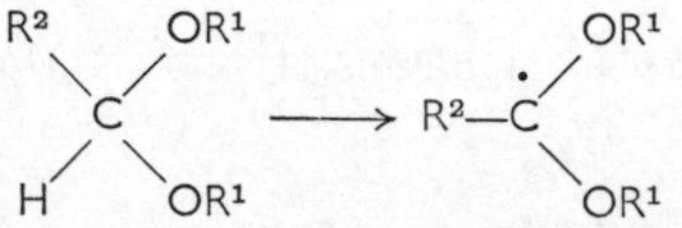

$$
\begin{array}{c}
\underset{H}{\overset{R^2}{\diagdown}}\underset{OR^1}{\overset{OR^1}{C}} \longrightarrow R^2-\overset{OR^1}{\underset{OR^1}{\overset{\cdot}{C}}} \tag{58}
\end{array}
$$

(63)

I. Bromination of acetals

While the action of N-bromosuccinimide on acetals of aliphatic aldehydes predominantly causes substitution in the methylene group[168], bromine attacks the acetal group in the absence of a neighboring methylene group. Acetals of benzaldehyde[168–170] and α-keto aldehydes[171] are easily brominated by N-bromosuccinimide. The unstable products of bromination (**64**) decompose immediately into ester and alkyl bromide (equation 59a).

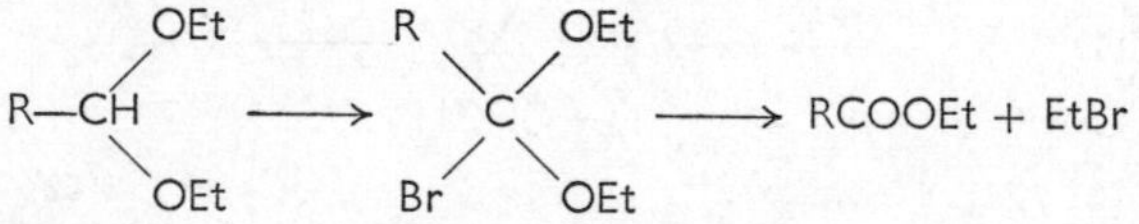

$$
R-\underset{OEt}{\overset{OEt}{CH}} \longrightarrow \underset{Br}{\overset{R}{\diagdown}}\underset{OEt}{\overset{OEt}{C}} \longrightarrow RCOOEt + EtBr \tag{59a}
$$

(64)

Cyclic acetals yield esters of brominated alcohols, for example **65** is formed from benzaldehyde ethylene acetal[169]. Chlorination of

$$C_6H_5COOCH_2CH_2Br$$

(65)

cyclic acetals of formaldehyde gives analogously formic esters of chlorinated alcohols (equation 59b)[172,173].

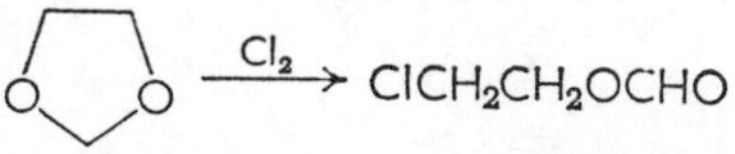

$$
\text{(dioxolane)} \xrightarrow{Cl_2} ClCH_2CH_2OCHO \tag{59b}
$$

2. Autooxidation of acetals

Acetals of aldehydes react frequently with oxygen even at room temperature. Terephthalaldehyde tetramethyl acetal can be obtained in a pure form only by recrystallization under nitrogen[70]. A compound with a peroxide structure (66) was first isolated by Criegee (reaction 60a)[174].

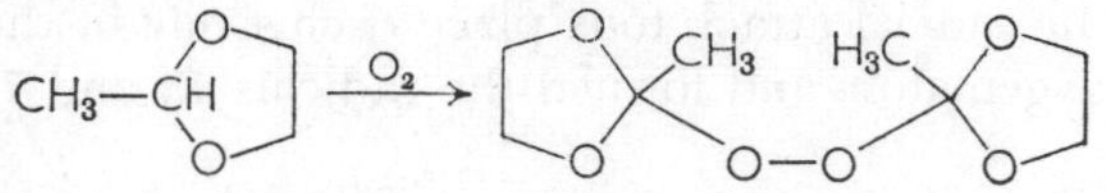

$$\text{CH}_3-\text{CH} \xrightarrow{\text{O}_2} \qquad\qquad (60a)$$

(66)

Acetal hydroperoxides (67 and 68) were obtained by Rieche and Schmitz. These hydroperoxides were formed from the ethylene

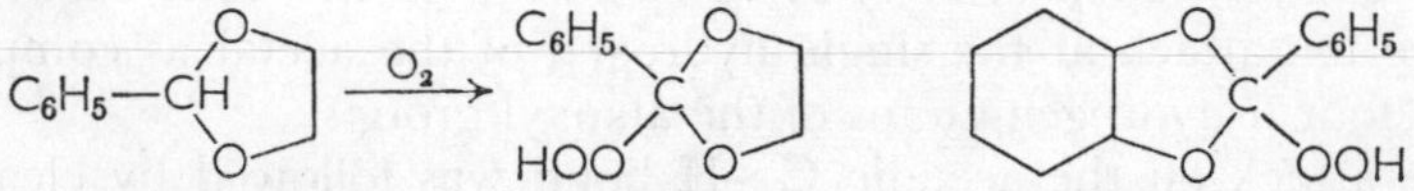

$$\text{C}_6\text{H}_5-\text{CH} \xrightarrow{\text{O}_2}$$

(67)   (68)

acetals[169] of benzaldehyde, *p*-chlorobenzaldehyde and terephthalaldehyde, as well as from benzylidene compounds[170] of *cis*- and *trans*-1,2-cyclohexanediol. Autooxidation of cyclic acetals of α,β-unsaturated compounds was recently investigated[175]. Three types of products were isolated: hydroperoxides (69), peroxides (70) and spirocyclic peroxides (71), the latter being rearrangement products of the hydroperoxides, preferably formed in the presence of acids (reaction 60b).

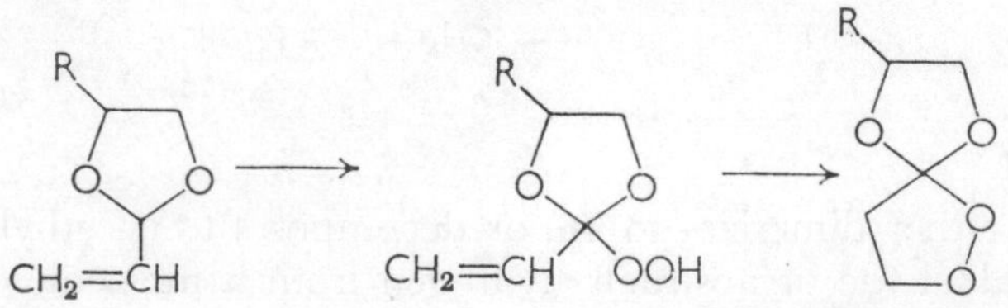

$$\qquad\qquad (60b)$$

(69)   (71)

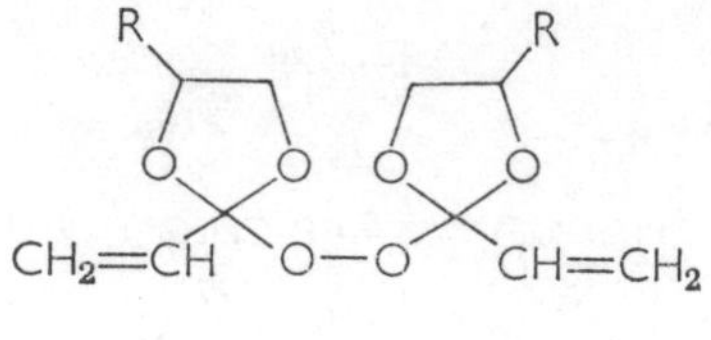

(70)

3. Radical attacks by decomposing peroxides

Kuhn and Wellman[170] decomposed di-*t*-butyl peroxide in butyraldehyde diethyl acetal at 120–140°. The acetal **72** was attacked by *t*-butoxy radicals, methyl radicals and also by radicals derived from the acetal. The radical attack took place exclusively in the neighborhood of an oxygen atom and formed the radicals **73** and **74** (reaction

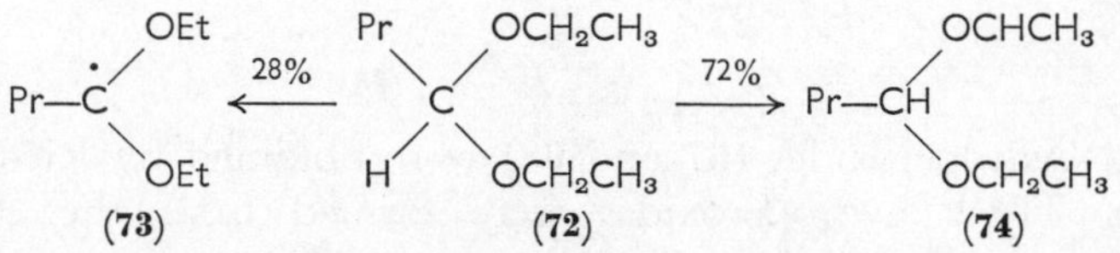

(61a)

61a). The formation of 28% of **73** and 72% of **74** shows slight preference for attack at the single hydrogen of the acetal as compared to the four α-hydrogen atoms of the alkoxyl groups.

The attack on the acetalic C—H bond was followed by cleavage into an ethyl radical and ethyl butyrate (equation 61b). The attack on

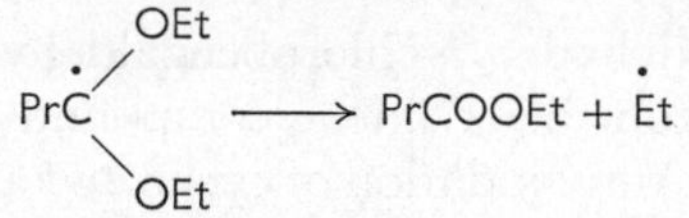

$$Pr\dot{C}\diagup_{\displaystyle OEt}^{\displaystyle OEt} \longrightarrow PrCOOEt + \dot{E}t \qquad (61b)$$

the alkoxyl hydrogen was followed by several competitive reactions. The first step is the cleavage to yield a carbonyl compound (acetaldehyde) and a new radical (**75**) (equation 61c). Subsequently, the

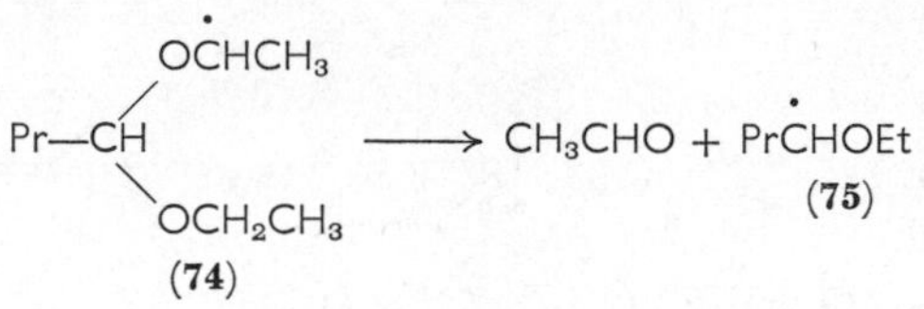

$$Pr—CH \longrightarrow CH_3CHO + Pr\dot{C}HOEt \qquad (61c)$$

radical **75** either dimerizes to **76**, or decomposes to an ethyl radical and butyraldehyde or abstracts hydrogen from a molecule of acetal forming butyl ethyl ether (**77**) (equation 62). In analogy to equation

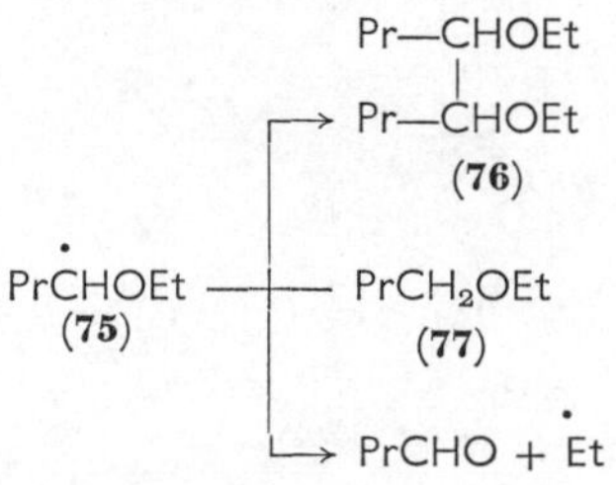

(62)

(57) decomposing peroxide transformed benzaldehyde ethylene acetal to ethyl benzoate (equation 63)[177]. Photoactivated acetone

$$C_6H_5\overset{O}{\underset{O}{\overset{|}{C}}}H \longrightarrow C_6H_5COOCH_2CH_3 \qquad (63)$$

may act as the initiating radical. Illuminating cyclic acetals in acetone Elad and Youssefyeh also obtained the isomeric esters[178].

An addition product of formaldehyde diethyl acetal with maleic ester was obtained in the presence of decomposing peroxide (equation 64)[179].

$$CH_2\overset{OEt}{\underset{OEt}{\big\langle}} + MeOCOCH{=}CHCOOMe \longrightarrow MeOCO\overset{CH(OEt)_2}{\underset{}{\overset{|}{C}}}HCH_2COOMe \qquad (64)$$

4. Thermal decomposition of acetals

It was recently observed[180] that acrolein dibutyl acetal (**78**) under nitrogen, in the absence of initiators, polymerizes at 130–150° to a low molecular weight product containing mainly units of butyl acrylate and acrolein acetal. The polymerization goes through radicals since hydroquinone acts as an inhibitor. Butanol was found among the volatile products. It was therefore assumed that the initiation was the radical decomposition shown in equation (65).

$$CH_2{=}CH{-}\overset{OBu}{\underset{OBu}{\overset{|}{C}}}H \longrightarrow CH_2{=}CH{-}\overset{\cdot}{C}HOBu + Bu\overset{\cdot}{O} \qquad (65)$$

$$\text{(78)} \qquad\qquad\qquad \text{(79)}$$

Though radicals like **79** are easily formed by hydrogen abstraction, the decomposition of **78** into two radicals according to equation (62) is surprising. Even if the additional stabilization of radical **79** by the double bond is taken into account, it is to be considered that simple acetals decompose markedly only at about 450°[181].

VI. REFERENCES

1. *Beilstein Handbuch der organischen Chemie I*, Vol. 1, p. 617.
2. O. Rebuffat, *Gazz. Chim. Ital.*, **17**, 408 (1887) (through *Beilstein I*, Vol. 1,

p. 621); H. Meerwein, Th. Bersin and W. Burneleit, *Chem. Ber.*, **62**, 1008 (1929).

3. W. Traube, *Chem. Ber.*, **40**, 4944 (1907).
4. P. Lipp, J. Buchkremer and H. Seeles, *Ann. Chem.*, **499**, 1 (1932).
5. E. Kober and C. Grundmann, *J. Am. Chem. Soc.*, **80**, 5550 (1958).
6. B. Helferich and H. Köster, *Ber. Deut. Chem. Ges.*, **56**, 2088 (1923).
7. A. Rieche and E. Schmitz, *Chem. Ber.*, **91**, 2693 (1958).
8. W. Treibs and R. Schöllner, *Chem. Ber.*, **94**, 2983 (1961).
9. K. L. Wolf and K. Merkel, *Z. Physik. Chem.*, **187**, 61 (1940).
10. W. Herold, *Z. Elektrochem.*, **38**, 633 (1932); **39**, 566 (1933).
11. J. D. Roberts and M. C. Caserio, *Basic Principles of Organic Chemistry*, W. A. Benjamin, New York, 1964, p. 444.
12. E. A. Halevi in *Progress in Physical Organic Chemistry*, Vol. 1, Interscience Publishers, New York, 1963, p. 177.
13. O. H. Wheeler, *J. Am. Chem. Soc.*, **79**, 4191 (1957).
14. D. G. Kubler and L. E. Sweeney, *J. Org. Chem.*, **25**, 1437 (1960).
15. H. Adkins and A. E. Broderick, *J. Am. Chem. Soc.*, **50**, 499 (1928).
16. F. E. McKenna, H. V. Tartar and E. C. Lingafelter, *J. Am. Chem. Soc.*, **75**, 604 (1953).
17. F. E. McKenna, H. V. Tartar and E. C. Lingafelter, *J. Am. Chem. Soc.*, **71**, 729 (1949).
18. Anon., Schimmel & Co. Ber. Schimmel u. Co. (1933), 78–81 (from *Chem. Abstr.*, **28**, 5041g (1934)).
19. J. Cantacuzène, *Bull. Soc. Chim. France*, 763 (1962).
20. B. Helferich, *Ber. Deut. Chem. Ges.*, **52**, 1123 (1919) and later works; H. Bredereck, *Angew. Chem.*, **69**, 406 (1957).
21. W. Lüttke, *Chem. Ber.*, **83**, 571 (1950)
22. C. D. Hurd and W. H. Saunders, *J. Am. Chem. Soc.*, **74**, 5324 (1952).
23. Reviews: H. Meerwein in Houben-Weyl, *Methoden der Organischen Chemie*, Vol. VI/3 (Ed. E. Müller), Georg Thieme Verlag, Stuttgart, 1965, pp. 199–293; O. Bayer in Houben-Weyl, *Methoden der Organischen Chemie*, Vol. 7 (Ed. E. Müller), Georg Thieme Verlag, Stuttgart, 1954, pp. 413–453; J. A. van Allan, *Org. Chem. Bull.*, **23**, 2 (1951); W. Friedrichsen in *Ullmanns Encyklopädie der technischen Chemie*, 3rd ed., Vol. 3, Verlag Urban und Schwarzenberg, München, 1953, p. 13.
24. J. D. Roberts and M. C. Caserio, *Basic Principles of Organic Chemistry*, W. A. Benjamin, New York, 1964, p. 447.
25. W. H. Hartung and H. Adkins, *J. Am. Chem. Soc.*, **49**, 2517 (1927).
26. C. Djerassi, L. A. Mitscher and B. J. Mitscher, *J. Am. Chem. Soc.*, **81**, 947 (1959).
27. (a) E. P. Oliveto, C. Gerold and E. W. Hershberg, *J. Am. Chem. Soc.*, **76**, 6113 (1954); (b) M. M. Janot, X. Lusinchi and R. Goutarel, *Bull. Soc. Chim. France*, 2109 (1961).
28. H. Adkins and E. W. Adams, *J. Am. Chem. Soc.*, **47**, 1368 (1925).
29. S. M. McElvain and M. J. Curry, *J. Am. Chem. Soc.*, **70**, 3781 (1948).
30. H. E. Simmons and D. W. Wiley, *J. Am. Chem. Soc.*, **82**, 2290 (1960).
31. H. Adkins and B. H. Nissen, *Organic Synthesis*, Vol. 1, John Wiley and Sons, New York, pp. 1–2.
32. A. Skrabal and M. Zlatewa, *Z. Phys. Chem.*, **119**, 305 (1926).

33. F. R. Galiano, D. Rankin and G. J. Mantell, *J. Org. Chem.*, **29**, 3424 (1964).
34. A. Skrabal and H. H. Eger, *Z. Phys. Chem.*, **122**, 349 (1926).
35. W. L. Howard and N. D. Lorette, *J. Org. Chem.*, **25**, 525 (1960).
36. E. Fischer and G. Giebe, *Ber. Deut. Chem. Ges.*, **30**, 3053 (1897).
37. E. Fischer and G. Giebe, *Ber. Deut. Chem. Ges.*, **31**, 545 (1898).
38. E. Fischer and E. Hoffa, *Ber. Deut. Chem. Ges.*, **31**, 1991 (1898).
39. E. Salmi, *Ber. Deut. Chem. Ges.*, **71**, 1803 (1938).
40. R. D. Haworth and A. Lapworth, *J. Chem. Soc.*, **121**, 81 (1922).
41. W. Voss, *Ann. Chem.*, **485**, 283 (1931).
42. B. Helferich and J. Hausen, *Ber. Deut. Chem. Ges.*, **57**, 795 (1924).
43. N. B. Lorette and W. L. Howard, *J. Org. Chem.*, **26**, 3112 (1961).
44. L. Claisen, *Ber. Deut. Chem. Ges.*, **29**, 1005 (1896); **40**, 3903 (1907).
45. F. A. Long and M. A. Paul, *Chem. Rev.*, **57**, 965 (1957).
46. R. Leutner, *Monatsh. Chem.*, **60**, 329 (1932); N. B. Lorette and W. L. Howard, *J. Org. Chem.*, **26**, 3112 (1961).
47. H. Ueberwasser, K. Heusler, J. Kalvoda, C. Meystre, P. Wieland, G. Anner and A. Wettstein, *Helv. Chim. Acta*, **46**, 344 (1963).
48. J. J. Brown, R. H. Lenard and S. Berstein, *Experientia*, **18**, 309 (1962); *J. Am. Chem. Soc.*, **86**, 2183 (1964).
49. C. Djerassi and M. Gorman, *J. Am. Chem. Soc.*, **75**, 3704 (1953).
50. H. Meerwein, K. Bodenbrenner, P. Borner, Fr. Kunert, K. W. Müller, H. J. Sasse, H. Schrodt and J. Spille, *Angew. Chem.*, **67**, 374 (1955).
51. R. L. Shriner and R. B. Moffet, *J. Am. Chem. Soc.*, **63**, 1694 (1941).
52. W. C. Baird and R. L. Shriner, *J. Am. Chem. Soc.*, **86**, 3142 (1964).
53. Review on α-haloethers: H. Gross and E. Höft, *Z. Chem.*, **4**, 401 (1964).
54. W. Reppe and coworkers, *Ann. Chem.*, **596**, 86 (1955).
55. W. Flaig, *Ann. Chem.*, **568**, 24 (1950).
56. F. Kröhnke, G. Kröhnke and H. Bernhardt, *J. Prakt. Chem.*, 4, **11**, 249 (1960).
57. W. Koenigs and E. Knorr, *Chem. Ber.*, **34**, 957 (1901).
58. J. Conchie, G. Levy and C. A. Marsh, *Advan. Carbohydrate Chem.*, **12**, 163 (1957).
59. A. Bachmann, *Ann. Chem.*, **218**, 44 (1883).
60. R. S. Juvet and J. Chiu, *J. Am. Chem. Soc.*, **83**, 1560 (1961).
61. N. B. Lorette and W. L. Howard, *J. Org. Chem.*, **25**, 521, 525 (1960).
62. E. H. Pryde, D. J. Moore, H. M. Teeter and J. C. Cowan, *J. Org. Chem.*, **29**, 2083 (1964).
63. C. Piantadosi, C. E. Anderson, E. A. Brecht and C. L. Yarbro, *J. Am. Chem. Soc.*, **80**, 6613 (1958).
64. J. A. Nieuwland, R. R. Vogt and W. L. Fookey, *J. Am. Chem. Soc.*, **52**, 1018 (1930); H. D. Hinton and J. A. Nieuwland, *J. Am. Chem. Soc.*, **52**, 2892 (1930).
65. G. Hamprecht, *Ger. Pat.*, 802,877 and 803,834 (1948) (cf. *Chem. Zentr* (1951) II, 1509, *Chem. Abstr.*, **45**, 8029h (1951)).
66. W. Reppe, *Ann. Chem.*, **601**, 81 (1956).
67. R. Paul, *Bull. Soc. Chim. France*, **1**, 5, 971 (1934).
68. K. Weisermel and M. Lederer, *Chem. Ber.*, **96**, 77 (1963).
69. F. Arndt, L. Loewe and M. Ozansoy, *Ber. Deut. Chem. Ges.*, **73**, 779 (1940).

70. E. Schmitz, *Chem. Ber.*, **91**, 410 (1958).
71. R. Kuhn and H. Trisch, *Chem. Ber.*, **94**, 2258 (1961).
72. M. Bergmann and A. Miekeley, *Ber. Deut. Chem. Ges.*, **64**, 802 (1931); E. P. Kohler and C. R. Addinall, *J. Am. Chem. Soc.*, **52**, 3728 (1930).
73. T. I. Temnikova and B. A. Gontarev, *J. Gen. Chem. USSR*, **34**, 24 (1964); C. L. Stevens and A. J. Weinheimer, *J. Am. Chem. Soc.*, **80**, 4072 (1958).
74. A. Rieche and E. Schmitz, *Chem. Ber.*, **89**, 1254 (1956).
75. E. Tschitschibabin, *Ber. Deut. Chem. Ges.*, **37**, 186 (1904); G. D. Bachman, *Org. Synth.*, Coll., Vol. II, p. 323 (1943); S. M. McElvain, R. L. Clarke and G. D. Jones, *J. Am. Chem. Soc.*, **64**, 1967 (1942); M. J. Ansell and B. Gadsby, *J. Chem. Soc.*, 3318 (1958).
76. N. C. Deno, *J. Am. Chem. Soc.*, **69**, 2233 (1947).
77. J. P. Copenhaver, *U.S. Pat.*, 2,527,533 (1950); (*Chem. Abstr.*, **45**, 1622i (1951)); F. G. Joung, Union Carbide Carbon Corp., *U.S. Pat.*, 2,556,312 (1949); (*Chem. Abstr.*, **46**, 1031i (1952)).
78. F. Šorm and J. Smrt, *Chem. Listy*, **47**, 413 (1953); *Chem. Abstr.*, **49**, 175 (1955).
79. B. W. Howk and J. C. Sauer, *J. Am. Chem. Soc.*, **80**, 4607 (1958).
80. L. I. Sacharkin and I. M. Chorlina, *Bull. Acad. Sci. USSR, Div. Chem. Sci. Eng. Transl.* 2255 (1959); *Chem. Abstr.*, **54**, 10837h (1960).
81. F. Piacenti, *Gazz. Chim. Ital.*, **92**, 225 (1962).
82. A. Wohl and M. Lange, *Ber. Deut. Chem. Ges.*, **41**, 3612 (1908); E. Kober and C. Grundmann, *J. Am. Chem. Soc.*, **80**, 5547 (1958).
83. J. E. Mackenzie and A. F. Joseph, *J. Chem. Soc.*, **85**, 790 (1904).
84. B. Wladislaw and A. M. J. Ayres, *J. Org. Chem.*, **27**, 281 (1962).
85. B. Belleau and N. L. Weinberg, *J. Am. Chem. Soc.*, **85**, 2525 (1963).
86. L. Horner and E. Lingnau, *Ann. Chem.*, **573**, 30 (1951).
87. C. Martius and H. Eilingsfeld, *Ann. Chem.*, **607**, 159 (1957).
88. J. Meisenheimer, *Ann. Chem.*, **323**, 205 (1902); see however K. L. Serois, *J. Am. Chem. Soc.*, **87**, 5495 (1965).
89. R. I. Longley, Jr., and W. S. Emerson, *J. Am. Chem. Soc.*, **72**, 3079 (1950); W. E. Parham and H. E. Holmquist, *J. Am. Chem. Soc.*, **73**, 913 (1951).
90. P. A. S. Smith, L. O. Krbechek and W. Rezemann, *J. Am. Chem. Soc.*, **86**, 2025 (1964).
91. W. Friedrichsen in *Ullmanns Encyklopädie der technischen Chemie*, Vol. 3, Verlag Urban und Schwarzenberg, München, 1953, p. 13.
92. *Chem. Eng. News*, **42**, No. 30, 25 (1964).
93. S. G. Matsoyan, M. A. Eliazyan and E. Ts. Gevorkyan, *Polymer Sci. (USSR), Eng. Transl.*, **4**, 1515 (1962); *Chem. Abstr.* **59**, 1764g (1963)).
94. Review: J. Mitchell, Jr., *Org. Anal.*, **1**, 305 (1953).
95. E. D. Bergmann and S. Pinchas, *Rec. Trav. Chim.*, **71**, 161 (1952).
96. S. A. Barker, E. J. Bourne, R. M. Pinkard and D. H. Whiffen, *J. Chem. Soc.*, 802 (1959).
97. W. Brügel and R. Oster, *Angew. Chem.*, **68**, 441 (1956).
98. K. Nukada, *Spectrochim. Acta*, **18**, 745 (1962).
99. L. M. Jackmann, *Application of NMR-Spectroscopy in Organic Chemistry*, Pergamon Press, Oxford, 1959, p. 54.
100. S. A. Barker, J. Homer, M. C. Keith and L. F. Thomas, *J. Chem. Soc.*, 1538 (1963).

101. W. Tochtermann, U. Walter and A. Mannschreck, *Tetrahedron Letters*, 2981 (1964).

102. K. Nukada, O. Yamamoto, T. Suzuki, M. Takeuchi and M. Ohnishi, *Anal. Chem.*, **35**, 1892 (1963).

103. H. Fribolin, S. Kabuss, W. Maier and A. Lüttringhaus, *Tetrahedron Letters*, 683 (1962)

104. T. A. Crabb, *Tetrahedron Letters*, 679 (1964).

105. H. A. Christ, P. Diehl, H. R. Schneider and H. Dahn, *Helv. Chim. Acta*, **44**, 865 (1961).

106. K. Biemann, D. C. DeJongh and H. K. Schnoes, *J. Am. Chem. Soc.*, **85**, 1673 (1963).

107. D. J. DeJongh and K. Biemann, *J. Am. Chem. Soc.*, **86**, 67 (1964).

108. Z. Pelah, D. H. Williams, H. Budzikiewicz and C. Djerassi, *J. Am. Chem. Soc.*, **86**, 3722 (1964).

109. E. G. Howard and R. V. Lindsay, Jr., *J. Am. Chem. Soc.*, **82**, 158 (1960).

110. F. Fischer and H. Riese, *J. Prakt. Chem.*, **12**, 177 (1961).

111. J. Smrt and F. Šorm, *Collection Czech. Chem. Commun.*, **27**, 73 (1962); M. Smith, D. H. Rammler, I. H. Goldberg and H. G. Khorana, *J. Am. Chem. Soc.*, **84**, 430 (1962); F. Cramer and K. H. Scheit, *Angew. Chem.*, **74**, 717 (1962).

112. W. Nagata, *Tetrahedron*, **13**, 287 (1961).

113. S. M. McElvain, *Chem. Rev.*, **45**, 453 (1949); A. Guyer, A. Bieler and E. Pedrazzeti, *Helv. Chim. Acta*, **39**, 423 (1956).

114. H. Baganz, K. H. Dossow and W. Hohmann, *Chem. Ber.*, **86**, 148 (1953).

115. P. R. Johnson, H. M. Barnes and S. M. McElvain, *J. Am. Chem. Soc.*, **62**, 964 (1940); S. M. McElvain and D. Kundiger, *Org. Syn.*, **23**, 45 (1943).

116. R. Mayer and K. F. Funk, *Angew. Chem.*, **73**, 578 (1961).

117. W. E. Parham and E. L. Anderson, *J. Am. Chem. Soc.*, **70**, 4187 (1948).

118. J. E. Christensen and L. Goddman, *J. Am. Chem. Soc.*, **83**, 3827 (1961).

119. R. Bonnet, V. M. Clark, A. Giddey and A. Todd, *J. Chem. Soc.*, 2087 (1959).

120. B. Belleau, *Can. J. Chem.*, **35**, 651 (1957).

121. B. Palameta and N. Zambeli, *J. Org. Chem.*, **29**, 1026 (1964).

122. S. Bernstein and R. H. Lenhard, *J. Am. Chem. Soc.*, **77**, 2331 (1955).

123. R. Rumpf and S. Marlier, *Bull. Soc. Chim. France*, 187 (1959).

124. U. Schmidt and P. Grafen, *Chem. Ber.*, **92**, 1177 (1959).

125. W. L. Howard and I. H. Brown, *J. Org. Chem.*, **26**, 1026 (1961).

126. C. Blumberg, A. D. Vreugdenhill and T. Homsma, *Rec. Trav. Chim.*, **82**, 355 (1963); R. A. Mallory, S. Rovinski and I. Scheer, *Proc. Chem. Soc.*, 416 (1964).

127. H. Meerwein, H. Allendörfer, P. Beekmann, Fr. Kunert, H. Morschel, F. Pawellek and Kl. Wunderlich, *Angew. Chem*, **70**, 211 (1958).

128. A. Maggiolo, S. J. Niegowski and A. L. Tumolo, *138th Meeting Am. Soc. 1960, Abstracts*, p. 10p (quoted by C. C. Price and A. L. Tumolo in *J. Am. Chem. Soc.*, **86**, 4691 (1964)).

129. J. M. O'Gorman and H. J. Lucas, *J. Am. Chem. Soc.*, **72**, 5489 (1950); C. A. McKenzie and J. H. Stocker, *J. Am. Chem. Soc.*, **77**, 3148 (1955); F. Stasiuk, W. A. Shephard and A. N. Bourns, *Can. J. Chem.*, **34**, 123 (1956).

130. M. M. Kreevoy and R. W. Taft, Jr., *J. Am. Chem. Soc.*, **77**, 3146 (1955).

131. M. M. Kreevoy, C. R. Morgan and R. W. Taft, Jr., *J. Am. Chem. Soc.*, **82**, 3064 (1960).
132. M. M. Kreevoy and R. W. Taft, Jr., *J. Am. Chem. Soc.*, **77**, 5590 (1955).
133. R. W. Taft, Jr., in *Steric Effects in Organic Chemistry* (Ed. M. S. Newman), John Wiley and Sons, New York, 1956, pp. 636–641.
134. A. Lüttringhaus and G. Schill, private communication.
135. Cs. Szàntay and E. Schmitz, *Chem. Ber.*, **95**, 1759 (1962).
136. J. Meisenheimer, *Ber. Deut. Chem. Ges.*, **45**, 2537 (1912).
137. *Beilstein, Handbuch der Organischen Chemie VII*, p. 425; G. W. Griffin and A. K. Price, *J. Org. Chem.*, **29**, 3192 (1964).
138. W. Franke, R. Kraft, D. Tietjen and H. Weber, *Chem. Ber.*, **86**, 793 (1953).
139. R. H. Levin, *J. Am. Chem. Soc.*, **76**, 546 (1957).
140. O. Exner, *Chem. Listy*, **50**, 779 (1956); *Chem. Abstr.*, **50**, 15477g (1956).
141. A. Rieche and Ch. Bischoff, *Chem. Ber.*, **94**, 2457 (1961).
142. A. Rieche and Ch. Bischoff, *Chem. Ber.*, **94**, 2722 (1961).
143. D. L. Heywood and B. Philipps, *J. Org. Chem.*, **25**, 1699 (1960).
144. B. Philipps, F. C. Frostrick, Jr., and P. S. Starcher, *J. Am. Chem. Soc.*, **79**, 5982 (1957).
145. L. Claisen, *Ber. Deut. Chem. Ges.*, **31**, 1018 (1898).
146. S. Akiyoshi and K. Okuno, *J. Am. Chem. Soc.*, **76**, 693 (1954); W. B. Hughes and R. D. Kleene, *J. Am. Chem. Soc.*, **76**, 5161 (1954).
147. A. Geuther, *Ann. Chem.*, **218**, 38 (1883); F. Straus and H. Heinze, *Ann. Chem.*, **493**, 191 (1932).
148. S. Hünig, *Angew. Chem.*, **76**, 400 (1964).
149. O. Grummit and J. A. Searns, *J. Am. Chem. Soc.*, **77**, 3136 (1955).
150. M. F. Schostakowski, V. M. Vlasov and A. A. Nikiforov, *J. Gen. Chem. USSR Eng. Transl.*, **34**, 1686 (1964).
151. D. B. Killian, G. P. Hennion and J. A. Nieuwland, *J. Am. Chem. Soc.*, **57**, 544 (1935).
152. O. Wichterle, J. Stepek and V. Brajko, *Collection Czech. Chem. Commun.*, **26**, 1099 (1961).
153. M. A. Dolliver, T. L. Gresham, G. B. Kistiakowski, E. A. Smith and W. E. Vaughan, *J. Am. Chem. Soc.*, **60**, 441 (1938).
154. M. F. Ansell and B. Gadsby, *J. Chem. Soc.*, 3388 (1958).
155. W. F. Gresham, *U.S. Pat.* 2,479,068 v. 5.6.1947/16.8.1949, C. 1950, I 2282; S. M. McElvain and Ch. H. Stammer, *J. Am. Chem. Soc.*, **73**, 915 (1951); H. Baganz and C. Vitz, *Chem. Ber.*, **86**, 395 (1953).
156. R. Paul and S. Tchelitcheff, *Bull. Soc. Chim. France*, 844 (1951); *Chem. Abstr.*, 4282f (1953).
157. M. Müller-Conradi and K. Pieroh, *U.S. Pat.* 2,165,962 (1939); C. 1940, I 1423; O. Bayer in *Houben-Weyl, Methoden der organischen Chemie*, Georg Thieme Verlag, Stuttgart, Vol. 7/1, p. 116 (1954).
158. R. I. Hoaglin and D. H. Hirsch, *J. Am. Chem. Soc.*, **71**, 3468 (1949).
159. H. H. Inhoffen, F. Bohlmann, K. Bartram, G. Rummert and H. Pommer, *Ann. Chem.*, **570**, 54 (1950).
160. O. Isler, H. Lindlar, M. Montavon, R. Rüegg and P. Zeller, *Helv. Chim. Acta*, **39**, 249 (1956).
161. A. Schönberg and K. Pracfeke, *Tetrahedron Letters*, **30**, 2043 (1964).
162. R. D. Youssefyeh, *J. Am. Chem. Soc.*, **85**, 3901 (1963).

163. R. D. Youssefyeh, *Tetrahedron Letters*, **32**, 2161 (1964).
164. E. L. Eliel, V. W. Badding and M. N. Rerick, *J. Am. Chem. Soc.*, **84**, 2371 (1962).
165. L. J. Sacharkin, V. J. Stanko and J. A. Tschapowski, *Bull. Acad. Sci. USSR, Div. Chem. Sci., Eng. Transl.*, **6**, 11 (1962).
166. C. S. Rondestvedt, Jr., and G. J. Mantell, *J. Am. Chem. Soc.*, **82**, 6419 (1960); **84**, 3307 (1962); C. S. Rondvestvedt, *J. Am. Chem. Soc.*, **84**, 3319 (1962).
167. A. Rieche and E. Schmitz, *Chem. Ber.*, **90**, 531 (1957).
168. E. N. Marvell and M. C. Joncich, *J. Am. Chem. Soc.*, **73**, 973 (1951).
169. A. Rieche, E. Schmitz and E. Beyer, *Chem. Ber.*, **91**, 1935 (1958).
170. A. Rieche, E. Schmitz, W. Schade and E. Beyer, *Chem. Ber.*, **94**, 2926 (1961).
171. J. B. Wright, *J. Am. Chem. Soc.*, **77**, 4883 (1955).
172. H. Baganz and L. Domaschke, *Chem. Ber.*, **91**, 653 (1958).
173. L. A. Cort and R. G. Pearson, *J. Chem. Soc.*, 1682 (1960).
174. R. Criegee in Houben-Weyl, *Methoden der organischen Chemie*, 4th ed., Vol. VIII, p. 23, Georg Thieme Verlag, Stuttgart, 1952.
175. C. K. Ikeda, R. A. Braun and B. E. Sorenson, *J. Org. Chem.*, **29**, 286 (1964).
176. L. P. Kuhn and C. Wellmann, *J. Org. Chem.*, **22**, 774 (1957).
177. E. S. Huyser and Z. Garcia, *J. Org. Chem.*, **27**, 2716 (1962).
178. D. Elad and R. D. Youssefyeh, *Tetrahedron Letters*, 2189 (1963).
179. A. Nagasaka, S. Nukina and P. Oda, *J. Chem. Soc. Japan, Ind. Chem. Sect.*, **58**, 46 (1955).
180. J. H. Davies and P. Kirby, *Chem. Ind. (London)*, 194 (1964).
181. M. J. Molera, J. Centeno and J. Orza, *J. Chem. Soc.*, 2234 (1963); 2311 (1963) and subsequent papers.

CHAPTER 8

Photochemistry of the C—O—C group

Dov Elad

The Weizmann Institute of Science, Rehovoth, Israel

I. INTRODUCTION

The photochemistry of ethers and related compounds (e.g. epoxides, acetals, and hemiacetals) is still a relatively unexplored region. Although activity in this field has increased recently, much further work remains to be done and synthetic exploitation is still open to investigation. Some work in the carbohydrate field has been published[1], and some light-induced reactions of acetals are mentioned in patent literature[2]; however, the photochemistry of acetals and related compounds still awaits further research and investigation.

In photochemical reactions only light which is absorbed by a molecule is effective in producing a chemical reaction. This primary photochemical process results in an increase in the energy content of the molecule due to absorption of a photon, and leads to changes in the electronic, vibrational, or rotational energies of the molecule. The primary process is followed by secondary processes, some of which lead to chemically reactive species, such as free radicals. These in turn lead to chemical transformations. A number of reviews dealing with the theoretical aspects of these processes have appeared[3]; these aspects will therefore not be discussed here.

Photochemical reactions are usually divided into two main types: (a) direct light-induced or nonsensitized reactions and (b) photosensitized reactions[4,5]. In the first case (a) light is absorbed directly by one of the reactants which subsequently undergoes a chemical reaction. In the second case (b) a substance which is added to the system serves as a 'catalyst', absorbing the light and transferring its excitation energy to one of the reactants, which subsequently undergoes a chemical reaction (reactions 1, 2, and 3). Various impurities present in

$$A \xrightarrow{h\nu} A^* \qquad (1)$$

$$A^* + B \longrightarrow A + B^* \qquad (2)$$

$$B^* \longrightarrow Products \qquad (3)$$

$$(A = photosensitizer; \quad B = reactant)$$

samples may serve as photosensitizers. It should be obvious that in sensitized reactions the wavelength of light required to produce a chemical reaction will depend on the light absorption of the photosensitizer and not on the absorption of the reactants.

Saturated ethers and acetals absorb light at wavelengths below 2000 Å[6–11]. Therefore photoreactions must be induced by light of relatively short wavelength in direct light-induced reactions; however, photosensitized reactions can be effected by light of longer wavelength through the use of a proper photosensitizer.

Photochemical reactions, like other chemical reactions, involve cleavage and formation of bonds; these processes can be either homolytic or heterolytic. Both C—O and C—H bond cleavages have been reported in photolyses of ethers and epoxides. Ethers possess a potentially reactive C—H bond in the α position to the ether linkage[12,13]. Cleavage of this bond leads to free radicals of the type $R^1\dot{C}HOR^2$. Such radicals have been formed by hydrogen atom abstraction from the ether by radicals produced from thermal decomposition of peroxides[14,15]. Similar radicals may be produced in photochemical processes, either by direct irradiation[16,17] or by the use of a photosensitizer or a photoinitiator*[18], such as acetone or benzophenone. The ether radicals, once produced, may participate in a variety of chemical reactions. It might be noted that resonance forms as illustrated by **1** contribute to the stabilization of ether radicals. It has also

$$R^1\ddot{O}\dot{C}HR^2 \longleftrightarrow R^1\overset{+}{\ddot{O}}\overset{-}{C}HR^2$$
(**1**)

been suggested that the inductive effect of the oxygen in the ether molecule facilitates the abstraction of the hydrogen atom from the α position to give the derived α-ether radical[12].

II. PHOTOCHEMICAL REACTIONS OF ETHERS

A. Photolysis of Ethers and Epoxides

The photolysis of ethers and epoxides with ultraviolet light of short wavelength (< 2000 Å) has been reported by a number of groups[19-21]. The direct photochemical decomposition of ethylene oxide in the vapor phase has been reported[19] to yield methane, ethane, hydrogen, and carbon monoxide as well as small amounts of formaldehyde and acetaldehyde. The mercury-sensitized decomposition of the same compound at room temperature has been shown[20] to produce carbon monoxide, hydrogen, ethane, traces of ketene and ethylene, and large amounts of aldehydes. The mercury-photosensitized decomposition of butylene-2,3-oxide[21] at 25° led to ethylene, propylene, acetaldehyde, propionaldehyde, isobutyraldehyde, ethyl methyl ketone, methane, ethane, carbon monoxide, and hydrogen.

The photolysis of trimethylene oxide (oxetane) in the gas phase gave ethylene and formaldehyde (reaction 4), while tetrahydrofuran led to ethylene and acetaldehyde under similar conditions (reaction 5)[19]. The stability of these cyclic ethers when exposed to ultraviolet irradiation

$$C_3H_6O \xrightarrow{h\nu} C_2H_4 + HCHO \tag{4}$$

$$C_4H_8O \xrightarrow{h\nu} C_2H_4 + CH_3CHO \tag{5}$$

* The term *photosensitizer* (or sensitizer) is used in this chapter for a compound which initiates a photochemical process through light absorption and does not undergo a chemical change itself. The term *photoinitiator* is used for a compound which undergoes a chemical transformation while initiating a photochemical reaction.

from hydrogen discharge lamps showed marked variation with ring size. Trimethylene oxide was shown to be very unstable and decomposed relatively rapidly, while tetrahydrofuran was more stable and decomposed more slowly. When an oxygen filter, which absorbs at wavelengths below 1750 Å, was used the decomposition of tetrahydrofuran, while not arrested, proceeded at a markedly slower rate. It is of interest that ethylene oxide has unexpected stability and required the greatest energy for excitation. It is claimed[8] that the lone pair of electrons are more involved with the ring and less available either for excitation or sharing than in the other ethers.

The photolysis of aliphatic ethers in the gas phase with light of wavelength less than 2000 Å has also been studied[22]. Diethyl ether is reported to yield ethylene, acetaldehyde, and formaldehyde in significant quantities. The process is in general assumed to yield carbonyl compounds accompanied by other products. Aldehydes and ketones react further to form ketenes (reaction 6). The photolysis of dimethyl

$$
\underset{\substack{|\\R}}{\overset{\substack{H\\|}}{H-C}}-C=O \xrightarrow{h\nu} \underset{\substack{|\\R}}{\overset{\substack{R\\|}}{H-C}}=C=O \qquad (6)
$$

$$(R = H, \text{ alkyl})$$

ether gave formaldehyde[22]. Ethylene and acetaldehyde which appear at a later stage are thought to be produced by secondary processes.

Vapor-phase photolysis of a variety of oxetanes was studied[11]. Ethylene and formaldehyde were obtained in the photolysis of oxetane (reaction 7a) while 2,2-dimethyloxetane (reaction 7b) was cleaved in two ways, either to ethylene plus acetone or to formaldehyde plus isobutylene. Photolysis of 2-phenyloxetane (reaction 7c) in isooctane led to ethylene and formaldehyde together with other products. The reaction can be summarized by reaction (7).

$$
\begin{array}{c}
\underset{\substack{|\\H_2C-O}}{\overset{\substack{R^1\\|}}{H_2C-C}}-R^2 + h\nu \longrightarrow
\begin{cases}
\longrightarrow H_2C=O + H_2C=\underset{R^2}{\overset{R^1}{C}} \\[2em]
\longrightarrow \underset{R^2}{\overset{R^1}{C}}=O + H_2C=CH_2
\end{cases}
\end{array} \qquad (7)
$$

((a) $R^1 = R^2 = H$;

(b) $R^1 = R^2 = CH_3$;

(c) $R^1 = H$; $R^2 = C_6H_5$)

The photolyses of aliphatic and cyclic ethers as well as epoxides in solution with light of wavelength greater than 2000 Å have been investigated[16,17]. The photolysis of aliphatic ethers is reported to give unidentified products whereas the photolysis of dioxane led to the two diastereoisomeric forms of dioxanyldioxane (reaction 8)[16]. The product results most probably from the dimerization of dioxanyl radicals.

$$\hspace{4cm} (8)$$

Racemate and *meso* compound

The photolysis of epoxides in solution with light of wavelength 2537 Å led to carbon–oxygen bond cleavage[17]. It has been indicated that in unsymmetrical epoxides both carbon–oxygen bonds undergo homolytic cleavage. Thus, irradiation of propylene oxide gave acetone, propionaldehyde, isopropyl alcohol, and n-propyl alcohol. Cyclohexene oxide gave cyclohexanone and cyclohexanol under similar conditions, whereas styrene oxide yielded acetophenone, 2-phenylethanol, and 1-phenylethanol. The sequence of the photochemical decomposition of propylene oxide, which is applicable to the breakdown of other epoxides, is demonstrated in Scheme 1.

$$(9)$$

$$(10)$$

$$(11)$$

$$(12)$$

$$(13)$$

$$4 \longrightarrow CH_3\overset{\displaystyle O}{\overset{\|}{C}}-\dot{C}H_2 \qquad\qquad (14)$$
$$(5)$$

$$5 + 5 \longrightarrow CH_3COCH_2CH_2COCH_3 \qquad\qquad (15)$$

$$5 + CH_3CH\overset{\displaystyle O}{\overbrace{\qquad}}CH_2 \longrightarrow CH_3\overset{\displaystyle O}{\overset{\|}{C}}CH_3 + 4 \qquad\qquad (16)$$

SCHEME 1.

This sequence of reactions does not constitute the only possible mechanism for these reactions. It is suggested that the intermediate biradicals formed from the initial cleavages are converted, by subsequent radical reactions, into alcohols and ketones. Some of the intermediate radicals have been found to dimerize and to add to 1-octene. The ratio of $C_{(1)}$—O to $C_{(2)}$—O bond cleavage was found to be about 25:1 with propylene oxide and about 1:1 with styrene oxide[17].

B. Photolysis of Aromatic Ethers and Aryl Esters

Photolysis of aromatic ethers or of compounds containing an ether linkage attached to the aromatic ring (e.g. aryl esters) usually results in rearrangement of the irradiated molecule. This rearrangement involves cleavage of a carbon–oxygen bond followed by migration of a group from the oxygen atom to the aromatic nucleus; phenolic products are also obtained. Irradiation of a solution of diphenyl ether in isopropyl alcohol at room temperature is reported to lead to the formation of p-hydroxydiphenyl and phenol (reaction 17)[23]. Similarly,

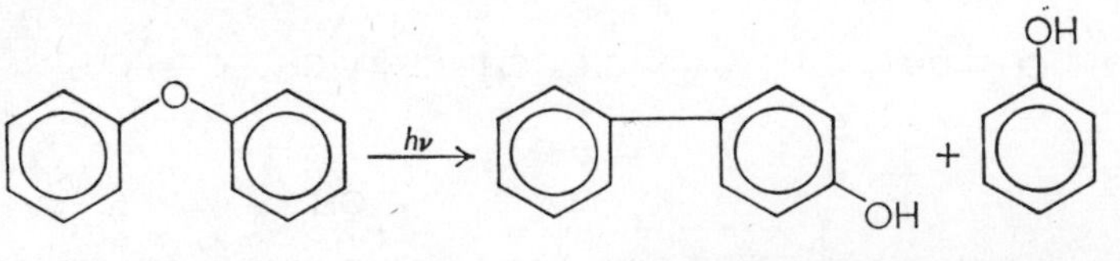

benzyl phenyl ether gave p-benzylphenol, whereas irradiation of allyl phenyl ether gave equal amounts of p-allylphenol and phenol (reaction 18). The isomers obtained in these reactions differ from those obtained in the nonphotochemical processes.

The photochemical rearrangements of phenoxyacetic acids were similar to those of simple aryl ethers[24]. These acids were shown to

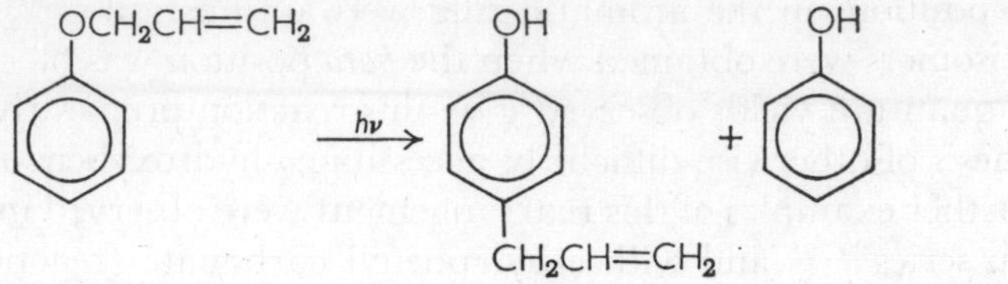

$$(18)$$

rearrange to the derived 2-coumaranones and *p*-hydroxyphenylacetic acids, via migration of the acetic acid residue from the ether oxygen to the *ortho* and *para* positions of the aromatic ring (reaction 19). The

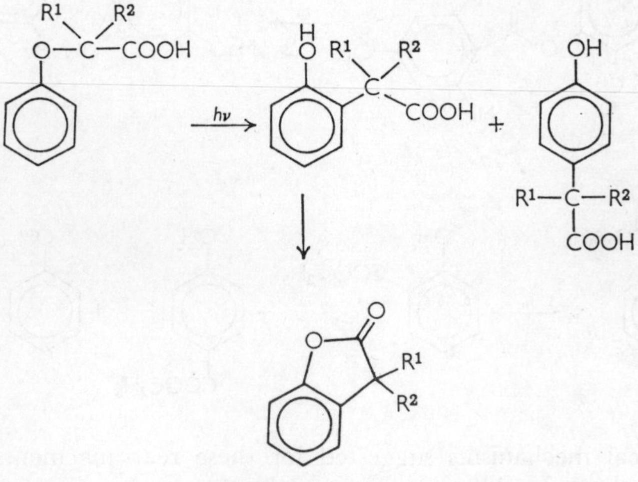

$$(19)$$

((a) $R^1 = R^2 = H$;
(b) $R^1 = H$; $R^2 = CH_3$;
(c) $R^1 = R^2 = CH_3$)

photoinduced Fries rearrangment of aryl esters has been shown to yield *o*- and *p*-hydroxyaryl methyl ketones or hydroxyaryl aryl ketones (reaction 20) [25]. Mixtures of *ortho* and *para* isomers were obtained when

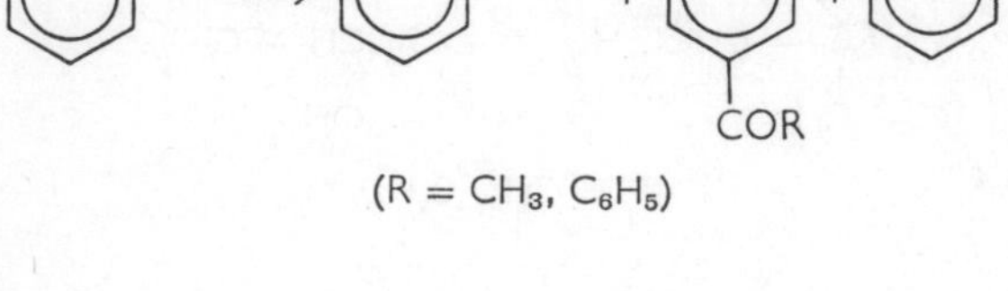

$$(20)$$

$(R = CH_3, C_6H_5)$

both positions in the aromatic ring were unsubstituted[25], while only *ortho* isomers were obtained when the *para* position was blocked[26]. The high quantum yields observed give this reaction preparative value for synthesis of otherwise difficultly accessible *o*-hydroxybenzophenones.

Further examples of this rearrangement were observed in the griseo-fulvin series[27, 28] and with ethyl phenyl carbonate (reactions 21 and 22)[29].

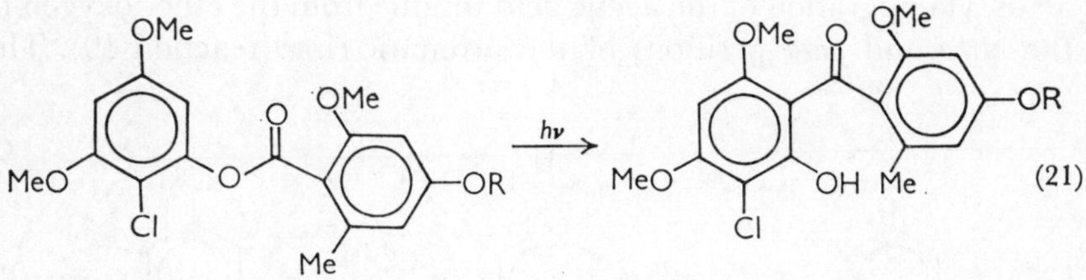

(21)

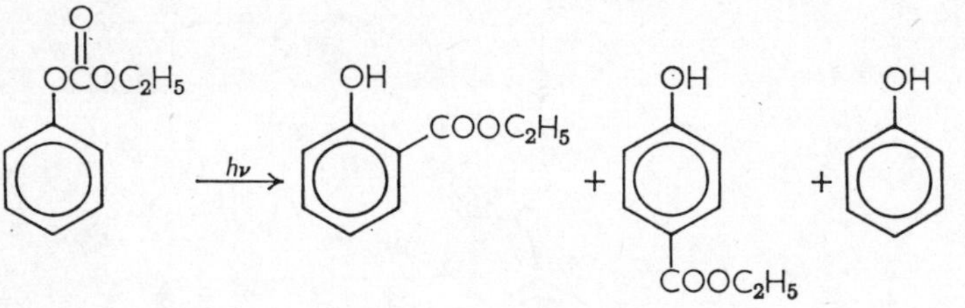

(22)

Radical mechanisms suggested for these rearrangements involve either intramolecular rearrangement[25], or cleavage to two radicals followed by recombination[26]. Both these mechanisms differ from the mechanism of the usual Fries rearrangement and frequently lead to different products. Further examples of the photo-Fries rearrangement have been published recently[30].

The photoisomerizations of epoxy ketones yielded a variety of products[31-34a]. Aromatic epoxy ketones were shown to isomerize to ketols[34b], whereas aliphatic ones underwent a rearrangement to β-diketones (reactions 23 and 24)[32-34a]. Similar reactions in the steroid

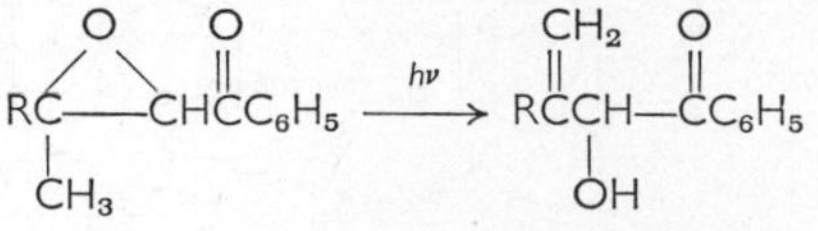

(23)

$(R = CH_3, C_6H_5)$

$$C_6H_5-\overset{\underset{|}{O}}{\underset{CH_3}{C}}-CHC-CH_3 \xrightarrow{h\nu} C_6H_5\overset{O}{C}-\overset{CH_3}{\underset{H}{C}}-\overset{O}{C}CH_3 \quad (24)$$

field have been investigated[32] and led to the appropriate diketones as well as to keto aldehydes. These reactions involve photoexcitation of the carbonyl group which subsequently leads to the observed products.

C. Photooxidation of Ethers

The autooxidation of ethers is a well-known reaction and has been reviewed[35]. This reaction yields the α-hydroperoxides of the ethers in addition to compounds resulting from further reactions of these products. This oxidation, which can be induced by a variety of reagents, is known to be accelerated by light[36] and has been shown[37] to be photosensitized by benzophenone to yield the derived α-hydroperoxides (reaction 25). A number of ethers have been converted by

$$R^1CH_2OR^2 \xrightarrow[\text{Sensitizer; } O_2]{h\nu} R^1\underset{\underset{OOH}{|}}{CHOR^2} \quad (25)$$

this method into hydroperoxides. Both aliphatic and alicyclic ethers underwent this reaction and this method can be of synthetic utility.

D. Photoreactions of Ethers with Carbonyl Compounds

Carbonyl compounds are among the common photosensitizers used in organic photochemistry[38]. These compounds may also serve as photoinitiators in photochemical reactions, e.g. the photoactivated carbonyl compound may abstract a hydrogen atom from a donor[5,39]. Ethers can act as hydrogen atom donors in reactions of this type due to the reactivity of the α hydrogens in these compounds and lead to ether free radicals, which subsequently react with the various species present. Thus acetone and benzophenone have been found to react with ethers under ultraviolet irradiation to give the derived carbinols (reactions 26 and 27)[18,37]. The presence of ether free radicals is

$$\text{(structure)} \xrightarrow[R_2C=O]{h\nu} \text{(structure)} \quad (26)$$

12*

$$\text{(ring with two O)} \xrightarrow[R_2C=O]{h\nu} \text{(ring with C(R)(R)-OH)} \qquad (27)$$

$$(R = CH_3, C_6H_5)$$

further demonstrated by the formation of dehydrodimers of the ethers, such as dioxanyl dioxane, in these and similar reactions.

Phenanthrenequinone was shown to react with cyclic or open-chain ethers under ultraviolet irradiation (reaction 28)[40,41]. This 1,4-

$$\text{(phenanthrenequinone)} \xrightarrow[\text{Ether}]{h\nu} \text{(product with OR, OH)} \qquad (28)$$

$$R = \text{(dioxane ring)} , \quad \text{(tetrahydrofuran ring)} , \quad -CH_2-O-C_6H_5, \quad -CH_2-O-\text{cholestan}$$

addition was found to be reversible, since irradiation of the product led to the formation of phenanthrenequinone and phenanthrenequinhydrone. The reaction of a variety of quinones and α-diketones with dioxane was examined; tetrachloro-o-benzoquinone, acenaphthalenequinone, benzil, and camphorquinone gave the appropriate adducts. p-Quinones, such as p-naphthoquinone, and 9,10-anthraquinone failed to react[42].

E. Photochemical Cyanation of Ethers

Irradiation of saturated aliphatic or cyclic ethers in the presence of ClCN produces the corresponding α-cyano ethers[43]; higher yields were obtained in the presence of acetone (reaction 29). When unsymmetrical

$$R^1OCH_2R^2 + ClCN \xrightarrow{h\nu} R^1OCHR^2 + HCl \qquad (29)$$
$$\underset{\displaystyle CN}{|}$$

ethers were used, mixtures of the derived α-cyano ethers were obtained. Cyclic ethers yielded α-cyano ethers as the major product as well as products of substitution at other positions. The presence of sodium bicarbonate in the mixture increases the yields of the cyano ethers by neutralizing the hydrogen chloride produced. A free-radical chain mechanism was proposed for this reaction (Scheme 2).

$$Cl\text{—}CN \xrightarrow{h\nu} \dot{C}l + \dot{C}N \tag{30}$$

$$Cl\text{—}Cl \xrightarrow{h\nu} 2\,\dot{C}l \tag{31}$$

$$R^1OCH_2R^2 + \dot{C}l \longrightarrow R^1O\dot{C}HR^2 + HCl \tag{32}$$

$$R^1O\dot{C}HR^2 + Cl\text{—}CN \longrightarrow R^1OCHR^2 + \dot{C}l \tag{33}$$
$$\underset{\displaystyle CN}{|}$$

$$\dot{C}l + \dot{C}l \longrightarrow Cl_2 \tag{34}$$

$$\dot{C}l + \dot{C}N \longrightarrow ClCN \tag{35}$$

$$R^1O\dot{C}HR^2 + \dot{C}N \longrightarrow R^1OCHR^2 \tag{36}$$
$$\underset{\displaystyle CN}{|}$$

SCHEME 2.

F. Photochemical Reaction of Peresters with Ethers

It has been found that ethers react readily with peresters upon exposure to ultraviolet irradiation in the presence of copper ions (reaction 37)[44]. Thus, irradiation of a mixture of diethyl ether, t-butyl

$$CH_3CH_2OCH_2CH_3 + CH_3\overset{\displaystyle O}{\overset{\displaystyle \|}{C}}\text{—}O\text{—}O\text{—}Bu\text{-}t \xrightarrow[CuBr]{h\nu} CH_3CH_2OCHCH_3 \tag{37}$$

with the product $1\text{-ethoxyethyl acetate}$ bearing:
$$\underset{\displaystyle \underset{\displaystyle CH_3}{\overset{\displaystyle |}{C}=O}}{\overset{\displaystyle |}{O}}$$

peracetate, and either cuprous bromide or cupric 2-ethyl hexanoate at 35° produced 1-ethoxyethyl acetate in 75% yield. Other peresters, e.g. t-butyl perbenzoate, reacted with ethers in a similar manner. The reaction was applied to cyclic ethers, e.g. tetrahydrofuran and dioxane, leading to α-acetoxy ethers (reactions 38 and 39). The thermal reaction of tetrahydrofuran and *t*-butyl peracetate yields 2-*t*-butoxytetrahydrofuran, whereas the photochemical reaction produces the 2-acetoxy derivative in 75% yield. The photochemical reaction of

$$
\text{(THF)} + CH_3\overset{\displaystyle O}{\overset{\displaystyle \|}{C}}\text{—O—O—Bu-}t \xrightarrow[\text{CuBr}]{h\nu} \text{(2-acetoxy-THF)} \tag{38}
$$

$$
\text{(1,4-dioxane)} + CH_3\overset{\displaystyle O}{\overset{\displaystyle \|}{C}}\text{—O—O—Bu-}t \xrightarrow[\text{CuBr}]{h\nu} \text{(dioxanyl acetate)} \tag{39}
$$

1,4-dioxane with peracetate produced dioxanyl acetate which was identical with the product of the thermal reaction. The reaction catalyzed either by light or by copper ions proceeded at a much slower rate than the reactions catalyzed by both light and copper ions. To date only a preliminary report on these reactions has appeared.

G. Photoadditions of Ethers to Alkenes

A number of photoaddition reactions of ethers have been reported[45–47]. The photoaddition of cyclic ethers, such as tetrahydrofuran, tetrahydropyran, and 1,4-dioxane to terminal alkenes led to the derived α-substituted ethers (reaction 40). This photoalkylation can be induced directly by light or initiated photochemically by acetone[45]. In the latter case higher yields were obtained (reaction 40). Photo-

$$
\text{(cyclic ether)} + C_6H_{13}CH{=}CH_2 \xrightarrow[\text{Acetone}]{h\nu} \text{(α-substituted ether-CH}_2\text{CH}_2\text{C}_6\text{H}_{13}\text{)} \tag{40}
$$

$$
X = -CH_2-, \ -CH_2CH_2-, \ -CH_2O-
$$

additions of cyclic ethers to nonterminal alkenes have also been reported. Thus, tetrahydrofuran has been shown to react with tetracyanoquinomethane and tetracyanoethylene under ultraviolet irradiation[46]. α-Substituted cyclic ethers are the major products of the reactions, e.g. reaction (41). In the case of tetracyanoethylene the re-

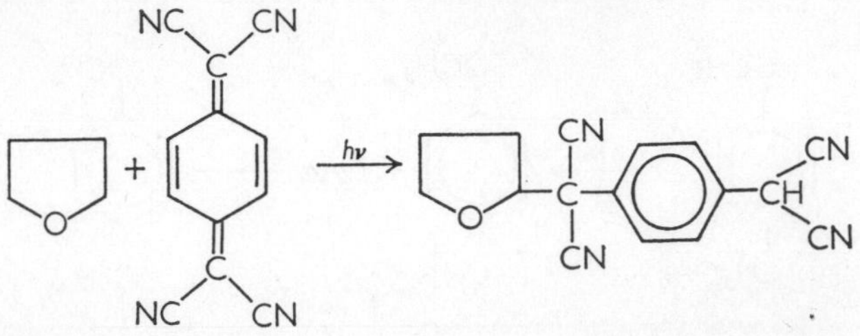

(41)

action proceeds further according to reaction (42). The photoaddition

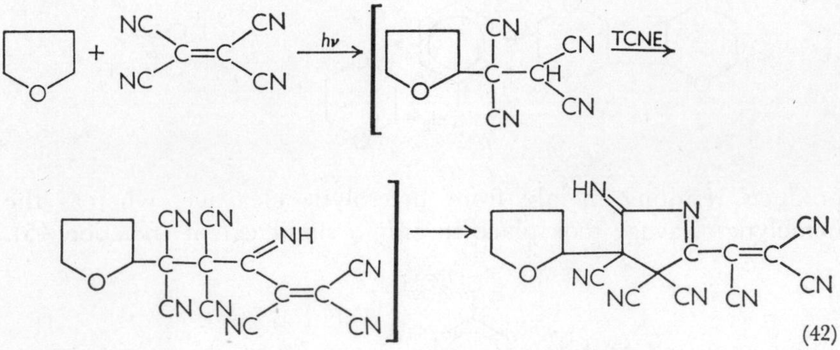

(42)

of tetrahydrofuran and its derivatives to maleic anhydride also led to
the derived α-substituted tetrahydrofurans (reaction 43) [47].

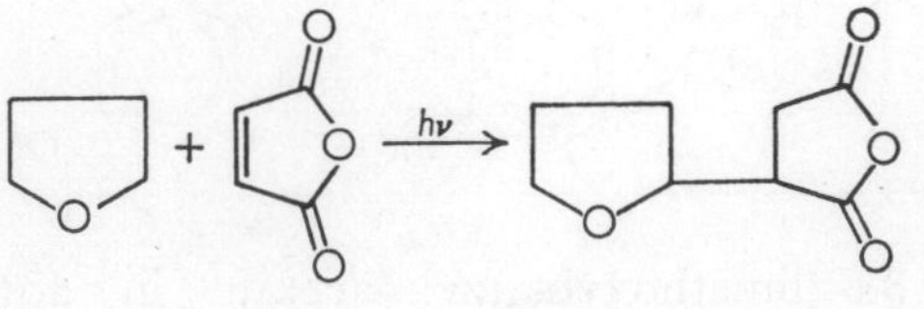

(43)

H. Solvolytic Photochemical Reactions

Some solvolytic photochemical reactions in which ethers were involved have been reported [48,49]. The photolyses of 4-methoxybenzyl
acetate, 3-methoxybenzyl acetate, and 3,5-dimethoxybenzyl acetate in
aqueous dioxane have been studied. It was found that 4-methoxy-
benzyl acetate essentially afforded exclusively free-radical products,

expected from homolytic generation of 4-methoxybenzyl and acetoxyl radicals (reaction 44) [48]. Irradiation of 3-methoxybenzyl acetate led to

products resulting mainly from heterolytic cleavage, whereas the homolytic cleavage took place to only a slight extent (reaction 45).

Photolysis of 3,5-dimethoxybenzyl acetate in aqueous dioxane afforded 3,5-dimethoxybenzyl alcohols through an ionic mechanism (reaction 46). Products of free-radical fission were not detected in this reaction. Irradiation of aryl trityl ethers led to the appropriate phenols (reaction 47) [49]. In these reactions m-nitrophenyl trityl ether underwent a more efficient photochemical solvolysis than the *para* isomer, in contrast to the nonphotochemical solvolysis. An ionic mechanism was suggested for this reaction [49].

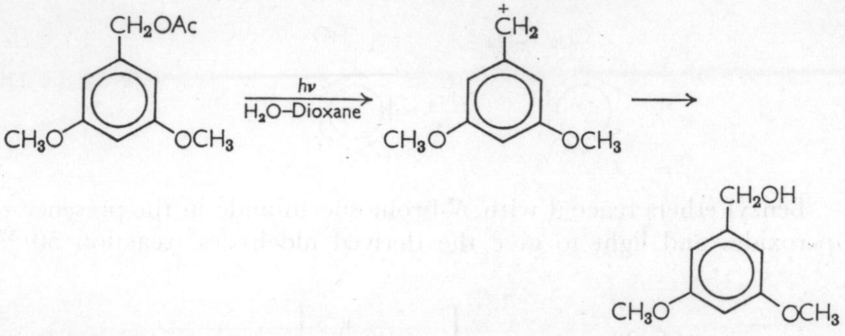

(46)

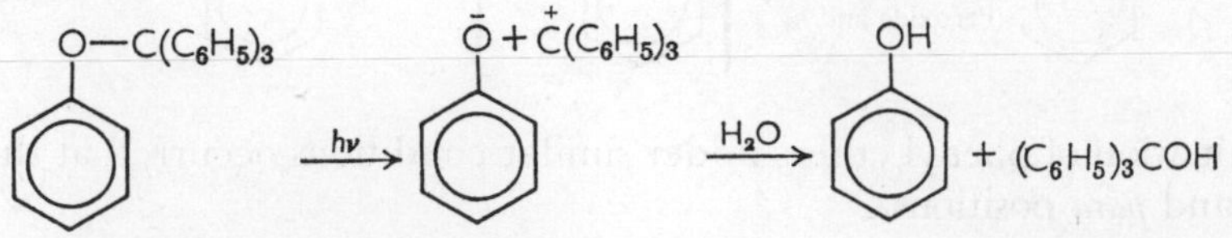

(47)

I. Photohalogenation of Ethers

Extensive studies of halogenation and photohalogenation of ethers have been reported[50]. Photochlorination of saturated acylic and cyclic ethers leads to α-chloro ethers as primary products which undergo further chemical reactions (reaction 48). The product composition

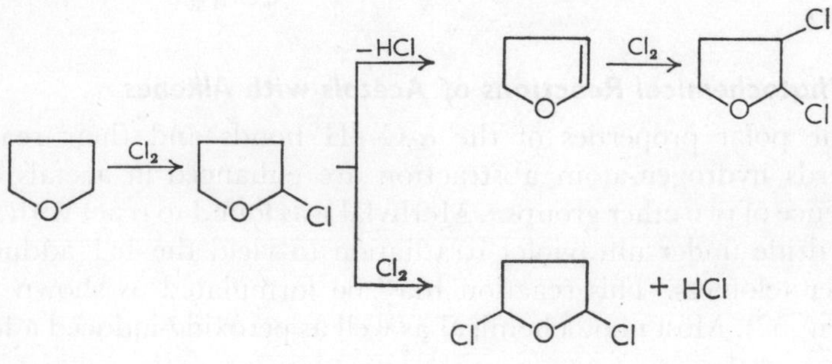

(48)

of these reactions has been found to be dependent on temperature and the relative amount of chlorine used.

Photobromination of benzyl methyl ethers with elemental bromine led to the corresponding benzaldehydes (reaction 49)[51].

$$(49)$$

Benzyl ethers reacted with *N*-bromosuccinimide in the presence of peroxides and light to give the derived aldehydes (reaction 50)[52].

$$(50)$$

Bromination of phenyl ethers under similar conditions occurred at the *ortho* and *para* positions.

J. Photochemical Reaction of Acid Chlorides with Ethers

Irradiation of acetyl chloride in ether solutions with light of wavelength 2540 Å led to α-acetyl ethers (reaction 51)[53].

$$(51)$$

K. Photochemical Reactions of Acetals with Alkenes

The polar properties of the α-C—H bonds and their reactivity towards hydrogen-atom abstraction are enhanced in acetals by the presence of two ether groups[2]. Methylal was found to react with maleic anhydride under ultraviolet irradiation to yield the 1:1 adduct and higher telomers. This reaction may be formulated as shown by reaction (52). Most photochemical as well as peroxide-induced additions

$$(52)$$

of acetals to alkenes are reported in the patent literature. The products described may have useful commercial applications, but further investigation is required[54,55].

L. Photochemical Conversion of Acetals into Esters

Irradiation of acetals of *o*-nitrobenzaldehyde led to the formation of the appropriate esters of *o*-nitrosobenzoic acid (reaction 53)[56].

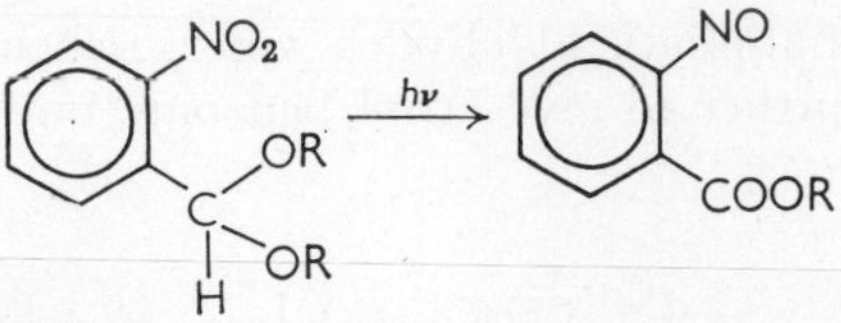

(53)

Cyclic acetals of *o*-nitrobenzaldehyde reacted analogously (reaction 54)[57]. This reaction has been applied in the carbohydrate and steroid fields[58–61].

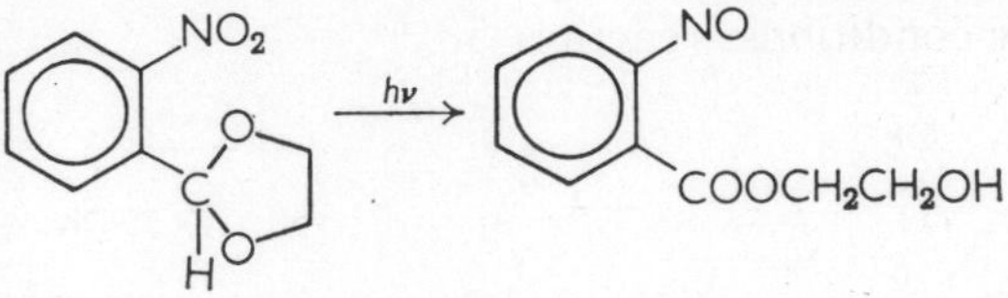

(54)

The photochemical acetone-initiated conversion of cyclic acetals of aldehydes into the corresponding carboxylic esters has also been reported[62]. The reaction probably proceeds through hydrogen atom abstraction from the acetal by the photoactivated acetone molecule followed by C—O bond cleavage (reaction 55).

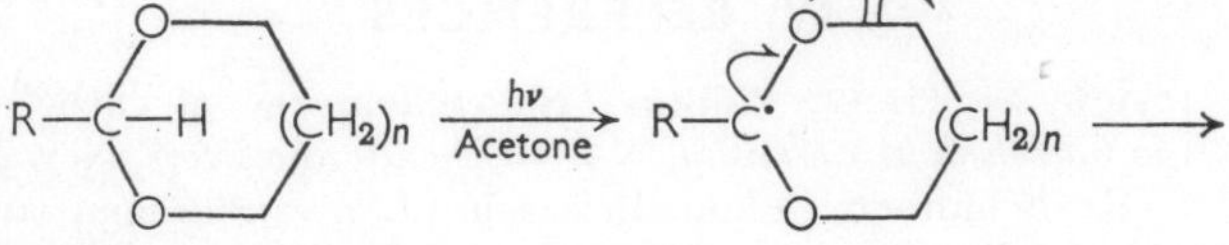

$$RCOOCH_2(CH_2)_n\overset{\cdot}{C}H_2 \xrightarrow{R^1H} RCOOCH_2(CH_2)_nCH_3 \qquad (55)$$

(n = 0 or 1)

M. Bromination of Acetals with N-Bromosuccinimide

Acetals can be brominated readily with *N*-bromosuccinimide in the presence of light (reaction 56)[63]. α-Bromo acetals were obtained in the

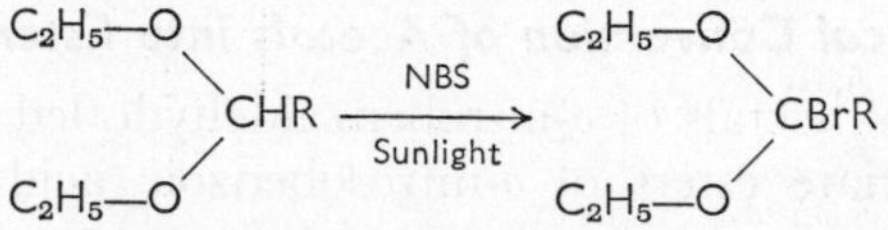

$$
\begin{array}{c}
C_2H_5-O \\
\diagdown \\
CHR \\
\diagup \\
C_2H_5-O
\end{array}
\xrightarrow[\text{Sunlight}]{\text{NBS}}
\begin{array}{c}
C_2H_5-O \\
\diagdown \\
CBrR \\
\diagup \\
C_2H_5-O
\end{array}
\tag{56}
$$

$$(R = CH_3, C_2H_5, \text{n-Pr, i-Pr})$$

case of acetals of aliphatic aldehydes, whereas benzaldehyde diethyl-acetal reacted further to give ethyl benzoate under these conditions (reaction 57)[63].

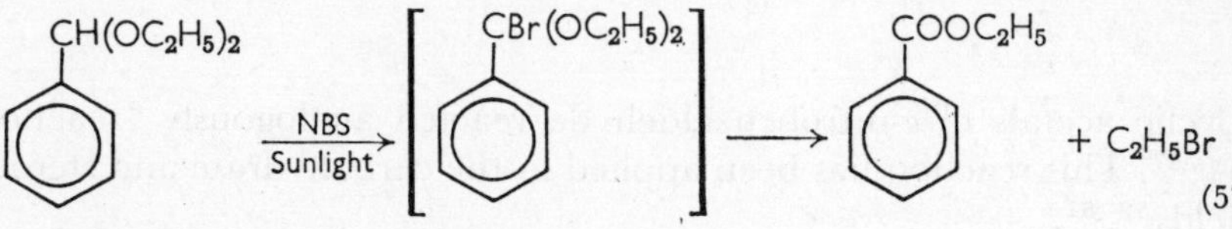

$$\tag{57}$$

Dialkylacetals of α-keto aldehydes were converted into α-keto esters under similar conditions (reaction 58)[64].

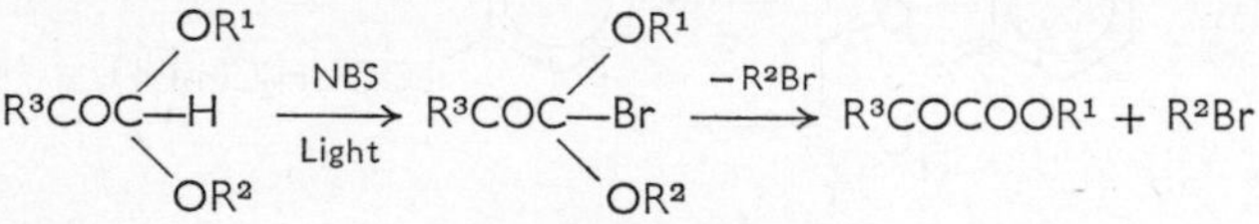

$$
\begin{array}{c}
OR^1 \\
\diagup \\
R^3COC-H \\
\diagdown \\
OR^2
\end{array}
\xrightarrow[\text{Light}]{\text{NBS}}
\begin{array}{c}
OR^1 \\
\diagup \\
R^3COC-Br \\
\diagdown \\
OR^2
\end{array}
\xrightarrow{-R^2Br}
R^3COCOOR^1 + R^2Br
\tag{58}
$$

$$(R^1 = R^2 = \text{alkyl})$$

III. ACKNOWLEDGEMENTS

The author is indebted to Dr. M. B. Rubin and Dr. C. H. Krauch for most valuable comments.

IV. REFERENCES

1. For a review see G. O. Phillips 'Photochemistry of carbohydrates' in *Advances in Carbohydrate Chemistry*, No. 18, Academic Press, New York, 1963, p. 9; cf. K. Schaffner, 'Photochemische Umwandlungen ausgewählter Naturstoffe' in *Progress in the Chemistry of Organic Natural Products*, No. 22 (Ed. L. Zechmeister), Springer-Verlag, Wien, 1964, p. 1.
2. C. Walling, *Free Radicals in Solution*, John Wiley and Sons, New York, 1957, p. 287.

3. T. Forster, *Z. Electrochem.*, **56**, 716 (1952); R. M. Hochstrasser and G. B. Porter, *Quart. Rev. (London)*, **14**, 146 (1960); W. A. Noyes, Jr., G. B. Porter, and J. E. Jolley, *Chem. Rev.*, **56**, 49 (1956); J. P. Simons, *Quart. Rev. (London)*, **13**, 3 (1959); J. N. Pitts, Jr., F. Wilkinson, and G. S. Hammond, *Advances in Photochemistry*, Vol. 1, Interscience Publishers, New York, 1963, p.1; see reference 1(b).

4. G. O. Schenck in *Präparative Organische Photochemie* (Ed. A. Schönberg), Springer-Verlag, Wien, 1958, p. 211.

5. G. S. Hammond and N. J. Turro, *Science*, **142**, 1541 (1963).

6. L. W. Pickett, N. J. Hoeflich, and T.-C. Liu, *J. Am. Chem. Soc.*, **73**, 4865 (1951).

7. G. Scheibe and H. Grieneisen, *Z. Physik Chem.*, **B25**, 52 (1934).

8. G. Fleming, M. M. Anderson, A. J. Harrison, and W. Pickett, *J. Chem. Phys.*, **30**, 351 (1959).

9. A. J. Harrison and D. R. W. Price, *J. Chem. Phys.*, **30**, 357 (1959).

10. G. J. Hernandez, *J. Chem. Phys.*, **38**, 2233 (1963).

11. J. D. Margerum, J. N. Pitts, Jr., J. G. Rutgers, and S. Searles, *J. Am. Chem. Soc.*, **81**, 1549 (1959).

12. C. Walling, *Free Radicals in Solution*, John Wiley & Sons, New York, 1957, pp. 287, 412, and references cited therein.

13. G. Sosnovsky, *Free Radical Reactions in Preparative Organic Chemistry*, The Macmillan Co., New York, 1964, pp. 370, 380.

14. T. J. Wallace and R. J. Gritter, *Tetrahedron*, **19**, 657 (1963) and references cited therein.

15. N. I. Shuikin and B. L. Lebedev, *Izv. Akad. Nauk. SSSR. Ser. Khim.*, 533 (1962).

16. K. Pfordte, *Ann. Chem.*, **625**, 30 (1959).

17. R. J. Gritter and E. C. Sabatino, *J. Org. Chem.*, **29**, 1965 (1964).

18. K. Shima and S. Tsutsumi, *Bull. Chem. Soc. (Japan)*, **36**, 121 (1963).

19. R. Gomer and W. A. Noyes, Jr., *J. Am. Chem. Soc.*, **72**, 101 (1950).

20. R. J. Cvetanovic, *Can. J. Chem.*, **33**, 1684 (1955).

21. R. J. Cvetanovic and L. C. Doyle, *Can. J. Chem.*, **35**, 605 (1957).

22. A. J. Harrison and J. S. Lake, *J. Phys. Chem.*, **63**, 1489 (1959).

23. M. S. Kharasch, G. Stampa, and W. Nudenberg, *Science*, **116**, 309 (1959).

24. O. P. Kelly and J. T. Pinhey, *Tetrahedron Letters*, *No. 46*, 3427 (1964).

25. J. C. Anderson and C. B. Reese, *J. Chem. Soc.*, 1781 (1963).

26. H. Kobsa, *J. Org. Chem.*, **27**, 2293 (1962).

27. C. H. Kuo, R. D. Hoffsommer, H. L. Slates, D. Taub, and N. L. Wendler, *Chem. Ind. (London)*, 1627 (1960).

28. D. Taub, C. H. Kuo, H. L. Slates, and N. L. Wendler, *Tetrahedron*, **19**, 1 (1963).

29. C. Pac and S. Tsutsumi, *Bull. Chem. Soc. (Japan)*, **37**, 1392 (1964).

30. R. A. Finnegan and J. J. Mattice, *Tetrahedron*, **21**, 1015 (1965) and references cited therein.

31. S. Bodforss, *Chem. Ber.*, **51**, 214 (1918).

32. C. Lehmann, K. Schaffner, and O. Jeger, *Helv. Chim. Acta*, **45**, 1031 (1962).

33. C. K. Johnson, B. Doming, and W. Reusch, *J. Am. Chem. Soc.*, **85**, 3894 (1963).

34. (a) Cf. K. Schaffner, 'Photochemie Umwandlungen ausgewählter Natur-stoffe' in *Progress in the Chemistry of Organic Natural Products*, No. 22 (Ed. L. Zechmeister), Springer-Verlag, New York, 1964, p. 19; (b) H. E. Zimmerman, B. R. Cowley, C.-Y. Tseng, and J. W. Wilson, *J. Am. Chem. Soc.*, **86**, 947 (1964).

35. C. Walling, *Free Radicals in Solution*, John Wiley & Sons, New York, 1957, p. 412.

36. W. C. Wolfe, *Anal. Chem.*, **34**, 1328 (1962).

37. G. O. Schenck, H. D. Becker, K.-H. Schulte-Elte, and C. H. Krauch, *Chem. Ber.*, **96**, 509 (1963).

38. W. G. Herkstroeter, A. A. Lamola, and G. S. Hammond, *J. Am. Chem. Soc.*, **86**, 4537 (1964).

39. G. S. Hammond, W. P. Baker, and W. M. Moore, *J. Am. Chem. Soc.*, **83**, 2795 (1961).

40. M. B. Rubin, *J. Org. Chem.*, **28**, 1949 (1963).

41. M. B. Rubin and P. Zwitkowitz, *J. Org. Chem.*, **29**, 2362 (1964).

42. M. B. Rubin, personal communication.

43. E. Müller and H. Huber, *Chem. Ber.*, **96**, 2319 (1963).

44. G. Sosnovsky, *J. Org. Chem.*, **28**, 2934 (1963).

45. D. Elad and R. D. Youssefyeh, *J. Org. Chem.*, **29**, 2031 (1964).

46. J. Diekmann and C. J. Pedersen, *J. Org. Chem.*, **28**, 2879 (1963).

47. R. L. Jacobs and G. G. Ecke, *J. Org. Chem.*, **28**, 3036 (1963).

48. H. E. Zimmerman and V. R. Sander, *J. Am. Chem. Soc.*, **85**, 915 (1963).

49. H. E. Zimmerman and S. Somasekhara, *J. Am. Chem. Soc.*, **85**, 922 (1963) and references cited therein.

50. For summary see G. Sosnovsky, *Free Radical Reactions in Preparative Organic Chemistry*, The Macmillan Co., New York, 1964, p. 367.

51. D. G. Markees, *J. Org. Chem.*, **23**, 1490 (1958).

52. M. Okawara, H. Sato, and E. Imoto, *J. Chem. Soc. Japan Ind. Chem. Sec.*, **58**, 924 (1958).

53. M. Schmidt, *Angew. Chem.*, **77**, 216 (1965).

54. T. M. Patrick, Jr., *U.S. Pat.* 2,628,238 (1953); *Chem. Abstr.*, **48**, 711 (1954).

55. T. M. Patrick, Jr., *U.S. Pat.* 2,716,660 (1955); *Chem. Abstr.*, **49**, 16523 (1955).

56. E. Bamberger and F. Elgar, *Chem. Ann.*, **371**, 319 (1910).

57. E. Bamberger and F. Elgar, *Chem. Ann.*, **475**, 288 (1929).

58. I. Tanasescu, *Bull. Soc. Chim. France*, **39**, [4] 1443 (1926).

59. I. Tanasescu and M. Ionescu, *Bull. Soc. Chim. France*, **7**, [5] 84 (1940), and references cited therein.

60. I. Tanasescu, F. Hodosan, and I. Jude, *Acad. Rep. Populare Romine Filiana Cluj, Sutdii Cercetari Chim.*, **11**, 309 (1960); through *Chem. Abstr.*, **58**, 4619 (1963).

61. I. Tanasescu and S. Mager, *Acad. Rep. Populare Romine, Filiana Cluj, Studii Cercetari Chim.*, **13**, 69 (1962); through *Chem. Abstr.*, **59**, 11637 (1963).

62. D. Elad and R. D. Youssefyeh, *Tetrahedron Letters*, No. 30, 2189 (1963).

63. E. N. Marwell and M. J. Joncich, *J. Am. Chem. Soc.*, **73**, 973 (1951).

64. J. B. Wright, *J. Am. Chem. Soc.*, **77**, 4883 (1955).

CHAPTER **9**

Reactions of cyclic ethers

Roy J. Gritter

IBM Research Laboratory, San Jose, California, U.S.A.

I. INTRODUCTION

The cyclic ethers as a class of compounds have several features which they share with other heterocyclic compounds, but they do have one feature which adequately distinguishes them from the others. The feature which they have in common with the cyclic sulfides and amines is that the ring can be opened, often readily[1]. The ring-opening rates of the three classes of compounds normally follow the order: 2- > 3- > 4- > 5- > 6-membered ring. The inclusion of the two-membered ring can be questioned, but it does give some insight into the reactions of these compounds.

The distinguishing characteristic of the cyclic ethers is that the ring *can* be opened in a single bimolecular reaction, which involves no pre-equilibrium step, to produce good yields of products[1]. In comparison, azacycloalkanes require a preequilibrium with a Lewis acid and the thiacycloalkanes will more often than not form a polymeric product under these reaction conditions. The rates of the ring-opening reactions are related to the stabilities of the anions produced $(-S^- > -O^- > -N^-)$. Thus a cyclic sulfide would be expected to be the most reactive of the three heterocyclics in any specific-sized ring system[1].

A. Reviews

The preparation and chemistry of two members of the cyclic ether series have recently been reviewed in detail. The epoxides have been covered before 1960–1961 by Rosowsky[2] in a chapter which included over two thousand references and the oxetanes before 1961 by Searles[3] in the same book. For this reason, the coverage in this chapter of these two members will stress material published since 1960–1961 and mechanistic details of interest. Topsom[4] has written on recent advances in the chemistry of simple oxygen heterocyclics including material up to 1963. There are other general reviews on epoxides that can be mentioned. The article on the Prileschejew reaction (reaction of perester on an olefin) appeared in *Organic Reactions* in 1953[5] and was recently brought up-to-date by Karnojitzky[6]. Additional surveys include one on the synthesis of new epoxy compounds by Batzer and Nikles[7], a brief one by Batzer[8], and an intensive coverage of the mechanisms of epoxide reactions by Parker and Isaacs[9]. Dean recently reported on the naturally occurring epoxides[10].

It is interesting that no review, other than brief descriptions in recent texts[4], on the chemistry or synthesis of the five-, six-, or higher-membered rings has appeared since the report by Winstein and Henderson[11]. The treatise edited by Rodd[12] glosses over these compounds very rapidly. For this reason, an attempt will be made to cover the chemistry and synthesis of at least the five- and six-membered ring compounds moderately extensively, but not necessarily completely.

B. Bond Energies

The ease of ring opening of the cyclic ethers can be related directly to their thermodynamic properties. Gray and Williams[13] summarized the data for the formation of diradicals from the cyclic ethers and these are given in Table 1. Cox[14] evaluated the strain and conjugation energies in a large number of cyclic systems and found that the differences between the experimental and calculated heats of formation could be determined. The heats derived by him are also given in Table 1 and are quite self-explanatory.

TABLE 1. The bond energies of the cyclic ethers.

Cyclic ether	Bond-dissociation energy[13] (kcal/mole)	$H_{f^\circ(g)}(\text{expt.}) - H^\circ_{(g)}(\text{calc.})$[14]
Ethylene oxide	47·7	28
Propylene oxide	50·5–51·5	26·4
Oxetane	—	—
Tetrahydrofuran	68·6	6·7
Tetrahydropyran	71·2	2·2

A slightly different, but still classical, approach has been used by Pell and Pilcher[15] who measured the heats of combustion of the cyclic ethers and other related compounds. From these data they were able to obtain the strain energies tabulated in Table 2. Several comments made by these authors are quite informative. They pointed out that the strain energy in the four-membered ring is only slightly less than that in the three-membered ring; the cyclic sulfides as a group have much less strain than the cyclic alkanes, ethers, or amines and this probably relates to the larger orbital size of the sulfur atom; tetra-hydropyran is the only six-membered ring to exhibit strain.

TABLE 2. Strain energies in cyclic systems (kcal/mole)[15].

Ring size	Alkane	Ether	Sulfide	Imine
3	27·43	27·28	19·78	26·87
4	26·04	25·51	19·64	
5	6·05	5·63	1·97	5·80
6	−0·02	1·16	−0·27	−0·15

Cox[14] considered the slight strain in the six-membered ring to be angular in origin, since a carbon–oxygen bond is slightly shorter than a carbon–carbon bond. The large strain in the four-membered ring fits in well with the latest data on the bond distances and bond angles for that system[16].

From these considerations it can be seen that the reactions of these compounds will often be unexpected and their synthesis sometimes difficult. This is because the three- and four-membered rings can *sometimes* be treated to give a product with the ring *intact* and the five-, six-, and higher-membered rings can *sometimes* be *opened*.

C. Physical Measurements

Several specific physical characteristics of the cyclic ethers can be described. The first of these is the contribution of the rings to the optical rotatory dispersion of a molecule, where only the epoxide group has been studied. Djerassi[17] found that oxirane rings contributed to the dispersion curves at 290 mμ, and in a manner opposite in sign to the alkyl group. The mass spectral fragmentation pattern of these compounds has been sparsely studied as is evident from the recent books on the subject[18-21]. It appears, however, that the cyclic ethers are important to mass spectrographic analysis, for one can deuterate compounds in a stereospecific manner by the reduction of an epoxide with lithium aluminum deuteride[22].

The infrared spectral characteristics of the small rings were described in the reviews mentioned above; however, the decisive assignments for the epoxide rings were recently made by Potts[23]. It has also been reported that long range effects of groups on infrared bands are possible in these compounds[24].

The transmission of conjugation through the epoxide ring is a point of interest and it is supported by recent reports. Most measurements of conjugation utilize ultraviolet spectra, thus they involve excited states and not the ground state of the molecule. For this reason, comparison studies with the corresponding olefins and cyclopropane systems can be most meaningful. Recent measurements of the acidities[25] and ultraviolet spectra[26] of substituted cyclopropanes and epoxides support the fact that conjugation does occur in both systems and that no specific orientation of the ring is necessary with cyclopropanes. This last fact should be compared to a previous report which suggests that conjugation through an epoxide ring does require specific orientation[27]. An explanation for the conjugation through the epoxide ring has been presented which considers that there is enough strain in the carbon–oxygen bonds to allow the oxygen atoms to be involved in no-bond resonance[28]. The authors further clarified their contention by suggesting that forms with a negative charge on the oxygen atom, which have been neglected in previous calculations, are important in the excited state and that these can explain the conjugation found. The ultraviolet spectra of the four- to six-membered rings have also been recently reexamined[29].

The measurement of the nuclear magnetic resonance spectra of the cyclic oxides has been an area of constant interest, although little work on the larger rings has been reported since the first definitive studies[30-33]. The epoxide ring has been examined in a variety of modes and the coupling constants for a large number of substituted epoxides are available[34-38]. Other aspects of importance to the understanding of the nuclear magnetic resonance spectra of epoxides involve general studies[39-41], studies on styrene oxides[42,43], a study of propylene oxide[44], highly inclusive studies of steroid epoxides[45,46], measurements on sugar epoxides[47], researches concerned with the signs of the coupling constants involved[48,49], a determination of the solvent dependence of the coupling constants in styrene oxide[50], and a study as to whether a ring current exists in the epoxide ring[51].

Several of the above-mentioned aspects must be discussed more completely, for they contain specific details of interest. Tori and his coworkers[46] have reported on the steroidal epoxides, where the epoxide rings were both the α and β isomers at a number of positions. They found the proton signal of the α isomer generally at a higher field than that of the β isomer. They compared their results to those from a large number of other epoxides. In addition, they considered their data in the light of the Karplus[52] correlation (gives the angular dependence of coupling constants of the various protons) and the electro-negativity of the groups involved. In another study, Tori and other co-workers[51] concluded that there is a ring current in epoxides, and thus conjugation exists through an epoxide ring; this is also indicated by the ultraviolet spectra. This ring current and other factors have a shielding effect on neighboring protons. In somewhat the same way, the ^{13}C—H coupling constants were used to calculate that there is about 12% ionic character in the carbon–oxygen bond in epoxides[53].

One final consideration concerning the nuclear magnetic resonance spectra of epoxides, and especially styrene oxide, is the sign of the coupling constants. Swalen and Reilly[34] chose the three coupling constants in styrene oxide to be positive, and other work[48] indicated that the signs should all be the same, i.e. either all positive or all negative. The most recent study[50], which considered the influence of solvents and the effect of an increase in dielectric constant of the solvent on the nuclear magnetic resonance spectrum, suggests that the values should all be positive. Other methods will certainly be used to clarify this situation.

D. Basicity, Inertness, and Solvent Properties

The basicity of the cyclic ethers has been a subject of interest, par-tially because of its relation to the solvent properties of the ethers, but also for theoretical reasons (they are more basic than the straight-chain ethers). The available data have been obtained by measuring the interaction of the oxygen with a Lewis acid, such as sulfuric acid[54], stannic chloride[55,56], boron trifluoride[57-59], and perchloric acid[60] and with iodine[61], molybdenum carbonyl[62], magnesium carbonyl[62], phenylmagnesium carbonyl with ultraviolet light catalysis[62], and also by infrared spectrophotometry[63,64]. The order of basicity for the specific ring sizes is 4- > 5- > 6- > 3-membered ring > Et_2O[54,61], but it can be influenced by steric effects in substituted compounds[63]. The metal carbonyls gave varied results[62].

Tamres and his coworkers[61] have shown that the situation is not as well understood as was thought, for they found that 7-oxabicyclo-[2.2.1]heptane was less basic than an epoxide in aqueous acid. In comparison, the ring-size order measured by the iodine-complex equilibria method in heptane was 4- > bicyclic ether > 5- > 6-membered ring. They attributed this change to a solvation effect, for in the bicyclic ether the oxygen is almost surrounded by a 'hydrocarbon cage' which not only reduces the chance of solvent stabilization of the oxonium ion obtained by protonation, but also shields one side of the oxygen atom[65].

One of the major uses of tetrahydrofuran results from its being a solvent of high solvating power (undoubtedly related to its basicity) and sometimes from its novel directing influence. In general, it is non-reactive toward ring opening by a nucleophile at room temperature, and thus, for example, has been used with Grignard reagents in reactions conducted at room temperature[66]. It has also been used for free-radical arylations[67]. The major use of tetrahydrofuran has been with organometallics, where it has been found to be an unusually good solvent and in some cases has actually caused sluggish reactions to proceed[68]. Gilman[69-71] has developed these two aspects in his studies of the lithium metal cleavages of heterocyclic compounds (1) to form organometallics (2)[68], and also in the synthesis and further reactions of organometallics (reaction 2)[71].

$$CH_2{=}CHCH_2MgCl + (C_6H_5)_3SiH \xrightarrow[\substack{\text{but not}\\ \text{Et}_2\text{O or}\\ \text{C}_6\text{H}_5\text{CH}_3}]{\text{THF}} C_6H_5CH_2MgCl + (CH_2{=}CHCH_2)$$
$$(3) \qquad\qquad\qquad\qquad\qquad\qquad (4) \qquad (C_6H_5CH_2)_2SiH \quad (2)$$
$$(5)$$

Another specific use of tetrahydrofuran has been in hydride reductions where tetrahydrofuran dissolved more of the reactants than did diethyl ether[72]; it made reduction with $NaBH_4$ and $Al(BH_4)_3$[73] extremely rapid, and gave complete solution when diborane and boron trichloride were used[74]. Its usefulness in the formation of Grignard reagents can be exemplified by stating that in tetrahydrofuran chlorobenzene will form a Grignard reagent[75]; this will not readily occur in diethyl ether. Some Grignard reagents formed in tetrahydrofuran favor Wurtz-type reactions (dimer formation) more than normal reactions[76], give ring opening of oxetane in 80% yield[77,78], and permit nonflammable Grignard reagents to be formed[79]. The last mentioned will occur when toluene is used as a solvent and one mole of cyclic ether is available for each mole of organometallic compound.

When alkali metal derivatives of organic compounds are involved in a reaction it has been found that tetrahydrofuran shortens the time necessary for the reaction to take place; e.g. for a Claisen reaction[80], it varies the reactivity of a carbanion and greatly enhances the amount of carbon alkylation of an ambident ion[81] (dimethyl sulfoxide and dimethylformamide give oxygen alkylation)[82], affects free radical ion (ketyl) reactivities[83], and permits the formation of aromatic (naphthalene and phenanthrene with Na, Li, and K)[84] and vinyllithium[85] carbanions. Tetrahydrofuran affects a Wittig reaction by changing the *cis/trans* ratio; 75% *cis* is produced as compared to 95% *cis* produced by dimethylformamide[86]. Finally, its use in phenylchromium chemistry must be mentioned, where its use gave unexplained results until it was realized that the tetrahydrofuran formed a strong complex with triphenylchromium (equation 3)[87]. The three molecules of tetrahydro-

$$CrCl_3 + 3\ C_6H_5MgBr \xrightarrow{\text{THF}} (C_6H_5)_3Cr^{III} \cdot 3THF\ (Violet) \qquad (3)$$
$$\text{(6)} \qquad\qquad\qquad\qquad \text{(7)}$$

furan of the complex (7) were removed when the complex was treated with large amounts of diethyl ether[87].

$$7 + Excess\ Et_2O \longrightarrow (C_6H_5)_3Cr^{III}\ (Black) \qquad (4)$$
$$\text{(8)}$$

E. Polymerization

The formation of polymers from the cyclic ethers is of some commercial interest, where the epoxides are of greatest importance. A study which relates the basicity of the cyclic ether to the rate of polymerization has been described[88], and an attempt to form a polymer from an epoxide by a free-radical displacement reaction (see section III.G) was reported as being a failure[89]. Most of the general material on epoxides is covered in recent treatises on polymers[90,91], while additional material on optically active monomers[92], mechanism[93], stereochemistry[94], and optically active catalysts[95] can be added.

Oxetanes are rarely polymerized commercially[96], but tetrahydrofuran can be polymerized quite readily. The polymerization of tetrahydrofuran was reviewed in 1960[97], and can be brought up-to-date by the inclusion of articles where cocatalysts were used[98], where the purity of the cocatalyst produced wide changes in product molecular weight[99,100], where *p*-benzoquinone diazide (9) was used as the catalyst[101], and where some of the many parameters (ceiling temperature, equilibrium conversion at specific temperatures, etc.) were determined[102].

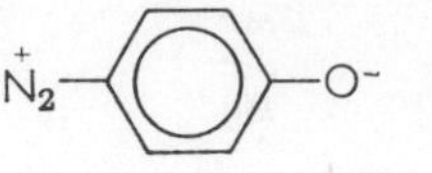

$$\overset{+}{N}_2\!-\!\!\langle\bigcirc\rangle\!-\!O^-$$

(9)

II. SYNTHESIS OF EPOXIDES

A. Classical Methods

The majority of epoxide syntheses involve the standard reagents, e.g. a peracid attacking an olefin or a ring closure of a halohydrin. Recent interesting findings about these methods indicate that the peracid oxidation gives a product in which a steric directive effect is evident. This work has been summarized by Henbest[103]; it was shown that 85% epoxidation could occur at the α face (side away from the substituent) of a cyclic 3-substituted olefin, depending on the solvent. This has been shown to be a steric effect of the substituent groups in alkylcyclopentenes (equation 5)[104,105]. The peracid method has also given the 2-butene oxides in high stereospecificity ($>95\%$) and in good yields (50–60%)[106]. However, the one-step procedure of using calcium hypochlorite has distinct advantages, for the yields with disubstituted olefins (2-butenes) are 80–90% and with tetrasubstituted ones, 20–60%[107,108].

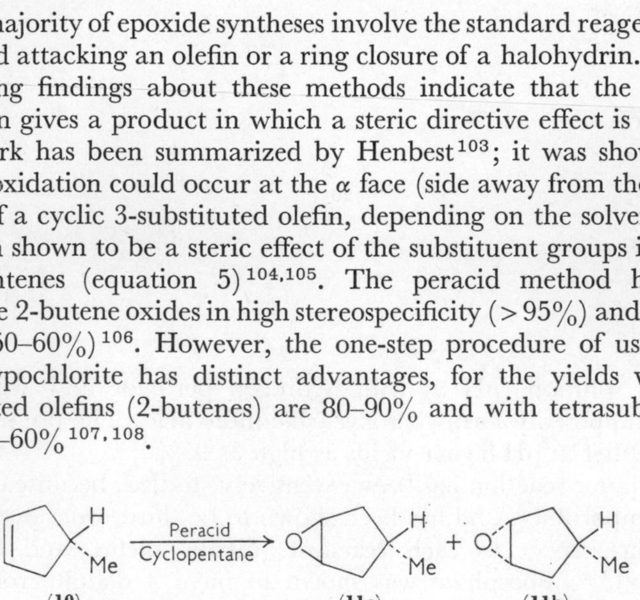

(5)

(10) (11a) (11b)

82% trans 18% cis

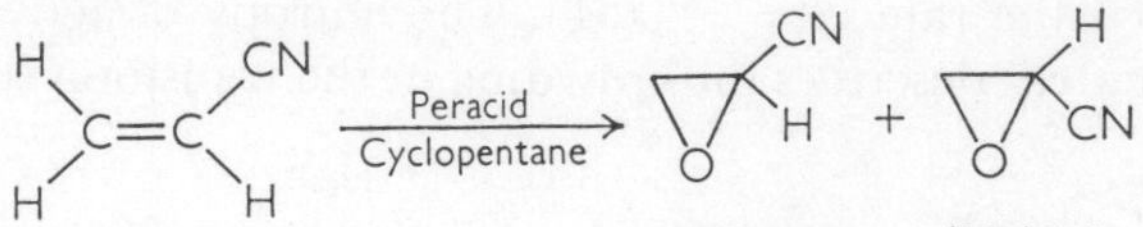

(6)

(12) (13a) 95% (13b) 5%

Epoxidation rates with peracids appear to be the same in almost every solvent[109-111]. This suggests intramolecular hydrogen bonding, which is shown in equation (7)[111].

$$\underset{(14)}{\overset{C}{\underset{C}{\parallel}}} + \underset{(15)}{\overset{O-C-R}{\underset{H\cdots O}{\overset{\parallel}{\bigcirc}}}} \longrightarrow \underset{(16)}{\overset{C}{\underset{C}{\searrow}}} \overset{O\cdots C-R}{\underset{H\cdots O}{\overset{\parallel}{\bigcirc}}} \longrightarrow \underset{(17)}{\triangleright O} + \underset{(18)}{\overset{O=C-R}{\underset{H}{\overset{}{\bigcirc}}}} \quad (7)$$

Isotope studies with ^{18}O indicate that the epoxide oxygen comes from one of the peroxy oxygens in an acyl peroxide[112], and this has resulted in the postulation of the mechanism shown in equation (8)[112]. It was discovered by Payne[113] that epoxidation with a peracid could occur

$$(8)$$

in *basic* solution (pH 9) with hydrogen peroxide and acetonitrile, which supposedly forms peroxycarboimidic acid. The use of a phosphate buffer at pH 8 gave yields as high as 95%[114].

This latter reaction has been extensively studied, because of its synthetic importance, and has been shown to be third order overall; first order in respect to each reactant (nitrile, olefin, and hydrogen peroxide)[115]. Phosphate was shown to have a definite role in the transition state of the reaction and a Hammett relation study showed that electron-attracting substituents on the benzonitrile accelerated the rate ($\rho = 0.57$) and electron-attracting groups in the olefin (styrene) slowed the rate ($\rho = -0.51$). The entropy of activation (-50 e.u.) adequately describes the crowding in the transition state (22)[115].

$$(22)$$

The almost constant rate at various values of pH and changes in rate with a change in polarity of the solvent strongly suggests that internal hydrogen bonding is also involved in the peramidine (**22**) as it is involved in the peracids (equation 7). Pertungstic acid has been shown to epoxidize, but only when a free hydroxyl group is alpha to the olefin[116]. The transition state appears to be one with considerable polar (electrophilic) character.

The transition state of ethylene oxide formation from ethylene chlorohydrin has been defined by Swain and his coworkers[117]. They were able to describe the reaction of the chlorohydrin with base from kinetic isotope effects and solvent correlations involving a transition state where epoxide formation was 100% complete (**23**). The extent of breaking of the carbon–chlorine bond in the transition state is not

(23)   (24)

yet known. This transition-state picture can be compared to that of the formation of tetrahydrofuran from 4-chlorobutanol, where the isotope effects and solvent correlations indicated that epoxide formation is only 25% complete (**24**). Based on this work, Swain has added a 'solvation rule' to his previously defined 'reacting-bond rule'. The latter rule states that electron-donating substituents lengthen the nearest reacting bond(s), but that they have an alternating effect on more remote bonds. The solvent rule suggests that a proton being transferred from one oxygen to another in an organic reaction should lie in an entirely stable potential at the transition state and not form bonds nor give rise to primary isotope effects.

Zimmerman[118] has recently redefined his views on epoxide formation in unsaturated ketones, for at one time he could not find any stereospecificity in the hydroxide-catalyzed product formation. He has

(25)   (26)   (27)

since reported that the amount of stereoselectivity is dependent on the departing anion, and efficient ones (Cl^- and $C_6H_5CO_2^-$) compete effectively with rotation such that the original conformation is trapped as the epoxide (equation 9).

B. Special Reagents

Recently a large number of special reagents have been applied to the synthesis of epoxides; these will be described in some detail.

1. Wittig reagent

One of the first of these new methods involved the utilization of the reaction of the Wittig reagent (29) with an aldehyde or ketone to produce the epoxide which may or may not rearrange to the corresponding aldehyde[119]. This reaction was recently briefly covered in a review

$$(C_6H_5)_2C{=}O + (C_6H_5)_3Sb{=}CH_2 \rightarrow \left[\begin{array}{c} (C_6H_5)_2C-O^- \\ | \\ CH_2-Sb^+ \\ | \\ (C_6H_5)_3 \end{array} \right] \rightarrow (C_6H_5)_2C\overset{O}{\overbrace{\qquad}}CH_2$$

$$\qquad (28) \qquad\qquad (29) \qquad\qquad\qquad\qquad (30) \qquad\qquad\qquad (31)$$

$$+ (C_6H_5)_3Sb \quad (10)$$

$$(32)$$

where not only the phosphorus compounds were illustrated, but also the corresponding antimony and arsenic compounds[120].

2. Phosphorus triamide

Another phosphorus-containing reagent, hexamethylphosphoramide or trisdimethylaminophosphine (34) was first used by Mark[121] to prepare substituted stilbene oxides (35) in good yields. He found that the *trans* product predominated and that an electron-withdrawing

$$ArCHO + [(Me)_2N]_3P \longrightarrow ArCH\overset{O}{\overbrace{\qquad}}CHAr + [(CH_3)_2N]_3PO \qquad (11)$$

$$\quad (33) \qquad\quad (34) \qquad\qquad\qquad (35) \qquad\qquad\qquad (36)$$

substituent in the aldehyde was necessary for the reaction to proceed to the product. If an electron-donating group were on the ring, only an adduct would form, which would not decompose to the epoxide. Some representative yields are given in Table 4. This reaction was recently used by Newman[122] to prepare 38 in 81% yield (the first

TABLE 4. Syntheses with trisdimethylaminophosphine (**34**)[121].

Aldehyde	% Yield	*trans/cis* ratio
o-Chlorobenzaldehyde	90	1·38
p-Chlorobenzaldehyde	40	4·0
m-Nitrobenzaldehyde	80	2·9
p-Formylbenzaldehyde	95	1·1
1-Naphthaldehyde	80	1·1
2-Thienylaldehyde	87	1·1

epoxide formally derived from an aromatic compound). The product rearranged on treatment with acid to 9-phenanthrol.

$$\underset{(37)}{} \xrightarrow[C_6H_6]{P[NMe_2]_3} \underset{(38)}{} \tag{12}$$

3. Carbenes

Singlet methylene in comparison to triplet methylene has been shown to add to acetone to give isobutylene oxide[123]. This fact readily explains why diphenylcarbene reacts with aldehydes to give the corresponding epoxide[124].

4. Sulfonium and oxosulfonium ylides

Corey and Chaykovsky[125,126] were the first to use dimethyloxosulfonium methylide (**39**) and dimethylsulfonium methylide (**40**) for the

$$\underset{(39)}{Me_2\overset{+}{S}\overset{O}{\diagdown}_{CH_2^-}} \qquad \underset{(40)}{Me_2\overset{+}{S}=\overset{-}{C}H}$$

synthesis of epoxides. They found that the oxoylide (**39**) was more reactive and gave several different products while the sulfonium methylide (**40**) would give only epoxides, in yields of 55–97%. A complete

13 + c.e.l.

description of their techniques has now been published[127]. Franzen has also reported syntheses with these ylides[128].

$$(C_6H_5)_2CO + Me_2\overset{+}{S}O\overset{-}{C}H_2 \longrightarrow (C_6H_5)_2\overset{O}{\overset{\triangle}{C---CH_2}} + Me_2SO \qquad (13)$$
$$\quad (28) \qquad\qquad (39) \qquad\qquad\qquad\qquad (31) \qquad\qquad (41)$$

The stereochemical behavior of these two ylides has been a topic of major interest. Johnson and his coworkers[129] have shown that when diphenylsulfonium benzylide reacts with benzaldehyde, the stilbene oxide produced (72% yield) is stereospecifically *trans*. Bly and Bly[130] have shown that dimethyl oxoylide with bicyclo[2.2.1]heptane-7-one (42) gives the *anti*-epoxide (43) exclusively. The rearrangement of this

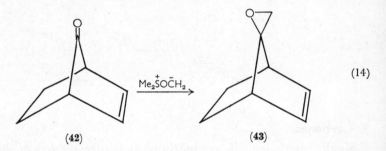

$$(14)$$

$$(42) \qquad\qquad\qquad\qquad\qquad (43)$$

epoxide to the aldehyde will be commented on under section III.E. The greater steric effects and more strenuous experimental requirements of the diphenylsulfonium benzylide are evident since with cyclohexanone it did not give a product under normal conditions, but only at low temperature (−70 to −50°) and in the presence of a stronger base (phenyllithium).

Corey[127] extensively discussed the similarities and differences of the reagents, of the types of reactions, and of the influence of groups, etc., in epoxidation. He pointed out that the oxosulfonium ylide reacts by the equatorial addition of methylene, while the sulfonium ylide gives a preference for axial addition. To illustrate this, Corey showed that the dimethyl ylide (40) when reacting with 4-*t*-butyl-cyclohexanone, for example, gives a stereospecific reaction to give one epoxide in 90% yield. This epoxide could be reduced to pure *trans*-4-*t*-butyl-1-methylcyclohexanol.

The stereospecificity involved was recently carried to its ultimate with steroids when it was reported that the oxoylide 39 reacted with a

3-keto steroid to form only the α-oxide (oxygen axial) in 79% yield and the ylide **40** reacted with the same ketone to form only the β-oxide (oxygen equatorial) in 90% yield[131].

$$
\begin{array}{c}
\text{(44)} \xrightarrow{\overset{+}{Me_2}\overset{..}{S}O\overline{C}H_2} \quad \text{(45) } \alpha\text{-oxide} \\[2em]
\xrightarrow{\overset{+}{Me_2}\overset{..}{S}\overline{C}H_2} \quad \text{(46) } \beta\text{-oxide}
\end{array}
\tag{15}
$$

5. Nitric acid

The use of 90–100% nitric acid on tetra-(p-nitrophenyl)ethylene at 0° gave the corresponding epoxide[132]. This is the first reported case of this type of epoxidation and it is undoubtedly due to the high electrophilicity of the double bond.

6. Oxygen

Cvetanovic[133] has extensively studied the direct formation of an epoxide from an olefin and oxygen in the gas phase. The mechanism of this reaction in the liquid phase has been studied by Brill[134] who showed that intermediate hydroperoxy species were involved and that 50% yields of epoxide were possible. Subsequently, Indictor and Brill[135] have shown that t-butyl hydroperoxide would work and that the epoxidation is catalyzed by metal acetylacetonates. Others have measured the rates of the oxygen reaction with cyclic olefins[136] and it appears that the same types of intermediates seem to be involved in the pyrolysis of peroxides[137]. Some of the mechanistic postulates of the previous workers have been supported, for a recent isotopic carbon study of the reaction indicated that hydrogen-atom shifts do occur in this reaction[138].

This type of method has been found to be especially effective for the synthesis of epoxides of the highly negatively substituted olefins, for it works well for the preparation of the tetracyano-[139] and tetrafluoroethylene[140] epoxides. In the latter, either heat, ultraviolet light, or ionizing radiation is effective in initiating the reaction. A similar type of reaction is the photosensitized oxidation of hydroxy olefins of steroids with hematoporphyrin and oxygen to give an epoxide in a stereospecific reaction [141].

C. Chloro Epoxides

One interesting type of epoxide is the chloro epoxide which has been shown to be stable under certain conditions (however, see section III.G). The initial attempt to prepare chloro epoxides was made in the 1880's [142]; however, Walling and Fredericks [143] were the first to show that the simplest member could be synthesized and, interestingly, by a free-radical reaction (equation 16). This synthesis fails with other

$$
\underset{(47)}{\overset{O}{CH_2\!-\!CH_2}} + \underset{(48)}{Me_3COCl} \longrightarrow \underset{(49)}{\overset{O}{CH_2\!-\!CHCl}} + \underset{(50)}{Me_3COH} \qquad (16)
$$

chlorinating agents, such as chlorine [144]. A second synthesis is the acid-catalyzed decomposition of monochloroethylene carbonate in 34%

$$
\underset{(51)}{\overset{H_2C\!-\!CHCl}{\underset{OC\diagdown O\diagup CO}{|}}} \overset{H_2SO_4}{\underset{\Delta}{\longrightarrow}} \underset{(49)}{\overset{O}{H_2C\!-\!CHCl}} \overset{Standing.}{\longrightarrow} \underset{(52)}{ClCH_2CHO} \qquad (17)
$$

yield (equation 17) [145]. Phenylated derivatives are more readily synthesized and have greater stability. A recent synthetic sequence is that described in equations (18) and (19) [146]. Other attempts at the

$$
\underset{(53)}{C_6H_5CCl_2CO_2Me} \overset{LiAlH_4}{\longrightarrow} \underset{(54)}{C_6H_5CCl_2CH_2OH} \qquad (18)
$$

$$
\underset{}{54} \overset{NaOH}{\underset{61\%}{\longrightarrow}} \underset{(55)}{\overset{Cl}{\underset{O}{C_6H_5C\!-\!CH_2}}} \longrightarrow \underset{(56)}{C_6H_5COCH_2Cl} \qquad (19)
$$

synthesis of the phenylchloro epoxides have led to rearranged products (see section III.E).

D. Oxirenes

A final topic to be considered in epoxide syntheses is the attempted preparation and possible existence of acetylene oxides or oxirenes. Before 1958 little effort had been made to synthesize these compounds. The attempts have been described by Franzen[147].

In the same paper, Franzen described an experiment of his which, if successful, would have been evidence for the oxirene **60**. However, the intermediate **58** did not react as planned, for the product did not show the expected scrambling of the isotopic labeling in the resultant acid (equation 20).

$$(C_6H_5)_2C={}^{14}C=O \longrightarrow \text{Products}$$
$$(59)$$

$$\uparrow$$

$$C_6H_5{}^{14}COCN_2C_6H_5 \longrightarrow C_6H_5{}^{14}CO-\ddot{C}-C_6H_5 \longrightarrow$$
$$(57) \qquad\qquad\qquad (58)$$

$$[C_6H_5{}^{14}C={}^{14}CC_6H_5] \longrightarrow (C_6H_5)_2{}^{14}CH{}^{14}CO_2H$$
$$(60) \qquad\qquad\qquad (61)$$

$$(20)$$

Two other groups of workers have tried a more direct method of synthesis, which utilized a classical epoxide synthesis technique[148,149]. Both groups used diphenylacetylene (**62**) and one also used phenylacetylene[148]. Both groups postulated the existence of the oxirene

$$\left[\underset{(63)}{C_6H_5C\!\!\!\overset{O}{\triangle}\!\!\!CC_6H_5} \right]$$
and/or

$$C_6H_5C\equiv CC_6H_5 \xrightarrow{RCO_3H} \left[\underset{(64)}{C_6H_5C\!\!\!\overset{O}{\square}\!\!\!CC_6H_5} \right] \longrightarrow \underset{5-51\%}{C_6H_5COCOC_6H_5} \quad (21)$$
$$(62)$$
and/or

$$\left[C_6H_5C\!\!\!\overset{\overset{+}{O}H}{=}\!\!\!CC_6H_5 \right]$$

intermediate **63** and one group suggested that additional dioxy compounds could be involved as intermediates[149]. Phenylacetylene gave phenylacetic acid (38%) and benzoic acid (25%) under the reaction conditions.

III. REACTIONS OF EPOXIDES

A. General Reactions

I. Oxidation

Epoxides have been found to give α-hydroxy ketones in yields of 55–75% when they are oxidized with dimethyl sulfoxide in the presence of BF_3 (equation 22)[150].

$$C_6H_5\overset{O}{\overset{\displaystyle\frown}{CH}}{-}CH_2 + Me_2SO \xrightarrow{BF_3} C_6H_5COCH_2OH + Me_2S \qquad (22)$$
$$\text{(65)} \qquad\qquad \text{(66)} \qquad\qquad\quad \text{(67)} \qquad\quad \text{(68)}$$

2. Reduction

The study of Eliel and Rerick[151,152] on the lithium aluminum hydride reduction of epoxides to alcohols, where they showed that the hydride attacks the least substituted position of the epoxide, is still the major study in this area. Subsequent work has shown that mixtures of alcohols can result from substituted styrene oxides and that the ratio produced indicates that bond breaking has progressed further than bond formation in the transition state[153]. This relates to the greater stability of the benzyl carbonium ion relative to the 2-phenethyl carbonium ion, one of which would be involved as an intermediate in the transition state[154]. Other hydride compounds such as diborane[155] and $LiAlH(O\text{-}t\text{-}Bu)_3$[156] also give an alcohol, however, the latter reagent is a slow-reacting species.

Two reductions of stereochemical interest can be mentioned. The first is the reduction of 4-*trans*-*t*-butylcyclohexene oxide with pure lithium aluminum hydride to give 90% 4-*trans*-alcohol and 10% *cis*-3-alcohol (the *cis* oxide gives the opposite ratio in the same amounts) and with the hydride plus aluminum chloride to give (by equatorial attack) stereospecifically pure 3-*trans*-alcohol[157]. The use of lithium aluminum deuteride indicated that the formation of the minor product followed the sequence outlined in equations (23) and (24). The second reduction is that of *exo*-norbornene oxide with lithium aluminum hydride to give a mixture of 2-*exo*-alcohol and 7-norborneol[158]. It was

$$(23)$$

$$\textbf{(69)} \qquad\qquad \textbf{(70)} \qquad\qquad \textbf{(71)}$$

$$(24)$$

$$\textbf{(71)} \qquad\qquad \textbf{(72)}$$

found that the ratio of products depends on the solvent and temperature of the reaction. A carbonium ion intermediate is obviously involved.

In catalytic reductions of epoxides, Pd–C with hydrogen gives high stereospecificity[159,160] and Raney nickel low selectivity[159,160] with cyclic oxides. Hydrogenation with $[Co^{II}(CN)_5]^{3-}$ as catalyst affords only 2-phenethyl alcohol from styrene oxide[161].

3. Formation of heterocyclic compounds

A number of different heterocyclic compounds are formed from epoxides of various structures with specific reagents. α-Acetylene epoxides with phosphines form 1-phospholine oxides[162], β-acetylene epoxides with phosphines give lactones[163], 3,4-epoxy esters with BF_3 form tetrahydrofurans[164], epoxides with ketones form 2,3-dihydrofurans[165], and epoxides with anhydrous hydrogen fluoride form dioxolanes[166].

There are many reactions with amines and hydrazines which can be mentioned. Carboethoxyhydrazine with epoxides forms tetrahydrooxadiazinones[167], butadiene dioxide with hydrazine gives 1,4-addition to form piperidazine, and 1,2-disubstituted hydrazines with epoxides give pyrazolidines[168,169]. Epoxides with diimides give imidazolidones[170], with cyanamides give oxazolidines[171], with carbon disulfide and an amine salt give cyclic carbamates or thiocarbamates[172,173], with amines give isooxazolopyrazines and azetidinium salts[174], and 1-chloro epoxides with thiourea give 2-aminothiazoles[175]. The first known displacement reaction of an epoxide on an alkyl halide (benzyl bromide) under mild conditions was utilized by having the intermediate form a piperazine upon the addition of an amine[176].

B. Specific Reagents

One novel reaction of epoxides discovered by Eisenmann[177] involves the reaction of carbon monoxide, metal carbonyl, alcohol, and an epoxide to form β-hydroxy esters in yields of 20–40% (equation 25).

$$CH_3CH\!-\!CH_2 + CO + CH_3OH + Co_2(CO)_2 \longrightarrow CH_3\overset{OH}{\underset{|}{CH}}CH_2CO_2CH_3 \qquad (25)$$

$$\text{(73)} \qquad\qquad \text{(74)} \qquad \text{(75)} \qquad\qquad \text{(76)}$$

This reaction was further studied by Heck[178] who gave a mechanistic explanation of the reaction, and by other workers who showed that aldehydes could also be obtained[179,180]. It was also shown that alcohols, ketones, ethers, and esters accelerate the reaction of $Co(CO)_8$ with epoxides[181]. Eisenmann[182] has reported that epoxides can be rearranged to ketones in 70–80% yield with the same catalyst.

The unusual deoxygenation of epoxides with phosphines as first reported by Denney[183] has been studied from a mechanistic point of view by Bissing[184]. He found that the equilibria in equation (26) are

$$R_3^3P + R^1HC\!-\!CHR^2 \;\rightleftharpoons\; R_3^3\overset{+}{P}\!-\!CHR^2 \longrightarrow R^1CH\!=\!CHR^2 + R_3^3PO$$
$$\underset{O^-\!-\!CHR^1}{}$$

$$\text{(77)} \qquad \text{(78)} \qquad\qquad \text{(79)} \qquad\qquad \text{(80)} \qquad\qquad \text{(81)}$$

$$R_3^3P\!=\!CHR^2 + R^1CHO \longrightarrow R_3^3PO + $$

$$\text{(82)} \qquad\qquad \text{(83)} \qquad\qquad \text{(81)} \qquad \text{(85)}$$

$$\text{(26)}$$

involved and that entropy, and not enthalpy, differences determine the product ratios[185]. Another deoxygenation reagent has been found to be potassium xanthate[186].

The formation of a cyclopropyl ring from an epoxide was reported to be possible by the action of a phosphorane salt (86) on an epoxide[187], subsequently also β-keto phosphonates were found to be effective[188]. Tomoskozi[189] has shown that mechanistically the two reagents plus phosphinates and phosphine oxides react by the same

$$\underset{\substack{| \\ C_6H_5 \\ \textbf{(86)}}}{\overset{\substack{Et \\ |}}{Me-P^+}}-CH^--C_6H_5 + \underset{\textbf{(65)}}{C_6H_5\overset{O}{\overset{\triangle}{CH-CH_2}}} \longrightarrow \underset{\textbf{(87)}}{C_6H_5\overset{CHC_6H_5}{\overset{\diagup\diagdown}{CH-CH_2}}} + \underset{\substack{| \\ C_6H_5 \\ \textbf{(88)}}}{\overset{\substack{Et \\ |}}{Me-P}\rightarrow O} \quad (27)$$

Optically active   50% Retention

mechanism. He has shown with optically active compounds that an intramolecular S_N2 process is involved with inversion occurring at the asymmetric center in active styrene oxide (equations 28 and 29).

$$\underset{\textbf{(89)}}{C_6H_5\overset{*}{CH}\overset{O}{\overset{\triangle}{-CH_2}}} + \underset{\textbf{(90)}}{\overset{PO(OEt)_2}{\overset{|}{^-CHCO_2R}}} \longrightarrow \underset{\textbf{(91)}}{\overset{\substack{O \quad PO(OEt)_2 \\ \diagup \quad \diagup \\ \quad CH}}{C_6H_5\overset{*}{H}C\text{——}CH_2}} \quad (28)$$

$$\textbf{91} \longrightarrow \underset{\textbf{(92)}}{C_6H_5\overset{CHCO_2R}{\overset{\diagup\diagdown}{{}^*CH-CH_2}}} + \underset{\textbf{(93)}}{PO_2^-(OEt)_2} \quad (29)$$

A metallic reagent of interest which reacts with epoxides is $(n\text{-Pr})_3GeBr$ which gives an alkoxy germane and this hydrolyzes to a β-bromo alcohol[190]. Selenium dioxide with an amine salt as a catalyst gives a cyclic selenite[191]. Grignard reagents on steroidal epoxides have been found to give two types of reaction, for it was discovered that an epoxide on a ring juncture gives ring opening to the substituted alcohol, however, the epoxides on 'free' sites rearrange to give the next smallest ring[192].

Tetracyanoethylene oxide (95) has been found to give quite unusual reactions, for with olefins it gives tetrahydrofurans, with acetylene it gives 3,4-dihydrofuran and with aromatics (except anthracene) it gives tetrahydrofurans (see equation 30)[121,193,194]. Anthracene gave a product where the ring attacked the 9,10-positions in the normal mode[194]. The rates of the reactions were olefin > acetylene > arene, as one might predict.

The treatment of epichlorohydrin with KCN gives a 2-cyanodi-

$$\underset{\textbf{(94)}}{C_6H_6} + \underset{\textbf{(95)}}{\overset{(CN)_2}{\underset{(CN)_2}{\triangleright O}}} \longrightarrow \underset{\textbf{(96)}}{\overset{(CN)_2}{\underset{(CN)_2}{\bigcirc}}} \quad (30)$$

hydroaniline derivative[195]. The reaction of styrene oxide with ethyl malonate[196,197] affords both 3- and 4-phenylbutyrolactone, and not just the 4-phenyl compound, with one group reporting the ratio of products to be 50:50[196] and the other 60:40[197].

An extensive study of the rates of the reactions of a large group of epoxides with potassium iodide in dioxane–water as solvent must be mentioned[198]. A number of epoxides substituted with highly complex groups were examined to determine the influence of the groups on the rates of the ring-opening reaction.

The reaction of epichlorohydrin with amines is of constant interest because of its commercial usefulness in preparing polymers and highly crosslinked materials. Under controlled conditions it is possible to prepare ammonium salts[199], quarternary hydroxides in the presence of water, and salts in the absence of water[200]. Tertiary amines do not always give a product, though under slightly different conditions instead of the expected product **100**, product **99** was given[201]. In comparison, epoxy ethers give α-aminocarbonyl compounds with

$$CH_2\!\!-\!\!CHCH_2Cl + Me_3N \longrightarrow Me_3\overset{+}{N}CH\!\!=\!\!CHCH_2OH \qquad (31)$$
$$\text{(97)} \qquad\qquad \text{(98)} \qquad\qquad \text{(99)}$$

$$Me_3\overset{+}{N}CH_2CH\!\!-\!\!\!-\!\!CH_2$$
$$\text{(100)}$$

amines[202], but with acid give hydroxy ketones by β-carbon–oxygen cleavage in a highly stereospecific manner[203]. Support for Steven's[203] mechanism for this reaction based on ^{18}O evidence has been given by Hite and his coworkers (equation 32)[204].

$$\text{(101)} \qquad\qquad\qquad \text{(102)} \qquad\qquad\qquad \text{(103)}$$

C. Acid Cleavages

Catalyzed hydrolyses of epoxides have been an area of continuing interest culminating in the work of Long and Paul[205a], who showed that there is a base-catalyzed reaction, an acid-catalyzed reaction, and a pH-independent reaction with water. Parker and Isaacs[9] further clarified these areas in their rigorous examination of the mechanisms of epoxide reactions.

Of primary importance to an understanding of the acid-catalyzed hydrolysis is the finding by two different workers that the volume of activation is negative[206, 207]. This fact lends support to the $A2$ mechanism for these hydrolyses instead of the $A1$ mechanism assigned by Long and Paul[205a] on the basis of a Hammett acidity-function correlation. Long and Paul[205a] found that there was a close relationship between the rates and h_0, which suggested that there was no water molecule in the transition state. The new data suggest that the Hammett relationship gave the wrong conclusion, which has been shown to be the case in other situations[205b] and that equation (33) depicts the reaction path.

$$\underset{\diagdown}{\overset{\diagup}{C}}\!\!-\!\!\underset{\diagdown}{\overset{\diagup}{C}} + H^+ \rightleftharpoons \underset{\diagdown}{\overset{\diagup}{C}}\!\!-\!\!\underset{\diagdown}{\overset{\diagup}{C}} \overset{H_2O}{\underset{Slow}{\longrightarrow}} \underset{|}{\overset{OH}{-C}}\!\!-\!\!\underset{|}{\overset{\overset{+}{O}H_2}{C}} \longrightarrow \underset{|}{\overset{OH}{-C}}\!\!-\!\!\underset{|}{\overset{OH}{C}}- + H^+ \quad (33)$$

Study has continued in the area of the product ratios produced with mineral-acid catalysis of ring opening[207]. The sequence in equation (34) illustrates the influence of electronegative groups. Phenyl-substi-

$$\underset{(104)}{R\!-\!\overset{\overset{\displaystyle O}{\diagup\diagdown}}{CH}\!\!-\!\!CH_2} \xrightarrow[Et_2O]{AlCl_3} \underset{(105)}{R\overset{OH}{\underset{|}{CH}}CH_2OCH_2CH_3} + \underset{(106)}{R\overset{OH}{\underset{|}{CH}}CH_2Cl} \quad (34)$$

R = ClCH₂⁻, F₃C⁻   79–92%   21– 8%

R = CH₃⁻   20–10%   80–90%

tuted epoxides gave only aldehydes when aluminum chloride was used as the catalyst[208]. The stereospecificity of ring opening of a *trans*-chlorocyclohexene oxide (107) to a *trans*-chloro-*trans*-hydroxycyclohexane ethyl ether (108) indicates an S_N2-type reaction where the halogen group enhances ether formation by depleting the electron density at the $C_{(1)}$ atom[209]. In comparison, an amide group has been found to give a neighboring-group effect in the cleavage by hydrogen chloride

$$(35)$$

(107)   **(108)**   **(109)**

trans   *trans–trans*

in benzene of *trans*-phenylglycidylate (equation 36) to give a stereo-specific ring opening involving intermediate **111**, and to produce

$$(36)$$

(110)   **(111)**   **(112)**

threo-chlorohydrin[210]. When hydrogen chloride in methanol was used the *erythro* product was formed. The *cis*-epoxide gives only *threo* product[210].

A highly inclusive study was made by Virtanen[211]; he considered the uncatalyzed cleavage reaction and two different acid-catalyzed reactions in a wide variety of solvents, with four different nucleophiles and at temperatures ranging from 20 to 80°. He found the rate of cleavage was retarded to different extents with organic solvents depending on the polarity of the solvent. In work toward the same goal, Parker has continued his studies of the transition state of the cleavage reaction and has adequately bolstered his views that bond breaking has progressed further than bond making in the transition state[212]. The yields of the two possible chlorohydrins produced from

TABLE 5. Data on the acid-catalyzed ring opening of epoxides by the chloride ion[213].

R in RCH—CH$_2$	pH	Normal product[a]		Abnormal product[a]	
		% Yield	Rate, $10^5 k_N$	% Yield	Rate, $10^5 k_A$
Ethyl	7·0	84	1·21	16	0·23
Ethenyl	7·0	14	0·5	86	3·3
Chloromethyl	7·0	100	6·30	0	<0·13
Methoxymethyl	7·0	100	1·80	0	<0·04
Ethyl	4·5	77	2·40	23	0·72
Ethyl	3·8	69	7·5	31	3·4
Ethyl	3·6	68	10·5	32	4·9

[a] See equation (38) for the meaning of normal and abnormal.

different epoxides are given in Table 5[213]. Under neutral conditions, electron-withdrawing groups accelerate the 'normal' (i.e. where the nucleophile attacks the least-substituted carbon) and retard the 'abnormal' reaction of epoxides. However, in the acid-catalyzed reaction (equations 37 and 38) electron-withdrawing groups retard the normal ring-opening reaction. Parker has explained these facts by a consideration of the preequilibrium between the epoxide (**104**) and its conjugate acid (**113**) in the acid-catalyzed reaction[213].

$$
\underset{\textbf{(104)}}{RCH\!\!-\!\!CH_2} + H_3O^+ \overset{K}{\rightleftharpoons} \underset{\textbf{(113)}}{\overset{+O-H}{RCH\!\!-\!\!CH_2}} + H_2O \qquad (37)
$$

$$
\underset{\textbf{(114)}}{\overset{+O-H}{RCH\!\!-\!\!CH_2}} + Cl^- \overset{k}{\longrightarrow} \underset{\substack{\textbf{(115)}\\ \text{Normal}}}{\overset{OH}{RCHCH_2Cl}} + \underset{\substack{\textbf{(116)}\\ \text{Abnormal}}}{\overset{Cl}{RCHCH_2OH}} \qquad (38)
$$

A number of studies have involved organic acid catalysis of cleavage[214–221]. The stereochemistry of ring opening under these conditions is *trans* as predicted, with trichloroacetic acid giving faster rates than β-chloropropionic acid[214]. The rates are first order in each reactant with acetic and related acids[215–217], and there is an approximate 20-fold increase in rate when a salt of the acid is used[215–217]; the rates are dependent on the structures of the epoxides[218]. These facts have led to the postulation of complex **117** as an intermediate in these

$$
\left[K^+ \; \underset{RCO_2^{\delta-}}{\overset{RCO_2^{\delta-}}{\cdots H^+ \cdots O\!\!-\!\!\underset{\delta\delta+}{\overset{\delta\delta-}{\triangleleft}}}} \right]
$$

$$
\textbf{(117)}
$$

TABLE 6. Products from the acid-catalyzed ring opening
of D-styrene oxide[221].

Acid	% Yield		% Inversion
	Abnormal[a]	Normal[b]	
Acetic	10	72	62
Trichloroacetic	27	65	37
Benzoic	25	54	50
Mesitoic	33	60	50

[a] Product (β-OH) resulting from attack at the α-carbon.
[b] Product (α-OH) resulting from ring opening at the β-carbon.

acid salt-catalyzed cleavages[219]. The ring opening with acetic acid has been shown to give a mixture of hydroxy acetates in which acyl migration has taken place[220, 221]. When mesitoic acid is used no migration occurs and the true ratio of products is discernable[221]. Product ratios from this type of study are given in Table 6, where the epoxide involved was the optically active D-styrene oxide[221].

D. Base Cleavages

The acidic and basic ring opening of epoxides has been compared in two systems to give interesting results. The details are given in equation (39)[222]. The rates of the reactions differ widely[223]. From

$$
\begin{array}{l}
\text{cis-epoxide} \left\{ \begin{array}{ll} \text{Basic} \longrightarrow & \text{on 2-carbon} \\ \text{Acidic} \longrightarrow & \text{on 1-carbon} \end{array} \right. \\[2em]
\underset{(118)}{C_6H_5\overset{O}{\overset{\displaystyle\frown}{CH}}\text{———}CHC_6H_5} \qquad\qquad (39) \\[2em]
\text{trans-epoxide} \left\{ \begin{array}{ll} \text{Basic} \longrightarrow & \text{on 1-carbon} \\ \text{Acidic} \longrightarrow & \text{on 2-carbon} \end{array} \right.
\end{array}
$$

Parker's studies it is known that bond breaking is far advanced in the transition state in acidic hydrolysis, thus the stability of the intermediate carbonium ion is directly involved in the acid-catalyzed reaction[212].

The base-catalyzed ring opening of epoxides normally involves a mixture of an alcohol or phenol, base, and epoxide[224]. If uncontrolled, or if appropriate conditions are used, polymers result[225]. Phenol is often used[224–229], and with it the reaction rate can be shown to be dependent on the phenolate concentration[224], and to have an activation energy of 16·6 kcal/mole with ethylene oxide[225]. There are definite steric effects which relate to the termolecular complex envisaged[227, 228], and a structure for the complex (122) has been described (equations 40 and 41)[226]. The use of alcohols in this context has also been of interest and this has led to kinetic studies with different substrates[229–231].

In the reaction of epoxides with amines, recent studies have involved measurements of rates under different conditions and with different amines[232–234], a consideration of steric effects with varying alkyl groups in the amine[235, 236], a measurement of steric and electronic effects in the epoxide[237], and a determination of the effect of catalysts[238]. A summary of the knowledge of the amine–epoxide reactions

$$C_6H_5OH + C\overset{O}{\triangle}C + C_6H_5ONa \rightleftharpoons \underset{(121)}{\underset{\underset{Na}{C_6H_5O\cdots\overset{\overset{\overset{O}{\triangle}}{H}}{\cdots}OC_6H_5}}{}} \tag{40}$$

(119) (120)

$$121 \longrightarrow \underset{(122)}{\underset{\underset{Na}{C_6H_5O\cdots\overset{\overset{O-CH_2}{\underset{CH_2}{H}}}{\cdots}OC_6H_5}}{}} \longrightarrow \underset{(123)}{C_6H_5OCH_2CH_2OH} + \underset{(120)}{C_6H_5ONa} \tag{41}$$

before 1962 is available which utilizes an application of the Hansson equation for this system[239,240]. This equation, like the Hammett equation from which it is derived, gives a correlation of multiple variations in structure as related to reactivity.

Other specific knowledge is also available. Parker and his colleagues[241–244] have studied normal (β-carbon) versus abnormal (α-carbon) attack on substituted styrene oxides (Table 7) with benzyl-

TABLE 7. Reaction of substituted styrene oxides with benzylamine in methanol[243].

Styrene oxide	% Normal isomer[a]	$10^5 k_N$[a]	$10 k_A$[b]
3,4-Dimethyl	30	3·54	8·26
p-CH$_3$	47	3·92	4·42
m-CH$_3$	61	4·45	2·84
H	62	5·67	3·48
m-CH$_3$O	57	5·52	4·16
p-Br	63	4·72	2·77
m-Cl	73	6·55	2·48
m-CF$_3$	78	5·80	1·63

Solvent effects on the reaction of styrene oxide with benzylamine[244].

Solvent	$10^7 k_N$[a]	$10^7 k_A$[b]
Methanol	582	358
Ethanol	490	138
2-Methyl-2-butanol	98	32
Acetonitrile	2·8	0·45

[a] Attack of the amine on the β-carbon of styrene oxide (rate = k_N).
[b] Rate of attack on the α-carbon.

amine and have shown that substituents and solvents greatly affect the ratios of products. Electron-withdrawing groups enhance the normal reaction, and vice versa. From their studies they were able to assign a Hammett ρ of 0.87 for the normal reaction and a ρ of -1.15 for the abnormal reaction[242]. Methanol when used as a solvent was found to give ρ values closer to zero than ethanol[243], and protic solvents were found to give a specific electrophilic assistance to ring cleavage as compared to aprotic solvents[244]. Other solvent effects on the reactions of amines with glycidyl ether were: xylene, $\rho = 0.70$; 1,1,2,2-tetra-chloroethane, $\rho = 0.00$; and nitrobenzene, $\rho = -0.80$[245]. The transition state for these reactions with ethylene oxide has been postulated to be **124**[246].

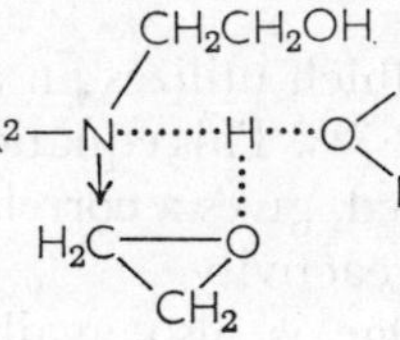

$$
\begin{array}{c}
CH_2CH_2OH \\
R^2-N\cdots\cdots H\cdots O \diagdown^{R^1}_H \\
H_2C \diagdown \diagup O \\
CH_2
\end{array}
$$

(**124**)

E. Rearrangements

Although enol ester epoxides require only heat to rearrange them to acyloxy ketones (reaction 42)[247], fortunately most epoxides are

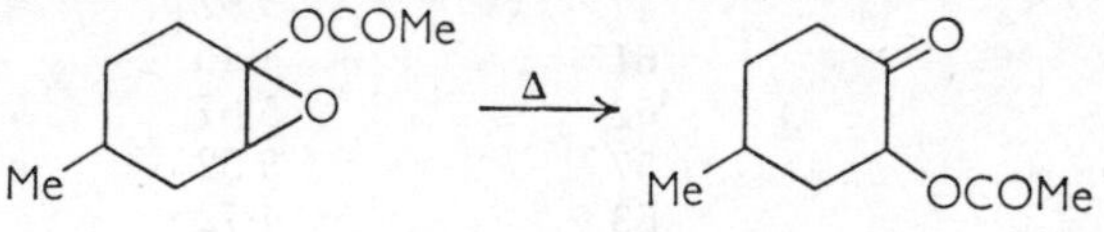

(42)

more stable. However, the acid-catalyzed rearrangement of epoxides to carbonyl compounds is a constant threat in their synthesis with peresters. For this reason the recently discovered syntheses which occur at pH 8–9 (see section II.A) are especially important.

A peracid-caused rearrangement was evident in the attempted synthesis of the monoepoxide of bicyclo[2.2.1]heptadiene (**125**) where bicyclo[3.0.1]-1-hexene-6-carboxaldehyde (**126**) was produced in 70% yield[248]. This has been shown to occur via the acid-catalyzed rearrangement of the intermediate epoxide[249]. Also, in the attempted synthesis of a chloro epoxide of 1,2-diphenylethylene, ring opening with

$$\text{(125)} \quad \xrightarrow{\text{Peracid}} \quad \text{(126)} \quad \text{—CHO} \qquad (43)$$

chlorine atom migration occurred to form a chloro ketone (equation 44) [250, 251]. It was further discovered that in acylic and alicyclic systems

$$\underset{\text{(127)}}{\overset{\displaystyle C_6H_5}{\underset{H}{>}}C=C\overset{\displaystyle Cl}{\underset{C_6H_5}{<}}} \xrightarrow{\text{Peracid}} \underset{\text{(128)}}{\overset{\displaystyle C_6H_5}{\underset{H}{>}}C\overset{O}{\underset{}{\triangle}}C\overset{\displaystyle Cl}{\underset{C_6H_5}{<}}} \xrightarrow{H^+} \underset{\text{(129)}}{C_6H_5\overset{\displaystyle Cl}{\underset{}{C}}HCOC_6H_5} \qquad (44)$$

both hydrogen and chlorine can migrate [252]. Another rearrangement involving chlorine attachment followed by chlorine removal is that in equations (45) and (46) [253].

$$\underset{\text{(97)}}{CH_2\overset{O}{\underset{}{\triangle}}CHCH_2Cl} \xrightarrow[\text{FeCl}_3]{\text{RMgX}} \underset{\text{(130)}}{ClCH_2COCH_2Cl} \qquad (45)$$

$$130 \xrightarrow{\text{RMgX}} \underset{\text{(131)}}{ClCH_2\overset{O^-}{\underset{R}{C}}CH_2Cl} \xrightarrow{\text{FeCl}_3} \underset{\text{(132)}}{\triangle\overset{OH}{\underset{R}{<}}} \qquad (46)$$

The specific rearrangement of a monosubstituted epoxide to an aldehyde has been used as a synthetic tool in simple systems [254], and also in complex bicyclic systems [130]. An excellent example is the rearrangement of α-pinene oxide (133) [255], which was based on a previous

$$\underset{\text{(133)}}{\text{[structure]}} \xrightarrow{H^+} \underset{\text{(134)}}{\text{—CHO}} \quad \text{and not} \quad \underset{\text{(135)}}{\text{[structure]}} \qquad (47)$$

report[256]. Almost concurrent with the use of this rearrangement, in an attempt to synthesize the ketone, it was reported that a mixture of an aldehyde and ketones is produced by the action of zinc bromide on limonene (**136**) and carvementhene oxides[257]. Even an acid-

$$(48)$$

(**136**)   (**134**)   (**137**)   (**138**)

washed gas chromatographic column was found to be sufficiently reactive to rearrange caryophyllene oxide[258]. In chalcone epoxides, the effect of substituents in the rings has been found to influence the product percentages, as one might predict[259]. An attempt to form a bicyclic oxide from an epoxy olefin by rearrangement failed[260].

As mentioned in section II.B.4, the epoxide **43** produced by Bly and Bly[130] in their study of the bicyclic ketone **42** was found to give a rearrangement to an aldehyde with BF$_3$. The rearrangement was found to occur stereospecifically and they postulated the mechanism shown in

$$(49)$$

(**139**)   (**140**)

(**141**)   (**142**)

equation (49), involving a π-bridged intermediate carbonium ion (**140**). The interaction of BF_3 with steroid epoxides has been studied by Hartshorn and Kirk[261–263] who showed that either methyl or methylene migration can occur. For example when the 4,5-epoxy ketones of cholestane were studied, the α,α-epoxide (4-equatorial oxygen) gave the A-nor-B-homo product and the β,β-epoxide (4-axial oxygen) gave methyl migration and no ring-size changes[261]. The migration ratios when the epoxide group is in various other positions are also dependent on stereochemistry; 'axial cleavage' has been shown to be preferred to 'equatorial cleavage'[261,262]. The presence or absence of groups, such as the acetoxy group, in various positions has also been found to affect the migration ratios[263].

Other agents which cause rearrangement are the phosphine oxides which have been shown to give both stereochemical isomerization, as well as cause a rearrangement to carbonyl products, with the phosphine oxide recovered unchanged[264].

Transannular hydride shifts in the reactions of epoxides were first reported by Cope[265,266] some years ago. He showed recently that trifluoroacetic acid would give 100% transannular rearrangement with *cis*-cyclooctene oxide[265]. The hydride shifts are either 1,3- or 1,5-migrations[266]. In comparison, 1-octene oxide with trifluoroacetic acid gave mainly 1,2-diol, with only 0·7% of the 1,3-diol, 0·5% of the 1,4-diol, 0·3% of the 1,5-diol, 0·2% of the 1,6-diol, and 0·1% of the 1,7-diol[267]. The peracid on the olefin gave only 1-octene oxide. When an olefinic group was present in the cyclooctene oxide, the acid-catalyzed reaction gave at least five different products and thermal isomerization gave 1,2- and 1,5-hydride shifts, ring contraction, and other reactions[268].

The base-catalyzed ring openings and rearrangements of epoxides are few, but quite novel. Payne[269] found that reaction (50) occurred

$$\underset{\textbf{(143)}}{\overset{O}{\underset{}{\triangle}}}\text{CH}_2\text{—CHCMe}_2 \xrightarrow[\text{NaOH}]{\text{aq.}} \text{HOCH}_2\text{CH}\underset{\textbf{(144)}}{\overset{O}{\underset{}{\triangle}}}\text{CMe}_2 \qquad (50)$$

in 92% yield. The formation of a primary alcohol from a tertiary alcohol is unusual, but has been reported previously[270]. The reaction of a halo-substituted epoxide (**145**) definitely did not proceed as expected (equation 51), but rather as is illustrated in equation (52)[271]. A similar reaction was shown to occur between butyllithium and the

$$\underset{(145)}{\text{CH}_2\text{—CHCCl}_3} \xrightarrow[\quad]{\text{CH}_3\text{Li}} \; \not\to \; \underset{(146)}{\overset{\text{OH}}{\underset{|}{\text{CH}_3\text{CH}_2\text{CHCCl}_3}}} \tag{51}$$

$$\textbf{145} \xrightarrow{\text{CH}_3\text{Li}} \underset{(147)}{\text{H}_2\text{C—CHCCl}_2} \longrightarrow \underset{(148)}{\overset{\text{O}^-}{\underset{|}{\text{CH}_2\text{CH}=\text{CCl}_2}}} \tag{52}$$

monochloro epoxide (equation 53), but only the *trans* product formed from either *cis* or *trans* epoxide[272]. When phenyllithium was used the

$$\underset{(97)}{\text{ClCH}_2\text{CH—CH}_2} \xrightarrow[\text{THF}]{\text{n-BuLi}} \underset{(149)}{\overset{\text{H}}{\underset{\text{Cl}}{\diagup}} \text{C}=\text{C} \overset{\text{CH}_2\text{OH}}{\underset{\text{H}}{\diagdown}}} \tag{53}$$

normal epoxide ring opening occurred[272]. This latter type of ring opening also results when 1,1-diphenylethylene oxide (**31**) is brought into reaction with phenylmagnesium bromide. Phenyllithium gives a mixture of products from the latter epoxide, partially by a carbanion mechanism (equations 54 and 55)[273].

$$\underset{(31)}{(\text{C}_6\text{H}_5)_2\text{C—CH}_2} \xrightarrow{\text{C}_6\text{H}_5\text{Li}} \underset{(150)}{(\text{C}_6\text{H}_5)_2\text{C—CH}} \longrightarrow \underset{(151)}{\overset{\text{O}^-}{\underset{|}{(\text{C}_6\text{H}_5)_2\text{C}=\text{CH}}}} \tag{54}$$

$$\textbf{151} \longrightarrow \underset{(152)}{(\text{C}_6\text{H}_5)_2\text{CH—CHO}} \xrightarrow{\text{C}_6\text{H}_5\text{Li}} \underset{(153)}{\overset{\text{OH}}{\underset{|}{(\text{C}_6\text{H}_5)_2\text{CHCHC}_6\text{H}_5}}} \tag{55}$$

What is probably the most outstanding item in the base-catalyzed rearrangements of epoxides is the postulation of a carbene intermediate (**156**)[274]. The reaction is outlined in equation (56). This type of carbene intermediate could also be involved in the rearrangements of cyclooctene oxide with base as reported by Cope and his co-workers[265, 266].

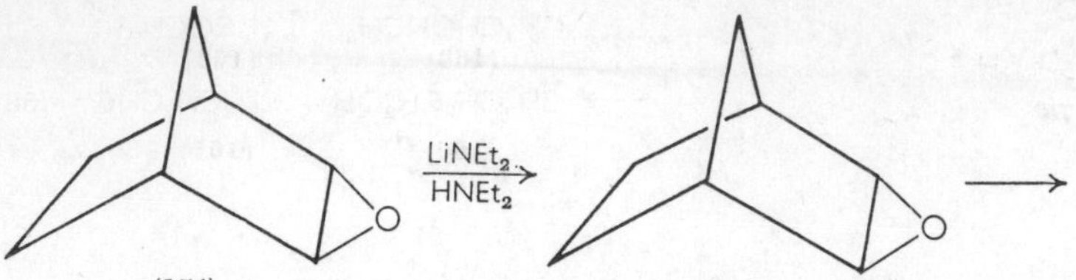

(154) (155)

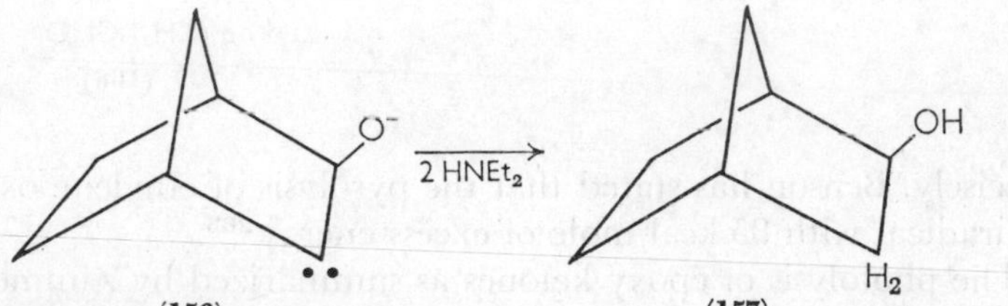

(156) (157)

(56)

F. Photochemistry

The photolytic transformation of epoxides to other products has been of interest for many years. Cvetanovic[275] has given many of the details and Zimmerman[276] has summarized much of the available knowledge in his writings on mechanistic photochemistry.

Much of the initial photochemical research with epoxides involved gas-phase photolyses with ethylene oxide in which acetaldehyde was the major product[277,278]. Further studies with more complex epoxides indicated that aldehydes were also produced[279], apparently by a free-radical rearrangement of an alkyl group or hydrogen atom (equation 57). No other example of a free-radical alkyl group or hydrogen-atom shift had previously been reported[280].

$$CH_3CH \overset{O}{\diagdown\!\!\diagup} CHCH_3 \xrightarrow{h\nu} (CH_3)_2CHCHO \qquad (57)$$

(158) (159)

A reaction of epoxides which involves ring opening would be expected to proceed with difficulty[281], and the low yield of products from the liquid-phase photolysis of various epoxides bears this out[282]. The action of ultraviolet light on a neat epoxide was found to give epoxide ring opening (equations 58 and 59), in both possible modes to give two different diradical intermediates[282]. No rearranged products were found even when the tests for aldehyde were carried out very

$$\underset{(73)}{CH_3CH\overset{O}{\overline{}}CH_2} \xrightarrow{h\nu} Diradicals \left[\begin{array}{l} \longrightarrow \underset{(163)}{Cl\,I_3CHOHCH_3} + \underset{(162)}{CH_3COCH_3} \\ \longrightarrow \underset{(160)}{CH_3CH_2CH_2OH} + \underset{(161)}{CH_3CH_2CHO} \quad (58) \end{array} \right.$$

$$\underset{(158)}{CH_3CH\overset{O}{\overline{}}CHCH_3} \xrightarrow{h\nu} Diradicals \longrightarrow \underset{(164)}{CH_3CH_2CHOHCH_3} + \underset{(165)}{CH_3CH_2COCH_3}$$

$$\text{and no } \underset{(166)}{(CH_3)_2CHO} \qquad (59)$$

precisely. Benson has stated that the pyrolysis of ethylene oxide gives a diradical with 85 kcal/mole of excess energy[283].

The photolysis of epoxy ketones as summarized by Zimmerman[276] and extensively studied by him had a much greater yield than those photochemical reactions mentioned above. This is undoubtedly because the energy is absorbed by the molecule via the carbonyl and not the epoxide group. Two different reaction paths have been postulated by Zimmerman[284] in these reactions, the first involving the formation of an unsaturated hydroxy ketone (168)[285,286], and the second the formation of a saturated diketone (170)[287,288]. If an alkyl

$$\underset{(167)}{CH_3CH\overset{O}{\overline{}}CHCO-} \longrightarrow \underset{(168)}{CH_2{=}CHCHOHCO-} \qquad (60)$$

$$\underset{\underset{R}{|}}{-C}\overset{O}{\overline{}}\underset{(169)}{CHCO-} \longrightarrow -CO\underset{\underset{R}{|}}{-}\underset{(170)}{CHCO-} \qquad (61)$$

group is present it will migrate but a phenyl group will not[287,288]. Jeger[289] has suggested that the migrating group actually becomes free in the alkyl shift. This reaction appears to support the findings of Cvetanovic[279].

Another type of photochemical rearrangement involves the valence tautomerism of cyclic epoxy ketones to pyrylium salts (172) and pyrones. Ullman[290-292] discovered and has examined this transformation, although others have studied somewhat similar systems[293,294].

In 2,3-diphenylindenone oxide (**171**) the energy requirement for re-arrangement is greater than 68 kcal/mole, however, if *trans*-stilbene

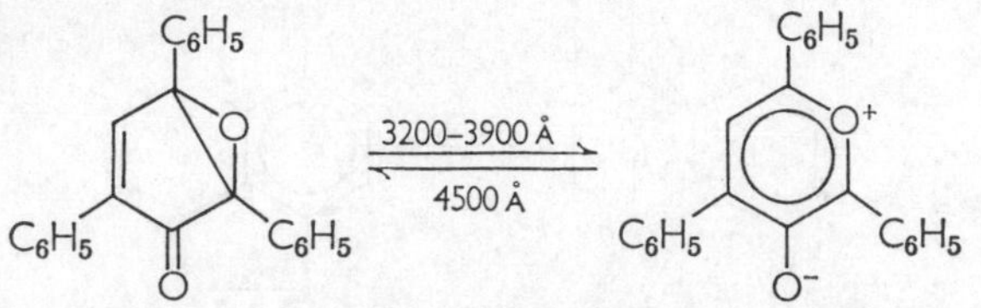

$$(62)$$

(**171**)　　　　　　　　　　(**172**)

(**173**) or certain other compounds are added the reaction will occur with a much lower activation energy. This is schematized in equations (63), (64), and (65). This reaction sequence has resulted in **171** being

$$C_6H_5CH{=}CHC_6H_5 \xrightarrow{\text{u.v.}} C_6H_5\overset{\uparrow\bullet}{CH}{-}\overset{\uparrow\bullet}{CH}C_6H_5 \qquad (63)$$

(**173**)　　　　　　　　　　(**174**)

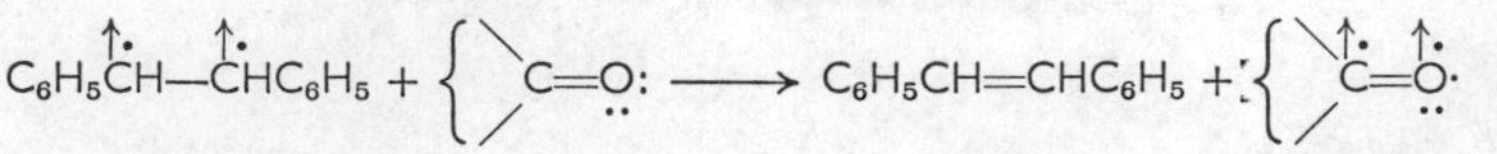

$$(64)$$

(**174**)　　　　　　　　(**175**)　　　　　　　(**176**)

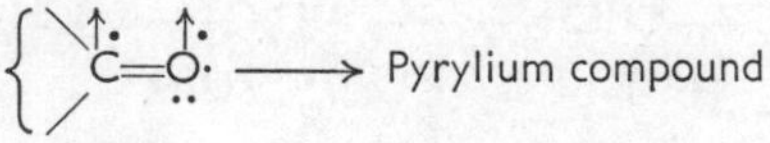

$$(65)$$

(**176**)　　　　　　　　　(**172**)

designated as a triplet-state indicator[292]. A final valence tautomerism involves either the formation of a pyrylium compound (**179**) or a pyrone (**177**)[293]. A somewhat similar photochemical dienone–phenol

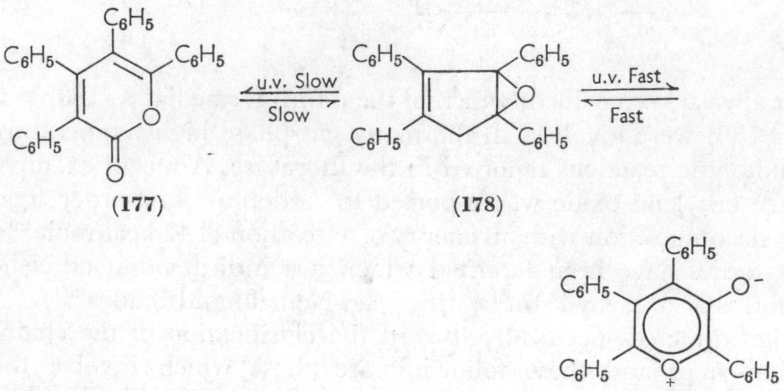

(**177**)　　　　　　　　　　(**178**)

$$(66)$$

(**179**)

rearrangement involving a five-membered oxide ring can be mentioned in this context purely for comparison purposes (equation 67) [295].

$$(67)$$

$$(180) \qquad (181)$$

G. Free-radical Chemistry

The free-radical reactions of epoxides involve four different types of reactions as chain-initiation steps, given in equations (68) to (71). It

$$(68)$$

$$(182) \qquad (183)$$

$$(69)$$

$$(182) \qquad (184)$$

$$(70)$$

$$(182) \qquad (185)$$

$$(71)$$

$$(182) \qquad (186)$$

has not always been evident which of the four intermediates (**183, 184, 185,** or **186**) were involved in the many gas-phase high temperature and photolytic reactions reported in the literature. A recent example is where ethylene oxide was reported to undergo a first-order free-radical decomposition with an energy of activation of 42 kcal/mole [296]. Many studies have been reported which just indicate that ethylene oxide forms acetaldehyde on heating (e.g. Neufeld and Blades [297]).

Studies directed specifically toward the clarification of the chain-initiation steps and those following are those which involve the presence of radical-trapping species, such as olefin and chlorine. The alkyl peroxide-catalyzed reaction of epoxides was shown to involve several different types of free-radical reactions and to be quite consistent mechanistically for a variety of epoxides[298]. The sequence is outlined in equations (72) to (75). From the yields of product, 11% of ketone **191**, it is evident that the first reaction proceeds with difficulty.

$$CH_3\overset{\displaystyle O}{\overset{\displaystyle \diagup\diagdown}{CH}}\text{---}CH_2 + RO\cdot \longrightarrow CH_3\overset{\displaystyle O}{\overset{\displaystyle \diagup\diagdown}{\underset{\displaystyle \cdot}{C}}}\text{---}CH_2 + ROH \qquad (72)$$
$$\text{(73)} \qquad\qquad\qquad \text{(187)}$$

$$CH_3\overset{\displaystyle O}{\overset{\displaystyle \diagup\diagdown}{\underset{\displaystyle \cdot}{C}}}\text{---}CH_2 \longrightarrow CH_3COCH_2\cdot \qquad (73)$$
$$\text{(187)} \qquad\qquad \text{(188)}$$

$$CH_3COCH_2\cdot + CH_2{=}CHC_6H_{13} \longrightarrow CH_3COCH_2CH_2\overset{\displaystyle \cdot}{C}HC_6H_{13} \longrightarrow \text{2-Hendecanone} \qquad (74)$$
$$\text{(188)} \qquad\quad \text{(189)} \qquad\qquad\qquad \text{(190)} \qquad\qquad\qquad\qquad \text{(191)}$$

$$CH_3COCH_2\cdot + CH_3\overset{\displaystyle O}{\overset{\displaystyle \diagup\diagdown}{CH}}\text{---}CH_2 \longrightarrow CH_3COCH_2\overset{\displaystyle \overset{\displaystyle O\cdot}{|}}{C}H_2CHCH_3 \longrightarrow$$
$$\text{(188)} \qquad\qquad \text{(73)} \qquad\qquad\qquad\qquad \text{(192)}$$
$$CH_3COCH_2CH_2CHOHCH_3 \quad (75)$$
$$\text{(193)}$$

This could be expected from the known hybridization of the carbon–hydrogen bond broken in equation (72)[13]. The rearrangement to the keto radical (equation 73) was found to occur with every epoxide. The olefin-addition reaction occurred readily when sufficient olefin was present, but the free-radical displacement reaction (equation 75) began to compete as the temperature of the reaction was raised to 200°[298]. An attempt was made to study the mechanism of this displacement reaction more extensively, however, it failed with cyclohexene oxide[299]. A similar result was reported in section I.E in the attempted free-radical polymerization of propylene oxide by this method[89].

The formation of the acetonyl radical **188** from the epoxide radical **187** has been studied by a comparison of the rates of decomposition of benzoyl peroxide in propylene oxide and in acetone[300]. Of special interest were the rates of the induced decomposition of the benzoyl peroxide in the two solvents, for the epoxy radical should, and did, give a greater rate of decomposition (0·850 l/mole h at 80°) than the acetonyl radical from acetone (0·692 l/mole h at 80°). The rearrangement reaction was found to have an activation energy of 2·7 kcal/mole[300]. This apparently is large enough for products from the epoxy free radical to be formed at ambient temperature or below, for Walling and Fredericks[143] showed that ethylene oxide could be chlorinated with t-butyl hypochlorite (equation 16). Chlorine in carbon tetrachloride has been shown to chlorinate epoxides (equations 76 and 77), however, under these conditions the product is the ring-opened

$$\overset{O}{\underset{(47)}{CH_2\!-\!-\!CH_2}} \xrightarrow{Cl_2} \underset{(52)}{ClCH_2CHO} + \underset{(194)}{ClCH_2CH_2OH} + \underset{(195)}{ClCH_2CO_2CH_2CH_2Cl} \qquad (76)$$

$$\overset{O}{\underset{(73)}{CH_3CH\!-\!-\!CH_2}} \xrightarrow{Cl_2} \underset{(196)}{ClCH_2COCH_3} \qquad (77)$$

product[144]. The presence of alcohol and ester in the product (194) indicates that a number of other free-radical reactions are also occurring.

The other type of initiation process indicated above where a carbon–hydrogen bond is broken was also shown to occur with several epoxides. This β-abstraction (equation 78) leads to another ring-opening

$$(78)$$

(197)   (198)

$$(79)$$

(198)   (199)   (200)   (201)

$$\overset{O}{\underset{(202)}{CH_3CH_2CH\!-\!-\!CH_2}} \longrightarrow \underset{(203)}{CH_3CH\!=\!CHCH_2OH} + \underset{(204)}{CH_3CH\!=\!CHCHO} \qquad (80)$$

or rearrangement reaction of epoxides (equation 79)[301]. The ring-opening reaction has also been reported by Huyser and Munson[302] who formed the intermediate free radical in a different manner (equations 81 and 82).

$$Cl_3C\cdot + CH_2{=}CHCH{-\!-}CH_2 \longrightarrow Cl_3CCH_2\overset{\cdot}{C}HCH{-\!-}CH_2 \qquad (81)$$
$$\text{(205)} \qquad \text{(206)} \qquad\qquad \text{(207)}$$

$$207 \longrightarrow Cl_3CCH_2CH{=}CHCH_2O\cdot \longrightarrow \textit{trans-Alcohol} \qquad (82)$$
$$\text{(208)}$$

The authentication of the oxide ring opening occurring in both possible modes to form two different diradical intermediates resulted from the products produced in the ultraviolet light photolyses of various epoxides (see above)[282]. The reaction is illustrated in equation (83) (cf. equations 70 and 71).

$$CH_3CH{-\!-}CH_2 \longrightarrow CH_3\overset{\cdot}{C}H{-}CH_2O\cdot + CH_3\overset{\cdot}{C}HCH_2\cdot \longrightarrow \text{Products} \quad (83)$$
$$\text{(73)} \qquad\qquad \text{(209)} \qquad\qquad \text{(210)}$$

IV. PREPARATION OF OXETANES

An extensive coverage of the syntheses of oxetanes has been made by Searles[3], and there has been a recent review, which is not as readily available, on the synthesis of the parent compound, oxetane or trimethylene oxide[303]. The synthetic methods described in these reviews mainly involve cyclizations of a 1,3-diol or its half ester[304]. Results obtained by these methods are well illustrated by the synthesis of oxetane-d_6 in 99·9% purity and in a good yield (46%)[305].

The major development in the synthesis of oxetanes is the utilization of a photochemical technique to prepare many complex compounds. This type of reaction was first carried out in 1909[306], but Buchi[307] has shown (equation 84) that many interesting products can be formed,

$$PhCHO + Me_2C{=}CHMe \xrightarrow{\text{u.v.}} \underset{Ph}{\overset{O\rule{1.2em}{0.4pt}Me}{\boxed{}}}\rule[0pt]{0pt}{0pt}Me_2 \qquad (84)$$
$$\text{(33)} \qquad\quad \text{(211)} \qquad\qquad \text{(212)}$$

and in good yield. Srinivasan[308] showed that an oxetane could be synthesized by an intramolecular reaction (equation 85) even though

$$\underset{\text{(213)}}{Me{-}\overset{\overset{\textstyle O}{\|}}{C}\underset{\underset{\textstyle CH_2{-}CH_2}{|}}{\overset{\overset{\textstyle CH_2}{\|}}{\underset{|}{C}H}}} \xrightarrow{\text{u.v.}} \underset{\text{(214)}}{Me{-}\boxed{}} \qquad (85)$$

unsubstituted oxetane had previously been shown to break down to formaldehyde and ethylene (equation 86)[309]. The development of this

$$\underset{\textbf{(215)}}{\square} \xrightarrow{\text{u.v.}} \underset{\textbf{(216)}}{\overset{\text{O}}{\underset{\text{CH}_2}{\|}}} + \underset{\textbf{(217)}}{\overset{\text{CH}_2}{\underset{\text{CH}_2}{\|}}} \tag{86}$$

synthetic method was carried forward by several workers[310,311], and Hammond[312] has reviewed the progress made up to 1963.

In work directed toward the scope and mechanism of the ketone–olefin reaction, it has been shown that with benzophenone the yield of oxetane (5–93%) depends on the olefin[313]: bulky olefins tend to give poorer yields. p-Quinone gives interesting products[314], and the reaction with benzophenone and isobutylene is of possible commercial value (yield 63%)[315]. Disubstituted olefins, such as fumaronitrile[316], and furan[310], can also be used. The intramolecular synthesis will also occur with ultraviolet light at the carbonyl group wavelength (equation 87)[317]. A slightly different mechanism operates with α-alkoxy ketones (equation 88)[318,319].

$$\underset{\textbf{(218)} \ trans}{\text{CH}_3\text{COCH}_2\text{CH}_2\underset{\text{H}}{\overset{\text{H}}{>}}\text{C}{=}\text{C}\underset{\text{CH}_3}{\overset{}{<}}} \xrightarrow{h\nu} \underset{\textbf{(219)}}{\text{CH}_3{-}\overset{\text{CH}_3}{\underset{}{\square}}{}^{\text{H}}} + \ cis\text{-}\textbf{218} \tag{87}$$

$$\underset{\textbf{(220)}}{\text{R}^1\text{COCH}_2\text{OCH}_2\text{R}^2} \xrightarrow{h\nu} \underset{\textbf{(221)}}{\text{R}^1{-}\overset{\text{OH}}{\underset{\text{O}}{\square}}{}^{\text{R}^2}} \tag{88}$$

$(\text{R}^1 = \text{C}_6\text{H}_5 \text{ or } t\text{-Bu}$
$\text{R}^2 = \text{H or Me})$

The direct mechanism studies[312,313,317,320,321] have shown that the light is first absorbed by the carbonyl group to go to the n, π^* state (ketones that will not give the n, π^* state will not give oxetanes) of the ketone (equation 89), and/or, triplet–triplet transfer can occur to give the triplet state of the olefin (equation 90). In the latter state cis to trans isomerization of the olefin can occur (equation 91), and/or, the

n, π^* state of the carbonyl reacts with the olefin in a stepwise manner which permits isomerization, and the product forms. Schematically the steps in equations (89) to (93) are operative. It is expected that

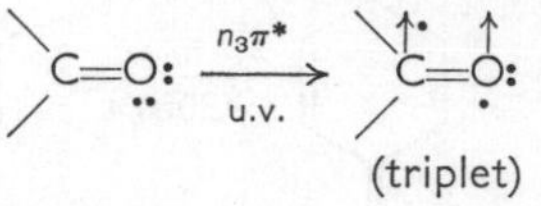

$$\diagover{C}{=}\diagover{O}{:} \xrightarrow[\text{u.v.}]{n_3\pi^*} \diagover{C}{=}\diagover{O}{:} \qquad (89)$$

(triplet)

$$\diagover{C}{=}O + \diagover{C}{=}C \longrightarrow \diagover{C}{=}O: + \diagover{C}{-}C \qquad (90)$$

trans (singlet) (triplet)

$$\text{and/or} \quad \diagover{C}{-}C \longrightarrow \diagover{C}{-}C \qquad (91)$$

trans *cis*

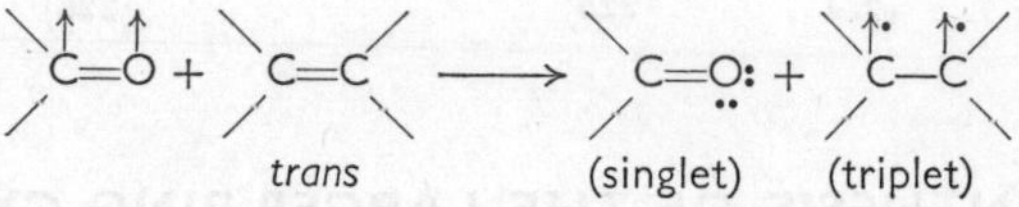

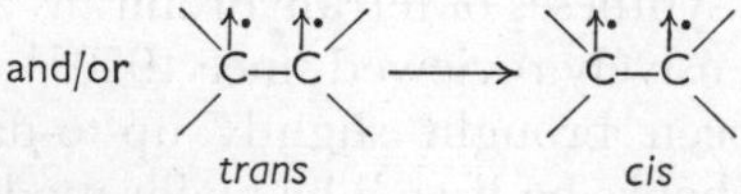

$$\text{and/or} \quad \diagover{C}{-}C + \overset{O}{\underset{\|}{C}} \longrightarrow \overset{-C-O}{\underset{C\uparrow\ C\uparrow}{}} \qquad (92)$$

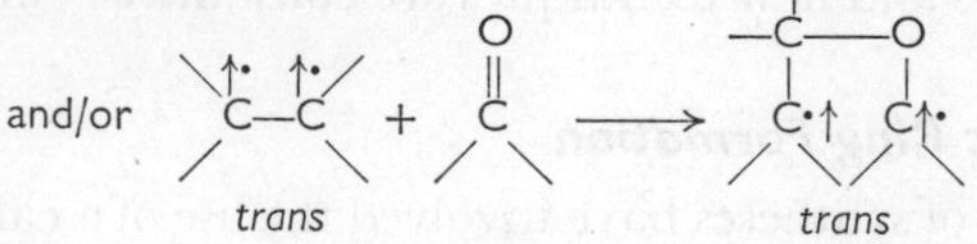

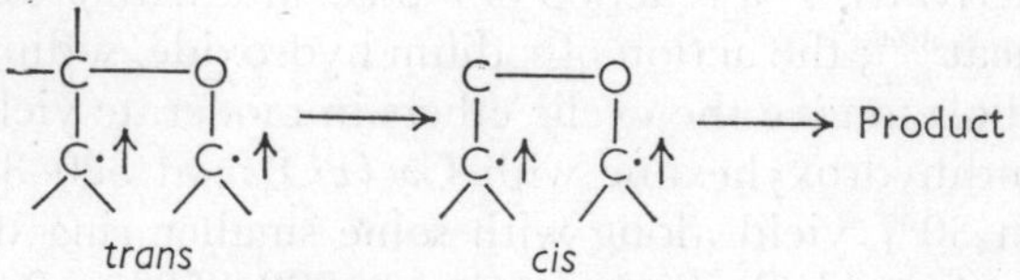

trans *trans*

$$\overset{-C-O}{\underset{C\cdot\uparrow\ C\cdot\uparrow}{}} \longrightarrow \overset{C-O}{\underset{C\cdot\uparrow\ C\cdot\uparrow}{}} \longrightarrow \text{Product} \qquad (93)$$

trans *cis*

much further clarification of the mechanism(s) of these oxetane syntheses will be forthcoming.

It has been shown also that a β-alkoxy ketone (**222**) with ultraviolet light will give a five-membered hydroxylated cyclic ether (**223**) [321],

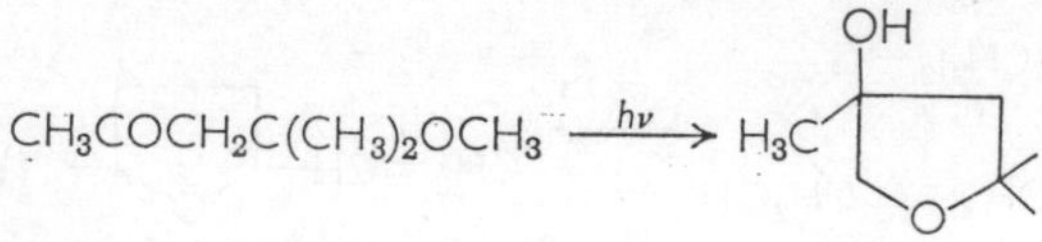

$$CH_3COCH_2C(CH_3)_2OCH_3 \xrightarrow{h\nu} \text{H}_3\text{C} \underset{O}{\overset{OH}{\diagover{}{}}} \qquad (94)$$

(**222**) (**223**)

and that an unsaturated six-membered ring can be formed from a dicnc and a quinone (equation 95)[322].

$$(95)$$

(224)   (225)   (226)

V. SYNTHESIS OF THE LARGER-RING CYCLIC ETHERS

The reactions and syntheses of tetrahydrofurans and tetrahydropyrans have not been extensively reviewed since 1950[11]; the synthesis of these compounds has been brought slightly up-to-date in an article by Topsom[4] and the books he lists. The major mode of synthesis of these compounds has been and still is by diol and halohydrin cyclization, but new reagents and new techniques are constantly being introduced.

A. Nucleophilic Ring Formation

Newer modes of syntheses have involved the use of a cation exchange resin and diols to give yields of around 80%[323] of tetrahydropyrans, furans, and their derivatives; a reaction of a diacetate with p-toluene-sulfonic acid and heat[324]; the action of sodium hydroxide, sodium sulfate, and heat on diols to give the cyclic ethers in moderate yields[325]; the reaction of 1,6-dihydroxyhexane with $Ca_3(PO_4)_2$ at 320–380° to oxacycloheptane in 30% yield along with some smaller ring derivatives[326]; the action of an Al_2O_3–SiO_2 catalyst at 220–258° on 2-substituted diols to give the corresponding cyclic ethers in yields of about 70%[327]; the reaction of diols with cyanuric chloride to give cyanuric acid and the cyclic ether[328]; a synthesis using the action of oxalic acid on a diol, isomerization also taking place (equation 96)[329]; and a cyclization by the action of dimethyl sulfoxide on the diol[330,331]. The

$$(96)$$

(227)   (228)

latter system will probably be further developed to raise the yields above the present 70% for tetrahydrofuran in 14 hours, 47% for tetrahydropyran in 24 hours, and 24% for oxacycloheptane in 24 hours, since the method appears to be simpler than many of the previous ones mentioned. Swain[117] has made an important mechanistic study of the halohydrin–hydroxide ring-closure reaction (see section II.A).

Special syntheses in the higher cyclic ether series are the photochemical ones mentioned above[321,322], hydrogenation of furan derivatives with hydrogen and nickel catalysts[332], hydrogenation with Ni–Cu catalysts to give tetrahydrofuran in 95% yield[333], hydrogenation with a ruthenium catalyst[334], a reduction of a γ-lactone with lithium aluminum hydride to a tetrahydropyran derivative[335], hydroboration of olefins to glycols which subsequently formed tetrahydrofuran derivatives[336], rearrangements of tetrahydrofuran derivatives with Al_2O_3 to tetrahydropyran derivatives (equation 97)[337], carbene

$$\text{(229)} \qquad \text{(230)} \qquad \text{(231)} \tag{97}$$

reactions with furan and methylene to give a dihydrofuran (**234**) and a tetrahydrofuran derivative (oxalan, **235**)[338], a novel diazoketone

$$\text{(232)} \qquad \text{(233)} \qquad \text{(234)} \qquad \text{Oxalan (235)} \tag{98}$$

cyclization reaction to give a 3-ketotetrahydrofuran as shown in Table 8[339], cyclization reactions of methoxybromo alkanes with $FeCl_3$ as the catalyst to give quantitative yields of tetrahydrofuran and pyran and also 75–80% of the 2-alkyltetrahydrofuran and 70% of the oxacycloheptane[340,341], cyclization of chlorohydroxy alkane to a large number of substituted cyclic ethers with sodium and potassium hydroxide as the base[342], the transformation of cyclic sulfites to tetrahydrofuran compounds[343], and various oxidations[344–360].

TABLE 8. Cyclic decomposition of a diazoketone[309].

$$ROCH_2CH_2COCHN_2 \xrightarrow{H^+} \quad \longrightarrow \quad + R^+$$

R	% Yield
Me	5
i-Pr	15
t-Bu	40
Benzyl	41

B. Oxidative Ring Formation

The oxidations are of particular interest because of their varied nature and great importance. One of the oldest is the autooxidation of hydrocarbons with oxygen and no catalyst[344,345] or with γ-irradiation initiation[346], where derivatives of all the cyclic ethers are formed. The chemistry involved has been reviewed by Fish[347]. The reaction sequence in equations (99) to (101) illustrates the reaction and the

$$Me_2CH(CH_2)_2CHMe_2 \xrightarrow{O_2} Me_2CH(CH_2)_2\overset{\bullet}{C}Me_2 \qquad (99)$$
$$\textbf{(236)} \qquad\qquad\qquad \textbf{(237)}$$

$$237 \xrightarrow[\text{Several steps}]{O_2} Me_2CH(CH_2)_2\overset{OH}{\underset{|}{C}}Me_2 \qquad (100)$$
$$\textbf{(238)}$$

$$238 \longrightarrow Me_2\overset{\bullet}{C}(CH_2)_2\overset{O-O-H}{\underset{|}{C}}Me_2 \longrightarrow Me_2\underset{O}{\diamond}Me_2 + \cdot OH \qquad (101)$$
$$\textbf{(239)} \qquad\qquad \textbf{(240)}$$

intramolecular hydrogen-atom abstraction involved[344]. This same type of reaction has been found to result when hypochlorites are decomposed in solution (equation 102)[348].

The treatment of an alcohol under conditions in which cationic oxygen is produced from an intermediate hypochlorite was utilized by

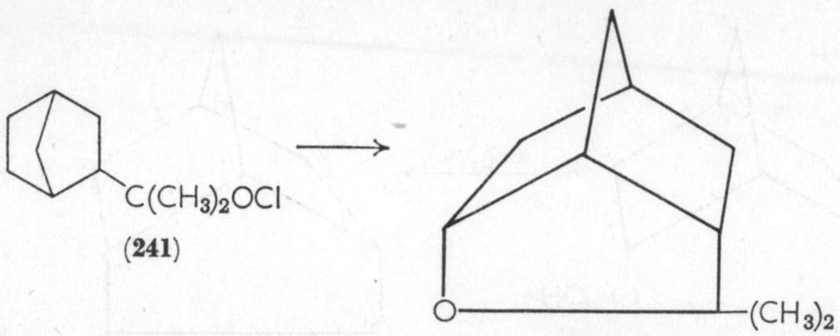

Corey[350] to prepare a tetrahydrofuran derivative (equation 103). This reaction has recently been expanded by using silver oxide and bromine

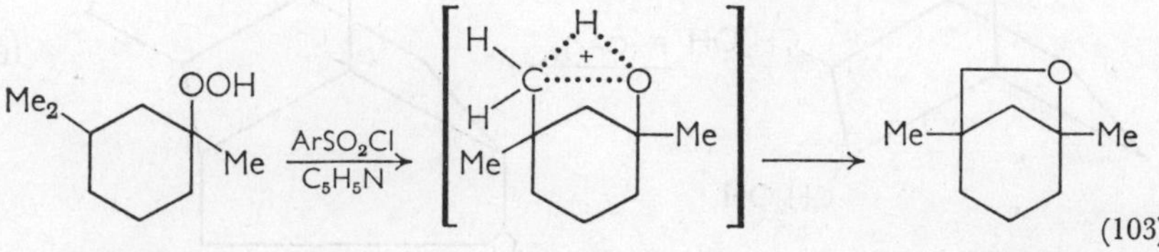

on an alcohol to give yields of cyclic oxide of over 50% (equation 104)[351]. Instead of the mechanism as shown above with a positive

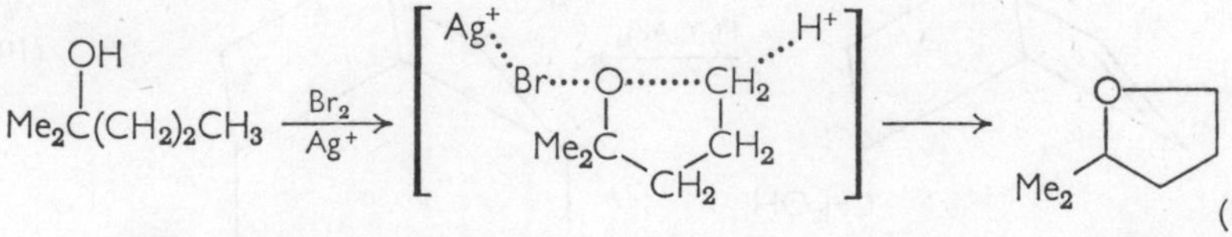

oxygen intermediate (**247**), however, a later report has suggested that an alkoxyl radical intermediate is involved[352].

Closely related to the above reactions, especially in light of the last comments, are those reactions which involve an intramolecular free-radical reaction of a hydroxyl group. The chemistry of this reaction has been reviewed in two separate articles which stress the action of hypoiodite and lead tetraacetate on an alcohol[353,354]. The development of the second reaction, especially in bicyclic compounds, has been an area of active interest and the examples in equations (105) to (107) illustrate this[355-357]. The formation of an acetoxy derivative

14+c.e.l.

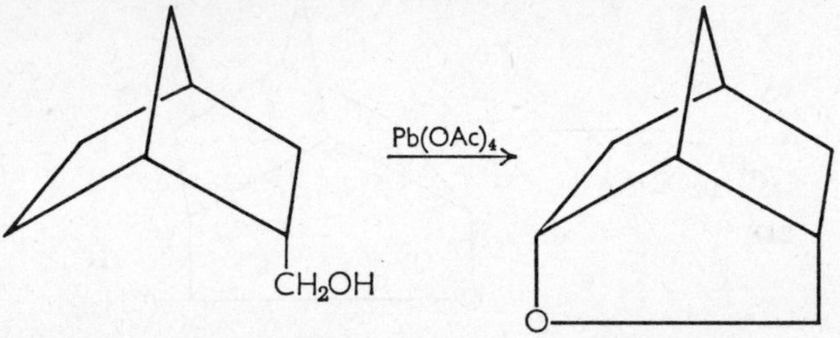

(105)

(249)   **(250)**

(106)

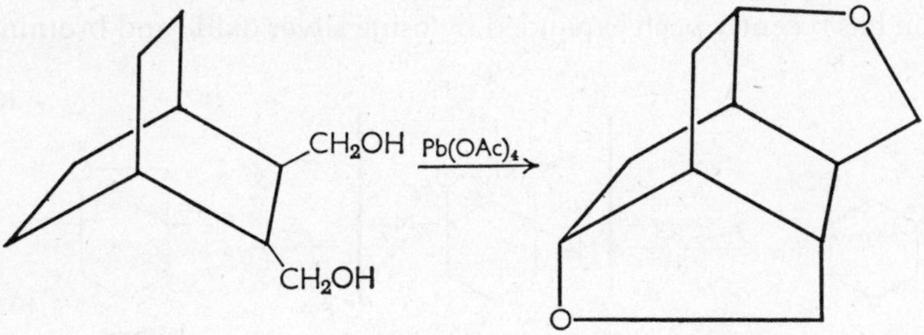

(251)   **(252)**

(107)

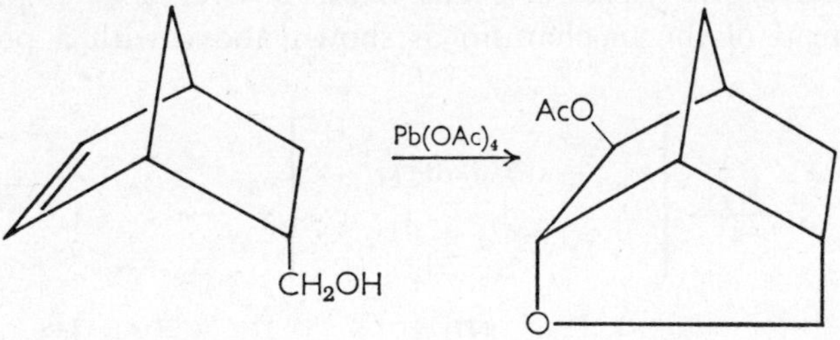

(253)   **(254)**

(**254**) when an olefin is used is common and quite useful (equation 107)[358]. Tetrahydropyran derivatives can be formed as well as the five-membered ring[359], and the reaction has also shown its utility in the synthesis of medium-sized ring compounds (**256**)[360]. Moriarty has

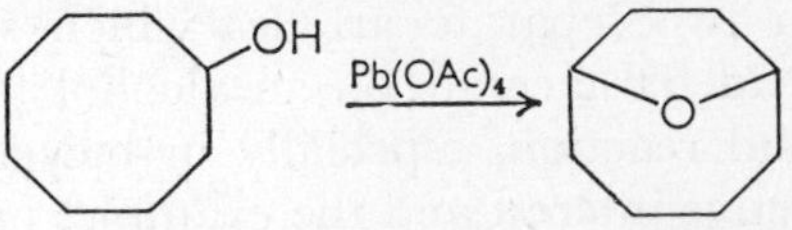

(108)

(255)   **(256)**

suggested that the activation energy for the cyclization is 6–8 kcal/mole and that reaction sequence (109) is involved with two separate electron

$$
\text{H OH} \longrightarrow \left[\text{H..O-H} \atop \text{Pb(OAc)}_3 \right] \longrightarrow \text{O} + \text{Pb(OAc)}_2 + 2\,\text{HOAc} \quad (109)
$$

$$(257) \qquad\qquad (258) \qquad\qquad (259)$$

transfers[360,361]. It appears that this method will be extremely useful in preparing bicyclic oxides, especially when one considers the effort involved in synthesizing them by other methods[362].

VI. CHEMICAL REACTIONS OF CYCLIC ETHERS

A. Cleavage of Cyclic Ethers

A sharp line of demarcation exists between the epoxides and the other cyclic ethers because of the general unreactivity of the latter, especially in ring-opening reactions involving nucleophiles. Oxetane reacts with a Grignard reagent to give the ring-opened product (equation 110)[77], but the acid-catalyzed ring openings of the cyclic ethers

$$
\text{O} + \text{RMgX} \longrightarrow \text{RCH}_2\text{CH}_2\text{CH}_2\text{OH} \quad (110)
$$

$$(215)$$

are more common, even though in general they do not proceed as readily as with epoxides, if at all[363].

In reactions which involve nucleophilic ring openings, or conditions close to this, tetrahydrofuran (259) has been found to be cleaved by

$$
(\text{C}_6\text{H}_5)_3\text{CMgBr} + \text{O} \longrightarrow (\text{C}_6\text{H}_5)_3\text{C(CH}_2)_4\text{OH} \quad (111)
$$

$$(260) \qquad (259) \qquad\qquad (261)$$

tritylmagnesium bromide in 95% yield (equation 111)[364], by lithium aluminum hydride with added aluminum chloride in good yield[365], with trityl sodium triphenylboron to give the alcohol after hydrolysis[366], and with diphenylchlorophosphine (**262**) plus magnesium to give the alkylated phosphorus compound (equation 112)[367]. Ger-

$$(C_6H_5)_2PCl + Mg + \underset{(262)}{\boxed{}} \longrightarrow (C_6H_5)_2P(CH_2)_4OH \quad (112)$$

$$(263)$$

manium and silicon compounds are also able to cleave these cyclic ethers[367]. Diborane (**264**) will cleave the compounds to give orthoborate esters (**265**) which can be hydrolyzed to the alcohols[368,369].

$$\underset{(264)}{\boxed{}} + B_2H_6 \longrightarrow \underset{(265)}{B(O\text{-}n\text{-}Bu)_3} \xrightarrow{H_2O} 3\,n\text{-}BuOH + \underset{(266)}{H_3BO_3} \quad (113)$$

When the reaction is carried out in the presence of iodine, hydroxy iodides are produced (equation 114)[370].

$$\underset{(264)}{\boxed{(CH_2)_x}} + B_2H_6 + I_2 \longrightarrow \underset{(267)}{B(O(CH_2)_xI)_3} \xrightarrow{H_2O} \underset{(268)}{HO(CH_2)_xI} + H_3BO_3 \quad (114)$$

Catalytic conversions usually involve a transformation to a carbonyl compound at the same time. These reactions have been studied extensively by Shuiken and his coworkers in Russia[371-378]. When tetrahydropyran and its derivatives are treated with 10% Pd–C at 300–350°, the aldehyde (from tetrahydropyran) or corresponding ketone is produced in 70–80% yield (equation 115)[371,378]. Derivatives of

$$\underset{(269)}{\boxed{\,R}} \xrightarrow[\Delta]{10\%\ \text{Pd-C}} \underset{(270)}{CH_3(CH_2)_3COR} \quad (115)$$

oxetane form a mixture of hydrocarbons and carbon monoxide under the same conditions (equation 116)[373]. When R was cyclohexyl the

$$\text{(271)} \quad \square\!\!-\!\!R \xrightarrow[\text{Pd-C}]{\Delta} RCH_2CH_3 + RCH\!=\!CH_2 + CO \qquad (116)$$

$$(R = CH_3, C_5H_{11}, C_6H_{11})$$

yield of alkane and alkene was 70 and 30%, respectively. A TiO_2-Al_2O_3 catalyst was found to split out formaldehyde to give olefinic

$$\text{(272)} \quad \xrightarrow[\Delta]{TiO_2\text{-}Al_2O_3} C_6H_5CH_2CH\!=\!CHCH_3 \text{(and isomers)} + CH_2O \qquad (117)$$
$$\text{(273)}$$

products[374-376], and a Cu–Al alloy with hydrogen gave the corresponding primary alcohol (274) in preference (80–95%); a Ni–Al catalyst gave a mixture (equation 119), with appropriate cyclic ethers[377].

$$\text{(271)} \quad \square\!\!-\!\!R \xrightarrow[H_2]{Cu\text{-}Al} R(CH_2)_2CH_2OH \qquad (118)$$
$$\text{(274) } 90\text{–}95\%$$

$$\text{(271)} \quad \square\!\!-\!\!R \xrightarrow{Ni\text{-}Al} CH_3CH_2CHOHR + R(CH_2)_3OH \qquad (119)$$
$$\text{(275)} \qquad \text{(276)}$$

The acid-catalyzed ring opening of the cyclic ethers with $TiCl_4$, $SbCl_5$, and PBr_3 gave the appropriate dihalides in 70–75, 50–55, and 90% yields, respectively[379], $AlCl_3$ with benzene (involving alkylation of the latter) gave a γ-phenylalcohol[380], $ZnCl_2$ plus methanesulfonyl bromide yielded a mixture of products containing diethers and dibromides[381], thiourea gave a hydroxy mercaptan[382], chloro silanes gave a chloroalkoxy silane[383], lithium chloride and BF_3 with acetic anhydride gave chloroalkyl acetates only when lithium chloride was added[384], and PCl_3 and $ZnCl_2$ gave dihalides and chloroalkoxydichloro phosphines[385].

B. Intact-ring Reactions

The chemical reactions of the intact ring are still few in number. Oxidation of tetrahydrofuran with RuO_4 in CCl_4 affords the lactone in quantitative yield[386], and dehydrogenation of 3,4-diphenyltetrahydrofuran with sulfur gives the corresponding furan[387]. The replacement of the oxygen in tetrahydropyran and in 2- and 3-alkyltetrahydropyran with sulfur occurs in yields of 50–70% when a ThO_2–Al_2O_3 catalyst and hydrogen sulfide are used at 300° (equation 120)[388,389].

$$\qquad\qquad\qquad\qquad\qquad\qquad\qquad\qquad (120)$$

(276)   (277) 55%

C. General and Special Reactions

The chemical reactions of substituted tetrahydrofurans are of interest for the knowledge they give on the character of the ring. The reactions of tetrahydrofurfuryl alcohol are quite important, especially the rearrangement of the alcohol to dihydropyran[390] (reaction 121).

$$\qquad\qquad\qquad\qquad\qquad\qquad\qquad\qquad (121)$$

(278)   (279)

The appearance of the labeling in the 6-position (279) would not be predicted, especially in the nonstatistical amount found. A mechanism for this process could be that in equations (122) and (123)[390]. The

$$\qquad\qquad\qquad\qquad\qquad\qquad\qquad\qquad (122)$$

(280)   (281)   (279a)

$$\qquad\qquad\qquad\qquad\qquad\qquad\qquad\qquad (123)$$

(281)   (282)   (279b)

pyrolysis of the benzoate of the same alcohol gave a ring-opened product (285)[391]. When the corresponding acetate is treated with

(283)   (284)

$$CH_3CH{=}CHCOCH_3 + C_6H_5CO_2H \quad (124)$$
(285)   (286)

$ZnCl_2$, 3-acetoxytetrahydropyran is produced[392]. The formation of a Grignard reagent from the bromide (287) gives an unexpected product

(287)   (288)

in 80% yield[393] (reaction 125). It was suggested that the reaction involved a tautomerization to an open-chain compound which gave the reaction and ultimately the product. It would seem that the reaction is much more complex than was suggested.

(289)   (290)   (291)

$$(Bs = p\text{-}BrC_6H_4\overset{..}{S}O_2)$$

A novel type of reaction is depicted in equation (126)[394]. A kinetic study indicated that neighboring-group participation was involved, and it is of considerable interest that the tetrahydrofuranyl group was two to three times better than the methoxy group in participation[394]. The kinetic details are given in Table 9.

TABLE 9. Rates of solvolysis of brosylate[a] esters in acetic acid[394].

Compound	Temp. (°c)	$10^5 k$ (sec^{-1})
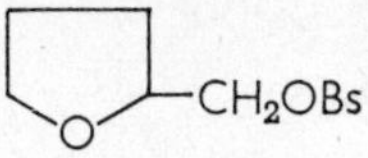 —CH$_2$OBs (tetrahydrofuran)	80	0·094
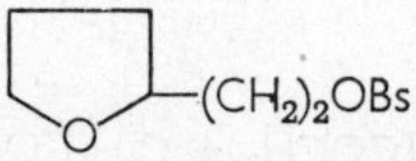 —(CH$_2$)$_2$OBs	80	0·193
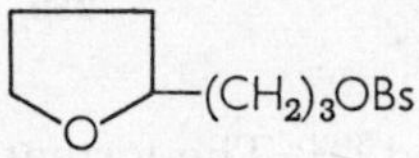 —(CH$_2$)$_3$OBs	80 (50)	188 (12)
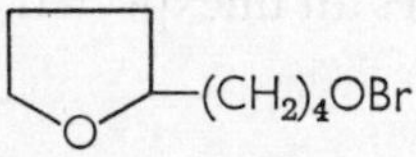 —(CH$_2$)$_4$OBr	80	21·5
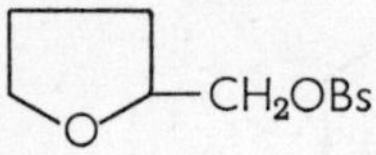 —CH$_2$OBs (tetrahydropyran)	80	0·0139
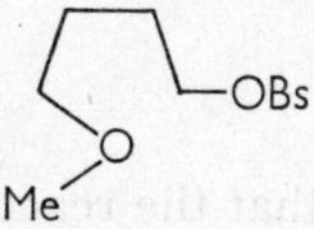 —OBs (Me)	50	4·58

[a] Brosylate = p-bromobenzenesulfonate.

It is possible to replace an α-halo atom with a strong nucleophile, thus reaction (127) occurs with the 2-chlorotetrahydropyrans and

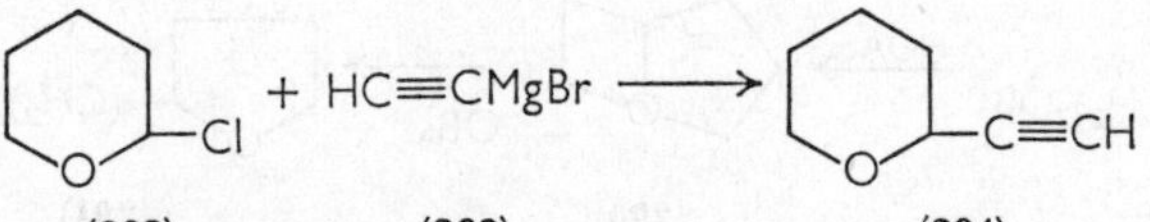

$$\text{(292)} \quad \overset{\text{—Cl}}{\bigcirc} + HC\equiv CMgBr \longrightarrow \overset{\text{—C}\equiv CH}{\bigcirc} \quad (127)$$

(292)   (293)   (294)

-furans in yields of about 60%[395]. A similar reaction is that of a Wittig reagent (296) on a hydroxy ether, which reacts as the aldehyde[396].

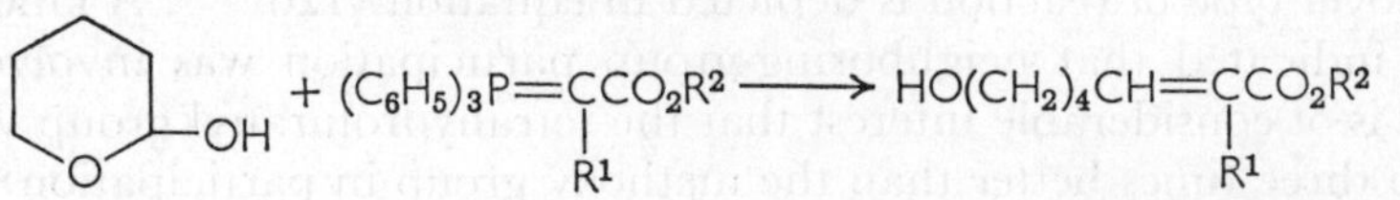

$$\text{(295)} \quad \overset{\text{—OH}}{\bigcirc} + (C_6H_5)_3P{=}CCO_2R^2 \longrightarrow HO(CH_2)_4CH{=}CCO_2R^2 \quad (128)$$
$$\overset{|}{R^1} \qquad\qquad \overset{|}{R^1}$$

(295)   (296)   (297)

Carbene insertion may take place on the α hydrogen (equations 129 and 130)[397]. The main product from these reactions (**301** and **304**) is

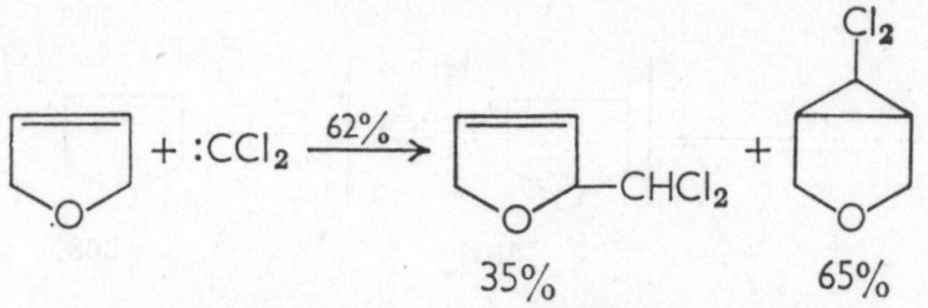

$$+ :CCl_2 \xrightarrow{62\%} \quad -CHCl_2 \; + \quad \tag{129}$$

35%   65%

(**298**)   (**299**)   (**300**)   (**301**)

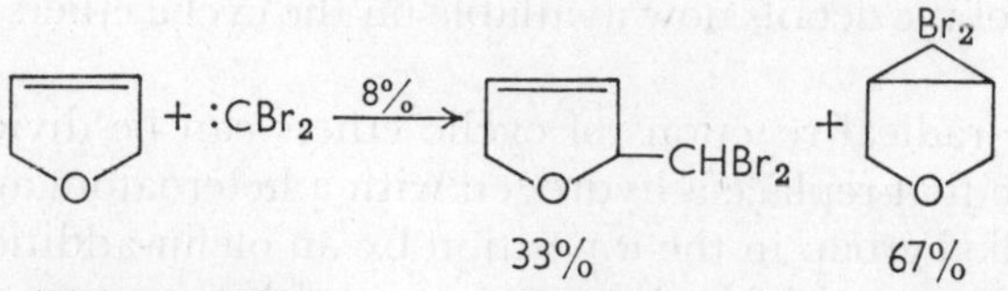

$$+ :CBr_2 \xrightarrow{8\%} \quad -CHBr_2 \; + \quad \tag{130}$$

33%   67%

(**298**)   (**302**)   (**303**)   (**304**)

the result of the normal mode of attack on the unsaturated linkage. Thus, the addition of a carbene to both the 2,3- and 3,4-positions (cf. equation 98) of the five-membered ring cyclic ether is authenticated, and has been found to occur with both the 2,3- and 3,4-positions of the six-membered ring cyclic ether to give the corresponding cyclopropyl compounds[398, 399]. Unsaturated pyrans and furans have also been found to undergo hydroformylation[400], to add HOCl to give mixtures of products[401], and to react with alcohols with acid catalysis to give moderately stable acetals[402].

D. Free-radical Reactions

The final type of reaction of the cyclic ethers (excluding epoxides) which will be discussed are their free-radical reactions. It can be predicted, by consideration of transition states **305** and **307**, that the atom

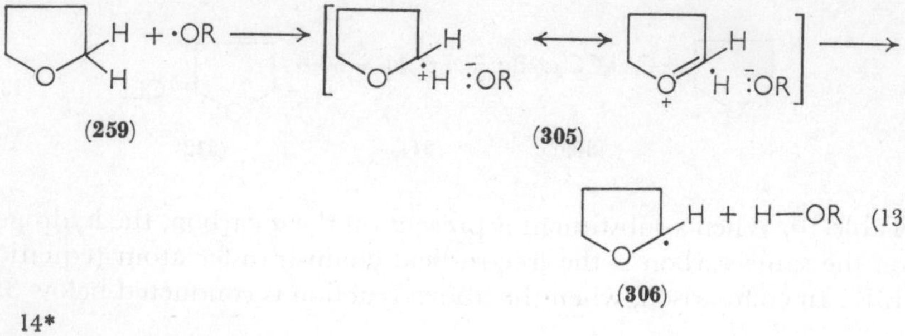

$$\begin{array}{c} H \\ H \end{array} + \cdot OR \longrightarrow \left[\begin{array}{c} H \\ {}^{+}H \; \dot{\mathstrut}OR \end{array} \longleftrightarrow \begin{array}{c} H \\ H \; \dot{\mathstrut}OR \\ + \end{array} \right] \longrightarrow$$

(**259**)   (**305**)

$$\begin{array}{c} H + H-OR \end{array} \tag{131}$$

(**306**)

which should undergo reaction is the α hydrogen. The products of the reactions bear out the prediction. The use of free-radical reactions in

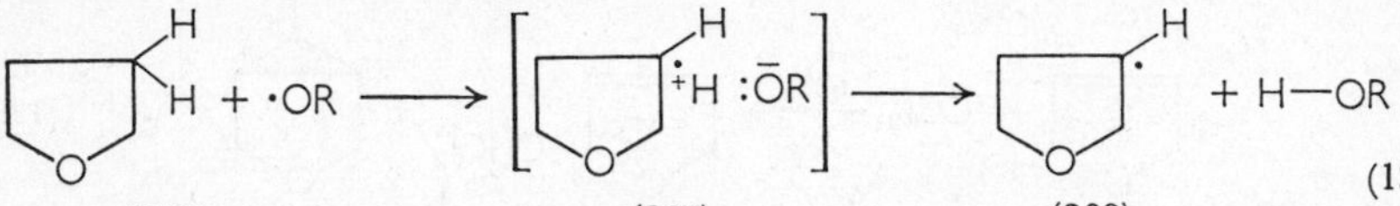

(259)   (307)   (308)   (132)

preparative organic chemistry has been the subject of a book[403], however, little of the details now available on the cyclic ethers are included in it.

The free-radical reactions of cyclic ethers can be divided into two types, those that replace a hydrogen with a heteroatom and those that place an alkyl group in the α position by an olefin-addition reaction.

The replacement of hydrogen occurs with oxygen and ultraviolet light to form the lactone[404]. Some researchers believe that the ultraviolet spectrum of the reaction mixture indicates that a molecular charge-transfer complex is formed between the ether and oxygen[404]. Alkoxy groups can be introduced by Lawesson's method (equation 133)[405]. When an alcohol and copper chloride are added to the reac-

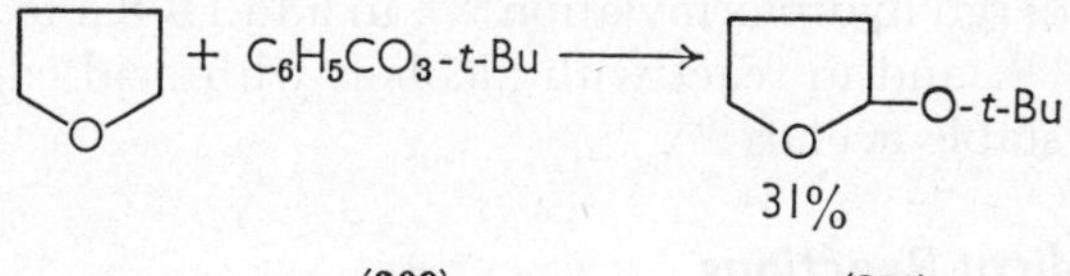

(309)   (310)
31%   (133)

tion mixture, the alcohol replaces the t-butyl group in the product (equation 134)[406]. The yields of this type of reaction are given in

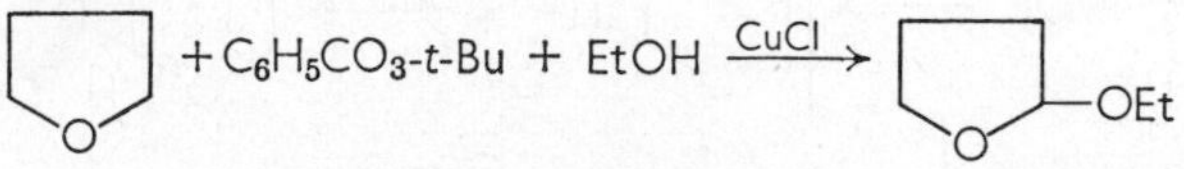

(309)   (311)   (312)   (134)

Table 10. When a substituent is present on the α carbon, the hydrogen on the same carbon is the free-radical chain-transfer atom (equation 135). In comparison, when the above reaction is conducted below 35°

TABLE 10. Yields of products from perester alkoxylations[406].

Added alcohol	% Yield	
	With tetrahydrofuran	With tetrahydropyran
Ethyl	40	
Isopropyl	44	38
t-Butyl	57	38
Hexyl	52	30

$$(135)$$

and with copper ions or copper and ultraviolet light present, the product is the corresponding α-acyloxy compound (315) in about 35%

$$(136)$$

yield[407]. A review article has been published on these reactions by the major researchers in the field[408].

Horner and his coworkers[409] discovered the free-radical replacement of hydrogen with halogen in cyclic ethers, when they were conducting a mechanistic study of the chlorination of ethers and traces of oxygen were present. Ultraviolet light readily catalyzes the reaction at −30 to −40° and gives some 2,5-dichlorotetrahydrofuran[410]. It was also found that some attack would occur in the 3-position when the 2-position was chlorinated (equation 137)[411]. Copper chloride with

$$(137)$$

ultraviolet light was found to give chlorination amongst other reactions[412], and cyanogen chloride was found to give a mixture of cyano ethers[413]. The yields of the products (equations 138 and 139)

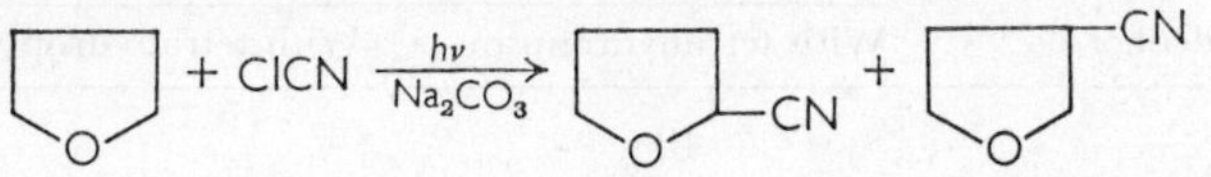

$$91\% \quad\quad\quad 9\%$$
$$(319) \quad\quad\quad (320)$$
(138)

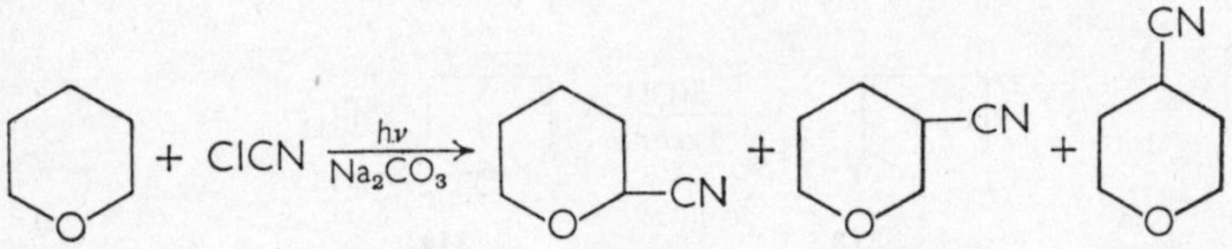

$$84\% \quad\quad 10\% \quad\quad 4\%$$
$$(322) \quad\quad (323) \quad\quad (324)$$
(139)

(321)

were increased greatly by the addition of acetone, which brings out the free-radical character of the reaction very adequately[413].

The free-radical alkylation of cyclic ethers was first illustrated by Huyser[414]. He showed that 2-methoxytetrahydropyran (326) would rearrange to methyl valerate (325) in about 40% yield with an alkyl

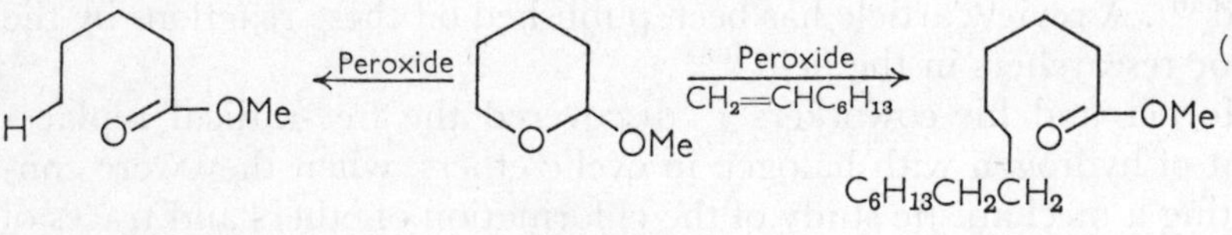

(140)

(325)   (326)   (327)

peroxide catalyst. When an olefin, such as 1-octene, was present the product was methyl tridecanoate (328). The reaction involves a novel ring opening, illustrated in equation (141), which occurs via a chain

(141)

(326)   (328)

mechanism[414]. It was shown that a cyano olefin would also alkylate the α carbon, but with no ring opening[415]. Gritter and Wallace[416] found that alkylation of tetrahydropyran, tetrahydrofuran, and oxetane to form ketones occurred to different extents and that there was another ring opening involved (equation 142). This second ring-opening reaction was somewhat similar to that discovered by Huyser[414], but involved a hydrogen-atom shift (equation 143). It was

$$\text{(329)} \qquad \text{(330)} \qquad \text{(331)} \tag{142}$$

$$\text{(332)} \qquad \text{(333)} \tag{143}$$

$$\textbf{333} \xrightarrow[\text{Several steps}]{C_6H_{13}CH = CH_2} CH_3(CH_2)_7COCH_2CH_3 \tag{144}$$

$$\text{(334)}$$

suggested that the differences in the yields of products (41% from the six-membered ring cyclic ether, 39% from the five-, and 14% from the four-) depended on the ease of formation of the initial free radical and data on this are given in Table 11[416]. The data indicate the ease of

TABLE 11. Ease of formation of free radicals from the cyclic ethers[a416].

Reactant	Reactivity relative to benzene[a]
Cyclohexane	25·0
Benzene	1·0
Toluene	10·7
Oxetane	1·4
Tetrahydrofuran	15·7
Tetrahydropyran	15·0
1,2-Epoxybutane	2·7
Styrene oxide	11·3
Propylene oxide	1·1

[a] These data were obtained by measuring the ratio of t-butyl alcohol to acetone formed when t-butyl peroxide was decomposed in the neat compounds.

formation of a radical, such as **329**. A second reason relates to the ener-
getics of the transition states for the hydrogen-atom shift rearrangement, where a four-, five-, and six-membered ring is involved. The
three transition states are illustrated in structures **335**, **336**, and **337**,
and based on thermodynamic considerations the stability order is
335 > 336 > 337[416].

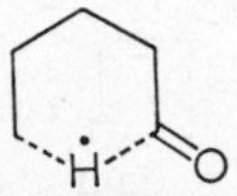

(**335**) 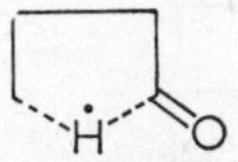   (**336**) 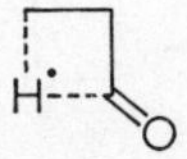   (**337**)

In addition to the additions of cyclic ethers to 1-octene illustrated
above, tetrahydrofuran has been shown to add to ethylene at high
temperatures to give 21% of product[417], and 2-methyltetrahydro-
furan was alkylated in the same way to give the 5-ethyl product and
2-pentanone[418]. The same workers also showed that the reaction
occurs with a peroxide catalyst[419]. Tetrahydrofuran could be alkylated
with maleic anhydride and a peroxide catalyst to give a high yield
(70%) of adduct, however, tetrahydropyran would not alkylate under
these conditions[420]. Acetylene will add about as well as an olefin to
give the 2-vinyl product from both tetrahydrofuran and tetrahydropyran[421]. No ring-opened product was isolated from these last two
examples nor from the ultraviolet light-initiated addition of the same
cyclic ethers to an olefin[422].

One final example which should be mentioned to indicate that free-
radical addition does not always occur is the failure of reaction
(145)[423]. It was thought that the energy required for the initial step

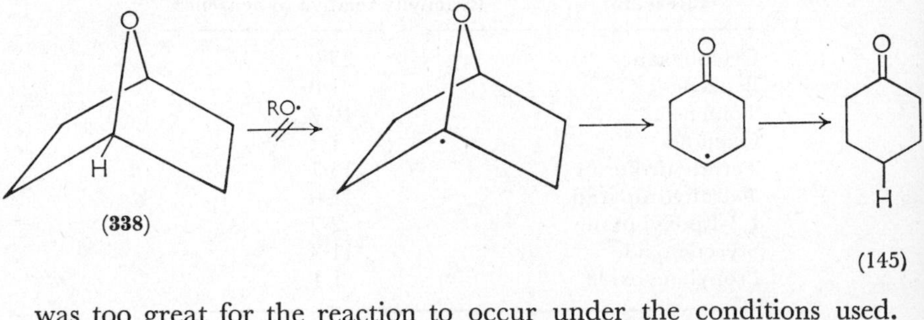

(**338**)

(145)

was too great for the reaction to occur under the conditions used.
Others have subsequently reported that the bridgehead carbon–
hydrogen bond is quite strong[424].

VII. REFERENCES

1. A. Weissberger, Ed., *Heterocyclic Compounds with Three- and Four-Membered Rings*, Parts I and II, Interscience Publishers, New York, 1964.
2. A. Rosowsky, reference 1, pp. 1–523.
3. S. Searles, Jr., reference 1, pp. 983–1068.
4. R. D. Topsom, *Rev. Pure Appl. Chem.*, **14**, 127 (1964).
5. D. Swern in *Organic Reactions*, Vol. 7 (Ed. R. Adams), John Wiley and Sons, New York, 1953, pp. 378–433.
6. V. J. Karnojitzky, *Chim. Ind. (Paris)*, **92**, 381 (1964).
7. H. Batzer and E. Nickles, *Chimia*, **16**, 57 (1962).
8. H. Batzer, *Chem. Ind. (London)*, 179 (1964).
9. R. E. Parker and N. S. Isaacs. *Chem. Revs.*, **59**, 737 (1959).
10. F. M. Dean, *Naturally Occurring Oxygen Ring Compounds*, Butterworths, London, 1963.
11. S. Winstein and R. B. Henderson in *Heterocyclic Compounds*, Vol. I (Ed. R. C. Elderfield), John Wiley and Sons, New York, 1950, pp. 1–60.
12. E. H. Rodd, *Chemistry of Carbon Compounds*, Vol. IV, Elsevier Publishing Co., Amsterdam, 1957.
13. P. Gray and A. Williams, *Trans. Faraday Soc.*, **55**, 760 (1959).
14. J. D. Cox, *Tetrahedron*, **19**, 1175 (1963).
15. A. S. Pell and G. Pilcher, *Trans. Faraday Soc.*, **60**, 71 (1964).
16. S. I. Chen, J. Zinn, and W. D. Gwinn, *J. Chem. Phys.*, **34**, 1311 (1961).
17. C. Djerassi, W. Klyne, T. Norin, G. Ohloff, and E. Klein, *Tetrahedron*, **21**, 163 (1965).
18. F. W. McLafferty, *Mass Spectral Correlations*, Adv. in Chem. Series, Vol. 40, Washington, 1963.
19. F. W. McLafferty, *Mass Spectrometry of Organic Ions*, Academic Press, New York, 1963.
20. H. Budzikiewicz, C. Djerassi, and D. Williams, *Interpretation of Mass Spectra of Organic Compounds*, Holden-Day, San Francisco, 1964.
21. H. Budzikiewicz, C. Djerassi, and D. Williams, *Structure Elucidation of Natural Products by Mass Spectrometry*, Holden-Day, San Francisco, 1964.
22. E. J. Corey and G. A. Gregoriou, *J. Am. Chem. Soc.*, **81**, 3124 (1959).
23. W. J. Potts, *Spectrochim. Acta*, **21**, 511 (1965).
24. Z. Jedlinski and R. Hippe, *Roczniki Chem.*, **38**, 1137 (1964); *Chem. Abstr.*, **61**, 16029 (1964).
25. C. A. Kaplan, *Dissertation Abstr.*, **24**, 3982 (1964).
26. A. L. Goodman and R. H. Eastman, *J. Am. Chem. Soc.*, **86**, 908 (1964).
27. R. S. Mohrbacken and N. H. Cromwell, *J. Am. Chem. Soc.*, **79**, 401 (1957).
28. L. A. Strait, R. G. Ketcham, D. K. Jambotka, and M. K. Hrenoff, *Colloq. Spectros. Intern.*, **3**, 125 (1961).
29. G. J. Hernandez, *J. Chem. Phys.*, **38**, 2233 (1963).
30. I. H. Primas, K. Frei, and H. H. Guenthard, *Helv. Chim. Acta*, **41**, 35 (1958).
31. B. K. Wasson, J. A. Kernan, and J. M. Parker, *Can. J. Chem.*, **41**, 3070 (1963).
32. P. K. Korver, P. J. Van Der Haak, H. Steinberg, and Th. J. DeBoer, *Rec. Trav. Chim.*, **84**, 129 (1965).

432   R. J. Gritter

33. K. Nukada, *Bull. Chem. Soc. Japan*, **33,** 1606 (1960).
34. C. A. Reilly and J. D. Swalen, *J. Chem. Phys.*, **32,** 1378 (1960).
35. F. S. Mortimer, *J. Mol. Spectry.*, **5,** 199 (1960).
36. B. P. Dailey, A. Gawer, and W. C. Neiken, *Disc. Faraday Soc.*, **34,** 18 (1962).
37. J.-M. Lehn and J.-J. Riehl, *Mol. Phys.*, **8,** 33 (1964).
38. K. L. Williamson, C. A. Lanford, and C. R. Nicholson, *J. Am. Chem. Soc.*, **86,** 762 (1964).
39. J. I. Musher, *Mol. Phys.*, **4,** 311 (1961).
40. M. H. Gianni, E. L. Stogryn, and C. M. Orlando, Jr., *J. Phys. Chem.*, **67** 1385 (1963).
41. R. P. Jeffries, R. S. Rosich, and D. E. White, *Tetrahedron Letters*, 1853 (1963).
42. D. D. Elleman and S. L. Manatt, *J. Mol. Spectry.*, **9,** 477 (1962).
43. S. J. Brois, *J. Org. Chem.*, **27,** 3532 (1962).
44. J. I. Musher and R. G. Gordon, *J. Chem. Phys.*, **36,** 3097 (1962).
45. A. D. Cross, *J. Am. Chem. Soc.*, **84,** 3206 (1962).
46. K. Tori, T. Komeno, and T. Kakagawa, *J. Org. Chem.*, **29,** 1136 (1964).
47. D. H. Buss, L. Hough, L. D. Hall, and J. F. Manville, *Tetrahedron*, **21,** 69 (1965).
48. H. Shimizu and Y. Hama, *Bull. Chem. Soc. Japan*, **37,** 763 (1964).
49. K. L. Williamson, C. A. Lanford, and C. R. Nicholson, *J. Am. Chem. Soc.*, **86,** 762 (1964).
50. S. L. Smith and R. H. Cox, *J. Mol. Spectry.*, **16,** 216 (1965).
51. K. Tori, K. Kitahonoki, Y. Takano, H. Tanida, and T. Tsuji, *Tetrahedron Letters*, 559 (1964).
52. M. Karplus, *J. Chem. Phys.*, **30,** 11 (1959).
53. P. R. Certain, V. S. Watts, and J. H. Goldstein, *Theo. Chim. Acta*, **2,** 324 (1964).
54. E. M. Arnett and C. Y. Wu, *J. Am. Chem. Soc.*, **84,** 1684 (1962); E. M. Arnett in *Progress in Physical Organic Chemistry*, Vol. 1 (Eds. S. G. Cohen, A. Streitwieser, Jr., and R. W. Taft), Interscience Publishers, New York, 1964, pp. 223–403.
55. E. T. Hitchcock and P. J. Elving, *Anal. Chim. Acta*, **28,** 301 (1963).
56. F. J. Cioffi and S. T. Zendielsky, *J. Phys. Chem.*, **67,** 357 (1963).
57. H. E. Wirth, M. J. Jackson and H. W. Griffiths, *J. Phys. Chem.*, **62,** 871 (1952).
58. D. E. McLaughlin, M. Tamres, S. Searles, Jr., and S. Nukina, *J. Inorg. Nucl. Chem.*, **17,** 112 (1961).
59. H. E. Wirth and P. I. Slick, *J. Phys. Chem.*, **66,** 2277 (1962); M. Okada, K. Sugama, and Y. Yamachita, *Tetrahedron Letters*, 2329 (1965).
60. R. R. Jay, *Anal. Chem.*, **36,** 667 (1964).
61. M. Tamres, S. Searles, Jr., and J. M. Goodenow, *J. Am. Chem. Soc.*, **86,** 3934 (1964).
62. W. Strohmeier, C. Barbeau and D. Hobe, *Chem. Ber.*, **96,** 3254 (1963).
63. E. Lippert and H. Prigge, *Ann. Chem.*, **659,** 81 (1962).
64. I. M. Ginzburg, E. S. Petrov, and A. I. Shatenshtein, *Zh. Obshch. Khim.*, **34,** 2294 (1964); *Chem. Abstr.*, **61,** 9380 (1964).
65. M. Veyret and M. Gomel, *Compt. Rend.*, **258,** 4506 (1964).
66. H. Normant, *Bull. Soc. Chim. France*, 1444 (1957).

67. C. S. Rondestvedt, Jr., and O. Vogl, *J. Am. Chem. Soc.*, **77,** 3401 (1955).

68. H. Gilman and J. J. Dietrich, *J. Org. Chem.*, **22,** 851 (1957).

69. H. Gilman and J. J. Dietrich, *J. Am. Chem. Soc.*, **80,** 380 (1958).

70. H. Gilman and S. Gray, *J. Org. Chem.*, **23,** 1476 (1958).

71. H. Gilman and R. A. Tomasi, *J. Am. Chem. Soc.*, **81,** 137 (1959).

72. L. M. Soffer and M. Katz, *J. Am. Chem. Soc.*, **78,** 1705 (1956).

73. S. Hillers and G. Sokolous, *Latvijas PSR Zinatnu Akad. Vestis*, 85 (1959); *Chem. Abstr.*, **54,** 241 (1960).

74. H. C. Brown and P. A. Tierney, *J. Inorg. Nucl. Chem.*, **9,** 51 (1959).

75. H. E. Ramsden, A. E. Balint, W. R. Whitford, J. J. Walburn, and R. Cserr, *J. Org. Chem.*, **22,** 1202 (1957).

76. L. Groizeleau-Miginiac, *Ann. Chim. (Paris)*, **6,** 1071 (1961).

77. T. Cuvigny and H. Normant, *Compt. Rend.*, **254,** 316 (1962).

78. L. Miginiac-Groizeleau, *Bull. Soc. Chim. France*, 1449 (1963).

79. T. Leigh, *Chem. Ind. (London)*, 426 (1965).

80. S.-O. Lawesson and T. Buoch, *Acta Chem. Scand.*, **13,** 1717 (1959).

81. H. E. Zaugg, *J. Am. Chem. Soc.*, **83,** 837 (1961).

82. N. Kornblum, R. Seltzer, and P. Haberfield, *J. Am. Chem. Soc.*, **85,** 1148 (1963).

83. D. G. Powell and E. Warhurst, *Trans. Faraday Soc.*, **58,** 953 (1962).

84. H. Normant and B. Angelo, *Bull. Soc. Chim. France*, 1988 (1961).

85. R. Waack and P. E. Stevenson, *J. Am. Chem. Soc.*, **87,** 1183 (1965).

86. L. D. Bergel'son, V. A. Vaver, and M. M. Shemyakin, *Izv. Akad. Nauk SSSR, Otd. Khim. Nauk.*, 729 (1961); *Chem. Abstr.*, **55,** 22196 (1961).

87. H. H. Zeiss and W. Herwig, *J. Am. Chem. Soc.*, **80,** 2913 (1958).

88. S. Iwatsuki, N. Takigawa, M. Okada, Y. Yamashita, and Y. Ishii, *Polymer Letters*, **2,** 549 (1964).

89. A. Iku, M. Okuno, and R. Oda, *Bull. Chem. Soc. Japan*, **37,** 570 (1964).

90. F. P. Greenspan in *Chemical Reactions of Polymers* (Ed. E. M. Fettes), Interscience Publishers, New York, 1964; L. E. St. Pierre, A. S. Kastans, and A. C. Farthing, in *Polyethers*, Part I, Vol. XIII of *High Polymers* (Ed. N. G. Gaylord), Interscience Publishers, New York, 1963.

91. J. Furukava and T. Saegusa, *Polymer Reviews*, Vol. 3, Interscience Publishers, New York, 1963.

92. T. Tsuruta, S. Inoue, M. Ishimori, and N. Yoshida, *J. Polymer Sci., Ser. C*, **4,** 267 (1963).

93. E. C. Steiner, R. R. Pelletier, and R. O. Trucks, *J. Am. Chem. Soc.*, **86,** 4678 (1964).

94. E. J. Vandenberg, *J. Polymer Sci., Ser. B*, **2,** 1085 (1965).

95. N. S. Chu and C. C. Price, *J. Polymer Sci., Ser. A*, **1,** 1105 (1963).

96. I. Penczek and S. Penczek, *Makromol. Chem.*, **67,** 203 (1963).

97. H. Meerwein, D. Delfs, and H. Morschell, *Angew. Chem.*, **72,** 927 (1960).

98. P. R. Johnston, *J. Appl. Polymer Sci.*, **9,** 461, 467 (1965).

99. K. Weissermel and E. Noelker, *Makromol. Chem.*, **68,** 140 (1963).

100. D. Sims, *J. Chem. Soc.*, 864 (1964).

101. J. K. Stille, P. Cassidy, and L. Plummer, *J. Am. Chem. Soc.*, **85,** 1318 (1963).

102. C. E. H. Bawn, R. M. Bell, and A. Ledwith, *Polymer*, **6,** 95 (1965).

103. H. B. Henbest, *Proc. Chem. Soc.*, 159 (1963).

434   R. J. Gritter

104. M. Mousseron, M. Mousseron-Canet, and G. Phillippe, *Compt. Rend.*, **258,** 3705 (1964); *Chem. Abstr.*, **61,** 560 (1964).

105. B. Rickborn and S.-Y. Lwo, *J. Org. Chem.*, **30,** 2212 (1965).

106. D. J. Pasto and C. C. Cumbo, *J. Org. Chem.*, **30,** 1271 (1965).

107. M. M. Morsumzade, F. G. Ismailova, and N. G. Abdullaew, *Azerb. Khim. Zh.*, 71 (1962); *Chem. Abstr.*, **59,** 2745 (1963).

108. M. M. Morsumzade and F. G. Ismailova, *Azerb. Khim. Zh.*, 59 (1964); *Chem. Abstr.*, **62,** 6447 (1965).

109. N. N. Schwartz and J. H. Blumbergs, *J. Org. Chem.*, **29,** 1976 (1964).

110. Y. Suhara, *Tokyo Kogyo Shikensho Hokoku*, **57,** 370 (1962); *Chem. Abstr.*, **61,** 14611 (1964).

111. Y. Suhara, *Tokyo Kogyo Shikensho Hokoku*, **57,** 377 (1962); *Chem. Abstr.*, **61,** 14612 (1964).

112. F. D. Greene and W. Adam, *J. Org. Chem.*, **29,** 136 (1964).

113. G. B. Payne, *Tetrahedron*, **18,** 763 (1962).

114. Y. Ogata and Y. Sawaki, *Tetrahedron*, **20,** 2065 (1964).

115. Y. Ogata and Y. Sawaki, *Bull. Chem. Soc. Japan*, **38,** 194 (1965).

116. H. C. Stevens and A. J. Kaman, *J. Am. Chem. Soc.*, **87,** 734 (1965).

117. C. G. Swain, D. A. Kuhn, and R. L. Schowen, *J. Am. Chem. Soc.*, **87,** 1553 (1965).

118. H. E. Zimmerman and G. A. Zimmerman, *Meeting Am. Chem. Soc., April 1965*, Abstr., p. 8P.

119. M. C. Henry and G. Wittig, *J. Am. Chem. Soc.*, **82,** 563 (1960).

120. A. Maercker in *Organic Reactions*, Vol. 14 (Ed. A. C. Cope), John Wiley and Sons, New York, 1965, p. 383.

121. V. Mark, *J. Am. Chem. Soc.*, **85,** 1884 (1963).

122. M. S. Newman and S. Blum, *J. Am. Chem. Soc.*, **86,** 5598 (1964).

123. J. N. Bradley and A. Ledwith, *J. Chem. Soc.*, 3480 (1963).

124. A. Schönberg and K. Junghans, *Chem. Ber.*, **97,** 2539 (1964).

125. E. J. Corey and M. Chaykovsky, *J. Am. Chem. Soc.*, **84,** 867 (1962).

126. E. J. Corey and M. Chaykovsky, *J. Am. Chem. Soc.*, **84,** 3782 (1962).

127. E. J. Corey and M. Chaykovsky, *J. Am. Chem. Soc.*, **87,** 1353 (1965).

128. V. Franzen and H. E. Driesen, *Chem. Ber.*, **98,** 1881 (1963).

129. A. W. Johnson, V. J. Hruby, and J. L. Williams, *J. Am. Chem. Soc.*, **86,** 918 (1964).

130. R. K. Bly and R. S. Bly, *J. Org. Chem.*, **28,** 3165 (1963).

131. C. E. Cook, R. C. Corby, and M. E. Wall, *Tetrahedron Letters*, 891 (1965).

132. J. H. Gorwin, *J. Chem. Soc.*, 3980 (1963).

133. R. J. Cvetanovic, *Can. J. Chem.*, **36,** 623 (1958).

134. W. F. Brill, *J. Am. Chem. Soc.*, **85,** 141 (1963).

135. N. Indictor and W. F. Brill, *J. Org. Chem.*, **30,** 2074 (1965).

136. I. S. Roch and J. C. Balaceanu, *Bull. Soc. Chim. France*, 1393 (1964).

137. L. Batt and S. W. Benson, *J. Chem. Phys.*, **36,** 895 (1962).

138. E. R. White, H. G. Davis and E. S. Hammack, *J. Am. Chem. Soc.*, **87,** 1175 (1965).

139. W. J. Linn and R. E. Benson, *Meeting Am. Chem. Soc., Jan. 1964,* Abstr. p. 13C; W. J. Linn, O. W. Webster, and R. E. Benson, *J. Am. Chem. Soc.*, **87,** 3651 (1965).

140. V. Caglioti, A. D. Site, M. Lenzi, and A. Mele, *J. Chem. Soc.*, 5430 (1964).

141. A. Nickon and W. L. Mendelson, *J. Am. Chem. Soc.*, **85,** 1894 (1963).
142. A. Sabanejeff, *Ann. Chem.*, **216,** 268 (1883).
143. C. Walling and P. S. Fredericks, *J. Am. Chem. Soc.*, **84,** 3326 (1962).
144. V. S. Etlis, N. N. Trofimov, and G. A. Razuvaev, *Zh. Obshch. Khim.*, **38,** 2784 (1964).
145. M. Zief and C. H. Schramm, *Chem. Ind.* (*London*), 660 (1964).
146. A. Kirrmann, P. Duhamel, and M. R. Mouri Bimorghi, *Bull. Soc. Chim. France*, 3264 (1964).
147. V. Franzen, *Ann. Chem.*, **614,** 31 (1958).
148. R. N. McDonald and P. A. Schwab, *J. Am. Chem. Soc.*, **86,** 4866 (1964).
149. J. K. Stille and D. D. Whitehurst, *J. Am. Chem. Soc.*, **86,** 4871 (1964).
150. T. Cohen and T. Tsuji, *J. Org. Chem.*, **26,** 1681 (1961).
151. E. L. Eliel and M. Rerick, *J. Am. Chem. Soc.*, **82,** 1362 (1960).
152. E. L. Eliel and M. Rerick, *J. Am. Chem. Soc.*, **84,** 2356 (1962).
153. J. J. Baron, Jr., *Dissertation Abstr.*, **22,** 2580 (1962).
154. G. E. Heasley, *Dissertation Abstr.*, **22,** 2988 (1962).
155. H. C. Brown and B. C. Subba Rao, *J. Am. Chem. Soc.*, **82,** 681 (1960).
156. H. C. Brown and P. M. Weissman, *Israel J. Chem.*, **1,** 430 (1963).
157. B. Rickborn and J. Quartucci, *J. Org. Chem.*, **29,** 3185 (1964).
158. H. Kwart and T. Takeshita, *J. Org. Chem.*, **28,** 670 (1963).
159. D. H. Kelly, *Dissertation Abstr.*, **24,** 974 (1963).
160. N. I. Shuikin, E. Kovach, I. F. Bel'skii, and M. Bartok, *Dokl. Akad. Nauk SSSR*, **136,** 1120 (1961); *Chem. Abstr.*, **55,** 17616 (1961).
161. J. Kwiatek, I. L. Mador, and J. K. Seyler, *J. Am. Chem. Soc.*, **84,** 304 (1962).
162. A. B. Naselow, *Dissertation Abstr.*, **24,** 1400 (1963).
163. G. Vollema and J. F. Arens, *Rec. Trav. Chim.*, **82,** 305 (1963).
164. W. V. McConnell and W. H. Moore, *Meeting Am. Chem. Soc., April 1964*, Abstr., p. 18N.
165. J. Huet and J. Dreux, *Compt. Rend.*, **258,** 4570 (1964).
166. G. Farges and A. Kergomard, *Bull. Soc. Chim. France*, 51 (1963).
167. M. Rosenblum and C. Steel, *Meeting Am. Chem. Soc., April 1965*, Abstr. p. 60P.
168. R. Gabler and H. R. Meyer, *Agnew. Chem.*, **72,** 942 (1962).
169. H. R. Meyer and R. Gabler, *Helv. Chim. Acta*, **46,** 2685 (1963).
170. K. Gulbins and K. Hamann, *Chem. Ber.*, **94,** 3287 (1961).
171. A. E. Kretov and I. S. Matveev, *Zh. Obshch. Khim.*, **30,** 1837 (1960); *Chem. Abstr.*, **55,** 15464 (1961).
172. V. S. Etlis, L. N. Grobov, and G. A. Razuvaev, *Dokl. Akad. Nauk SSSR*, **140,** 623 (1961); *Chem. Abstr.*, **56,** 11528 (1961).
173. G. A. Razuvaev, V. S. Etlis, and L. N. Grobov, *Zh. Obshch. Khim.*, **32,** 994 (1962); *Chem. Abstr.*, **58,** 2356 (1963).
174. J. H. Ross, D. Baker, and A. T. Coscia, *J. Org. Chem.*, **29,** 824 (1964).
175. A. A. Durgaryan, *Izv. Akad. Nauk Arm. SSR, Khim. Nauk*, **14,** 51 (1961); *Chem. Abstr.*, **56,** 465 (1962).
176. H. Howell, G. B. Butler, and H. H. Sisler, *J. Org. Chem.*, **27,** 1709 (1962).
177. J. L. Eisenmann, R. L. Yamantino, and J. F. Howard, Jr., *J. Org. Chem.*, **26,** 2102 (1961).
178. R. F. Heck, *J. Am. Chem. Soc.*, **85,** 1460 (1963).

179. Y. Takegami, C. Yokokawa, Y. Watanabe, and H. Masada, *Bull. Chem. Soc. Japan*, **37**, 672 (1964).

180. Y. Takegami, C. Yokokawa, and Y. Watanabe, *Bull. Chem. Soc. Japan*, **37**, 677 (1964).

181. Y. Takegami, C. Yokokawa, and Y. Watanabe, *Bull. Chem. Soc. Japan*, **37**, 935 (1964).

182. J. L. Eisenmann, *J. Org. Chem.*, **27**, 2706 (1962).

183. M. J. Boskin and D. B. Denney, *Chem. Ind. (London)*, 330 (1959).

184. D. E. Bissing, *Meeting Am. Chem. Soc., Sept. 1964*, Abstr. p. 12S.

185. D. E. Bissing and A. J. Speziale, *J. Am. Chem. Soc.*, **87**, 2683 (1965).

186. J. F. McGhie, W. A. Ross, F. J. Julietti, G. Swift, G. Usher, N. M. Waldron, and B. E. Grimwood, *Chem Ind. (London)*, 460 (1964).

187. W. E. McEwen, A. Blade-Font, and C. A. VanderWerf, *J. Am. Chem. Soc.*, **84**, 677 (1962).

188. H. Normant and G. Sturtz, *Compt. Rend.*, **256**, 1800 (1963).

189. I. Tomoskozi, *Tetrahedron*, **19**, 1969 (1963).

190. R. M. Pike and A. A. Lavigne, *Rec. Trav. Chim.*, **83**, 883 (1964).

191. V. S. Etlis, L. M. Degtyareva, and G. A. Razuvaev, *Zh. Obshch. Khim.*, **32**, 1508 (1962); *Chem. Abstr.*, **58**, 3302 (1963).

192. P. Rao and J. C. Uroda, *Tetrahedron Letters*, 1117 (1964).

193. W. J. Linn and R. E. Bensen, *J. Am. Chem. Soc.*, **87**, 3657 (1965); W. J. Linn, *J. Am. Chem. Soc.*, **87**, 3665 (1965).

194. P. Brown and R. C. Cookson, *Proc. Chem. Soc.*, **185** (1964).

195. F. Johnson and J. P. Heeschen, *J. Org. Chem.*, **29**, 3252 (1964).

196. P. M. G. Bavin, D. P. Hansell, and R. G. W. Sprickett, *J. Chem. Soc.*, 4535 (1964).

197. C. H. DePuy, F. W. Breitbeil, and K. L. Eilers, *J. Org. Chem.*, **29**, 2810 (1964).

198. H. Hopff and P. Lienhard, *Helv. Chim. Acta*, **45**, 1741 (1962).

199. T. Kuwamura and E. Kameyama, *Kogyo Kagaku Zasshi*, **67**, 592 (1964); *Chem. Abstr.*, **61**, 6973 (1964).

200. F. T. Shostak, S. M. Serikbawa, and N. Ya. Lyubman, *Teoriya i Prakf. Ionnogo Obmena, Akad. Nauk Kaz. SSR, Tr. Resp. Soveshch*, 7 (1962); *Chem. Abstr.*, **61**, 6975 (1964).

201. D. M. Burness, *J. Org. Chem.*, **29**, 1862 (1964).

202. C. Hung Chang, *Dissertation Abstr.*, **25**, 2224 (1964).

203. C. L. Stevens and A. J. Weinheimer, *J. Am. Chem. Soc.*, **80**, 4072 (1958).

204. T. B. Zalucky, S. Marathe, L. Malspeis, and G. Hite, *J. Org. Chem.*, **30**, 1324 (1965).

205. (a) F. A. Long and M. A. Paul, *Chem. Rev.*, **57**, 935 (1957); (b) J. F. Bunnett, *J. Am. Chem. Soc.*, **83**, 4978 (1961).

206. I. E. Walley, *Trans. Faraday Soc.*, **55**, 815 (1959).

207. W. J. LeNoble and M. Duffy, *J. Phys. Chem.*, **68**, 619 (1964).

208. N. G. Needler, *Dissertation Abstr.*, **24**, 1401 (1963).

209. J. Hine, *Physical Organic Chemistry*, 2nd ed., McGraw-Hill Book Co., New York, 1962, p. 163.

210. C. C. Tung and A. J. Speziale, *J. Org. Chem.*, **28**, 2009 (1963).

211. P. O. I. Virtanen, *Ann. Acad. Sci. Fennicae, Ser. AII*, 89 (1963); *Chem. Abstr.*, **61**, 2921 (1964).

212. J. K. Addy and R. E. Parker, *J. Chem. Soc.*, 915 (1963).
213. J. K. Addy and R. E. Parker, *J. Chem. Soc.*, 644 (1965).
214. G. Berti, F. Bottari and B. Macchia, *Gazz. Chim. Ital.*, **90**, 1783 (1960).
215. N. N. Lebedev and K. A. Gus'kov, *Kinetika i Kataliz*, **4**, 116 (1963); *Chem. Abstr.*, **59**, 3735 (1963).
216. N. N. Lebedev and K. A. Gus'kov, *Kinetika i Kataliz*, 787 (1964); *Chem. Abstr.*, **62**, 3898 (1965).
217. N. N. Lebedev and K. A. Gus'kov, *Kinetika i Kataliz*, **4**, 581 (1963); *Chem. Abstr.*, **59**, 15136 (1963).
218. M. W. Miller, *J. Org. Chem.*, **28**, 1148 (1963).
219. N. N. Lebedev and K. A. Gus'kov, *Kinetika i Kataliz*, **5**, 446 (1964); *Chem. Abstr.*, **61**, 8150 (1964).
220. T. Cohen, M. Dughi, V. A. Notaro, and G. Pinkus, *J. Org. Chem.*, **27**, 814 (1962).
221. G. Berti, F. Bottari, and B. Macchia, *Ann. Chim. (Rome)*, **52**, 1101 (1962).
222. F. Fischer and H. Rönsch, *Chem. Ber.*, **94**, 901 (1961).
223. S. Sakai and Y. Ishii, *Kogyo Kagaku Zasshi*, **61**, 1473 (1958); *Chem. Abstr.*, **56**, 13088 (1961).
224. F. Patat and B. Wojtech, *Makromol. Chem.*, **37**, 1 (1962).
225. Y. Ishii, Y. Nishikawa, and H. Kato, *Kogyo Kagaku Zasshi*, **63**, 2177 (1960); *Chem. Abstr.*, **57**, 8523 (1962).
226. F. Patat and E. Wittmann, *Z. Naturforsch., Ser. A*, **18**, 169 (1963).
227. S. Sakai, T. Sugiyama, and Y. Ishii, *Kogyo Kagaku Zasshi*, **66**, 355 (1963); *Chem. Abstr.*, **59**, 12605 (1963).
228. V. F. Shvets and N. W. Lebedev, *Tr. Mosk. Khim. Tekhnol. Inst.*, 79 (1963); *Chem. Abstr.*, **62**, 7603 (1965).
229. W. J. Belanger and J. H. Denham, *Am. Chem. Soc. Div. Paint, Plastic, Printing Chem., Preprints*, **18**, 10 (1958); *Chem. Abstr.*, **58**, 2335 (1963).
230. Y. Ishii, S. Ito, and Y. Nishikawa, *Kogyo Kagaku Zasshi*, **63**, 1751 (1960); *Chem. Abstr.*, **57**, 9642 (1962).
231. S. Sekiguchi, I. Takase, and K. Matsui, *Kogyo Kagaku Zasshi*, **66**, 12827 (1963); *Chem. Abstr.*, **60**, 14346 (1964).
232. N. N. Lebedev and M. M. Smirnova, *Kinetika i Kataliz*, **2**, 519 (1961); *Chem. Abstr.*, **56**, 8052 (1961).
233. N. N. Lebedev and M. M. Smirnova, *Izv. Vysshykh Uchebn. Zavedenii, Khim. i Khim. Tekhnol.*, **3**, 104 (1960); *Chem. Abstr.*, **54**, 16149 (1960).
234. I. I. Yukel'son and R. M. Terekhin, *Tr. Vovonezhsk. Tekhnol. Inst.*, **16**, 31 (1960); *Chem. Abstr.*, **58**, 3286 (1963).
235. Y. Oshiro, K. Asado, and S. Komori, *Kogyo Kagaku Zasshi*, **65**, 187 (1962); *Chem. Abstr.*, **58**, 2333 (1963).
236. V. M. Al'bitskaya, A. A. Petrov, and E. M. Blyakhman, *Zh. Obshch. Khim.*, **31**, 2166 (1961); *Chem. Abstr.*, **56**, 2363 (1961).
237. M. Freifelder and G. R. Stone, *J. Org. Chem*, **26**, 1477 (1961).
238. Y. Oshiro, T. Tsunoda and S. Komori, *Kogyo Kagaku Zasshi*, **64**, 2132 (1961); *Chem. Abstr.*, **57**, 2054 (1962).
239. J. Hannson, *Svensk Kem. Tidskr.*, **66**, 351 (1954).
240. P. R. Wells, *Chem. Rev.*, **63**, 201 (1963).
241. J. K. Addy, R. M. Laird, and R. E. Parker, *J. Chem. Soc.*, 1708 (1961).
242. R. M. Laird and R. E. Parker, *J. Am. Chem. Soc.*, **83**, 4237 (1961).

243. R. M. Laird and R. E. Parker, *J. Chem. Soc.*, 6065 (1963).
244. R. E. Parker and B. W. Rockctt, *J. Chem. Soc.*, 2569 (1965).
245. S. Sakai, T. Sugiyama, and Y. Ishii, *Kogyo Kagaku Zasshi*, **67**, 333 (1964); *Chem. Abstr.*, **61**, 1724 (1964).
246. Y. Oshiro and S. Komori, *Kogyo Kagaku Zasshi*, **65**, 1830 (1962); *Chem. Abstr.*, **59**, 1447 (1963).
247. A. L. Draper, W. J. Heilman, W. E. Schaefer, H. J. Shine, and J. N. Shoolery, *J. Org. Chem.*, **27**, 2727 (1962).
248. J. Meinwald, S. S. Labana, and M. S. Chadra, *J. Am. Chem. Soc.*, **85**, 582 (1963).
249. J. Meinwald, S. S. Labana, L. L. Labana, and G. H. Wahl, Jr., *Tetrahedron Letters*, 1789 (1965).
250. R. N. McDonald and P. S. Schwab, *J. Am. Chem. Soc.*, **85**, 4004 (1963).
251. R. N. McDonald and P. A. Schwab, *J. Org. Chem.*, **29**, 2458 (1964).
252. R. N. McDonald, P. A. Schwab, and T. E. Tabor, *J. Am. Chem. Soc.*, **85**, 820 (1963).
253. C. H. DePuy, R. A. Klein, and G. M. Dappen, *J. Org. Chem.*, **27**, 3742 (1962).
254. M. S. Malinorskii and A. G. Yudasina, *Zh. Obshch. Khim.*, **30**, 1831 (1960); *Chem. Abstr.*, **55**, 7341 (1961).
255. M. P. Hartshorn, D. N. Kirk, and A. F. A. Wallis, *J. Chem. Soc.*, 5494 (1964).
256. E. E. Royals and L. L. Harell, Jr., *J. Am. Chem. Soc.*, **77**, 3405 (1956).
257. R. L. Settine, G. L. Parks, and G. L. K. Hunter, *J. Org. Chem.*, **29**, 616 (1964).
258. I. C. Nigam and L. Levi, *J. Org. Chem.*, **30**, 653 (1965).
259. H. Griseback and W. Barz, *Chem. Ber.*, **97**, 1688 (1964).
260. D. J. Goldsmith and C. J. Cheer, *J. Org. Chem.*, **30**, 2264 (1965).
261. M. P. Hartshorn and D. N. Kirk, *Tetrahedron*, **20**, 2547 (1964).
262. M. P. Hartshorn and D. N. Kirk, *Tetrahedron*, **20**, 2943 (1964).
263. J. W. Blunt, M. P. Hartshorn and D. M. Kirk, *Tetrahedron*, **21**, 559, 1547 (1965).
264. D. E. Bissing and A. J. Speziale, *J. Am. Chem. Soc.*, **87**, 1405 (1965).
265. A. C. Cope, J. M. Grisar, and P. E. Peterson, *J. Am. Chem. Soc.*, **81**, 1640 (1959).
266. A. C. Cope, G. A. Berchtold, P. E. Peterson, and S. H. Sharman, *J. Am. Chem. Soc.*, **82**, 6366 (1960).
267. A. C. Cope, L. J. Fleckenstein, S. Moon, and H. E. Petree, *J. Am. Chem. Soc.*, **85**, 3752 (1963).
268. A. C. Cope and J. K. Hecht, *J. Am. Chem. Soc.*, **84**, 4872 (1962).
269. G. B. Payne, *J. Org. Chem.*, **27**, 3819 (1962).
270. S. J. Angyal and P. T. Gilham, *J. Chem. Soc.*, 3691 (1957).
271. W. Reeve and L. W. Fine, *J. Am. Chem. Soc.*, **86**, 880 (1964).
272. D. F. Hoeg, J. E. Forrette, and D. I. Luck, *Tetrahedron Letters*, 2059 (1964).
273. J. Bornstein, M. A. Joseph, and J. E. Shields, *J. Org. Chem.*, **30**, 801 (1965).
274. J. K. Crandall, *J. Org. Chem.*, **29**, 2830 (1964).
275. R. J. Cvetanovic in *Advances in Photochemistry*, Vol. 1 (Eds. W. A. Noyes, Jr., G. S. Hammond, and J. N. Pitts, Jr.), Interscience Publishers, New York, 1963, pp. 115–182.

276. H. E. Zimmerman in *Advances in Photochemistry*, Vol. 1 (Eds. W. A. Noyes, Jr., G. S. Hammond, and J. N. Pitts, Jr.), Interscience Publishers, New York, 1963, pp. 183–208.

277. R. Gomer and W. A. Noyes, Jr., *J. Am. Chem. Soc.*, **72,** 101 (1950).

278. R. J. Cvetanovic, *Can. J. Chem.*, **33,** 1684 (1955).

279. R. J. Cvetanovic and L. C. Doyle, *Can. J. Chem.*, **35,** 605 (1957).

280. C. Walling in *Molecular Rearrangements*, Vol. 1 (Ed. P. de Mayo), Interscience Publishers, New York, 1963, pp. 407–456.

281. G. Fleming, M. M. Anderson, A. J. Harrison, and L. W. Pickett, *J. Chem. Phys.*, **30,** 351 (1959).

282. R. J. Gritter and E. C. Sabatino, *J. Org. Chem.*, **29,** 1965 (1964).

283. S. W. Benson, *J. Chem. Phys.*, **40,** 105 (1964).

284. H. E. Zimmerman, B. R. Cowley, C.-Y. Tseng, and J. W. Wilson, *J. Am. Chem. Soc.*, **86,** 947 (1964).

285. O. Jeger, K. Schaffner, and H. Wehrli, *J. Pure Appl. Chem.*, **9,** 555 (1964).

286. H. E. Zimmerman and R. D. Sinkin, *Tetrahedron Letters*, 1843 (1964) and articles cited.

287. C. K. Johnson, B. Dominy, and W. Reusch, *J. Am. Chem. Soc.*, **85,** 3895 (1963).

288. C. K. Johnson, B. Dominy, and W. Reusch, *J. Am. Chem. Soc.*, **85,** 3994 (1963).

289. H. Wehrli, C. Lehmann, K. Schaffner, and O. Jeger, *Helv. Chim. Acta*, **47,** 1336 (1964).

290. E. F. Ullman, *J. Am. Chem. Soc.*, **85,** 3529 (1963).

291. E. F. Ullman and W. A. Henderson, Jr., *J. Am. Chem. Soc.*, **86,** 5050 (1964).

292. E. F. Ullman, *J. Am. Chem. Soc.*, **86,** 5357 (1964).

293. J. M. Dunston and P. Yates, *Tetrahedron Letters*, 505 (1964).

294. A. Padwa, *Tetrahedron Letters*, 813 (1964).

295. R. Villotti, A. Cervantes, and A. D. Cross, *J. Chem. Soc.*, 3621 (1964).

296. L. Crocco, I. Glassman, and I. E. Smith, *J. Chem. Phys.*, **31,** 506 (1959).

297. M. L. Neufeld and A. T. Blades, *Can. J. Chem.*, **41,** 2956 (1963).

298. T. J. Wallace and R. J. Gritter, *Tetrahedron*, **19,** 657 (1963).

299. E. C. Sabatino, *Ph.D. Thesis*, University of Connecticut, 1963.

300. R. A. Bouffard, *Ph.D. Thesis*, University of Connecticut, 1964.

301. R. J. Gritter and E. C. Sabatino, *J. Org. Chem.*, **28,** 3437 (1963).

302. E. S. Huyser and L. R. Munson, *J. Org. Chem.*, **30,** 1436 (1965).

303. M. Bartok and J. Apjok, *Acta Univ. Szeged, Acta Phys. Chem.*, **8,** 133 (1962); *Chem. Abstr.*, **59,** 6337 (1963).

304. O. Kovacs, Z. Tuba, J. Weisz and G. Schneider, *Izv. Akad. Nauk SSSR, Otd. Khim.*, 130 (1962); *Chem. Abstr.*, **57,** 11135 (1962).

305. W. S. Lafferty, R. C. Lord, and D. W. Mayo, *J. Org. Chem.*, **29,** 2799 (1964).

306. E. Paterno and G. Chieffi, *Gazz. Chim. Ital.*, **39,** 341 (1909).

307. G. Büchi, C. G. Inman, and E. S. Lipinsky, *J. Am. Chem. Soc.*, **76,** 4327 (1954).

308. R. Srinivasan, *J. Am. Chem. Soc.*, **82,** 775 (1960).

309. J. D. Margerum, J. N. Pitts, Jr., J. G. Rutgers, and S. Searles, Jr., *J. Am. Chem. Soc.*, **81,** 1549 (1959).

310. S. Toki, K. Shima, and H. Sakurai, *Bull. Chem. Soc. Japan*, **38,** 760 (1965).

311. N. C. Yang, M. Nussim, M. J. Jorgenson, and S. Murov, *Tetrahedron Letters*, 3657 (1964).
312. G. S. Hammond and N. J. Turro, *Science*, **142**, 1541 (1963).
313. D. R. Arnold, R. L. Hinman, and A. H. Glick, *Tetrahedron Letters*, 1425 (1964).
314. D. Bryce-Smith and A. Gilbert, *Proc. Chem. Soc.*, 87 (1964).
315. H. J. Cenci, *U.S. Pat.*, 3,146,180, Aug. 25, 1964; *Chem. Abstr.*, **61**, 10658 (1964).
316. J. J. Beereboom and M. S. Wittenau, *J. Org. Chem.*, **30**, 1231 (1965).
317. H. Morrison, *J. Am. Chem. Soc.*, **87**, 932 (1965); *Tetrahedron Letters*, 3653 (1964).
318. P. Yates and A. G. Azabo, *Tetrahedron Letters*, 485 (1965).
319. R. B. LaCount and C. E. Griffin, *Tetrahedron Letters*, 1549 (1965).
320. A. A. Lamola, P. A. Leermaker, G. W. Byers, and G. S. Hammond, *J. Am. Chem. Soc.*, **87**, 2322 (1965).
321. D. J. Coyle, *Meeting Am. Chem. Soc.*, *Sept. 1964*, Abstr. p. 24S.
322. J. A. Barthrop and B. Hesp, *Proc. Chem. Soc.*, 195 (1964).
323. E. Switak, *Compt. Rend.*, **240**, 1544 (1955).
324. S. Olsen and R. Bredock, *Chem. Ber.*, **91**, 1589 (1958).
325. L. F. Schmoyer and L. C. Case, *Nature*, **187**, 592 (1960).
326. L. Kh. Freidlin, V. Z. Sharf, and N. S. Andreev, *Izv. Akad. Nauk SSSR, Otd. Khim. Nauk*, 373 (1961); *Chem. Abstr.*, **55**, 19774 (1961).
327. Yu. K. Yur'ev and O. M. Revenko, *Vestn. Mosk. Univ., Ser. II, Khim.*, **17**, 68 (1962); *Chem. Abstr.*, **58**, 4500 (1963).
328. A. J. Matuszko and M. S. Chang, *Chem. Ind. (London)*, 822 (1963).
329. G. Ohloff, K. H. Schulte-Elte, and B. Willhalm, *Helv. Chim. Acta*, **47**, 602 (1964); *Chem. Abstr.*, **60**, 13275 (1964).
330. B. T. Gillis and P. E. Beck, *J. Org. Chem.*, **28**, 1388 (1963).
331. V. J. Traynelis, W. L. Hergenrother, H. T. Hanson, and J. A. Valicenti, *J. Org. Chem.*, **29**, 123 (1964).
332. N. I. Chouikin and I. F. Belski, *Bull. Soc. Chim. France*, 1556 (1956).
333. P. A. Moshkin, *Vopr. Ispol'z. Pentozansoderzh. Syr'ya, Tr. Vses. Soveshch. Riga*, 225 (1955); *Chem. Abstr.*, **53**, 15048 (1959).
334. A. A. Ponomarev and A. S. Chegolya, *Zh. Obshch. Khim.*, **34**, 1193 (1964); *Chem. Abstr.*, **61**, 1819 (1964).
335. J. T. Edward and J. M. Ferland, *Chem. Ind. (London)*, 975 (1964).
336. A. I. Meyers and K. Baburso, *J. Hetero. Chem.*, **1**, 203 (1964).
337. G. Descotes, B. Giroud-Abel, and J. C. Martein, *Compt. Rend.*, **258**, 6460 (1964).
338. E. Müller, H. Kessler, H. Fricke, and H. Suhr, *Tetrahedron Letters*, 1047 (1963).
339. J. H. S. Weiland, *Rec. Trav. Chim.*, **83**, 81 (1964).
340. A. Kirrmann and N. Hamaide, *Bull. Soc. Chim. France*, 789 (1957).
341. A. Kirrmann and L. Wartski, *Compt. Rend.*, **259**, 2857 (1964).
342. M. Bartok and A. S. Gilde, *Acta Phys. Chem.*, **9**, 25, 37 (1963).
343. R. G. Gillis, *J. Org. Chem.*, **25**, 651 (1960).
344. F. F. Rust, *J. Am. Chem. Soc.*, **79**, 4000 (1957).
345. A. P. Zeelenberg and A. F. Bickel, *J. Chem. Soc.*, 4014 (1961).
346. P. J. Luecchesi and W. Bartok, *J. Am. Chem. Soc.*, **82**, 4528 (1960).

347. A. Fish, *Quart. Rev. Chem. Soc.*, **18**, 243 (1964).
348. F. D. Greene, M. L. Savitz, F. D. Osterholtz, H. H. Lau, W. N. Smith, and P. M. Zanet, *J. Org. Chem.*, **28**, 55 (1963).
349. A. C. Cope, R. S. Bly, M. M. Martin, and R. C. Peterson, *J. Am. Chem. Soc.*, **87**, 3111 (1965).
350. E. J. Corey and R. W. White, *J. Am. Chem. Soc.*, **80**, 6686 (1958).
351. R. A. Sneen and N. P. Matheny, *J. Am. Chem. Soc.*, **86**, 3905 (1964); **86**, 5503 (1964).
352. M. Akhtar, P. Hunt, and P. B. Dewhurst, *J. Am. Chem. Soc.*, **87**, 1807 (1965).
353. K. Heusler and J. Kalvoda, *Angew. Chem.*, **3**, 525 (1964).
354. M. Akhtar in *Advances in Photochemistry*, Vol. 2 (Eds. W. A. Noyes, Jr., G. S. Hammond, and J. N. Pitts), Interscience Publishers, New York, 1964, pp. 263–304.
355. V. M. Micovic, R. I. Mamuzic, D. Jeremic, and M. Lj. Mihailovic, *Tetrahedron Letters*, 2091 (1963).
356. K. Katahonoki and A. Matsuura, *Tetrahedron Letters*, 2263 (1964).
357. V. M. Micovic, S. Stojcic, S. Mladenovic, and M. Stefanonic, *Tetrahedron Letters*, 1559 (1965).
358. R. M. Moriarty and K. Kapodia, *Tetrahedron Letters*, 1165 (1964).
359. D. Hauser, K. Schaffner, and O. Jeger, *Helv. Chim. Acta*, **47**, 1883 (1964).
360. R. M. Moriarty and H. G. Walsh, *Tetrahedron Letters*, 465 (1965).
361. A. C. Cope, M. Gordon, S. Moon, and C. H. Park, *J. Am. Chem. Soc.*, **87**, 3119 (1965).
362. F. Bohlman, H. J. Schulz, and J. Riemann, *Tetrahedron Letters*, 1705 (1964).
363. P. Chabrier and J. Seyden-Penne, *Bull. Soc. Chim. France*, **2074** (1961).
364. F. R. Jensen and R. L. Bedard, *J. Org. Chem.*, **24**, 874 (1959).
365. W. J. Bailey and F. Marktscheffel, *J. Org. Chem.*, **25**, 1797 (1960).
366. G. Wittig and G. Kolb, *Chem. Ber.*, **93**, 1469 (1960).
367. A. Y. Garner and A. A. Tedeschi, *J. Am. Chem. Soc.*, **84**, 4734 (1964) and previous references noted.
368. J. Kollonitsch, *J. Am. Chem. Soc.*, **83**, 1515 (1961).
369. J. Kollonitsch, *U.S. Pat.*, 3,112,336, Nov. 26, 1963; *Chem. Abstr.*, **60**, 2766 (1964).
370. G. F. Freeguard and L. H. Long, *Chem. Ind.* (*London*), 1582 (1964).
371. I. F. Bel'skii and N. I. Shuikin, *Dokl. Akad. Nauk SSSR*, **127**, 91 (1959); *Chem. Abstr.*, **54**, 267 (1960).
372. N. I. Shuikin, I. F. Bel'skii, and R. A. Karakhanow, *Z. Chem.*, **3**, 222 (1963).
373. N. I. Shuikin, M. Bartok, E. Kovoch, and I. F. Bel'skii, *Izv. Akad. Nauk SSSR, Otd. Khim.*, 1653 (1962); *Chem. Abstr.*, **58**, 4492 (1963).
374. N. I. Shuikin and V. V. An, *Izv. Akad. Nauk SSSR, Otd. Khim. Nauk*, 1508 (1960); *Chem. Abstr.*, **55**, 524 (1961).
375. N. I. Shuikin and V. V. An, *Izv. Akad. Nauk SSSR, Ser. Khim.*, 1478 (1963); *Chem. Abstr.*, **59**, 13923 (1963).
376. E. Kovach, N. I. Shuikin, M. Bartok, and I. F. Bel'skii, *Izv. Akad. Nauk SSSR, Otd. Khim. Nauk*, 124 (1962); *Chem. Abstr.*, **57**, 11136 (1962).
377. N. I. Shuikin, O. Kovacic, I. F. Bel'skii, and M. Bartok, *Acta Chim. Akad. Sci. Hung.*, **38**, 115 (1963); *Chem. Abstr.*, **60**, 5430 (1964).

378. N. I. Shuikin, R. A. Karakhavow, and I. I. Ibrahimov, *Izv. Akad. Nauk SSSR, Ser. Khim.*, 165 (1965).

379. N. I. Shuikin and I. F. Bel'skii, *Dokl. Akad. Nauk SSSR*, **111**, 1048 (1956); *Chem. Abstr.*, **51**, 9568 (1957).

380. I. P. Tsukervanik and Ch. Sh. Kadyrov, *Dokl. Akad. Nauk Uz. SSR*, 31 (1958); *Chem. Abstr.*, **53**, 16083 (1959).

381. G. Sieben, *Ann. Chem.*, **631**, 180 (1960).

382. C. S. Rondestvedt, Jr., *J. Org. Chem.*, **26**, 3024 (1961).

383. N. I. Shuikin, I. E. Grushko, and I. F. Bel'skii, *Dokl. Akad. Nauk SSSR*, **141**, 649 (1961); *Chem. Abstr.*, **56**, 12829 (1961).

384. R. D. Youssefyeh and Y. Mazur, *Tetrahedron Letters*, 1287 (1962).

385. N. I. Shuikin, I. F. Bel'skii, and I. E. Grushko, *Izv. Akad. Nauk SSSR, Otd. Khim. Nauk*, 557 (1963); *Chem. Abstr.*, **59**, 2750 (1963).

386. L. M. Berkowitz and P. N. Rylander, *J. Am. Chem. Soc.*, **80**, 6682 (1958).

387. D. G. Farnum and M. Burr, *J. Org. Chem.*, **28**, 1387 (1963).

388. Yu. K. Yur'ev and O. M. Revenko, *Zh. Obshch. Khim.*, **31**, 1883 (1961); *Chem. Abstr.*, **55**, 27298 (1961).

389. Yu. K. Yur'ev and O. M. Revenko, *Zh. Obshch. Khim.*, **32**, 1822 (1962); *Chem. Abstr.*, **58**, 4505 (1963).

390. W. J. Gensler and G. L. McLeod, *J. Org. Chem.*, **28**, 3194 (1963).

391. D. M. A. Armitage and C. L. Wilson, *J. Am. Chem. Soc.*, **81**, 2437 (1959).

392. D. Gagnaire and A. Butt, *Bull. Soc. Chim. France*, 309 (1961).

393. N. I. Shuikin and G. K. Vasilevskaya, *Dokl. Akad. Nauk SSSR*, **159**, 395 (1964); *Chem. Abstr.*, **62**, 6449 (1965).

394. G. T. Kwiatkowski, S. J. Kavarnos, and W. D. Closson, *J. Hetero. Chem.*, **2**, 11 (1965).

395. L. Gouin, *Ann. Chim.* (*Paris*), **5**, 529 (1960).

396. L. D. Bergel'son and M. M. Shemyakin, *Tetrahedron*, **19**, 149 (1963).

397. J. C. Anderson, D. G. Lindsay and C. B. Reese, *J. Chem. Soc.*, **4874** (1964).

398. R. S. Shank and H. Shechter, *J. Org. Chem.*, **24**, 1825 (1959).

399. S. Olsen, *Acta Chem. Scand.*, **5**, 1168 (1951).

400. J. Falbe and F. Korte, *Chem. Ber.*, **97**, 1104 (1964); *Chem. Abstr.*, **61**, 634 (1964).

401. G. Descotes and J. C. Soula, *Bull. Soc. Chim. France*, 2639 (1964).

402. M. Kratochvil and J. Jonas, *Spisy Prirodovedecke Fak. Univ. Brne*, **447**, 419 (1963); *Chem. Abstr.*, **62**, 3992 (1965).

403. G. Sosnovsky, *Free Radical Reactions in Preparative Organic Chemistry*, Macmillan Co., New York, 1964.

404. R. D. Olson and V. I. Stenberg, *Proc. N. Dakota Acad. Sci.*, **17**, 50 (1964); *Chem. Abstr.*, **60**, 6384 (1964).

405. S.-O. Lawesson and C. Berglund, *Acta Chem. Scand.*, **14**, 1854 (1960).

406. S.-O. Lawesson and C. Berglund, *Arkiv Kemi*, **17**, 475 (1961).

407. G. Sosnovsky, *Tetrahedron*, **21**, 871 (1965).

408. G. Sosnovsky and S.-O. Lawesson, *Angew. Chem.*, **3**, 269 (1964).

409. L. Horner, B. Anders and O. Basedow, *Ann. Chem.*, **635**, 46 (1960).

410. H. Gross, *Angew. Chem.*, **72**, 268 (1960).

411. M. Kratochvil and I. Hort, *Collection Czech. Chem. Comm.*, **27**, 52 (1962).

412. J. K. Kochi, *J. Am. Chem. Soc.*, **84**, 2131 (1962).

413. E. Mueller and H. Huber, *Chem. Ber.*, **96**, 2319 (1963).

414. E. S. Huyser, *J. Org. Chem.*, **25**, 1820 (1960).
415. J. Diekmann and C. J. Pedersen, *J. Org. Chem.*, **28**, 2879 (1960).
416. T. J. Wallace and R. J. Gritter, *J. Org. Chem.*, **27**, 3067 (1962).
417. N. I. Shuikin and B. L. Lebedev, *Dokl. Akad. Nauk SSSR*, **139**, 131 (1961); *Chem. Abstr.*, **56**, 1417 (1962).
418. N. I. Shuikin and B. L. Lebedev, *Izv. Akad. Nauk SSSR*, 2195 (1961); *Chem. Abstr.*, **57**, 11139 (1962).
419. N. I. Shuikin and B. L. Lebedev, *Izv. Akad. Nauk SSSR*, 533 (1962); *Chem. Anstr.*, **57**, 15044 (1962).
420. R. L. Jacobs and G. G. Ecke, *J. Org. Chem.*, **28**, 3036 (1963).
421. N. I. Shuikin, B. L. Lebedev, and V. G. Nikol'skii, *Dokl. Akad. Nauk SSSR*, **158**, 692 (1964); *Chem. Abstr.*, **62**, 3998 (1965).
422. D. Elad and R. D. Youssefyeh, *J. Org. Chem.*, **26**, 2031 (1964).
423. H. G. Walsh, *Senior Thesis*, University of Connecticut, 1961.
424. D. E. Applequist and L. Kaplan, *J. Am. Chem. Soc.*, **87**, 2194 (1965).

CHAPTER **10**

Methods of formation of the ether linkage

Henry Feuer

Purdue University, Lafayette, Indiana, U.S.A.

and

John Hooz

University of Alberta, Edmonton, Canada

I. INTRODUCTION

One of the earliest recorded methods for the formation of the ether linkage goes back to 1544, when Valerius Cordus[1] described the preparation of ethyl ether from ethanol and oil of vitriol.

The pioneering work of Alexander William Williamson in the period 1850–1860 not only established the correct formula of ethyl ether but also contributed a very important method for the synthesis of ethers; namely, the reaction of alkoxides with alkyl halides. Since its inception more than 100 years ago, the utility of this method has become well documented by a continuous flow of publications in which the original procedure has undergone considerable modifications.

The discussions in this chapter deal mainly with recent developments in the synthesis of ethers. These also include mechanistic considerations whenever they may serve to clarify and predict conditions advantageous to the formation of the C—O—C bond.

The formation of α-haloalkyl ethers, ethynyl ethers, vinyl ethers, and the addition of alcohols and phenols to olefins have not been considered in this chapter, because they have been treated adequately elsewhere*.

II. NUCLEOPHILIC SUBSTITUTIONS

A. Reactions of Alkoxides with Alkyl Halides

Conversion of an alcohol into an effective nucleophile, which displaces a good leaving group from some other substrate, constitutes one of the important methods for forming the C—O—C bond (equation 1).

$$R^1O^- + R^2X \longrightarrow R^1OR^2 + X^- \tag{1}$$

In the preparations of simple and mixed ethers from alkyl halides and alkoxides, the original procedure of Williamson[2] has undergone many variations both with regard to the preparation of the alkoxides and with regard to the reaction medium.

Reactions are carried out with preformed alkoxides in inert solvents, or in an excess of the alcohol in which the halide is dissolved, or in

* See references 175–183.

liquid ammonia[3]. In general, higher yields are obtained in the latter solvent with metal phenolates, which are more soluble than metal alcoholates and induce less dehydrohalogenation in the alkyl halides. Alkyl bromides afford higher yields of ethers because they are more reactive than alkyl chlorides and are less susceptible to dehydrohalogenation than alkyl iodides. Also, an improvement in yield is realized at elevated pressures (Table 1)[4].

TABLE 1. Preparation of ethers in liquid ammonia.

R in RONa	Alkyl halide	Time (h)	Max. pressure (atm)	% Yield
Bu	BuBr	1	1	8
Bu	BuBr	1	10	28
Am	AmCl	2	2·7	3
Am	AmBr	2	2·7	32
Am	AmBr	5	2·7	33
Am	AmI	2	2·7	17
Am	BuCl	2	3	0
Am	BuBr	2	3	28
Ph	AmBr	2	3	45

The liquid ammonia method has been adapted for the alkylation of carbohydrates[5] and is claimed to be superior to the reaction with silver oxide and alkyl iodide[6] or dimethyl sulfate and alkali[7].

Various methods are employed to convert higher molecular weight alcohols into their salts. These include the use of sodium hydride[8] and sodium amide[9], or the refluxing of sodium or potassium in high-boiling solvents such as benzene[10], toluene[11], dioxane[12], or xylene[13] with the mixture of alcohol and alkyl halide. In some cases, sodium naphthalene[14] is employed.

The correct choice of the alkyl halide–alcoholate combination is often critical for successful ether preparations. Kirner[15] has found that while the reaction of furfuryl chloride with a number of alcoholates affords ethers in high yield, tetrahydrofurfuryl chloride does not react under the same conditions. On the other hand, mixed ethers are readily obtained with the combination tetrahydrofurfuryl alcohol–alkyl bromide[16].

The usual method for preparing optically active ethers by the reaction of an alkyl halide with alkali alcoholates leads in the case of phenyl methyl carbinyl ethers to partially racemized products[17]. This is caused by partial racemization of the alcohol in the conversion into the alcoholate[18], especially in the presence of traces of oxidizing agents[19]. By employing the procedure of Purdie[6] in which alcohols are converted into ethers with an alkyl iodide–silver oxide mixture, Mislow[20] prepared optically pure ethyl α-methylbenzyl ether. Also, Streitwieser[21] converted (+)-2-octanol and (+)-2-butanol to the corresponding ethyl ethers in high optical purity by using ethyl bromide. But this procedure caused some racemization in the conversion of benzyl-α-d alcohol into its ethyl ether. The highest optical rotation for ethyl benzyl-α-d ether was obtained from benzyl-α-d tosylate and alcoholic sodium ethoxide[22].

In the preparation of ethers, in which secondary or tertiary alkyl groups are involved, difficulties are encountered because of side-reactions, mostly of the $E2$ type. These can be minimized in mixed ether preparations by employing secondary or tertiary alcohols as the nucleophiles. This procedure is not applicable to the synthesis of simple ethers such as di-t-butyl ether, but the reaction between t-butyl chloride and silver carbonate leads to t-butyl ether in 35% yield[23]. More convenient methods involve the acid-catalyzed condensation of t-butyl alcohol or isobutylene with the corresponding alcohols[24] and the reaction of t-butyl perbenzoate with Grignard reagents[25] (see section IV.B).

B. Reactions of Aryl Oxides with Alkyl Halides

Procedures for alkylating phenols follow largely those of alcohols except that weaker bases can be employed because of the higher acidity of phenols. The method of Claisen[26] which is especially suitable with the more reactive alkyl halides, such as allylic halides, has been used extensively (reaction 2). By this method White and coworkers[27]

$$p\text{-ClC}_6\text{H}_4\text{OH} + \text{CH}_2\text{=CHCH}_2\text{Br} \xrightarrow[\text{CH}_3\text{COCH}_3]{\text{K}_2\text{CO}_3} p\text{-ClC}_6\text{H}_4\text{OCH}_2\text{CH=CH}_2 \quad (2)$$

have prepared in high yield a number of alkyl *para*-substituted phenyl ethers.

The reaction of phenols with halohydrins[28] and with dihaloalkanes[29] in ethanolic sodium ethoxide constitutes a convenient route to aryloxy alcohols and aryloxy alkyl halides; and the higher reactivity of one of the chlorine atoms in 1,1,2-trichloro-2,2-difluoroethane has been utilized to prepare a number of 1-aryloxy-1,1-difluoro-2,2-dichloroethanes[30].

A novel procedure for preparing benzyl ethers at room temperature by converting substituted phenols into phenolates with strongly basic anion-exchange resins such as IRA-400 and Dowex 1-X4 is due to the work of Rowe and coworkers[31]. Both column and batch techniques are applicable.

The preparation of alkyl picryl ethers from silver picrate is successful at 0° with the C_1–C_3 iodides, the n-butyl, isobutyl, and isoamyl iodides, and also at −60° with isopropyl iodide[32]. Surprisingly, the reaction is unsuccessful with 2-butyl, n-pentyl, and 2-pentyl iodide and gives rise to picric acid. This acid is again the sole product when alkyl bromides are employed as the alkylating agents.

Reactions of polyhydric phenols with alkyl iodides and alkali lead to oxygen- and carbon-alkylated products[33] and in the case of phloroglucinol the only product is the completely methylated 1,3,5-trioxo-2,2,4,4,6,6-hexamethylcyclohexane. However, by keeping the reaction mixture acidic during the addition of sodium methylate, 1,3,5-trimethoxybenzene is obtained. As shown by Wenkert[34], mixtures of oxygen- and carbon-alkylated products can also result with monohydric phenols. The reaction of sodium 2-naphthoxide with methyl iodide in toluene gives preponderantly 1-methyl-2-naphthol, and with n-butyl bromide both oxygen- and carbon-alkylation products are obtained in a 1·4:1 ratio. 1,1-Dimethyl-2(1H)-naphthalenone is the major product (88% yield) from sodium 1-methyl-2-naphthoxide and methyl iodide (reaction 3).

Factors which influence oxygen- against carbon-alkylation in reactions of monohydric phenols with alkyl and the highly reactive allyl and benzyl halides have been studied extensively by Kornblum and

15+c.e.l.

coworkers[35] and their important contributions and conclusions will be discussed in section II.H.

C. Reactions of Alkoxides with Aryl Halides

The displacement of halogen in aromatic compounds by alkoxide usually requires high temperatures, and the resulting ethers are obtained in low yield. More favorable results are obtained with poly-halobenzenes in which the combined inductive effects of the halogens are operative. The reaction of 1,3,5-trichlorobenzene with excess alcoholic sodium ethoxide for 50 hours at 170° affords 3,5-dichloro-1-ethoxybenzene and 5-chloro-1,3-diethoxybenzene (yields unstated)[36]. Nucleophilic attack on hexachlorobenzene is highly accelerated in such solvents as pyridine, picoline, and lutidine. For example the reaction time with sodium methoxide, which in refluxing methanol requires one hour, is reduced to one minute, affording 90% of 1-methoxy-2,3,4,-5,6-pentachlorobenzene[37]. Due to the combined inductive effect of the fluorine atoms, hexafluorobenzene is about 10^7 times more reactive than fluorobenzene[38] at 50° in the bimolecular reaction with sodium methoxide, and the energy of activation of the former is about 10 kcal/mole lower[39].

The displacement of halogen on the aromatic ring by nucleophiles is greatly facilitated by the presence of electron-withdrawing groups in the *ortho* and *para* positions. In the preparations of nitrophenyl ethers, low concentration of the alkoxide and temperatures below 70° lead to high yields. In concentrated solutions and at higher temperatures the reducing action of alkoxides on the nitrohalobenzenes becomes prevalent and azoxy compounds are formed[40]. The reducing action can be inhibited by oxidizing agents such as manganese dioxide[41]. The trifluoromethyl group also facilitates the substitution of chlorine by alkoxide, and the order of reactivity of the various compounds investigated is[42]:

$$2,4,6\text{-}(CF_3)_3C_6H_2Cl > 2,4\text{-}(CF_3)_2C_6H_3Cl > 2,6\text{-}(CF_3)_2C_6H_3Cl > 2,5\text{-}(CF_3)_2C_6H_3Cl >$$
$$4\text{-}CF_3C_6H_4Cl > 2\text{-}CF_3C_6H_4Cl > 3\text{-}CF_3C_6H_4Cl \approx 3,5\text{-}(CF_3)_2C_6H_3Cl$$

The rate of replacement of halogen by methoxide in methanol in *o*- and *p*-nitrohalobenzenes and in 2,4-dinitrohalobenzenes decreases in the order $F > Cl > Br > I$[43]. In the presence of triethylamine, primary alcohols react exothermically with 2,4-dinitrofluorobenzene (reaction 4) while higher temperatures are required with secondary and tertiary alcohols[44]. Compound 1 is much more reactive with alcohols and phenols in the presence of potassium fluoride than in other bases. The reaction proceeds essentially in neutral medium and the yield is almost quantitative (Table 2)[45].

TABLE 2. Ether formation from 2,4-dinitrofluorobenzene (1) with various alcohols and phenols according to equation (4).

R in ROH	Time (h)	% Yield
Ethyl	1	93
Octadecyl	5	81
1-Naphthyl	0·5	97
2-Naphthyl	0·5	93
p-Isooctylphenyl	0·5	95
o-Diphenyl	0·5	99
p-Diphenyl	0·5	95
o-Carboxymethylphenyl	1	95
N-Phenyl-1,2,3,4-tetrahydro-3-quinolinyl	5	79

$$O_2N-\underset{(1)}{\underset{NO_2}{\bigcirc}}-F + ROH + KF \xrightarrow{100-110°} O_2N-\underset{(2)}{\underset{NO_2}{\bigcirc}}-OR + KHF_2 \quad (4)$$

Although nitro groups in the *meta* positions do not exert much activation on halogen atoms, the situation is different in 1,3,5-trinitrobenzene. Here one of the nitro groups is readily substituted by alcohols in strongly alkaline media[46] or at rather mild basic conditions in 76% aqueous methanol in the presence of either sodium or potassium bicarbonate or sodium carbonate[47]. The failure of other weak bases to catalyze the reaction indicates that the bicarbonate and carbonate ion play a specific role in the displacement reaction. It was suggested that the course of this transformation is analogous to that presented by Bunnett[48] for the von Richter reaction. The essential feature of the mechanism is the nucleophilic attack of bicarbonate ion on the position *ortho* to the nitro group to give a Meisenheimer type o-quinonoid intermediate which undergoes subsequent transformations to the final product (reaction 5). Recently, Rosenblum[49] has proposed a modification for the mechanism in the von Richter reaction in order to account for the fact that nitrogen is a product of the reaction. But this modification does not seem to be applicable to the case under discussion.

$$(5)$$

Alkyl 2,4-dinitrophenyl ethers undergo transetherification in basic media with alcohols in the C_1-C_4 range and with polyhydric alcohols[50]. The reaction is reversible when R^1 is alkyl but irreversible when R^1 is aryl (reaction 6). The rate of formation of phenol in the

$$(6)$$

irreversible exchange between 2,4-dinitrodiphenyl ether and methoxide ion is proportional to the product of the concentration of the original ether and methoxide. Electron-withdrawing groups in the 4'-position increase the rate, while electron-donating groups in the 2'- or 4'-position of the phenyl group decrease it. The effect of the substituent on the rate coefficient satisfies Hammett's equation, giving a ρ value of $+1\cdot46 \pm 0\cdot04$[51]. The data can be explained by the formation of an activated complex (3). An electron-attracting group Y would not only speed up the formation of the complex but would also accelerate fission of the carbon–oxygen bond (x) because of the bond-weakening effect on (x).

(3)

A solid red-colored intermediate of the type **3** was isolated by Meisenheimer[52] on treating either 2,4,6-trinitroanisole with potassium ethoxide or 2,4,6-trinitrophenetole with potassium methoxide (reaction 7). The possibility of such covalent complexes being true inter-

mediates in aromatic S_N2 type processes has been considered by many investigators and the subject has recently been discussed in detail[53]. Based on a low-temperature (-60 to $-80°$) kinetic study by optical methods, the formation at a fast rate of a charge-transfer complex which rearranges in a slow step to the Meisenheimer complex, has been suggested[54] in the reaction between 2,4,6-trinitroanisole and sodium ethoxide. But based on recent nuclear magnetic resonance studies, Servis[55] is of the opinion that initially the unstable anion (**4**) is formed in the reaction between 2,4,6-trinitroanisole and sodium methoxide in dimethyl sulfoxide, which then rearranges very rapidly to the Meisenheimer-type complex (reaction 8). The apparent first-order rate coefficient for the rearrangement at $30°$ is 4×10^{-3} sec^{-1}.

On the basis of nuclear magnetic resonance spectra, Crampton and Gold[56] have also ruled out the formation of charge-transfer complexes in reactions of methyl picrate or 1,3,5-trinitrobenzene with methanolic potassium methoxide. They conclude that the products of these reactions have the structure of covalent complexes.

D. Reactions of Aryl Oxides with Aryl Halides

The displacement of halogens by the action of aryl oxides on aryl halides usually requires temperatures above 300° in the absence of catalysts and is not practical for the preparation of diaryl ethers. Ullmann's discovery[57] of the catalytic effect of copper powder, especially with aryl bromides, has widened the applicability of this reaction, and the subject has been surveyed in detail by Ungnade[58]. Usually a catalyst is not needed with activated aryl halides. The reaction of *o*- or *p*-chloronitrobenzene with potassium phenoxide in water affords the corresponding ethers in good yield, but no ether is obtained if the phenolate part contains a nitro group[59]. According to equation (9),

bis(nitrophenyl) ethers are obtained in high yield in dimethylformamide as a solvent (Table 3)[60]. The limitations of this reaction are that

TABLE 3. Preparation of bis(nitrophenyl) ethers according to equation (9).

Nitrophenoxide	Nitrochlorobenzene	Reaction time (h)	% Yield
o	*o*	18	72
p	*o*	4·5	61
p	*p*	16	79
m	*p*	1	73
m	*o*	5	60

dry potassium nitrophenolates must be used and that sodium salts may not be substituted for potassium salts. With potassium 3-nitrophenoxide and 3-nitrochlorobenzene the ether was not obtained; instead, a small amount of a reduction product, 3,3'-dichloroazobenzene, was isolated.

Substituted 2,4-dinitrophenyl ethers of monohydric and dihydric phenols are formed in high yield from 2,4-dinitrofluorobenzene (reaction 4) in acetone with catalytic amounts of triethylamine[61]. This method is recommended for the characterization of phenols, and constitutes an improvement over previous procedures which are based on the reaction of phenols with 2,4-dinitrochlorobenzene[62]. Conversion of phenols into sodium phenolates with sodium hydride in benzene and subsequent addition of 1 and dimethylformamide also leads to substituted phenyl ethers in excellent yield[63].

E. Reactions of Aryl Oxides with Diphenyliodonium Salts

The high susceptibility of diaryliodonium salts to nucleophilic attack has been utilized to prepare, under relatively mild reaction conditions, diphenyl ethers in which the aryl group does not require activation by electron-withdrawing substituents (reaction 10)[64]. Reac-

$$\left[R-C_6H_4-I-C_6H_4-R \right]^+ X^- \;+\; (6) \;\xrightarrow[H_2O,\ 100°]{NaOH}\; (7) \quad (10)$$

(5)   (6)   (7)

tions with different salts of 5 (X = Br$^-$, Cl$^-$, and ClO$_4^-$) and 6 (R^1, R^2, R^3 = H) gave 7 (R, R^1, R^2, R^3 = H) in yields of 72, 66, and 65%, respectively, indicating that the associating ions do not compete with the phenoxide ion. High yields of 7 are obtained on refluxing equimolar amounts of 5, 6, and sodium hydroxide for 24 hours (Table 4).

The mechanism of the hydrolysis of diaryliodonium salts has been investigated extensively[65]. Results with unsymmetrically substituted phenyliodonium salts have shown that the direction of cleavage is unaffected by the nature of the substituents, the solvent, catalysts, and

TABLE 4. Preparation of substituted diaryl ethers according to
equation (10).

5(X = Br⁻)		7				
R	6	R	R¹	R²	R³	% Yield of 7
H	Isovanillin	H	OMe	CHO	H	84
Me	Phenol	Me	H	H	H	86
Me	Guaiacol	Me	OMe	H	H	64
Me	Vanillin	Me	OMe	H	CHO	63
Me	Isovanillin	Me	OMe	CHO	H	65

the associated anion. Hydrolysis is retarded by acid and strongly catalyzed by cuprous ion, but this does not change the product composition. These observations are not consistent with an S_N1 or S_N2 process
and it seems likely that a homolytic mechanism is involved in the
hydrolytic cleavage of the carbon–iodine bond.

F. Alkylations with Dialkyl Sulfates and Arylsulfonic Esters

Activation of the hydroxyl group is usually a prerequisite for obtaining good yields in the alkylation of alcohols with dialkyl sulfates. For
example acetylenic alcohols react under relatively mild conditions[66].
Higher reaction temperatures and anhydrous conditions are required
with unactivated alcohols, and employment of magnesium alcoholates
has led to good yields of the methyl and ethyl ethers of C_3–C_5 alcohols[67, 68]. Alkylation of C_1–C_8 sodium alcoholates with di-(β-fluoro-
ethyl) sulfate at 100° leads to β-fluoroethyl alkyl ethers in 54–67%
yield[69].

In contrast to alcohols, the etherification of phenols proceeds quite
readily with dialkyl sulfates. The reactions are exothermic, and external heating is usually not required[70].

Alkylation of alcohols with esters of arylsulfonic acids has found
some application, but depending on the nature of the alkyl group the
elimination reaction, leading to olefins, may become more important
than the substitution reaction. Olefin formation can sometimes be
decreased if the correct ester–alcoholate combination is employed.
Isopropyl propyl ether is obtained in 55% yield from propyl benzene-
sulfonate and sodium isopropoxide, while the reverse combination only
affords the ether in 27% yield[71]. Conversion of 2-methyl-1-butanol
into its sodium salt with sodium hydride in a refluxing mixture of
xylene and t-butyl alcohol, and addition of methyl tosylate, gives

methyl ether in 45% yield[72]. Ethylene glycol is converted into the mono- and dioctadecyl ethers in yields of 56 and 25% on treatment with n-octadecyl tosylate in the presence of sodium carbonate at 170–185° for 4 hours. The octadecyl ethers of 1-butanol (60%), 1-octanol (67%), 2-octanol (30%), 1-octadecanol (67%), and benzyl alcohol (40%) are prepared similarly[73].

Etherification of phenols with alkyl aryl sulfonates has found wide application, and usually higher yields are obtained with primary than with secondary alkyl esters[74]. Phenol and butyl tosylate in 10% aqueous sodium hydroxide give butoxybenzene in 73% yield[75] and under similar conditions, 2-methyl-5-nitrophenol is converted into C_1–C_5 ethers (Me 60%, Et 52%, Pr 72%, Bu 70%, and Am 73%)[76]. By taking advantage of the lower reactivity of the chlorine atom in nucleophilic displacements, the β-chloroethyl group has been introduced into phenols and naphthols. Yields are as high as 80% and very little of the diphenyl and dinaphthyl ethylene ethers are formed[77].

G. Etherification in Acidic Medium

The formation of ethers by the dehydration of alcohols only occurs in the presence of acids; it is especially suitable for the synthesis of mixed ethers in which one of the radicals is tertiary and the other primary. The role of the acid is to convert the hydroxyl group of the alcohol into a better leaving group by formation of an oxonium salt. The ether is then formed by the nucleophilic attack of an alcohol molecule on the salt in a bimolecular reaction, as in the case of normal primary alcohols, or in a unimolecular reaction when tertiary, allylic, acetylenic, and aryl alcohols are involved. Secondary alcohols undergo reaction by either the S_N2 or S_N1 mechanism (reaction 11).

$$ROH \xrightleftharpoons{H^+} [ROH_2]^+ \begin{cases} \xrightleftharpoons{ROH} [RO\cdots R\cdots OH_2]^+ \atop H \longrightarrow R_2O + H_3O^+ \\ \xrightleftharpoons{} [R^+ + H_2O] \xrightleftharpoons{ROH} R_2O + H^+ \end{cases} \qquad (11)$$

It is uncertain whether, in the preparation of ethers from primary alcohols and concentrated sulfuric acid, the acid functions only as a catalyst or whether alkyl hydrogen sulfates are actually formed as intermediates which, on subsequent nucleophilic attack by alcohol, are converted into the ether. Diethyl ether was obtained in 95% yield when ethanol was passed through concentrated sulfuric acid at 140°,

15*

and only in 70% yield when the acid was replaced by ethyl hydrogen sulfate. Moreover, sulfur dioxide was evolved in copious amounts[24]. The case of concentrated sulfuric acid might be unique and certainly does not carry over to dilute sulfuric acid or to the many Lewis type acids which are being employed as catalysts. For example there was no evidence of alkyl hydrogen sulfate formation when ethanol alone or mixed with *t*-butyl alcohol was treated with 15% sulfuric acid at 70°, although the mixture gave a quantitative yield of *t*-butyl ethyl ether[24]. Furthermore, Van Alphen[78] established that hydrochloric acid is an excellent catalyst for the preparation of diethyl ether under conditions at which ethyl chloride does not react with ethanol.

A successful synthesis of an ether is very often dependent upon the proper choice and amount of the catalyst, the reaction temperature, and experimental procedure[79]. In the preparation of mixed ethers, containing *t*-butyl and primary alkyl radicals, Norris and Rigby[24] established that 15% sulfuric acid, an excess of the primary alcohol, and removal of the ether–water azeotrope during the reaction gave the highest yield of *t*-butyl alkyl ethers (Me 95%, Et 95%, Pr 68%, and Bu 52%). A higher concentration of sulfuric acid was necessary to obtain mixed ethers with primary–secondary alcohols, but simple ethers also formed and the overall yield was low. On the other hand, the synthesis of *t*-butyl isopropyl ether was successful (82% yield) when sulfuric acid was replaced by sodium hydrogen sulfate and *t*-butyl alcohol was very slowly added to the hot reaction mixture.

Cationic-exchange resins have been used successfully in place of sulfuric acid for preparing simple ethers from primary alcohols. Swistak and Mastagli[80], by employing elevated pressures with alcohols boiling below 100°, obtained C_3–C_{12} simple ethers in yields ranging from 60 to 80%. Similar results are reported by Shuikin and coworkers[81] with alcohols in the C_6–C_{10} range. But negligible amounts of ether resulted from secondary alcohols, the major product being olefins[80].

Etherification of alcohols in which the cationic intermediate is stabilized by mesomerism is accomplished under rather mild conditions. However, rearrangements have been reported[82,83] to occur with alcohols such as 1,4-hexadien-3-ol and 4-hexen-1-yn-3-ol which, on treatment with methanol and dilute sulfuric acid, gave 5-methoxy-1,3-hexadiene and 5-methoxy-3-hexen-1-yne, respectively (reactions 12 and 13).

$$\underset{\substack{| \\ OH}}{H_2C{=}CHCHCH{=}CHCH_3} \xrightarrow[H_2SO_4]{CH_3OH} \underset{\substack{| \\ OCH_3}}{H_2C{=}CHCH{=}CHCHCH_3} \qquad (12)$$

$$\underset{\text{HC}\equiv\text{CCHCH}=\text{CHCH}_3}{\overset{\text{OH}}{|}} \xrightarrow[\text{H}_2\text{SO}_4]{\text{CH}_3\text{OH}} \underset{\text{HC}\equiv\text{CCH}=\text{CHCHCH}_3}{\overset{\text{OCH}_3}{|}} \qquad (13)$$

Examples of facile ether formation from allyl alcohols are the quantitative conversion of 2-cyclopentenol into 2,2′-dicyclopentenyl ether at room temperature in the presence of catalytic amounts of hydrochloric acid[84], and the preparation of ethers from $\alpha,\alpha,\gamma,\gamma$-tetraalkylated t-allyl alcohols and a catalytic amount of dilute sulfuric acid at room temperature (reaction 14 and Table 5)[85].

$$\underset{\underset{\text{R}^1}{|}}{\overset{\overset{\text{CH}_3}{|}}{(\text{CH}_3)_2\text{C}=\text{CHCOH}}} \xrightarrow[\text{H}_2\text{SO}_4]{\text{R}^2\text{OH}} \underset{\underset{\text{R}^1}{|}}{\overset{\overset{\text{CH}_3}{|}}{(\text{CH}_3)_2\text{C}=\text{COR}^2}} \qquad (14)$$

TABLE 5. Preparation of ethers from allyl alcohols according to equation (14).

| Alcohol | % Yield of products | | | | | | |
| | R^2 | | | | | | |
R^1	Me	Et	Pr	Bu	i-Bu	i-Am	Allyl
CH_3CH_2	70	60	42	45	—	43	53
$CH_3(CH_2)_2$	78	60	63	51	—	—	—
$CH_3(CH_2)_3$	68	58	48	41	—	—	—
$(CH_3)_2CH(CH_2)_2$	83	68	63	45	40	35	67
$C_6H_5CH_2$	79	60	48	—	—	—	65

The various methods by which phenyl carbinols are etherified have largely come from investigations which were primarily concerned with the existence of carbonium ions and in particular with their formation, stability, and reactions. The discovery[86] that addition of triphenylacetic acid dissolved in 100% sulfuric acid to cold methanol (reactions 15, 16, and 17) afforded, upon dilution with ice water, triphenylmethyl methyl ether (8) instead of the expected ester, suggested a quick and useful preparation of triphenylmethyl alkyl ethers from triphenyl carbinol. That the formation of (8) from the acid occurs via

$$(C_6H_5)_3CCO_2H + 2\,H_2SO_4 \longrightarrow (C_6H_5)_3CCO^+ + H_3O^+ + 2\,HSO_4^- \qquad (15)$$

$$(C_6H_5)_3CCO^+ \longrightarrow (C_6H_5)_3C^+ + CO \qquad (16)$$

$$(C_6H_5)_3C^+ + CH_3OH \Longrightarrow (C_6H_5)_3COCH_3 + H^+ \qquad (17)$$
$$(8)$$

a stable ion is well documented by the fact that the van't Hoff i factor was found to be 4 and that the presence of carbon monoxide was established. Diphenylacetic acid and bis-(p-chlorophenyl) acetic acid are converted into bis(diphenylmethyl) ether (15% yield) and bis-(p,p'-dichlorodiphenyl methyl) ether (88% yield)[87].

The preparation of triphenylmethyl alkyl ethers in 100% sulfuric acid is complicated by their tendency to undergo cleavage, which is catalyzed by bisulfate ion, into triphenylmethane and aldehydes. Methods which have been used to obviate this difficulty, and which have also been quite successful with diphenyl carbinols, employ catalytic amounts of p-toluenesulfonic acid and azeotropic removal with benzene of the ether as it is formed[88,89].

Sulfonation is often responsible for the low yield in which ethers are obtained from diphenylcarbinols in 100% sulfuric acid[90]. While dimesityl carbinol and methanol gave a 98% yield of the ether in 100% sulfuric acid, no ether was obtained from benzhydrol (9)[91]. However, the diphenylmethyl methyl ether was obtained in 67% yield when a carbon tetrachloride solution of 9 was stirred into 100% sulfuric acid and the resulting red solution poured into methanol[90]. Also, dibenzhydryl ether (10) was obtained in 67% yield when methanol was replaced by water. Compound 10 formed in 90% yield, when 9 and 85% phosphoric acid were heated at 75° for 10 minutes (reaction 18)[92], and in a quantitative yield when a benzene solution of 9 was passed through an alumina column at room temperature[93]. By the latter procedure, α-phenylethanol was converted into bis-(α-phenylethyl) ether in 75% yield.

$$C_6H_5CH(OH)C_6H_5 \xrightarrow{85\% \ H_3PO_4} (C_6H_5)_2CH-O-CH(C_6H_5)_2 \qquad (18)$$
$$\quad (9) \qquad\qquad\qquad\qquad\qquad\qquad (10)$$

H. Mechanism of Nucleophilic Substitutions

In view of several recent comprehensive reviews on the up-to-date developments in nucleophilic aromatic substitutions[94-96] and nucleophilic substitutions on saturated carbon[97,98], a survey on these subjects is not needed. We will concern ourselves only with new data involving the factors which influence the formation of the C—O—C bond.

I. Importance of the leaving group

In nucleophilic substitutions, the nature of the alkyl group of the substrate, the leaving group, the attacking nucleophile, the solvent, and the temperature are important factors which influence the course of the reaction, and in particular the extent of substitution against elimination. It is well established that in bimolecular nucleophilic reactions with alkyl halides, the $S_N2/E2$ ratio is not significantly altered by the nature of the halide, although the ratio decreases in the order RCl > RBr > RI. The striking difference of tosylate as a leaving group in such reactions has been emphasized in recent investigations. Bishop and DePuy[99] have measured the rate of reaction of alkyl iodides, bromides, and tosylates in ethanol in the presence of ethoxide, and the data show that the tosylates are much less reactive than the corresponding iodides and often less reactive than the corresponding bromides (Table 6). This is strikingly different in the case of solvolytic reactions where the relative solvolysis rates in ethanol are Tos:I:Br $\approx$ 20:2:1[97].

TABLE 6. Rates of reaction with EtO$^-$ in EtOH.

Compound	Temp. (°c)	Rate (1×10^{-4})	% E2	Ref.
$CH_3CH(CH_3)CH_2Br$	55	1·40	60	100
$CH_3CH(CH_3)CH_2OTs$	55	1·80	44	99
$CH_3CH_2CH_2Br$	40	1·26	9	100
$CH_3CH_2CH_2OTs$	40	4·58	Small	99
$C_6H_5CH_2CH_2I$	30	26·60	~100	101
$C_6H_5CH_2CH_2Br$	30	4·10	96	101
$C_6H_5CH_2CH_2OTs$	30	1·20	33	101
$p\text{-}ClC_6H_4CH_2CH_2I$	30	105·0	100	101
$p\text{-}ClC_6H_4CH_2CH_2Br$	30	18·8	100	101
$p\text{-}ClC_6H_4CH_2CH_2OTs$	30	2·93	20	101
$p\text{-}CH_3OC_6H_4CH_2CH_2I$	30	9·56	100	101
$p\text{-}CH_3OC_6H_4CH_2CH_2Br$	30	1·73	100	101
$p\text{-}CH_3OC_6H_4CH_2CH_2OTs$	30	0·86	20	101
$m\text{-}BrC_6H_4CH_2CH_2I$	30	203	100	101
$m\text{-}BrC_6H_4CH_2CH_2Br$	30	37·1	100	101
$m\text{-}BrC_6H_4CH_2CH_2OTs$	30	5·53	67	101

Veeravagu and coworkers[102] have provided clear evidence for the difference between primary alkyl bromides and alkyl tosylates at conditions which would be expected to favor greatly the $E2$-type elimination reaction. For example 1-bromooctadecane (11), on treatment with 0·9 N potassium t-butoxide in t-butyl alcohol at 40°, undergoes 83·7% elimination and 16·3% substitution at a slower rate ($k = 2·32 \times 10^5$) than 1-octadecyl tosylate (12) ($k = 15·10 \times 10^5$ l/mole sec), which undergoes 100% substitution. The difference in the ratio of bimolecular substitution and elimination was also established by product analysis of reactions in which compounds **11** and **12** were refluxed for 20 hours with 1 N potassium t-butoxide in absolute t-butyl alcohol. Under similar reaction conditions, employing the weaker base, sodium methoxide, substitution is the predominant feature with compounds **11** and **12**. The differences between the bromides and tosylates do not carry over to the respective β-phenylethyl and β-mesitylethyl compounds. In every case, 100% elimination was observed on treatment with potassium t-butoxide. It is rather remarkable that the more bulky mesityl group is as effective as the phenyl group in stabilizing, through conjugation, the incipient double bond of the $E2$ transition state. In contrast to the reaction with potassium t-butoxide, treatment of β-mesitylethyl tosylate with sodium methoxide gave 79% substitution and only 5% elimination.

Dimethyl sulfoxide (DMSO) enhances the reactivity of potassium t-butoxide toward sulfonate esters to such an extent that reactions are complete within 30 minutes at 20–25° for 0·5 M solutions of the ester[103]. In contrast to the t-BuO$^-$–t-BuOH system, in which primary alkyl esters of aryl sulfonates undergo about 100% substitution[102], 20–25% elimination is reported in the t-BuO$^-$–DMSO combination, and the $S_N2/E2$ ratio is not markedly influenced by changes in the leaving group (Table 7). It is probably due to the greater proton

TABLE 7. Effect of the leaving group on the reaction of 1-hexyl sulfonates in the t-BuO$^-$–DMSO system at 20–25°.

Leaving group	% Ether	% 1-Alkene
$C_6H_5OSO_2^-$	69	20
p-$CH_3C_6H_4OSO_2^-$	67	20
p-$BrC_6H_4OSO_2^-$	76	20
p-$NO_2C_6H_4OSO_2^-$	29	8·2
$CH_3OSO_2^-$	33	12·5
$CH_3(CH_2)_3OSO_2^-$	46	20

abstracting power of t-BuO$^-$ in DMSO that some elimination does take place with the primary alkyl esters. The $S_N2/E2$ ratio is decreased in the t-BuO$^-$–DMSO system with esters of primary alcohols containing α-alkyl substituents (30–40% ether and 20–30% alkene) while esters of secondary alcohols give a negligible quantity of ether and 80% alkene (Table 8).

TABLE 8. Reactions of alkyl benzenesulfonates with potassium t-butoxide in dimethyl sulfoxide at 20–25° (reaction time 30 minutes)[103].

Parent alcohol of benzenesulfonate	Alkene (%)[a]	Alkyl t-butyl ether (%)[a]
Cyclohexylcarbinol	26	60
1-Hexanol	20	69
1-Octanol	24	67
2-Methyl-1-butanol	22	39
2-Ethyl-1-butanol	27	40
Cyclohexanol	83	trace
Cyclopentanol	76	—
2-Octanol	{51 (1-Octene) / 28 (2-Octene)	trace

[a] Gas chromatography analysis of reaction extracts.

2. Factors promoting oxygen alkylation

The results of recent investigations by Kornblum and collaborators[104] have contributed to the recognition of several factors which control the reaction of ambient anions, such as phenoxide, in nucleophilic reactions.

3. Role of solvent

It has been shown that solutions of salts of phenol or p-alkylphenols, in a wide variety of solvents, react bimolecularly with allyl or benzyl halides to give largely the corresponding ethers and only traces of carbon-alkylated products. These solvents include various alcohols, ethers, and dimethylformamide. However, when these reactions are executed in strongly hydrogen-bonding solvents such as water, phenol, and fluorinated alcohols, substantial amounts of *ortho* and *para* carbon-alkylated products are obtained in addition to ethers (Table 9). Such solvent effects have also been observed by Barner and Schmid[105] in reactions of sodium phenoxide with allyl bromide, and by Zook and Russo[106] who reported that ethylation of sodiodiphenylacetophenone in diethylene glycol dimethyl ether occurs almost exclusively at the oxygen atom to give the enol ether 1,2,2-triphenyl-1-ethoxyethene

TABLE 9. Effect of solvents on the product distribution in the homogeneous alkylation of phenolic salts[a, 104].

Solvent	Salt	Alkylating agent	% Yield Oxygen alkylation	% Yield Carbon alkylation[b]
t-Butyl alcohol	Sodium phenoxide	Allyl bromide	100[c]	
Diethyl ether	Sodium p-t-octyl-phenoxide	Allyl bromide[d]	99	
Dimethylform-amide	Sodium phenoxide	Allyl chloride	100[c]	
		Ally bromide	91	
		Benzyl chloride	100[c]	
Ethanol	Sodium phenoxide	Allyl chloride	100[c]	
Ethylene glycol dimethyl ether	Sodium phenoxide	Allyl chloride	99	
		Allyl bromide	100[c]	
		Benzyl chloride	100[c]	
		Benzyl bromide[d]	99	
	Sodium p-t-octyl-phenoxide	Allyl bromide[d]	98	
Methanol	Sodium phenoxide	Allyl chloride	100[c]	
		Allyl bromide	96	
		Benzyl chloride	100[c]	
Phenol[e]	Sodium phenoxide	Allyl chloride	22[c]	78[c]
		Allyl bromide	23[c]	77[c]
		Benzyl chloride	22	69
2,2,3,3-Tetra-fluoro-1-propanol	Sodium phenoxide	Allyl chloride	58	37
2,2,2-Trifluoro-ethanol	Sodium phenoxide	Allyl bromide	37	42
		Benzyl chloride	62	26
Tetrahydrofuran	Sodium phenoxide	Allyl chloride	96	
		Allyl bromide	94	
		Benzyl chloride	100[c]	
Water	Sodium phenoxide	Allyl chloride	49	41
		Allyl bromide	51	38
		Benzyl chloride	65	24
	Sodium p-cres-oxide	Allyl chloride	67	25
		Allyl bromide	58	30

[a] All reactions conducted at 27° except when otherwise noted.
[b] Includes dialkylated products.
[c] By vapor-phase chromatography.
[d] At 35°.
[e] At 43°.

(13). However, in t-butyl alcohol, carbon alkylation to give α,α-diphenylbutyrophenone (14) occurs to the extent of 25% (reaction 19).

$$[C_6H_5\overset{\overset{\displaystyle O}{\|}}{C}C(C_6H_5)_2]^-\,Na^+ + C_2H_5Br \xrightarrow{\ t\text{-BuOH}\ } 13 + C_6H_5\overset{\overset{\displaystyle O}{\|}}{C}C(C_6H_5)_2CH_2CH_3 \quad (19)$$
$$(14)$$

$$\downarrow (CH_3OCH_2CH_2)_2O$$

$$\overset{\textstyle OC_2H_5}{\underset{(13)}{C_6H_5C=C(C_6H_5)_2}}$$

The influence of solvents on the ratio of oxygen- and carbon-alkylation products is explained[104] by the ability of the powerful hydrogen-bonding solvents to solvate the aryl oxide oxygen so strongly that its availability for nucleophilic displacement is greatly decreased. As a consequence, the otherwise less reactive *ortho* and *para* carbon atoms of the aryl oxide can compete successfully in the nucleophilic displacement.

The nature of the solvent is even more critical in alkylations with β-naphthol[107], where the nucleophilicity of the α carbon and of the naphthoxide oxygen are more evenly balanced. Because of this competition, not only strongly hydrogen-bonding solvents, but even those of low dielectric constant, without hydrogen-bonding capacity, give substantial amounts of carbon alkylation. It is only in *aprotic solvents* with *high dielectric* constant that ether formation predominates (Table 10). To account for the effect of aprotic solvents of low dielectric constant, it is suggested that sodium β-naphthoxide exists in these solvents as ion pairs and as higher aggregates, and that oxygen alkylation is disfavored by the large separation of the sodium cation and the developing halide ion in the transition state (15). On the other hand, carbon alkylation is favored, for in the transition state (16) the sodium cation

(15)   (16)

TABLE 10. Solvent effect in reactions of benzyl bromide with
sodium β-naphthoxide[a, 107].

Solvent	Dielectric constant[b]	% Oxygen alkylation	% Carbon alkylation[c]
Dimethylformamide[d]	37	97	0
Dimethyl sulfoxide[e]	45	95	0
Ethylene glycol dimethyl ether	7	70	22
Tetrahydrofuran	7	60	36
Methanol	33	57	34
Ethanol	24	52	28
2,2,2-Trifluoroethanol	27	7	85
Water	80	10	84
Benzene–Water		7	83

[a] All reactions performed at room temperature unless otherwise stated.
[b] Temperature 20–25°.
[c] Includes dialkylated products.
[d] At 10–15°; a duplicate run at 35° gives 93% oxygen and 1% carbon alkylation.
[e] A duplicate run at 40° gives 95% oxygen and 1% carbon alkylation.

is in close proximity to the developing halide ion. This coulombic
factor will decrease in aprotic solvents of high dielectric constant, such
as dimethyl sulfoxide, in which the reacting species may again be an
ion pair or the free naphthoxide ion, and oxygen alkylation will be
favored.

Cram and Grosser[108] have advanced similar considerations to
explain stereochemical consequences due to ion-pair formation in
carbanion systems.

4. Role of alkyl halides

The proportion of oxygen and carbon alkylation is also dependent
on the nature of the alkyl halide. As seen in Tables 11 and 12, reactions of sodium β-naphthoxide with methyl iodide and propyl bromide
afford, even in aqueous media, a preponderance of oxygen-alkylated
products. In contrast, β-naphthoxide and benzyl bromide give in the
same reaction medium, 84% of carbon-alkylated products. At present,
no explanation is available to account for the relationship between the
structure of the alkyl halide and the amount of oxygen against carbon
alkylation in various solvents.

The ratio of oxygen against carbon alkylation is also dependent on

Table 11. Reaction of methyl iodide with sodium
β-naphthoxide[a, 107].

Solvent	% Oxygen alkylation	% Carbon alkylation
Dimethylformamide[b]	91	3
Dimethyl sulfoxide[b]	90	4
Ethylene glycol dimethyl ether	86	10
Tetrahydrofuran	80	13
Ethanol	83	12
2,2,2-Trifluoroethanol	57	34
Water	66	30

[a] All reactions conducted at room temperature except when otherwise noted.
[b] At 30°.

Table 12. Reaction of n-propyl bromide with
sodium β-naphthoxide[a, 107].

Solvent	% Oxygen alkylation	% Carbon alkylation
Dimethylformamide[b]	98	0
Dimethyl sulfoxide[b]	95	0
Ethylene glycol dimethyl ether	96	0
Tetrahydrofuran	96	0
Ethanol	95	trace
2,2,2-Trifluoroethanol	81	10
Water	88	5

[a] All reactions performed at room temperature unless otherwise stated.
[b] At 35°.

Table 13. Alkylation of potassium
2,6-di-t-butylphenoxide.

Alkyl iodide	% Oxygen alkylation	% Carbon alkylation
Methyl	88	6
Ethyl	11	66
Isopropyl[a]	0	100

[a] Only 28% of the halide undergoes substitution; elimination of hydrogen iodide accounts for the remainder.

the steric requirement of the alkyl halide. This has been well demonstrated[109] in alkylations of potassium 2,6-di-t-butylphenoxide. As can be seen in Table 13, on treatment with a set of alkyl halides of increasing steric requirement, a clear shift from oxygen to carbon alkylation occurs.

III. ETHERS FROM ALCOHOLS, PHENOLS, AND CARBODIIMIDES

Although alcohols are inert toward carbodiimides at ordinary temperatures, a reaction occurs at elevated temperatures to produce O-alkylpseudoureas. Thus 17 ($R^1 = C_6H_5$) gave a quantitative yield of 18 ($R^2 = Et$) when an alcoholic solution of the carbodiimide was heated in a sealed tube (equation 20)[110]. The same reaction occurs at

$$R^1N{=}C{=}NR^1 + R^2OH \xrightarrow[\text{R}^2\text{O}^-]{\text{Heat or}} \underset{\substack{|\\ OR^2 \\ \textbf{(18)}}}{R^1NHC{=}NR^1} \qquad (20)$$
$$\textbf{(17)}$$

ambient temperatures[111] or in the cold[112,113] in the presence of sodium alkoxide. Excellent yields of N,N'-diaryl-O-alkyl pseudoureas have been obtained by both methods*. Phenols also react with diaryl- and dialkylcarbodiimides to form the corresponding oxygen ethers†. The reversibility of the reaction between phenols and dicyclohexylcarbodiimide (DCC) has been demonstrated[115].

In 1962, Vowinkel reported[116] that aryl alkyl ethers could be prepared from an equimolar mixture of a phenol, an alcohol, and DCC (equation 21, R = primary alkyl group, DCU = N,N'-dicyclohexylurea). The reaction was conducted in an inert solvent in a sealed tube

$$\text{ArOH} + \text{ROH} + \text{DCC} \longrightarrow \text{ArOR} + \text{DCU} \qquad (21)$$

at room temperature for 30 days. Whereas the synthesis was successful employing primary alcohols, the method was quite sensitive to steric effects; the use of secondary or tertiary alcohols or *ortho*-substituted phenols led to little or none of the desired mixed ether.

---

* Khorana[111] reports the failure of dicyclohexylcarbodiimide to react with alcohols using the base-catalyzed method under the mild conditions in which N,N'-diarylcarbodiimides give excellent yields of 18 ($R^1 =$ aryl, $R^2 =$ alkyl).

† Nitrophenols behave abnormally. At elevated temperatures the oxygen–ether adducts from nitrophenols and diaryl- as well as dialkylcarbodiimides rearrange to carbamides[114,115].

An improvement of this method was subsequently described[117] in which phenols, alcohols, and DCC were heated (at about 100°) in a sealed tube without solvent. Yields of ethers from *meta*- and *para*-substituted phenols were in the range 84–91%. *Ortho*-substituted phenols required longer reaction times before comparable yields could be obtained. The mechanism of aryl alkyl ether formation postulated by Vowinkel involves initial formation of a phenol–DCC adduct **19** (equation 22), protonation of adduct **19** to give **20** followed by attack of primary alcohol on **20** to give rise to products (reaction 24).

$$\text{ArOH} + \text{DCC} \rightleftharpoons \underset{\textbf{(19)}}{C_6H_{11}N\!\!=\!\!\overset{\displaystyle OAr}{\overset{|}{C}}\!\!-\!\!NHC_6H_{11}} \tag{22}$$

$$\textbf{19} + H^+ \rightleftharpoons \underset{\textbf{(20)}}{C_6H_{11}\overset{+}{N}H\!\!=\!\!\underset{\displaystyle OAr}{\overset{|}{C}}\!\!-\!\!NHC_6H_{11}} \tag{23}$$

$$\textbf{20} + RCH_2OH \longrightarrow RCH_2OAr + H^+ + DCU \tag{24}$$

Recently this work was repeated by Bach[118] and excellent yields were confirmed (87–92%). An alternative mechanism was suggested which discounted equation (24) as the product-determining step. Bach explained the reaction in terms of equations (25) and (26). Although a phenol–DCC adduct (**19**) would be expected to form faster than an alcohol–DCC adduct (**21**), the demonstrated reversibility[115] of equation (22) would permit a build-up of alkyl pseudourea ether (**21**) (equation 25). Attack of phenoxide ion (equation 26) completes the

$$\text{DCC} + \text{EtOH} \longrightarrow \underset{\textbf{(21)}}{EtO\overset{\displaystyle NC_6H_{11}}{\underset{\displaystyle NHC_6H_{11}}{C}}} \tag{25}$$

$$ArO^- + \overset{\displaystyle H}{\underset{\displaystyle H}{\overset{CH_3}{C}}}\!\!-\!\!O\!\!-\!\!\overset{\displaystyle \overset{+}{N}HC_6H_{11}}{\underset{\displaystyle NHC_6H_{11}}{C}} \longrightarrow ArOEt + DCU \tag{26}$$

process. The poor yields obtained using secondary and tertiary alcohols are readily accommodated by invoking steric hindrance to S_N2

displacement in equation (26). Discrimination between the two mechanisms was made by employing ^{18}O-labeled alcohol in the phenol–primary alcohol–DCC system. According to Vowinkel's scheme (equation 24) labeled oxygen would only appear in the ether whereas Bach's formulation (equation 26) predicts the [18]O would appear only in the dicyclohexylurea. In the system phenol–Et[18]OH–DCC, mass spectroscopic analysis revealed that all the label appeared in the urea. Thus the mechanism described by equation (24) does not prevail whereas the data are in accord with S_N2 attack by phenoxide ion on an alkylpseudourea ether intermediate (equation 26).

It should be mentioned that although this method lacks generality, the ease of workup* and the high degree of purity of the resulting crude ether renders this an attractive alternative to the Williamson synthesis.

IV. ETHERS FROM PEROXY COMPOUNDS

A. Reaction of Organometallics with Dialkyl Peroxides

Gilman and Adams[119] found that diethyl peroxide reacts with phenylmagnesium bromide to give a 34% yield of phenetole (equation 27, $R^1 = R^2 = Et$, $R^3 = C_6H_5$, $M = MgBr$). The potential synthetic

$$R^1OOR^2 + R^3M \longrightarrow R^1OR^3 + R^2OM \qquad (27)$$

utility of this reaction remained unexplored for 25 years until the availability of di-t-butylperoxide prompted Campbell and coworkers[120] to reinvestigate this method as a possible route to t-butyl alkyl ethers. These investigators found that little or no reaction occurred in the case of the tertiary-aliphatic and phenyl Grignard reagents. However, Grignard reagents derived from primary and secondary bromides gave the desired t-butyl alkyl ethers (reaction 28) albeit in poor

$$\text{(a)} \longrightarrow Me_3COMgBr + RCH_2CH_2OCMe_3$$
$$\text{(b)} \longrightarrow Me_3COH + Me_3COMgBr + RCH=CH_2 \qquad (28)$$

* Product ethers are isolated by chromatography on alumina. It is reported that crystalline ethers have the correct melting point after removing solvent, and that liquid ethers are pure (correct refractive index) without distillation.

yield (about 20%). Significant by-products were olefins derived from the organometallic and *t*-butyl alcohol. These results were rationalized in terms of a scheme in which direct displacement on peroxidic oxygen gave rise to product ether (path a), and competitive olefin formation followed a course (path b) analogous to the known reduction of hindered ketones by the β-hydrogen atom[121] of the Grignard reagent.

Subsequently Edward and collaborators[122] compared the reactivity of phenyllithium and phenylmagnesium bromide toward one unsymmetrical and several symmetrical dialkyl peroxides (equation 29).

$$R^1OOR^2 + C_6H_5M \longrightarrow C_6H_5OR^2 + R^1OM \qquad (29)$$
$$(M = Li, MgBr)$$

Although dimethyl peroxide reacted equally well with both the lithium and magnesium compounds, other peroxides gave higher yields of ethers when phenyllithium was employed. Thus C_6H_5Li and $t\text{-}Bu_2O_2$ gave a 39% yield of $t\text{-}BuOC_6H_5$ while, as previously noted, C_6H_5MgBr failed to react, even under forcing conditions. By way of contrast, higher yields of *t*-butyl ethers are obtained from the organomagnesium reagent and *t*-butyl perbenzoate (*vide infra*).

Although triphenylmethylsodium reacted with dimethyl peroxide to give a methyl ether, the triphenylmethyl radical failed to react. An ionic mechanism consistent with this finding involves nucleophilic displacement on oxygen (reaction 30). A similar mechanism was postu-

$$\text{(C}_6\text{H}_5)_3\text{C} \overset{\overset{\displaystyle R}{|}}{\underset{}{\text{O}}}\text{OR} \longrightarrow \text{(C}_6\text{H}_5)_3\text{COR} + \text{RO}^- \qquad (30)$$

lated for the reactions of phenyllithium. To explain ether formation in the reaction of a Grignard reagent with a dialkyl peroxide, the transition state* **22** was suggested in which the phenyl group, owing to its

* The formulation of the phenyl Grignard reagent as a complex of $(C_6H_5)_2Mg$ and $MgBr_2$ was based on the findings of Dessy and Handler, *J. Am. Chem. Soc.*, **80**, 5824 (1958). In the light of more recent results, among others, G. D. Stucky, and R. E. Rundle, *J. Am. Chem. Soc.*, **85**, 1002 (1963), and E. C. Ashby and M. B. Smith, *J. Am. Chem. Soc.*, **86**, 4363 (1964), the transition state might be reasonably reformulated as

bulk, was partially bonded to the oxygen atom bearing the less bulky alkyl substituent. This is in accord with the exclusive formation of anisole from methyl t-butyl peroxide ($\mathbf{22}$, $R^1 = Me$, $R^2 = t$-Bu).

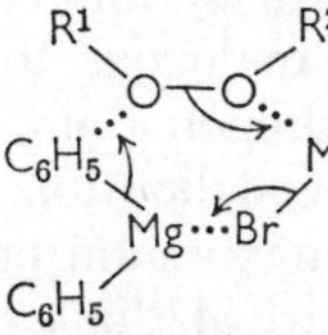

(22)

B. Reaction of Organometallics with t-Butyl Perbenzoate

A valuable method for the preparation of t-butyl ethers was introduced by Lawesson and Yang[25] in 1959. By reacting t-butyl perbenzoate with a variety of Grignard reagents under mild conditions (0–5°), good yields of t-butyl ethers and benzoic acid were obtained. The reaction was formulated as in reaction (31). The Grignard reagents

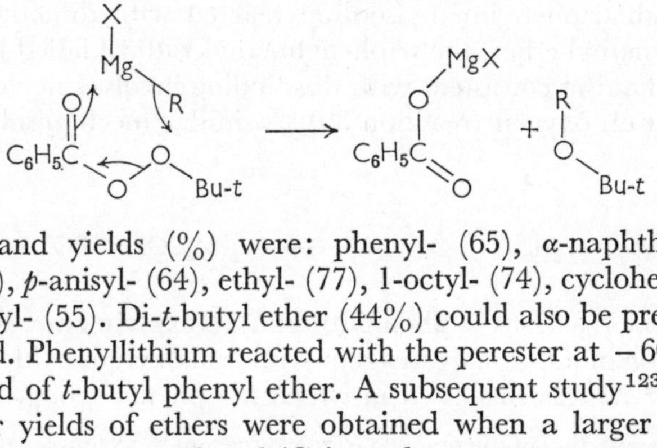

(31)

employed and yields (%) were: phenyl- (65), α-naphthyl- (69), p-tolyl- (81), p-anisyl- (64), ethyl- (77), 1-octyl- (74), cyclohexyl- (57), and 2-propyl- (55). Di-t-butyl ether (44%) could also be prepared by this method. Phenyllithium reacted with the perester at $-60°$ to give a 59% yield of t-butyl phenyl ether. A subsequent study[123] revealed that higher yields of ethers were obtained when a larger excess of Gignard reagent was employed (Grignard reagent:perester $\approx$ 1·5:1). Organolithium reagents were found to give lower yields of ethers; high-boiling products were formed presumably through preferential attack of the lithium compound on the carbonyl group.

The reaction of Grignard reagents with t-butyl perbenzoate appears to have particular merit when applied to the synthesis of t-butyl aryl ethers. In such cases, the conventional Williamson synthesis fails and the usual method of preparation, the acid-catalyzed addition of isobutylene and phenols, must be conducted under special conditions[124] such that nuclear alkylation of the phenol is suppressed.

C. Reaction of Tervalent Phosphorus Compounds with Dialkyl Peroxides

The reaction of dialkyl peroxides with tervalent organophosphorus compounds to give rise to ethers has been formulated as an Arbuzov process by Horner and Jurgeleit (reaction 32) [125]. In this manner, di-

$$R_3P + R^1OOR^1 \longrightarrow [R_3\overset{+}{P}OR^1\overset{-}{O}R^1] \longrightarrow R_3PO + R^1OR^1 \qquad (32)$$

ethyl peroxide gave ethyl ether with triethylphosphine at 80°, and *t*-butyl peroxide reacted with triphenylphosphine (110–120°) to give di-*t*-butyl ether. The ionic mechanism was invoked since no experimental evidence (sensitivity toward oxygen or initiation of polymerization) for a free-radical mechanism could be found.

In marked contrast, Walling and Rabinowitz [126] reacted dicumyl peroxide and di-*t*-butyl peroxide with triethyl phosphite thermally and photochemically, and obtained triethyl phosphate and hydrocarbon products arising from alkyl-radical dimerization and disproportionation. The reaction was postulated as proceeding through an intermediate phosphoranyl radical (reactions 33, 34, and 35). Since no

$$ROOR \longrightarrow 2\ RO^\bullet \qquad (33)$$

$$RO^\bullet + (EtO)_3P \longrightarrow (EtO)_3\overset{\bullet}{P}OR \longrightarrow R^\bullet + (EtO)_3PO \qquad (34)$$

$$2\ R^\bullet \longrightarrow R\!-\!R \qquad (35)$$

di-*t*-butyl ether was detected, Walling, Basedow, and Savas [126] reinvestigated the reaction of di-*t*-butyl peroxide with triphenylphosphine and found products consistent with the postulated free-radical process. Since Walling's product analyses were performed by gas–liquid chromatography, whereas Horner's was based on a distillation temperature, it appears that equation (32) is erroneous.

D. Thermolysis of Triarylmethyl Peroxides

The thermal decomposition of triarylmethyl peroxides usually proceeds by aryl migration to the initially formed alkoxy radical followed by dimerization. Wieland [127] obtained a 70% yield of benzpinacol diphenyl ether from thermolysis of triphenylmethyl peroxide via the sequence shown by reaction (36). The same product was obtained by

$$(C_6H_5)_3C\!-\!O\!-\!O\!-\!C(C_6H_5)_3 \longrightarrow 2\ (C_6H_5)_3CO^\bullet \longrightarrow$$

$$2\ (C_6H_5)_2\overset{\bullet}{C}\!-\!OC_6H_5 \longrightarrow (C_6H_5)_2\overset{\overset{\displaystyle OC_6H_5}{|}}{C}\!-\!\overset{\underset{\displaystyle OC_6H_5}{|}}{C}(C_6H_5)_2 \qquad (36)$$

treating triphenylmethyl hydroperoxide with ferrous salts (reactions 37 and 38)[128].

$$(C_6H_5)_3C\!-\!O\!-\!OH + Fe^{2+} \longrightarrow Fe^{3+} + OH^- + (C_6H_5)_3CO^{\cdot} \qquad (37)$$

$$(C_6H_5)_3CO^{\cdot} \longrightarrow (C_6H_5)_2\overset{\cdot}{C}\!-\!OC_6H_5 \longrightarrow Dimer \qquad (38)$$

If the thermal decomposition is conducted in a solvent which itself is a good radical source, mixed coupling products may result. Thus thermolysis of *t*-butyl triphenylmethyl peroxide in cumene gave a 60% yield of 1-phenoxy-2-methyl-1,1,2-triphenylpropane (reaction 39), the

$$(C_6H_5)_3C\!-\!O\!-\!O\!-\!C(CH_3)_3 + C_6H_5CH(CH_3)_2 \longrightarrow$$

$$\underset{\underset{OC_6H_5}{|}}{\overset{\overset{C_6H_5}{|}}{(C_6H_5)_2C\!-\!C(CH_3)_2}} + CH_4 + (CH_3)_2CO \quad (or\ (CH_3)_3COH) \quad (39)$$

coupling product of $(C_6H_5)_2\overset{\cdot}{C}\!-\!OC_6H_5$ and $C_6H_5\overset{\cdot}{C}(CH_3)_2$. The α-phenylethyl analog was also obtained (50% yield) using ethylbenzene in place of cumene.

From a study of the relative migratory aptitude of aryl groups in the thermal decomposition of several *t*-butyl aryldiphenylmethyl peroxides in cumene (reactions 40 and 41), Kharasch and coworkers[128] estab-

$$\underset{\underset{Ar}{|}}{(C_6H_5)_2C\!-\!O\!-\!O\!-\!C(CH_3)_3} \longrightarrow (CH_3)_3CO^{\cdot} + \underset{\underset{Ar}{|}}{(C_6H_5)_2C\!-\!O^{\cdot}} \qquad (40)$$

$$\underset{\underset{Ar}{|}}{(C_6H_5)_2C\!-\!O^{\cdot}} \longrightarrow \underset{\underset{Ar}{|}}{(C_6H_5)_2\overset{\cdot}{C}\!-\!OAr} + \underset{\underset{Ar}{|}}{C_6H_5\overset{\cdot}{C}\!-\!OC_6H_5} \overset{C_6H_5\overset{\cdot}{C}(CH_3)_2}{\longrightarrow}$$

$$\underset{\underset{C_6H_5}{|}}{\overset{\overset{OAr}{|}}{(C_6H_5)_2C\!-\!C(CH_3)_2}} + \underset{\underset{C_6H_5O}{|}\ \underset{C_6H_5}{|}}{\overset{\overset{Ar}{|}}{C_6H_5C\!-\!C(CH_3)_2}} \quad (41)$$

lished that α-naphthyl and *p*-biphenyl migrated equally readily and were about six times faster than phenyl or *p*-tolyl.

V. ETHERS FROM THE SMILES REARRANGEMENT

A group of intramolecular nucleophilic aromatic substitution reactions extensively investigated by Smiles[129] and his school may be represented by the general expression shown by reaction (42). A

$$(42)$$

variety of such rearrangements have been observed in which —ZH may be —OH, —SH, —NHR, —CONHR, —SO$_2$NHR, or —SO$_2$H, while X may be O, S, SO, or SO$_2$, although not all combinations of —ZH and X are allowed[130].

The reaction is usually conducted in basic media and it is generally agreed that the mechanism involves ionization of —ZH to —Z$^-$ followed by nucleophilic attack of $-Z^-$ on C$_1$ (ring B) displacing —X$^-$ [131]. In the majority of examples studied, ring B was activated (most frequently by an o- or p-NO$_2$ group), although the first observed instances of this rearrangement involved naphthalene derivatives containing no activating groups at all[129]. Aromatic ring A does not appear to be a requirement for rearrangement to occur[132].

Typical examples of this transformation are reactions 43a and 43b. The latter reaction proceeds quantitatively.

$$(43a)$$

$$(43b)$$

McClement and Smiles[133] determined the rates of rearrangement of a series of sulfones (23) with substituents in ring A (reaction 44). The effect that substituents exerted on the rearrangement rate was ascribed to an interesting and subtle electronic interplay among substituents.

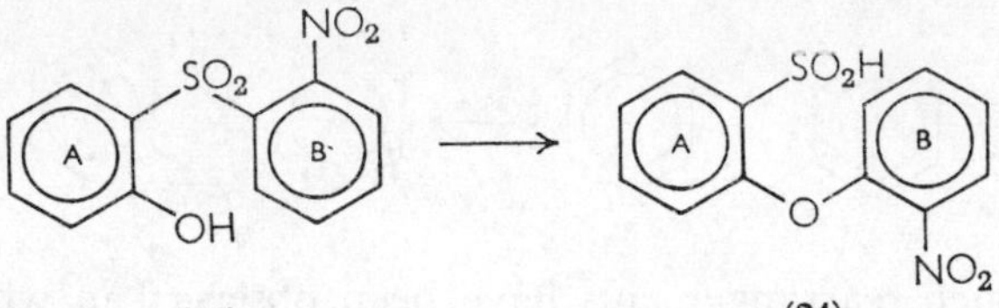

$$(44)$$

$$(23) \qquad\qquad (24)$$

From theoretical considerations and from the experimental work of Smiles, and subsequently Bunnett[134], one would predict that re-arrangement should be enhanced by electron release to ionized hydroxyl and electron withdrawal from the sulfone linkage. Rate retardation should be observed by introducing electron-attracting groups which influence hydroxyl more than the sulfone group or by electron-donating groups which interact with the sulfone substituent more strongly than with the ionized hydroxyl.

It was approximately determined[133] that a 6-methyl substituent increased the rate more than ten-fold over the 6-unsubstituted deriva-tive. This was interpreted as a manifestation of electron release from the methyl to the sulfone group thereby rendering the sulfone group less efficient at withdrawing electrons from the hydroxyl group. As a result, the nucleophilicity of the ionized hydroxyl in the 6-methyl derivative was enhanced over that of the 6-unsubstituted compound and the rate was correspondingly greater for the former. This inter-pretation was rendered untenable by the subsequent experiments of Okamoto and Bunnett[134], showing a very much higher rate enhance-ment for this case.

The latter investigators determined the rates of rearrangement of sulfones 25, 26, 27, and 28 in order to sort out contributions due to

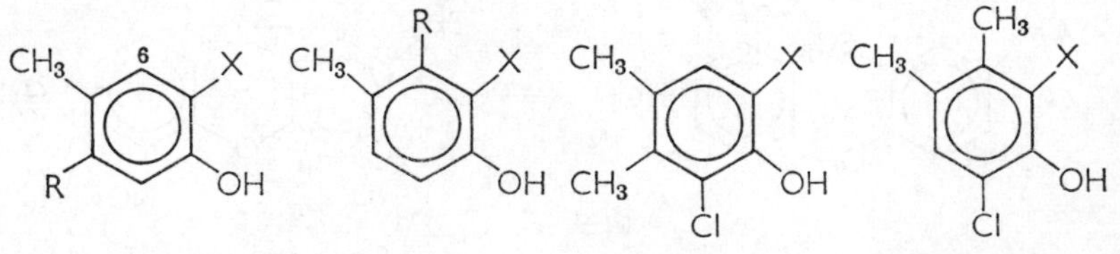

$$(25) \qquad\qquad (26) \qquad\qquad (27) \qquad\qquad (28)$$

(a) R = H
(b) R = CH$_3$
(c) R = Cl
(d) R = Br
X = $-SO_2C_6H_4NO_2$-o

(b) R = CH$_3$ X = SO$_2$C$_6$H$_4$NO$_2$-o X = $-SO_2C_6H_4NO_2$-o
(c) R = Cl
(d) R = Br
X = $-SO_2C_6H_4NO_2$-o

steric and electronic effects. They found that the rate was retarded by a methyl group (25b) or a chlorine atom (25c) in the 4-position in accord with the above-mentioned considerations. Sulfone (25b) rearranged only slightly more slowly than 25a, and this was considered to be primarily a reflection of the methyl group interacting with the sulfone group since electron release from methyl occurs more efficiently to a *para* than to a *meta* position. The ten-fold decrease in rate of 25c and 25d relative to 25a was ascribed primarily to electron withdrawal from ionized hydroxyl by the halogen atom. A chlorine atom in the 3-position also caused a slight rate decrease. These effects, however, are small compared to the steric effects of 6-substituents.

Electronically a 6-substituent should exert a similar effect to the same substituent in the 4-position; consequently rate differences exhibited by 6- and 4-substituted isomers could be taken as a measure of the magnitude of a steric effect. Comparison of the rates of rearrangement of 27 and 28, and 25b and 26b, respectively, revealed the 6-methyl derivative to react approximately 500,000 times faster than the 6-hydrogen isomer. Moreover, the 6-chloro isomer 26c showed the same large rate acceleration; this was also true for the 6-bromo compound 26d. Since both electron-releasing as well as electron-attracting 6-substituents caused similar enormous rate enhancements, the earlier notion of Smiles must be abandoned, and the view that rate acceleration is due to a steric effect is assured. It was suggested[134] that the marked steric acceleration caused by 6-substituents was the result of regulating the rotational conformations of the anionic species which led to transition state 29. A consideration of the various conformations

(29)

of the 6-hydrogen and 6-substituted compounds which could lead to 29 indicated that steric repulsions between substituents and the carbon atoms of ring B were least severe for the latter isomers. Hence 6-substituted compounds, regardless of the electronic effect exerted by the 6-substituent, rearranged faster than the 6-hydrogen derivative.

VI. ETHERS FROM DIAZO COMPOUNDS

A. Methylation of Alcohols by Means of Diazomethane

Although nonacidic hydroxyl groups are generally inert toward diazomethane, several reports have appeared citing the successful methylation of alcohols with diazomethane in conjunction with various catalysts (equation 45). In an early study, Meerwein and

$$ROH + CH_2N_2 \xrightarrow{\text{Catalyst}} ROCH_3 + N_2 \qquad (45)$$

Hinz[135] showed that n-BuOH could be methylated using $ZnCl_2$, $MgCl_2$, or $FeCl_3$ as catalysts, although yields were only of the order of 25%. Furthermore, $B(OEt)_3$ catalyzed the methylation of EtOH (69%) and n-PrOH (24%), but not of n-BuOH and i-PrOH. $Al(OBu)_3$ permitted the methylation of n-BuOH (83%); $Al(O-i-Pr)_3$ catalysis afforded i-PrOCH$_3$ (77%). Similarly, $Sb(OBu)_3$ as catalyst permitted the preparation of n-BuOCH$_3$ (73%), but $Sb(O-i-Pr)_3$ was ineffective in catalyzing the formation of i-PrOCH$_3$. Although other catalysts were also explored and none proved to be of general preparative significance, nevertheless this early study is of interest for having set the stage for subsequent more successful developments.

In 1958, Caserio, Roberts, Neeman, and Johnson[136] established that the methylation of a variety of alcohols could be successfully conducted by employing fluoboric acid* as catalyst. In this manner, methyl ethers of simple primary and unhindered secondary alcohols could be obtained in 84–98% yields. The reactions were conducted in diethyl ether, or preferably, methylene chloride as solvent, at 0–25° in the presence of 0·6–8 mole percent fluoboric acid. Methylene chloride as solvent generally gave higher yields, more rapid reaction, and required less catalyst than reactions employing diethyl ether as solvent. Tertiary and moderately hindered secondary alcohols gave lower yields, slower reaction, and were accompanied by the formation of polymethylene, which could be diminished by using lower temperatures.

Some typical results are the methylation of n-octanol (87%), cyclohexanol (92%), t-amyl alcohol (66%), and dimethylphenylcarbinol

---

* A protic acid such as hydrochloric acid is itself consumed by reaction with diazomethane since the intermediate methyldiazonium ion reacts preferentially with the acid anion rather than the alcohol. The judicious choice of fluoboric acid rested on the expectation that the methyldiazonium cation would react more rapidly with the alcohol as nucleophile, since the consumption of fluoboric acid by diazomethane would require scission of a B—F bond.

(30%). Isoborneol (hindered hydroxyl) failed to be methylated. Triphenylcarbinol also did not undergo alkylation, but instead formed trityl fluoborate.

From competition experiments on the isomeric butanols, the relative rates of methylation were determined to be primary:secondary: tertiary = 2·2:1·3:1·0. The relative rates of methylation of the epimeric cholestanols were in the ratio $3\beta(\text{eq}):3\alpha(\text{ax}) = 1\cdot3:1$. Although the relative rates are in the expected order, the rather small spread reflects the lack of great steric selectivity for this methylation procedure. However, the primary and secondary hydroxyl groups of 2,3-dimethylascorbic acid (**30**) proved to be sufficiently different to permit preferential methylation of the primary hydroxyl group forming the trimethyl ether **31** (equation 46).

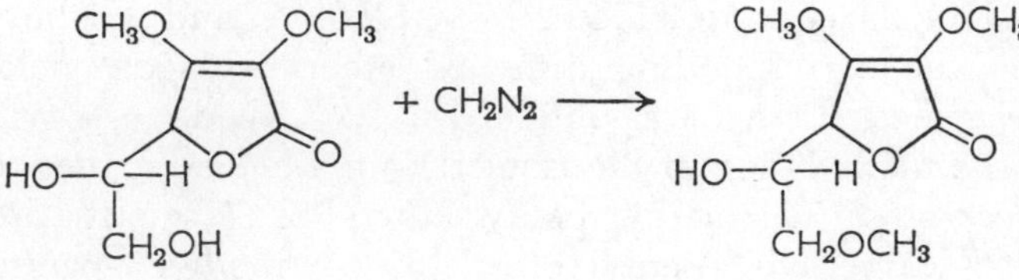

$$+ \text{CH}_2\text{N}_2 \longrightarrow \tag{46}$$

(**30**)　　　　　　　　　　　　　　(**31**)

Since this methylation procedure gives a product with the same configuration as the starting alcohol, reaction apparently occurs directly at the oxygen atom. α-Cholestanyl methyl ether is obtained from α-cholestanol, and the β-ether from β-cholestanol, each in 98% yield.

The method also permits the direct conversion (difficult by any other direct methylation procedure) of desoxycorticosterone (**32a**) into 21-methoxyprogesterone (**32b**) and testosterone (**32c**) into 17-β-methoxyandrost-4-en-3-one (**32d**). In subsequent work [137,138], it was established that a competing process in the case of α,β-unsaturated ketones is homologation to a β,γ-unsaturated ketone.

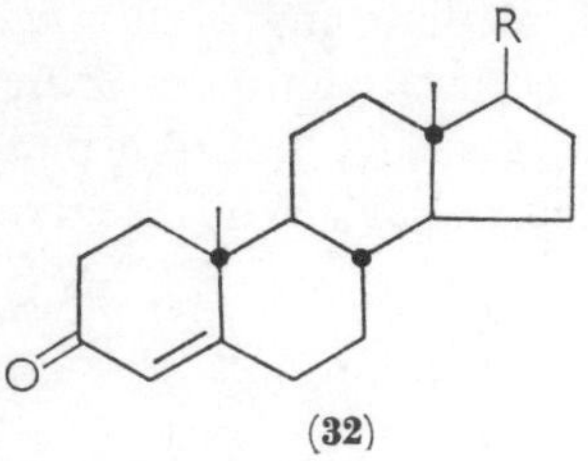

(a) R = COCH$_2$OH
(b) R = COCH$_2$OCH$_3$
(c) R = OH
(d) R = OCH$_3$
(e) R = COCHN$_2$

(**32**)

Weakly acidic phenols also reacted with diazomethane employing fluoboric acid catalysis; estradiol was transformed to the dimethyl ether in 81% yield. Phenols with pK_a 9·5 to 10·2 gave poor to fair yields of methyl ethers.

Although no extensive study was made, an adaptation of the above procedure employing diazoethane afforded *trans*- and *cis*-1-methyl-2-ethoxycyclopentane from the corresponding secondary alcohols in 26 and 17% yields, respectively.

In addition to fluoboric acid, it was established that boron trifluoride etherate (method of Newman and Beal[149], *vide infra*) was effective in catalyzing the methylation of alcohols with diazomethane.

Similarly, Müller and Rundel[139], employing 10 mole percent boron trifluoride etherate as catalyst, obtained 70–80% yields of the corresponding ethers from cyclohexanol, diphenylcarbinol, n-octyl alcohol, crotyl alcohol, and cholesterol. t-$BuOCH_3$ was prepared in 40% yield. Glycols, $HOCH_2(CH_2)_nCH_2OH$ (n = 1,2,3,4), and 1,4-butynediol also gave the corresponding dimethyl ethers in good yields, and glycerine trimethyl ether was obtained in 73% yield.

From the methylation of the isomeric amyl alcohols, the following yields were obtained: methyl pentyl ether (72%), methyl isopentyl ether (75%), methyl 3-pentyl ether (69%), methyl t-pentyl ether (44%), or primary:secondary:tertiary = 1·7:1·55:1·0.

It was also determined that ethylation of alcohols by diazoethane was likewise catalyzed by boron trifluoride etherate but yields were in the range 15–20%.

B. α-Alkoxy Ketones from α-Diazo Ketones

Several groups of investigators have determined that the reaction of α-diazo ketones with alcohols in the presence of appropriate catalysts gives α-alkoxy ketones (equation 47), i.e. the reaction proceeds without

$$R^1COCHN_2 + R^2OH \xrightarrow{\text{Catalyst}} R^1COCH_2OR^2 + N_2 \qquad (47)$$

intervention of the Wolff rearrangement. This catalytic effect has been ascribed to 'deactivation' of the intermediate involved (*vide infra*).

In the absence of a catalyst and at moderate temperatures, mixtures are obtained. The diazo ketone (**33**) gave 30% benzoin methyl ether (**34**) and 70% methyl diphenyl acetate (**35**, Wolff rearrangement

$$C_6H_5COCN_2C_6H_5 + CH_3OH \longrightarrow C_6H_5COCHC_6H_5 + (C_6H_5)_2CHCO_2CH_3 \qquad (48)$$

$$\text{(33)} \qquad\qquad\qquad\qquad \underset{OCH_3}{|} \qquad \text{(35)}$$

$$\text{(34)}$$

product) in methanol at 50° (reaction 48)[140]. Elevated temperatures appear to favor the Wolff rearrangement; thus diazo ketones are converted into benzyl esters in refluxing benzyl alcohol[141].

Moderate temperatures and the presence of a suitable catalyst permit the conversion of the diazo ketones to the corresponding ketol ether. Aeberli and Erlenmeyer[142] employed cupric oxide in methanol to convert a diazo ketone-substituted thiazole into the α-alkoxy ketone. Similarly, Casanova and Reichstein[143], and Plattner and coworkers[144] were successful in preparing ketol ethers from several steroidal diazo ketones using cupric oxide as catalyst. However, the Wolff rearrangement product, methyl phenyl acetate, was obtained by the action of this catalyst on α-diazoacetophenone in methanol[143].

Yates[145] established, contrary to previous claims[146], that copper bronze was not a suitable general catalyst for the Arndt–Eistert sequence, but rather, was efficacious in converting α-diazo ketones into α-alkoxy ketones. The action of copper on 1-diazo-2-nonadecanone in hot ethanol afforded a 68% yield of 1-ethoxy-2-nonadecanone. By treating α-diazoacetophenone with copper in the appropriate alcohol, the following α-keto ethers were also prepared: α-methoxyacetophenone (55%), α-ethoxyacetophenone (60%), α-(1-hexoxy)acetophenone (20%), and α-(t-butoxy)acetophenone (30%). The reaction of phenol with α-diazoacetophenone in the presence of copper gave, in addition to α-phenoxyacetophenone (63%), a 26% yield of 2-phenylbenzofuran. The diazoethane derivative, α-diazopropiophenone, was also shown to give the corresponding α-ethoxy ketone (52%) with copper in ethanol.

These reactions may be interpreted[145] in terms of a keto carbene (or keto carbene–copper complex) intermediate undergoing nucleophilic attack at the methine carbon by an unshared electron pair on oxygen, followed by a prototropic shift (reactions 49a and 49b). In the absence

$$RCOCHN_2 \xrightarrow{\text{Cu}} RCOCH: + N_2 \qquad (49a)$$

$$R^1COCH: + R^2OH \longrightarrow R^1CO\bar{C}H\overset{+}{O}R^2 \longrightarrow R^1COCH_2OR^2 \qquad (49b)$$
$$\underset{H}{|}$$

of nucleophiles, diazo ketones are converted into diacylethylenes by treatment with copper[147] (or copper salts)[148] in inert solvents such as benzene, toluene, or ligroin. The enediones, formally dimers of the keto carbenes, probably arise by attack of the keto carbene (or more

16+c.e.l.

likely, keto carbene–catalyst complex) on excess diazo ketone (reaction 50).

$$2\ RCOCHN_2 \longrightarrow RCOCH{=}CHCOR \tag{50}$$

Boron trifluoride etherate was shown by Newman and Beal[149] to be very effective in catalyzing the reaction of diazo ketones and alcohols (reaction 51). The reaction appears to be quite general even when

$$ArCOCHN_2 + ROH \xrightarrow{\ BF_3\ } ArCOCH_2OR + N_2 \tag{51}$$

t-butyl alcohol is employed, although appreciable amounts of catalyst cause hydrolysis of the t-butyl ether to the corresponding phenacyl alcohol. Yields of ethers obtained by this method are, in general, superior to the copper- or cupric oxide-catalyzed reactions. Typical results are the preparation of α-methoxyacetophenone (79%), α-ethoxyacetophenone (81%), α-isopropoxyacetophenone (69%), α-t-butoxy-p-methoxyacetophenone (57%), and α-methoxypropiophenone (60%). Aluminum chloride or stannic chloride could be used in place of boron trifluoride etherate; they produce comparable results. The extension[150] of the boron trifluoride etherate method for steroids enabled the conversion of 21-diazoprogesterone (**32e**) to 21-methoxy-progesterone (**32b**) to proceed in essentially quantitative yield.

C. Miscellaneous Reactions

Although the thermal and photochemical decomposition of diazo compounds in alcohols has been employed to prepare ethers, other methods are frequently more desirable from a preparative viewpoint.

The reaction of diazo compounds with unsaturated alcohols appears to favor ether rather than cyclopropane formation. D'yakonov[151] obtained benzhydryl allyl ether (major product) as well as smaller amounts of benzophenone azine and 1-(hydroxymethyl)-2,2-diphenyl-cyclopropane from the thermal decomposition of diphenyldiazo-methane in allyl alcohol (reaction 52).

$$(C_6H_5)_2CN_2 + CH_2{=}CHCH_2OH \longrightarrow (C_6H_5)_2CHOCH_2CH{=}CH_2 +$$

$$ + (C_6H_5)_2C{=}N{-}N{=}C(C_6H_5)_2 \tag{52}$$

The copper-catalyzed decomposition of ethyl diazoacetate in allyl alcohol gave a 52% yield of ethyl allyloxyacetate and 7% of ethyl *trans*-2-(hydroxymethyl)cyclopropanecarboxylate (reaction 53) [151].

$$N_2CHCOOC_2H_5 + CH_2{=}CHCH_2OH \xrightarrow{Cu} CH_2{=}CHCH_2OCH_2COOC_2H_5 +$$

$$\underset{HOCH_2 \quad H}{\overset{H \quad COOC_2H_5}{\triangle}} \qquad (53)$$

Photolysis of an ethereal solution of diazomethane and cyclopenten-4-ol, however, gave neither the ether nor the cyclopropyl derivative; diethyl ether solvent was apparently preferentially attacked [152].

From the photolysis of diphenyldiazomethane in methanol, a 70% yield of benzhydryl methyl ether was obtained [153]. Kirmse has noted the formal acid–base relationship existing between carbenes and carbonium ions (reaction 54) and has suggested that benzhydryl methyl

$$R_2C{:} + H^+ \xrightleftharpoons{} R_2CH^+ \qquad (54)$$

ether formation is the result of diphenylcarbene accepting a proton to form the diphenylcarbonium ion followed by reaction with methanol solvent. This mechanism was preferred over an alternative scheme involving protonation of diphenyldiazomethane in an excited state on the basis of quantum-yield determinations. Photolysis of diphenyl-diazomethane in lithium azide–methanol gave benzhydryl methyl ether and benzhydryl azide in virtually the same ratio as that obtained from solvolysis of benzhydryl chloride (reaction 55).

$$(C_6H_5)_2CN_2 \xrightarrow{h\nu} (C_6H_5)_2C{:} \xrightarrow{H^+} (C_6H_5)_2\overset{+}{C}H \begin{array}{l} \xrightarrow{CH_3OH} (C_6H_5)_2CHOCH_3 \\[6pt] \xrightarrow{N_3^-} (C_6H_5)_2CHN_3 \end{array} \qquad (55)$$

Azine monoxides (prepared by peracetic acid oxidation of azines) undergo cleavage to the diazo hydrocarbon and carbonyl compound photolytically, thermally, or by treatment with acid (reaction 56).

$$\underset{\overset{|}{O^-}}{\overset{R}{Ar\overset{|}{C}}}{=}N{-}\overset{+}{N}{=}\overset{R}{\overset{|}{C}}Ar \longrightarrow Ar{-}\overset{R}{\overset{|}{C}}{-}N_2 + Ar{-}\overset{R}{\overset{|}{C}}{=}O \qquad (56)$$

Aldehydes and ethers are obtained in good yield from the reaction of an azine oxide with an alcohol (or phenol) under acid catalysis (reaction 57). Some representative examples are the formation of benzyl

$$
\overset{\overset{\displaystyle O^-}{|}}{ArCH{=}N{-}\underset{+}{N}{=}CHAr} + ROH \xrightarrow{H^+} ArCHO + ArCH_2OR \tag{57}
$$

ethyl ether (78% yield), benzyl butyl ether (90% yield), benzyl cyclohexyl ether (74% yield), and benzyl phenyl ether (73% yield). In each case, the aldehyde was also obtained in greater than 75% yield. The reaction is believed to proceed by initial protonation on oxygen followed by the addition of water to give an intermediate which fragments to aldehyde and diazo compound; reaction of the latter with alcohol gives the ether (reaction 58)[154].

$$
\overset{\overset{\displaystyle O^-}{|}}{ArCH{=}N{-}\underset{+}{N}{=}CHAr} \xrightarrow{H^+} \overset{\overset{\displaystyle OH}{|}}{ArCH{=}N{-}\underset{+}{N}{=}CHAr} \xrightarrow{H_2O}
$$

$$
\overset{\overset{\displaystyle OH}{|}}{\underset{\overset{|}{H}}{ArCH{=}N{-}\overset{+}{N}{-}}\underset{\overset{|}{OH}}{CHAr}} \longrightarrow ArCHO + [H_3O^+] + ArCHN_2 \xrightarrow{ROH} ArCH_2OR \tag{58}
$$

D. The Reaction of Aromatic Diazonium Compounds with Alcohols

Although Griess[155] originally reported that benzene was produced by the action of ethanol on benzenediazonium salts, subsequent experimentation[156] established that the thermal decomposition of a diazonium salt in an alcoholic solution gave a mixture of the aryl alkyl ether and an aromatic hydrocarbon (reaction 59). Benzenediazonium

$$
ArN_2{}^+X^- + C_2H_5OH \longrightarrow ArH + ArOC_2H_5 + N_2 + CH_3CHO + HX \tag{59}
$$

chloride, for example, on treatment with ethanol, gave phenetole (61%) and benzene (5%). Anisole (major product) and some benzene were produced when benzenediazonium sulfate was boiled with methanol.

The decomposition of benzenediazonium chloride in aqueous solution leading to phenol is a first-order reaction, the rate of which is almost completely unaffected by the presence of other ions (e.g. chloride, bromide, nitrate, and sulfate) in moderate concentration. In the presence of chloride ion, both phenol and chlorobenzene are produced. Benzenediazonium nitrate, bromide, and sulfate, in the complete absence of chloride ion, decomposed at the same rate as benzenediazonium chloride. An S_N1 mechanism is in accord with these observations, involving rate-determining loss of nitrogen from the diazonium salt, followed by a fast reaction of the aryl cation with water to give phenol, and, in the presence of chloride ion, chlorobenzene (reactions 60, 61, and 62)[157, 158].

$$ArN_2^+ \longrightarrow Ar^+ + N_2 \tag{60}$$

$$Ar^+ + H_2O \rightleftharpoons AroH + H^+ \tag{61}$$

$$Ar^+ + Cl^- \longrightarrow ArCl \tag{62}$$

By analogy with the above considerations, the expected product from the thermal decomposition of a diazonium salt in an alcohol is the alkyl aryl ether, and it is generally accepted that ether formation involves heterolytic cleavage of the C—N bond of the diazonium salt, followed by reaction of the aryl cation with alcohol (reaction 63). The

$$Ar^+ + ROH \longrightarrow ArOR + H^+ \tag{63}$$

reduction product arises primarily by a homolytic path (reaction 64),

$$Ar^\bullet + RCH_2OH \longrightarrow ArH + R\overset{\bullet}{C}HOH \tag{64}$$

although a hydride-transfer mechanism (reaction 65) has also been postulated[159].

$$Ar^+ + RCH_2OH \longrightarrow ArH + R\overset{+}{C}HOH \tag{65}$$

When benzenediazonium fluoborate is thermally decomposed in methanol in the presence of air, the reaction mixture becomes acidic; nitrogen is liberated quantitatively and anisole (93%) is the major product[160]. This is in accord with the proposed heterolytic mechanism which requires that one mole of H^+ and one mole of nitrogen is formed for each mole of diazonium salt decomposed. In the presence of sodium acetate (Gomberg–Bachmann conditions[161]) and absence of oxygen, benzene (85–90%) is the principal product; some anisole and biphenyl are produced along with a trace amount of azobenzene. The oxidation of methanol to formaldehyde (about 85%) accompanies the formation of benzene[160]. Under these conditions the homolytic portion of the reaction has effectively intervened.

The factors that influence the reaction course are the alcohol employed, the nature of substituents in the diazonium salt, the acidity, and the presence of oxygen.

In general, the yield of ether decreases at the expense of the reduction product as the alcohol is changed from methyl to ethyl or higher alkyl. Thus treatment of benzenediazonium fluoroborate with methanol, ethanol, n-butyl alcohol, and isopropyl alcohol, respectively, in the presence of air, gave the corresponding ethers in yields of 93%, 66%, 57%, and 43%. The first-order rates of decomposition in methanol, ethanol, and isopropyl alcohol were within about 10% of each other. This insensitivity of rate to small variation in alcohol structure is understandable in terms of a heterolytic cleavage of the diazonium salt to give the corresponding ethers[159]. The rate of decomposition is about twice as fast in alcohols as in water; this is in the direction expected for a reaction in which there is charge dispersion in the transition state.

Benzenediazonium sulfate, when decomposed in amyl alcohol, is reported to give 30% of the ether. When the bisdiazonium chloride derived from benzidine was treated with ethanol, biphenyl (80%) was obtained, whereas decomposition with methanol gave only a trace of the biaryl and a 65% yield of 4,4′-dimethoxybiphenyl.

The introduction of substituents such as halogen atoms, nitro groups, or carboxyl groups tends to favor the replacement of the diazonium group by hydrogen at the expense of ether formation. The presence of a methyl group or a methoxyl substituent, on the other hand, appears to favor ether formation. Although the available data do not justify broad generalizations, it would seem that this effect is maximal when the substituent is *ortho* to the diazo function, intermediate in the *meta* position, and weakest in the *para* position[159,162]. For example the diazotized *o*-, *m*-, and *p*-toluidines, on treatment with ethanol, give the corresponding ethers in yields of 50%, 40%, and 20%, respectively.

Diazotized *o*-, *m*-, and *p*-chloroanilines, as well as the isomeric bromoanilines, on treatment with ethanol, give only the reduction product. Similarly, only reduction is observed in the reaction of either diazotized *o*-chloro- or *o*-bromoaniline with methanol. The *m*-chloro- and *m*-bromoanilines, however, give mainly the ether when decomposed in either ethanol or methanol. The *p*-chloro compound gives only the ether in methanol but only the reduction product in ethanol. Identical results were reported for the *p*-bromo diazonium salt, but it was subsequently established that bromobenzene is the major product in methanol[159,162].

The results of a recent study have rendered it possible to emphasize either the heterolytic or homolytic process by the choice of suitable conditions. The following examples illustrate this point.

Diazotized m- and p-aminotoluenes, when thermally decomposed in methanol in the presence of air (to inhibit the radical process), gave the respective ethers in yields of 95% and about 84%. Diazotized p-anisidine could be converted either into hydroquinone dimethyl ether or into anisole in high yield, depending on whether oxygen was present or absent. p-Bromobenzenediazonium bisulfate, when decomposed thermally in methanol, gave a preponderance (66–84% yield) of reduction product; in the presence of oxygen a 70% yield of p-bromoanisole results[159].

A systematic study of the decomposition of several diazonium salts with methanol under conditions considered most favorable for ether formation, namely, in the presence of oxygen and added acid, as well as conditions considered most favorable for reduction, i.e. nitrogen atmosphere and no added acid, gave the following interesting results. Under the former set of conditions, benzenediazonium bisulfate gave 94% of anisole, the p-toluenediazonium salt yielded 97% of p-methoxytoluene, the p-bromobenzenediazonium ion formed the ether in 73% yield, the p-nitrobenzenediazonium salt afforded a 49% yield of p-nitroanisole, and hydroquinone dimethyl ether was formed in 79% yield from p-methoxybenzenediazonium bisulfate. Under a nitrogen atmosphere and in the absence of added acid the yields of the above-listed ethers were, respectively, 73%, 42%, 3%, 20%, and 4%[159].

A study of the photodecomposition of the p-nitrobenzenediazonium salt in ethanol and methanol solutions revealed that the dominant primary reaction was the formation of p-nitrophenyl radical[163]. In ethanol solution, for example, in addition to nitrobenzene (major product) the α- and β-arylethanols as well as the 1,4- and 2,3-butanediols and acetaldehyde were formed, but no dinitrobiphenyl. These results have been rationalized in terms of the primary process shown in reaction (66). The small amounts (about 3·5%) of ether formed

$$ArN_2{}^+X^- \xrightarrow{h\nu} Ar^{\bullet} + N_2 + {}^{\bullet}X \tag{66}$$

and the increase in acidity of the photolyzed solution as the reaction progressed was interpreted in terms of the heterolytic process given by reaction (67).

$$ArN_2{}^+X^- \xrightarrow{h\nu} Ar^+ + N_2 + X^- \tag{67}$$

The photoinduced decomposition of several other diazonium salts in methanol solution has led to the surprising result that the product distribution for the photo process is essentially identical with that of the 'dark' decomposition[159]. For example the photoinduced decomposition of the p-nitrobenzenediazonium salt in methanol gave nitrobenzene and p-nitroanisole in yields of 80% and 13%, respectively, whereas the 'dark' decomposition yielded the reduction product in 82% yield and the ether in 4% yield. The 'dark' reaction of p-toluenediazonium bisulfate with methanol afforded the reduction product and ether in yields of 4% and 91%, respectively; the photoinduced decomposition gave toluene (12%) and p-methoxytoluene (85%).

VII. ETHERS PRODUCED BY KOLBE ELECTROLYSIS

Methanol and water are commonly employed solvents for the Kolbe anodic decarboxylation of carboxylic acids and the Kolbe dimer is to a varying degree accompanied by such by-products as nondimeric saturated hydrocarbons, olefins, alcohols, esters, and ethers (Hofer–Moest reaction).

It has been suggested that the Hofer–Moest path involves oxidation of electrolytically produced radicals to carbonium ions which then attack the solvent (reaction 68). Ether formation is suggestive of a

$$R^1COO^- \longrightarrow R^1COO^{\bullet} \longrightarrow R^{1\bullet} \longrightarrow R^{1+} \xrightarrow{R^2OH} R^1OR^2 \qquad (68)$$

cationic rather than a free-radical intermediate since radical attack on alcohol would be expected to give rise to hydrocarbon by hydrogen abstraction rather than ether[164].

Rearranged Hofer–Moest products are frequently obtained, but significantly such products are exclusively monomeric whereas dimeric products prove to be unrearranged. This is consistent with rearranged products arising from 1,2-alkyl shifts involving a cationic intermediate and unrearranged dimer arising from radical coupling. Thus Dauben and Muhs[164] obtained, in addition to 58% unrearranged Kolbe dimer, 13% of 1-methylcycloheptylmethyl ether and 11% 1-methylcycloheptene from the electrolysis of 1-methylcyclohexylacetic acid in methanol, presumably via reaction (69). Similar behavior was noted for 1-methylcyclopentylacetic acid[164].

In general, the yield of Kolbe dimer decreases at the expense of ether as phenyl groups (or other carbonium ion stabilizing groups) are substituted on the carbon atom *alpha* to the carboxylate function. For

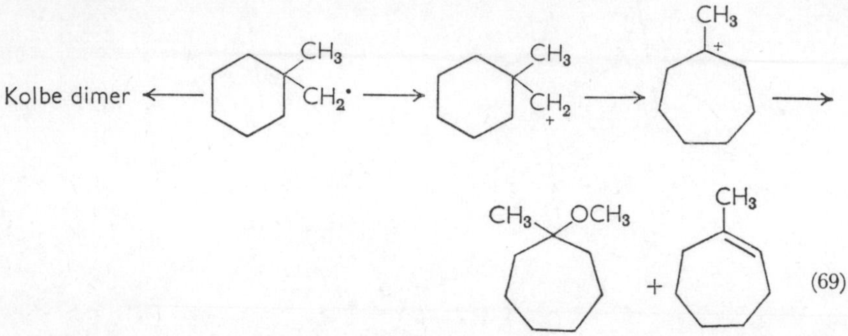

(69)

example the electrolysis of diphenylacetic acid in a methanol–pyridine mixture gave tetraphenylethane (9% yield) and methyl benzhydryl ether (42% yield)[165]; subsequently the yield of ether was raised to 80% by using a methanol–triethylamine mixture[166]. Similarly, trityl methyl ether was the major product from the electrolysis of triphenylacetic acid in methanol[167]. Anodic oxidation of the sodium salt of 2,3,3-triphenylpropanoic acid (**36**) in methanol gave no coupling product (reaction 70), the only product being methyl 1,2,2-triphenylethyl ether (**37**)[168].

$$(C_6H_5)_2CH-\underset{\underset{C_6H_5}{|}}{CH}-COO^-Na^+ \xrightarrow[CH_3OH]{Anode} (C_6H_5)_2CH-\underset{\underset{C_6H_5}{|}}{CH}-OCH_3 \qquad (70)$$

(**36**)   (**37**)

Corey and coworkers have established that Hofer–Moest products become increasingly important at higher voltages[169]. Thus electrolysis (50 v) of either exo- or endo-norbornane-2-carboxylic acid (**38** or **39**) in methanol–triethylamine produced, as the only ether product, the exo isomer **40**. When optically active **39** was employed, product ether **40** was racemic. Electrolytic oxidation of either exo- or endo-5-norbornene-2-carboxylic acid (**41** or **42**) in methanol–triethylamine gave 3-methoxynortricyclene (**43**). Thus, the ethers produced are in complete accord with a cationic intermediate[170].

Further evidence which implicates such an intermediate is the fact that electrolysis (150 v) of cholesteryl-3β-carboxylic acid in methanol yielded 6β-methoxy-3,5-cyclocholestane, the characteristic solvolysis product obtained from cholesteryl tosylate[171], and a mixture of 6β-methoxy-Δ⁴-cholestene and 4β-methoxy-Δ⁶-cholestene, obtained previously from methanolysis of epicholesteryl tosylate[171].

16*

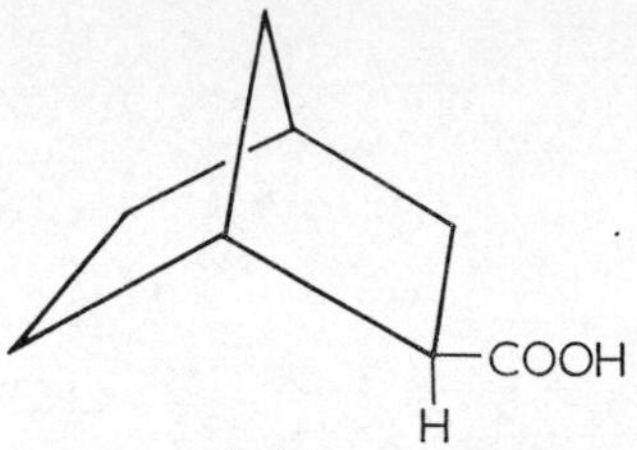

(38)

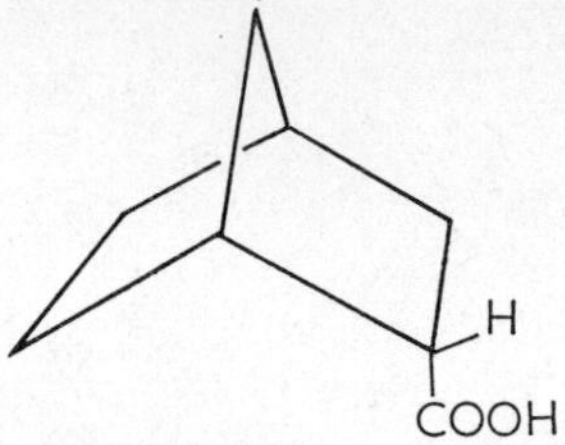

(39)

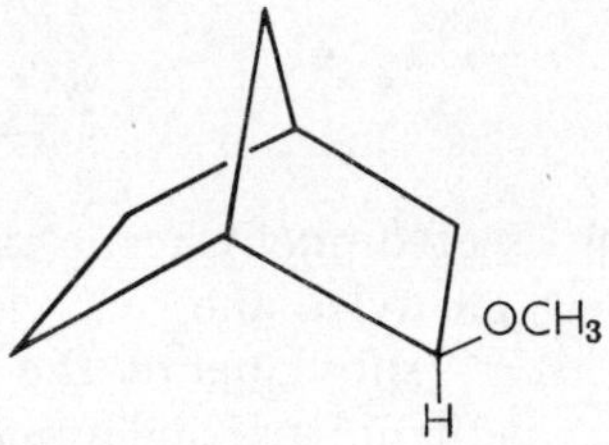

(40)

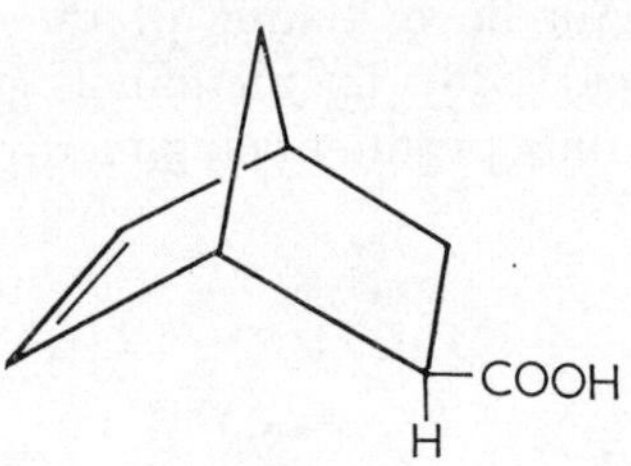

(41)

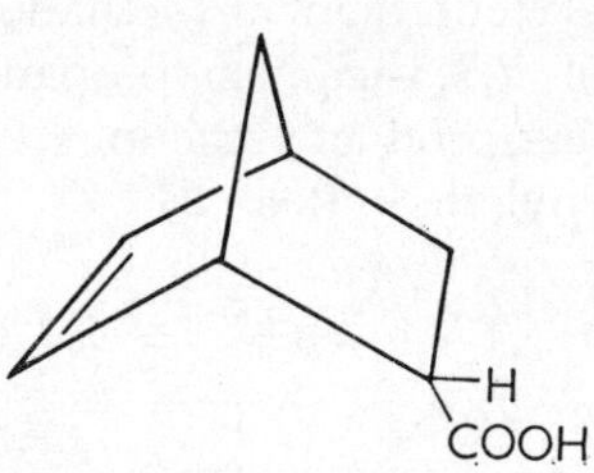

(42)

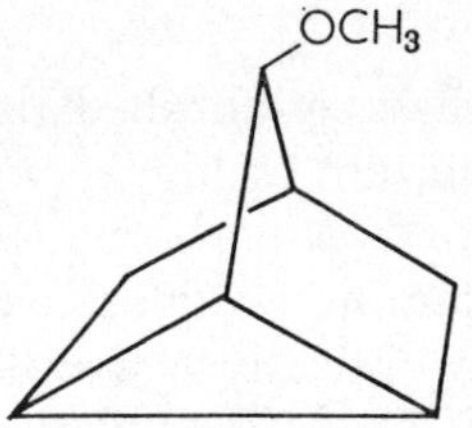

(43)

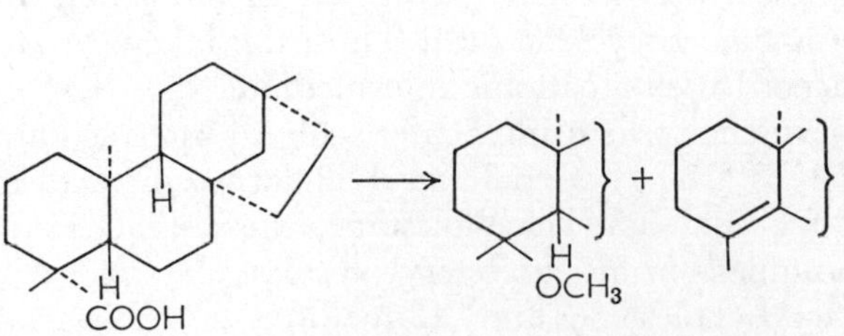

(44) → (45) + (46)

(71)

The anodic reaction of isostevic acid (**44**) in methanol gave a mixture of ether **45** and β-elimination product **46** (reaction 71); similarly, anodic decarboxylation of **47** in methanol gave rise to ether **48** and olefin **49** (reaction 72) [172]. (High pH caused hydrolysis of 3-OAc.)

This anodic decarboxylation-solvolysis method has proved useful for the synthesis of acetals and mixed acetals. Benzophenone dimethyl acetal was obtained (74% yield) from the electrolysis of α-methoxy-diphenylacetic acid in methanol; electrolysis of α-ethoxyphenylacetic acid and α-ethoxydiphenylacetic acid, respectively, in methanol provided the corresponding methyl ethyl acetals in over 70% yield[173].

As already mentioned, electrolysis of triphenylacetic acid in methanol gave trityl methyl ether. Interestingly, electrolysis of the next higher homolog, 3,3,3-triphenylpropanoic acid, in methanol gave the 1,4-phenyl migration product, phenyl 3,3-diphenyl-3-methoxypropanoate,[174] which may have arisen via reaction (73).

VIII. REFERENCES

1. F. Beilstein, *Handbuch der Organischen Chemie*, Vol. I, Verlag von L. Voss, Hamburg, 1893, p. 293.
2. W. Williamson, *J. Chem. Soc.*, **4**, 106, 229 (1852).
3. G. F. White, A. B. Morrison, and E. G. E. Anderson, *J. Am. Chem. Soc.*, **46**, 961 (1924)
4. T. H. Vaughn, R. R. Vogt, and J. A. Nieuwland, *J. Am. Chem. Soc.*, **57**, 510 (1935).
5. I. E. Muscat, *J. Am. Chem. Soc.*, **56**, 693, 2450 (1934).
6. T. Purdie and J. C. Irvine, *J. Chem. Soc.*, **83**, 1021 (1903).
7. W. N. Haworth, *J. Chem. Soc.*, **107**, 8 (1915).
8. C. D. Hurd and W. H. Saunders, Jr., *J. Am. Chem. Soc.*, **74**, 5324 (1952); W. G. Dauben and G. H. Berezin, *J. Am. Chem. Soc.*, **85**, 468 (1963).
9. R. Cornubert and H. LeBihan, *Bull. Soc. Chim. France*, **43**, 74 (1928).
10. J. R. Lewis and C. W. Shoppee, *J. Chem. Soc.*, 1375 (1955); R. C. Fuson and B. Freedman, *J. Org. Chem.*, **23**, 1161 (1958); C. R. Narayanan and K. N. Iyer, *J. Org. Chem.*, **30**, 1734 (1965).
11. R. L. Letsinger and J. G. Traynham, *J. Am. Chem. Soc.*, **70**, 3342 (1948); R. H. Baker, *J. Am. Chem. Soc.*, **70**, 3857 (1948); J. Meinwald and S. L. Emerman, *J. Am. Chem. Soc.*, **78**, 5087 (1956).
12. C. R. Hauser and S. W. Kantor, *J. Am. Chem. Soc.*, **73**, 1437 (1951).
13. G. M. Bennett and A. L. Hock, *J. Chem. Soc.*, 472 (1927); D. Wasserman and C. R. Dawson, *J. Org. Chem.*, **8**, 73 (1943); E. A. Talley, A. S. Hunter, and E. Yanovsky, *J. Am. Chem. Soc.*, **73**, 3528 (1951).
14. P. G. Stevens and S. A. V. Deans, *Can. J. Chem.*, *Ser. B*, **17**, 290 (1939); F. L. M. Pattison, W. C. Howell, and R. G. Woolford, *Can. J. Chem.*, **35**, 141 (1957).
15. W. R. Kirner, *J. Am. Chem. Soc.*, **50**, 1955 (1928).
16. W. R. Kirner, *J. Am. Chem. Soc.*, **52**, 3251 (1930).
17. K. Mislow, *J. Am. Chem. Soc.*, **73**, 3954 (1951).
18. E. D. Hughes, C. K. Ingold, and A. D. Scott, *J. Chem. Soc.*, 1201 (1937).
19. W. E. Doering and J. C. Aschner, *J. Am. Chem. Soc.*, **71**, 839 (1949).
20. K. Mislow, *J. Am. Chem. Soc.*, **73**, 4043 (1951).
21. A. Streitwieser, Jr. and A. C. Waiss, Jr., *J. Org. Chem.*, **27**, 290 (1962).
22. A Streitwieser, Jr. and J. R. Wolfe, Jr., *J. Am. Chem. Soc.*, **81**, 4912 (1959).
23. J. L. E. Erickson and W. H. Ashton, *J. Am. Chem. Soc.*, **63**, 1769 (1941).
24. J. F. Norris and G. W. Rigby, *J. Am. Chem. Soc.*, **54**, 2088 (1932); D. R. Stevens, *J. Org. Chem.*, **20**, 1232 (1955).

25. S.-O. Lawesson and N. C. Yang, *J. Am. Chem. Soc.*, **81**, 4230 (1959).
26. L. Claisen and O. Eisleb, *Ann. Chem.*, **401**, 21 (1913).
27. W. N. White, D. Gwynn, R. Schlitt, C. Girard, and W. Fife, *J. Am. Chem. Soc.*, **80**, 3271 (1958).
28. R. E. Rindfusz, P. M. Ginnings, and V. L. Hannack, *J. Am. Chem. Soc.*, **42**, 157 (1920); H. Gilman and L. Fullhart, *J. Am. Chem. Soc.*, **67**, 1585 (1945); A. F. Lindenstruth and C. A. Vander Werf, *J. Am. Chem. Soc.*, **73**, 4209 (1951); J. F. Kerwin, G. C. Hall, F. J. Milnes, I. H. Witt, R. A. McLean, E. Macko, E. J. Fellows, and G. E. Ullyot, *J. Am. Chem. Soc.*, **73**, 4162 (1951); F. Toda and M. Nakagawa, *Bull. Chem. Soc. Japan*, **33**, 223 (1960).
29. C. S. Marvel and A. L. Tanenbaum, *J. Am. Chem. Soc.*, **44**, 2645 (1922); A. Lüttringhaus, *Ann. Chem.*, **528**, 181 (1937); J. B. Cloke, E. Stehr, T. R. Steadman, and L. C. Westcott, *J. Am. Chem. Soc.*, **67**, 1587 (1945); F. J. Buckle, F. L. M. Pattison, and B. C. Saunders, *J. Chem. Soc.*, 1471 (1949); B. W. Horrom and H. E. Zaugg, *J. Am. Chem. Soc.*, **79**, 1754 (1957); A. A. Aroyan and S. G. Titanyan, *Izv. Akad. Nauk Arm. S.S.R., Khim. Nauk*, **10**, 283 (1957); E. Berry, H. Lee, E. Miller, and D. R. S. Spessard, *J. Sci. Lab., Denison Univ.*, **44**, 128 (1958); J. N. Ashley, R. F. Collins, M. Davis, and N. E. Sirett, *J. Chem. Soc.*, 3298 (1958); M. Nakagawa and F. Toda, *Tetrahedron Letters*, **2**, 51 (1961).
30. E. T. McBee and R. O. Bolt, *Ind. Eng. Chem.*, **39**, 412 (1947).
31. E. J. Rowe, K. L. Kaufman, and C. Piantadosi, *J. Org. Chem.*, **23**, 1622 (1958).
32. G. E. Philbrook and D. J. Massey, *J. Am. Chem. Soc.*, **73**, 3454 (1951).
33. J. Herzig and F. Wenzel, *Monatsh.*, **27**, 581 (1906); J. Herzig and Br. Erthal, *Monatsh.*, **32**, 491 (1911); R. Fabre, *Ann. Chim. (Paris)*, **18**, 53 (1922).
34. E. Wenkert, R. D. Youssefyeh, and R. G. Lewis, *J. Am. Chem. Soc.*, **82**, 4675 (1960).
35. N. Kornblum, R. A. Smiley, R. K. Blackwood, and D. C. Iffland, *J. Am. Chem. Soc.*, **77**, 6269 (1955); N. Kornblum and A. P. Lurie, *J. Am. Chem. Soc.*, **81**, 2705 (1959).
36. T. R. Rubin and A. A. Brooks, *J. Am. Chem. Soc.*, **75**, 2517 (1953).
37. A. L. Rocklin, *J. Org. Chem.*, **21**, 1478 (1956).
38. C. W. L. Bevan and G. C. Bye, *J. Chem. Soc.*, 3091 (1954); B. A. Bolto, M. Liveris, and J. Miller, *J. Chem. Soc.*, 750 (1956).
39. J. Burdon, W. B. Hollyhead, and C. R. Patrick, *J. Chem. Soc.*, 4663 (1964).
40. C. Willgerodt, *Chem. Ber.*, **15**, 1002 (1882); K. Brand, *J. Prakt. Chem.*, **67**, 145 (1903); A. V. Blom, *Helv. Chim. Acta*, **4**, 297, 510, 1029 (1921); L. McMaster and A. C. Magill, *J. Am. Chem. Soc.*, **50**, 3038 (1928).
41. L. Laloi and P. Rumpf, *Compt. Rend.*, **258**, 940 (1964).
42. E. T. McBee, R. O. Bolt, P. J. Graham, and R. F. Tebbe, *J. Am. Chem. Soc.*, **69**, 947 (1947).
43. B. A. Bolto, J. Miller, and V. A. Williams, *J. Chem. Soc.*, 2926 (1955).
44. W. B. Whalley, *J. Chem. Soc.*, 2241 (1950).
45. N. N. Vorozhtsov, Jr., and G. G. Iacobson, *Zh. Obshch. Khim.*, **28**, 40 (1958).

46. C. A. Lobry de Bruyn and F. H. van Leent, *Rec. Trav. Chim.*, **14**, 150 (1895); F. Reverdin, *Org. Syn.*, **1**, 219 (1941).
47. P. T. Izzo, *J. Org. Chem.*, **24**, 2026 (1959).
48. J. F. Bunnett and M. M. Rauhut, *J. Org. Chem.*, **21**, 944 (1956).
49. M. Rosenblum, *J. Am. Chem. Soc.*, **82**, 3797 (1960).
50. Y. Ogata and M. Okano, *J. Am. Chem. Soc.*, **71**, 3211 (1949).
51. Y. Ogata and M. Okano, *J. Am. Chem. Soc.*, **71**, 3212 (1949).
52. J. Meisenheimer, *Ann. Chem.*, **323**, 205 (1902).
53. L. J. Andrews and R. M. Keefer, *Molecular Complexes in Organic Chemistry*, Holden Day, San Francisco, 1964, p. 148.
54. J. B. Ainscough and E. F. Caldin, *J. Chem. Soc.*, 2528, 2540, 2546 (1956).
55. K. L. Servis, *J. Am. Chem. Soc.*, **87**, 5495 (1965).
56. M. R. Crampton and V. Gold, *J. Chem. Soc.*, 4293 (1964).
57. F. Ullmann and P. Sponagel, *Ber. Deut. Chem. Ges.*, **38**, 2211 (1905).
58. H. E. Ungnade, *Chem. Rev.*, **38**, 405 (1946).
59. L. C. Raiford and J. C. Colbert, *J. Am. Chem. Soc.*, **48**, 2652 (1926).
60. J. J. Randall, C. E. Lewis, and P. M. Slagan, *J. Org. Chem.*, **27**, 4098 (1962).
61. J. D. Reinheimer, J. P. Douglass, H. Leister, and M. B. Voelkel, *J. Org. Chem.*, **22**, 1743 (1957).
62. R. W. Bost and F. Nicholson, *J. Am. Chem. Soc.*, **57**, 2368 (1935).
63. W. H. Pirkle and J. L. Zabriskie, *J. Org. Chem.*, **29**, 3124 (1964).
64. F. M. Beringer, A. Brierley, M. Drexler, E. M. Gindler, and C. C. Lumpkin, *J. Am. Chem. Soc.*, **75**, 2708 (1953); J. R. Crowder, E. E. Glover, M. F. Grundon, and H. X. Kaempfen, *J. Chem. Soc.*, 4578 (1963).
65. E. S. Lewis and C. A. Stout, *J. Am. Chem. Soc.*, **76**, 4619 (1954); F. M. Beringer and E. M. Gindler, *J. Am. Chem. Soc.*, **77**, 3203 (1955); F. M. Beringer, E. J. Geering, I. Kuntz, and M. Mausner, *J. Phys. Chem.*, **60**, 141 (1956); A. N. Nesmeyanov, L. G. Makarova, and T. P. Tolstaya, *Tetrahedron*, **1**, 145 (1957); M. C. Caserio, D. L. Glusker, and J. D. Roberts, *J. Am. Chem. Soc.*, **81**, 336 (1959); F. M. Beringer, E. M. Gindler, M. Rapoport, and R. J. Taylor, *J. Am. Chem. Soc.*, **81**, 351 (1959).
66. B. Gredy, *Ann. Chim. (Paris)*, **4**, 5 (1935); W. Reppe and Coworkers, *Ann. Chem.*, **596**, 1 (1955); R. Heilmann, R. Glenat, and G. de Gaudemaris, *Bull. Soc. Chim. France*, 284 (1952); J. F. Gillespie and C. C. Price, *J. Org. Chem.*, **22**, 780 (1957).
67. E. M. Marks, D. Lipkin, and B. Bettman, *J. Am. Chem. Soc.*, **59**, 946 (1937).
68. V. Cherchez, *Bull. Soc. Chim. France*, **43**, 762 (1928).
69. H. Kitano and K. Fukui, *J. Chem. Soc. Japan, Ind. Chem. Sect.*, **58**, 355 (1955).
70. F. Ullmann, *Ann. Chem.*, **327**, 114 (1903).
71. P. Truchet and M. Graves, *Bull. Soc. Chim. France*, **51**, 686 (1932).
72. N. Allentoff and G. F. Wright, *J. Org. Chem.*, **22**, 1 (1957).
73. D. A. Shirley, J. R. Zietz, Jr., and W. H. Reedy, *J. Org. Chem.*, **18**, 378 (1953).
74. F. Drahowzal and D. Klaman, *Monatsh.*, **82**, 588 (1951); D. A. Shirley and W. H. Reedy, *J. Am. Chem. Soc.*, **73**, 458 (1951).
75. V. C. Sekera and C. S. Marvel, *J. Am. Chem. Soc.*, **55**, 348 (1933).
76. L. Katz and W. E. Hamlin, *J. Am. Chem. Soc.*, **73**, 2801 (1951).

77. G. R. Clemo and W. H. Perkin, Jr., *J. Chem. Soc.*, **121**, 642 (1922); R. M. Herbst and P. Johnson, *J. Org. Chem.*, **17**, 693 (1952).
78. J. Van Alphen, *Rec. Trav. Chim.*, **49**, 754 (1930).
79. J. B. Senderens, *Compt. Rend.*, **179**, 1015 (1924); **181**, 698 (1925); **182**, 612 (1926).
80. E. Swistak and P. Mastagli, *Compt. Rend.*, **239**, 709 (1954).
81. N. I. Shuikin, N. A. Pozdnyak, and T. P. Dobrynina, *Izv. Akad. Nauk SSSR, Ser. Khim*, 1705 (1964).
82. E. R. H. Jones and J. T. McCombie, *U.S. Pat.*, 2,429,411 (1947).
83. I. M. Heilbron, E. R. H. Jones, and B. C. L. Weedon, *J. Chem. Soc.*, 81, 88 (1945).
84. K. Alder and F. H. Flock, *Chem. Ber.*, **89**, 1732 (1956).
85. V. I. Pansevich-Kolyada, Z. B. Idelchik, and L. A. Kureichik, *Zh. Obshch. Khim.*, **25**, 1481 (1955); V. I. Pansevich-Kolyada and I. E. Osipenko, *Zh. Obshch. Khim.*, **28**, 641, 909 (1958); V. I. Pansevich-Kolyada and B. K. Bogush, *Zh. Obshch. Khim.*, **29**, 1198 (1959); V. I. Pansevich-Kolyada and T. A. Galaysheva, *Zh. Obshch. Khim.*, **30**, 469 (1960).
86. H. A. Smith and R. J. Smith, *J. Am. Chem. Soc.*, **70**, 2400 (1948).
87. C. M. Welch and H. A. Smith, *J. Am. Chem. Soc.*, **75**, 1412 (1953).
88. E. J. Salmi and E. Renconen, *Chem. Ber., Ser. B*, **72**, 1107 (1939).
89. E. F. Pratt and J. D. Draper, *J. Am. Chem. Soc.*, **71**, 2846 (1949).
90. C. M. Welch and H. A. Smith, *J. Am. Chem. Soc.*, **72**, 4748 (1950).
91. R. C. Fuson and H. L. Jackson, *J. Am. Chem. Soc.*, **72**, 351 (1950).
92. D. Y. Curtin and S. Leskowitz, *J. Am. Chem. Soc.*, **73**, 2630 (1951).
93. Chi-Hua Wang, *J. Org. Chem.*, **28**, 2914 (1963).
94. J. F. Bunnett, *Quart. Rev., London*, **12**, 1 (1958).
95. J. Sauer and R. Huisgen, *Angew. Chem.*, **72**, 294 (1960).
96. S. D. Ross in *Progress in Physical Organic Chemistry*, Vol. 1 (Ed. S. G. Cohen, A. Streitwieser Jr., and R. W. Taft), Interscience Publishers, New York, 1963, p. 1.
97. A. Streitwieser, Jr., *Chem. Rev.*, **56**, 571 (1956).
98. C. A. Bunton, *Nucleophilic Substitution at a Saturated Carbon Atom*, Vol. I (Ed. E. D. Hughes), Elsevier Publishing Company, Amsterdam, 1963.
99. C. A. Bishop and C. H. DePuy, *Chem. Ind. (London)*, 297 (1959).
100. M. L. Dhar, E. D. Hughes, C. K. Ingold, and S. Masterman, *J. Chem. Soc.*, 2055 (1948).
101. C. H. DePuy and D. H. Froemsdorf, *J. Am. Chem. Soc.*, **79**, 3710 (1957).
102. P. Veeravagu, R. T. Arnold, and E. W. Eigenmann, *J. Am. Chem. Soc.*, **86**, 3072 (1964).
103. C. H. Snyder and A. R. Soto, *J. Org. Chem.*, **29**, 742 (1964).
104. N. Kornblum, P. J. Berrigan, and W. J. Le Noble, *J. Am. Chem. Soc.*, **82**, 1257 (1960); **85**, 1141 (1963).
105. R. Barner and H. Schmid, *Helv. Chim. Acta*, **43**, 1393 (1960).
106. H. D. Zook and T. J. Russo, *J. Am. Chem. Soc.*, **82**, 1258 (1960).
107. N. Kornblum, R. Seltzer, and P. Haberfield, *J. Am. Chem. Soc.*, **85**, 1148 (1963).
108. D. J. Cram and L. Grosser, *J. Am. Chem. Soc.*, **85**, 3890 (1963).
109. N. Kornblum and R. Seltzer, *J. Am. Chem. Soc.*, **83**, 3668 (1961).
110. F. Lengfeld and J. Stieglitz, *Ber. Deut. Chem. Ges.*, **27**, 926 (1894).

111. H. G. Khorana, *Can. J. Chem.*, **32**, 227 (1954).
112. J. Stieglitz, *Ber. Deut. Chem. Ges.*, **28**, 573 (1895).
113. F. B. Dains, *J. Am. Chem. Soc.*, **21**, 136 (1899).
114. M. Busch, G. Blume, and E. Pungs, *J. Prakt. Chem.*, **79**, 513 (1909).
115. E. Vowinkel, *Chem. Ber.*, **96**, 1702 (1963).
116. E. Vowinkel, *Chem. Ber.*, **95**, 2997 (1962).
117. E. Vowinkel, *Angew. Chem.*, *Intern. Ed. Engl.*, **2**, 218 (1963).
118. F. L. Bach, *J. Org. Chem.*, **30**, 1300 (1965).
119. H. Gilman and C. H. Adams, *J. Am. Chem. Soc.*, **47**, 2816 (1925).
120. T. W. Campbell, W. Burney, and J. L. Jacobs, *J. Am. Chem. Soc.*, **72**, 2735 (1950).
121. F. C. Whitmore and R. S. George, *J. Am. Chem. Soc.*, **64**, 1239 (1942); G. E. Dunn and J. Warkentin, *Can. J. Chem.*, **34**, 75 (1956).
122. G. A. Baramki, H. S. Chang, and J. T. Edward, *Can. J. Chem.*, **40**, 441 (1962).
123. S. O. Lawesson and C. Frisell, *Arkiv Kemi*, **17**, 393 (1961); S. O. Lawesson, C. Berglund, and S. Grönwall, *Acta Chem. Scand.*, **15**, 249 (1961).
124. D. R. Stevens, *J. Org. Chem.*, **20**, 1232 (1955); R. S. Bowman, D. R. Stevens, and W. E. Baldwin, *J. Am. Chem. Soc.*, **79**, 87 (1957).
125. L. Horner and W. Jurgeleit, *Ann. Chem.*, **591**, 138 (1955); L. Horner and H. Hoffmann in *Newer Methods of Preparative Organic Chemistry*, Vol. 2 (Ed. W. Foerst), Academic Press, New York, 1963, pp. 176–178.
126. C. Walling and R. Rabinowitz, *J. Am. Chem. Soc.*, **81**, 1243 (1959); C. Walling, O. H. Basedow, and E. S. Savas, *J. Am. Chem. Soc.*, **82**, 2181 (1960).
127. H. Wieland, *Ber. Deut. Chem. Ges.*, **44**, 2550 (1911).
128. M. S. Kharasch, A. C. Poshkus, A. Fono, and W. Nudenberg, *J. Org. Chem.*, **16**, 1458 (1951).
129. L. A. Warren and S. Smiles, *J. Chem. Soc.*, 914 (1931), and subsequent papers in this series.
130. For a more extensive coverage see J. F. Bunnett and R. E. Zahler, *Chem. Rev.*, **49**, 273 (1951); also see reference 94.
131. A. A. Levy, H. C. Rains, and S. Smiles, *J. Chem. Soc.*, 3264 (1931).
132. B. A. Kent and S. Smiles, *J. Chem. Soc.*, 422 (1934).
133. C. S. McClement and S. Smiles, *J. Chem. Soc.*, 1016 (1937).
134. T. Okamoto and J. F. Bunnett, *J. Am. Chem. Soc.*, **78**, 5357 (1956); J. F. Bunnett and T. Okamoto, *J. Am. Chem. Soc.*, **78**, 5363 (1956).
135. H. Meerwein and G. Hinz, *Ann. Chem.*, **484**, 1 (1930).
136. M. C. Caserio, J. D. Roberts, M. Neeman, and W. S. Johnson, *J. Am. Chem. Soc.*, **80**, 2584 (1958); M. Neeman, M. C. Caserio, J. D. Roberts, and W. S. Johnson, *Tetrahedron*, **6**, 36 (1959).
137. W. S. Johnson, M. Neeman, and S. P. Birkeland, *Tetrahedron Letters*, 1 (1960); W. S. Johnson, M. Neeman, S. P. Birkeland, and N. A. Fedoruk, *J. Am. Chem. Soc.*, **84**, 989 (1962).
138. H. O. House, E. J. Grubbs, and W. F. Gannon, *J. Am. Chem. Soc.*, **82**, 4099 (1960).
139. E. Müller and W. Rundel, *Angew. Chem.*, **70**, 105 (1958); E. Müller, M. Bauer, and W. Rundel, *Z. Naturforsch.*, *Ser. B*, **14**, 209 (1959); (*Chem. Abstr.*, **53**, 21613d (1959)).

140. G. Schroeter, *Ber. Deut. Chem. Ges.*, **42**, 3356 (1909).
141. A. L. Wilds and A. L. Meader, Jr., *J. Org. Chem.*, **13**, 763 (1948).
142. M. Aeberli and H. Erlenmeyer, *Helv. Chim. Acta*, **31**, 28 (1948); H. Erlenmeyer and M. Aeberli, *Helv. Chim. Acta*, **33**, 503 (1950).
143. R. Casanova and T. Reichstein, *Helv. Chim. Acta*, **32**, 647 (1949); R. Casanova and T. Reichstein, *Helv. Chim. Acta*, **33**, 417 (1950).
144. H. Heusser, C. R. Engel, and P. A. Plattner, *Helv. Chim. Acta*, **32**, 2475 (1949).
145. P. Yates, *J. Am. Chem. Soc.*, **74**, 5376 (1952).
146. W. E. Bachmann and W. S. Struve in *Organic Reactions*, Vol. 1 (Ed. R. Adams), John Wiley and Sons, New York, 1942, p. 38; B. Eistert in *Newer Methods of Preparative Organic Chemistry*, Vol. 1, Interscience Publishers, New York, 1948, p. 513.
147. C. Grundmann and H. Trischmann, *Ann. Chem.*, **536**, 29 (1938).
148. See W. Kirmse, *Carbene Chemistry*, Academic Press, New York, 1964, Chap. 7, for a more extensive discussion of keto carbenes.
149. M. S. Newman and P. F. Beal, *J. Am. Chem. Soc.*, **72**, 5161 (1950).
150. W. W. Zarbach and C. R. Tamorria, *J. Org. Chem.*, **22**, 1127 (1957).
151. I. A. D'yakonov, *Zh. Obshch. Khim.*, **21**, 1986 (1951); *Chem. Abstr.*, **46**, 6591 (1952); I. A. D'yakonov and N. D. Pirogova, *Zh. Obshch. Khim.*, **21**, 1979 (1951); *Chem. Abstr.*, **46**, 6590 (1952).
152. S. Winstein and J. Sonnenberg, *J. Am. Chem. Soc.*, **83**, 3235 (1961).
153. W. Kirmse, L. Horner, and H. Hoffmann, *Ann. Chem.*, **614**, 19 (1958); W. Kirmse, *Ann. Chem.*, **666**, 9 (1963); W. Kirmse, *Angew. Chem., Intern. Ed. Engl.*, **2**, 554 (1963).
154. L. Horner, W. Kirmse, and H. Fernekess, *Chem. Ber.*, **94**, 279 (1961).
155. P. Griess, *Phil. Trans. Roy. Soc. London, Sci., Ser. A*, **154**, 683 (1864).
156. I. Remsen and W. R. Orndorff, *Am. Chem. J.*, **9**, 387 (1887); A. Hantzsch and E. Jochem, *Chem. Ber.*, **34**, 3337 (1901).
157. E. Pfeil, *Ann. Chem.*, **561**, 220 (1948); E. S. Lewis and W. H. Hinds, *J. Am. Chem. Soc.*, **74**, 304 (1952).
158. J. C. Cain and F. Nicoll, *J. Chem. Soc.*, **81**, 1412 (1902); **83**, 47 (1903); H. A. H. Pray, *J. Phys. Chem.*, **30**, 1417, 1477 (1926); M. L. Crossley, R. H. Kienle, and C. H. Benbrook, *J. Am. Chem. Soc.*, **62**, 1400 (1940); E. A. Moelwyn-Hughes and P. Johnson, *Trans. Faraday Soc.*, **36**, 948 (1940); J. S. P. Blumberger, *Rec. Trav. Chim.*, **49**, 259 (1930); W. A. Waters, *J. Chem. Soc.*, 226 (1942); H. Zollinger, *Azo and Diazo Chemistry*, Interscience Publishers, New York, 1961, Chap. 7.
159. D. F. De Tar and T. Kosuge, *J. Am. Chem. Soc.*, **80**, 6072 (1958).
160. D. F. De Tar and M. N. Turetzky, *J. Am. Chem. Soc.*, **77**, 1745 (1955).
161. For a recent study of the Gomberg-Bachmann reaction see C. Rüchardt and E. Merz, *Tetrahedron Letters*, 2431 (1964); C. Rüchardt and B. Freudenberg, *Tetrahedron Letters*, 3623 (1964).
162. A. Hantzsch and R. Vock, *Ber. Deut. Chem. Ges.*, **36**, 2061 (1903); J. H. C. Winston, *Am. Chem. J.*, **31**, 119 (1904); F. K. Cameron, *Am. Chem. J.*, **20**, 229 (1898); I. Remsen and R. O. Graham, *Am. Chem. J.*, **11**, 319 (1889); P. Griess, *Ber. Deut. Chem. Ges.*, **21**, 978 (1888); G. F. Weida, *Am. Chem. J.*, **19**, 547 (1897); N. Kornblum, *Organic Reactions*, Vol. 2, John Wiley and Sons, New York, 1949, Chap. 7.

163. W. E. Lee, J. G. Calvert, and E. W. Malmberg, *J. Am. Chem. Soc.*, **83**, 1928 (1961).
164. C. Walling, *Free Radicals in Solution*, John Wiley and Sons, New York, 1957, p. 581; C. Walling in *Molecular Rearrangements* (Ed. P. de Mayo), Part 1, Interscience Publishers, New York, 1963, p. 420.
165. A. J. v.d. Hoek and W. T. Nauta, *Rec. Trav. Chim.*, **61**, 845 (1942).
166. M. Finkelstein and R. C. Petersen, *J. Org. Chem.*, **25**, 136 (1960).
167. R. P. Linstead, B. R. Shepard, and B. C. L. Weedon, *J. Chem. Soc.*, 3624 (1952).
168. W. A. Bonner and F. D. Mango, *J. Org. Chem.*, **29**, 430 (1964).
169. E. J. Corey, N. L. Bauld, R. T. La Londe, J. Casanova, Jr., and E. T. Kaiser, *J. Am. Chem. Soc.*, **82**, 2645 (1960).
170. S. Winstein and D. Trifan, *J. Am. Chem. Soc.*, **74**, 1147, 1154 (1952); J. D. Roberts, E. L. Trumbull, W. Bennett, and R. Armstrong, *J. Am. Chem. Soc.*, **72**, 3116 (1950).
171. D. D. Evans and C. W. Shoppee, *J. Chem. Soc.*, 540 (1953); E. M. Kosower and S. Winstein, *J. Am. Chem. Soc.*, **68**, 4354 (1956).
172. J. A. Waters, E. D. Becker, and E. Mosettig, *J. Org. Chem.*, **27**, 4689 (1962); J. A. Waters, *J. Org. Chem.*, **29**, 428 (1964).
173. B. Wladislaw and A. M. J. Ayres, *J. Org. Chem.*, **27**, 281 (1962).
174. H. Breederveld and E. C. Kooyman, *Rec. Trav. Chim.*, **76**, 297 (1957).
175. L. Summers, *Chem. Rev.*, **55**, 301 (1955).
176. J. F. Arens in *Advances in Organic Chemistry*, Vol. 2 (Ed. R. A. Raphael, E. C. Taylor, and H. Wynberg), Interscience Publishers, New York, 1960, p. 117.
177. M. F. Shostakovskii, A. V. Bogdanova, and G. I. Plotnikova, *Russ. Chem. Rev. Eng. Transl.*, **33**, 66 (1964); M. F. Shostakovskii, E. P. Gracheva, and N. K. Kul'bovskaya, *Russ. Chem. Rev. Eng. Transl.*, **30**, 207 (1961).
178. R. A. Raphael, *Acetylenic Compounds in Organic Synthesis*, Butterworths, London, 1955, Chap. 1.
179. S. Patai and Z. Rappoport in *The Chemistry of Alkenes* (Ed. S. Patai), Interscience Publishers, London, 1964, Chap. 8.
180. K. Ichikawa, K. Nishimura, and S. Takayama, *J. Org. Chem.*, **30**, 1593 (1965).
181. H. C. Beyerman and G. J. Heiszwolf, *J. Chem. Soc.*, 755 (1963).
182. R. D. Morin and A. E. Bearse, *Ind. Eng. Chem.*, **43**, 1596 (1951).
183. J. Chatt, *Chem. Rev.*, **48**, 7 (1951).

CHAPTER **11**

The polyethers

Charles C. Price

University of Pennsylvania, Philadelphia, U.S.A.

I. INTRODUCTION

A. General Properties

During the last decade there has been a remarkable surge forward in discovery and development which has seen the commercial production of many new high polymeric materials with ether oxygen as part of the backbone of the polymer chain. The following examples are polymers in which the ether oxygens are separated by one to four aliphatic carbons or an aromatic ring.

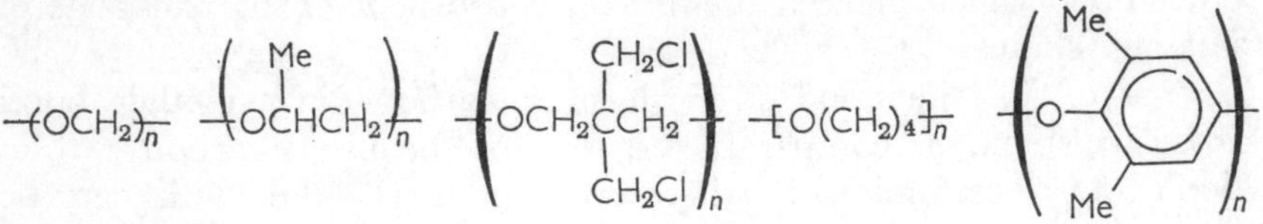

$$-(OCH_2)_n \quad \left(OCHCH_2\right)_n^{Me} \quad \left(OCH_2CCH_2\right)_n^{CH_2Cl}{}_{CH_2Cl} \quad \left[O(CH_2)_4\right]_n \quad \left(O-\underset{Me}{\overset{Me}{\bigcirc}}\right)_n$$

The polyaldehydes, in addition to the moldable plastic poly-formaldehyde, now include a clear, tough oriented film from high-melting crystalline isotactic polyacetaldehyde[1a]. In addition to poly-urethane rubbers from low molecular weight poly(propylene gylcols), a vulcanizable high molecular weight copolymer of propylene oxide with an unsaturated alkylene oxide is now available with an interesting combination of low temperature, dynamic, solvent- and ozone-resistant properties.

High molecular weight crystalline poly(phenyl glycidyl ether) gives orientable films and fibers melting well above 200°. Bis(chloromethyl)-oxetane resins, in spite of their high cost, have such unusual properties of solvent resistance, strength, moldability and dimensional stability that they maintain a unique place in the range of synthetic plastics.

Polytetrahydrofuran is believed to make an important contribution to the properties of the new 'synthetic leathers', such as Corfam; this is because of discoveries of catalysts producing polymers with an unusual degree of purity of bifunctionality and because of its tendency to crystallize easily under stress and to resist hydrolytic and oxidative decomposition.

Because of the thermal stability of the aryl ether linkage, recent discoveries of polymerization processes for the preparation of poly-xylenol (PPO) give promise of useful development of this new material with an unusual and interesting combination of properties[1b].

All of these discoveries and developments, which have been made within a decade, certainly suggest that polyethers are destined to assume a major role among the synthetic polymeric materials which are so important as resins, rubbers, films and fibers. The scope of this development is reflected in recent publications[2-4]. Because of these recent detailed and extensive publications, it is the purpose of this article to summarize the major concepts relating to the formation and properties of these compounds, without presenting exhaustive documentation.

Before undertaking a discussion of the chemistry of polyethers, it is pertinent to remind the reader of the important characteristics of an ether bond which make it useful as a constituent of the backbone of polymer chains.

First of all, the bond strength of a carbon–oxygen ether bond (84·0 kcal/mole) is comparable to that of the usual carbon–carbon bond (83·1 kcal/mole). Furthermore, the aryl ether link can be further strengthened due to resonance interaction with the aromatic system (reaction 1). This partial double-bond character has been considered as one important reason for the thermal stability of diphenyl ether.

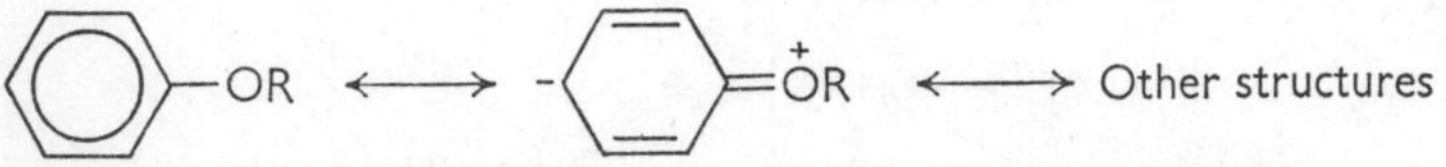

(1)

The other significant property of ether linkages is their low barrier to rotation. While this is about 3 kcal/mole for the carbon–carbon single bond, it is only about 1·2 kcal/mole for the aliphatic ethers. This low barrier to rotation was one of the reasons for selecting the poly-(propylene oxide) chain as a superior candidate structure for a synthetic elastomer[5].

B. Epoxide Polymerization

The various procedures useful for polymerizing epoxides can be classified into three main categories, so far as the mechanism of the propagation step is concerned, namely, anionic, cationic and coordination rearrangement; these mechanisms are represented by reactions (2), (3) and (4), respectively.

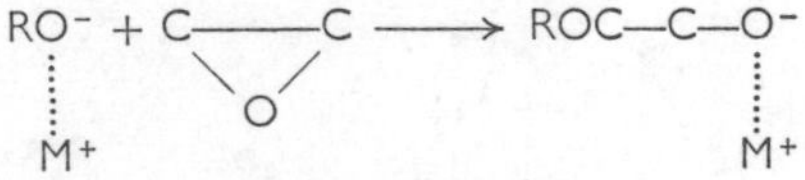

(2)

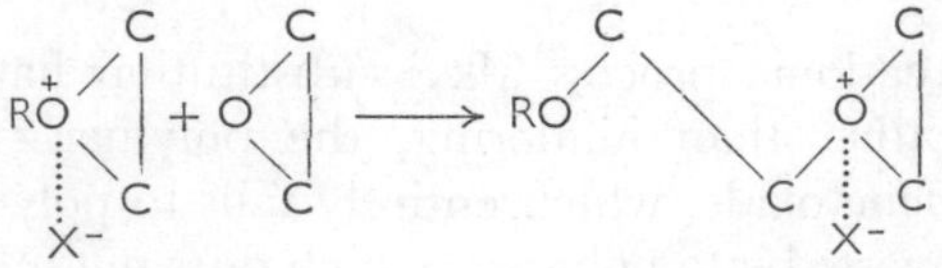

(3)

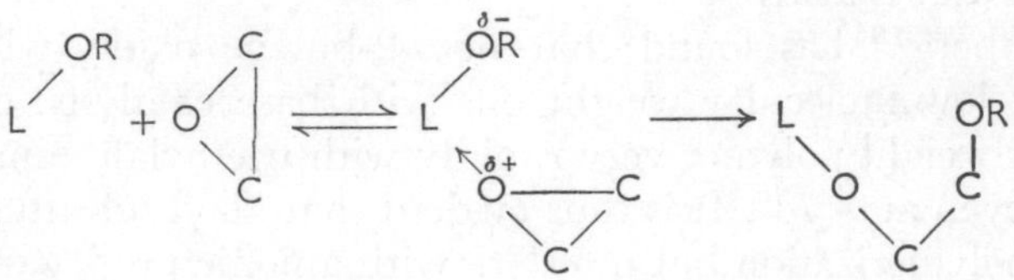

(4)

The anionic or base-catalyzed reaction proceeds best for ethylene oxide. Even with propylene oxide a chain-transfer process intervenes and limits the molecular weight to about 5000[6-8]. Gee has shown that the nucleophilic attack proceeds principally at the primary, rather than the secondary carbon atom (reaction 5)[7]. With tetramethylene

$$RO^- + CH_2\!\!-\!\!CH\!\!-\!\!CH_3 \begin{cases} \xrightarrow{k_p} ROCH_2\overset{\underset{\textstyle CH_3}{|}}{C}HO^- \\ \xrightarrow[k_t]{} ROH + CH_2\!\!=\!\!CHCH_2O^- \end{cases} \tag{5}$$

oxide[9] the hydrogen-abstraction reaction dominates and an almost quantitative yield of an allyl alcohol results (reaction 6).

$$Me_2C\!\!-\!\!CMe_2 \xrightarrow[\text{t-BuO}^-]{\text{DMSO}} CH_2\!\!=\!\!\overset{\underset{\textstyle Me}{|}}{C}\!\!-\!\!\overset{\underset{\textstyle OH}{|}}{C}Me_2 \tag{6}$$

$$95\%$$

The chain-transfer process not only limits molecular weight, but introduces allyl ether end-groups[10]. The recognition of an unusually sharp line in the infrared spectra of poly(propylene oxide), prepared by base catalysis but without treatment with water in any way, and its identification as the *cis*-propenyl ether band[11] led to the suggestion shown by reaction (7) for the mechanism of the loss of the allyl ether end-groups[6,8,12–14].

$$\text{\scriptsize\leavevmode} OCH_2CH\!\!=\!\!CH_2 \xrightarrow{\text{Base}} OC\!\!=\!\!CCH_3 \xrightarrow{H_2O} OH + CH_3CH_2CHO \tag{7}$$

For the cationic process alkyl substitution has a major effect in favoring, rather than hindering, the polymerization. For example tetramethylene oxide, which entirely fails to polymerize with base, is rapidly converted into polymer, which does not melt at 300°, by treatment with Lewis acids[15].

Vandenberg[16] has found that *trans*-2-butene oxide, which gives only very low molecular weight oils with base catalysts, gives high molecular weight polymer very rapidly with triethylaluminum–water catalyst, even at −78°. It is thus evident that alkyl substituents favor cationic polymerization but interfere with anionic propagation.

In the coordination rearrangement scheme, which will be discussed more fully in the section on stereoselective polymerization, a Lewis acid metal (L) as its alkoxide coordinates reversibly with the monomer. This product can then rearrange, introducing a monomer unit between the catalyst center and the alkoxide group, freeing a coordination site for the next step.

The nature of the coordination site (L) is not established, but some evidence bearing on its general features will be presented in a following section.

Evidence available to date indicates that all three propagation steps proceed exclusively with inversion of configuration at the epoxide-ring carbon undergoing nucleophilic attack[16,17,27].

II. STEREOCHEMISTRY OF POLYMER CHAINS

For nearly thirty years, ever since the acceptance of the concept of high-polymer molecules by Staudinger[18], there has been much speculation and research concerning the stereochemistry of such 'giant' molecules. These questions may be divided into two major categories, those related to *configuration* of carbon atoms and those related to *conformation* of the main-chain bonds. We may illustrate these problems by considering the structural formula (1_p) for a vinyl polymer (reaction 8). While it was once considered that 'free rotation'

$$n \; CH_2{=}CH \atop \quad\;\; X \longrightarrow \left(CH_2{-}CH{-}CH_2{-}CH{-}CH_2{-}CH \atop \qquad\quad X \qquad\;\; X \qquad\;\; X \right)_{\frac{n}{3}} \qquad (8)$$

$$(1_m) \qquad\qquad\qquad\qquad (1_p)$$

$$(X = Ph, Cl, OCOR, COOR, CN, etc.)$$

occurred at the carbon–carbon bonds of such a molecule, it is now recognized that usually three stable rotational arrangements are possible, with definite although low barriers (about 3 kcal/mole) between the stable arrangements **2, 3** and **4**.

trans	skew$_1$	skew$_2$
(2)	(3)	(4)

The conformational arrangements of chains are affected by many factors, such as physical state (crystalline, melt or solution), the nature of the substituent X and the configuration of the atom holding X. For example crystalline polyethylene (X = H) contains chains with all-*trans* arrangements. Crystalline isotactic polypropylene (X = CH_3) has a regular sequence alternating between *trans* and *skew*$_1$ which results in a helically coiled chain conformation; the molecules are consequently linear and rod-like. Amorphous polystyrene and polyvinyl acetate have a random sequence of all three conformations, resulting in a randomly coiled chain conformation.

However, while the conformation of polymer chains presents interesting theoretical and fundamental questions which also have great significance for the important practical properties of plastics, rubbers, films and fibers, these are not the subject of this present discussion. Rather we will consider the question of the *configuration* of polymer molecules. This aspect of polymer stereochemistry may be illustrated by **5** which shows a segment of a polymer chain in the all-*trans* conformation.

(5)

The arrangement indicated, with the substituted groups X all on the *same* side of the planar, zig-zag polymer chain, is now called *isotactic* as suggested by Natta[19], while the arrangement in which the sequence of placement of X alternates regularly is called *syndiotactic*. A random sequence of isotactic and syndiotactic is called *atactic*. This *configurational* difference is built into the polymer chain and is not altered by such changes in physical state as melting or dissolution.

Although Schildknecht[20] reported that he could make polyvinyl ethers with different physical properties by polymerization under different conditions and correctly ascribed the difference to a more regular configurational arrangement in some samples, it was not until 1955 that discoveries were reported of conditions for preparing stereoregular polymers; these discoveries have had enormous practical impact on the polymer industry and have intensely stimulated fundamental research around the world on the mechanism of these remarkable stereoregulated polymerization processes, which resemble enzyme reactions in their amazing stereoselectivity. In that year Natta[19] published his first report on the preparation of crystalline polypropylene (m.p. 170°), making use of catalysts discovered earlier by Ziegler.

On the basis of the repeat distance along the fiber axis, as determined by x-ray diffraction (6·5 Å), Natta[19] concluded that the polymer chains must have a regular helical arrangement of alternating *trans* and *skew*$_1$ conformations and therefore that the configuration must be isotactic. A scale model of isotactic polypropylene in the all-*trans* conformation (**5**, X = CH$_3$) shows that the methyl groups overlap and it is this steric hindrance of adjacent methyl groups which presumably makes the linear all-*trans* conformation less stable than the helically coiled arrangement.

Also in 1955 Pruitt and Baggett[21] obtained a patent disclosing that an iron catalyst would convert DL-propylene oxide into a polymer which was remarkable in two major respects. Firstly, the product had a molecular weight in the range of 10^5 to 10^6, orders of magnitude greater than any reported earlier by conventional acid or base catalysts. Secondly, it could be easily fractionated into amorphous and crystalline fractions, the latter having a melting point of 70° and a clear-cut crystalline x-ray pattern.

Recognizing the interesting stereochemical features of propylene oxide and its polymer, i.e., that the configurational differences in the polymer arise from truly asymmetric carbon atoms (not pseudo-asymmetric*, as in polypropylene and vinyl polymers), that the polymer therefore should be optically active, and that the asymmetric atom of the polymer also exists as an asymmetric atom in the monomer, in 1952 a program to synthesize and polymerize optically active propylene oxide was undertaken (reaction 9). The L-monomer and

$$n \ H_2C\!\!-\!\!\overset{O}{\frown}\!\!CH \longrightarrow \left(CH_2CHOCH_2CHOCH_2CHO\right)_{\frac{n}{3}}$$

$$\underset{CH_3}{|} \qquad \underset{CH_3}{|} \quad \underset{CH_3}{|} \quad \underset{CH_3}{|} \qquad (9)$$

(**6**$_m$)   (**6**$_p$)

DL-, L-, D-

polymer were prepared in 1955[22] and the optically active, crystalline polymer was shown to have the same x-ray pattern as the optically inactive crystalline polymer made by Pruitt and Baggett[21].

Thus in 1955 the discovery of catalysts producing isotactic polypropylene from propylene and producing isotactic polypropylene oxide from DL-propylene oxide were both reported. While the former

---

* A pseudoasymmetric atom has four different groups, but two of them differ only in being nonidentical mirror images.

has reached earlier major commercial application, the latter has had features such as those mentioned above, which have made it possible to derive more detailed experimental information on the mechanism of this reaction. This discussion will, of course, deal largely with the latter, although the close relationship of olefin and olefin oxide will be emphasized. Note that monomer and polymer **1** are related to monomer and polymer **6** by replacing an electron pair in the former by an oxygen atom.

III. STEREOSELECTIVE POLYMERIZATION OF PROPYLENE OXIDE

As has been the case for isotactic polypropylene, where innumerable catalysts have now been discovered with varying capabilities, many catalysts have been discovered [23-25] for isotactic poly(propylene oxide) in addition to that first reported [21].

The original iron catalyst has been proposed to have the structure shown by (reaction 10).

$$FeCl_3 + 4\,\mathbf{6_m} \xrightarrow{\text{Et}_2\text{O}} ClFe\left(\overset{\overset{\displaystyle CH_3}{|}}{OCHCH_2}\overset{\overset{\displaystyle CH_3}{|}}{OCHCH_2Cl}\right)_2 \tag{10}$$

$$(\mathbf{7})$$

Price and Osgan [23] found that, among many Lewis acid metal alkoxides, aluminum isopropoxide activated by zinc chloride (**8**) was superior. Later diethylzinc–water (**9**) [24] or triethylaluminum–water–acetylacetone (**10**) [25] were found to be remarkably active stereospecific catalysts for propylene oxide and related monomers. The

$$\text{DL-}\mathbf{6_m} \xrightarrow{\mathbf{7}} \text{DL-}\mathbf{6_p} + \text{DL-}\mathbf{6_p} \tag{11}$$

Amorphous (75%) rubber,   Crystalline (25%) m.p. 70°,
molecular weight about 10^5 molecular weight about 10^6

separation of the atactic and isotactic polymer in this case (reaction 11) can be readily and cleanly accomplished by dissolution in acetone and chilling to about $-30°$. The isotactic portion separates and is collected while the amorphous rubbery fraction is recovered by evaporation of acetone and then by freeze-drying from frozen benzene. Approximately similar proportions of atactic and isotactic polymer are obtained by the other catalysts, although the Furukawa (**9**) [24] and Osgan (**8**) [23] catalysts give somewhat less and the Vandenberg (**10**) [25] catalyst somewhat more of the crystalline fraction.

Interesting features of these catalysts have been revealed by a study of the polymer they produce from D-monomer[26]. The surprising fact learned was that, whereas D-6_m gave only D-6_p in 95% yield by non-stereoselective potassium hydroxide catalysis, the stereoselective catalysts gave a very considerable proportion of amorphous, soluble polymer, as indicated in Table 1.

TABLE 1. Properties of amorphous and crystalline polymer fractions from D-propylene oxide.

Catalyst	Amorphous				Crystalline			
	% Yield	$[\eta]^a$	$[\alpha]_D^{20}$	$k_D/k_L{}^b$	$[\eta]$	$[\alpha]_D^{20}$	M.p.	$k_D/k_L{}^c$
Fe (7)	60	1·01	$-10°$	3·3	4·10	$-23°$	75	>300
Al–Zn (8)	50	0·38	$-18·5°$	7·7	1·19	$-28·6°$	68	~ 44
Zn (9)	30	0·92	$-5·1°$	2·5	2·75	$-26·8°$	62	~ 24

^{a} $[\eta]$ = intrinsic viscosity = $1·4 \times 10^{-4}$ MW$^{0·8}$ (in benzene at 25°).

^{b} k_D = propagation rate for D-unit adding as a D-unit; k_L = propagation rate for D-unit adding as an L-unit. $k_L/k_D = (50 - [\alpha]_{20}^D)/50$.

^{c} $k_D/k_L = \dfrac{18}{75 - \text{m.p.}} \times 17$; since the m.p. for crystalline polymer from DL-6_m is about the same, this also represents the ratio of isotactic to nonisotactic placements.

The formation of substantial amounts of amorphous fraction by these catalysts indicates that there are not only catalyst sites capable of selecting from DL-monomer only D- or only L-units for long sequences of highly isotactic polymer, but that there are also catalyst sites capable of taking all D-monomer and creating polymer with a substantial fraction of random units. The various catalysts differ quantitatively in this capacity to invert some of the asymmetric centers. For example Furukawa catalyst (9) produced only 28% of amorphous polymer, but it has almost 50% L-units. Osgan catalyst (8) gave a much larger yield of amorphous polymer (62%) but this contained only about 10% of L-units, as estimated from its high optical activity.

It is also possible to estimate the sequence length of the crystalline isotactic polymer from the melting point, if we assume that the depression of melting point can arise from one syndiotactic placement as 'impurity' in the same way that it can arise from end-groups as 'impurities'. Since isotactic polymer of 3000 molecular weight (degree of polymerization equal to 50) has a melting point of 56° and the 'purest' isotactic polymer, that from catalyst 7, melting point 75°, we may estimate that the isotactic polymer from Osgan catalyst (**8**), melting point 68°, has an average isotactic sequence length of about forty-four and that from Furukawa catalyst (**9**) a sequence length of about twenty*.

Using the Furukawa catalyst as an example we may conclude that there must be some catalyst sites which are stereoselective and, even from DL-monomer, that they will select so as to produce polymer chains with an average sequence of about twenty-four isotactic placements between syndiotactic placements. There are other sites which produce atactic polymer, even from L-monomer, with almost a completely random sequence of units.

In addition to sites which produce partially or largely racemized amorphous poly(propylene oxide) from D-monomer and isotactic sites which produce isotactic poly-(D-propylene oxide) even from DL-monomer, it has recently been shown by Vandenberg[27] that his catalyst (**10**) will *invert* the configuration of one asymmetric center of *meso*-2-butene oxide, producing an optically inactive but stereo-specific DL-polymer (**11$_p$**) (reaction 12).

(**11$_m$**) (**11$_p$**) (12)

meso-2-butene oxide

m.p. about 100°, > 90%
(and all *l*-isomer)

The stereochemistry of this polymerization must involve a high degree of selection, successive ring opening occurring with inversion at $C_{(l)}$ at one stereospecific site, with inversion at $C_{(d)}$ at another, in order to produce racemic isotactic polymer. These results prove that selective inversion is also possible by stereoselective catalysts.

In addition to this important contribution, Vandenberg[25] also discovered that triethylaluminum–water catalyst (**12**) in heptane solution at −78°, which gave amorphous, atactic polymer from **11$_m$**, nevertheless gave stereoregular crystalline polymer from *trans*-2-butene oxide

---

* From an entirely different analysis, based on x-ray and density data, S. L. Aggarwal (*148th Meeting Am. Chem. Sci., Sept. 1964*, Chicago, Illinois) estimated isotactic sequence lengths about one-half those we have estimated from melting-point data.

(13_m) (reaction 13). Here also there was stereoselection and inversion of one asymmetric center of each monomer unit.

$$n \quad \begin{matrix} H_3C \overset{(d)}{\diagdown} \overset{}{C} \overset{}{\diagup} H \\ \overset{}{C} \\ H \overset{(d)}{\diagup} \overset{}{\diagdown} CH_3 \end{matrix} O \xrightarrow[-78°]{\text{Catalyst } \mathbf{12}} \left(\overset{(d)}{\underset{CH_3}{CH}} - \overset{(l)}{\underset{CH_3}{CH}} - O - \overset{(d)}{\underset{CH_3}{CH}} - \overset{(l)}{\underset{CH_3}{CH}} - O - \overset{(d)}{\underset{CH_3}{CH}} - \overset{(l)}{\underset{CH_3}{CH}} - O \right)_{\frac{n}{3}}$$

DL- (or D-)   m.p. about 160°, 97%   (13)

(13_m)   (13_p)

Furukawa, Tsuruta and coworkers[28] have shown that diethylzinc activated by L-borneol is not only capable of partially racemizing asymmetric centers of L-monomer, but also partially resolving DL-monomer, producing partially optically active isotactic polymer from DL-propylene oxide. Furthermore, the monomer recovered is enriched in the opposite isomer. Thus the optically active catalyst made with L-borneol not only produced isotactic polymer but selectively does so more readily from L- than from D-monomer. Such selectivity could *not* be produced by catalysts made from diethylzinc–water–D-6_m or from 7 and D-6_m or from 8 and D-6_m[26].

Very recently Tsuruta[37] has shown that a catalyst prepared from diethylzinc and an oligomer of D-propylene oxide prepared from monomer and sodium methoxide was stereoselective in favor of L-monomer (reactions 14 and 15).

$$\text{D-}\mathbf{6_m} \xrightarrow{NaOCH_3} CH_3O \left(CH_2 \overset{\overset{CH_3}{|}}{CH} O \right)_8 H \xrightarrow{(C_2H_5)_2 Zn} \text{Catalyst} \qquad (14)$$

$$\text{Catalyst} \xrightarrow{\text{DL-}\mathbf{6_m}} (\text{DL} + \text{L})\text{-}\mathbf{6_p} + (\text{DL} + \text{D})\text{-}\mathbf{6_m} \qquad (15)$$

IV. CATALYST STUDIES

The nature of the Pruitt and Baggett catalyst (7) has been the subject of several recent investigations. Gee, Higginson and Jackson[29] have prepared it under strictly anhydrous conditions and then studied the effect of addition of controlled amounts of water. In the absence of water, the reaction had an induction period, followed by a rate of conversion first order in both catalyst and monomer. Addition of water (up to two moles per mole of iron) had the following effects: (*a*) elimination of the induction period, (*b*) first an increase in rate (up to one mole) and then a decrease in rate and (c) a steady increase in the fraction of product which was crystalline (from 15% anhydrous to 85% at two moles of water). They confirmed the earlier proposal for the structure of the catalyst (7) and suggested that the function of water was to hydrolyze the alkoxide links producing oxygen links between iron atoms.

It had been observed earlier that bulk polymerization with catalyst (7), which was initially homogeneous, produced a precipitate on heating to polymerization temperature of 80° and that polymer grew upward from this precipitate in an unstirred vessel.

The magnetic characteristics of the Pruitt and Baggett catalyst have also been the subject of a careful investigation made by Makishima[30]. Ferric chloride in ether was found to have a broad band (600 gauss) in the electron spin resonance spectrum and was shown to have five unshared electrons by magnetic susceptibility measurements. A catalyst solution made from ferric chloride and propylene oxide

(7)

showed a narrow electron spin resonance band (60 gauss) and three unshared electrons. These data were interpreted on the basis that ferric chloride exists as the dimer in ether, broadening the electron spin resonance band, whereas 7 is unimolecularly dispersed, perhaps due to chelation effects.

The reaction of diethylzinc with water to produce catalyst 9 has also been studied carefully by Furukawa[24, 31] and by Herold, Aggarwal and Neff[32]. The course of the reaction seems well established (reaction 16).

$$\text{EtZnEt} + \text{H}_2\text{O} \xrightarrow{\text{Fast}} \text{EtH} + \text{EtZnOH} \xrightarrow{\text{Slow}} \text{EtH} + (\text{ZnO})_n \qquad (16)$$

The 'zinc oxide' formed by the second step is aggregated to such an extent that it gives no measurable depression of the freezing point of dioxane, but it does give clear solutions. Since ordinary zinc oxide has very little catalytic activity, conversion of the 'active' zinc oxide catalyst to its normal state of aggregation or crystallinity may represent the very slow catalyst deactivation process.

Tsuruta[28] has shown that the reaction of alcohols with diethylzinc also proceeds in two steps (reaction 17) and believes that amorphous zinc dialkoxide so produced is an active catalyst for conversion of 6_m into isotactic 6_p.

$$\text{EtZnEt} + \text{ROH} \xrightarrow{\text{Fast}} \text{EtZnOR} + \text{EtH} \xrightarrow[\text{ROH}]{\text{Slow}} \text{ROZnOR} + \text{EtH} \qquad (17)$$

The intermediate ethylzinc alkoxide has been isolated in the crystalline state (for $R = CH_3$) and shown to be a less effective catalyst than the dialkoxide.

V. CONCEPTS OF MECHANISM

In 1956, Price and Osgan[22] proposed the coordination-propagation scheme shown by reaction (18) to explain the stereoselective polymerization of propylene oxide by catalyst 7. Such a mechanism

$$
\overset{\displaystyle OR}{\underset{(7)}{\diagdown\text{Fe}\diagup}}
\underset{k_{-1}}{\overset{k_1}{\rightleftharpoons}}
\overset{\displaystyle \overset{\delta-}{OR}}{\underset{\underset{\displaystyle (14)}{\underset{|}{\overset{\delta+}{O}-\overset{|}{C}HCH_3}}}{\diagdown\text{Fe}\diagup}}
\xrightarrow{k_2}
\overset{\displaystyle OR}{\underset{O-CH_2\quad CH_3}{\diagdown\text{Fe}\diagup\qquad\diagdown CH\diagup}}
\qquad (18)
$$

adequately accounts for the kinetics observed by Gee[29]. It predicts that alkoxide groups attached to the metal might become end-groups in the polymer, as has been observed by Price and Ebert[33] for catalyst 8 and by Tsuruta[28] for diethylzinc activated by 9-anthranylmethanol and tritiated methanol. The close proximity of an asymmetric center in R and the asymmetric carbon of the incoming propylene oxide molecule could explain the stereoselection and the optical activity arising when $R = \text{D-bornyl}$[28].

The generation of a 'free' carbonium center at the asymmetric secondary carbon atom of 14 could account for the partial inversion of $\text{D-}6_m$ which must occur in the formation of the amorphous fraction of polymer by catalyst 7. Ring opening with retention of configuration cannot explain the data of Vandenberg, however, who found inversion occurred in the stereospecific polymerization of cis-2-butene oxide (11_m). It would therefore seem likely that ring opening may occur in a similar manner for propylene oxide at stereoselective sites. In this case, an inversion mechanism would presumably occur preferentially at the primary carbon atom and would not be evident since this carbon atom is not asymmetric. Thus of the two possibilities for the mechanism of ring opening at stereoselective sites originally considered in 1956 by Price and Osgan (see footnote 17, reference 22), ring opening at the asymmetric atom with selective retention of configuration or ring opening at the primary carbon atom (also, of course, with retention of configuration at the asymmetric carbon), the second seems now almost certainly the correct choice.

It is still not possible to decide whether the stereospecific coordinate propagation reaction occurs on a single metal atom or involves two or more. For inversion of configuration to occur at one carbon atom during ring opening, the two oxygen atoms and the carbon atom must be essentially linear and the oxygen–oxygen distance should be about 3 Å. Furukawa has estimated the distance between two oxygen atoms attached to any of a number of hexacoordinate metals as between 2·8 and 2·9 Å, so perhaps the model 15 is geometrically feasible. The oxygen–oxygen distance in 16 would be only slightly larger (due to

(15)   (16)

the fact that the $\stackrel{\frown}{MOM}$ angle may be somewhat greater than 90°). However, model 15, with the metal hexacoordinate, would have another atom directly above and one directly below the metal M. Since at least one hydrogen atom on the carbon atom undergoing inversion must be directed toward M, it would seem that this arrangement could not have enough room inside the strained four-membered ring to accommodate even one hydrogen atom. The model 16, however, would not only involve much less angular strain, because the ring is now six membered, but would have much more room to accommodate the inwardly directed hydrogen atom (or atoms). It is therefore Gee's opinion[29] and ours that the two-centered model (16) can much more satisfactorily account for the inversion of one carbon atom in ring opening.

There have been several suggestions as to why stereoselective catalysts produce isotactic (rather than syndiotactic) polymer from propylene oxide. Essentially, any mechanism must make use of the stereochemistry of the preceding unit in order to direct the stereochemistry of the incoming unit.* Corey[34] expanded the Price–Osgan one-center mechanism in an interesting and clever way for this purpose. Assuming a hexacoordinate metal atom, the Corey proposal can be represented as reaction (19). The polymer chain is attached by

$$(19)$$

an alkoxide bond at $O_{(2)}$ and forms a chelate five-membered ring by coordination of the penultimate oxygen $(O_{(1)})$. The incoming monomer is first attached by coordination through oxygen $(O_{(3)})$ and rearrangement with ring opening then occurs producing a second chelate ring. The two five-membered rings are folded at nearly a 90° angle on the $Fe–O_{(2)}$ axis. Corey proposes that these two rings could form at this sharp angle only if the methyl groups were directed *outward* from the fold, which in fact would produce isotactic polymer. The major problem with the Corey hypothesis is the fact that isotactic polymer is produced by ring opening of propylene oxide at the methylene group, with inversion of configuration, so that the objections raised to model **15** hold for the Corey model also.

The earlier suggestion that the noncrystalline[22] fraction accompanying the optically active crystalline poly(propylene oxide) from D-propylene oxide was formed by 'cationic' opening at the secondary center, accompanied by racemization, has recently been shown to be incorrect[17,27,35]. Vandenberg[27] has reported that inversion of configuration occurred at the expoxide-ring carbon atom undergoing nucleophilic attack when *cis*- and *trans*-2-butene oxides were polymerized by either cationic or coordination-rearrangement type

---

* Tsuruta[28c] has recently resolved DL-isotactic **6**$_p$ and believes this supports the view that asymmetery of the catalyst site, not merely the asymmetry of the preceding unit of the chain, must be responsible for the stereoselection.

catalysts. These observations have been extended to *cis-* and *trans-*dideuteroethylene oxides for all three catalyst types (reactions 20 and 21)[17,35]. Thus the course of reaction has been shown to involve ring

$$(20)$$

$$(21)$$

(Catalyst = *t*-BuOK in dimethyl sulfoxide, $Et_3Al \cdot H_2O$, $Et_2Zn \cdot H_2O$, $FeCl_3$, (propylene oxide)$_4$)

opening with inversion of configuration at both primary[17] and secondary[27] carbon atoms.

Tumulo[36] discovered a procedure for degradation of poly(propylene oxide) through treatment with ozone followed by lithium aluminum hydride. By this procedure essentially one ether bond is cleaved to two hydroxyl groups for every equivalent of ozone consumed. By using 50 mole per cent of ozone an appreciable yield of dipropylene glycol was formed (reaction 22). It was shown that the three structural

$$(22)$$

isomers, diprimary, disecondary and primary–secondary could be readily separated and identified by gas–liquid chromatography. When high molecular weight crystalline polymer was used, the molecular weights and melting points for the samples were as summarized in Table 2. The dimer fraction from this polymer was over 99% of the unsymmetrical glycol **19** in agreement with a regular istotactic, head-to-tail structure.

TABLE 2. Isotactic poly(propylene oxide) by ozone cleavage of a sample with molecular weight 215,000 (m.p. 68·5°, $[\eta] = 2·53$).

Mol. wt.	$[\eta]$	M.p. (°c)	Proportion of O_3 (mg/g)	Equiv. 6_p/equiv. O_3[a]	Degree of polymerization
215,000	2·53	75	—	—	—
18,000	0·33	64·5	3·25	254	310
2,000	—	56	24·0	34·5	34·5
1,800	—	56·5	23·8	34·7	31
920	—	36	89	9·3	15·9
833	—	33·5	92	9·0	14·4

[a] Should equal D.P. (degree of polymerization) if each ozone molecule randomly cleaved one ether linkage.

$$CH_3 \quad CH_3 \qquad\qquad CH_3 \qquad CH_3 \qquad\qquad\qquad CH_3 \qquad CH_3$$
$$HOCH_2CHOCHCH_2OH \qquad HOCHCH_2OCH_2CHOH \qquad HOCH_2CHOCH_2CHOH$$
$$(\mathbf{17}) \qquad\qquad\qquad (\mathbf{18}) \qquad\qquad\qquad\qquad (\mathbf{19})$$

For the noncrystalline fractions from several different catalyst systems, the proportion of symmetrical glycols was considerable[17], indicating head-to-head, tail-to-tail sequences in the polymer chain. The results are summarized in Table 3. The excellent agreement

TABLE 3. Head-to-head structure and optical activity in poly(propylene oxides).

Catalyst	Polymer m.p.	$[\alpha]_D^{20}$	% Head-to-head glycol	
			Experimental	Calculated[a]
Zn (9)	Amorphous	−5	39	40
Fe (7)	Amorphous	−10	33	30
Al	Amorphous	−18·5	25	13[b]
KOH	56	−20	10	10
Zn (9)	68·5	−25	<1	0

[a] Calculated percentage head-to-head glycol = $2(25 - [\alpha]_D^{20})$.

[b] This apparent discrepancy may arise because the data on optical activity were from polymer made with catalyst 8 while the data on head-to-head structure were from catalyst 12.

between the percentage of glycol which is head-to-head ($\mathbf{17} + \mathbf{18}$) and the percentage of inversion from optical rotation data[25] supports the view that the irregularity causing noncrystallinity is indeed structural as well as configurational*. A reasonable hypothesis to explain these

* E. J. Vanderberg (private communication) has observed approximately the same proportion of head-to-head dimer units when amorphous fractions of 6_p are degraded by a different procedure.

facts would be that isotactic catalyst sites are highly selective for ring opening at the primary carbon (presumably with inversion at this carbon) producing only head-to-tail sequences and, from D-monomer, only D-units along the chain.

The catalyst sites producing amorphous polymer apparently have a far lesser selectivity with respect to opening at the primary or secondary carbon atom. When D-propylene oxide is the monomer, those units incorporated by opening at the primary carbon ('normal') will retain a D-configuration at the asymmetric secondary carbon. Those monomer units incorporated by opening at the secondary carbon ('abnormal') will provide units head-to-head with respect to 'normal' units and will have the configuration of the asymmetric secondary carbon atom inverted from D- to L-configuration.

These observations offer further support to the model **16** for the catalyst site.

Tsuruta's[28] observations that D-borneol will activate diethylzinc to give a catalyst producing partially active D-isotactic polymer and correspondingly leaving L-monomer unreacted supports the view that D-borneol (but *not* D-monomer[26] or many other optically active alcohols)[37] can produce catalyst sites retaining asymmetry from the initiator and selectively resolving the DL-monomer in the coordination stage. One might explain this remarkable discovery by assuming that one or more of the unfilled ligand positions of **16a** is occupied by the bornyl residue (OR^2). One requirement for retention of optical activity

(**16a**)

(R^1 = growing polymer chain, R^2 = D-bornyl)

at this catalyst site may be the unreactivity of the R^{2}O group in migration during the rearrangement stage. Many alkyl groups do migrate, becoming polymer chain end groups[28b,33]. Perhaps the bornyl group is sufficiently hindered to resist attack by the coordinated epoxide in the rearrangement step.

VI. POLY(PHENYLENE OXIDES)

In the search for more stable polymeric substances, the stability of diphenyl ether has served as a stimulus. The carbon–oxygen bond in aryl ethers is considerably more resistant to thermal, acid and oxidative cleavage than the alkyl ether bond, due to resonance with the ring (reaction 23); this decreases the basicity of the oxygen and imparts some double-bond character to the ether link.

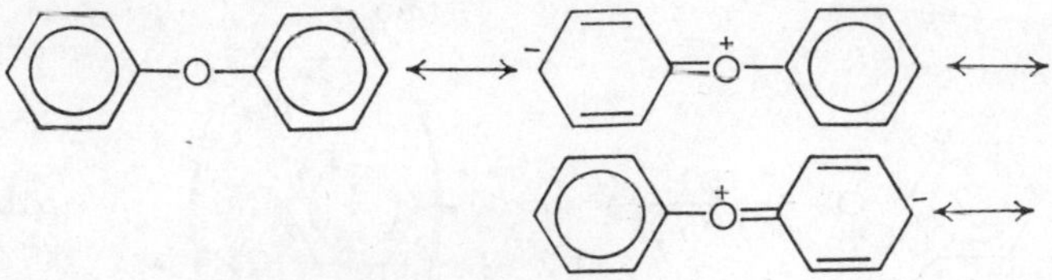

(23)

The most successful efforts to incorporate this linkage as the building unit of high polymer has been in the case of polyxylenol[38,39] which has recently been developed commercially and will be sold under the designation of PPO (poly(phenylene oxide))[1b].

Over half a century ago Hunter[40] made an extensive investigation of the amorphous products formed from trihalophenols under a variety of conditions and concluded that they were polymers involving condensation with elimination of a halogen atom per unit, producing polymer with both *ortho* and *para* linkages and a molecular weight of about two thousand (reaction 24).

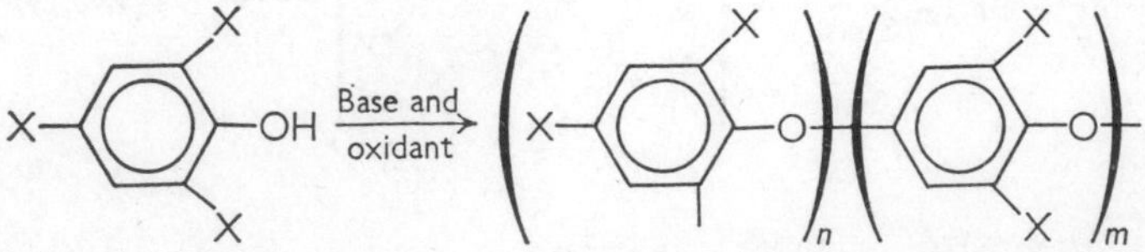

(24)

We were interested in extending these observations to monohalophenols to give units of fixed structure and to explore the mechanism of this interesting polycondensation reaction. The most suitable monomers were found to be 4-halo-2,6-dialkylphenols, with primary alkyl groups. 4-Bromo-2,6-xylenol was found to be indefinitely stable in alkaline solution, no measurable nucleophilic displacement of halogen occurring in a week. Addition of a one-electron oxidizing agent such as ferricyanide ion, iodine or lead dioxide, which are particularly effective in converting 2,4,6-tri-*t*-butylphenol into its stable blue free radical, leads to polymerization in a few seconds with quantitative liberation of bromide ion (reactions 25 and 26). The

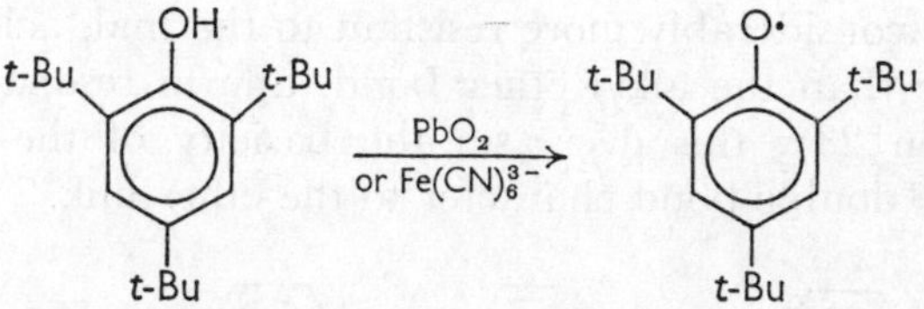

(25)

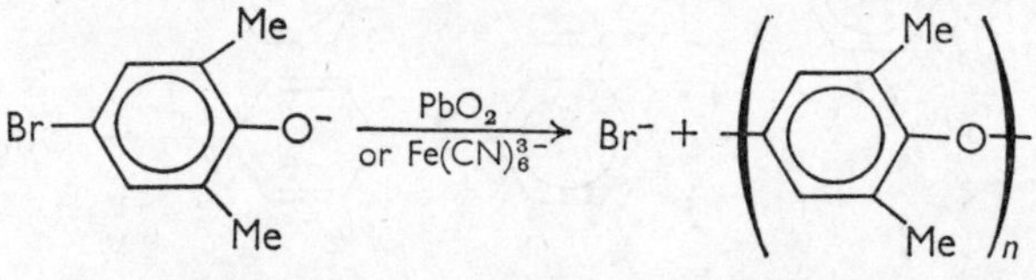

molecular weight ~ 25,000

(20)   (21)

(26)

polymerization process is greatly facilitated by a layer of benzene to dissolve the polymer as it is formed. It has been proposed that the polymerization proceeds through phenoxy-radical attack on phenolate ions, probably at the water–benzene interface (Xyl = *p*-xylylene unit) (reaction 27).

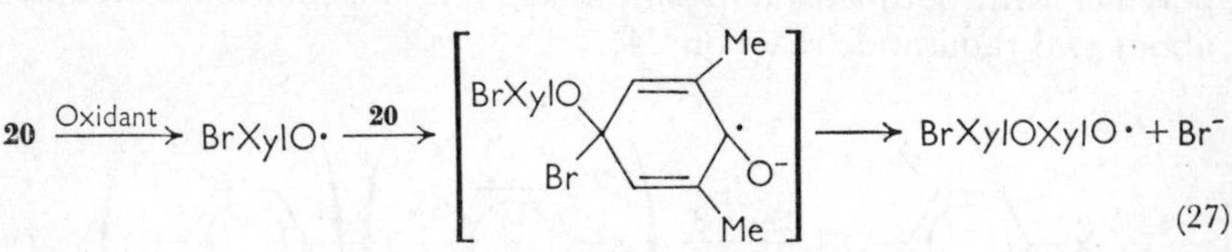

(27)

Solvolysis of the α-bromo ether (**22**) should occur exceedingly readily to give bromide ion and a dimeric phenolic radical which can then attack another bromoxylenolate ion to continue the propagation reaction. The process is thus a typical chain-reaction process in which a chain grows rapidly to high molecular weight and eventually terminates. Thus polymer at even 5% conversion has high molecular weight.

Concurrently with our work on the haloxylenol polymerization, Hay[39] discovered a new oxidative polymerization process for xylenol itself producing the same polymer (reaction 28). They have reported

$$(28)$$

(21)

molecular weight 20,000–100,000

many interesting features of this remarkable and important process listed as follows:

1. It is a polycondensation reaction, proceeding stepwise to give dimer, trimer, etc. Thus at 50% conversion the product is a low molecular weight oil and dimer and trimer polymerize as readily as monomer.

2. The dimer methyl ether is an inert diluent in polymerizing monomer.

3. The importance of the phenolic hydrogen is further supported by the fact that monomer with O-^{2}H polymerizes more slowly than with OH ($k_H/k^2_H = 2.5$). In contrast 4-^{2}H monomer polymerizes at a rate virtually identical to the normal monomer.

Since we[41] found the polyxylenol made by either the Hay or the Price–Staffin procedure can be crystallized, this would suggest that *only* the 4-hydrogen atom is affected by the Hay oxidative polymerization scheme. The special relation of the *ortho* and *para* positions in both is further supported by the need to have the 2,6-methyl groups, and the hindering effect of adding two more in the 3,5-positions. When we[41] made a study of monomer with 3- and 4-^{3}H we were therefore surprised to find that there was some retention of 4-^{3}H and some loss of 3-^{3}H during the polymerization[42]. The course shown by Scheme 1 was suggested to account for all these observations[42].

Radical–radical coupling to give **24** is promoted by the resonance between the 'diradical' (**23a**) and zwitterionic (**23b**) states through the chain of atoms all having $2p–\pi$-type orbital resonance potential. Direct loss of the 4-hydrogen atom evidently competes with proton migration to produce the intermediate **24** in which the 4-hydrogen atom has become equivalent to one of the two 3-hydrogens. The resonance depicted by **23a** and **23b** must stabilize intermediates of this type as readily when the phenonium ring unit and the terminal

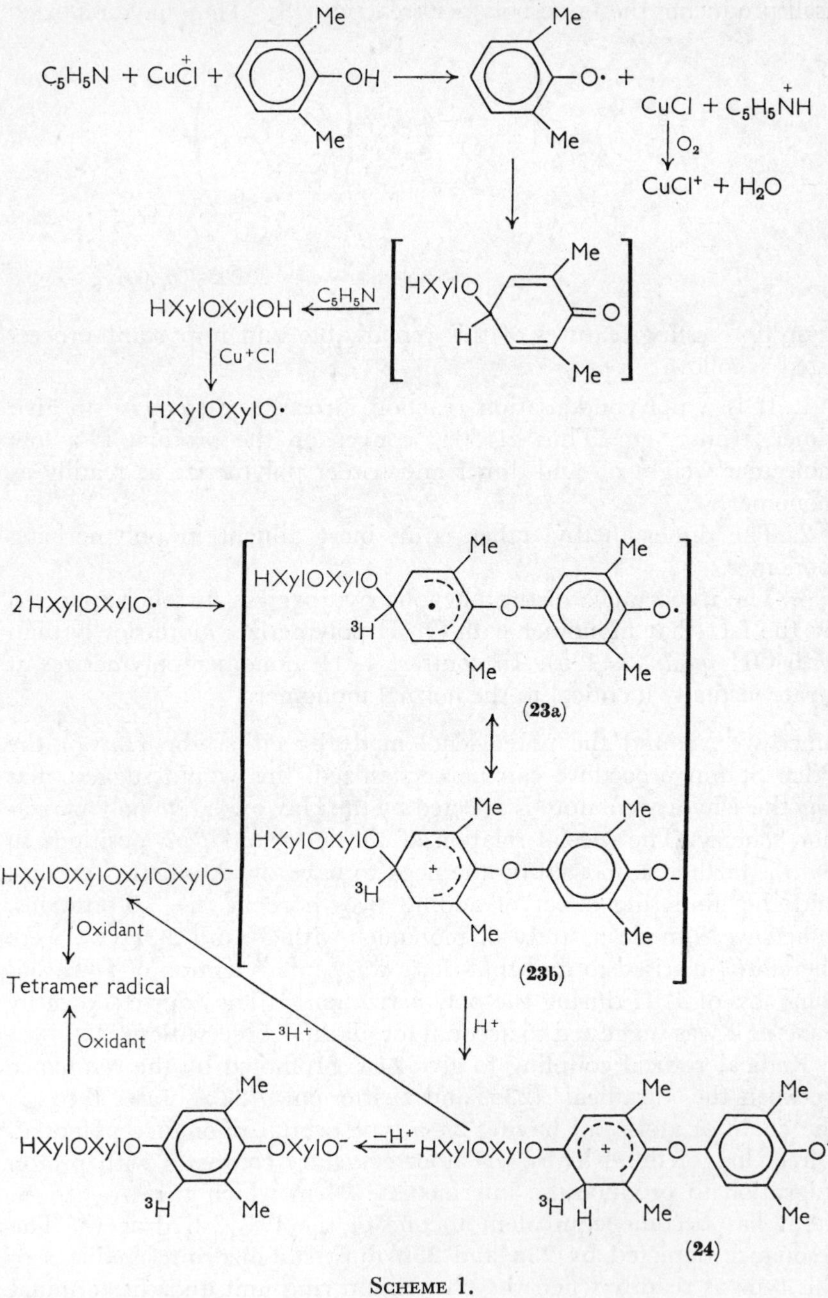
Me
C_5H_5N + CuCl + OH
O·
CuCl + $C_5H_5\overset{+}{N}H$
O_2
$CuCl^+$ + H_2O
HXylO
H
O
C_5H_5N
HXylOXylOH
Cu^+Cl
HXylOXylO·
2 HXylOXylO·
HXylOXylO
^3H
(23a)
(23b)
HXylOXylOXylOXylO$^-$
Oxidant
Tetramer radical
$-^3H^+$
H^+
HXylOXylO
OXylO$^-$
$-H^+$
(24)

SCHEME 1.

phenolate ring are separated by hundreds of intervening phenylene oxide units as when they are adjacent.

Both the oxidative coupling and the halo-displacement polymerization procedures are highly sensitive to the nature of the 2,6-substituents. When either of these is hydrogen, no high polymer is formed. With 2,6-di-*t*-butyl groups, oxidative coupling gives a dimeric diphenoquinone and the bromo-displacement reaction fails to give polymer. Allyl groups in the 2- or 2,6-positions inhibit polymerization by oxidative coupling, but produce polymer (or copolymers) with allylic side-chains by bromodisplacement polymerization.

Dewar[43] has reported that poly(phenylene oxides) can be prepared from diazooxides (reaction 29).

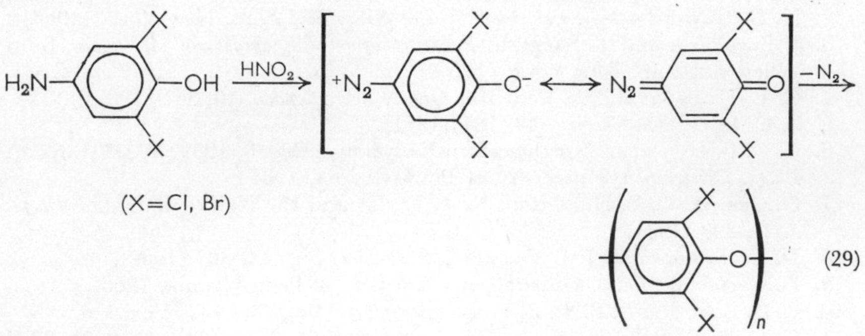

H2N
OH
HNO2
X
(X=Cl, Br)
+N2
O−
N2
O
−N2
n

(29)

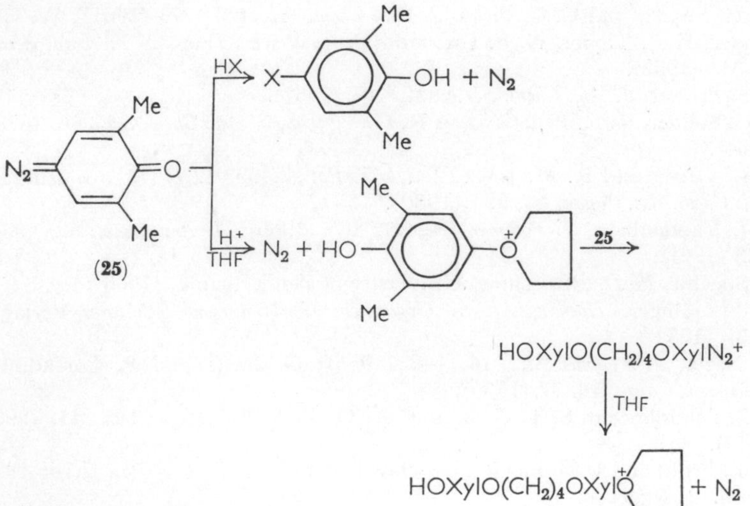

Me
HX
X
OH + N2
N2
O
(25)
H+
THF
N2 + HO
25
HOXylO(CH2)4OXylN2+
THF
HOXylO(CH2)4OXylO
+ N2

(30)

The halogen atoms have been ascribed an important role in the carbene–methylene interconversion in this polymerization[43b].

Efforts to extend this reaction for the case of $X = CH_3$ gave no polymeric products except in THF[44,45] or dioxane (reaction 30)[45].

In this process, the THF (or dioxane) oxygen displaces the diazo group. The resulting oxonium ion then undergoes nucleophilic attack by the diazoöxide oxygen. This sequence leads to a 1:1 copolymer of alternating aryl and alkyl units.

VII. REFERENCES

1. (a) H. Tani and N. Oguni, *Polymer Letters*, **3**, 123 (1965); (b) *Chem. Eng. News*, Dec. 7, 1964, p. 57; April 26, 1965, p. 48.
2. N. G. Gaylord (Ed.), *Polyethers*, John Wiley and Sons, New York, (1963).
3. J. Furukawa and T. Saegusa, *Polymerization of Epoxides and Aldehydes*, John Wiley and Sons, New York, (1963).
4. C. E. H. Bawn and A. Ledwith, *Quart. Rev., London*, **16**, 361 (1962).
5. C. C. Price, *The Chemist*, **38**, 131 (1961).
6. C. C. Price, *Lecture*, Northwestern University, Dec. 8, 1959; W. H. Snyder, *Ph.D. Dissertation*, University of Pennsylvania, 1961.
7. G. Gee, W. C. E. Higginson, K. J. Taylor and M. W. Trenholme, *J. Chem. Soc.*, 4298 (1961).
8. D. M. Simons and J. J. Verbanc, *J. Polymer Sci.*, **44**, 303 (1960).
9. D. Carmelite, *Ph.D. Dissertation*, University of Pennsylvania, 1966.
10. C. C. Price and L. E. St. Pierre, *J. Am. Chem. Soc.*, **78**, 2432 (1956).
11. G. C. Dege, R. L. Harris and H. S. MacKenzie, *J. Am. Chem. Soc.*, **81**, 3374 (1959).
12. W. H. Snyder and C. C. Price, *J. Am. Chem. Soc.*, **83**, 1773 (1961); W. H. Synder, K. J. Taylor, N. S. Chu and C. C. Price, *Trans. N.Y. Acad. Sci.*, **24**, 341 (1962).
13. T. S. Prosser, *J. Am. Chem. Soc.*, **83**, 1701 (1961).
14. E. C. Steiner, R. R. Pelletier and R. O. Trucks, *J. Am. Chem. Soc.*, **86**, 4678 (1964).
15. T. L. Cairns and R. M. Joyce, Jr., *U.S. Pat.*, 2,455,912 (1948); S. Ishida, *Bull. Chem. Soc. Japan*, **33**, 924 (1960).
16. E. J. Vandenberg, *J. Polymer Sci.*, **47**, 486 (1960); *J. Am. Chem. Soc.*, **83**, 3538 (1961).
17. R. Spector, *Ph.D. Dissertation*, University of Pennsylvania, (1965).
18. H. Staudinger, *Hochmolecularen Organische Verbindungen*, Springer-Verlag, Berlin (1932).
19. G. Natta, *J. Polymer Sci.*, **16**, 143 (1955); G. Natta and P. Corradini, *Makromol. Chem.*, **16**, 77 (1955).
20. C. E. Schildknecht, S. T. Gross and A. O. Zoss, *Ind. Eng. Chem.*, **41**, 1998 (1949).
21. M. E. Pruitt and J. M. Baggett (to Dow Chemical Co.), *U.S. Pat.*, 2,706,182 (April 12, 1955).

22. C. C. Price and M. Osgan, *J. Am. Chem. Soc.*, **78**, 4787 (1956).
23. C. C. Price and M. Osgan, *J. Polymer Sci.*, **34**, 153 (1959).
24. J. Furukawa, T. Tsuruta, R. Sakata, T. Saegusa and A. Kawasaki, *Makromol. Chem.*, **32**, 90 (1959).
25. E. J. Vandenberg, *J. Polymer Sci.*, **47**, 485 (1960).
26. N. S. Chu and C. C. Price, *J. Polymer Sci.*, *Ser. A*, **1**, 1105 (1963).
27. E. J. Vandenberg, *Polymer Letters*, **2**, 1085 (1964); *U.S. Pat.*, 3,065,187 (1962).
28. (a) S. Inoue, T. Tsuruta and J. Furukawa, *Makromol. Chem.*, **53**, 215 (1962);
    (b) S. Inoue, T. Tsuruta and N. Yoshida, *Makromol. Chem.*, **79**, 34 (1964);
    (c) T. Tsuruta, S. Inoue and I. Isukuma, *Makromol. Chem.*, in press.
29. G. Gee, W. C. E. Higginson and J. B. Jackson, *Polymer*, **231** (1962).
30. S. Makishima, private communication.
31. M. Ishimori and T. Tsuruta, *Makromol. Chem.*, **64**, 190 (1963).
32. R. J. Herold, S. L. Aggarwal and V. Neff, *Can. J. Chem.*, **41**, 1368 (1963).
33. P. E. Ebert and C. C. Price, *J. Polymer Sci.*, **34**, 157 (1959).
34. E. J. Corey, *Tetrahedron Letters*, **2**, 1 (1959).
35. C. C. Price and R. Spector, *J. Am. Chem. Soc.*, **87**, 2069 (1965).
36. A. L. Tumolo, *Ph.D. Dissertation*, University of Pennsylvania, 1963; *J. Poly. Sci.*, in press.
37. S. Inoue, Y. Yokota, N. Yoshida and T. Tsuruta, *Makromol. Chem.*, **81**, 191 (1965).
38. C. C. Price and G. Staffin, *Army–Navy–Air Force Elastomer Conference, Dayton, Ohio, Oct. 1958*; *J. Am. Chem. Soc.*, **82**, 3632 (1960).
39. A. S. Hay, H. S. Blanchard, G. F. Endres and J. W. Eustance, *J. Am. Chem. Soc.*, **81**, 6335 (1959); see also *Am. Chem. Soc. Div. Polymer Chem.*, Preprint **2**, 319, 326, 331, 340 (Sept. 1961); *J. Polymer Sci.*, **58**, 581 (1962).
40. W. H. Hunter and M. A. Dahlen, *J. Am. Chem. Soc.*, **54**, 2459 (1932).
41. W. A. Butte, Jr., C. C. Price and R. E. Hughes, *J. Polymer Sci.*, **61**, S28 (1962).
42. W. A. Butte, Jr. and C. C. Price, *J. Am. Chem. Soc.*, **84**, 3567 (1962).
43. (a) M. J. S. Dewar and A. N. James, *J. Chem. Soc.*, 917 (1958); (b) M. J. S. Dewar and K. Narayanaswami, *J. Am. Chem. Soc.*, **86**, 2422 (1964).
44. J. K. Stille, P. Cassidy and L. Plummer, *J. Am. Chem. Soc.*, **85**, 1318 (1963).
45. T. Kunitake and C. C. Price, *J. Am. Chem. Soc.*, **85**, 761 (1963).

CHAPTER **12**

Interconversion of C—O—C, C—S—C, and C—Se—C groups

VÁCLAV HORÁK

Charles University, Prague, Czechoslovakia

and

JÜRGEN GOSSELCK

The University, Giessen, Germany

I. INTRODUCTION

Ethers, organic sulfides, and selenides are three types of structurally related compounds containing an atom from Group VIb of the periodic table. As they are typical representatives of oxygen-, sulfur-, and selenium-containing organic compounds, respectively, they are suitable for a comparative study of those properties which are functions of the particular heteroatom. Taking both physical and chemical properties into account, the observed differences can be divided into two classes. The first comprises those differences which are due to different molecular weights and are best considered as quantitative. The second class includes those differences which appear to be of qualitative nature; they are related to the location of the heteroatom in its particular row of the periodic table, i.e. to the electronic configuration and properties of the atomic orbitals which are of fundamental importance to the chemical properties of the element. The possible use of d orbitals in sulfur and selenium provides these heavier elements with distinctly different properties as compared with oxygen. Qualitative differences between oxygen- and sulfur-containing compounds are generally of a more profound nature than those between sulfur- and selenium-containing ones.

These variations in properties can be made use of in practical applications: one of these is the interconversion of ethers, organic sulfides, and selenides. Studies of exchange reactions of compounds with heteroatoms from Group VIb have so far proceeded mostly along lines determined purely by practical requirements. Most attention has been paid to reactions which convert easily accessible compounds into relatively inaccessible ones. This is an understandable tendency, but unfortunately it imposes an arbitrary limitation on the scope of the studies. Because of this, a rather incomplete picture of the field is given by the literature. Most papers deal with the conversion of oxygen-containing compounds into sulfur- or selenium-containing compounds, and reactions involving the former two classes of compounds have been studied much more thoroughly than those involving selenium-containing compounds.

Many theoretically interesting interrelations between oxygen-, sulfur-, and selenium-containing organic compounds await further studies and it is hoped that the present chapter might provide some incentive.

The main subject of this work is the interconversion of ethers, organic sulfides, and selenides. The methods used to effect these changes are usually quite general and can sometimes be applied to all nucleophiles derived from the particular heteroatom. Examples have been chosen so as to keep the contents as homogenous as possible. On the other hand, some reactions are discussed in a more general manner, as it was clearly undesirable to take detailed information out of a broader context. This suggests some possibilities which have so far been neglected.

II. THEORETICAL CONSIDERATIONS

The data given in this section characterize some of the basic properties of oxygen, sulfur, and selenium, both as elements and in compounds. They should help to establish a general picture of the basic problems in the chemistry of organic compounds containing these three elements, which in turn should be helpful in giving some idea of the possibilities of interconverting ethers, organic sulfides, selenides, and some additional related compounds. Most of the data are summarized in Table 1.

Table 1 clearly shows the higher degree of similarity between selenium and sulfur than between sulfur and oxygen, especially in electronegativity, covalent bond energies, and ionization energy. The difference in the covalent radius between oxygen and sulfur is similarly much greater than that between sulfur and selenium. This factor is important in steric effects as is clearly seen, for example, from the difference in the energy barriers to free rotation along the C—O and C—S bonds. The decrease in bond angle in the heavier elements acts in the opposite direction. Electron distribution, which is a function of the electronegativity of the heteroatom, in dimethyl ether and its sulfur and selenium analogs demonstrates the inductive effect of these elements, just as the σ_m values do, at least approximately. Differences in the ratio of the σ_p and σ_m values provide an approximate measure of the conjugative properties of the heteroatoms. The lower conjugative properties of the heavier elements can be explained by a less efficient overlap of $2p$ with $3p$ orbitals as compared with $2p$ with $2p$ orbitals.

A fundamental difference in the properties of sulfur and selenium in comparison with those of oxygen is due to the former two being able to expand their valence shells. This involves the d orbitals of sulfur and selenium, and provides a basis for so-called d-orbital resonance which can be represented by reactions (1) and (2). In this chapter it is only possible to refer the reader to a comprehensive review[9].

TABLE 1. Atomic properties[a] of oxygen, sulfur, and selenium.

Property[a]	Bond or compound[b]	Oxygen	Sulphur	Selenium
Atomic weight		16·000	32·066	78·96
B.p. (°c)	Me$_2$X	−24·9	37·3	58
	Ph$_2$X	258·3	296–297	301–302
Covalent radius of X (Å)	Y—X	0·66	1·04	1·17
	Y=X	0·55	0·94	1·07
Energy barrier of internal rotation (kcal/mole)	Me—XMe	3·1	2·0	
	Me—XH	3·4	1·5	
Bond angle (degrees)	HX̂H	104·45 ± 0·1	92·2 ± 0·1	91·0 ± 1
	MeX̂Me	111 ± 3	105 ± 3	
	ClX̂Cl	110 ± 1	102 ± 3	
Electronic configuration (last shell)		{ 2, 6 (2s^2, 2p^4)	2, 8, 6 (3s^2, 3p^4)	2, 8, 18, 6 (4s^2, 4p^4)
Electronegativity according to Pauling		3·5	2·5	2·4
Experimental covalent bond energy (kcal/mole)	X—X	118·3	76	65
Calculated covalent bond energy (from electronegativities) (kcal/mole)	X—X	81·0	50	44
Heat of atomization (kcal/mole)	X—X	59·14	53·25	48·37
First ionization energy of X (kcal/mole)		314	239	225
Experimental covalent bond energy (kcal/mole)	X—H	109·4	87	67
	C—X	84·0	62·0	
	C=X	169 ± 5	114	
Individual bond moment	C—X	0·86	0·95	
	C=X	2·40	2·80	
Charge localized in Me	Me$_2$X	0·13	0·05	0·07
Charge localized in X	Me$_2$X	−0·30	−0·11	−0·13
Basicity (pK_a) (H_0 units)		−2·05	−5·1	
Hammett constant (σ_m)	—XMe	0·115	0·15	
(σ_p)	—XMe	−0·268	0·00	
(σ_m)	—XH	0·121	0·25	
(σ_p)	—XH	−0·37	0·15	

[a] For a detailed discussion of these properties see references 1–8.
[b] X = O, S, or Se atom.

$$-\overset{|}{\underset{|}{\text{C}}}-\text{S}- \longleftrightarrow -\overset{|}{\text{C}}=\bar{\text{S}}- \tag{1}$$

$$\text{CH}_3\text{S}-\langle\bigcirc\rangle-\bar{\text{O}} \longleftrightarrow \text{CH}_3\bar{\text{S}}=\langle\bigcirc\rangle=\text{O} \tag{2}$$

Basicity is an important factor in the interconversion of ethers, sulfides, and selenides. Proton affinity decreases in the series $\text{Me}_2\text{O} > \text{Me}_2\text{S} > \text{Me}_2\text{Se}$, as does affinity towards BF_3. On the other hand, the order of affinities towards BH_3 and BMe_3 is different: $\text{Me}_2\text{S} > \text{Me}_2\text{Se} \sim \text{Me}_2\text{O}$. The affinity of Lewis acids towards both Me_2S and Me_2Se is in the order $\text{BH}_3 > \text{BF}_3 > \text{BMe}_3$[10].

The formation of complexes with transition metal ions also plays an important role in the interconversion discussed. In this case the strength of the complex-forming bond increases with increasing atomic number; in the case of reaction of $p\text{-MeXC}_6\text{H}_4\text{SO}_3^-$ (X = O, S, Se) with Ag^+ ions, the methoxy compound does not react at all and the complex formed by the methylseleno derivative is 1·3 kcal/mole stronger than that formed by the methylthio derivative[11].

In most cases relevant to the oxygen, sulfur, and selenium interconversion, nucleophilicity towards a saturated carbon atom plays a significant role. This strongly promotes the reactivity of sulfur-containing nucleophiles in comparison with the oxygen-containing ones: $\text{C}_4\text{H}_9\text{S}^- > \text{C}_6\text{H}_5\text{S}^- > \text{S}_2\text{O}_3{}^{2-} > \text{SC}(\text{NH}_2)_2 > \text{SCN}^- > \text{OH}^- > \text{C}_6\text{H}_5\text{O}^- > \text{MeCOO}^- > \text{H}_2\text{O}$[12].

Much important information available for oxygen- and sulfur-containing compounds is missing for selenium derivatives. In these cases the fact that the latter are closely related to their sulfur analogs provides a useful first approximation.

III. SYNTHETIC METHODS

A. Conversion of Ethers and Acetals

I. Thermal methods

The energy required to effect C—O bond cleavage and convert ethers into sulfides is met by carrying out the reaction at an elevated temperature.

The cases where the reaction is carried out without the use of a catalyst are not common. One example is the reaction of benzyl 2-quinolyl ether with thiophenol at 150–170°, yielding benzyl phenyl sulfide (reaction 3)[13]. The cleavage is facilitated in this case by the

$$\text{[quinoline]}-OCH_2Ph + PhSH \xrightarrow{150-170°} PhCH_2SPh + \text{[quinoline]}-OH \tag{3}$$

stability of the benzyl group, either in the cationic or in the radical form. The reaction is in a way analogous to the oxygen–sulfur conversion in thio O-acid esters, which is more often used for practical purposes*. An example is the thermal rearrangement of methyl esters of xanthogenic acids, an intramolecular reaction of the type shown by reaction (4). This rearrangement has found frequent practical use in

$$-\overset{|}{C}-O-\underset{\overset{\|}{S}}{C}-OCH_3 \longrightarrow -\overset{|}{C}-S-\underset{\overset{\|}{O}}{C}-OCH_3 \tag{4}$$

the chemistry of carbohydrates[14], β-amino alcohols[15], and esters of thio O-acids[16]. Particularly important is the thermal rearrangement of O,O-diphenyl thiocarbonate to O,S-diphenyl thiocarbonate in view of the usual reluctance of the phenolic C—O bond to break in any manner (reaction 5)[17].

$$Ph-O-\underset{\overset{\|}{S}}{C}-O-Ph \longrightarrow Ph-S-\underset{\overset{\|}{O}}{C}-O-Ph \tag{5}$$

Much work has been devoted to the conversion of ethers into sulfides using contact catalysis and high temperatures ($> 300°$). Chemisorption at the active surface of the catalyst, usually Al_2O_3, $Al_2O_3 + K_2WO_4$[18], ThO_2[19], or ZrO_2[20], leads at this high temperature to fission of C—O bonds, including those which are not weakened by structural features. The reaction has been used mostly for the preparation of mono- and polyalkyl-substituted cyclic sulfides from the corresponding ethers (reaction 6)[21–24]. Because of the reaction conditions, structural

---

* Thiocarboxylic acids of the form $RC(=O)SH$ are termed S-acids (e.g. thioacetic S-acid, CH_3COSH); acids $RC(=S)OH$ are termed O-acids (IUPAC rules).

$$H_2S + \;\; \boxed{}_{O} \;\; \xrightarrow[300°]{Al_2O_3} \;\; \boxed{}_{S} \tag{6}$$

features in the reactant or in the reaction intermediate may result in isomerization of the product, to the thermodynamically most stable form; for example, a four-membered ring may expand to a five-membered ring[25,26]. The formation of dihydrothiopyran from tetrahydrofuryl alcohol and hydrogen sulfide (Al_2O_3, 300°)[27] is analogous to the formation of dihydropyran. Under more drastic conditions disproportionation occurs, giving rise to thiopyran and tetrahydrothiopyran (reaction 7)[28]. Using almost identical conditions, furan has been

$$\boxed{}_{S} \xleftarrow[300°]{Al_2O_3} \boxed{}_{O}\!-\!CH_2OH + H_2S \xrightarrow[450°]{Al_2O_3} \boxed{}_{S} + \boxed{}_{S} \tag{7}$$

converted into thiophene (reaction 8)[29].

$$H_2S + \;\; \boxed{}_{O} \;\; \xrightarrow[400°]{Al_2O_3} \;\; \boxed{}_{S} \tag{8}$$

To complete the picture of the scope of the method, it seems desirable to mention the preparation of mercaptans and thiophenols from hydroxy compounds[30]. A different type of reaction is the conversion of n-butyl alcohol into thiophene by reaction with SO_2. The catalyst (Al_2O_3 + 10% Cr_2O_3) promotes dehydrogenation in addition to dehydration[31].

2. Acid catalysis

The conversion of both acyclic and cyclic ethers into sulfides has been affected in some cases by acid catalysts. The procedure is a special application of a general method for the preparation of sulfur from oxygen-containing compounds, starting with ethers[32], alcohols[33-39], or carboxylic acid esters (reactions 9 and 10)[40,41] and

$$\boxed{}_{O}\!-\!CH_3 + PhSH \xrightarrow{Na[BH_4]\cdot BF_3} PhSCH_2CH_2CH_2\underset{\underset{OH}{|}}{CH}CH_3 \tag{9}$$

$$\begin{array}{c}
\text{Ph} \quad \text{COOH} \\
\diagdown \diagup \\
\text{C} \\
\diagup \diagdown \\
\text{Ph} \quad \text{OH}
\end{array}
+ \text{HSCH}_2\text{COOH} \xrightarrow{\text{H}_2\text{SO}_4}
\begin{array}{c}
\text{Ph} \quad \text{COOH} \\
\diagdown \diagup \\
\text{C} \\
\diagup \diagdown \\
\text{Ph} \quad \text{SCH}_2\text{COOH}
\end{array}
\qquad (10)$$

leading to sulfides, mercaptans, sulfones, and isothiuronium salts, respectively. Both Brönsted and Lewis acids may be used. The acids most commonly used are H_2SO_4[39], HClO_4[38], hydrogen halides[42], HCOOH[40], and the $\text{Na[BH}_4]\text{BF}_3$ complex[32]. Depending on the oxygen-containing starting material and the catalyst, lower or higher temperatures are used. Especially mild conditions may be used with compounds in which the C—O bond is easily cleaved, such as t-butoxy or benzyloxy compounds. Even n-alkyl ethers may be used for the reaction if HI is used as catalyst (reaction 11)[42].

$$(11)$$

3. Conversion of epoxides

Conversion of epoxides into episulfides is a special case of the conversion of ethers into sulfides. The reaction course is determined by the reagent used and by the reaction conditions. The thiocyanate anion and thiourea are suitable reagents for episulfide formation.

In acidic media these reagents open the epoxide ring and form a 2-hydroxyalkyl thiocyanate or a 2-hydroxyalkyl isothiuronium salt (reaction 12)[43]. Reactions of epoxides with other sulfur-containing

$$(12)$$

nucleophiles, such as hydrogen sulfide[44], mercaptans[45], thioacetic S-acid[46], and the sulfite anion[45], give products of similar nature (reaction 13). 2-Substituted alcohols are usually the final products in

$$t\text{-BuCH}_2\overset{\overset{\displaystyle CH_2SCH_3}{|}}{\underset{\underset{\displaystyle CH_3}{|}}{C}}\text{—OH} \xleftarrow{\;\;\text{NaSCH}_3\;\;} t\text{-BuCH}_2\text{—}\overset{\overset{\displaystyle CH_2}{\diagup\diagdown O}}{\underset{\underset{\displaystyle CH_3}{|}}{C}} \xrightarrow{\;\;\text{Na}_2\text{SO}_3\;\;} t\text{-BuCH}_2\text{—}\overset{\overset{\displaystyle CH_2SO_3Na}{|}}{\underset{\underset{\displaystyle CH_3}{|}}{C}}\text{—OH} \qquad (13)$$

the absence of another reactive center; the halogen atom in the epichlorohydrin molecule leads to further reaction as shown by reaction (14) [47].

$$\underset{\text{O}}{CH_2\text{—}CHCH_2Cl} \xrightarrow{\;\;H_2S\;\;} S\langle\;\rangle\text{—OH} \qquad (14)$$

On the other hand, in basic media, epoxides react with the thiocyanate anion or thiourea with the formation of episulfides (reaction 15) [48–50]. A weakly alkaline medium is preferable since episulfides

$$\underset{S}{CH_3CH\text{—}CH_2} \xleftarrow[\;\;H_2O\;\;]{\text{KCNS}} \underset{O}{CH_3CH\text{—}CH_2} \xrightarrow[\;\;H_2O,H_3PO_4\;\;]{\text{HCNS}} \underset{OH}{CH_3CHCH_2SCN} \qquad (15)$$

polymerize in strongly basic media. Under these conditions episulfides are also formed from products of the acid-catalyzed reaction, so that the 2-hydroxy compounds in equation (12) are reaction intermediates [43]. The cyclization of these compounds to episulfides is related to cyclization of various 2-substituted mercaptans such as halo [51], tosyloxy [52], acyloxy [46], and thiocyano [53] (not hydroxy) derivatives, which also yields episulfides. A counterpart of cyclic intermediates (see section IV) proved in the formation of episulfides from 2-hydroxy compounds mentioned above, is O,S-ethylene thiocarbonate. This compound also yields ethylene episulfide in slightly alkaline media [54]. It has proved to be an excellent mercaptoethylating agent, particularly for primary and secondary amines (reaction 16).

$$\underset{H_2C}{\overset{H_2C}{\diagdown}}\overset{|}{\underset{\diagup}{S}} \xleftarrow{\;\;\text{Na}_2\text{CO}_3\;\;} \begin{bmatrix} O \\ | \\ \text{—}C\text{=}O \\ | \\ S \end{bmatrix} \xrightarrow[\text{toluene}]{\;\;R^2NH\;\;} R^2NCH_2CH_2SH \qquad (16)$$

Similarly, ethylene episulfide and propylene-1,3-sulfide are formed from ethylene carbonate and propylene-1,3-carbonate, respectively, by the action of the thiocyanate ion (reaction 17)[55]. The reaction of

$$(17)$$

carbon disulfide and KOH with epoxides in methanol leads initially to trithiocarbonates via unisolated intermediates (reaction 18)[49]. β-

$$(18)$$

Propiolactone is another compound which resembles an epoxide in its reactivity, due to the presence of a small ring. Its reactions with sulfur-containing nucleophiles have been used to prepare a series of β-carboxyethyl derivatives of sulfur-containing compounds; e.g. β-arylmercapto acids are formed by the reaction of mercaptans with β-propiolactone under basic catalysis (reaction 19)[56].

$$(19)$$

4. Conversion of O-alkyltropolones

Tropolone, its O-alkyl and O-tosyl derivatives, and 2-halotropones undergo a substitution reaction with sulfur-containing nucleophiles such as hydrogen sulfide, thiols, and thio S-acids. 2-Alkylmercapto-tropones and di-2-tropyl sulfide can be prepared in this manner (reaction 20)[57,58]. Substituted tropolone derivatives other than 5-monosubstituted tropolene usually give two isomeric products in which the alkylmercapto and carbonyl groups are in different positions; for instance, this behavior is shown by colchicine and its methyl ether

$$(X = OCH_3, OH, Cl, OTos\text{-}p)$$

(reaction 21). The reaction can be performed in both acidic and alkaline media; in the latter case, especially in the presence of an excess of

mercaptide ions and in highly basic media, it may be accompanied by rearrangement of the carbon skeleton and formation of benzoic acid derivatives[58, 59].

An analogous nucleophilic substitution of an alkoxy group on the benzene ring can be effected in cases where the alkoxy group is activated by nitro groups (reaction 22)[60].

5. Conversion of pyrones, pyrylium cations, alkoxymethylene ketones, and related compounds

γ-Pyrone is converted into γ-thiopyrone by reaction with NaSH (reaction 23)[61]. The reaction has not been widely used and it fails in

$$(23)$$

some cases: it is impossible, for example, to prepare 3-hydroxy-γ-thiopyrone from 3-hydroxy-γ-pyrone and γ-selenapyrone from γ-pyrone[61].

A similar conversion occurs with alkoxymethylene ketones and esters[62] or amides of alkoxymethylene carboxylic acids which are structurally related to pyrone (reaction 24)[63]. Similar behavior is ex-

$$C_2H_5OCH{=}CHCOOC_2H_5 \xrightarrow[\text{NaHSO}_4]{\text{PhSH}} PhSCH{=}CHCOOC_2H_5 \qquad (24)$$

hibited by hydroxymethylene ketones or the corresponding α-formyl ketones which are their tautomers (reaction 25)[63,64]. In several cases

$$(25)$$

(R¹ = H, COCH₃
R² = C₂H₅, H)

the reaction is carried out using either acid catalysts or, with the higher-boiling thiophenol, elevated temperature.

The pyrylium cation itself also undergoes an exchange reaction with the sulfide anion in alkaline media and gives the thiapyrylium ion (reaction 26)[65]. The reaction of 4-alkoxypyrylium ions with mercaptans proceeds differently, the alkoxy group being exchanged for an alkylmercapto group and the pyrylium ring remaining intact (reaction 27)[66].

$$(26)$$

$$(27)$$

6. The use of P_2S_5

In exceptional cases thioethers can be prepared from ethers using P_2S_5. The reaction was effected with a bisditertiary ether (reaction 28)[67]. However, the main field of application of the method is the

$$(28)$$

oxygen–sulfur conversion in carbonyl compounds[68], amides[69], and γ-dicarbonyl compounds[70-73]. The reaction produces thioketones[68], thioamides[69], thiophenes[70,71,73], and thiazoles[72]; the example given (reaction 29) is taken from the chemistry of imino esters[74].

$$(29)$$

7. Conversion of acetals and glycosides

Acetals[75,76], ketals[77], and glycosides[78] can be converted into mercaptals, mercaptols, and thioglycosides by the action of mercaptans, usually with acid catalysts (reactions 30 and 31). These products can

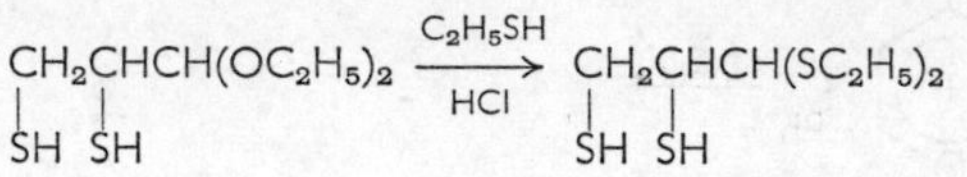

$$CH_2CHCH(OC_2H_5)_2 \ \underset{HCl}{\overset{C_2H_5SH}{\longrightarrow}} \ CH_2CHCH(SC_2H_5)_2 \qquad (30)$$
$$\underset{SH \ \ SH}{} \qquad\qquad\qquad \underset{SH \ \ SH}{}$$

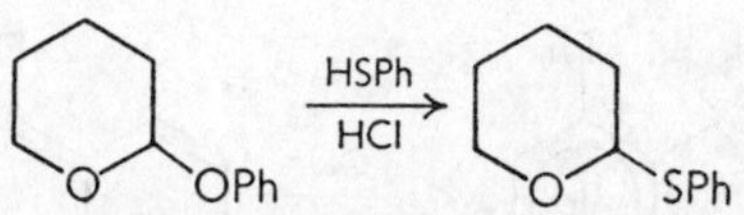

(31)

also usually be obtained directly from carbonyl compounds and mer-captans[79–83], again with acid catalysts. The common catalysts are HCl[75–78, 81, 82], HCl + ZnCl$_2$[83], p-toluenesulfonic acid[80], or BF$_3$[79]. In some cases the use of carbonyl compounds as starting materials can lead to products of different nature; e.g. the reaction of mercaptans with ketones yields vinyl sulfides (reactions 32 and 33)[83, 84]. The

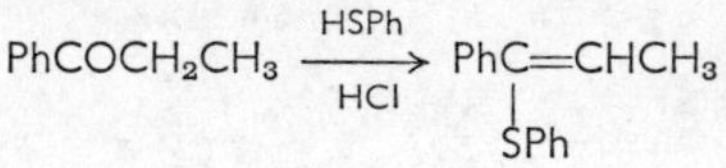

$$PhCOCH_2CH_3 \ \underset{HCl}{\overset{HSPh}{\longrightarrow}} \ PhC{=}CHCH_3 \qquad (32)$$
$$\underset{SPh}{}$$

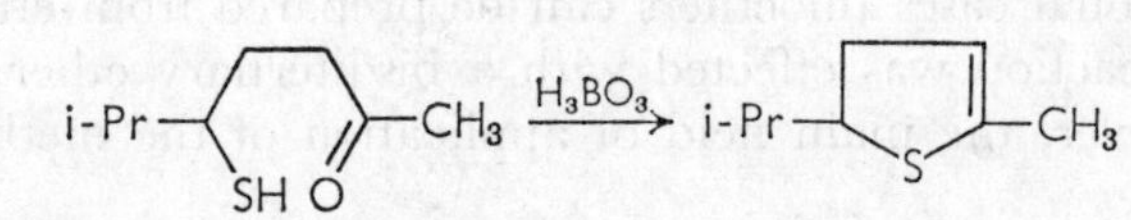

(33)

reaction with hydroxycarbonyl compounds (including sugars) and their derivatives yields mercaptals or mercaptols rather than thio-glycosides (reaction 34)[85]. For the sake of completeness the formation

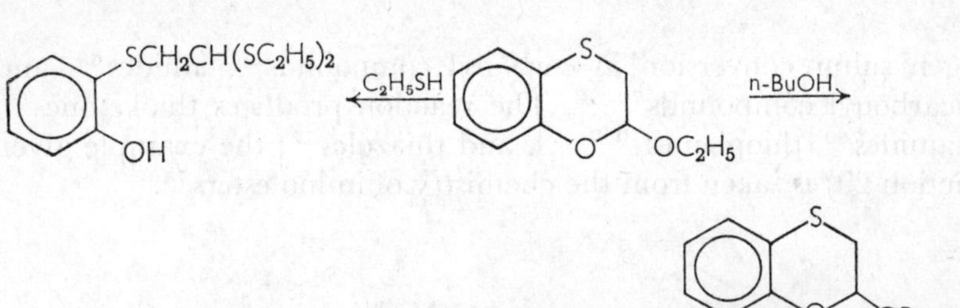

(34)

of s-trithianes from carbonyl compounds and hydrogen sulfide under acid catalysis should also be mentioned (reaction 35)[86, 87].

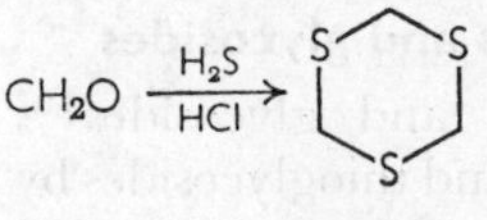

$$CH_2O \ \underset{HCl}{\overset{H_2S}{\longrightarrow}} \qquad\qquad (35)$$

In a similar way carbonyl compounds and amines (primary and secondary) react with hydrogen sulfide and mercaptans to form α-aminosulfides; this reaction (36) is analogous to the Mannich reaction[88-90].

$$(36)$$

Similar reaction schemes are used for the preparation of selenium-containing compounds. The reaction of H_2Se (catalyzed by HCl) with aldehydes[91,92] and ketones[92] yields selenoaldehydes and selenoketones, respectively, and, with selenols[93], selenoacetals, and selenoketals. In a special case BrMgSeH was used[94] for the preparation of a selenoaldehyde. The condensation of chloral with H_2Se[95]

$$CCl_3CH(OH)_2 \xrightarrow[\text{HCl}]{H_2Se} \left[\begin{matrix} CCl_3CH- \\ | \\ OH \end{matrix} \right]_2 Se \qquad (37)$$

(reaction 37) and the conversion of acridone into selenoacridone should be mentioned here[96].

8. Reactions analogous to alkylation by Mannich bases

β-Acetoxynitropropane[97] and some o-hydroxymethylphenols[98,99] react with sulfur nucleophiles, especially mercaptans, to give the corresponding sulfides (reaction 38). The substitution of a particular

$$\begin{matrix} CH_3CHCH_2NO_2 \\ | \\ OCOCH_3 \end{matrix} \xrightarrow[\text{NaOC}_2H_5]{\text{HSR}} \begin{matrix} CH_3CHCH_2NO_2 \\ | \\ SR \end{matrix} \qquad (38)$$

oxygen-containing group proceeds under conditions which are similar to those characteristic for alkylation reactions by Mannich bases.

B. Conversion of Organic Sulfides, Mercaptals (Mercaptols), and Analogous Selenium Compounds

1. Acid catalysis

Certain sulfides are cleaved hydrolytically in acidic media, usually with formation of the corresponding hydroxy derivative or of the tautomeric carbonyl compound. This reaction has been effected with an alkylmercapto group in the 2-position of the pyrimidine ring (reaction 39) [100–102]. Alkylmercaptodienes are hydrolyzed to α,β-

$$\text{(39)}$$

unsaturated ketones by the action of HCl in methanol; the mercaptan formed may react with one of the other reactive sites in the molecule (reaction 40) [103]. Some sulfones and sulfoxides are cleaved hydrolytic-

$$\text{(40)}$$

ally; this may be regarded as a two-step cleavage of sulfides (see next section). Conversion of a mercapto into a hydroxy group can be effected via the sulfide as intermediate; acid catalysis is used for the

$$\text{(41)}$$

C—S bond fission (reaction 41) [104]. There are no recorded instances of an organic sulfide being converted into an ether in this manner.

2. Oxidation products as intermediates

In some cases the oxidation of sulfides to sulfoxides or sulfones is used to facilitate the fission of a C—S bond during acid-catalyzed hydrolysis (reaction 42) [105,106]. This approach has been particularly

$$\text{(42)}$$

successful with mercaptals and mercaptols[107] and has often been used in sugar chemistry (reaction 43)[108]. The reaction can be effected

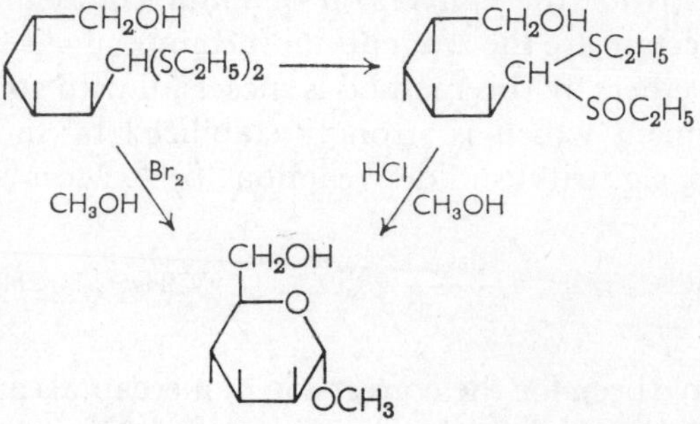

(43)

either in two steps, oxidation and hydrolysis separately, or in one step. The recommended reagent for the latter procedure is bromine; its action in methanol leads to methyl glycosides. The sulfur-containing components are split off as a disulphide. In one instance the same method gives benzylglyoxal[109]. In some cases the oxidation of sulfides, most often by hydrogen peroxide or bromine, is accompanied by a spontaneous rupture of the C—S bond[110,111]. Such a reaction has been carried out with triphenylmethylalkyl sulfides, t-butylalkyl sulfides[112], and 2-alkylmercaptopyrimidine; it yielded the corresponding hydroxy compounds. All these again are exceptionally reactive structures.

A single case of conversion of a sulfide into an ether through the corresponding sulfone in alkaline ethanolic media is known from xanthine chemistry (reaction 44)[41].

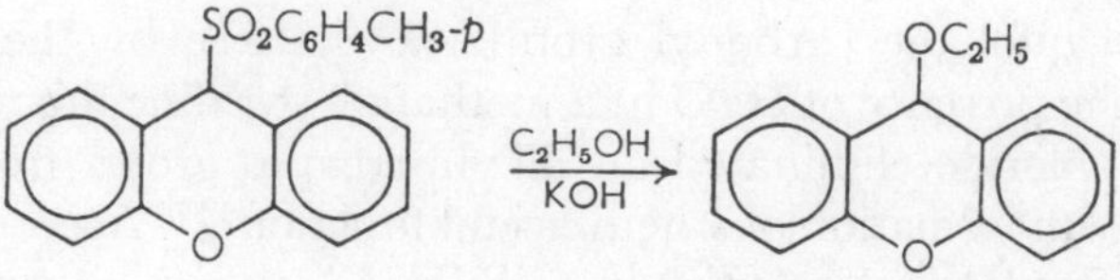

(44)

The conversion of an aromatic sulfide into an analogous selenide using the corresponding sulfone as an intermediate and elemental selenium as a reactant is shown in reaction (45)[113].

$$Ph_2SO_2 \xrightarrow[300°]{Se} Ph_2Se + SO_2$$

(45)

3. The use of the complexes of heavy metal salts or oxides

Salts and oxides of heavy metals, most often Hg^{II}, Ag^{I}, and Pb^{II}, are selective reagents for the conversion of sulfur compounds. Mercuric chloride and acetate are the reagents most commonly used. Conversion of sulfides into ethers by this method is successful with compounds containing a fragment which is strongly stabilized by inductive or resonance effects, e.g. trityl sulfide (reaction 46)[36]. Most applications of

$$Ph_3CSC_6H_4CH_3\text{-}o \xrightarrow[CH_3OH]{HgCl_2} Ph_3COCH_3 + ClHgSC_6H_4CH_3\text{-}o \qquad (46)$$

the method have been for the conversion of mercaptals and mercaptols into acetals and ketals[114,115], glycosides[116], hemiacetals[117], or carbonyl compounds[118,119], according to the reaction conditions used. The reaction has often been used in sugar chemistry. The conversion of a mercaptal of an acetylated sugar into an acetal is effected by the action of mercuric chloride in methanol in the presence of HgO[115] or $CdCO_3$[114]; the latter bind the liberated hydrochloric acid. A methyl glycoside was formed from a sugar mercaptal by the action of $HgCl_2$ in methanol (reaction 47)[116]. In the molecule of a fully O-substituted

$$\begin{array}{cc}
CH(SC_2H_5)_2 & CH(OCH_3)_2 \\
| & | \\
CH_2 & CH_2 \\
| & | \\
CH_3COOCH & \xrightarrow[\substack{CdCO_3 \\ HgCl_2 \\ CH_3OH}]{} \quad CH_3COOCH \\
| & | \\
HCOCOCH_3 & HCOCOCH_3 \\
| & | \\
HCOCOCH_3 & HCOCOCH_3 \\
| & | \\
CH_2OCOCH_3 & CH_2OCOCH_3
\end{array} \qquad (47)$$

sugar mercaptol the carbonyl group was set free by the action of $HgCl_2$ in the presence of HgO in a methanol–pyridine mixture[118,119]. Mercuric chloride eliminated an alkylmercapto group from a thioglycoside with formation of a hemiacetal function[117]. According to the conditions used, thio S-esters react with $HgCl_2$ to give either a product of reesterification[120] or of hydrolysis[121]. This method has also found wide application in the conversion of thione compounds into carbonyl compounds, e.g. in thioamides[122–124], trithiocarbonates[125], or trithiones[126]. In these cases $HgCl_2$ is occasionally replaced by lead or silver nitrates[122] or lead oxide[123,124].

An analogous application of heavy metal salts for the conversion of selenium compounds of similar structures are based on their $HgCl_2$ complex formation ability[127].

IV. DISCUSSION OF SYNTHETIC METHODS

The synthetic methods presented in the preceding section can be discussed from several viewpoints. The fundamental factors which can affect the mutual conversion of ethers, organic sulfides, and selenides are the polarization of the bond to be broken, the ability of a particular carbon atom to change its hybridization, stereoelectronic effects, the special reaction mechanisms which may in some cases facilitate the conversion considerably, and also external factors which may influence the reaction. In addition to factors relevant to the molecule in which the bond is being broken, we also have to take into account the reactivity of the atom or group which forms the new bond.

The main criterion in the conversion of ethers into organic sulfides and selenides is usually the case of cleavage of the C—O bond; the reactivity of the sulfur- or selenium-containing component (i.e. its nucleophilicity in most cases) is high enough not to be the limiting factor.

The polarity of the C—O bond in ethers hardly ever approaches the degree which it has, for example, in esters of strong mineral or organic acids (sulfates, nitrates, and p-toluenesulfonates) and which makes the latter important alkylating agents. Therefore, it is usually necessary to use other means of facilitating the C—O bond fission.

In some cases a purely thermal noncatalyzed reaction occurs. The small number of known cases of conversion of ethers into sulfides under these conditions makes it desirable to refer to information from better known areas, such as the thermal rearrangement of esters of thio O-acids to esters of thio S-acids. An example is the rearrangement of esters of xanthogenic acids; for the present purpose, we refer to this reaction route and not to the other possible one, i.e. the Tchugaev reaction, which yields olefins by a cyclic elimination mechanism[128]. The current explanation of the rearrangement of esters of thio O-acids involves a C—O bond fission leading to a formation of an ion pair which recombines under C—S bond formation (reaction 48)[16]. A

$$Ph_2CHOCPh \longrightarrow \left[Ph_2\overset{+}{C}H \overset{\bar{O}}{\underset{S}{\diagdown}} CPh \right] \longrightarrow Ph_2CHSCPh \qquad (48)$$

similar course is possible for the reaction of benzyl 2-quinolyl ether with thiophenol[13]. Mechanisms of this kind are favored by the stability of the carbonium ion. The thermal rearrangement of diphenyl carbonate appears rather remarkable, and since it is difficult to assume formation of a $C_6H_5{}^+$ ion[17], this reaction probably follows a different pathway.

It is more usual to carry out the conversion of ethers into sulfides under conditions of thermolysis on the active surface of a catalyst such as Al_2O_3. Chemisorption may effectively change the electronic structure of the reacting species; it even permits conversion of furan into thiophene[29], involving fission of a C—O bond which forms part of a delocalized π-electron system. A similar far-reaching change in the π-electron system has to be assumed in the conversion of phenol into thiophenol[30].

Besides chemisorption, acid catalysis may be used to increase the C—O bond polarization. The formation of dialkylhydroxonium cations is facilitated by the relatively high basicity of ethers as compared with sulfides and selenides. For example the pK_a values of tetrahydrofuran and tetrahydrothiophene differ by 3·05 H_0 units[129]. The large difference in basicity makes it possible to find reaction conditions where the starting material is protonated but the reaction product is not. This practically removes the reversibility of the reaction, which has to be taken into account, in other reactions where the difference in the basicity of the starting and resulting molecules is negligible, e.g. in acid-catalyzed transesterification. Such conditions prevail if the catalyst is an acid with an anion of low nucleophilicity. In the case of hydrogen halides formation of at least some alkyl halide as an intermediate is not completely ruled out. The same effect on the polarization of the C—O bond which is obtained by catalysis with Brönsted acids is obtained by the use of Lewis acids, most often BF_3.

C—O bond fission in the conversion of ethers into sulfides and selenides is facilitated by stereoelectronic factors in the ether. The most important of these factors is the stability of species such as benzyl- or allylcarbonium ions. This is important in the first place for uncatalyzed thermal methods, as well as for acid-catalyzed reactions including the reaction with P_2S_5. The fission of the C—O bond in phenol ethers required for oxygen–sulphur conversion is relatively difficult. In this case also the reaction is facilitated by suitable substitution in the benzene ring, which favors aromatic nucleophilic substitution in general (e.g. by nitro groups in the *ortho* or *para* position).

In *O*-alkyltropolones the situation is much more favorable for the splitting of the C—O bond. The reaction is acid catalyzed, making use of the comparatively high basicity of the compound, and the protonated form is stabilized by the electronically favorable substituted tropylium ion structure; this cation is a good reaction partner for the nucleophilic agent. On the other hand, base-catalyzed reactions often lead to undesirable rearrangements of the tropolone skeleton and give rise to derivatives of benzoic acid[130].

Another interesting area in which the conversion of oxygen compounds into sulfur-containing ones was used successfully was the chemistry of heterocycles of the pyrone and pyrylium cation types. The conversion of γ-pyrone into γ-thiopyrone and of the pyrylium cation into the thiopyrylium cation aroused additional interest by involving systems isoelectronic with tropone and the tropylium ion, respectively. Even though these molecules have pseudoaromatic character and a fairly delocalized π-electron system, they are susceptible to nucleophilic attack by sulfydryl or hydroxyl ions, and by amines. The nucleophilic attack occurs at the 2- and 6-positions, in good agreement with quantum-mechanical models of pyrone and the pyrylium ion as given by the simple Hückel molecular-orbital method[131,132]. The 4-position, which is electronically preferred but is not involved in reactions of a simple pyrylium cation, becomes the reaction center in the 4-methoxypyrylium cation. Reactions discussed in connection with pyrones are related to reactions involved in the conversion of alkoxymethylene ketones, ethers, amides, acids, hydroxymethylene ketones, and the tautomeric formyl ketones into the corresponding alkylmercaptomethylene derivatives; these systems are vinylogous to esters or thioesters of carboxylic acids.

Epoxides present a favorable structure for conversion into sulfur compounds. Like β-propiolactone, they are highly reactive because of an I strain in a small ring. Whereas the formation of β-hydroxyethyl sulfides appears to follow a simple reaction course, the formation of an episulfide represents a rather complex system of consecutive reactions. The primary products of the reaction of epoxides with thiocyanate ions or with thiourea are stable in acidic media and episulfides are formed in alkaline media only. The nucleophilic attack at the other carbon center is preceded by migration, which has been proved to involve a cyclic intermediate (reaction 49)[43]. The formation of this cyclic intermediate needs special steric requirements, as shown by the difference in the behavior of cyclopentene oxide and cyclohexene oxide towards thiourea. Whereas the latter reacts in the usual manner to give the episulfide, the former gives an entirely different reaction product,

18 + C.E.L.

$$\text{(epoxide)} \xrightarrow{\text{SC(NH}_2)_2} \quad \longrightarrow \quad \text{C(NH}_2)_2 \quad \longrightarrow \quad \text{(episulfide)} \tag{49}$$

namely N-(2-hydroxycyclopentyl)thiourea, proving that the reaction mechanism is different[43]. The primary nucleophilic attack is usually stereospecific and occurs with inversion at the reaction center. Because of the rigidity of the five-membered ring in the case of cyclopentene oxide, the resulting structure is incapable of reaching the conformation required for the cyclic intermediate. The formation of the episulfide from the epoxide involves inversion of configuration at both reaction centers.

The conversion of ethers is facilitated by special reaction mechanisms. The elimination–addition mechanism, which is assumed to operate mainly in alkylations by Mannich bases, should be mentioned since it seems to present a useful general viewpoint[133]. Mannich bases are well-known C-, N-, O-, and S-alkylating agents[134]. In view of the prevailing opinions on the mechanism of these alkylations, the existence of a close analogy between the behavior of Mannich bases and that of their oxygen-containing analogs, the β-alkoxyethyl ketones, appears quite probable. Aldols are unsuitable for the study of this analogy because of the acidity of the hydroxyl group which results in retroaldol reaction in alkaline media. On the other hand, phenoxymethanols behave as phenolic Mannich bases[98,99]. The case of 2-acetoxy-1-nitropropane also supports the view that there is such a close analogy[97]. Other evidence which supports this analogy is the similarity of the Mannich reaction to the reaction used to synthetize β-ketosulfides. Unlike the Mannich reaction, the latter often depends for its success on accidental experimental circumstances, such as solubility relations and the ability of the product to crystallize, e.g. the condensation of acetonedicarboxylic acid diester with aldehyde and hydrogen sulfide in the presence of piperidine was successful only when the reaction product separated and thus shifted the complicated system of equilibria in the desired direction[135].

The conversion of sulfur or selenium compounds into oxygen compounds usually requires entirely different reaction conditions. This is due to several circumstances. The basicity of sulfur-containing compounds is substantially lower than that of the oxygen analogs. Therefore, successful catalysis by acids *a priori* places more rigorous requirements on reaction conditions. Another handicap is lower nucleophilicity of the oxygen-containing reaction partners in comparison with sulfur-containing ones. On the other hand, some other properties by which sulfur and selenium differ from oxygen, especially complex formation with heavy metal ions, can be used to attain a high enough C—S bond polarity for fission to become possible.

Effective polarization of the C—S bond can be effected by conversion of S^{II} into a higher oxidation state. While sulfones are usually stable compounds and have been used as intermediates for the conversion of sulfides into ethers only in special cases, the fission of the C—S bond in sulfoxides is in general relatively easy. In a similar way the C—S bond cleavage is facilitated by the formation of a S-bromosulfonium cation in the degradation of *t*-butyl sulfides and triphenylmethyl sulfides by bromine[112]. A similar effect is achieved by transforming the sulfide into a sulfonium salt; this method proved valuable for the splitting of the C—S bond in sulfur-containing analogs of Mannich bases. Since in basic media practically irreversible elimination occurs and leads to the formation of an α,β-unsaturated ketone, the successful use of this method for the sulfur–oxygen conversion is mainly a problem of finding the suitable reaction conditions and the proper oxygen-containing nucleophile[136].

The most effective and at the same time very selective method for the splitting of the C—S bond is based on the formation of complexes between organic compounds containing bivalent sulfur and heavy metal ions, especially Hg^{2+}. $HgCl_2$ complexes of S^{II}-containing compounds are usually insoluble compounds which may be isolated[137]; under more severe conditions, particularly at elevated temperatures, they decompose in two possible manners. Complexes of sulfides containing n-alkyl or s-alkyl groups revert to the starting components (e.g. on steam distillation). In complexes of sulfides with a tertiary alkyl group the C—S bond breaks in mercaptals and mercaptols and the resulting products are a halomercuric mercaptide (RSHgCl) and the corresponding oxygen-containing derivative whose exact nature depends on the properties of the oxygen-containing nucleophile present in the reaction medium. This reaction course is irreversible as the mercaptan remains strongly bonded in the insoluble RSHgCl salt and the oxygen-containing products do not react with $HgCl_2$ to form complexes which might facilitate fission of the newly formed C—O bond.

V. REFERENCES

1. L. Pauling, *The Nature of the Chemical Bond*, 3rd ed., Cornell University Press, Ithaca, New York, 1960.
2. L. N. Ferguson, *Electron Structures of Organic Molecules*, Prentice-Hall, New York, 1953.
3. R. C. Brasted, *Comprehensive Inorganic Chemistry*, Vol. 8, P. Van Nostrand Co., New York, 1961.
4. R. T. Sanderson, *Chemical Periodicity*, Reinhold Publ. Corp., New York, 1960.
5. R. Connor in *Organic Chemistry, an Advanced Treatise*, Vol. I (Ed. H. Gilman), John Wiley and Sons, New York, 1953, p. 835.
6. Ch. C. Price and S. Oae, *Sulfur Bonding*, The Ronald Press Comp., New York, 1962.
7. W. A. Pryor, *Mechanisms of Sulfur Reactions*, McGraw-Hill Book Co., New York, 1962.
8. N. Kharash (Ed.), *Organic Sulfur Compounds*, Vol. I, Pergamon Press, New York, 1961.
9. G. Cilento, *Chem. Rev.*, **60**, 147 (1960).
10. W. A. G. Graham and F. G. A. Stone, *Chem. Ind. (London)*, 319 (1956).
11. S. Ahrland, J. Chatt, N. R. Davies, and A. A. Williams, *J. Chem. Soc.*, 264 (1958).
12. J. O. Edwards and R. G. Pearson, *J. Am. Chem. Soc.*, **84**, 16 (1962).
13. G. Illuminatti and H. Gilman, *J. Am. Chem. Soc.*, **71**, 3349 (1949).
14. K. Freudenberg and A. Wolf, *Chem. Ber.*, **60**, 232 (1927).
15. J. W. Batty and B. C. L. Weedon, *J. Chem. Soc.*, 786 (1949).
16. S. G. Smith, *Tetrahedron Letters*, **21**, 979 (1962).
17. H. R. Al-Kazimi, D. S. Tarbell, and D. Plant, *J. Am. Chem. Soc.*, **77**, 2479 (1955).
18. H. O. Folkins and E. L. Miller, *Ind. Eng. Chem. Process Design Dev.*, **1**, 271 (1962).
19. P. Sabatier and A. Mailhe, *Compt. Rend.*, **150**, 823 (1910); **150**, 1217 (1910); **150**, 1569 (1910).
20. K. Bauer (to I. G. Farbenind, A. G.), *U.S. Pat.*, 2,116,182 (1938); *Chem. Abstr.*, **32**, 5002[5] (1938).
21. Yu. K. Yur'ev and M. Prokina, *Zh. Obshch. Khim.*, **7**, 1868 (1937).
22. Yu. K. Yur'ev, *Zh. Obshch. Khim.*, **8**, 1934 (1938).
23. Yu. K. Yur'ev, E. G. Rozancev, and S. N. Godovikova, *Zh. Obshch. Khim.*, **28**, 2168 (1958).
24. Yu. K. Yur'ev and O. M. Revenko, *Zh. Obshch. Khim.*, **31**, 1883 (1961).
25. Yu. K. Yur'ev, S. V. Djatlovickaja, and I. S. Levi, *Vestnik Mosk. Univ.*, 55 (1952).

26. Yu. K. Yur'ev, I. K. Korobicina and L. A. Savina, *Dokl. Akad. Nauk SSSR*, **86**, 91 (1952).
27. Yu. K. Yur'ev and E. G. Vendelstejn, *Zh. Obshch. Khim.*, **22**, 687 (1952).
28. R. F. Naylor, *J. Chem. Soc.*, 2749 (1949).
29. Yu. K. Yur'ev and V. A. Tronova, *Zh. Obshch. Khim.*, **10**, 31 (1940).
30. S. A. Ballard and D. E. Winkler (to Shell Development Co.), *U.S. Pat.*, 2,438,838 (1948); *Chem. Abstr.*, **42**, 4609d (1948).
31. Yu. K. Yur'ev and L. I. Chmelnickij, *Zh. Obshch. Khim.*, **23**, 1725 (1953).
32. D. J. Pasto, *J. Am. Chem. Soc.*, **84**, 3777 (1962).
33. E. A. Fehnel and M. Carmack, *J. Am. Chem. Soc.*, **71**, 84 (1949).
34. I. W. Ruderman and E. M. Fettes, *J. Am. Chem. Soc.*, **71**, 2264 (1949).
35. M. P. Balfe, J. Kenyon, amd C. E. Searle, *J. Chem. Soc.*, 3309 (1950).
36. D. C. Gregg, H. A. Iddles, and P. W. Stearus, Jr., *J. Org. Chem.*, **16**, 246 (1951).
37. Ch. Barkenbus and P. Pauzera, *J. Org. Chem.*, **20**, 237 (1955).
38. M. E. Cain, M. B. Evans, and D. F. Lee, *J. Chem. Soc.*, 1694 (1962).
39. R. C. Cline, R. M. Fink, and K. Fink, *J. Am. Chem. Soc.*, **81**, 2521 (1959).
40. A. G. Davies and A. M. White, *J. Chem. Soc.*, 3300 (1952).
41. M. P. Balfe, J. Kenyon, and E. M. Thain, *J. Chem. Soc.*, 790 (1952).
42. U. Schmidt and P. Grafen, *Chem. Ber.*, **92**, 1177 (1959).
43. (a) E. E. Van Tamelen, *J. Am. Chem. Soc.*, **73**, 3444 (1951); (b) F. G. Bordwell and H. M. Andersen, *J. Am. Chem. Soc.*, **75**, 4949 (1953).
44. V. F. Martynov and N. A. Rozepina, *Zh. Obshch. Khim.*, **22**, 1577 (1952).
45. A. R. Graham, A. F. Millidge, and D. P. Young, *J. Chem. Soc.*, 2180 (1954).
46. L. W. C. Miles and L. N. Owen, *J. Chem. Soc.*, 817 (1952).
47. D. C. Dittmer and M. E. Christy, *J. Org. Chem.*, **26**, 1324 (1961).
48. Ch. C. Price and P. F. Kirk, *J. Am. Chem. Soc.*, **75**, 2396 (1953).
49. C. C. J. Culvenor, W. Davies, and K. H. Pausacker, *J. Chem. Soc.*, 1050 (1946).
50. E. E. Van Tamelen, *Org. Syn.*, Coll. Vol. IV, 232 (1963).
51. M. Delepine and P. Jaffeux, *Bull. Soc. Chim. France*, **27**, 740 (1920); **29**, 136 (1921).
52. W. Coltof (to Shell Development Co.), *U.S. Pat.*, 2,183,860 (1939); *Chem. Abstr.*, **34**, 2395³ (1940).
53. M. Delepine and P. Jaffeux, *Compt. Rend.*, **172**, 158 (1921).
54. D. D. Reynolds, M. K. Massad, D. L. Fields, and D. L. Johnson, *J. Org. Chem.*, **26**, 5109 (1961).
55. S. Searles, Jr., and E. F. Lutz, *J. Am. Chem. Soc.*, **80**, 3168 (1958).
56. T. L. Gresham, J. E. Jansen, F. W. Shaver, R. A. Bankert, W. L. Beears, and M. G. Prendergast, *J. Am. Chem. Soc.*, **71**, 661 (1949).
57. J. W. Cook, J. D. Loudon, and D. K. V. Steel, *J. Chem. Soc.*, 530 (1954).
58. T. Nozoe, M. Sato, and K. Matsui, *J. Chem. Soc. Japan*, **73**, 781 (1952); *Proc. Japan. Acad.*, **29**, 22 (1953).
59. G. Muller, B. P. Vaterlaus, and L. Velusz, *Bull. Soc. Chim. France*, 434 (1957).
60. S. S. Gitis, *USSR Pat.*, 137,925; *Chem. Abstr.*, **56**, 8638d.
61. R. Mayer, *Chem. Tech. (Berlin)*, **10**, 418 (1958).
62. W. J. Croxall, L. R. Freimiller, and E. Y. Shropshire, *J. Am. Chem. Soc.*, **72**, 4275 (1950).

63. H. Behringer and H. Weissauer, *Chem. Ber.*, **85**, 774 (1952).
64. R. E. Ireland and I. A. Marshall, *Chem. Ind. (London)*, 1534 (1960).
65. G. V. Boyd, *J. Chem. Soc.*, 55 (1959).
66. R. M. Anker and A. H. Cook, *J. Chem. Soc.*, 117 (1946).
67. R. F. Naylor, *J. Chem. Soc.*, 1532 (1947).
68. A. J. Kretov and J. F. Kommisarov, *Zh. Obshch. Khim.*, **5**, 388 (1935).
69. K. Kindler, *Ann. Chem.*, **431**, 187 (1923).
70. G. N. Jean and F. F. Nord, *J. Org. Chem.*, **20**, 1363 (1955).
71. Buu-Hoï and Nguyen-Hoán, *Rec. Trav. Chim.*, **67**, 309 (1948).
72. D. S. Tarbell, H. P. Hirschler, and R. B. Carlin, *J. Am. Chem. Soc.*, **72**, 3138 (1950).
73. H. Paul, *Chem. Ber.*, **93**, 2395 (1960).
74. A. I. Meyers, *J. Org. Chem.*, **25**, 1147 (1960).
75. A. A. Pavlic, W. A. Lazier, and F. K. Signaigo, *J. Org. Chem.*, **14**, 61 (1949).
76. R. A. Baxter, G. T. Newbold, and F. S. Spring, *J. Chem. Soc.*, 370 (1947).
77. M. F. Shostakovskiĭ, A. V. Bogdanova, G. I. Plotnikova, and A. N. Dolgikh, *Izv. Akad. Nauk SSSR, Otd. Khim. Nauk*, 1901 (1960).
78. W. E. Parham and D. M. DeLaitsch, *J. Am. Chem. Soc.*, **76**, 4962 (1954).
79. T. L. Cairus, G. L. Evans, A. W. Larcher, and B. C. McKusick, *J. Am. Chem. Soc.*, **74**, 3982 (1952).
80. M. W. Cronyn and E. Zavarin, *J. Org. Chem.*, **19**, 139 (1954).
81. M. L. Wolfrom and R. L. Brown, *J. Am. Chem. Soc.*, **63**, 1336 (1941).
82. H. Fiesselmann and F. Thoma, *Chem. Ber.*, **89**, 1907 (1956).
83. (a) E. Campaigne and R. Moss, *J. Am. Chem. Soc.*, **76**, 1269 (1954);
    (b) E. Campaigne and J. R. Leal. *J. Am. Chem. Soc.*, **76**, 1272 (1954).
84. L. Bateman and R. W. Glazebrook, *J. Chem. Soc.*, 2836 (1958).
85. W. E. Parham and J. D. Jones, *J. Am. Chem. Soc.*, **76**, 1068 (1954).
86. R. W. Bost and E. W. Constable, *Org. Syn.*, Coll. Vol. II, p. 610, 1943.
87. J. A. Stanfield and L. B. Reynolds, Jr., *J. Am. Chem. Soc.*, **74**, 2878 (1952).
88. G. F. Grillot, H. R. Felton, B. R. Garrett, H. Greenberg, R. Green, R. Clementi, and M. Moskowitz, *J. Am. Chem. Soc.*, **76**, 3969 (1954).
89. D. Collins and J. Graymore, *J. Chem. Soc.*, 4089 (1953).
90. H. Böhme, K. Dietz and K.-D. Leidreiter, *Arch. Pharm.*, **287**, 198 (1954).
91. (a) T. G. Pearson, R. H. Purcell, and G. S. Saigh, *J. Chem. Soc.*, 415 (1938);
    (b) H. J. Bridger and R. W. Pittman, *J. Chem. Soc.*, 1371 (1950).
92. R. E. Lyons and W. E. Brandt, *Chem. Ber.*, **60**, 824 (1927).
93. J. Loevenich, H. Fremdling, and M. Föhr, *Chem. Ber.*, **62**, 2857 (1929).
94. Q. Mingoia, *Gazz. Chim. Ital.*, **58**, 672 (1928).
95. D. T. Lewis, *J. Chem. Soc.*, 832 (1940).
96. K. Glen and R. Schaarschmidt, *Chem. Ber.*, **72**, 1252 (1939).
97. C. A. Grob and H. von Sprecher, *Helv. Chim. Acta*, **35**, 885, 902 (1952).
98. E. Ziegler and H. Lüdde, *Monatsh. Chem.*, **79**, 316 (1948).
99. U. Schmidt and G. Giesselmann, *Ann. Chem.*, **657**, 162 (1962).
100. R. H. Martin and J. Mathieu, *Tetrahedron*, **1**, 75 (1957).
101. F. H. S. Curd, M. I. Davis, E. C. Owen, F. L. Rose, and G. A. P. Tuey, *J. Chem. Soc.*, 370 (1946).
102. R. M. Dodson, E. R. Peterson, and J. K. Seyler, *J. Am. Chem. Soc.*, **72**, 3281 (1950).

103. J. Romo, M. Romero, C. Djerassi, and G. Rosenkranz, *J. Am. Chem. Soc.*, **73**, 1528 (1951).
104. G. H. Hitchings, G. B. Elion, E. A. Falco, and P. B. Russel, *J. Biol. Chem.*, **177**, 357 (1949).
105. C. W. Noel and R. K. Robins, *J. Am. Chem. Soc.*, **81**, 5997 (1959).
106. J. G. Nairn and H. Tieckelmann, *J. Org. Chem.*, **25**, 1127 (1960).
107. H. Kloosterziel, W. van der Ween, and H. J. Backer, *Rec. Trav. Chim.*, **71**, 1231 (1952).
108. (a) R. Kuhn, W. Baschang-Bister, and W. Dafeldecker, *Ann. Chem.*, **641**, 160 (1961); (b) R. Kuhn and F. A. Neugebauer, *Chem. Ber.*, **94**, 2629 (1961).
109. F. Weygand and H. J. Bestmann, *Chem. Ber.*, **90**, 1230 (1957).
110. L. Katz and H. S. Cohen, *J. Org. Chem.*, **19**, 767 (1954).
111. E. C. Taylor, O. Vogel, and C. C. Cheng, *J. Am. Chem. Soc.*, **81**, 2442 (1959).
112. C. R. Strauss, H. G. Guay, and H. J. Harwood, *J. Org. Chem.*, **29**, 1945 (1964).
113. N. M. Cullinane, N. M. E. Morgan, and C. A. I. Plummer, *Rec. Trav. Chim.* **56**, 629 (1937).
114. (a) H. R. Bolliger, *Helv. Chim. Acta*, **34**, 989 (1951); (b) H. R. Bolliger and M. D. Schmid, *Helv. Chim. Acta*, **34**, 1597 (1951).
115. D. L. MacDonald and H. G. Fletcher, Jr., *J. Am. Chem. Soc.*, **81**, 3719, (1959).
116. H. Zinner, K. Wessely, and H. Kristen, *Chem. Ber.*, **92**, 1618 (1959).
117. M. L. Wolfrom and Z. Yosizawa, *J. Am. Chem. Soc.*, **81**, 3477 (1959).
118. E. Pascu and J. W. Green, *J. Am. Chem. Soc.*, **58**, 1823 (1936).
119. O. T. Dalley and R. J. McIlroy, *J. Chem. Soc.*, 555 (1949).
120. A. F. Ferris and B. A. Schutz, *J. Org. Chem.*, **28**, 71 (1963).
121. L. B. Bos and J. A. Arens, *Rec. Trav. Chim.*, **82**, 339 (1963).
122. J. Goerdeler and H. Horstmann, *Chem. Ber.*, **93**, 671 (1960).
123. A. R. Katritzky, *J. Chem. Soc.*, 2586 (1955).
124. T. S. Gardner, E. Wenis, and J. Lee, *J. Org. Chem.*, **19**, 753 (1954).
125. C. G. Overberger and P. V. Bonsignore, *J. Am. Chem. Soc.*, **80**, 5427 (1958).
126. B. Böttcher, *Chem. Ber.*, **81**, 376 (1948).
127. F. Challenger and H. E. North, *J. Chem. Soc.*, 68 (1934).
128. G. L. Connor and H. R. Nace, *J. Am. Chem. Soc.*, **74**, 5454 (1952).
129. E. M. Arnett and Ch. Y. Wu, *J. Am. Chem. Soc.*, **84**, 1680 (1962).
130. T. Nozoe in *Non-Benzenoid Aromatic Compounds* (Ed. D. Ginsburg), Interscience Publishers, New York, 1959, Chap. VII, pp. 407 ff.
131. R. Zahradník, C. Parkányi, and J. Koutecký, *Collection Czech. Chem. Commun.*, **27**, 1242 (1962).
132. R. Zahradník and J. Koutecký, *Collection Czech. Chem. Commun.*, **28**, 1120 (1963).
133. V. Horák and P. Zuman, *Collection Czech. Chem. Commun.*, **26**, 173 (1961).
134. H. Hellmann and G. Opitz, *β-Aminoalkylierung*, Verlag Chemie, Weinheim, 1960.
135. V. Horák and M. Černý, *Collection Czech. Chem. Commun.*, **18**, 379 (1953).
136. V. Horák, *Collection Czech. Chem. Commun.*, **28**, 1614 (1963).
137. F. Challenger, *Aspects of the Organic Chemistry of Sulphur*, Butterworths, London, 1959, pp. 16, 78.

CHAPTER **13**

The chemistry of thioethers; differences and analogies with ethers

L. BRANDSMA and J. F. ARENS

University of Utrecht, Holland

18*

I. INTRODUCTION

In this chapter the principal differences between the chemical behavior of ethers and thioethers are outlined. Most attention has been paid to the synthetic aspects. Because of the scope of the review the chemistry of thiophen and other cyclic sulfur compounds has not been considered. More extensive treatises on the chemistry of sulfur compounds are given in *Organic Chemistry of Bivalent Sulfur*, by E. E. Reid, in Houben–Weil, *Methoden der organischen Chemie: Schwefel-, Selen- und Tellur-verbindungen* and in *Organic Chemistry of Sulfur Compounds*, edited by N. Kharash.

II. REACTIONS INVOLVING CARBANIONS DERIVED FROM THIOETHERS

The presence of alkyl- or arylthio groups has a marked influence on the acidity of α-hydrogen atoms. These hydrogen atoms are much more easily split off as protons by bases than those in the α position relative to alkoxy or aryloxy groups. In some cases the abstraction of a proton may lead to a stable carbanion, but in many reactions an anionic group is eliminated from either a β carbon with formation of a double or triple bond, or from the same carbon leading to a carbene or from a γ-carbon atom with formation of a cyclopropane derivative. Prototropic isomerizations and condensation reactions also take place more easily with compounds in which hydrogen atoms are activated by thioether groups rather than by oxygen ether groups.

Many investigators consider the activating influence of thioether groups on α-hydrogens as evidence for the participation of the d orbitals of sulfur in anion stabilization; this means that the sulfur atom accommodates a decet of electrons[1]. For an oxygen atom such an expansion of the number of electrons in the valence shell is highly unfavorable. Indeed an explanation for the different behavior of sulfur compounds and their oxygen analogs towards basic reagents on the grounds of this theory seems to be the most satisfying, but in a number of other reactions a different kind of 'activation' may be considered (compare with section II.B). In this section we shall review the conversions of thioethers which can be regarded as being caused by 'activation' of hydrogen atoms by sulfur-containing groups.

A. Formation of and Conversions with Stable Carbanions

The formation of stable carbanions by abstraction of protons with the aid of bases is a well-known reaction. From the many examples we mention the formation of the diphenylmethide ion $((C_6H_5)_2\bar{C}H)$ from diphenylmethane $((C_6H_5)_2CH_2)$ and potassium amide in liquid ammonia[2], the formation of the anions $\bar{C}H_2COCH_3$ and $\bar{C}H_2COO$-t-C_4H_9 from acetone and t-butyl acetate, respectively, and alkali amides in liquid ammonia[3,5] (compare with reference 4). The hydrogen in malonic esters, e.g. $CH_2(COOC_2H_5)_2$, is readily split off by sodium ethoxide in alcohol with formation of the anion $\bar{C}H(COOC_2H_5)_2$. In all these compounds groups are present which can, by their electron-accepting properties, facilitate the abstraction of hydrogen and stabilize the carbanions formed by resonance.

There are no clear indications that the sulfur atom in ordinary dialkyl thioethers, e.g. $(C_2H_5)_2S$, has an influence on the reactivity of the α-hydrogen atoms towards strong bases, such as butyllithium or potassium amide. With aryl alkyl thioethers, e.g. $C_6H_5SCH_2CH_3$, and butyllithium in ether both *nuclear* metalation and substitution of an α-hydrogen of the alkyl group by lithium can take place[6]. Phenyl methyl thioether, $C_6H_5SCH_3$, is metalated only in the methyl group by butyllithium, while anisole $(C_6H_5OCH_3)$ gives a nuclear metalation product[7,8]. The solution of the metalated thioether can be converted with carbon dioxide (reaction 1). Other metalating reagents, e.g. $(C_2H_5)_2Sr$[6], are less specific in their reaction with phenyl methyl thioether.

$$C_6H_5SCH_3 + C_4H_9Li \longrightarrow C_6H_5SCH_2Li \xrightarrow{CO_2} C_6H_5SCH_2COOLi \qquad (1)$$

Recently it has been found, that when two or three alkylthio groups are present at the same carbon atom, like in thioacetals $(CH_2(SR)_2)$ and esters of thioorthoformic acids $(HC(SR)_3$ where R is alkyl or phenyl), hydrogen atoms attached to the same carbon are easily abstracted as protons. Thus solutions of the carbanions $\bar{C}H(SR)_2$ and $\bar{C}(SR)_3$ are obtained when the compounds are added to equivalent quantities of alkali amides in liquid ammonia[9-11]. The analogous oxygen compounds remain unchanged under these conditions.

The solutions of the carbanions, which have a greenish or brown colour, show a much higher electric conductivity than the alkali amide suspensions or solutions. Alkylation with primary and secondary alkyl halides is possible (reactions 2 and 3).

$$CH_2(SR^1)_2 + NH_2^- \xrightarrow[\text{Liq. NH}_3]{} {}^-CH(SR^1)_2 \xrightarrow[\text{Liq. NH}_3]{R^2Br} R^2CH(SR^1)_2 \qquad (2)$$

$$CH(SR^1)_3 + NH_2^- \xrightarrow{} {}^-C(SR^1)_3 \xrightarrow{R^2Br} R^2C(SR^1)_3 \qquad (3)$$

The strong nucleophilicity of the carbanions is demonstrated by their smooth reaction with bromoacetal ($BrCH_2CH(OC_2H_5)_2$)[12,13], a compound which is known to be much less reactive towards nucleophiles than alkyl halides (compare with reference 14).

The relative stability of the solutions of the carbanions may be attributed to resonance in which the sulfur atom attains a decet of electrons (reaction 4).

$$(4)$$

The easy *formation* of the carbanions is probably also due to electron acceptance by the sulfur atom: in the transition state the energy of activation of the hydrogen abstraction is lowered, because the sulfur atom assists in the uptake of the lone pair of electrons. The result cannot be due to the inductive ($-I$) effect, because then the highest acidity of the hydrogen atoms would be expected in the oxygen acetals ($CH_2(OR)_2$) and orthoformic esters ($HC(OR)_3$).

Formaldehyde diethylselenoacetal ($CH_2(SeR)_2$) can also be metalated and subsequently alkylated[15]. The metalation, however, only proceeds with potassium amide and even then rather slowly. This lower reactivity may be caused by the very low solubility of the selenoacetal in liquid ammonia.

Another type of stable carbanion is formed from 1-alkynyl thioethers ($R^1CH_2C\equiv CSR^2$) and allenyl thioethers ($R^1CH=C=CHSR^2$) with sodamide or lithium amide in liquid ammonia[16-18]. Probably in these cases also resonance stabilization plays an important role. Both types of compounds produce the same (mesomeric) anions. Hydrolysis of the solutions gives almost pure allenyl thioethers. The carbanions are extremely reactive towards alkyl halides and bromoacetal. Even with n-decyl bromide, which does not react with sodium alkynylides ($RC\equiv CNa$) in liquid ammonia because of its slight solubility, a smooth conversion takes place. The alkylation leads to allenyl thioethers which have the alkyl group introduced on the α-carbon atom.

The carbanions which have lithium as a cation react with ketones to give the carbinols.

Scheme 1 can be used to illustrate the conversions mentioned.

Very probably the acidity of the α-hydrogen atom in the allenyl thioethers ($R^1CH=C=CHSR^2$) is greater than that of the γ-hydrogen atoms in the isomeric 1-alkynyl thioethers ($R^1CH_2C\equiv CSR^2$) because the allenyl thioether is more readily converted into the carbanion with lithium amide $LiNH_2$ than the 1-alkynyl thioether.

A useful application of the allenyl thioethers is in the synthesis of enynes ($HC\equiv CCH=CH—$) outlined in Scheme 2[17,18]. The starting product 1-ethylthio-1-butyne ($CH_3CH_2C\equiv CSC_2H_5$) can easily be prepared from sodium acetylide ($NaC\equiv CH$), ethyl bromide and sulfur[19,20] in liquid ammonia, in an overall yield of greater than 50%.

The elimination of ethanethiol from the allenyl thioether derivatives possibly proceeds through the cumulenes $CH_2=C=C=CHR$ or $CH_2=C=C=CHCR^1R^2OH$, the anions of which isomerize to the metalated enyne derivatives.

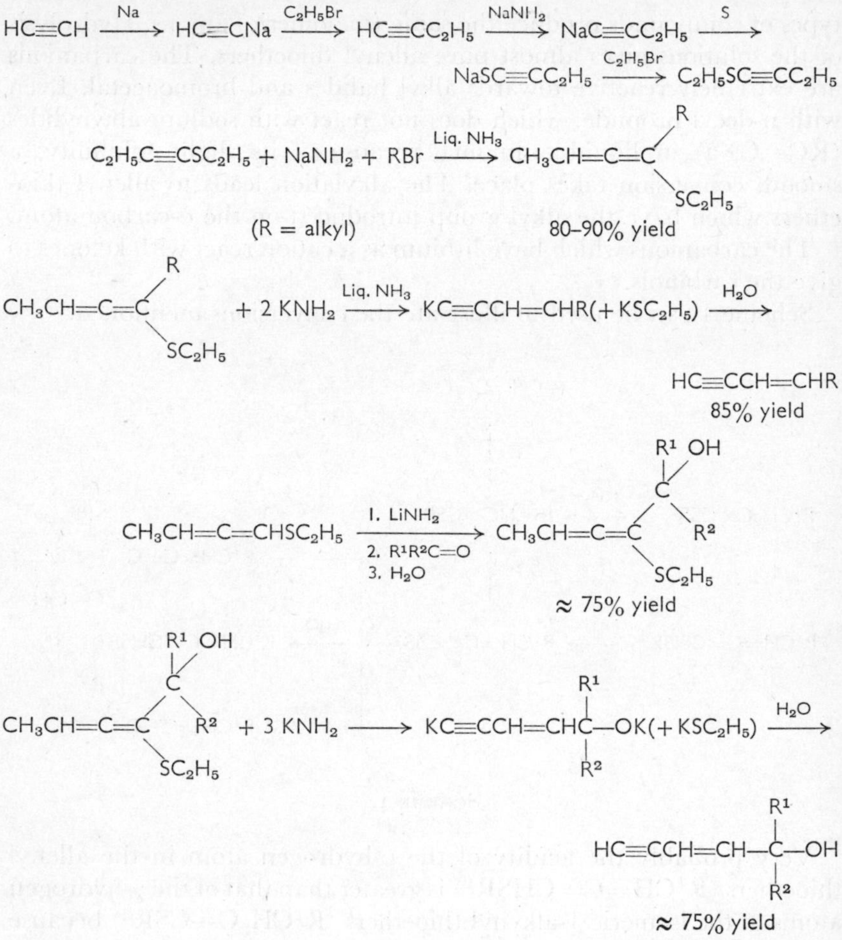

$$HC{\equiv}CH \xrightarrow{Na} HC{\equiv}CNa \xrightarrow{C_2H_5Br} HC{\equiv}CC_2H_5 \xrightarrow{NaNH_2} NaC{\equiv}CC_2H_5 \xrightarrow{S}$$

$$NaSC{\equiv}CC_2H_5 \xrightarrow{C_2H_5Br} C_2H_5SC{\equiv}CC_2H_5$$

$$C_2H_5C{\equiv}CSC_2H_5 + NaNH_2 + RBr \xrightarrow{Liq.\ NH_3} CH_3CH{=}C{\overset{R}{\underset{SC_2H_5}{\diagup\diagdown}}}$$

(R = alkyl)   80–90% yield

$$CH_3CH{=}C{\overset{R}{\underset{SC_2H_5}{\diagup\diagdown}}} + 2\ KNH_2 \xrightarrow{Liq.\ NH_3} KC{\equiv}CCH{=}CHR(+ KSC_2H_5) \xrightarrow{H_2O}$$

HC≡CCH=CHR
85% yield

$$CH_3CH{=}C{=}CHSC_2H_5 \xrightarrow[\substack{2.\ R^1R^2C{=}O \\ 3.\ H_2O}]{1.\ LiNH_2} CH_3CH{=}C{\overset{\overset{R^1\ OH}{\diagup\diagdown}}{\underset{SC_2H_5}{\diagup\diagdown}}}{}^{R^2}$$

≈ 75% yield

$$CH_3CH{=}C{\overset{\overset{R^1\ OH}{C}}{\underset{SC_2H_5}{\diagup\diagdown}}}{}^{R^2} + 3\ KNH_2 \longrightarrow KC{\equiv}CCH{=}CHC{\overset{R^1}{\underset{R^2}{\mid}}}{-}OK(+ KSC_2H_5) \xrightarrow{H_2O}$$

$$HC{\equiv}CCH{=}CH{-}C{\overset{R^1}{\underset{R^2}{\mid}}}{-}OH$$

≈ 75% yield

SCHEME 2.

The reactions of the ethers $R^1CH_2C{\equiv}COR^2$ and $R^1CH{=}C{=}CHOR^2$ with alkali amides in liquid ammonia are quite different from those of the sulfur analogs.

Propynyl ethers ($CH_3C{\equiv}COR^2$) and also the isomers $CH_2{=}C{=}CHOR$ are completely converted into propargyl ethers (reaction 5)[21].

$$CH_3C{\equiv}COR + NH_2{}^- \longrightarrow [\bar{C}H_2C{\equiv}COR \longleftrightarrow CH_2{=}C{=}\bar{C}OR] \longrightarrow$$

$$[\bar{C}H{=}C{=}CHOR \longleftrightarrow HC{\equiv}C\bar{C}HOR] \longrightarrow \bar{C}{\equiv}CCH_2OR \xrightarrow{H_2O} HC{\equiv}CCH_2OR$$

(5)

In contrast to the allenyl thioethers the allenyl ethers do not form anions of the type $R^1CH{=}C{=}\bar{C}OR^2$, since the electrical conductivity of suspensions of alkali amides in liquid ammonia does not rise after addition of $(CH_3)_3CCH{=}C{=}CHOR$. Furthermore this compound cannot be alkylated[22]. 1-Alkynyl ethers with at least two hydrogen atoms in the γ position and at least one in the δ position, e.g. $C_2H_5CH_2CH_2C{\equiv}COC_2H_5$, and allenyl ethers possessing at least one δ-hydrogen atom, e.g. $(CH_3)_2CHCH{=}C{=}CHOC_2H_5$, give 3,1-cnynes on treatment with two equivalents of potassium amide, probably through the sequence of reactions shown by Scheme 3, involving a 1,4-elimination[23, 24].

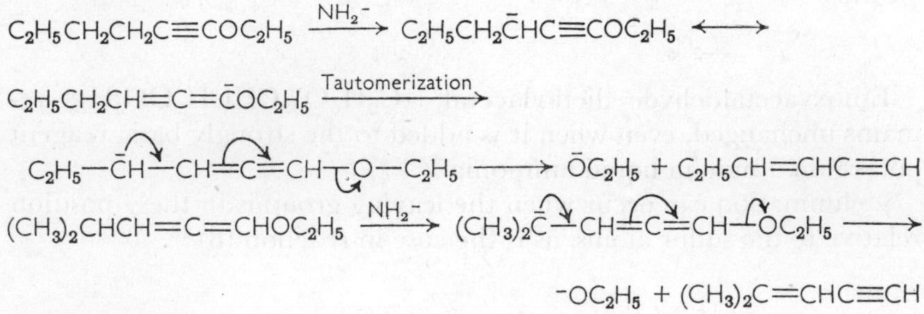

$$C_2H_5CH_2CH_2C{\equiv}COC_2H_5 \xrightarrow{NH_2^-} C_2H_5CH_2\bar{C}HC{\equiv}COC_2H_5 \longleftrightarrow$$

$$C_2H_5CH_2CH{=}C{=}\bar{C}OC_2H_5 \xrightarrow{\text{Tautomerization}}$$

$$C_2H_5{-}\bar{C}H{-}CH{=}C{=}CH{-}O{-}C_2H_5 \longrightarrow \bar{O}C_2H_5 + C_2H_5CH{=}CHC{\equiv}CH$$

$$(CH_3)_2CHCH{=}C{=}CHOC_2H_5 \xrightarrow{NH_2^-} (CH_3)_2\bar{C}{-}CH{=}C{=}CH{-}OC_2H_5 \longrightarrow$$

$$^-OC_2H_5 + (CH_3)_2C{=}CHC{\equiv}CH$$

SCHEME 3.

The first enyne is formed in moderate yields, together with ethyl caproate $(C_5H_{11}COOC_2H_5)$, caproic amide $(C_5H_{11}CONH_2)$ and caproic acid $(C_5H_{11}COOH)$. The by-products probably arise from the hydrolysis of a product formed by base-catalyzed addition of ammonia to the 1-alkynyl ether.

The second enyne is obtained in an excellent yield.

B. Elimination Reactions Attributable to the Activating Influence of Thioether Groups

Elimination of hydrogen and another group takes place with much more ease when the hydrogen atom is in the α position with respect to a sulfur atom than when it is in the α position with respect to an oxygen atom.

2-Hydroxyethyl alkyl thioethers $(HOCH_2CH_2SR)$, when treated with solid potassium hydroxide at $250°$, are converted into vinyl alkyl thioethers $(CH_2{=}CHSR)$, whereas the 2-hydroxy ethers are stable under these conditions (reaction 6)[25].

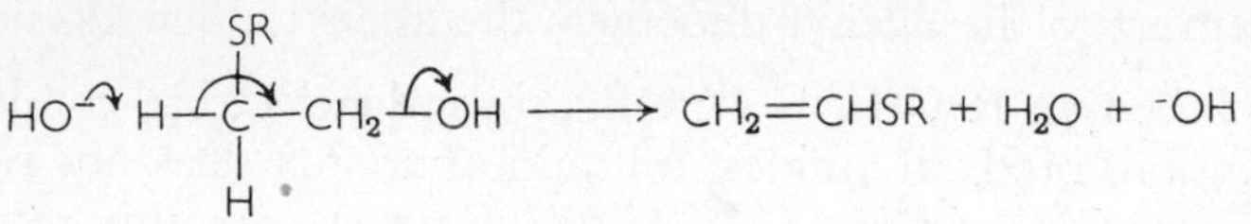

$$\text{HO}^{\curvearrowright}\text{H}-\overset{\overset{\displaystyle \text{SR}}{|}}{\underset{\underset{\displaystyle \text{H}}{|}}{\text{C}}}-\text{CH}_2\overset{\curvearrowleft}{}\text{OH} \longrightarrow \text{CH}_2{=}\text{CHSR} + \text{H}_2\text{O} + {}^-\text{OH} \qquad (6)$$

Ethanethiol is split off from ethylthioacetaldehyde diethylthioacetal, when this compound is heated with potassium butoxide[26]: as expected, the hydrogen atom, which is in the α position to *two* geminal ethylthio groups and which is thus more strongly activated than the methylene hydrogen atoms, is eliminated (reaction 7).

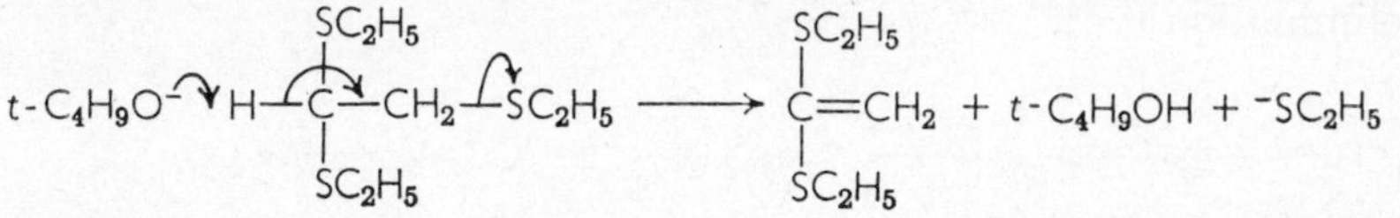

$$t\text{-}\text{C}_4\text{H}_9\text{O}^{\curvearrowright}\text{H}-\overset{\overset{\displaystyle \text{SC}_2\text{H}_5}{|}}{\underset{\underset{\displaystyle \text{SC}_2\text{H}_5}{|}}{\text{C}}}-\text{CH}_2\overset{\curvearrowleft}{}\text{SC}_2\text{H}_5 \longrightarrow \overset{\overset{\displaystyle \text{SC}_2\text{H}_5}{|}}{\underset{\underset{\displaystyle \text{SC}_2\text{H}_5}{|}}{\text{C}}}{=}\text{CH}_2 + t\text{-}\text{C}_4\text{H}_9\text{OH} + {}^-\text{SC}_2\text{H}_5 \quad (7)$$

Ethoxyacetaldehyde diethylacetal $((\text{C}_2\text{H}_5\text{O})_2\text{CHCH}_2\text{OC}_2\text{H}_5)$ remains unchanged, even when it is added to the strongly basic reagent potassium amide in liquid ammonia[27].

γ elimination can occur when the leaving group is in the γ position relative to the sulfur atoms, as is the case in reaction (8)[28].

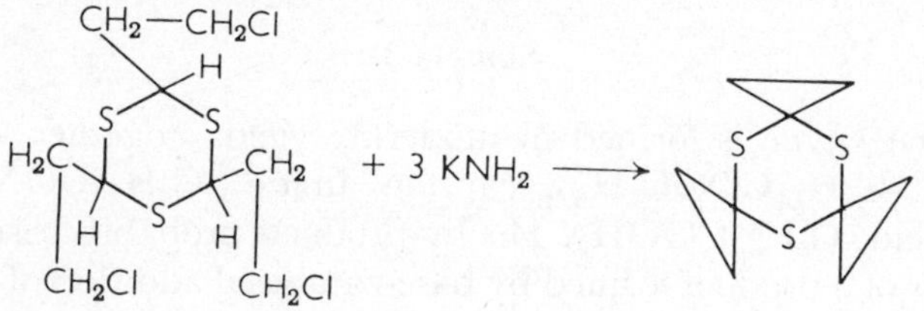

$$+\ 3\ \text{KNH}_2 \longrightarrow \qquad\qquad (8)$$

As mentioned in section II.A, orthothioesters $(\text{HC}(\text{SR})_3)$ form relatively stable carbanions with alkali amides in liquid ammonia; these carbanions can be alkylated. On standing the carbanions split off thiolate with formation of tetrakisalkylthio- or arylthioethene. Carbenes $(\text{:}\text{C}(\text{SR})_2)$ are thought[9,11] to be formed in the α elimination of the thiol. Scheme 4 may explain the phenomena most satisfactorily[9,11].

$$\text{HC}(\text{SR})_3 \xrightarrow{\text{NH}_2^-} {}^-\bar{\text{C}}(\text{SR})_3 \xrightarrow{-\bar{\text{S}}\text{R}} \text{:}\text{C}(\text{SR})_2$$

$$\bar{\text{C}}(\text{SR})_3 + \text{:}\text{C}(\text{SR})_2 \longrightarrow (\text{RS})_3\text{C}{-}\bar{\text{C}}(\text{SR})_2 \xrightarrow{-\bar{\text{S}}\text{R}} (\text{RS})_2\text{C}{=}\text{C}(\text{SR})_2$$

SCHEME 4.

1,2-Bis(-alkylthio- or -arylthio-)alkenes ($RSCH=CHSR$) react with sodamide in liquid ammonia or with butyllithium in ether, whereas the corresponding ethers are not attacked by these reagents (reactions 9 and 9a) [29-31].

$$RSCH=CHSR + 2\,NaNH_2 \longrightarrow NaSR + 2\,NH_3 + NaC\equiv CSR \qquad (9)$$

$$RSCH=CHSR + 2\,C_4H_9Li \longrightarrow LiSR + 2\,C_4H_{10} + LiC\equiv CSR \qquad (9a)$$

Treatment of 1-ethoxy-2-ethylthioethylene with butyllithium gives rise to the elimination of alcohol rather than thiol (reaction 10) [31].

$$C_2H_5OCH=CHSC_2H_5 + 2\,C_4H_9Li \longrightarrow LiC\equiv CSC_2H_5 + LiOC_2H_5 + 2\,C_4H_{10} \quad (10)$$

The fact that the latter compound does not react with sodamide in liquid ammonia (but only with the stronger base butyllithium), while 1,2-bis(ethylthio)ethylene is smoothly converted by sodamide, suggests that not only α-, but also β-alkylthio groups, have a certain influence upon the 'acidity' of hydrogen atoms. This type of reaction is analogous to the 1,2-elimination of hydrogen halide from vinyl halides ($CH_2=CHCl$) upon treatment with base.

Possibly such an influence may also be considered in the case of the elimination illustrated by reaction (11). Hydrolysis of the reaction mixture gives the diyne ($HC\equiv CC\equiv CR$) in excellent yields [32].

$$RC\equiv CCH=CHSC_2H_5 + 2\,NaNH_2 \xrightarrow{\text{Liq. NH}_3} NaSC_2H_5 + NaC\equiv CC\equiv CR + 2\,NH_3 \quad (11)$$

The enyne ethers ($CH_3C\equiv CCH=CHOC_2H_5$) are isomerized by the same procedure, the isomers being obtained in excellent yields (reaction 12) [32]. The homologs, e.g. $C_2H_5C\equiv CCH=CHOC_2H_5$, are

$$CH_3C\equiv CCH=CHOC_2H_5 + NaNH_2 \longrightarrow NaC\equiv CCH=CHCH_2OC_2H_5 \xrightarrow{H_2O}$$
$$HC\equiv CCH=CHCH_2OC_2H_5 \quad (12)$$

converted into tarry products, and only traces of the elimination product ($C_2H_5C\equiv CC\equiv CH$) have been isolated [33].

Vinyl ethyl thioether ($CH_2=CHSC_2H_5$) reacts with potassium amide with formation of thiolate and acetylide (reaction 13) [34]. This

$$CH_2=CHSC_2H_5 + 2\,KNH_2 \xrightarrow{\text{Liq. NH}_3} KC\equiv CH + KSC_2H_5 + NH_3 \qquad (13)$$

elimination is analogous to the elimination of HCl from vinyl chloride ($CH_2=CHCl$). The ether $CH_2=CHOC_2H_5$ does not react. The same elimination takes place with ketene thioacetal (reaction 14) [35].

$$CH_2=C(SC_2H_5)_2 + 2\,KNH_2 \longrightarrow KC\equiv CSC_2H_5 + KSC_2H_5 \qquad (14)$$

Unfortunately a comparison with the behavior of ketene acetal (CH_2=$C(OC_2H_5)_2$) is impossible, because this compound reacts with the solvent liquid ammonia.

Interesting differences emerge on comparing the behavior of ethers of butynediol towards bases with that of the analogous thioethers.

Enyne thioethers (RSC≡CCH=CH_2) (compare with reference 46) are formed by the action of sodium ethoxide in liquid ammonia on the bisthioethers of butynediol. Probably a 1,4-elimination of hydrogen and ^-SR takes place first, the intermediate cumulenic thioethers then undergo a prototropic conversion into the enyne thioethers. The first step in this isomerization is the abstraction of the α-hydrogen atom (reaction 15a) (compare section II.C).

$$RS-CH-C\equiv C-CH_2-SR \longrightarrow$$

$$\quad\quad\quad\quad H$$

$$\quad\quad\quad ^-OC_2H_5$$

$$[RSCH{=}C{=}C{=}CH_2] \xrightarrow[\text{conversion}]{\text{Prototropic}} RSC{\equiv}CCH{=}CH_2 \quad (15a)$$

1,4-Eliminations of alcohol from the bis(oxygen) ethers of butynediol by means of alkoxide do not take place in liquid ammonia, but require high temperatures[14]. The fact that the order of the double and triple bond in the enyne ethers (HC≡C—CH=$CHOR$) formed is the reverse of that for the previously mentioned enyne thioethers may indicate that the first step in the prototropic conversion of the intermediate cumulenic (oxygen) ethers is an abstraction of one of the δ-hydrogen atoms rather than of the hydrogen in the α position of the alkoxy group (reaction 15b).

$$R^1O-CH-C\equiv C-CH_2-OR^1 \longrightarrow$$

$$\quad\quad\quad\quad H$$

$$\quad\quad\quad ^-OR^2$$

$$[R^1OCH{=}C{=}C{=}CH_2] \xrightarrow[\text{conversion}]{\text{Prototropic}} R^1OCH{=}CHC{\equiv}CH \quad (15b)$$

$$(R^2 = \text{alkyl})$$

The production of RSC≡CCH=CH_2 from the mixed derivatives of butynediol ($RSCH_2C$≡CCH_2OR) and sodium ethoxide in liquid ammonia clearly demonstrates the difference in activation between the hydrogen atoms in the α position of the alkylthio groups and those in the α position of the alkoxy groups (reaction 15c).

$$RS-\underset{\underset{\underset{-OC_2H_5}{\downarrow}}{\overset{|}{H}}}{CH}-C\equiv C-CH_2-OR \longrightarrow$$

$$[RSCH=C=C=CH_2] \xrightarrow[\text{conversion}]{\text{Prototropic}} RSC\equiv CCH=CH_2 \quad (15c)$$

C. Prototropic Conversions of Unsaturated Thioethers

The reactions in sections II.A and II.B required a stoichiometrical quantity of the base for a complete conversion. The present section deals with prototropic conversions of unsaturated thioethers where the function of the base is that of a catalyst.

When an allyl thioether ($CH_2=CHCH_2SR$ where R is alkyl, aryl or allyl) is treated with a solution of sodium ethoxide in ethanol or with potassium butoxide, a rather smooth isomerization to the propenyl thioether ($CH_3CH=CHSR$) occurs, probably according to reaction (16) [36–38]. The isomerization of allylic (oxygen) ethers with potassium t-butoxide requires much higher temperatures [39].

$$CH_2=CHCH_2SR \xrightarrow[\text{EtOH}]{\text{NaOEt}} [CH_2=CH\bar{C}HSR \longleftrightarrow \bar{C}H_2CH=CHSR] \xrightarrow{\text{EtOH}}$$

$$CH_3CH=CHSR \, (+\text{NaOEt}) \quad (16)$$

β-Chloropropionaldehyde diethylthioacetal is converted with alcoholate into a ketene thioacetal, whereas β-chloropropionaldehyde acetal gives the normal elimination product (acrolein acetal). It can also be presumed that the chlorothioacetal gives first the normal product (acrolein thioacetal), but that this is subsequently isomerized to the ketene thioacetal, while the acetal of acrolein ($CH_2=CHCH(OC_2H_5)_2$) remains unchanged (reaction 17) [40, 41].

$$CH_2ClCH_2CH(SC_2H_5)_2 \xrightarrow{\text{Base}} CH_2=CHCH(SC_2H_5)_2 \longrightarrow$$

$$[CH_2=CH\bar{C}(SC_2H_5)_2 \longleftrightarrow \bar{C}H_2CH=C(SC_2H_5)_2] \xrightarrow[\text{solvent}]{\text{Protic}} CH_3CH=C(SC_2H_5)_2 \quad (17)$$

The isomerization of propargylic thioethers ($HC\equiv CCH_2SR$) proceeds very easily. Weak bases like sodium ethanethiolate ($NaSC_2H_5$)

are already capable of causing a partial conversion into the allenyl thioethers (CH_2=C=CHSR) even in liquid ammonia at the boiling point ($-33°$)[16]. With a small quantity of sodium ethoxide in liquid ammonia the isomerization to the propynyl thioethers (CH_3C≡CSR) is complete in a few minutes[16].

The rate of the isomerization in alcohol at about 40° has been measured[42, 43]; the conversion into the *allenic* intermediate proceeds much faster than the further isomerization to the propynyl thioether. The prototropic rearrangement can be represented by reaction (18).

$$HC\equiv CCH_2SR \xrightarrow{-OC_2H_5} [HC\equiv C-\bar{C}HSR \longleftrightarrow \bar{C}H=C=CHSR] \xrightarrow{EtOH}$$

$$CH_2=C=CHSR \xrightarrow{-OEt} [CH_2=C=\bar{C}SR \longleftrightarrow \bar{C}H_2C\equiv CSR] \xrightarrow{EtOH} CH_3C\equiv CSR$$

$$\text{(18)}$$

The oxygen analogs remain unchanged with sodium ethoxide in liquid ammonia. In ethanol a rather slow isomerization occurs, which only affords the allenyl ethers and no trace of the 1-propynyl ether (CH_3C≡COR)[44, 45].

Homologs of the propargyl thioethers (RCH_2C≡CCH_2SR) isomerize more slowly to the 1-alkynyl thioethers (RCH_2CH_2C≡CSR)[45].

In the prototropic conversion of thioethers with a 1,3-diyne system this conjugated system as a whole migrates (probably in several steps) (reaction 19)[45].

$$HC\equiv C-C\equiv C-CH_2SC_2H_5 \xrightarrow{Base} CH_3C\equiv CC\equiv CSC_2H_5 \qquad \text{(19)}$$

Other examples of rearrangements are the conversion of thioacetals of acetylenic aldehydes and of enyne thioethers. Both reactions can be carried out under mild conditions, namely, in liquid ammonia under the catalytic influence of sodium ethoxide (reactions 20 and 21)[46].

$$R^1C\equiv CCH(SR^2)_2 \longrightarrow R^1CH=C=C\underset{SR^2}{\overset{SR^2}{\diagup}} \qquad \text{(20)}$$

$$R^1CH=CHC\equiv CCH_2SR^2 \longrightarrow R^1CH=CHCH=C=CHSR^2 \qquad \text{(21)}$$

The corresponding oxygen compounds remain unchanged under similar conditions.

The lower reactivity of the oxygen compounds in the examples mentioned in this section may be attributed to lack of sufficient activation of the α-hydrogen atoms in the ethers.

D. Condensation Reactions

The presence of a thioether group can have an appreciable influence on the course of condensation reactions of esters. The required formation of carbanions is facilitated when a sulfur atom is in the α position.

In the Dieckmann condensation[47] of the diester CH_3OOCCH_2 $CH_2SCH_2COOCH_3$ the carbanion $CH_3OOCCH_2CH_2S\overset{-}{C}HCOOCH_3$ is formed more easily than $CH_3OOC\overset{-}{C}HCH_2SCH_2COOCH_3$. Therefore the kinetically controlled product consists mainly of **1**.

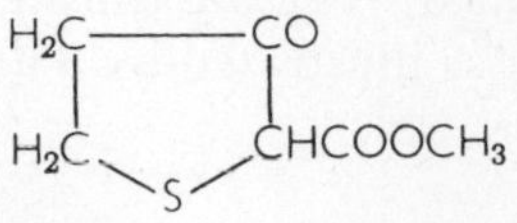

$$
\begin{array}{ccc}
H_2C & \!\!\!\!-\!\!\!\! & CO \\
| & & | \\
H_2C & & CHCOOCH_3 \\
& \diagdown_S\diagup &
\end{array}
$$

(1)

The difference between sulfur and oxygen is apparent (**1**) in the exclusive conversion of $CH_3OOCCH_2SCH_2OCH_2COOCH_3$, through $CH_3OOC\overset{-}{C}HSCH_2OCH_2COOCH_3$ as a precursor[48], into **2**.

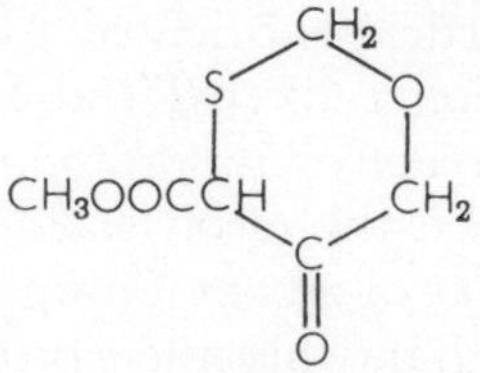

$$
\begin{array}{c}
CH_2 \\
S \diagup \quad \diagdown O \\
CH_3OOCCH \qquad CH_2 \\
\diagdown C \diagup \\
\| \\
O
\end{array}
$$

(2)

In the intermolecular condensations[49, 50] shown in reactions (22) and (23) the sulfur compound reacts faster than the oxygen analog.

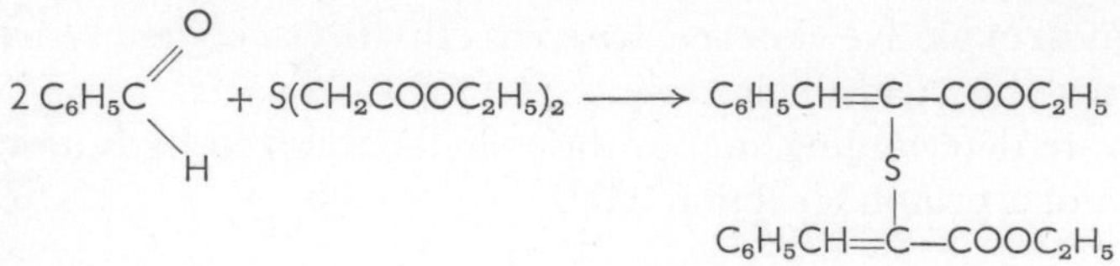

$$
2\ C_6H_5C\overset{\textstyle O}{\underset{\textstyle H}{\Big\langle}} + S(CH_2COOC_2H_5)_2 \longrightarrow
\begin{array}{c}
C_6H_5CH\!=\!C\!-\!COOC_2H_5 \\
| \\
S \\
| \\
C_6H_5CH\!=\!C\!-\!COOC_2H_5
\end{array}
\qquad (22)
$$

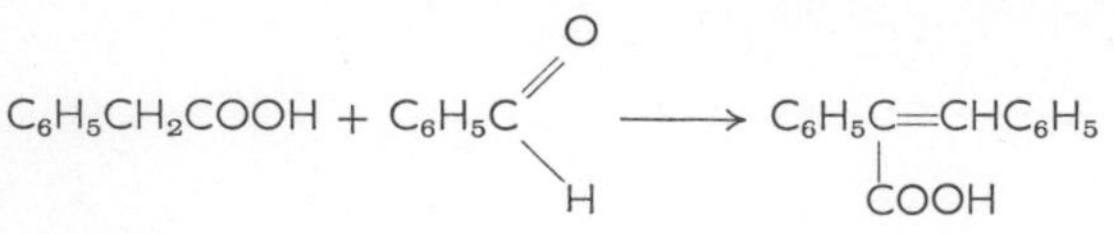

$$
C_6H_5CH_2COOH + C_6H_5C\overset{\textstyle O}{\underset{\textstyle H}{\Big\langle}} \longrightarrow
\begin{array}{c}
C_6H_5C\!=\!CHC_6H_5 \\
| \\
COOH
\end{array}
\qquad (23)
$$

III. ELECTROPHILIC AND NUCLEOPHILIC ADDITIONS TO THE UNSATURATED SYSTEM OF ALKENYL AND ALKYNYL THIOETHERS

A. Electrophilic Additions[51]

The orientation in the addition of electrophilic reagents to unsaturated ethers and thioethers, in which the alkoxy (—OR) or alkythio (—SR)group is conjugated with a double or triple bond, is governed by the positive electromeric ($+E$) effect of the alkoxy and alkylthio groups mentioned. The unsaturated systems show polarization during the reaction as illustrated by 3 and 4.

$$\overset{\beta}{C}=\overset{\alpha}{C}-\overset{..}{\underset{..}{X}}R \qquad \overset{\beta}{C}\equiv\overset{\alpha}{C}-\overset{..}{\underset{..}{X}}R$$
$$\underset{\delta^-\quad\delta^+}{\qquad} \qquad \underset{\delta^-\quad\delta^+}{\qquad}$$

(3)　　　　　　　　(4)

(X = O or S)

The β-carbon atom assumes a negative charge and it will be clear that the electrophilic particle is oriented towards this carbon atom. Because of this polarization 1-alkynyl and 1-alkenyl ethers and thioethers are much more reactive in proton-catalyzed reactions than alkynes and alkenes. Since the electron-donating effect of alkylthio groups is weaker than that of alkoxy groups, it can be expected that electrophilic additions with the thioethers proceed slower than with the ethers.

There is indeed a great difference between the rates of the acid-catalyzed addition of water to 1-alkynyl ethers[52-57] and the sulfur analogs. The conversion of ethoxyacetylene ($HC{\equiv}COC_2H_5$) with a 5 N solution of sulfuric acid to ethyl acetate ($CH_3COOC_2H_5$) proceeds with almost explosive violence, whereas ethylthioacetylene reacts much more slowly to yield thioacetate ($CH_3COSC_2H_5$)[58, 59].

The rate-determining step in these acid-catalyzed hydrations is the addition of a proton (reaction 24)[60].

$$R^1C{\equiv}CSR^2 \xrightarrow[\text{Slow}]{H^+} R^1CH{=}\overset{+}{C}SR^2 \xrightarrow[\text{Fast}]{H_2O} R^1CH{=}CSR^2 \xrightarrow{\text{Fast}} R^1CH_2COSR^2 \quad (24)$$
$$\underset{\underset{H\quad H}{\overset{+}{O}}}{\big|}$$

When the group R also contains an unsaturated system in conjugation with the heteroatom, the rates of hydration are diminished. In vinylthioethyne ($HC\equiv CSCH\equiv CH_2$) and vinyloxyethyne ($HC\equiv COCH\equiv CH_2$) the triple bond is attacked first (reaction 25)[61,62].

$$HC\equiv CXCH\equiv CH_2 \xrightarrow[H^+]{H_2O} CH_3COXCH\equiv CH_2 \qquad (25)$$

$$(X = O \text{ or } S)$$

Another example illustrating the difference in rate of reaction between unsaturated ethers and thioethers under electrophilic conditions is the Meyer–Schuster rearrangement of alkylthioethynyl carbinols[61,63,64], e.g. reaction (26).

$$\qquad (26)$$

The rearrangement can be carried out by shaking the carbinol with a 2–5 N solution of sulfuric acid in water. With the oxygen ethers this conversion may proceed explosively and a very dilute solution of acid has to be used[51]; the reaction of the sulfur analog is considerably slower.

The results of the acid-catalyzed hydrations of 1-ethoxy-2-ethylthioethene and -ethyne can be explained by the difference in strength of the polarizations caused by the ethoxy and ethylthio group[65]. The initial proton addition will take place at the most negative carbon atom of the unsaturated site, which is in the β position with respect to oxygen (reactions 27 and 28).

$$\qquad (27)$$

$$C_2H_5\ddot{O} - \underset{\times}{\overset{}{C}} \equiv \underset{\times}{\overset{}{C}} - \ddot{S}C_2H_5 \xrightarrow{H^+} C_2H_5O\overset{+}{C} = CHSC_2H_5 \xrightarrow{H_2O}$$

$$\overset{\displaystyle H \quad H}{\underset{\displaystyle C_2H_5OC=CHSC_2H_5}{\overset{O^+}{\diagdown\diagup}}} \longrightarrow C_2H_5O\overset{O}{\overset{\|}{C}}CH_2SC_2H_5 \quad (28)$$

For the results of the acid-catalyzed hydration of 1-ethoxy-2-ethylselenoethene[58] and 1-ethylthio-2-ethylselenoethene similar explanations can be given (reactions 29 and 30).

$$C_2H_5OCH=CHSeC_2H_5 \xrightarrow[H_2O]{H^+} \overset{\displaystyle O}{\underset{\displaystyle H}{\overset{\diagup}{\diagdown}C}}CCH_2SeC_2H_5 \quad (29)$$

$$C_2H_5SCH=CHSeC_2H_5 \xrightarrow[H_2O]{H^+} \overset{\displaystyle O}{\underset{\displaystyle H}{\overset{\diagup}{\diagdown}C}}CCH_2SeC_2H_5 \quad (30)$$

Vinyl ethers and thioethers are converted into acetaldehyde with dilute acid (reaction 31). Consecutive reactions may take place involv-

$$CH_2=CHXR \xrightarrow{H^+} CH_3\overset{+}{C}HXR \xrightarrow{H_2O} \overset{\displaystyle H \quad H}{\underset{\displaystyle CH_3\overset{|}{C}HXR}{\overset{O^+}{\diagdown\diagup}}} \longrightarrow CH_3\overset{O}{\overset{\diagup}{\underset{H}{\diagdown}}}C + RXH \quad (31)$$

$$(X = O \text{ or } S)$$

ing both products or one of the products with the starting material (reactions 32 and 32a).

$$CH_3\overset{O}{\overset{\diagup}{\underset{H}{\diagdown}}}C + 2\,RSH \longrightarrow CH_3CH(SR)_2 \quad (32)$$

$$CH_2=CHSR + RSH \xrightarrow[\text{addition}]{\text{Radical}} RSCH_2CH_2SR \quad (32a)$$

Peculiar, but not clearly understood, are the results of the acid-catalyzed hydration of β-haloalkenyl thioethers[66,67]. β-Bromovinyl ethyl thioether, for example, is converted into (ethylthio)acetaldehyde.

It is not known at which carbon atom of the double bond the initial proton addition takes place. Two attempts to reconstruct the formation of (ethylthio)acetaldehyde are represented by reactions (33a) and (33b).

$$CHBr{=}CHSC_2H_5 \xrightarrow{H^+} \overset{+}{C}HBrCH_2SC_2H_5 \xrightarrow{H_2O} \overset{H}{\underset{H}{>}}\overset{+}{O}{-}CHBrCH_2SC_2H_5 \longrightarrow$$

$$\overset{O}{\underset{H}{\parallel}}\!\!\!C CH_2SC_2H_5 \quad (33a)$$

$$CHBr{=}CHSC_2H_5 \xrightarrow{H^+} CH_2Br\overset{+}{C}HSC_2H_5 \xrightarrow{H_2O} \overset{H\quad H}{\underset{|}{\overset{\backslash\,/}{O^+}}}CH_2Br\overset{|}{C}HSC_2H_5 \longrightarrow$$

$$\underset{SC_2H_5}{\overset{OH}{CH_2Br\overset{|}{C}H}} \longrightarrow \underset{\overset{+}{\underset{C_2H_5}{\overset{|}{S}}\;H}}{\overset{OH}{CH_2{-}C}} \longrightarrow \underset{H}{\overset{O}{C_2H_5SCH_2C}} \quad (33b)$$

The homologs of β-halovinyl ethyl thioether yield alkylthioketones on treatment with acid. One of the possible mechanisms is given by reaction (34).

$$RCBr{=}CHSC_2H_5 \xrightarrow{H^+} RCHBr\overset{+}{C}H{-}SC_2H_5 \xrightarrow{H_2O} \underset{SC_2H_5}{\overset{OH}{RCHBr\overset{|}{C}H}} \;\rightleftarrows$$

$$\underset{\overset{+}{\underset{C_2H_5}{\overset{|}{S}}\;H}}{\overset{OH}{RCH{-}C}} \longrightarrow \underset{SC_2H_5}{\overset{OH}{RCH\overset{+}{C}H}} \longrightarrow \underset{SC_2H_5}{\overset{OH}{RCH(OH)\overset{|}{C}H}} \longrightarrow$$

$$RC(OH){=}CHSC_2H_5 \longrightarrow RCOCH_2SC_2H_5 \quad (34)$$

β-Haloalkenyl thioethers of the type $CHCl{=}C(R)SC_2H_5$ also give alkyl thioketones under similar conditions. Possibly episulfonium ions are intermediates in this case too (reaction 35).

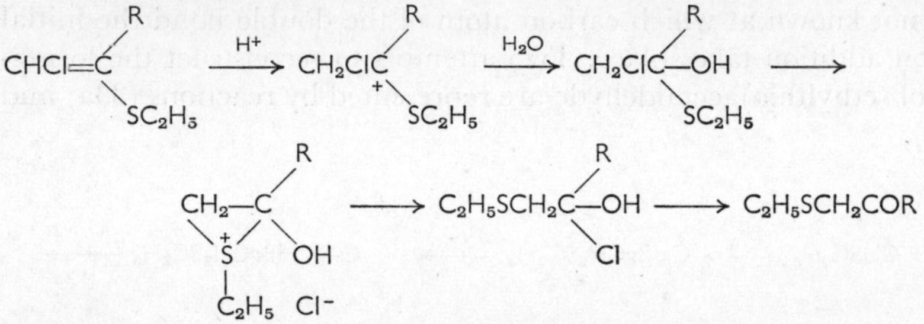

$$CHCl{=}C\overset{R}{\underset{SC_2H_5}{\diagup}} \xrightarrow{H^+} CH_2ClC\overset{R}{\underset{SC_2H_5}{\diagup}}{}^+ \xrightarrow{H_2O} CH_2ClC\overset{R}{\underset{SC_2H_5}{\diagup}}{-}OH \longrightarrow$$

$$CH_2{-}C\overset{R}{\diagup}\underset{\underset{\underset{C_2H_5}{|}}{\overset{+}{S}}{\diagdown}OH}{}\ Cl^- \longrightarrow C_2H_5SCH_2C\overset{R}{\underset{Cl}{\diagup}}{-}OH \longrightarrow C_2H_5SCH_2COR \quad (35)$$

With β-haloalkenyl(oxygen) ethers the initial proton addition must take place at the β-carbon atom, since α-halo aldehydes are obtained in good yields (reaction 36) [67,68].

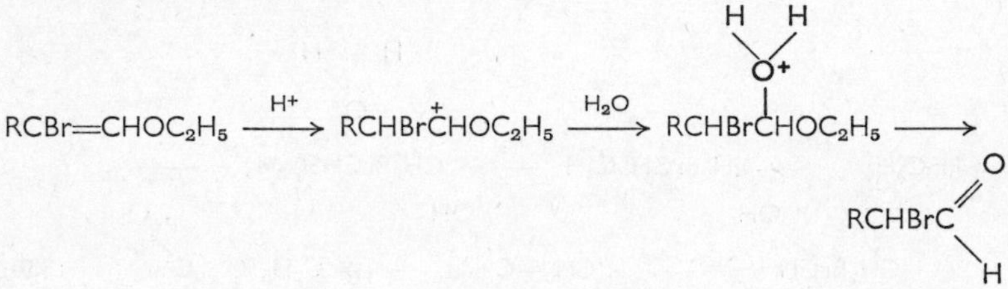

$$RCBr{=}CHOC_2H_5 \xrightarrow{H^+} RCHBr\overset{+}{C}HOC_2H_5 \xrightarrow{H_2O} RCHBr\overset{\overset{\displaystyle\overset{H\ \ H}{\diagdown\diagup}}{\underset{|}{O^+}}}{C}HOC_2H_5 \longrightarrow$$

$$RCHBrC\overset{\displaystyle O}{\underset{\diagdown H}{\diagup\kern-0.4em\diagup}} \quad (36)$$

(R = H or alkyl)

The electrophilic addition of thiols to vinyl ethers and thioethers [69,70] is catalyzed by sulfur dioxide. Oxygen must be carefully excluded in order to prevent radical addition which affords the adducts opposed to the Markovnikov rule (reactions 37 and 38).

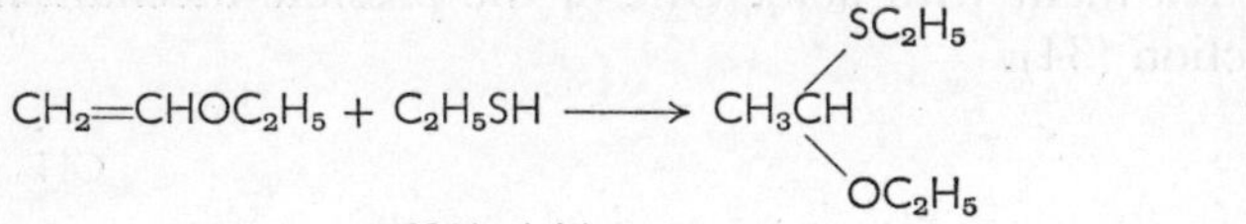

$$CH_2{=}CHOC_2H_5 + C_2H_5SH \longrightarrow CH_3CH\overset{\diagup SC_2H_5}{\diagdown OC_2H_5} \quad (37)$$

82% yield

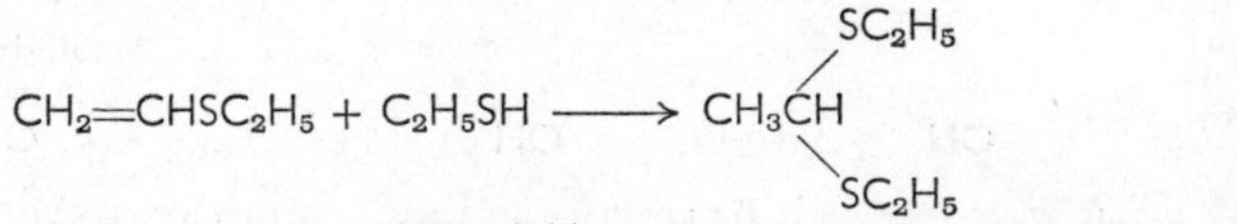

$$CH_2{=}CHSC_2H_5 + C_2H_5SH \longrightarrow CH_3CH\overset{\diagup SC_2H_5}{\diagdown SC_2H_5} \quad (38)$$

37% yield

The acid-catalyzed addition of alcohols to vinyl ethers proceeds more easily than that to vinyl thioethers, as may be concluded from reaction (39) [71].

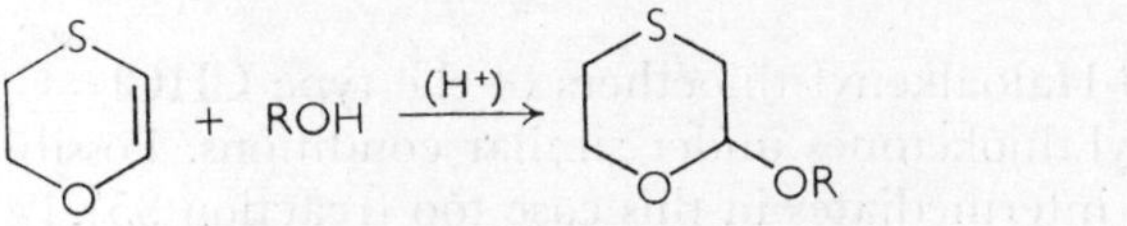

$$\text{[structure]} + ROH \xrightarrow{(H^+)} \text{[structure]OR} \quad (39)$$

The reaction between vinyl ethers and thioethers and between ethynyl ethers and thioethers proceeds easily with gaseous hydrogen chloride (reactions 40 and 41)[72,51]. Rate studies have not been undertaken.

$$CH_2=CHXR + HCl \longrightarrow CH_3CHClXR \qquad (40)$$

$$HC\equiv CXR + HCl \longrightarrow CH_2=C(Cl)XR \xrightarrow{HCl} CH_3CCl_2XR \qquad (41)$$
$$(X = O \text{ or } S)$$

A slightly more complicated electrophilic addition is the reaction of ketones and aldehydes with alkynyl ethers and thioethers ($RC\equiv CXC_2H_5$) with boron trifluoride etherate (($C_2H_5)_2O \cdot BF_3$) as a catalyst[73,74]. The α,β-unsaturated thiolesters formed in this reaction can be hydrolyzed to α,β-unsaturated acids in high yields[74].

B. Nucleophilic Additions to the Unsaturated System[51]

All available experimental evidence shows that in nucleophilic additions the nucleophilic particle is directed towards the α-carbon atom of the unsaturated bond in the oxygen ethers, but to the β-carbon atom when thioethers are employed (reactions 43 to 46).

$$-C\equiv CSR + BH \longrightarrow \underset{\underset{SR}{\diagup}}{\overset{B}{\diagdown}}C=C\overset{H}{\diagup} \tag{46}$$

From this it must be concluded, that contrary to the oxygen ethers alkenyl and alkynyl *thioethers* show a polarization in *nucleophilic additions* which is the opposite to that shown in electrophilic additions. This can again be attributed to the ability of sulfur to accommodate *ten* instead of eight electrons in its valence shell during the approach of the nucleophilic particle and in the transition state of the reaction.

The sulfur atom can therefore assist in the uptake of the electron pair provided by the nucleophilic reagent (reaction 47). The examples given by reactions (48) to (56) are typical.

$$\bar{B} + -C\equiv C-S- \longrightarrow [B-\overset{|}{C}=\bar{C}-S- \longleftrightarrow B-\overset{|}{C}=C=\bar{S}-] \overset{\text{Proton donor}}{\longrightarrow}$$
$$B-\overset{|}{C}=CH-S- \tag{47}$$

Vinyl alkyl and vinyl aryl thioethers add organolithium compounds (reaction 48)[75].

$$CH_2=CHSR^1 + \bar{R}^2\overset{+}{L}i \overset{\text{Ether}}{\longrightarrow} R^2CH_2CHLiSR^1 \tag{48}$$
$$(R^1 = \text{alkyl or phenyl, } R^2 = \text{alkyl})$$

The structure of these adducts can be proved by hydrolysis (reaction 49).

$$R^2CH_2CHLiSR^1 + H_2O \longrightarrow R^2CH_2CH_2SR^1 + LiOH \tag{49}$$

Vinyl ethers are cleaved by organolithium and Grignard compounds[75,76]; it is probable that an adduct is formed first (reaction 50).

$$CH_2=CHOR^1 + Li^+R^{2-} \longrightarrow CH_2-CH\overset{OR^1}{\underset{R^2}{\diagdown}} \longrightarrow$$

$$Li^+OR^{1-} + CH_2=CHR^2 \tag{50}$$

The nucleophilic addition of thiols to ethynyl ethers as well as to the thioethers proceeds very easily, even in liquid ammonia at its boiling point $(-33°)$ (reaction 51 and 52)[4,77-80].

$$HC\equiv COC_2H_5 + RSH \overset{\text{NaOC}_2H_5}{\underset{C_2H_5OH}{\longrightarrow}} CH_2=C\overset{OC_2H_5}{\underset{SR}{\diagdown}} \tag{51}$$

$$HC\equiv CSC_2H_5 + RSH \xrightarrow[C_2H_5OH]{NaOC_2H_5} RSCH=CHSC_2H_5 \qquad (52)$$

The addition of alcohols to ethynyl ethers and thioethers is a slower reaction, and refluxing for some hours is necessary (reactions 53 and 54)[8,59].

$$HC\equiv COC_2H_5 + C_2H_5OH \dashrightarrow[\text{}]{NaOC_2H_5} CH_2=C\overset{OC_2H_5}{\underset{OC_2H_5}{\big\langle}} \xrightarrow{C_2H_5OH} CH_3C\overset{OC_2H_5}{\underset{OC_2H_5}{-OC_2H_5}} \qquad (53)$$

$$HC\equiv CSC_2H_5 + C_2H_5OH \xrightarrow{NaOC_2H_5} C_2H_5OCH=CHSC_2H_5 \qquad (54)$$

Secondary amines can be added to ethynyl ethers and thioethers by refluxing the compounds (reactions 55 and 56)[51,58,81].

$$HC\equiv COC_2H_5 + (C_2H_5)_2NH \longrightarrow CH_2=C\overset{OC_2H_5}{\underset{N(C_2H_5)_2}{\big\langle}} \qquad (55)$$

$$HC\equiv CSC_2H_5 + (C_2H_5)_2NH \longrightarrow (C_2H_5)_2NCH=CHSC_2H_5 \qquad (56)$$

IV. REDUCTIVE CLEAVAGE OF THIOETHERS

A. Cleavage by Alkali Metals

The cleavage which ethers and thioethers undergo by the interaction with alkali metals is represented by reaction (57). The organometallic

$$R^1XR^2 + 2M \longrightarrow R^1XM + MR^2 \qquad (57)$$
$$(X = O \text{ or } S; R^1 \text{ and } R^2 \text{ are alkyl, aryl, allyl, or benzyl; } M = Li, Na \text{ or } K)$$

derivative MR^2 can react with the solvent, e.g. when liquid ammonia is used (reaction 58).

$$MR^2 + NH_3 \longrightarrow MNH_2 + R^2H \qquad (58)$$

It is generally accepted[82,83] that the reduction of ethers and thioethers involves a transfer of two electrons from the metal to the substrate. The reaction can consequently also be written as shown in equation (59). Probably the two electrons are transferred in two steps.

$$R^1XR^2 + 2e \longrightarrow R^1X^- + R^{2-} \qquad (59)$$

After the transfer of one electron a radical is formed which either quickly picks up another electron, or reacts with another like-radical.

There are indeed some cases, where the dimer of the radical $R^1\cdot$ is formed in small quantities (reactions 60 and 60a)[84,85].

$$R^1XR^2 + e \longrightarrow R^2X^- + R^1\cdot \tag{60}$$

$$2\,R^1\cdot \longrightarrow R^1R^1 \tag{60a}$$

Saturated aliphatic ethers[86] are in general much more difficult to cleave by alkali metals than thioethers. This difference in reactivity may again be attributed to the relative abilities of oxygen and sulfur to expand their electron shells. The ethers are stable towards the metals at temperatures below 200°, whereas thioethers react fairly smoothly in organic solvents, as well as in liquid ammonia (at ordinary pressure). The latter has the advantage that a homogenous reaction can take place: the alkali metals dissolve to give a blue colour, which disappears when the stoichiometrical quantity of the compound has been added.

The use of an organic solvent, e.g. hexane, is often required when the purpose of the cleavage is the preparation of an organometallic compound or one of its derivatives since in liquid ammonia the organometallics are solvolyzed. Calcium hexamine[83] ($Ca(NH_3)_6$) suspended in an organic solvent has a more specific action: dialkyl thioethers are not attacked, while the aryl thiol and the alkane are produced from alkyl aryl thioethers in good yields.

The cleavage of symmetrical dialkyl or diaryl thioethers gives good yields of the thiols[86,87]. In some cases the alkane, arising from the solvolysis of the organometallic compound, can also be isolated (reactions 61 and 62). The cleavage of t-butyl n-octyl thioether only affords n-octanethiol (reaction 63).

$$C_{10}H_{21}SC_{10}H_{21} + 2\,Na \xrightarrow{\text{Liq. NH}_3} C_{10}H_{21}SNa + C_{10}H_{21}Na \tag{61}$$

$$C_{10}H_{21}Na + NH_3 \longrightarrow NaNH_2 + C_{10}H_{22} \tag{62}$$

$$\text{n-}C_8H_{17}SC_4H_9\text{-}t + 2\,Li \xrightarrow{\text{CH}_3\text{NH}_2} \text{n-}C_8H_{17}SLi + \text{Other products} \tag{63}$$

From $\text{n-}C_8H_{17}SC_4H_9\text{-}t$ only $s\text{-}C_4H_9SLi$ is formed, while the cleavage of $s\text{-}C_4H_9S\text{-n-}C_4H_9$ gives equal quantities of $s\text{-}C_4H_9SLi$ and $\text{n-}C_4H_9SLi$. It appears from these and other examples that in the cleavage of unsymmetrical aliphatic thioethers the longest carbon chain is preferentially split off as a thiolate. Reaction of aryl alkyl thioethers with alkali metals always gives the aryl thiolate, while from unsymmetrical diaryl thioethers in general a mixture of both possible thiolates is formed. Cleavage of p-methoxyphenyl phenyl thioether results in the exclusive formation of the unsubstituted thiophenol (C_6H_5SH).

Aryl alkyl and diaryl ethers react with a liquid alloy of sodium and potassium or with solutions of these metals in liquid ammonia[86], e.g. reactions (64), (65) and (66). Allyl thioethers and benzyl thioethers

$$CH_3OC_6H_5 + 2\,K \xrightarrow[-33°]{Liq.\,NH_3} C_6H_5OK + CH_3K \qquad (64)$$

$$CH_3K + NH_3 \longrightarrow CH_4 + KNH_2 \qquad (65)$$

$$C_6H_5OC_6H_5 + 2\,Na \xrightarrow[20°]{Na/K} C_6H_5ONa + C_6H_5Na \qquad (66)$$

as well as their oxygen analogs are very readily cleaved. Some of these cleavage reactions can be applied to the preparation of organometallic compounds (reactions 67[88], 68[89], 69[85], 70[85] and 71[90]):

$$(CH_2{=}CHCH_2)_2O \xrightarrow[hexane,\,35°]{Na} CH_2{=}CHCH_2Na + CH_2{=}CHCH_2ONa \qquad (67)$$

$$C_6H_5CH_2OCH_3 \xrightarrow[THF,\,-10°\,to\,30°]{Li} C_6H_5CH_2Li + CH_3OLi \qquad (68)$$

$$CH_3SC_6H_5 + 2\,K \xrightarrow{Toluene} CH_3K + C_6H_5SK \;\Big\rbrace \qquad (69)$$

$$C_6H_5CH_3 + CH_3K \xrightarrow{} C_6H_5CH_2K + CH_4 \qquad (70)$$

$$C_6H_5SCH_2C_6H_5 \xrightarrow{Na} C_6H_5SNa + NaCH_2C_6H_5 \qquad (71)$$

The ether $C_6H_5OCH_2C_6H_5$ gives in addition to C_6H_5ONa and $NaCH_2C_6H_5$ the rearranged product $C_6H_5CH(ONa)C_2H_5$. The easy cleavage of benzyl thioethers is widely used in peptide synthesis for the protection of the mercapto group in cysteine. *S*-Benzylcysteine is prepared[91] from cystine in liquid ammonia by reduction with sodium followed by benzylation with benzyl chloride. After completion of the peptide synthesis the benzyl group is removed by reduction with sodium in liquid ammonia (see, for example, the synthesis of gluta-thion[92]).

It is possible to cleave the C—S bond in unsaturated thioethers[93], without reducing the double bond, by controlled addition of the alkali metal, e.g. (reaction 72). This reaction deserves a more extensive study.

$$C_2H_5CH{=}C(C_2H_5)SC_6H_7CH_3\text{-}p \xrightarrow[Liq.\,NH_3]{Na} C_2H_5CH{=}CHC_2H_5 + p\text{-}CH_3C_6H_7{-}SNa \qquad (72)$$
$$\text{(after hydrolysis)}$$

B. Desulfurization with Raney Nickel

Desulfurization by means of Raney nickel has been reviewed by several authors[94-96] and therefore we have not treated this subject extensively. Only the principle of desulfurization and some examples illustrating its use in organic syntheses are mentioned. It is believed that the first step in the desulfurizations involves a chemisorption of the sulfur atom on the surface of the catalyst. Fission of the C—S bond then takes place with formation of two free radicals. Depending on the quantity of hydrogen absorbed by the catalyst, hydrogenation, dimerization or recombination of the radicals may occur. These possibilities may be represented by reaction (73). Degassed catalysts give greater yields of the dimers and recombination products.

$$R^1SR^2 \longrightarrow R^1\cdot + R^2\cdot \left\{ \begin{array}{l} \longrightarrow R^1H + R^2H \\ \\ \longrightarrow R^1R^1 + R^1R^2 + R^2R^2 \end{array} \right. \tag{73}$$

Desulfurization has found a wide variety of applications. In the total synthesis of cantharidine (7) (compare reference 94 with 24) the intermediate 5 is desulfurized, yielding the compound 6 with the angular methyl groups in the desired configuration. Oxidative degradation of 6 leads to cantharidine (reaction 74).

(5)

(6)   (7)   (74)

Of interest is a recently developed method for the synthesis of o-di-t-butyl-substituted heterocyclic compounds[97]. The last step involves cleavage with Raney nickel of a tetramethyl-substituted sulfur-containing ring, thus producing 4,5-di-t-butylimidazole (reaction 75).

$$\text{(75)}$$

The desulfurization reaction is also a useful tool in structural studies; among other reactions it has been used for the degradation of biotine (compare reference 94) (reaction 75a). It is possible to remove a

$$\text{(75a)}$$

benzylthio group without reducing double bonds (compare reference 94 with 103) (reaction 76).

3-(Benzylthio)-3,5-cholestadiene   3,5-Cholestadiene

$$\text{(76)}$$

A carbonyl group can be reduced to a methylene group by converting the compound with a thiol into the mercaptal or mercaptole and removing the sulfur-containing group with Raney nickel (reaction 77).

$$\text{(77)}$$

19+C.E.L.

In some cases, especially when a neutral medium is required, the Raney-nickel method is more advantageous than the Clemmensen or Wolf–Kishner reduction of the carbonyl group.

V. CLEAVAGE OF THIOETHERS BY NUCLEOPHILIC SUBSTITUTION AT SULFUR AND AT CARBON

A. General

There are two types of nucleophilic substitution leading to the loss of a thioether group.

In the first type the sulfur atom is attacked by the reagent and one of the organic residues to which it was bound is expelled as an anion. This may finally take up a proton from the solvent. Similar reactions of oxygen ethers are unknown. In the second type a carbon atom linked to sulfur is attacked by the reagent leading to the expulsion of a thiolate group (reaction 78). Conversions of the second type are common for

$$
\begin{array}{c}
\text{Attack at S} \\
\longrightarrow \quad BSR + -\overset{|}{\underset{|}{C}}^- \xrightarrow[\substack{\text{(from the} \\ \text{solvent)}}]{H^+} -\overset{|}{\underset{|}{C}}-H + BSR \\
-\overset{|}{\underset{|}{C}}-SR + B^- \\
\longrightarrow \quad B-\overset{|}{\underset{|}{C}}- + RS^- \\
\text{Attack at C}
\end{array}
\qquad (78)
$$

oxygen ethers too, and even proceed more easily with the latter, doubtless because of the stronger inductive effect of alkoxy groups.

B. Nucleophilic Substitution at the Heteroatom

There are many examples of organic nucleophilic substitutions occurring at atoms other than carbon, but curiously the reactions have received little attention or have been misinterpreted[98]. These substitutions can be expected when stable anions like alkynyl anions can be expelled.

The conversion of 1-chloro-2-phenylacetylene with butyllithium into lithium phenylacetylide and butyl chloride, is an example of such a process (reaction 79). 1-Bromo-2-phenylacetylene reacts in an analogous way with Grignard compounds (reaction 80).

$$
C_6H_5C{\equiv}\overset{\frown}{C}-Cl \quad \overset{\frown}{C_4H_9Li^+} \longrightarrow C_6H_5C{\equiv}\bar{C}Li^+ + C_4H_9Cl \qquad (79)
$$

$$C_6H_5C \equiv C - Br \qquad CH_3\overset{+}{M}gBr \longrightarrow C_6H_5C \equiv \bar{C}MgBr^+ + CH_3Br \qquad (80)$$

Nucleophilic substitution at sulfur has been observed with some alkynyl thioethers, having the systems —C≡C—SR and —CH= CH—C≡C—SR (compare, however, section II.A), and with ortho-thiocarbonic esters $(C(SR)_4)$. There are no examples of a similar cleavage of the C—O bond. The facile reaction of the sulfur compounds is probably due to the assistance of the sulfur atom in the uptake of the electron pair provided by the nucleophilic reagent; this assistance lowers the energy of the transition state.

The examples given by reactions (81) to (85) are typical[99–102]. No

$$(CH_3)_3CC \equiv CSC_2H_5 + KNH_2 \xrightarrow{\text{Liq. NH}_3} (CH_3)_3CC \equiv CK + NH_2SC_2H_5 \qquad (81)$$

trace of alkyne is found after hydrolysis of the reaction mixture of the oxygen ether $(CH_3)_3CC \equiv COC_2H_5$ (compare reaction 81) with potassium amide, but only a mixture of the acid $(CH_3)_3CCH_2COOH$ and the amide $(CH_3)_3CCH_2CONH_2$. These compounds are probably formed by hydrolysis of an adduct of potassium amide and the alkynyl ether.

$$\overset{CH_2OH}{\underset{|}{RCH}} - C \equiv CSC_2H_5 + 2\ KNH_2 \longrightarrow \overset{CH_2OK}{\underset{|}{RCH}} - C \equiv CK + NH_2SC_2H_5 \qquad (82)$$

$$\bigcirc\!\!=\!\!CHC \equiv CSCH_3 + KNH_2 \longrightarrow \bigcirc\!\!=\!\!CHC \equiv CK + NH_2SCH_3$$
$$(83)$$

$$C(SR)_4 + LiNH_2 \xrightarrow{\text{Liq. NH}_3} Li^+C(SR)_3 + NH_2SR \longrightarrow :C(SR)_2 + {}^-SR \longrightarrow \text{Products} \qquad (84)$$
$$(R = \text{alkyl or aryl})$$

$$C(SR)_4 + C_4H_9Li \longrightarrow C_4H_9SR + Li^+\bar{C}(SR)_3 \longrightarrow :C(SR)_2 \longrightarrow \text{Products} \qquad (85)$$

The C—Se bond in alkynyl selenoethers is more easily cleaved than the C—S bond[99]. The disproportionation of ethylselenoacetylene $(HC \equiv CSeC_2H_5)$ which takes place under the catalytic influence of sodium ethoxide or sodium ethanethiolate (reaction 89) must be considered as the consequence of a nucleophilic attack of the base (B^-) at the selenium atom (reaction 86). Dialkyl ethynyl phosphines $(HC \equiv CP(R)_2)$ react in a similar way in liquid ammonia.

$$HC\equiv CSeC_2H_5 + B^- \; \rightleftarrows \; BSeC_2H_5 + HC\equiv\bar{C}$$
$$\text{(Nucleophilic substitution)} \qquad (86)$$

$$HC\equiv\bar{C} + HC\equiv CSeC_2H_5 \; \rightleftarrows \; HC\equiv CH + \bar{C}\equiv CSeC_2H_5$$
$$\text{(Transmetalation)} \qquad (87)$$

$$\bar{C}\equiv CSeC_2H_5 + BSeC_2H_5 \; \rightleftarrows \; C_2H_5SeC\equiv CSeC_2H_5 + B^-$$
$$\text{(Nucleophilic substitution)} \qquad (88)$$

$$2\,HC\equiv CSeC_2H_5 \; \rightleftarrows \; HC\equiv CH + C_2H_5SeC\equiv CSeC_2H_5 \qquad (89)$$

From this overall equation it appears that the base (B^-) plays the role of a catalyst. In liquid ammonia the reaction proceeds almost completely to the right, because of the insolubility of the last product.

Ethylthioacetylene $(HC\equiv CSC_2H_5)$ remains unchanged under similar conditions.

Bis(ethylthio)acetylene $(C_2H_5SC\equiv CSC_2H_5)$, when treated with phenyllithium in ether, gives a mixture of products, as ethylthioacetylene, phenyl ethyl thioether and phenylacetylene (after hydrolyzing the reaction mixture). Probably nucleophilic substitution at sulfur is involved in the formation of these products, as is expressed in equations (90) to (92).

$$C_2H_5SC\equiv CSC_2H_5 + C_6H_5Li \longrightarrow LiC\equiv CSC_2H_5 + C_6H_5SC_2H_5 \qquad (90)$$
$$\text{(Substitution at sulfur)}$$

$$C_2H_5SC\equiv CSC_2H_5 + C_6H_5Li \longrightarrow LiSC_2H_5 + C_6H_5C\equiv CSC_2H_5 \qquad (91)$$
$$\text{(Substitution at carbon)}$$

$$C_6H_5C\equiv CSC_2H_5 + C_6H_5Li \longrightarrow C_6H_5C\equiv CLi + C_6H_5SC_2H_5 \qquad (92)$$
$$\text{(Substitution at sulfur)}$$

The reaction of disulfides with Grignard compounds with organolithium compounds or with alkali alkynylides belongs to the class of nucleophilic substitutions at sulfur, which produces thioethers (R^1SR^2) (reaction 93) [103, 81]. An example of this class of substitution is given by reaction (94).

$$R^1S\!-\!S + {}^-R^2[MgBr]^+ \text{ (or Li or Na)} \longrightarrow$$

$$R^1S^-[MgBr]^+ \text{ (or } Li^+ \text{ or } Na^+) + R^2SR^1 \qquad (93)$$

$$C_2H_5S\!-\!SC_2H_5 + NaC\!\equiv\!CC_3H_7 \xrightarrow{\text{Liq. NH}_3} C_2H_5SNa + C_2H_5SC\!\equiv\!CC_3H_7 \qquad (94)$$

Instead of disulfides, thiolsulfonates may be used to advantage in those cases when a reaction of the desired product with thiolate has to be avoided (reaction 95)[104].

$$C_2H_5SSO_2C_2H_5 + NaC\!\equiv\!COR \longrightarrow C_2H_5SC\!\equiv\!COR + C_2H_5SO_2Na \qquad (95)$$

C. Nucleophilic Substitution at the α-Carbon Atom of Thioethers

Several ethers and thioethers can be cleaved by nucleophilic reagents according to reaction (96)[86,90].

$$\bar{B} + R^1\!-\!XR^2 \longrightarrow BR^1 + \bar{X}R^2 \qquad (96)$$
$$(X = O \text{ or } S)$$

In general the oxygen ethers undergo such a fission more easily than thioethers; this can be attributed to the stronger inductive effect of an —OR group when compared with an —SR group. The nature of the groups R^1 and R^2 has a strong influence on the rate of the conversion, as will be apparent from the data below.

Occasionally the presence of Lewis acids facilitates the conversion, probably through coordination with the heteroatom; this aids the development of a positive charge at this atom.

The cleavage of ethers and thioethers by treating with potassium hydroxide[105] in ethanol has no preparative importance. The reaction only proceeds to a slight extent with aryl ethers (reaction 97). Thioanisole is stable under these conditions.

$$C_6H_5OCH_3 + {}^-OC_2H_5 \xrightarrow[200°]{\text{Ethanol}} CH_3OC_2H_5 + C_6H_5O^- \qquad (97)$$
$$(7\% \text{ conversion in 7 hours})$$

Phenyl alkyl ethers react smoothly with Grignard solutions at elevated temperatures, whereas the thioethers are quite stable[106], e.g. reaction (98).

$$C_6H_5OCH_3 + CH_3MgI \xrightarrow{\text{Ether}} C_6H_5OMgI + C_2H_6 \qquad (98)$$

Saturated aliphatic ethers and thioethers do not react with ethereal Grignard solutions.

Aryl alkyl and allyl alkyl ethers are readily cleaved at room temperature by phenylmagnesium bromide, the sulfur analogs require a much higher temperature and even then the reaction is incomplete (reaction 99)[107,108].

$$C_6H_5SCH_2CH{=}CH_2 + C_6H_5MgBr \xrightarrow[78°]{6\ h}$$

$$C_6H_5CH_2CH{=}CH_2 + C_6H_5SMgBr + \text{Starting material} \quad (99)$$

The nucleophilic cleavage of a C—O bond in acetals $(CH_2(OR)_2)$, orthoformic esters $(HC(OR)_3)$ and orthocarbonic esters $(C(OR)_4)$ occurs more easily than in ordinary ethers. An important application is the preparation of acetylenic acetals (reaction 100)[109].

$$HC(OR^1)_3 + R^2C{\equiv}CMgBr \xrightarrow{\text{Ether}} R^2C{\equiv}CCH(OR^1)_2 + R^1OMgBr \quad (100)$$

The presence of Lewis acids (magnesium bromide) in the reaction medium has a favorable influence on the reaction rate: when sodium alkynylides (dissolved or suspended in ether) are employed, the reactions proceed more slowly[110].

Formaldehyde thioacetals $(CH_2(SR)_2)$ and orthothioesters $(HC(SR)_3)$ are stable towards alkynyl–Grignard compounds under the same conditions. In thioacetals derived from aldehydes one of the —SR groups can be substituted (reaction 101)[111].

$$R^1CH(SR^2)_2 + R^3MgBr \longrightarrow R^2SMgBr + R^3R^1CHSR^2 \quad (101)$$

Vinyl thioethers $(R^1CH{=}CHSR^2)$ normally do not react with Grignard compounds, but with alkyllithium compounds a nucleophilic addition generally takes place (see section III.B). The following example, however, involves perhaps a nucleophilic substitution at carbon (reaction 102)[112].

$$C_6H_5CH{=}CHSC_6H_5 + C_4H_9Li \longrightarrow C_6H_5SLi + C_6H_5CH{=}CHC_4H_9 \quad (102)$$

Vinyl (oxygen) ethers appear to react similarly and give rise to alkene formation on prolonged heating with Grignard or alkyllithium compounds, e.g. reactions (103) and (104)[113] (compare with references 75 and 76).

$$CH_2{=}CHOC_4H_9 + C_6H_5MgBr \longrightarrow C_4H_9OMgBr + CH_2{=}CHC_6H_5 \quad (103)$$
$$\text{35\% yield}$$

$$\text{(pyran)} + n\text{-}C_8H_7MgBr \longrightarrow C_8H_7CH{=}CH(CH_2)_3OMgBr \quad (104)$$
$$\text{48\% yield}$$

It is not known whether these reactions are similar to S_N2 substitutions in the sense that the formation of the new bond and the cleavage of the C—O bond occur simultaneously; an addition–elimination mechanism could be considered as another possibility (reaction 105).

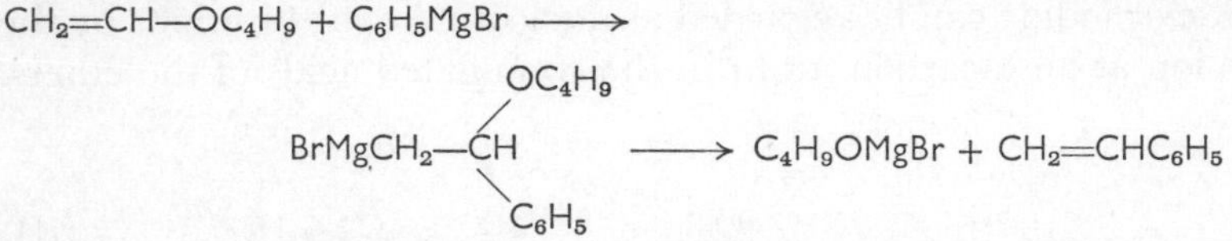

$$CH_2{=}CH{-}OC_4H_9 + C_6H_5MgBr \longrightarrow$$

$$BrMgCH_2{-}\overset{\displaystyle OC_4H_9}{\underset{\displaystyle C_6H_5}{CH}} \longrightarrow C_4H_9OMgBr + CH_2{=}CHC_6H_5 \quad (105)$$

The reaction between dihydropyran and a Grignard compound seems to be a direct displacement at carbon: the C—O rather than the =C—O bond is broken (reaction 106).

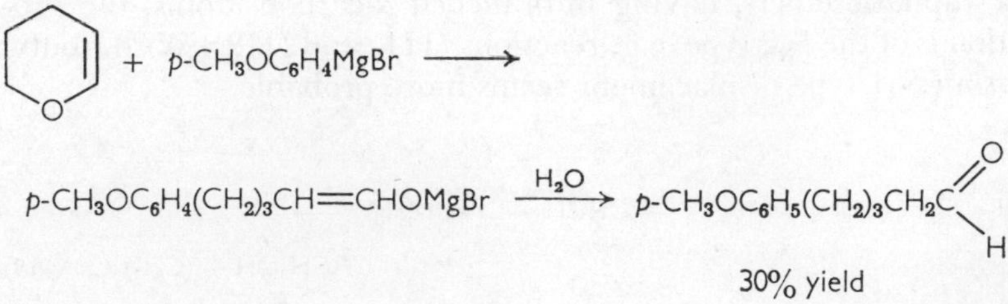

$$\text{(dihydropyran)} + p\text{-}CH_3OC_6H_4MgBr \longrightarrow$$

$$p\text{-}CH_3OC_6H_4(CH_2)_3CH{=}CHOMgBr \xrightarrow{H_2O} p\text{-}CH_3OC_6H_5(CH_2)_3CH_2C{\overset{O}{\underset{H}{\diagup}}} \quad (106)$$

30% yield

The alkoxy group in 1-alkynyl ethers can be readily displaced by an alkyl group or a dialkylamino group with formation of alkynes and yneamines, respectively (reactions 107 and 108)[114,115]. Adducts may also be intermediates in these cases.

$$R^1C{\equiv}COC_2H_5 + R^2Li \xrightarrow{\text{Ether}} R^1C{\equiv}CR^2 + LiOC_2H_5 \quad (107)$$

$$R^1C{\equiv}COC_2H_5 + R^2{}_2NLi \longrightarrow R^1C{\equiv}CNR^2{}_2 + LiOC_2H_5 \quad (108)$$

Nucleophilic substitution at sulfur as well as metalation takes place when 1-alkynyl thioethers are treated with butyllithium (reactions 109 and 110)[115].

$$RCH_2C{\equiv}CSC_2H_5 + C_4H_9Li \longrightarrow C_4H_9SC_2H_5 + RCH_2C{\equiv}CLi \quad (109)$$

(Nucleophilic substitution at S)

$$RCH_2C{\equiv}CSC_2H_5 + C_4H_9Li \longrightarrow RCHLiC{\equiv}CSC_2H_5 \rightleftharpoons RCH{=}C{=}CLiSC_2H_5 \quad (110)$$

(Metalation)

D. Cleavage of Ethers and Thioethers in the Presence of Hydrogen Halides and Lewis Acids

Important types of ether cleavage are those which are effected by hydrogen halides, acyl halides and Lewis acids[86,90].

I. Cleavage with hydrogen halides

The reactions of ethers and thioethers with hydrogen chloride, bromide or iodide can be regarded as nucleophilic substitutions by the halide ion at an α-carbon atom in the conjugated acids of the ethers.

$$CH_3CH_2\!-\!O\!-\!C_2H_5 + HI \longrightarrow CH_3CH_2\!-\!\overset{\overset{\displaystyle H}{|}+}{O}\!-\!C_2H_5 \qquad (111)$$

$$I^- + CH_3CH_2\!-\!\overset{\overset{\displaystyle H}{|}+}{O}\!-\!C_2H_5 \longrightarrow CH_3CH_2I + C_2H_5OH \qquad (112)$$

With aliphatic ethers, having unbranched α-carbon atoms, the substitution is of the S_N2 type, e.g. reactions (111) and (112). With t-butyl ethers an S_N1 type displacement seems more probable.

$$RCH_2\!-\!O\!-\!C(CH_3)_3 + HBr \longrightarrow RCH_2\!-\!\overset{\overset{\displaystyle H}{|}+}{O}\!-\!C(CH_3)_3 \longrightarrow$$

$$RCH_2OH + (CH_3)_3\overset{+}{C} \quad (113)$$

$$(CH_3)_3\overset{+}{C} + \overset{-}{Br} \longrightarrow (CH_3)_3CBr \qquad (114)$$

Thioethers are in general less reactive towards protonic and Lewis acids. The reason may be that the sulfur atom is too large to allow effective orbital overlap with a proton or with the electron-deficient atom of a Lewis acid; therefore generally no intermediate sulfonium compound is formed.

Anisole ($CH_3OC_6H_5$) can be converted into methyl bromide or iodide and phenol by heating for 2 hours at 130° with hydrogen bromide or iodide, whereas thioanisole ($CH_3SC_6H_5$) is stable under these conditions[116].

Reactions (115)[117] and (116)[118] may also illustrate the difference in reactivity between the C—O and C—S bonds. However, at low tem-

$$CH_3OC_6H_4SR + HBr \xrightarrow{\ 120–130° \ } HOC_6H_4SR + CH_3Br \qquad (115)$$
$$45\%$$

$$C_2H_5O\!-\!\underset{\underset{\displaystyle S}{}}{\boxed{}}\!-\!OC_2H_5 + HBr \longrightarrow HO\!-\!\underset{\underset{\displaystyle S}{}}{\boxed{}}\!-\!OH + 2\,C_2H_5Br$$
$$(116)$$

peratures dimethyl thioether forms an adduct with hydrogen iodide, which gives methyl iodide and methanethiol on heating (reaction 117)[90].

$$CH_3SCH_3 + HI \longrightarrow (CH_3)_2S.HI \longrightarrow CH_3I + CH_3SH \qquad (117)$$

Benzyl alkyl, benzyl aryl and dibenzyl ethers are very smoothly cleaved by heating with an aqueous solution of HBr with formation of benzyl bromide and the alcohol or phenol. The analogous thioethers remain unchanged under similar conditions.

The influence of substituents in the nucleus, however, can be very important; p-hydroxy- or alkoxybenzyl thioethers are readily converted by aqueous solutions of hydrogen halides[119]. The reason is, probably, that the p-hydroxy or alkoxy substituents by their electromeric effect promote the attack of a proton at sulfur and thus favor the cleavage (reaction 118). Acetals are very smoothly converted by

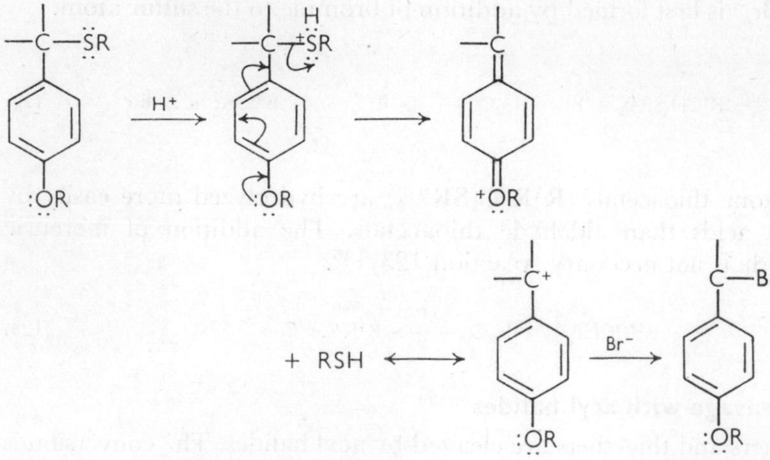

(118)

gaseous hydrogen chloride to α-chloro ethers, even at very low temperatures (reaction 119).

$$R^1CH(OR^2)_2 + HCl \underset{\longleftarrow}{\overset{-50°}{\longrightarrow}} R^1CHClOR^2 + R^2OH \qquad (119)$$

Thioacetals ($R^1CH(SR^2)_2$) are stable towards hydrogen chloride at these temperatures.

With aqueous solutions of acids, acetals are converted into aldehydes (reaction 120).

19*

$$R^1CH(OR^2)_2 + H_2O \xrightarrow{H^+} R^1\overset{\displaystyle O}{\underset{\displaystyle H}{C}} + 2\,R^2OH \qquad (120)$$

The alkoxy or aryloxy group in acetals can be substituted by alkyl- or arylthio groups; an application of this conversion is the preparation of thioacetals of acetylenic aldehydes (reaction 121)[120].

$$RC{\equiv}CCH(OC_2H_5)_2 + 2\,C_2H_5SH \xrightarrow{ZnCl_2} RC{\equiv}CCH(SC_2H_5)_2 + 2\,C_2H_5OH \quad (121)$$

The cleavage of thioacetals with dilute acids can only be effected when mercuric chloride is added[121,122]. The intermediate complex formed between the thioacetal and $HgCl_2$ is hydrolyzed more easily.

In another method of converting thioacetals into the corresponding aldehydes a mixture of bromine and water is employed (reaction 122)[123,124]. Probably a bromosulfonium bromide $[R^1CH(SR^2)_2\text{-}Br]^+Br^-$ is first formed by addition of bromine to the sulfur atom.

$$R^1CH(SR^2)_2 + Br_2 + H_2O \longrightarrow R^1\overset{\displaystyle O}{\underset{\displaystyle H}{C}} + R^2SSR^2 + 2\,HBr \qquad (122)$$

Ketone thioacetals $(R^1R^2C(SR^3)_2)$ are hydrolyzed more easily by dilute acids than aldehyde thioacetals. The addition of mercuric chloride is not necessary (reaction 123)[125].

$$R^1R^2C(SR^3)_2 + H_2O \xrightarrow{H^+} R^1R^2C{=}O + 2\,R^3SH \qquad (123)$$

2. Cleavage with acyl halides[86,90]

Ethers and thioethers are cleaved by acyl halides. The conversion is catalyzed by Lewis acids such as $AlCl_3$, $SnCl_4$ and $SbCl_5$. The uncatalyzed formation of alkyl halides from thioethers and acyl halides proceeds more slowly than that from ethers.

Diethyl thioether reacts only with acetyl bromide and iodide; the ethyl iodide formed reacts further with unconverted diethyl thioether (reactions 124 and 125)[126]. Orthothioformates $(HC(SR)_3)$ are

$$C_2H_5SC_2H_5 + CH_3\overset{\displaystyle O}{\overset{\displaystyle \|}{C}}{-}I \longrightarrow C_2H_5I + CH_3\overset{\displaystyle O}{\overset{\displaystyle \|}{C}}SC_2H_5 \qquad (124)$$

$$C_2H_5SC_2H_5 + C_2H_5I \longrightarrow (C_2H_5)_3S^+I^- \qquad (125)$$

more reactive and are cleaved readily by acetyl chloride (reaction 126)[127]. It is presumed that these conversions proceed through inter-

$$HC(SR)_3 + CH_3\overset{\overset{\displaystyle O}{\|}}{C}Cl \longrightarrow HCCl(SR)_3 + CH_3\overset{\overset{\displaystyle O}{\|}}{C}SR \qquad (126)$$

action of the heteroatom with the positively charged carbonyl carbon of the acyl halide (reaction 127).

$$CH_3\overset{\overset{\displaystyle Cl}{|}}{C}{=}O + R\overset{..}{\underset{..}{X}}R \longrightarrow R\overset{\overset{\displaystyle Cl^-}{|}}{\underset{\underset{\displaystyle CH_3}{\overset{\displaystyle |}{C}{=}O}}{X^+}}R \longrightarrow RCl + RX\overset{\overset{\displaystyle O}{\|}}{C}CH_3 \qquad (127)$$

3. Cleavage with Lewis acids[86,90]

Cleavage of ethers can be effected by heating with Lewis acids, e.g. MgI_2, $AlCl_3$. Again the lone pair of electrons at the heteroatom must be responsible for this occurrence (reaction 128). Anisole is there-

$$ROR + MgI_2 \longrightarrow R\overset{\overset{\displaystyle MgI}{|}}{\underset{\underset{\displaystyle I^-}{+}}{O}}R \longrightarrow RI + ROMgI \qquad (128)$$

fore completely converted into methyl iodide and phenoxymagnesium iodide by heating for one hour at 200° with MgI_2; on the contrary $C_6H_5SCH_3$ remains unchanged under these circumstances[117].

VI. REACTIONS OF HALO AND HYDROXY THIOETHERS

The α-, β-, γ- and δ-halo and hydroxy thioethers show interesting differences in properties. Furthermore their properties deviate from those of the oxygen analogs.

A. α-Halo Thioethers

α-Halo ethers and thioethers (CH_2HalXR or $RCHHalXR$ where $X = O$ or S) show a much higher reactivity towards nucleophilic reagents than primary or secondary alkyl halides, probably because they can form carbonium ions stabilized by resonance[128] (compare the reviews given in references 129 to 132 and references mentioned therein) (reaction 129). α-Chloro ethers and thioethers hydrolyze much

$$R^1CHHal\overset{..}{\underset{..}{X}}R^2 \xrightarrow{-Halogen} [R^1\overset{+}{C}H\overset{..}{X}R^2 \longleftrightarrow R^1CH\!=\!\overset{+}{X}R^2] \qquad (129)$$

$$(X = O \text{ or } S)$$

faster than alkyl chlorides (reaction 130). This reaction is first order, the rate-determining step being the ionization.

$$R^1CHClOR^2 \underset{\longleftarrow}{\overset{H_2O}{\rightleftharpoons}} R^1CH(OH)OR^2(+ \text{ HCl}) \rightleftharpoons R^1\overset{O}{\underset{H}{\overset{\parallel}{C}}} + R^2OH \qquad (130)$$

The α-chloro thioethers react considerably more slowly than the ethers, as may be expected from the lower $+E$ effect of an alkylthio group compared to an alkoxy group. Furthermore, part of the thiol formed in the hydrolysis reacts with the aldehyde with production of a thioacetal. The intermediate α-hydroxy thioethers are only stable at lower temperatures in aqueous solution (reactions 131 and 132).

$$R^1CHClSR^2 \underset{\longleftarrow}{\overset{H_2O}{\rightleftharpoons}} R^1CH(OH)SR^2(+HCl) \rightleftharpoons R^1\overset{O}{\underset{H}{\overset{\parallel}{C}}} + R^2SH \qquad (131)$$

$$R^1CH(OH)SR^2 + R^2SH \longrightarrow R^1CH(SR^2)_2 + H_2O \qquad (132)$$

Chloromethyl alkyl ethers (CH_2ClOR), especially those with a small alkyl group, react very vigorously with liquid ammonia; with the chloro thioethers the reaction is not instantaneous (reaction 133)[133].

$$CH_2ClXR + NH_3 \longrightarrow HCl.NH_2CH_2XR \qquad (133)$$
$$(X = O \text{ or } S)$$

With alcohols (R^2OH) or thiols (R^2SH) acetals or thioacetals are formed. Again the α-chloro ethers react much faster than the corresponding thioethers. Diethylaniline can be added in order to remove the hydrogen chloride liberated (reaction 134).

$$R^1CHClXR^2 + R^2XH \xrightarrow{C_6H_5N(C_2H_5)_2} R^1CH(XR^2)_2 + C_6H_5N(C_2H_5)_2.HCl \qquad (134)$$
$$(X = O \text{ or } S)$$

Instead of the free alcohols (phenols or thiols) the alcoholates, phenolates or thiolates can be used, the same product being produced.

Some other reactions with nucleophilic reagents have found useful applications, e.g. the reaction of alkynylmagnesium bromides or alkynyllithium compounds with α-chloro ethers or thioethers (reaction 135).

$$R^1C{\equiv}CMgBr(or\ RC{\equiv}CLi) + R^2CHClXC_2H_5 \xrightarrow{Ether} R^1C{\equiv}C-\overset{R^2}{\underset{|}{C}}HXC_2H_5 \quad (135)$$
$$(X = O\ or\ S)$$

The synthesis of the oxygen compounds in this manner proceeds more easily and with better yields than that of the thioethers; α-chloro ethers react with the Grignard solutions readily at −20 to 0°, whereas the chloro thioethers require refluxing for some time[134].

There is, however, a fundamental difference in the behavior of α-chloro ethers and thioethers towards organolithium, -sodium or -potassium compounds in liquid ammonia. The α-chloro ethers give the normal substitution products with alkynylides together with products of ammonolysis (reaction 136).

$$R^1C{\equiv}CNa + CH_2ClOR^2 \xrightarrow{Liq.\ NH_3} R^1C{\equiv}CCH_2OR^2 \quad (136)$$

However, when chloro thioethers (CH_2ClSR^2) are added to lithium, sodium or potassium alkynylides in liquid ammonia, instead of the expected 2-alkynyl thioethers ($R^1C{\equiv}CCH_2SR^2$), appreciable quantities of the thioacetals ($CH_2(SR^2)_2$) are formed. Lithium amide also converts the α-chloro thioethers into the thioacetals[135].

α-Halo thioethers of the type $R^1CH_2CHHalSR^2$ readily split off hydrogen halide[59] on heating at 70–110°. The hydrogen halide can be removed under reduced pressure or by the addition of a sterically hindered base, e.g. diethylaniline, alkenyl thioethers ($R^1CH{=}CHSR^2$) being produced. The α-halo(oxygen)ethers are also converted into alkenyl ethers ($R^1CH{=}CHOR^2$) on heating with bases like diethylaniline or dicyclohexylethylamine, but on thermal decomposition in the absence of these bases alkyl halides and aldehydes are formed rather than alkenyl ethers[129]. These reaction possibilities may be represented by reaction (137).

$$R^2XCH(Hal)CH_2R^1 \xrightarrow{-Hal^-} \begin{array}{c} R^2\overset{..}{\underset{..}{X}}\overset{+}{C}HCH_2R^1 \\ \updownarrow \\ R^2\overset{+}{X}{=}CHCH_2R^1 \end{array} \quad \begin{array}{l} \longrightarrow R^2Hal + R^1CH_2C\overset{O}{\underset{H}{\diagdown}} \\ \quad when\ (X = O) \\ \\ \overset{-H^+}{\longrightarrow} R^2XCH{=}CHR^1 \\ \quad (X = O\ or\ S) \end{array} \quad (137)$$

The removal of hydrogen halide from α-halo ethers and thioethers by means of sterically hindered bases generally affords the alkenyl ethers or thioethers in good yields. There is no marked difference between the rate of dehydrohalogenation of the ethers and thioethers in the preparative experiment.

A useful application of this elimination reaction is the synthesis from glutardialdehyde through the corresponding cyclic saturated dichloro derivatives of γ-4H-pyran and γ-4H-thiopyran, compounds unknown until recently (reactions 138 and 139)[136].

Another type of elimination[137] is the 1,1-dehydrohalogenation of chloromethyl ethers and thioethers by means of strong bases like t-butyllithium and potassium t-butoxide. The intermediate carbenes can be trapped by adding an alkene (reaction 140).

The dehydrohalogenation proceeds more smoothly with the thio-ethers than with the ethers. A possible reason therefore is that in the

$$ClCH_2XR + B^- \longrightarrow \bar{C}HClXR \longrightarrow$$

$$:CHXR \xrightarrow{Cyclohexene} \text{[structure]} \quad (140)$$

α-chloro thioethers the alkylthio group contributes to the activation of the α-hydrogen atoms (compare with section II.A).

B. β-, γ- and δ-Halo and Hydroxy Thioethers

One of the most striking properties of β-halo thioethers is their very fast hydrolysis. In this respect they resemble the α-halo thioethers. The phenomenon is attributed to the formation of an episulfonium ion in a rate-determining step. This intermediate is very readily attacked by water, a β-hydroxy thioether being produced (reaction 141).

$$\text{[structure]} \xrightarrow{Slow} Cl^- + \text{[structure]} \xrightarrow{Fast}{H_2O}$$

$$\overset{+}{O}H_2CH_2CH_2SR \longrightarrow HOCH_2CH_2SR + H^+ \quad (141)$$

In their turn β-hydroxy thioethers are very smoothly converted into β-halo thioethers, even by aqueous hydrochloric or hydrobromic acid, in a reversal of the preceding reaction.

The reactivity of β-halo ethers $(HalCH_2CH_2OR)$ and β-hydroxy ethers $(HOCH_2CH_2OR)$ is comparable with that of primary alkyl halides or primary alcohols and is much lower than that of their sulfur analogs. The hydrolysis of $ClCH_2CH_2OC_2H_5$ is slower than that of alkyl halides. β-Bromoethyl ethyl ether can be obtained from 2-ethoxy-ethanol and PBr$_3$ in yields which do not exceed 60% [138], the β-bromo thioether, on the contrary, can be prepared in very high yields (reaction 142) [139].

$$3 CH_2(OH)CH_2XC_2H_5 + PBr_3 \longrightarrow 3 CH_2BrCH_2XC_2H_5 + P(OH)_3 \quad (142)$$
$$(X = O \text{ or } S)$$

Consequently there are no indications for an interaction between oxygen and a β-halogen or a β-hydroxyl group in the oxygen ethers.

Many conversions of β-halo or β-hydroxy thioethers with nucleophilic reagents can be considered to proceed via an episulfonium ion.
In principle nucleophilic attack can take place on both carbon atoms
of the three-membered ring, so that in general two substitution
products must be expected. The ratio of these products depends on
the nature of the substituents.

The following examples may give an impression of the reaction
possibilities of β-halo and β-hydroxy thioethers[140–142].

β,β'-Dihydroxydiethyl thioether is very readily converted into a
diether, when treated with alcohol in the presence of acids. This con-
trasts with the fact, that the formation of ethers from hydroxy compounds usually requires drastic conditions. The intermediate formation

$$HOCH_2CH_2SCH_2CH_2OH \xrightarrow{H^+} \overset{CH_2}{\underset{CH_2}{\diagdown}}\overset{+}{S}-CH_2CH_2OH \xrightarrow{ROH}$$

$$ROCH_2CH_2SCH_2CH_2OH \longrightarrow ROCH_2CH_2-\overset{CH_2}{\underset{CH_2}{\diagup}}\overset{+}{S} \xrightarrow{ROH}$$

$$ROCH_2CH_2SCH_2CH_2OR \quad (143)$$

of episulfonium ions would elegantly explain the difference (reaction
143). The conversions shown in reactions (144) to (149) are also com-
prehensible when episulfonium ions are involved. Thioacetals with a

$$C_6H_5SCH(CH_3)CH_2OH \longrightarrow C_6H_5\overset{+}{S}\overset{CH_2\quad H}{\underset{CH_3}{\diagdown\diagup}}C \xrightarrow{SOCl_2} C_6H_5SCH_2CHClCH_3 \quad (144)$$

$$RSCH_2CHClC\equiv N \longrightarrow \overset{CH_2-CH-C\equiv N}{\underset{\underset{R}{\overset{+}{S}}}{\diagdown\diagup}} \xrightarrow{Liq.\ NH_3} NH_2CH_2CH(SR)C\equiv N$$

$$+ RSCH_2CH(NH_2)C\equiv N \quad (145)$$

$$CH_3SCH_2CHClCOOCH_3 \longrightarrow \overset{CH_2-CH-COOCH_3}{\underset{\underset{CH_3}{\overset{+}{S}}}{\diagdown\diagup}} \xrightarrow[100°]{KBr/DMF}$$

$$CH_2BrCH(SCH_3)COOCH_3 \quad (146)$$

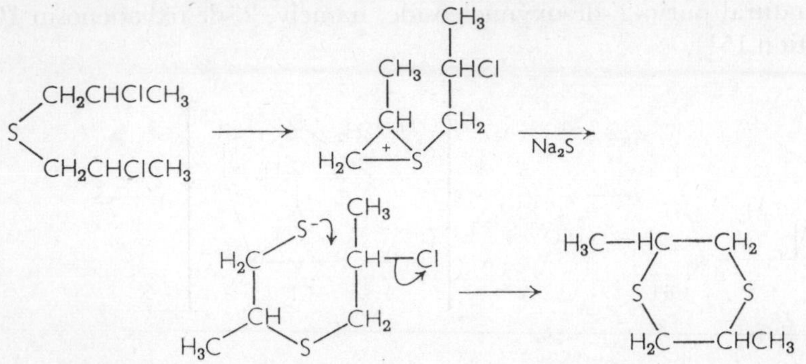

(147)

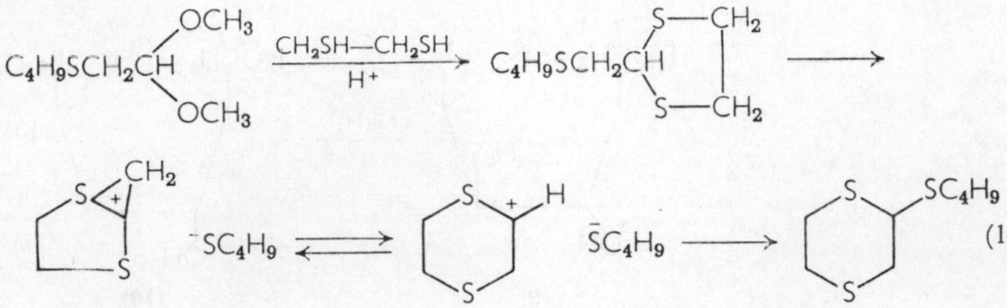

(148)

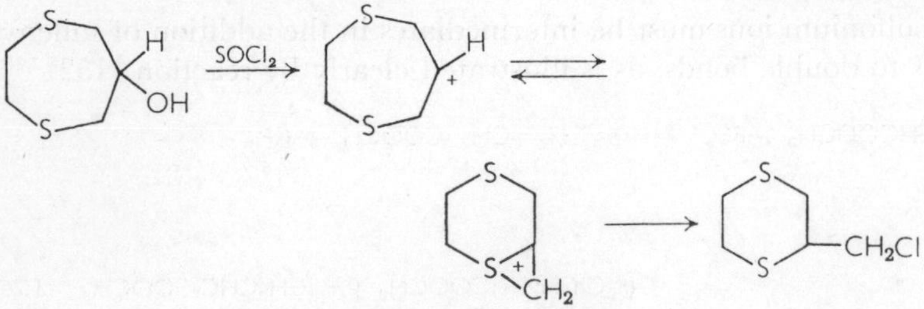

(149)

β-halogen, e.g. $ClCH_2CH(SC_2H_5)_2$, undergo a spontaneous elimination of hydrogen halide with formation of a rearranged product (reaction 150). The corresponding oxygen acetals are quite stable.

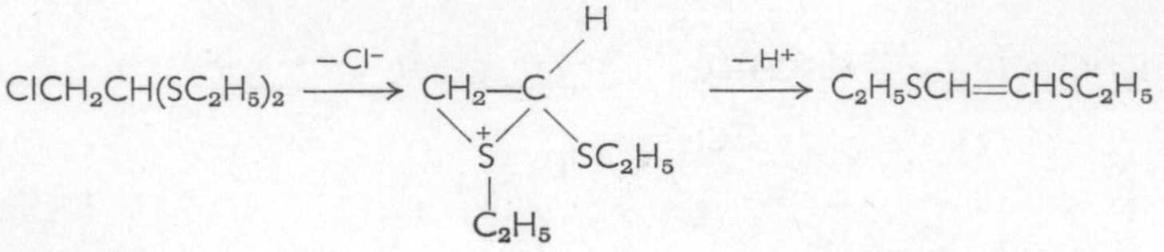

(150)

A valuable application [143] of the properties of β-halo thioethers is the isomerization of the 3-desoxy-3-(ethylthio)xylose derivative **8** into the 2-desoxy-2-(ethylthio)arabinose derivative **9** in the synthesis of the first natural purin-2′-desoxynucleoside, namely, 2′-desoxyadenosin **10** (reaction 151).

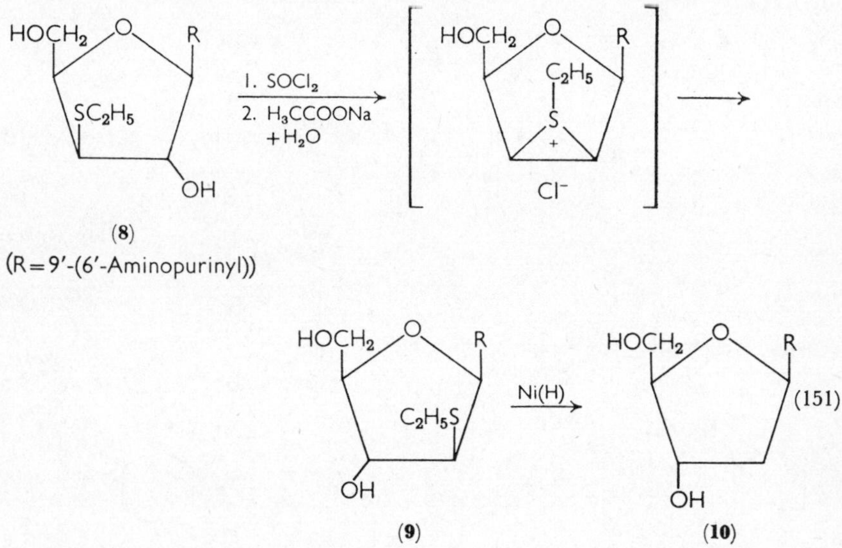

(**8**)

(R = 9′-(6′-Aminopurinyl))

(151)

(**9**)   (**10**)

Episulfonium ions must be intermediates in the addition of sulfenyl halides to double bonds, as is illustrated clearly by reaction (152)[140].

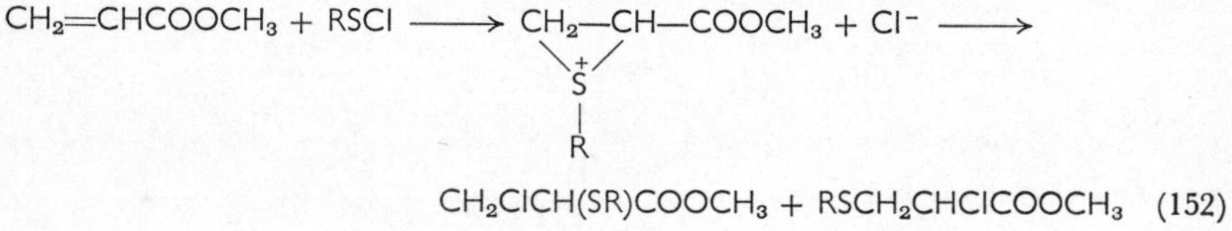

$$CH_2{=}CHCOOCH_3 + RSCI \longrightarrow CH_2{-}CH{-}COOCH_3 + CI^- \longrightarrow$$

$$CH_2CICH(SR)COOCH_3 + RSCH_2CHCICOOCH_3 \quad (152)$$

A possible explanation for the unexpected orientation in the addition of sulfur dichloride and sulfenyl chlorides to 1-alkynes[144,145] is the occurrence of episulfonium ions (reactions 153 and 154). These epi-

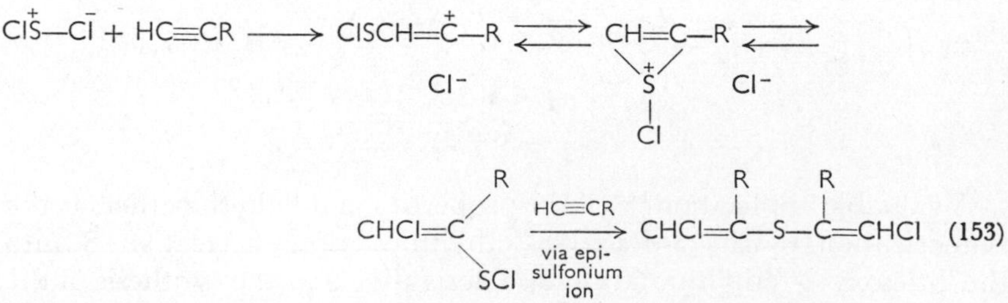

$$R^2SCl + HC\equiv CR^1 \longrightarrow R^2SCH\!\!=\!\!CR^1 \underset{\longleftarrow}{\overset{\longrightarrow}{}} CH\!\!=\!\!CR^1 \underset{\longleftarrow}{\overset{\longrightarrow}{}} CHCl\!\!=\!\!C \quad (154)$$

sulfonium ions may be invoked to explain the formation of the alkynyl thioethers $R^1C\equiv CSC\equiv CR^1$ and $R^1C\equiv CSR^2$ from $[CHCl\!\!=\!\!CR^1]_2S$ and $CHCl\!\!=\!\!CR^1SR^2$, respectively, by careful addition of lithium amide in liquid ammonia (reaction 155) [146,147].

$$CHCl\!\!=\!\!C\overset{R}{\underset{SC_2H_5}{}} \rightleftharpoons H\!-\!C\!\!=\!\!CR \longrightarrow RC\equiv CSC_2H_5 \quad (155)$$

γ-Halo thioethers [148], e.g. $ClCH_2CH_2CH_2SR$, are more difficult to hydrolyze than primary alkyl chlorides. Also their formation from γ-hydroxy thioethers proceeds more slowly than that of alkyl chlorides from alcohols, even when PCl_3 is used. A satisfactory explanation has not been given.

Neighboring-group interaction is favored in δ-halo and δ-hydroxy thioethers, because the required five-membered ring can be formed without strain. On standing, δ-bromo thioethers form a cyclic sulfonium bromide.

The rates of interconversion between the δ-halo and δ-hydroxy thioethers, though not as high as in the cases of the α- and β-substituted thioethers, are considerably higher than those of primary alkyl halides and alcohols. The intermediate species is the five-membered sulfonium ring (reaction 156).

$$R\overset{..}{S}: \quad CH_2\!\!-\!\!Cl \quad \rightleftharpoons \quad R\overset{+}{S}\!\!-\!\!-\!\!CH_2 \quad \overset{H_2O}{\rightleftharpoons} \quad RS \quad CH_2OH + Cl^- \quad (156)$$

As is known, ethers do not form oxonium salts with alkyl halides. In accordance with this no acceleration by 'neighboring-group interaction' is observed during reaction of δ-chloro ethers ($CH_2ClCH_2CH_2CH_2OR$);

the behavior of δ-substituted ethers resembles that of alkyl halides or alcohols.

It is interesting to note that δ-chloro ethers in the presence of metal chlorides such as $SbCl_5$ do form an intramolecular oxonium compound[149]. The $SbCl_5$ abstracts a Cl^- ion from the ether to form a stable anion $SbCl_6^-$ (reaction 157).

$$ \text{(157)} $$

Though six- and higher-membered cyclic sulfonium ions are stable, their rates of formation from the ω-halo or ω-hydroxy thioethers rapidly diminish with increasing length of the carbon chain. The probability of the halogen coming into a favored position by the coiling of the molecule becomes increasingly smaller. Accordingly there will be a continuous decrease in the rates of interconversion between the ω-halo and ω-hydroxy thioethers going from four to nine carbon atoms between the sulfur and the halogen or hydroxy group.

VII. MISCELLANEOUS REACTIONS OF THIOETHERS

A. Some Reactions of the Heteroatom[150,151]

Dialkyl thioethers readily add alkyl halides to form trialkylsulfonium halides (reaction 158); these compounds are soluble and highly ionized

$$ R_2^1S + R^2Hal \longrightarrow R_2^1R^2S^+Hal^- \tag{158} $$

in polar solvents. Methyl iodide reacts most readily, while the higher iodides and also alkyl bromides and chlorides combine less smoothly with the thioethers. The rate of formation decreases likewise with increasing length of the carbon chain in the thioethers. The influence of the solvent is very important; a polar solvent, e.g. methanol, is favorable. The alkylation is catalyzed by mercuric halides.

Unsaturated thioethers with a double or a triple bond, in which the sulfur atom is conjugated with the unsaturated system, e.g. $(CH_2{=}CH)_2S$, $(CH_3C{\equiv}C)_2S$ or $HC{\equiv}CSC_2H_5$, do not form sulfonium compounds under the usual conditions[152].

This difference in reactivity between saturated and unsaturated thioethers can be used for the removal of contaminating saturated thioethers in alkynyl thioethers[20]; the difference between the boiling points of ethylthioacetylene ($HC \equiv CSC_2H_5$) and diethyl thioether ($(C_2H_5)_2S$) is only 2 to 3°. When the ethynyl thioether is prepared from sodium acetylide, sulfur and ethyl bromide, about 25% yield of diethyl thioether is present as impurity. This can be removed by adding a proper quantity of methyl iodide. After some days standing at 20° a bottom layer separates consisting mainly of diethylmethyl sulfonium iodide. When the mixture is shaken with water, the sulfonium compound dissolves. Distillation of the upper layer results in purified ethylthioacetylene.

Ethers (R_2O) only form oxonium salts with alkyl halides when metal halides such as $SbCl_5$, $SnCl_4$ and $FeCl_3$ are added (reaction 159)[149].

$$R_2^1O + R^2Cl + SbCl_5 \longrightarrow R_2^1R^2O^+SbCl_6^- \tag{159}$$

Contrary to the trialkylsulfonium compounds the oxonium salts are only stable in nonaqueous media.

When triethyloxonium borofluorate and diethyl thioether are brought together, diethyl ether is liberated (reaction 160).

$$(C_2H_5)_3O^+BF_4^- + (C_2H_5)_2S \longrightarrow (C_2H_5)_2O + (C_2H_5)_3S^+BF_4^- \tag{160}$$

Dialkyl thioethers also form sulfonium compounds with strong acids; dimethyl thioether ($(CH_3)_2S$) dissolves in concentrated sulfuric acid with formation of the odorless compound $(CH_3)_2\overset{+}{S}H \cdot HSO_4^-$. On dilution with water dimethyl thioether is liberated again; dialkyl ethers behave similarly.

Thioethers with an ester group on the β-carbon atom, such as the methyl ester of 3-(methylthio)propionic acid ($CH_3SCH_2CH_2COOCH_3$) give unexpected results when they are subjected to strong acidic conditions[153]; the propionic ester yields dimethyl thioether ($(CH_3)_2S$) and bis-2-(carboxyethyl)thioether ($(HOOCCH_2CH_2)_2S$). An intermediate complex ion $CH_3\overset{+}{S}(H)CH_2CH_2COOH$ is thought to be formed in the strongly acidic medium. This ion might then be converted into the corresponding thetin ($(CH_3)_2\overset{+}{S}CH_2CH_2COOH$) and 3-mercaptopropionic acid ($HSCH_2CH_2COOH$). The dimethyl thioether, together with acrylic acid ($CH_2 = CHCOOH$), might be decomposition products of the thetin. The bis-2-(carboxyethyl)thioether (($HOOC$-$CH_2CH_2)_2S$) would be formed by addition of 3-mercaptopropionic acid ($HSCH_2CH_2COOH$) to acrylic acid ($CH_2 = CHCOOH$).

Alkylthioacetic acids ($RSCH_2COOH$) remain unchanged on boiling with concentrated solutions of strong acids. Probably the carboxyl group in this position renders the unshared electrons of the sulfur atom unavailable, so that coordination of a proton is hindered. The intermediate occurrence of thetins can also explain the formation of dimethyl thioether and homocystein ($HSCH_2CH_2CH(NH_2)COOH$) from methionin ($CH_3SCH_2CH_2CH(NH_2)COOH$) and 18 N sulfuric acid.

The products formed from thioethers and halogens at low temperatures can be regarded as sulfonium compounds. At room temperature the halogen migrates to the carbon chain or to the aromatic ring, while hydrogen halide is evolved, e.g. reactions (161) and (162). The adducts

$$CH_3SCH_3 + Cl_2 \xrightarrow{\text{Low temp.}} (CH_3)_2\overset{+}{S}ClCl^- \longrightarrow CH_3SCH_2Cl \qquad (161)$$

$$Ph_2S + Br_2 \longrightarrow Ph_2\overset{+}{S}BrBr^- \longrightarrow p\text{-}BrC_6H_4SPh + HBr \qquad (162)$$

of thioethers and iodine are more stable. They have a characteristic absorption band at 308 mμ. Aliphatic thioethers can be detected even in very low concentrations by this reaction[154].

Thioethers can also take up two molecules of bromine or iodine. Dibenzyl thioether forms a 'tetraiodide' at 120° in acetic acid (reaction 163)[155]. From β,β'-dichlorodiethyl thioether (($CH_2ClCH_2)_2S$) and

$$(C_6H_5CH_2)_2S + I_2 \longrightarrow (C_6H_5CH_2)_2\overset{+}{S}I\cdots I^- \xrightarrow{I_2} (C_6H_5CH_2)_2S^+I\cdots I_3^- \qquad (163)$$

two molecules of bromine an un stable adduct ($ClCH_2CH_2)_2S^+Br\cdots$ Br_3^- is obtained[156], which readily converts into the relatively stable ($ClCH_2CH_2)_2S^+Br\cdots Br^-$ (m.p. 44°). The adducts of halogens with selenides and tellurides are more stable. The tendency of the selenium atom to add bromine is so strong, that only one double bond in divinyl selenoether can take up bromine (reaction 164)[157]. Tetrachlorodivinyl

$$(CH_2{=}CH)_2Se + Br_2 \longrightarrow CH_2BrCHBrSeCH{=}CH_2 \xrightarrow{Br_2}$$

$$\begin{array}{c} Br \\ | \\ CH_2BrCHBr\overset{+}{S}e{-}CH{=}CH_2 \qquad (164) \\ | \\ Br^- \end{array}$$

selenoether similarly adds chlorine to the selenium atom (reaction 165)[158]. It is reported that ethers can also form oxonium dibromides

$$[CHCl{=}CCl]_2Se + Cl_2 \longrightarrow [CHCl{=}CCl]_2Se^+{-}Cl\cdots Cl^- \qquad (165)$$

$R_2O \cdot Br_2$. The heat of formation is less than in the case of the thio-ethers.

Alkyl thioethers react with chloramine-T and chloramine-B with formation of sulfilimines, compounds having distinctive melting points (reaction 166)[159].

$$R_2^1S + R^2SO_2N\overset{\displaystyle Cl}{\underset{\displaystyle Na}{<}} \longrightarrow R_2^1\overset{+}{S}-\overset{-}{N}SO_2R^2$$

$$(R^2 = CH_3C_6H_4-, \quad C_6H_5-) \tag{166}$$

Of particular interest are the ylides obtained from some sulfonium compounds. When for instance a solution of fluorenyl-9-dimethyl-sulfonium bromide is treated with sodium hydroxide dimethylsul-fonium-9-fluorenylide is produced as a yellow precipitate (reaction 167)[160]. An important application[161] in the chemistry of sulfur ylides

$$\tag{167}$$

is the preparation of oxiranes by adding an aldehyde to a solution of an ylide; in some cases a ketone also gives good results (reaction 168).

$$(C_6H_5)_2\overset{+}{S}-CH_2R^1 \xrightarrow[\text{THF}]{\text{BuLi}} (C_6H_5)_2\overset{+}{S}-\overset{-}{C}HR^1 \xrightarrow{} (C_6H_5)_2\overset{+}{S}-CHR^1 \xrightarrow{}$$

$$R^1\overset{O}{\overset{\triangle}{CH-CHR^2}} + (C_6H_5)_2S \tag{168}$$

Ylides are formed as intermediates from benzyne (prepared *in situ* from *o*-chlorobromobenzene and butyllithium) and dialkyl thioethers[162]. The ylides undergo a Hoffmann degradation, alkyl phenyl thioethers and alkenes being formed, e.g. reaction (169).

$$\text{(o-chlorobromobenzene)} + C_4H_9Li \xrightarrow[20°]{\text{Ether}} \left[\text{(benzyne)} \right] \xrightarrow{n\text{-}C_5H_{11}SC_5H_{11}}$$

$$\text{(ylide with } \overset{+}{S} \text{--}C_5H_{11}, CH_2, H\text{--}\overset{-}{C}\text{--}H, C_3H_7) \longrightarrow \text{(}C_6H_5SC_5H_{11}\text{)} + CH_2{=}CHC_3H_7 \quad (169)$$

The phenyl alkyl thioethers (and alkenes) are obtained in good yields. In the case of dimethyl thioether ($(CH_3)_2S$) as starting product phenyl methyl thioether ($C_6H_5SCH_3$), along with polymethylene ($(CH_2)_n$) is found.

When the generation of benzyne with butyllithium and the addition of the thioether ($(CH_3)_2S$) are carried out at low temperatures, the intermediate ylide can be trapped by adding perchloric acid to the mixture. Similar results are obtained with *o*-fluorophenylmagnesium bromide as a source of benzyne[163]. With allyl or benzyl thioethers the reaction mixtures are more complicated.

Ylide formation is thought to occur with saturated thioethers and dichlorocarbene, but no pure products have been obtained as yet[164].

Addition takes place between dialkyl thioethers and the triphenylmethyl radical to form an unstable compound (reaction 170)[165].

$$RSR + 2 Ph_3C\cdot \longrightarrow R_2S(CPh_3)_2 \qquad (170)$$

A very characteristic property of thioethers is the formation of well defined crystalline coordination complexes with salts of heavy metals[166]. These complexes can be used for the identification and isolation of thioethers; the thioethers can be recovered by decomposition of the complex with hydrogen sulfide, which converts the mercuric chloride in the complex into mercuric sulfide.

The most common complexes are those with $HgCl_2$. Some thioethers can combine with one molecule of $HgCl_2$ as well as with two; two molecules of the thioether or two alkylthio groups can also complex with only one molecule of $HgCl_2$. The complexes are usually prepared in alcohol. Other metal salts coordinating with sulfur are $PtCl_2$, $PtCl_4$, $PtBr_2$, $AuCl$, $AuCl_3$, $SnCl_4$, $IrCl_3$, $ZnCl_2$, ZnI_2, $SbCl_5$, $AlCl_3$, etc.

Thioethers can be oxidized to sulfoxides and sulfones[167,168]. The oxidation to the sulfoxides is more rapid than the conversion of the sulfoxides to the sulfones, so that it is in many cases possible to obtain the sulfoxide in a pure state (reaction 171). The oxidants most

$$R^1SR^2 \longrightarrow R^1\overset{O}{\underset{\uparrow}{S}}R^2 \longrightarrow R^1\overset{O}{\underset{\underset{O}{\downarrow}}{\overset{\uparrow}{S}}}R^2 \qquad (171)$$

frequently used are hydrogen peroxide (30%), peracids (e.g. C_6H_5COOOH), concentrated nitric acid, potassium permanganate and chromic trioxide, while in some cases iodosobenzene (C_6H_5IO) and ozone have been applied with good results. It is accepted that the oxidation of thioethers to the sulfoxides involves a nucleophilic attack *by* the sulfur atom *upon* the peroxide oxygen, while the oxidation of the sulfoxides to the sulfones must be regarded as a nucleophilic attack *by* the peracid *upon* the sulfur atom of the sulfoxide. The general equation (172) represents the oxidation to the sulfoxides.

$$R^1_2S + R^2OOH \longrightarrow R^1_2SO + R^2OH \qquad (172)$$
$$(R^2 = H, \text{ alkyl, acyl, } o\text{-HOOC—}C_6H_4CO, CF_3CO)$$

The ease of the oxidation depends on the structure of the groups linked to sulfur, and on the nature and the position of substituents in these groups. For instance, dialkyl thioethers such as $(C_2H_5)_2S$ are readily oxidized to sulfoxides and sulfones by hydrogen peroxide (30%), whereas unsaturated thioethers such as $CH_2{=}CHSR$ or $RSC{\equiv}CSR$ are hardly attacked by this reagent, and a very concentrated solution (70%) of H_2O_2 or a peracid are required.

Alkyl thioethers with electron-withdrawing substituents, e.g. CH_2ClCH_2SR, are less reactive than the unsubstituted dialkyl thioethers, while the latter compounds are much more easily oxidized than diaryl thioethers.

In the aryl series *p*-methyl and *p*-methoxy substituents increase and *p*-chloro and *p*-nitro substituents decrease reactivity towards H_2O_2. The oxidation of thioethers with ozone often gives quantitative yields of the sulfones or sulfoxides.

Some thioethers, especially of the allylic type, are autooxidized to some extent, with sulfoxides present among the products.

B. Halogenation of Saturated Thioethers[129-132]

The preparation of α-halo thioethers in good yields by the direct halogenation of saturated thioethers is limited to a few compounds, as in the case of the oxygen ethers. A more general method to obtain the α-halo thioethers is the introduction of gaseous hydrogen halide into a cooled mixture of an aldehyde and a thiol (reaction 173).

$$R^2SH + HCl + R^1C\overset{O}{\underset{H}{\diagdown}} \longrightarrow R^1CHClSR^2 + H_2O \tag{173}$$

Successful chlorinations with free chlorine can be carried out, e.g. with $(CH_3)_2S^{169}$, $CH_3SC_2H_5$, $(C_2H_5)_2S$ and $CH_3SCH_2C_6H_5$. In these cases the proper quantity of chlorine is introduced at $-20°$ into a mixture of the thioether and a solvent, e.g. CCl_4. The products obtained are respectively CH_2ClSCH_3, $CH_3SCHClCH_3$, $CH_3CHCl-SC_2H_5$ and $CH_3SCHClC_6H_5$. Sulfuryl chloride or thionyl chloride can be used instead of chlorine[170,171]. The chlorination at higher temperatures often leads to cleavage of the C—S bond with formation of sulfenyl halides $(RSCl)$ [172] or alkyl halides. Formaldehyde dimethylthioacetal is converted into a mixture of a chlorothioether and a sulfenyl chloride in high yields (reaction 174)[173].

$$CH_2(SCH_3)_2 + Cl_2 \longrightarrow CH_3SCl + CH_2ClSCH_3 \tag{174}$$

A possible mechanism for this cleavage is given by reaction (175).

$$CH_2(SCH_3)_2 + Cl_2 \longrightarrow \underset{\underset{SCH_3}{|}}{\overset{\overset{Cl}{\underset{|}{S^+}}}{CH_2}}\diagdown CH_3 \quad Cl^- \xrightarrow[\text{of Cl}^-\text{ at C}]{\text{Nucleophilic attack}} CH_3SCH_2Cl + CH_3SCl \tag{175}$$

Trithiane is converted by sulfur dichloride or monochloride into α,α'-dichlorodimethyl thioether in excellent yield (reaction 176)[174].

$$\underset{\underset{S}{H_2C}\diagup \diagdown CH_2}{\overset{\overset{CH_2}{S}\diagup \diagdown S}{||}} + 2\,SCl_2 \longrightarrow CH_2ClSCH_2Cl + CS_2 + 2\,HCl + S \tag{176}$$

The halogenation of thioethers proceeds according to an ionic mechanism; first a sulfonium halide is formed which splits off hydrogen halide (see section VII.A). Dimethyl thioether is chlorinated mainly to CH_2ClSCH_3 with the calculated amount of the chlorinating agent. In the further chlorination substitution takes place at the same carbon atom, $CHCl_2SCH_3$ and CCl_3SCH_3 being subsequently formed. The explanation given for this phenomenon is that the $-I$ effect of halogen substituents facilitates the introduction of a further halogen[171].

Only one bromine atom can be introduced into dimethyl thioether[175]. Possibly steric hindrance plays a role.

The halogenation of ethers is accelerated by ultraviolet irradiation, which suggests that a radical mechanism is involved[129]. The reaction is rather unspecific and yields a mixture of different halogenated ethers. In contrast to the thioethers the α-halo ethers are halogenated on the α'-carbon atom before a second hydrogen on the α-carbon atom is substituted. There are only a few reports of clean-cut halogenation of ethers. Dimethyl ether for instance can be chlorinated to CH_2ClOCH_3 and CH_2ClOCH_2Cl, while diethyl ether is converted into $(CH_3CHCl)_2O$ at $-30°$ with chlorine. At room temperature the β-hydrogen atoms are also substituted. Probably the α-chloro ether primarily formed splits off hydrogen halide, whereupon the resulting vinyl ether adds halogen (reaction 177). The easy formation of α,β-

$$R^1CH_2CH_2OR^2 + Cl_2 \longrightarrow R^1CH_2CHClOR^2 \xrightarrow{-Cl^-} R^1CH_2\overset{+}{C}HOR^2 \xrightarrow{-H^+}$$
$$R^1CH{=}CHOR^2 \xrightarrow{Cl_2} R^1CHClCHClOR^2 \quad (177)$$

dibromo ethers from bromine and α-chloro ethers (a reaction which also proceeds with α-chloro thioethers) is in concordance with this mechanism (reaction 178).

$$R^1CH_2CHClXR^2 + Br_2 \xrightarrow{(X = O \text{ or } S)} R^1CHBrCHBrXR^2 + HCl \quad (178)$$

C. Reaction of Dichlorocarbene with Unsaturated Thioethers

Unsaturated ethers and thioethers, including cyclic compounds in which the heteroatom is conjugated with a double bond, give the expected adducts with dichlorocarbene ($:CCl_2$) in good yields[167], when the latter is produced from ethyl trichloroacetate and from sodium methoxide or from sodium trichloroacetate. When it is generated from chloroform and potassium t-butoxide, the yields of the adducts are considerably lower (reaction 179)[177].

$$(179)$$

$$(X = O \text{ or } S)$$

A marked difference in the course of the reaction with dichloro-carbene is observed between allylic ethers and thioethers: the former give the normal adduct in high yields, as is illustrated by reaction (180)[178]. In the case of the sulfur analogs mainly two different

$$(180)$$

products are formed in a considerably lower total yield (reaction 181)[179].

$$(181)$$

Mesomeric anions may occur as intermediates (compare with section II.C) (reaction 182).

$$(182)$$

2,5-Dihydrofuran gives the expected adduct as well as an abnormal product with dichlorocarbene[180]. The ratio of these products depends, as in the reaction just mentioned, on the source of dichlorocarbene. In the case of ethyl trichloroacetate and sodium methoxide the quantity of the normal product is higher than when sodium trichloroacetate is employed (reaction 183). Noncyclic allyl thioethers react in a different

$$\text{(structure)} + :CCl_2 \longrightarrow \text{(structure)} + \text{(structure)} \quad (183)$$

way with dichlorocarbene; a mixture of two compounds is obtained in good yield (reaction 184)[164,181].

$$RSCH_2CH{=}CH_2 + :CCl_2 \longrightarrow RSC{-}CH{-}CH{=}CH_2 + RSC{=}CHCHCH_3 \quad (184)$$

A well-defined mechanism for the formation of these products is not known. Ylides ($(CH_2{=}CHCH_2)(R)\overset{+}{S}{-}\overset{-}{C}Cl_2$) are possible intermediates. When the double bond is separated from the alkylthio group by two methylene groups, the normal adduct is produced, but only in low yield (reaction 185).

$$RSCH_2CH_2CH{=}CH_2 + :CCl_2 \longrightarrow RSCH_2CH_2CH{-}CH_2 \quad (185)$$

The presence of saturated thioethers has been shown to inhibit the formation of 7,7-dichloronorcarane from cyclohexene and dichlorocarbene. In the same way the reaction of the double bond in $RSCH_2CH_2CH{=}CH_2$ with dichlorocarbene can be suppressed by the presence of the saturated system ($RSCH_2CH_2{-}$); nothing is known about the nature of this inhibiting effect.

D. Some Thermic Reactions of Thioethers

Contrary to the 1-alkynyl ethers ($R^1C{\equiv}COR^2$ where R^1, $R^2 =$ alkyl), the sulfur analogs are rather stable towards heating at elevated temperatures.

The 1-alkynyl ethers possessing at least one β-hydrogen atom in the saturated part of the molecule, e.g. $RC{\equiv}COCH_2CH_3$, undergo a pyrolytic cleavage with elimination of an alkene, e.g. ethene, when heated at 100–150°. The intermediate ketene immediately reacts with the starting material to produce a cyclobutenone derivative[51], e.g. reaction (186).

$$R-C\equiv C \quad H \quad O \quad H_2C \quad CH_2 \xrightarrow{-C_2H_4} RCH=C=O \xrightarrow{RC\equiv COC_2H_5} C_2H_5O-C=C-R \quad (186)$$

Alkynyl thioethers ($RC\equiv CSC_2H_5$) can be heated to 200° without decomposition. The acetylenic thioethers ($HC\equiv CSC_2H_5$ and $HC\equiv CS\text{-}t\text{-}C_4H_9$), other compounds have not yet been investigated, split off gaseous products on heating; these products consist mainly of a mixture of ethene and ethyne and isobutene, respectively. Thiophen derivatives are obtained in moderate yields[182]. The mechanism of this decomposition has not yet been investigated, but the thiophens may be formed from thioketene ($CH_2=C=S$), which is reported to be formed from ethylthioethyne at 500° under reduced pressure (reactions 187 and 188)[183].

$$2\ HC\equiv CSC_2H_5 \longrightarrow \boxed{}\text{-}SC_2H_5 \ (+\ CH_2=CH_2 + HC\equiv CH) \quad (187)$$

$$2\ HC\equiv C-S-t\text{-}C_4H_9 \longrightarrow \boxed{}\text{-}S-t\text{-}C_4H_9 \left(+ \ CH_2=C\!\!\begin{array}{l} CH_3 \\ CH_3 \end{array} \right) \quad (188)$$

A well-known thermal isomerization is the Claisen rearrangement[188] of allyl aryl ethers, which proceeds when the ether is heated at about 200°. The o-allylphenol is obtained in good yields.

The same reaction is observed with the thioethers, but the conversion proceeds more slowly and results in low yields of the o-allyl thiophenol[185], e.g. reaction (189).

(189)

Refluxing of phenyl allyl thioether for several hours in the presence of quinoline produces a mixture of two products (**13** and **14**), which are thought to have the *o*-allyl thiophenol as a precursor. Part of the phenyl allyl thioether possibly isomerizes under the catalytic influence of quinoline into phenyl propenyl thioether (compare section II.C), which polymerizes under the drastic reaction conditions. Scheme 5 may serve to explain the formation of **13** and **14**[186].

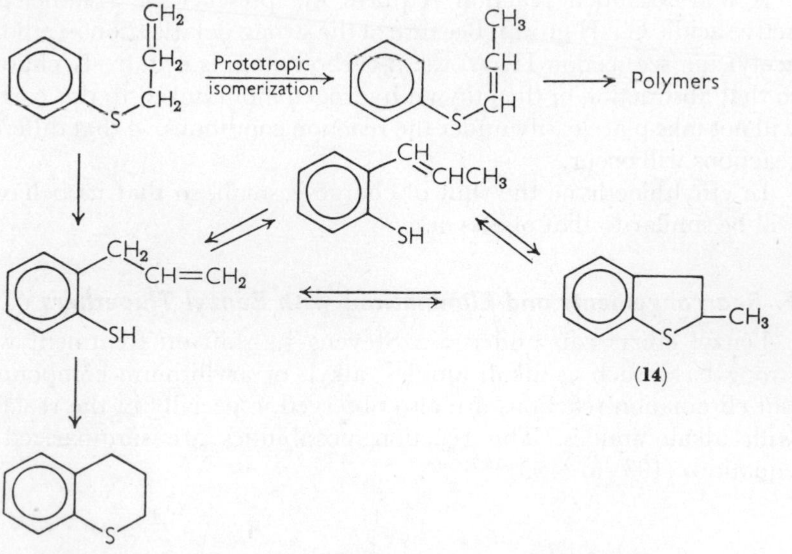

SCHEME 5.

E. Reaction of Acetylenic Thioethers under Mannich Conditions

Acetylenic ethers (HC≡COR) and the corresponding thioethers show a strong difference in their reactions with a mixture of a secondary amine and formaldehyde. Ethylthioethyne gives the expected condensation product in an excellent yield (reaction 190)[183].

$$HC{\equiv}CSC_2H_5 + HN(C_2H_5)_2 + HC\overset{O}{\underset{H}{\diagdown}} \longrightarrow (C_2H_5)_2NCH_2C{\equiv}CSC_2H_5 + H_2O \quad (190)$$

Ethoxyacetylene does not yield the Mannich product, but rather a β-dialkylamino ester, probably formed by addition of the hydrate of dialkylaminomethanol to the triple bond. Compounds in which the ethynyl hydrogen atom is replaced by a carbinol function react in a similar way under Mannich conditions (reactions 191 and 192)[51].

$$HC{\equiv}COC_2H_5 + (C_2H_5)_2NCH_2OH \cdot H_2O \longrightarrow (C_2H_5)_2NCH_2CH_2COOC_2H_5 \quad (191)$$

$$CH_3CH(OH)C{\equiv}COC_2H_5 + (C_2H_5)_2NCH_2OH \longrightarrow CH_3CH(OH)\overset{\overset{\displaystyle CH_2N(C_2H_5)_2}{|}}{C}H{-}COOC_2H_5 \quad (192)$$

A real Mannich reaction requires the presence of a sufficiently active acidic C—H group. Because of the strong polarization in ethoxy-acetylene (see section III.A) the β-carbon atom is negatively charged so that abstraction of the ethynyl hydrogen atom linked to this carbon will not take place easily under the reaction conditions, so that different reactions will occur.

In ethylthioethyne the shift of charge is small, so that its behavior will be similar to that of alkynes.

F. Rearrangements and Eliminations with Benzyl Thioethers

Benzyl ethers can undergo a Stevens 1,2-shift on treatment with strong bases such as alkali amides, alkyl- or aryllithium compounds, but elimination reactions are also observed, especially in the reaction with alkali amides. The reaction possibilities are summarized in equations (193) to (195)[187,188].

$$C_6H_5CH_2OR^1 \xrightarrow[\text{ether}]{R^2Li} C_6H_5\overset{\overset{\displaystyle Li}{|}}{C}HOR^1 \longrightarrow C_6H_5\overset{\overset{\displaystyle OLi}{|}}{C}HR^1 \quad (193)$$

$$(R^1 = \text{benzyl or alkyl}, \quad R^2 = \text{aryl or alkyl})$$

$$C_6H_5CH_2OCH_2C_6H_5 \xrightarrow[\substack{\text{ether or} \\ \text{liq. } NH_3}]{KNH_2} C_6H_5\overset{-}{C}HOCH_2C_6H_5 \xrightarrow{\text{1,2-shift}} C_6H_5\overset{\overset{\displaystyle O^-}{|}}{C}HCH_2C_6H_5$$

$$(194)$$

$$C_6H_5CH_2O—CH_2—CH_3 \xrightarrow{KNH_2} C_6H_5CH_2O—CH_2\bar{C}H_2 \xrightarrow{\text{1,2-Elimination}}$$

$$C_6H_5CH_2\bar{O} + CH_2{=}CH_2 \quad (195)$$

With diallyl ether and with its sulfur analog 1,2-shifts can also occur in the latter as a side-reaction in the prototropic conversion into dipropenyl thioether (reaction 196) (compare section II.C). With benzyl

$$CH_2{=}CH—CH_2—CH—CH_2CH{=}CH_2 \quad (196)$$

$$(X = O \text{ or } S)$$

thioethers both the rearrangement and the elimination proceed in a different way (reactions 197 and 198) [189].

$$(197)$$

$$(198)$$

On heating with potassium t-butoxide in dimethyl sulfoxide, hydrogen sulfide is eliminated from dibenzyl thioether and stilbene is obtained in moderate yields; the mechanism shown by reaction (199) is proposed[190].

$$C_6H_5CH_2SCH_2C_6H_5 \xrightarrow[\text{DMSO, 100°}]{\text{KO}-t\text{-}C_4H_9} C_6H_5\overset{-}{C}HSCH_2C_6H_5 \xrightarrow{\text{1,2-Shift}}$$

$$\underset{\overset{|}{S^-}}{C_6H_5CHCH_2C_6H_5} \xrightarrow{\text{KO}-t\text{-}C_4H_9} \underset{\overset{|}{S^-}}{C_6H_5C\overset{\frown}{-}CHC_6H_5} \longrightarrow H_2S + C_6H_5CH{=}CHC_6H_5 \quad (199)$$

VIII. REFERENCES

1. G. Cilento, *Chem. Rev.*, **60**, 147–167 (1960).
2. C. R. Hauser, C. F. Hauser and P. J. Hamrick, *J. Org. Chem.*, **24**, 397 (1959).
3. K. Shishido, Y. Kazama, H. Kodama and H. Nozaki, *J. Am. Chem. Soc.*, **81**, 5817 (1959).
4. J. R. Nooi and J. F. Arens, *Rec. Trav. Chim.*, **80**, 244 (1961).
5. H. O. House, *Modern Synthetic Reactions*, W. A. Benjamin, New York, 1965.
6. H. Gilman and F. J. Webb, *J. Am. Chem. Soc.*, **71**, 4062 (1949).
7. H. Gilman and F. J. Webb, *J. Am. Chem. Soc.*, **62**, 987 (1940).
8. V. Baliah and R. Varadachari, *J. Indian Chem. Soc.*, **31**, 666 (1954).
9. A. Fröling and J. F. Arens, *Rec. Trav. Chim.*, **81**, 1009 (1962).
10. W. E. Truce and F. E. Roberts, *J. Org. Chem.*, **28**, 961 (1963).
11. J. Hine, R. P. Bayer and G. G. Hammer, *J. Am. Chem. Soc.*, **84**, 1751 (1962).
12. L. Brandsma, unpublished results.
13. R. J. S. Beer and R. A. Slater, *J. Chem. Soc.*, 4069 (1964).
14. M. H. Durand, *Bull. Soc. Chim. France*, 2396 (1961).
15. L. Brandsma, unpublished results.
16. L. Brandsma, H. E. Wijers and J. F. Arens, *Rec. Trav. Chim.*, **82**, 1040 (1963).
17. P. P. Montijn and L. Brandsma, *Rec. Trav. Chim.*, **83**, 456 (1964).
18. L. Brandsma, C. Jonker and M. H. Berg, *Rec. Trav. Chim.*, **84**, 560 (1965).
19. L. Brandsma, H. E. Wijers and J. F. Arens, *Rec. Trav. Chim.*, **81**, 583 (1962).
20. L. Brandsma, H. E. Wijers and C. Jonker, *Rec. Trav. Chim.*, **83**, 208 (1964).
21. J. J. van Daalen, A. Kraak and J. F. Arens, *Rec. Trav. Chim.*, **80**, 810 (1961).
22. H. E. Wijers and L. Brandsma, unpublished results.
23. L. Brandsma, P. P. Montijn and J. F. Arens, *Rec. Trav. Chim.*, **82**, 1015 (1963).
24. P. P. Montijn, H. M. Schmidt, J. H. van Boom, H. J. T. Bos, L. Brandsma and J. F. Arens, *Rec. Trav. Chim.*, **84**, 271 (1965).
25. T. F. Doumani, *Chem. Abstr.*, 12669a (1954).
26. H. C. Volger and J. F. Arens, *Rec. Trav. Chim.*, **76**, 847 (1957); E. Rothstein, *J. Chem. Soc.*, 1553 (1940).
27. L. Brandsma, unpublished results.
28. C. C. Price and J. S. Vittimberga, *J. Org. Chem.*, **27**, 3736 (1962).

29. H. J. Boonstra and J. F. Arens, *Rec. Trav. Chim.*, **79**, 882 (1960).
30. W. E. Parham and P. L. Stright, *J. Am. Chem. Soc.*, **78**, 4783 (1956).
31. W. E. Parham, R. F. Motter and G. L. Mayo, *J. Am. Chem. Soc.*, **81**, 3386 (1959).
32. J. H. van Boom, P. P. Montijn, M. H. Berg, L. Brandsma and J. F. Arens, *Rec. Trav. Chim.*, **84**, 813 (1965).
33. L. Brandsma, unpublished results.
34. L. Brandsma and J. H. van Boom, unpublished results.
35. L. Brandsma and M. H. Berg, unpublished results.
36. D. S. Tarbell and W. E. Lovett, *J. Am. Chem. Soc.*, **78**, 2254 (1956).
37. D. S. Tarbell and M. A. McCall, *J. Am. Chem. Soc.*, **74**, 48 (1952).
38. C. C. Price and W. H. Snyder, *J. Org. Chem.*, **27**, 4639 (1962).
39. T. J. Prosser, *J. Am. Chem. Soc.*, **83**, 1701, 1773 (1961).
40. S. Oae, A. Choro and W. Tagaki, *Chem. Ind. (London)*, 304 (1962).
41. E. Rothstein, *J. Chem. Soc.*, 1558 (1940).
42. G. Pourcelot, P. Cadiot and A. Willemart, *Compt. Rend.*, **252**, 1630 (1961).
43. G. Pourcelot, M. Lequan, M. P. Simonnin and P. Cadiot, *Bull. Soc. Chim. France*, 1278 (1962).
44. G. Pourcelot, *Compt. Rend.*, **260**, 2847 (1965).
45. P. P. Montijn and L. Brandsma, unpublished results.
46. J. H. van Boom and L. Brandsma, unpublished results.
47. R. B. Woodward and R. H. Eastman, *J. Am. Chem. Soc.*, **68**, 2229 (1946).
48. W. H. Brehm and T. Levenson, *J. Am. Chem. Soc.*, **76**, 5389 (1954).
49. H. Stobbe, G. Ljungren and J. Freyberg, *Chem. Ber.*, **59**, 265 (1926).
50. V. Baliah and R. Varadachari, *Chem. Abstr.*, **49**, 3076 (1955).
51. J. F. Arens in *Advances in Organic Chemistry*, Vol. II (Eds. R. A. Raphael, E. C. Taylor and H. Wynberg), Interscience Publishers, New York, 1960.
52. T. L. Jacobs, R. Cramer and J. E. Hanson, *J. Am. Chem. Soc.*, **64**, 223 (1942).
53. A. E. Favorskiĭ and M. N. Shchukina, *Chem. Abstr.*, **40**, 4657 (1946); *Zh. Obshch. Khim.*, **15**, 394 (1945).
54. M. N. Shchukina, *Zh. Obshch. Khim.*, **18**, 1350 (1948).
55. G. Eglington, E. R. H. Jones, B. L. Shaw and M. C. Whiting, *J. Chem. Soc.*, 1860 (1954).
56. T. L. Jacobs, R. Cramer and F. T. Weiss, *J. Am. Chem. Soc.*, **62**, 1849 (1940).
57. J. Ficini, *Bull. Soc. Chim. France*, 1367 (1954).
58. H. C. Volger and J. F. Arens, *Rec. Trav. Chim.*, **77**, 1170 (1958).
59. H. J. Boonstra, L. Brandsma, A. M. Wiegman and J. F. Arens, *Rec. Trav. Chim.*, **78**, 252 (1959).
60. W. Drenth and H. Hogeveen, *Rec. Trav. Chim.*, **79**, 1002 (1960).
61. W. Drenth in *Chemistry of Organic Sulfur Compounds*, Vol. II (Ed. N. Kharash), Pergamon Press, New York, in press.
62. L. Brandsma and J. F. Arens, *Rec. Trav. Chim.*, **81**, 540 (1962).
63. G. L. Hekkert and W. Drenth, *Rec. Trav. Chim.*, **80**, 1285 (1961).
64. J. F. Arens, H. C. Volger, T. Doornbos, J. Bonnema, J. W. Greidanus and J. H. van den Hende, *Rec. Trav. Chim.*, **75**, 1459 (1956).
65. J. F. Arens, A. C. Hermans and J. F. Sperna Weiland, *Proc. Koninkl. Ned. Akad. Wetenschap.*, **B58**, 78 (1955).
66. J. F. Arens and T. Doornbos, *Rec. Trav. Chim.*, **75**, 482 (1956).

67. L. Brandsma, unpublished results.
68. M. F. Shostakovskiĭ and A. W. Bogdanova, *Chem. Abstr.*, **42**, 4519 (1948).
69. M. F. Shostakovskiĭ, E. N. Prilezhaeva and N. I. Uvarava, *Chem. Abstr.*, **49**, 9483 (1955).
70. M. F. Shostakovskiĭ, E. N. Prilezhaeva and E. S. Shapiro, *Chem. Abstr.*, **48**, 9311 (1954).
71. W. E. Parham, I. Gordon and J. D. Swalen, *J. Am. Chem. Soc.*, **74**, 1824 (1952).
72. M. F. Shostakovskiĭ and A. W. Bogdanova, *Zh. Obshch. Khim.*, **17**, 567 (1947).
73. H. Vieregge, H. J. T. Bos and J. F. Arens, *Rec. Trav. Chim.*, **78**, 664 (1959).
74. L. B. Bos and J. F. Arens, *Rec. Trav. Chim.*, **82**, 157, 339 (1963).
75. W. E. Parham and R. F. Motter, *J. Am. Chem. Soc.*, **81**, 2146 (1959).
76. C. M. Hill, R. M. Prigmore and G. J. Moore, *J. Am. Chem. Soc.*, **77**, 352 (1955).
77. H. J. Alkema and J. F. Arens, *Rec. Trav. Chim.*, **79**, 1257 (1960).
78. W. E. Truce, H. E. Hill and M. M. Boudakian, *J. Am. Chem. Soc.*, **78**, 2760 (1956).
79. E. Angeletti, F. Montanari and A. Negrini, *Gazz. Chim. Ital.*, **87**, 1115 (1957).
80. W. E. Truce, M. M. Boudakian, R. F. Heine and R. J. McManimie, *J. Am. Chem. Soc.*, **78**, 2743 (1956).
81. Th. R. Rix and J. F. Arens, *Proc. Koninkl. Ned. Akad. Wetenschap.*, **56**, 364 (1953).
82. A. J. Birch, *Quart. Rev (London)*, **4**, 69 (1950).
83. J. van Schooten, J. Knotnerus, H. Boer and P. M. Duinker, *Rec. Trav. Chim.*, **77**, 935 (1958).
84. W. E. Truce and J. J. Breiter, *J. Am. Chem. Soc.*, **84**, 1621 (1962).
85. G. Gerdil and E. A. C. Lucken, *J. Chem. Soc.*, 2857 (1963).
86. R. L. Burwell, *Chem. Rev.*, **54**, 672 (1954).
87. W. E. Truce, D. P. Tate and D. N. Burdge, *J. Am. Chem. Soc.*, **82**, 2872 (1960).
88. R. L. Letsinger and J. G. Traynham, *J. Am. Chem. Soc.*, **70**, 3342 (1948).
89. H. Gilman and H. A. McNinch, *J. Org. Chem.*, **26**, 3723 (1961).
90. D. S. Tarbell and D. P. Harnish, *Chem. Rev. (London)*, **49**, 1 (1951).
91. J. P. Greenstein and M. Winitz, *Chemistry of the Amino Acids*, Vol. II, John Wiley and Sons, New York, 1961, p. 1241.
92. V. Du Vigneaud and G. L. Miller, *J. Biol. Chem.*, **116**, 469 (1936).
93. W. E. Truce and J. J. Breiter, *J. Am. Chem. Soc.*, **84**, 1623 (1962).
94. G. R. Pettit and E. E. van Tamelen, *Org. Reactions*, **12**, 356 (1962).
95. H. Hauptmann and W. F. Walter, *Chem. Rev.*, **62**, 347 (1962).
96. R. Mozingo, D. E. Wolf, S. A. Harris and K. Folkers, *J. Am. Chem. Soc.*, **65**, 1013 (1943).
97. Hans Wijnberg and A. E. de Groot, *Chem. Comm.*, **1**, 171 (1965).
98. J. F. Arens, *Rec. Trav. Chim.*, **82**, 83 (1963).
99. L. Brandsma, *Rec. Trav. Chim.*, **83**, 307 (1964).
100. A Schaap, L. Brandsma and J. F. Arens, to be published.
101. J. H. van Boom, L. Brandsma and J. F. Arens, to be published.
102. G. A. Wildschut and J. F. Arens, unpublished results.

103. O. Foss, 'Ionic scission of the S—S bond' in *Organic Chemistry of Sulfur Compounds* (Ed. N. Kharash), Pergamon Press, New York, 1961, p. 83.
104. J. R. Nooi and J. F. Arens, *Rec. Trav. Chim.*, **81**, 533 (1962).
105. G. K. Hughes and E. O. P. Thompson, *Nature*, **164**, 365 (1949).
106. H. Simonis and P. Remmert, *Chem. Ber.*, **47**, 269 (1914).
107. A. Lüttringhaus, G. Wagner von Sääf, E. Sucker and G. Borth, *Ann. Chem.*, **557**, 62 (1945).
108. A. Lüttringhaus, G. Sääf and K. Hauschild, *Chem. Ber.*, **71**, 1673 (1938).
109. G. Gamboni and H. Schinz, *Helv. Chim. Acta*, **41**, 1603 (1958).
110. A. L. Kranzfelder and R. Vogt, *J. Am. Chem. Soc.*, **60**, 1714 (1938).
111. E. E. Reid, *Organic Chemistry of Bivalent Sulfur*, Part III, Chemical Publishing Co., New York, 1960, p. 332; compare also: M. F. Shotakovskii, M. R. Kulibekov and A. K. Cjorban, *J. Gen. Chem. USSR*, **34**, 2870 (1964).
112. W. E. Parham, M. A. Kalnins and D. R. Theissen, *J. Org. Chem.*, **27**, 2698 (1962).
113. C. M. Hill, G. W. Senter, L. Haynes and M. E. Hill, *J. Am. Chem. Soc.*, **76**, 4538 (1954).
114. P. P. Montijn, E. Harryvan and L. Brandsma, *Rec. Trav. Chim.*, **83**, 1212 (1964).
115. L. Brandsma and J. F. Arens, unpublished results.
116. G. K. Hughes and E. O. P. Thompson, *J. Proc. Roy. Soc. N. S. Wales*, **83**, 269 (1959).
117. C. M. Suter and H. L. Hansen, *J. Am. Chem. Soc.*, **54**, 4100 (1932).
118. W. I. Patterson and J. V. Karabinos, *Chem. Abstr.*, **40**, 4484 (1946).
119. J. Gierer and B. Alfredsson, *Chem. Ber.*, **90**, 1240 (1957).
120. J. H. van Boom and L. Brandsma, to be published.
121. B. Holmberg, *J. Pr.* [2] **135**, 57 (1932).
122. R. A. Baxter, G. T. Newbold and F. S. Spring, *J. Chem. Soc.*, 370 (1947).
123. F. Weygand and H. J. Bestmann, *Chem. Ber.*, **90**, 1230 (1957).
124. H. Böhme and H. J. Gran, *Ann. Chem.*, **577**, 68 (1952).
125. D. S. Tarbell and D. P. Harnish, *Chem. Rev.*, **49**, 71 (1951).
126. E. L. Gustus and P. G. Stevens, *J. Am. Chem. Soc.*, **55**, 378 (1933).
127. H. Böhme and J. Roehz, *Ann. Chem.*, **648**, 21 (1961).
128. C. C. Price and S. Oae, *Sulfur Bonding*, The Ronald Press Comp., New York, 1962, p. 9.
129. H. Gross and E. Höft, *Z. Chem.*, **4** [11], 401 (1964).
130. L. Summers, *Chem. Rev.*, **55**, 301 (1955).
131. H. Baganz, *Angew. Chem.*, **71**, 366 (1959).
132. H. Baganz and L. Domaschke, *Angew. Chem.*, **74**, 144 (1962).
133. L. Jirousek and J. V. Kostir, *Chem. Abstr.*, **45**, 542 (1951); L. Brandsma, unpublished.
134. J. H. van Boom and L. Brandsma, to be published.
135. L. Brandsma, unpublished results.
136. J. Strating, J. H. Keijer, E. Molenaar and L. Brandsma, *Angew. Chem.*, *Intern. Ed. Engl.*, 399 (1962). Compare also: L. Brandsma and J. F. Arens, *Rec. Trav. Chim.*, **81**, 33 (1961).
137. U. Schöllköpf and G. J. Lehmann, *Tetrahedron Letters*, 165 (1962).
138. G. C. Harryson and H. Diehl, *Org. Syn.*, Coll. Vol. III, John Wiley and Sons, New York, 1955, p. 370.

139. L. Brandsma, unpublished results.
140. K. D. Gundermann, *Angew. Chem.*, **75**, 1195 (1963).
141. F. P. Richter, F. B. Augustin, E. Koft and E. E. Reid, *J. Am. Chem. Soc.*, **74**, 4076 (1952).
142. C. S. Marvel and E. D. Weil, *J. Am. Chem. Soc.*, **76**, 63 (1954).
143. C. D. Anderson, L. Goodman and B. R. Baker, *J. Am. Chem. Soc.*, **81**, 3967 (1959).
144. L. I. Zakharkin, *Bull. Acad. Sci. USSR, Div. Chem. Sci.* (C.B. Transl.) 414 (1959).
145. A. Dondoni, G. Modena und G. Scorrano, *Chem. Abstr.*, **61**, 10613 (1964).
146. L. Brandsma and J. F. Arens, *Rec. Trav. Chim.*, **80**, 241 (1961).
147. L. Brandsma, unpublished results.
148. E. E. Reid, *Organic Chemistry of Bivalent Sulfur*, Part II, Chemical Publishing Co., New York, 1960, p. 231, 232 and 272 and references.
149. Houben–Weil, *Sauerstoffverbindungen*, Teil 3 (1965): H. Meerwein, *Oxoniumsalze*.
150. E. E. Reid, *Organic Chemistry of Bivalent Sulfur*, Vols. II and III, Chemical Publishing Co., New York, 1960.
151. Houben—Weil, *Methoden der organischen Chemie*, Schwefel-, Selen- und Tellurverbindungen.
152. H. J. Boonstra and L. Brandsma, unpublished results.
153. F. Challenger, *Aspects of the Organic Chemistry of Sulphur*, Butterworths, London, 1959, pp. 1–32.
154. S. H. Hastings, *Anal. Chem.*, **25**, 420 (1953).
155. F. Feigl and A. Bonoli, *Monatsh. Chem.*, **53**, 508 (1929).
156. C. S. Gibson and W. J. Pope, *J. Chem. Soc.*, **117**, 271 (1920).
157. L. Brandsma, unpublished results.
158. H. Brintzinger, K. Pfannstiel and H. Vogel, *Z. Anorg. Allgem. Chem.*, **256**, 75 (1948).
159. E. E. Reid, *Organic Chemistry of Bivalent Sulfur*, Vol. II, Chemical Publishing Co., New York, 1960, pp. 51 and 52.
160. C. K. Ingold and J. A. Jessop, *J. Chem. Soc.*, 713 (1930).
161. A. W. Johnson, V. J. Hruby and J. L. Williams, *J. Am. Chem. Soc.*, **86**, 918 (1964) and references mentioned therein.
162. H. Hellmann and D. Eberle, *Ann.*, **662**, 188 (1963).
163. V. Franzen, H. I. Joschek and C. Mertz, *Ann. Chem.*, **654**, 82 (1962).
164. W. E. Parham and S. H. Groen, *J. Org. Chem.*, **29**, 2214 (1964).
165. S. Bezzi and P. Lanza, *Gazz. Chim. Ital.*, **80**, 180 (1950).
166. E. E. Reid, *Organic Chemistry of Bivalent Sulfur*, Vol. II, Chemical Publishing Co., New York, 1960, pp. 52–60 and references mentioned therein.
167. D. Barnard, L. Bateman and J. I. Cunneen in *Organic Chemistry of Sulfur Compounds* (Ed. N. Kharash), Vol. I, Pergamon Press, New York, 1961, p. 229.
168. H. H. Szmant in *Organic Chemistry of Sulfur Compounds* (Ed. N. Kharash), Vol. I, Pergamon Press, New York, 1961, p. 154.
169. H. Böhme, H. Fischer and R. Frank, *Ann. Chem.*, **563**, 54 (1949).
170. F. G. Bordwell and B. M. Pitt, *J. Am. Chem. Soc.*, **77**, 572 (1955).
171. W. E. Truce, G. H. Birum and E. T. McBee, *J. Am. Chem. Soc.*, **74**, 3594 (1952).

172. N. Kharash and R. B. Langford, *J. Org. Chem.*, **28**, 1903 (1963).
173. H. Böhme and H. J. Grau, *Ann. Chem.*, **577**, 68 (1952); **581**, 137 (1953).
174. F. G. Mann and W. J. Pope, *J. Chem. Soc.*, 1172 (1923).
175. F. Boberg, G. Winter and G. R. Schultze, *Chem. Ber.*, **89**, 1160 (1956).
176. E. E. Schweizer and W. E. Parham, *J. Am. Chem. Soc.*, **82**, 4085 (1960);
     W. E. Parham, R. W. Soeder and R. M. Dodson, *J. Am. Chem. Soc.*, **87**, 321
     (1965); W. E. Parham, L. Christenser, S. H. Groen and R. M. Dodson,
     J. Org. Chem., **29**, 2211 (1964).
177. E. P. Prilezhaeva, N. P. Petukhova and M. F. Shostakovskiĭ, *Chem. Abstr.*,
     57, 13632 (1962).
178. W. E. Parham and L. D. Huestis, *J. Am. Chem. Soc.*, **84**, 813 (1962).
179. W. E. Parham and E. Koncos, *J. Am. Chem. Soc.*, **83**, 4034 (1961).
180. J. C. Anderson and C. B. Reese, *Chem. Ind.* (*London*), 575 (1963).
181. W. E. Parham and S. H. Groen, *J. Org. Chem.*, **30**, 728 (1965).
182. H. J. Boonstra and J. F. Arens, *Rec. Trav. Chim.*, **79**, 866 (1960).
183. E. G. Howard, *U.S. Pat.*, 3,035,030. (1962).
184. D. S. Tarbell, *The Claisen Rearrangement in Organic Reactions*, Vol. II, John
     Wiley and Sons, New York, 1946, p. 1.
185. C. D. Hurd and H. Greengard, *J. Am. Chem. Soc.*, **52**, 3356 (1930).
186. S. Y. Meyers, C. Rinaldi and L. Bonoli, *J. Org. Chem.*, **28**, 2440 (1963).
187. C. R. Hauser and S. W. Kantor, *J. Am. Chem. Soc.*, **73**, 1437 (1951).
188. P. T. Lansbury and V. A. Pattison, *J. Org. Chem.*, **27**, 1933 (1962).
189. C. R. Hauser, S. W. Kantor and W. R. Braser, *J. Am. Chem. Soc.*, **75**, 2660
     (1953).
190. T. J. Wallace, H. Pobiner, J. E. Hofmann and A. Schriesheim, *Proc. Chem.
     Soc.*, 137 (1963).

CHAPTER 14

Rearrangements of ethers

D. L. Dalrymple, T. L. Kruger, and W. N. White

University of Vermont, U.S.A.

I. INTRODUCTION

Although ethers are ordinarily classified as rather inert and unexciting substances chemically, certain specialized members of this class of compound undergo intriguing rearrangements under specified conditions. The mechanisms of these rearrangements depend on the structure of the ethers and the means of effecting the reaction. The products are usually isomeric hydroxy or carbonyl compounds and result from cleavage of one of the carbon–oxygen bonds. This chapter is devoted to a discussion of some of the more interesting classes of ether iso-merizations, i.e. the base-catalyzed Wittig rearrangement, the acid-promoted alkyl aryl ether rearrangement, the thermal Claisen rearrangement, and the heat or free-radical induced enol ether re-arrangement.

II. THE WITTIG REARRANGEMENT

A. *Introduction*

The base-catalyzed rearrangement of certain ethers to the isomeric carbinols (equation 1) was first recognized by Wittig in 1942[1].

$$C_6H_5CH_2OR \xrightarrow{C_6H_5Li} \begin{bmatrix} C_6H_5\overset{-}{C}HOR \\ Li^+ \end{bmatrix} \longrightarrow C_6H_5-\underset{R}{\overset{|}{CH}}-\overset{-}{O}Li^+ \qquad (1)$$

$$(1) \qquad\qquad\qquad (2) \qquad\qquad\qquad (3)$$

(R = phenyl or methyl)

Schlenk and Bergmann had reported in 1928 that the reduction of benzophenone dimethyl ketal (4) with sodium or lithium gave α-methylbenzhydrol (5), and that similar treatment of *sym*-diphenoxy-tetraphenylethane (6) gave trityl alcohol (7) (equations 2 and 3)[2].

$$(C_6H_5)_2C(OMe)_2 \xrightarrow{Na\ or\ Li} (C_6H_5)_2MeCOH \qquad (2)$$

$$(4) \qquad\qquad\qquad (5)$$

$$(C_6H_5)_2\underset{C_6H_5O}{\overset{|}{C}}-\underset{OC_6H_5}{\overset{|}{C}}(C_6H_5)_2 \xrightarrow{Na} (C_6H_5)_3COH \qquad (3)$$

$$(6) \qquad\qquad\qquad\qquad (7)$$

Wittig repeated this work in 1947 and suggested that the intermediates in the reductions and in the rearrangements are similar (equation 4)[3].

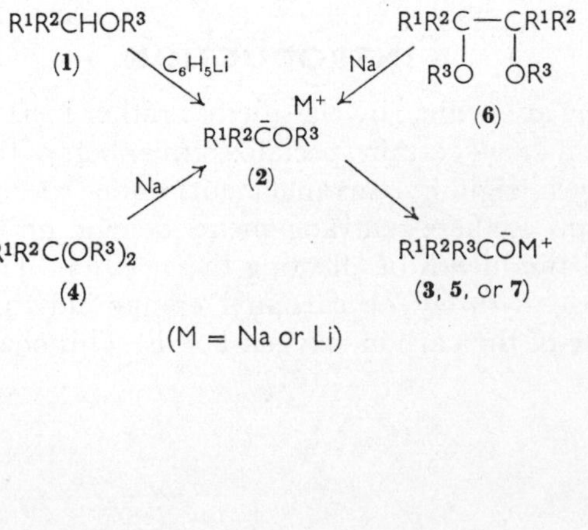

$$\begin{array}{ccc}
R^1R^2CHOR^3 & & R^1R^2C-CR^1R^2 \\
(1) & \searrow^{C_6H_5Li} \quad \overset{Na}{\swarrow} & R^3O \quad OR^3 \\
& M^+ \swarrow & (6) \\
& R^1R^2\overset{-}{C}OR^3 & \\
& \nearrow^{Na} \quad (2) \searrow & \\
R^1R^2C(OR^3)_2 & & R^1R^2R^3C\overset{-}{O}M^+ \\
(4) & & (3, 5, or 7)
\end{array} \qquad (4)$$

(M = Na or Li)

An even earlier observation of a possible Wittig rearrangement was made by Schorigin in 1924. He reported the isolation of benzhydrol from the reaction of benzyl phenyl ether with sodium[4]. The initially formed reduction product, benzyl sodium (**9**), may have acted as a base to catalyze the rearrangement of unreduced ether (equations 5 and 6).

$$C_6H_5CH_2OC_6H_5 \xrightarrow{2\ Na} C_6H_5CH_2{}^-Na^+ + C_6H_5O^-Na^+ \tag{5}$$
$$\text{(8)} \qquad\qquad\qquad \text{(9)} \qquad\qquad \text{(10)}$$

$$C_6H_5CH_2{}^-Na^+ + C_6H_5CH_2OC_6H_5 \rightleftharpoons C_6H_5CH_3 + C_6H_5CH^-Na^+ \tag{6}$$
$$\text{(9)} \qquad\qquad \text{(8)} \qquad\qquad\qquad\qquad\qquad C_6H_5O$$
$$\text{(11)}$$

$$\downarrow$$

$$(C_6H_5)_2CHO^-Na^+$$
$$\text{(12)}$$

B. The Mechanism of the Reaction

Several facts indicate that the first step of the reaction is proton abstraction from the α carbon of the ether. The ethers which rearrange readily are those in which this proton is relatively acidic (benzyl, allyl, phenacyl, etc.). Bases are required to effect the rearrangement (alkyl and aryl organometallics, amides (R_2N^-), and alkoxides have all been used). In addition kinetic studies have shown the rate of reaction to be first order in both ether and base[5].

The second step of the rearrangement (**2 → 3**) was studied by varying the nature of the migrating group in 9-fluorenyl ethers (**13**) and observing the effect on the yields of fluorenols (equation 7)[6]. It was found that the ease of migration decreased in the order: benzyl,

$$\text{(13)} \qquad\qquad\qquad\qquad \text{(14)} \tag{7}$$

fluorenyl, allyl > alkyl > aryl. Of the six compounds in which R was aryl, carbinol formation was observed only in the case when R was *p*-nitrophenyl. Hauser and Kantor obtained similar migratory aptitudes from the treatment of benzyl ethers with potassium amide: benzyl, allyl > *s*-butyl > methyl, ethyl, *neo*-pentyl, and phenyl; the last four in the sequence gave no carbinols[7]. Curtin observed that on heating α-phenylphenacyl (desyl) ethers in alcoholic potassium hydroxide the yields of alcohol decreased in the order: benzhydryl > benzyl > *p*-nitrophenyl > phenyl = 0[8,9].

These orders of reactivity would be expected if the migration step involved nucleophilic attack of the intermediate's anionic center on the migrating group's α carbon (equation 8)[7]. This mechanism re-

$$
\left[\begin{array}{c} R^1\!-\!\ddot{C}\!-\!O \\ \vphantom{.}\\ R^2 \end{array} \right]^{-} \; M^+ \longrightarrow R^1\!-\!\underset{R^2}{C} \underset{\bar{O}M^+}{\overset{C-}{\diagdown}} \tag{8}
$$

          (15)   **(16)**

sembles that established for the Stevens rearrangement of tetraalkylammonium salts (e.g. equation 9)[10]. The relative migratory abilities of

$$
C_6H_5COCH_2\overset{+}{N}(CH_3)_3 \xrightarrow[\Delta]{OH^-} \left[C_6H_5\overset{O}{\overset{\|}{C}}CH\!-\!\overset{+}{\underset{CH_3}{N}}\overset{CH_3}{\diagup} \right] \longrightarrow C_6H_5COCHN(CH_3)_2 \underset{CH_3}{|} \tag{9}
$$

        (17)   **(18)**

various groups are comparable in both rearrangements[10], and it has been found that sulfonium salts rearrange by the Stevens mechanism[11]. Since it was accepted that the latter was concerted, the mechanism in equation (8) was assumed to be correct[7].

Wittig studied the relative rates of rearrangement of various alkali metal salts of phenyl benzhydryl ether. The results suggested that the cation was coordinated with the oxygen rather than the carbanion (equation 10)[5]. The order of reactivity was Li > Na > K, i.e. the

$$
(C_6H_5)_2\overset{\overset{M}{|}}{C}\!-\!O\!-\!C_6H_5 \rightleftharpoons (C_6H_5)_2\bar{C}\!-\!\overset{+}{\underset{C_6H_5}{O}}\overset{M}{\diagup} \tag{10}
$$

        (19)   **(20)**

                        (M = Li,Na,K)

least dissociated salt rearranged fastest[5, 12]. It was also observed that the three salts had identical ultraviolet spectra ($\lambda_{max.} = 449$ mμ, $\varepsilon = 3\cdot2 \times 10^4$) indicating lack of differences in coordination at the benzhydryl chromophore[5]. If the ylid on the right in equation (10) is the form which rearranges fastest, the observed rates are reasonable. This intermediate (**20**) is also more like that in the Stevens rearrangement (equation 9) supporting a similar mechanism for the Wittig rearrangement (equation 11).

$$(C_6H_5)_2\overset{+}{C}-\overset{\underset{\displaystyle Li}{|}}{\underset{C_6H_5}{O}} \longrightarrow (C_6H_5)_3C-O^-Li^+ \tag{11}$$

$$\text{(20)} \hspace{5cm} \text{(21)}$$

In 1960 Stevens and coworkers published results which indicated that there were significant differences between the mechanisms for the two isomerizations[13]. One observation was that both α- and γ-methyl-allyl fluorenyl ethers gave as the major product 9-(1-buten-2-yl)-9-fluorenol (**24**) (equation 12), whereas in the Stevens rearrangement

$$\text{(22)} \hspace{8cm} \text{(12)}$$

$$\text{(24)} \hspace{5cm} \text{(23)}$$

allyl groups migrate with nearly 100% inversion in all cases[14]. They also found that $(-)$-9-fluorenyl α-phenylethyl ether (**25**) rearranged to racemic 9-(α-phenylethyl)-9-fluorenol (**26**) (equation 13) in contrast to the nearly complete retention of configuration observed in comparable Stevens rearrangements[15]. Further, they noted that while benzyl

(25)   (26)   (13)

phenacyl ether gave products derived from Wittig rearrangement, p-nitrobenzyl phenacyl ether gave only p-nitrotoluene and benzoic acid. All of these observations suggested cleavage of the ether to a carbanion and a ketone rather than $S_N i$ displacement.

The first of a series of papers by Schöllkopf on the Wittig rearrangement of optically active ethers also appeared in 1960[16]. He observed that reaction of benzyl or benzhydryl s-butyl ethers with n-butyllithium resulted in formation of carbinols with a large loss of optical activity. The amount of retention of configuration was found to decrease as the solvent polarity or temperature increased[16-18]. Control experiments indicated that neither the ether nor the carbinol is racemized under the reaction conditions indicating that optical activity is lost only during rearrangement[16-19]. In these same rearrangement experiments appreciable quantities of o- and p-s-butylbenzaldehyde were formed. These results are, like Stevens', explicable only by a cleavage–recombination mechanism for the isomerization (equation 14).

(27)   (28)   (14)

Product with   Product with
retention   inversion

In 1957 Wittig had argued that if such an intermediate was involved in the rearrangement of phenyl benzhydryl ether (29) with butyllithium, one would expect α-butylbenzhydrol (30) as a side-product[5] (equation 15). Using a 2:1 ratio of butyllithium and 29 in

$$(C_6H_5)_2CH-OC_6H_5 \xrightarrow{\text{BuLi}} \left[(C_6H_5)_2C=O \begin{array}{c} \\ \\ C_6H_5^- \end{array} Li^+ \right] \xrightarrow[\text{Et}_2O]{\text{BuLi}} (C_6H_5)_2C \begin{array}{c} OLi \\ \diagdown \\ Bu \end{array} \tag{15}$$

(29)   (30)

ethyl ether none of this alcohol was observed. In 1962 Lansbury and Pattison removed this last objection to an intermediate such as 28 by reporting that with a five-fold excess of methyllithium as base, dibenzyl ether gave appreciable amounts of α-phenylethanol, along with the normal product, benzyl phenyl carbinol (equation 16)[20a]. They found

$$(C_6H_5CH_2)_2O \xrightarrow{\text{MeLi}} C_6H_5CHCH_2C_6H_5 + C_6H_5CHCH_3 \tag{16}$$
$$\phantom{(C_6H_5CH_2)_2O \xrightarrow{\text{MeLi}} C_6H_5CH} | |$$
$$\phantom{(C_6H_5CH_2)_2O \xrightarrow{\text{MeLi}} C_6H_5C} OH OH$$

(31)   (32)   (33)

the ratio of 32 to 33 decreased from thirty-two to three as the polarity of the solvent increased (Table 1). Wittig's failure to observe any of compound 30 is reasonable as the solvent used (Et_2O) is even less polar than any of the mixtures in Table 1.

TABLE 1. Rearrangement products of dibenzyl ether (equation 16)[20a].

Solvent	%32	%33	Ratio (32/33)
1:1 Et_2O–THF[a]	97	3	32
1:1 THF–Et_3N	91	9	10
THF	82	18	4·5
1:1 THF–$(MeOCH_2)_2$	75	25	3

[a] THF = tetrahydrofuran.

Lansbury and Pattison have also reported that the rearrangements of benzyl cylcobutyl and benzyl cyclopropyl carbinyl ethers give the expected carbinols (equations 17 and 18)[20b]. The lack of 37 from the

$$C_6H_5CH_2O-\square \xrightarrow[\text{THF}]{\text{MeLi}} C_6H_5\overset{\overset{\displaystyle OH}{|}}{C}H-\square \tag{17}$$

(34)   (35)
                                 75%

$$C_6H_5CH_2OCH_2-\triangleleft \xrightarrow{\text{MeLi}}{\text{THF}} C_6H_5\overset{\underset{|}{OH}}{CH}CH_2-\triangleleft + C_6H_5\overset{\underset{|}{OH}}{CH}CH_2CH_2CH=CH_2 \quad (18)$$

(36)　　　　　　　　　　　　(37)　　　　　　　　(38)
　　　　　　　　　　　　　　94%　　　　　　　　6%

reaction of 34 makes an $S_N i$ mechanism unlikely since in displacement reactions of cyclobutyl compounds, significant amounts of cyclopropyl carbinyl products are usually formed[21]. The formation of 38 is explained by the facile ring opening of the cyclopropyl carbinyl anion (equation 19)[22].

$$\overset{H_2C}{\underset{H_2C}{\Large >}}CH-\overset{\curvearrowleft}{CH_2^-} \rightleftharpoons {}^-CH_2\overset{H_2C}{\underset{}{\Large >}}CH=CH_2 \quad (19)$$

(39)　　　　　　　　　　(40)

A study by Schöllkopf and coworkers of the Wittig rearrangement of a mixture of compounds 41 and 42 (equation 20) has shown that pro-

$$H-\bigcirc-CH_2OPr\text{-}i$$

(41)

$$D-\bigcirc-CH_2OBu\text{-}s$$

(42)

$$\xrightarrow{\text{BuLi}} \bigcirc-\overset{\underset{|}{OH}}{CH}-Bu\text{-}s + \bigcirc-\overset{\underset{|}{OH}}{CH}-Pr\text{-}i \quad (20)$$

(43)　　　　　　　　(44)

duct 44 contained 3–4% of the deuterium in 42 indicating only 6–8% intermolecular reaction[17,18]. That this was observed under conditions which result in approximately 80% racemization of optically active 42[18], indicates that an intimate or caged ion pair is a better representation of the intermediates than the free ions implied in 28 of equation (14).

A mechanism which is consistent with all the observations has been proposed by Lansbury and Pattison (equation 21)[20a]. Dissociation of 48 into ions (49) accounts for the racemization (equation 14), cross-products (equation 20), and base incorporation (equation 16). Two of these processes have been shown to be favored by polar solvents. However, Lansbury and Pattison have recently suggested that the rearrangement proceeds by cleavage of (47) to a pair of free radicals

$$R_2CH{-}O{-}CR_3 \underset{\overline{B}:M^+}{\rightleftharpoons} R_2\overset{M^+}{\overset{\vdots^-}{C}}{-}O{-}CR_3 \rightleftharpoons R_2\overset{-}{C}{-}\overset{M}{\overset{|^+}{O}}{-}CR_3$$

$$\qquad (45) \qquad\qquad\qquad (46) \qquad\qquad\qquad (47)$$

$$\left[R_2\overset{+}{C}{-}O\underset{R_3\overset{-}{C}}{\overset{\diagdown}{\cdots}}M \longleftrightarrow R_2C{=}O\underset{R_3C}{\overset{\diagdown}{\cdots}}M \right] \qquad (21)$$

$$(48)$$

$$R_2C{-}OM \underset{R_3C}{|} \qquad\qquad R_2C{=}\overset{+}{O}{-}M + R_3C^-$$
$$\text{or}$$
$$R_2C{=}O + R_3C^-M^+$$

$$(50) \qquad\qquad\qquad\qquad (49)$$

which recombine to give **50**[23]. This has the advantage of explaining the inertness of benzyl 1-apocamphyl ether to conditions which readily rearrange benzyl *t*-butyl ether[20a].

The formation of several side-products of the reaction have been explained in terms of the mechanism of equation (21). Among these are benzaldehyde and toluene produced during the rearrangement of dibenzyl ether[7], and *s*-butylbenzaldehyde (**51**) formed from benzyl *s*-butyl ether (equation 22)[17], and the significant amounts of alkenes and benzyl alcohol (**52**) obtained from alkyl benzyl ethers (equation 23)[17,24].

$$\left[\underset{}{\bigcirc}{-}CH{=}\overset{+}{O}{-}Li + \text{s-Bu}^- \longleftrightarrow + \underset{}{\bigcirc}{=}CH{-}OLi\,\text{s-Bu}^- \right] \longrightarrow$$

$$(49)$$

$$\text{s-Bu}\underset{H}{\diagup}\bigcirc{=}CH{-}O{-}Li \xrightarrow{-LiH} \text{s-Bu}{-}\bigcirc{-}CHO \qquad (22)$$

$$(51)$$

The production of phenol from the treatment of benzyl phenyl ether with butyllithium in diethyl ether illustrates another side-reaction[25a]. When the reaction was carried out in the presence of a large excess of isobutene, products were isolated which indicate that α elimination

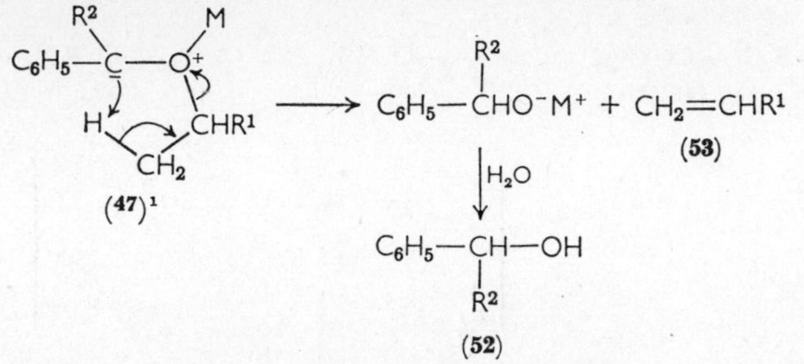

$$C_6H_5-CHO^-M^+ + CH_2{=}CHR^1 \quad (53)$$

(with structure **(47)** on left)

$$\downarrow H_2O$$

$$C_6H_5-CH-OH \quad (23)$$
$$\underset{R^2}{|}$$

(52)

((**a**) $R^1 = H$, $R^2 = C_6H_5$ (reference 23);
(**b**) $R^1 = Et$, $R^2 = H$ (reference 17))

occurred to form phenyl carbene (equation 24). No products from a Wittig rearrangement were observed. However, the same ether (**54**) with butyllithium in tetrahydrofuran was found to give 90% yield of the rearrangement product, benzhydrol, and only 3% of phenol.

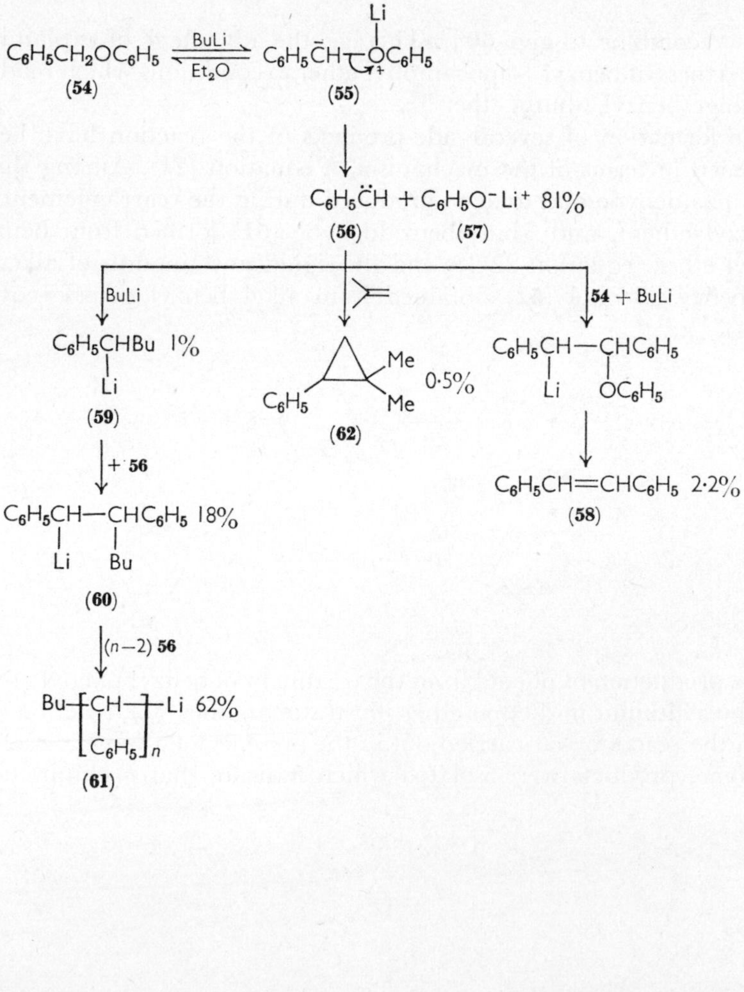

$$C_6H_5CH_2OC_6H_5 \underset{Et_2O}{\overset{BuLi}{\rightleftharpoons}} C_6H_5\bar{C}H\!-\!\overset{Li}{\underset{+}{O}}C_6H_5$$

(54)   **(55)**

$$\downarrow$$

$$C_6H_5\ddot{C}H + C_6H_5O^-Li^+ \quad 81\%$$

(56)   **(57)**

$$\underset{Li}{\overset{|}{C_6H_5CHBu}} \quad 1\%$$

(59)

$$\downarrow +\;56$$

$$\underset{Li\;\;\;\;Bu}{C_6H_5CH-CHC_6H_5} \quad 18\%$$

(60)

$$\downarrow (n{-}2)\;56$$

$$Bu\!-\!\!\left[\underset{C_6H_5}{CH}\right]_n\!\!-\!Li \quad 62\%$$

(61)

(center) C_6H_5 cyclopropane with Me, Me   0.5%

(62)

(right) $$\underset{Li\;\;\;\;OC_6H_5}{C_6H_5CH-CHC_6H_5}$$

$$\downarrow$$

$$C_6H_5CH{=}CHC_6H_5 \quad 2.2\%$$

(58)

$$(24)$$

Another interesting side-reaction has been reported recently by Schöllkopf and Rizk[25b]. Treatment of benzyl 2-butynyl ether (62a) with butyllithium gave, in addition to the expected 1-phenyl-3-pentynol-1 (62b), 1-(o-tolyl)-2-butynol-1 (62c) (equation 24a). The reaction is analogous to the Sommelet rearrangement of ammonium salts but no mechanism was postulated.

C. Miscellaneous Wittig-type Rearrangements

In at least two instances a Wittig-type rearrangement has been observed with sulfides. Thus dibenzyl sulfide when treated with potassium t-butoxide in dimethylformamide gives a 45% yield of stilbene (equation 25)[26]. Dibenzyl disulfide and dibenzyl sulfoxide also yield stilbene but in lower yields (17 and 10%, respectively). Benzyl phenyl

sulfide and benzyl phenyl sulfoxide were not observed to rearrange. Rearrangement of a mixture of 63a and 63b produced only 64a and 64b indicating the intramolecularity of the rearrangement.

Arens and coworkers have observed a Wittig-like rearrangement of benzyl 1-butynyl ether from (**65**) to 1-phenyl-2-pentynol-1 (**66**) using sodium amide in liquid ammonia (equation 26)[27].

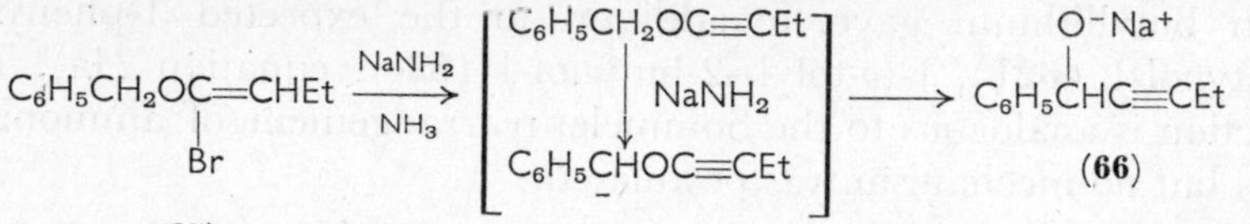
C6H5CH2OC=CHEt
Br
NaNH2
NH3
C6H5CH2OC≡CEt
NaNH2
C6H5CHOC≡CEt
O⁻Na⁺
C6H5CHC≡CEt

(26)

(**65**) (**66**)

D. Synthetic Utility of the Wittig Rearrangement

The Wittig rearrangement has little synthetic utility since the resulting carbinols can usually be obtained by more direct methods. One exception may be the synthesis of phenanthrenes from biphenyls reported by Wittig and coworkers in 1951 (equation 27)[28]. The overall yield is fair (about 50%) but the method does not seem to have been utilized to any extent.

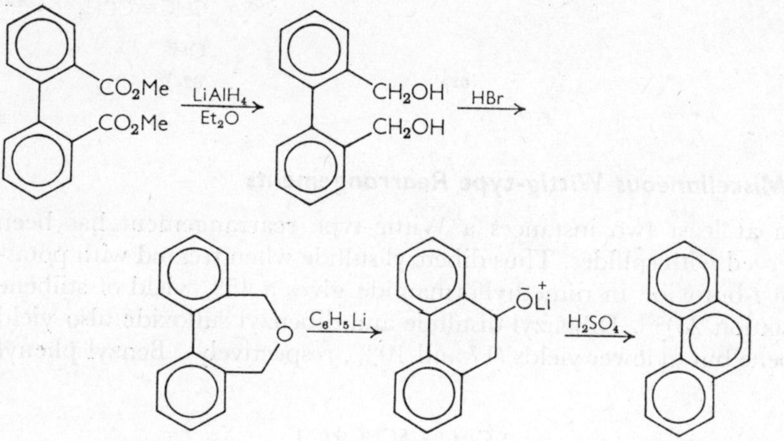
CO2Me
CO2Me
LiAlH4
Et2O
CH2OH
CH2OH
HBr
O
C6H5Li
OLi
H2SO4

(27)

III. ACID-CATALYZED ETHER REARRANGEMENTS

A. Introduction

Certain alkyl aryl ethers have been observed to rearrange to alkylphenols when treated with various Lewis acids (equation 28). The

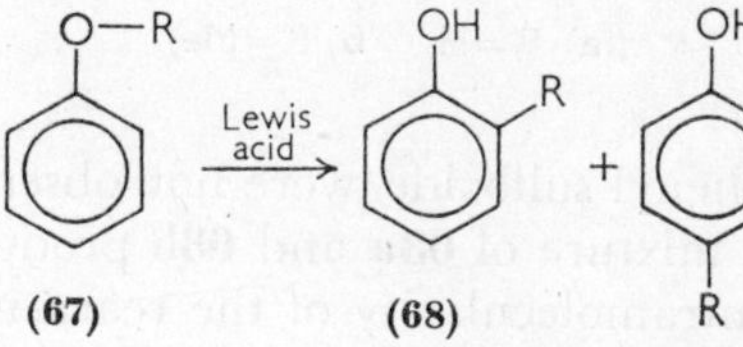
O—R
Lewis
acid
OH
R
+
OH
R

(28)

(**67**) (**68**) (**69**)

normal products are *ortho*- and *para*-alkylphenols if those positions are unsubstituted. Often the rearrangement is complicated by concurrent and/or subsequent reactions, and its course is quite dependent on the experimental conditions used. For these reasons it has not been studied as thoroughly as other ether rearrangements.

Further, the reaction lacks general synthetic utility, as the products are usually more readily obtained by direct alkylation of the phenol by acid- or base-catalyzed reactions.

B. Studies of the Mechanism

Numerous workers have attempted to determine whether the acid-catalyzed rearrangement of alkyl aryl ethers is intramolecular or intermolecular. The results have been somewhat contradictory leading to the conclusion that in most cases it is both. Thus, both isobutyl phenyl ether and *t*-butyl phenyl ether have been shown to rearrange on treatment with an equimolar amount of AlCl$_3$ to form *p*-*t*-butylphenol (equation 29) [29]. This would seem to indicate that isobutene or

$$
\begin{array}{ccc}
\text{OBu-}t & \text{OH} & \text{OBu-}i \\
\bigcirc \xrightarrow{\text{AlCl}_3} & \bigcirc \xleftarrow{\text{AlCl}_3} & \bigcirc \\
 & t\text{-Bu} & \\
(70) & (71) & (72)
\end{array}
\qquad (29)
$$

a free isobutyl group (isomerizable to a *t*-butyl group) is formed as an intermediate.

However, a year later Sprung and Wallis reported that optically active *s*-butyl *p*-tolyl ether gave optically active *o*-*s*-butyl *p*-cresol upon heating in a mixture of acetic and sulfuric acids (equation 30) [30]. Since

$$
\begin{array}{cc}
\text{OBu-}s & \text{OH} \\
\bigcirc \xrightarrow[\Delta]{\text{H}_2\text{SO}_4/\text{HOAc}} & \bigcirc^{\text{Bu-}s} \quad + \text{ Other products} \\
\text{Me} & \text{Me} \\
(73) & (74) \\
\alpha = +21{\cdot}4^\circ & \alpha = +2{\cdot}9^\circ
\end{array}
\qquad (30)
$$

the specific rotations of the two compounds were not known, no estimate could be made of the degree of racemization. Since then Hart and Elia have studied the rearrangement of optically active α-phenyl-ethyl aryl ethers [31], for which they determined the approximate specific rotations of the ethers and the phenolic products [32]. They showed that in the rearrangement of the phenyl and *p*-tolyl ethers of α-phenyl-ethanol (equations 31 and 32) the configuration of the α-phenylethyl

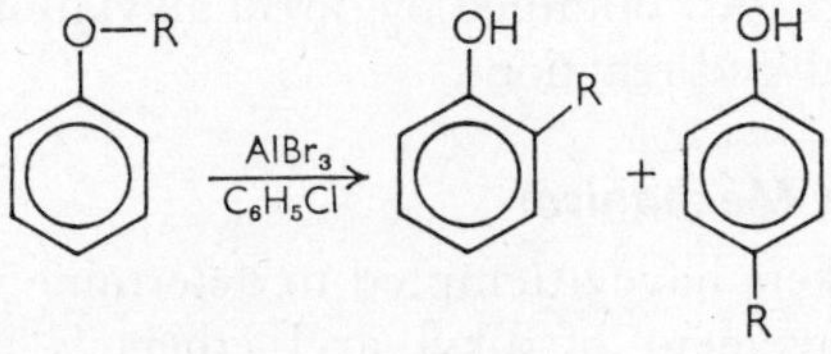

$$(31)$$

(75)   (76)   (77)
        19%   3%

$$(32)$$

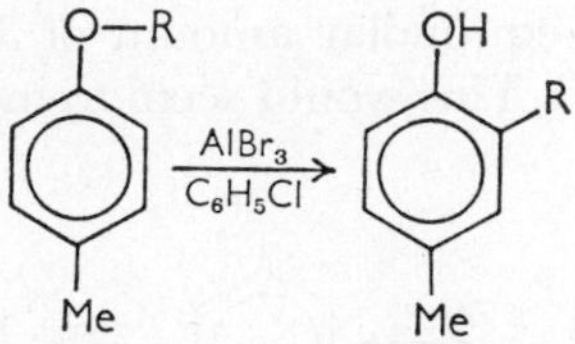

Me   Me
(78)   (79)
        41%

$$(R = C_6H_5\underset{\underset{Me}{|}}{C}H)$$

group was partially retained in the products (76% retention in **78** → **79**). This could only be explained by an intramolecular process in which the migrating α-phenylethyl group is not free to racemize. An alternative route involving alkylation of the solvent, chlorobenzene, followed by alkylation of the phenol liberated, both steps with inversion, was ruled out on the basis of the lack of optically active alkylated chlorobenzenes. Further, previous work had shown that such trans-alkylations result in racemic products (equation 33) [33].

In an attempt to determine the degree of intramolecularity of the rearrangement, Dewar and Puttnam carried out a series of experiments in which the product distributions from rearrangement were compared with those from Friedel–Crafts alkylation of phenols [34–37]. In a mixture of acetic and sulfuric acids they observed the alkylation of phenol (**84**) with *s*-butyl alcohol (**85**) to give a mixture of products (equation 34),

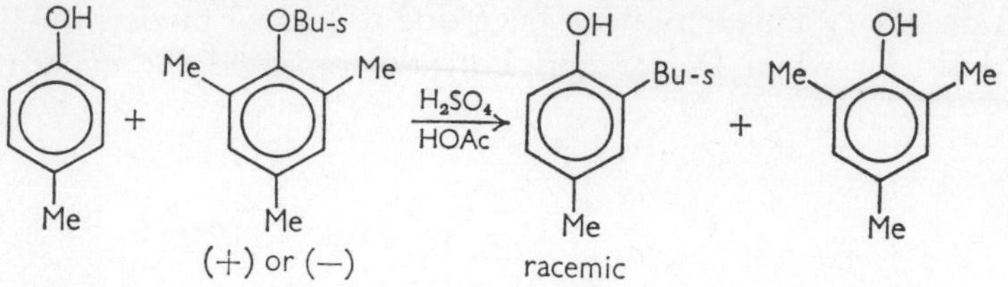

$$(33)$$

(80)   (81)   (82)   (83)

(+) or (−)   racemic

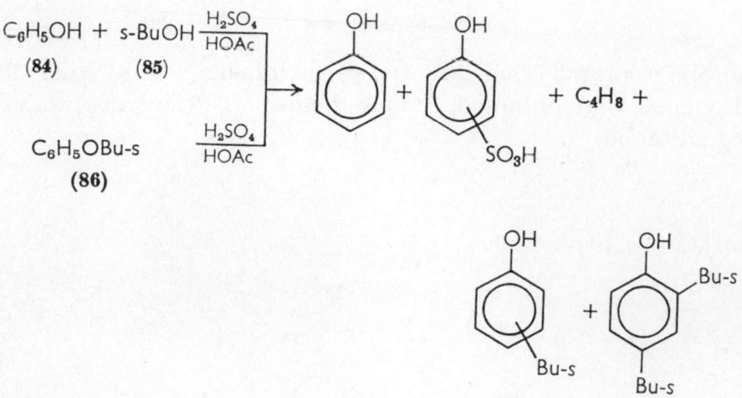

$$C_6H_5OH + s\text{-BuOH} \xrightarrow[\text{HOAc}]{H_2SO_4}$$

(84)   (85)

$$C_6H_5OBu\text{-}s \xrightarrow[\text{HOAc}]{H_2SO_4}$$

(86)

$$+ \ C_4H_8 \ +$$

$$(34)$$

(87)

in which the ratio of o- to p-s-butylphenol (87) was 0·55[35]. Phenyl s-butyl ether (86) under the same conditions gave the same products, but the ratio of *ortho* to *para* isomer was increased to 1·0, indicating some degree of intramolecularity in the rearrangement. Changing the acid and solvent to $AlBr_3$ in chlorobenzene this same ether (86) gave an *ortho*- to *para*-product ratio of 11[36], indicating a high degree of intramolecularity. Further, it was observed that the rearrangement (accompanied by cleavage to phenol and butene) was essentially complete in one hour at 5–10° giving a total yield of s-butylphenols of 24%. A mixture of phenol, s-butyl bromide, and $AlBr_3$ at the same temperature produced only 4% alkylated phenol after 24 hours. The use of $AlCl_3$ as a catalyst in the rearrangement of the isopropyl and s-butyl ethers of p-cresol resulted in product ratios comparable to those in the Friedel–Crafts alkylation of p-cresol with the corresponding alkyl chlorides[37].

In an early study by Gilbert and Wallis, no cross-products were observed when phenyl isopropyl ether (88) and p-tolyl s-butyl ether (89) were rearranged together in a mixture of sulfuric and acetic acids (equation 35) [33]. This may have been due to lack of modern methods of analysis, for when Dewar and Puttnam repeated the experiment

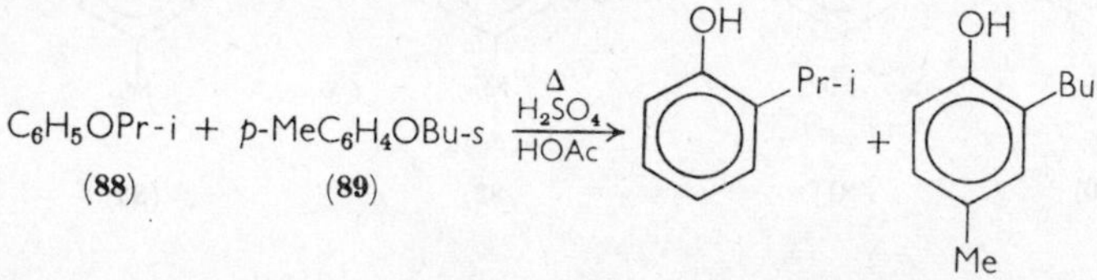

$$
C_6H_5OPr\text{-}i + p\text{-}MeC_6H_4OBu\text{-}s \xrightarrow[\text{HOAc}]{\overset{\Delta}{H_2SO_4}} \quad (35)
$$

(88)   (89)

(90)   (91)

using p-tolyl isopropyl ether (92) and p-ethylphenyl s-butyl ether (93) several phenols were obtained, among them one of the cross-products (96) (equation 36) [35].

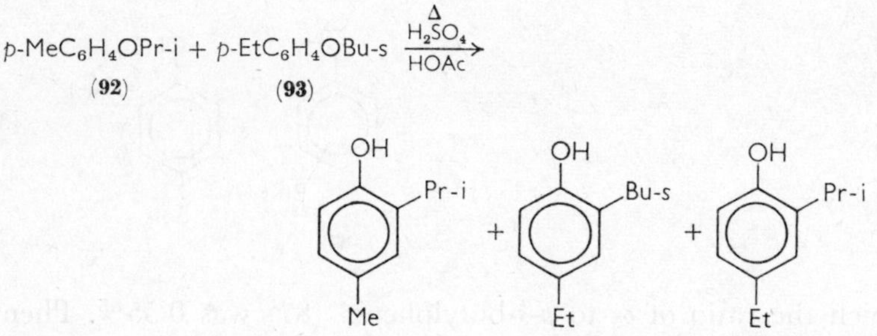

$$
p\text{-}MeC_6H_4OPr\text{-}i + p\text{-}EtC_6H_4OBu\text{-}s \xrightarrow[\text{HOAc}]{\overset{\Delta}{H_2SO_4}} \quad (36)
$$

(92)   (93)

(94)   (95)   (96)

No mechanism for the acid-catalyzed rearrangement of alkyl aryl ethers has met with complete acceptance. Dewar has postulated that the alkyl group migrates as a carbonium ion complexed with the π system of the phenol so as to retain its stereochemistry (equation 37) [36]. This has the advantage of explaining the increased *ortho* to *para* ratio of products formed in rearrangement against alkylation but lacks the substantiation of precedence or analogy. Whatever the mechanism of the intramolecular rearrangement, it is generally accompanied by intermolecular reactions involving complete cleavage of the ether. Further, it has been shown in certain cases that these reactions proceed at comparable rates and with apparently similar activation parameters [38,39]. The latter was demonstrated by Tarbell and Petropoulos by varying the temperature of the AlBr$_3$-catalyzed rearrangement and cleavage of benzyl phenyl ether (97) from -40 to $+25°$ and observing no change in product composition (equation 38) [39].

$$AX + C_6H_5OR \rightleftharpoons \left[\cdots \longrightarrow \cdots \longrightarrow \cdots \right] \longrightarrow \cdots \tag{37}$$

$(A = H \text{ or } AlX_2)$

$$C_6H_5OCH_2C_6H_5 \xrightarrow[C_6H_5Cl]{AlBr_3} C_6H_5OH + \text{(o-benzylphenol)} \tag{38}$$

$$\text{(97)} \qquad\qquad \text{(98)} \qquad \text{(99)}$$
$$\qquad\qquad\qquad\qquad 42\% \qquad 55\%$$

The acid-catalyzed rearrangement of allyl aryl ethers has also been observed, and the mechanism in this case seems to involve a six-membered cyclic transition state similar to the thermal Claisen rearrangement. Indeed, the enhanced rates of the latter reaction in acidic solvents are undoubtedly due to this competing mechanism (see section IV.B). In the presence of strong Lewis acids these ethers rearranged very rapidly even at low temperatures. Thus, allyl phenyl ether (100) treated with BF_3 at $-80°$ gave a 73% yield of tris-(o-allylphenyl) borate (101) which was readily hydrolyzed (both MeOH and H_2O were used) to o-allylphenol (102) (equation 39)[40]. In dilute

$$\xrightarrow{BX_3} \left[\cdots \right]_3 B \xrightarrow{ROH} \cdots \tag{39}$$

$$\text{(100)} \qquad\qquad \text{(101)} \qquad\qquad\qquad \text{(102)}$$

solutions the rearrangement gave nearly quantitative yields of *o*-allylphenol with no *para* or disubstituted products[41]. In the case of 2,6-xylyl allyl ether *m*- and *p*-allylxylenols were formed[42]. Analogous results were obtained with mesityl[41] and duryl[42] allyl ethers.

Schmid has shown that the allyl group migrates to the *ortho* position with inversion and to the *para* position without inversion[42], as in the Claisen rearrangement. Migration to the *meta* position gave mixtures of both types of phenols (**106** and **107**). On the basis of this evidence, Schmid proposed the mechanism in equation (40)[42]. The mechanism

of the migration from the *ortho* to the *meta* position (**104** → **106** + **107**) is not known, however, **106** was formed in preference to **107** in the case of R^1 = Me, R^2 = H (ratio **106/107** = 1·5)[42].

Piers and Brown have observed that when 2,6-dichlorophenyl allyl ether (**109**, Y = Cl) was rearranged at 130–155° in the presence of $ZnCl_2$ the major product was 2-allyl-4,6-dichlorophenol (**110** and **111**) (equation 41, $X = Y = Cl$)[43]. At higher temperatures the methyl-coumaran (112, $R = Cl$) was formed in greater yield. Reactions with

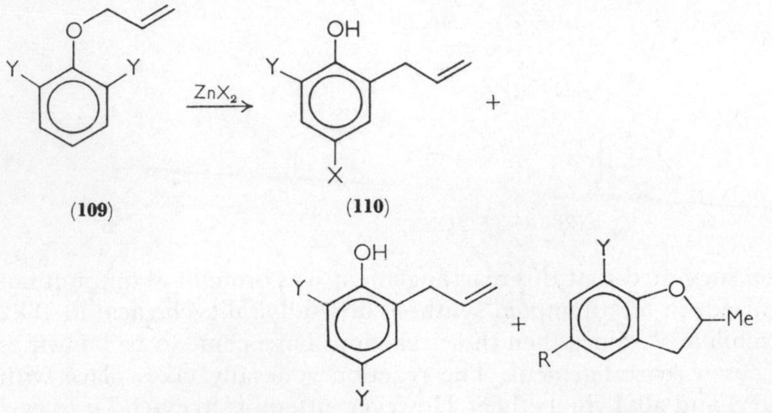

(109)   (110)

(111)   (112)

(R = X, Y, or H)

mixed halides ($X = Cl$, $Y = Br$ or $X = Br$, $Y = Cl$) at low temperatures (100–130°) gave a preponderance of 4-bromo isomer in both cases indicating formation of Y^+ followed by subsequent electrophilic substitution[44]. At higher temperatures (150°) the two isomers were formed in approximately equal amounts in each reaction. The relatively high temperatures at which these last reactions were performed leave some doubt about the degree to which normal Claisen rearrangements and intermolecular reactions competed with the acid-catalyzed Claisen rearrangement.

The above evidence suggests that the acid-catalyzed rearrangement of alkyl aryl ethers is at least in part intramolecular, but is usually accompanied by intermolecular reactions at comparable rates. The reactions often give mixtures of several products, and this is an additional reason why the rearrangement has little synthetic utility.

IV. THE CLAISEN REARRANGEMENT

A. Introduction

The thermal rearrangement of O-allyl enol ethers to form the isomeric γ,δ-unsaturated carbonyl compounds or the corresponding enols was discovered and studied by Claisen in 1912 (equations 42 and 43)[45].

$$RCH{=}CHOCH_2CH{=}CH_2 \xrightarrow{\Delta} \underset{\underset{CH_2CH{=}CH_2}{|}}{R\overset{O}{\overset{||}{C}H}CMe} \qquad (42)$$

$$\underset{Me}{|}$$

$$(R = CO_2Et, MeCO)$$

$$(43)$$

$$(R = CO_2Et, OMe)$$

Claisen suggested that this rearrangement was brought about, but not recognized, in an attempted synthesis of *O*-allylsalicyclic acid in 1882 by Scichilone[46]. Since then these reactions have come to be known as the Claisen rearrangement. The reaction generally takes place with allyl aryl and allyl vinyl ethers. However, attempts to extend it to aryl vinyl, aryl benzyl, aryl 3-propynyl, and aryl 4-buten-1-yl ethers have been largely unsuccessful[47] (compare, however, section IV.D).

A variation of the normal rearrangement of allyl aryl ethers occurs when the 2,6-positions in the aromatic nucleus are substituted (equation 44). This isomerization is frequently referred to as the *para*-Claisen rearrangement.

$$(44)$$

       (113)   **(114)**

Previous reviews of these rearrangements have been given by Tarbell[48] and Rhoads[49].

B. The Mechanism of the Reaction

I. The intermediate

The currently accepted mechanism of the rearrangement is essentially that suggested by Claisen in 1925[50]. He observed that the thermolysis of aryl 3-phenylallyl ethers yielded *o*-(1-phenylallyl)phenols, and from this result he postulated that the reaction was cyclic, intra-molecular, involved a dienone intermediate, and proceeded with the inversion of the allyl group (equation 45, path a). Path b was eli-minated because of the stability of intermediate **116b** under the conditions of the rearrangement.

$$(45)$$

Conclusive evidence for the intermediacy of a dienone was obtained by carrying out the rearrangement in the presence of a dienophile to trap the generated dienone (**119**) as the Diels–Alder adduct (**120**) (equation 46)[51–54]. Thermolysis of **120** gave the product of *para*-Claisen rearrangement of **118** (equation 44, R = Me)[51].

Further evidence for the proposed structure of the intermediate has been obtained by several groups. Schmid observed (equation 47) the formation of 30% of compound **124** and 70% of compound **125** from ether **121**[55]. Intermediates **122** and **123** would lead to 25% of **124** and 75% of **125** on a statistical basis.

Curtin found that rearrangement of either **126** or **127** gave both **128** and **129** as products (equation 48)[56,57]. For example heating **126** for 2 minutes at 230° in diethylaniline (DEA) gave a 25% yield of the

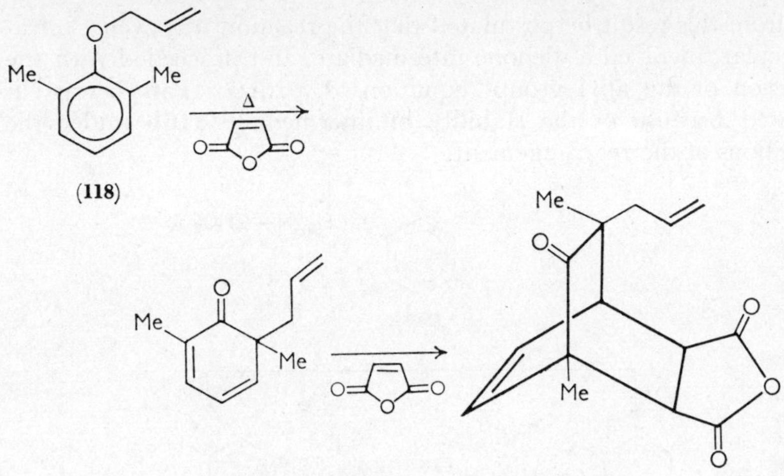

(118) (119) (120) (46)

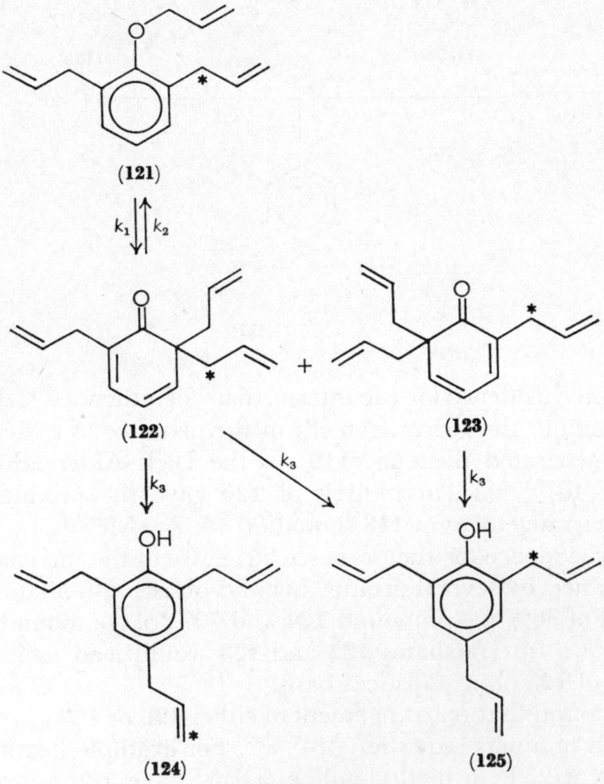

(121) (122) (123) (124) (125) (47)

(* = ^{14}C)

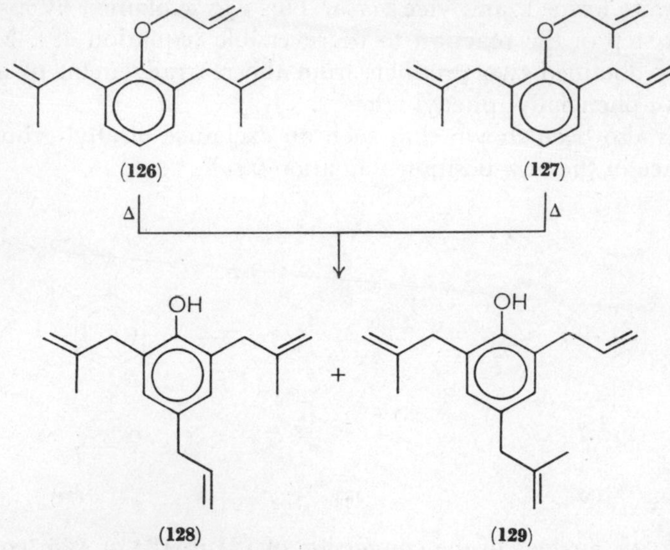

(126)   (127)

(48)

(128)   (129)

products (**128** and **129**) in a ratio of 56:44, whereas **127**, under similar conditions, gave a product ratio of 40:60. In experiments at higher temperatures or for longer periods of heating polymerization of both the starting material and the products became a major reaction. It was also observed that during the rearrangement of **126** significant amounts

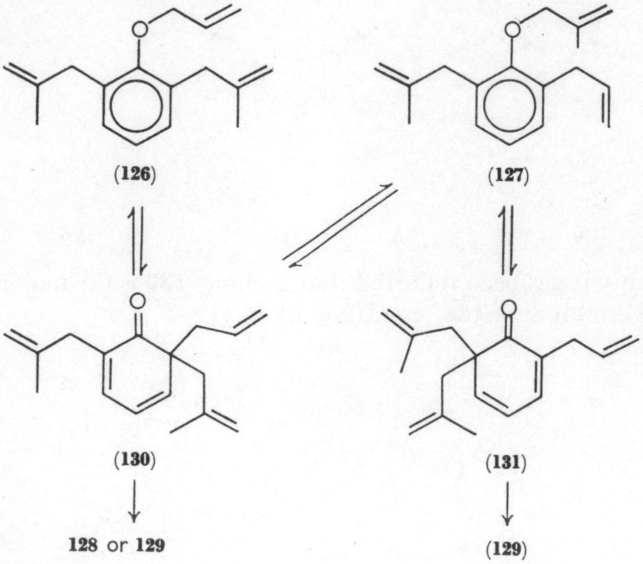

(126)   (127)

(49)

(130)   (131)

128 or 129   (129)

of **127** were formed, and vice versa. This was explained by assuming the first step of the reaction to be reversible (equation 49). Marvell similarly obtained two products from the rearrangement of allyl 2-allyl-6-(α-phenylallyl)phenyl ether[58].

It has also been shown that such an exchange of allyl groups can take place in the *para* position (equation 50)[59, 60].

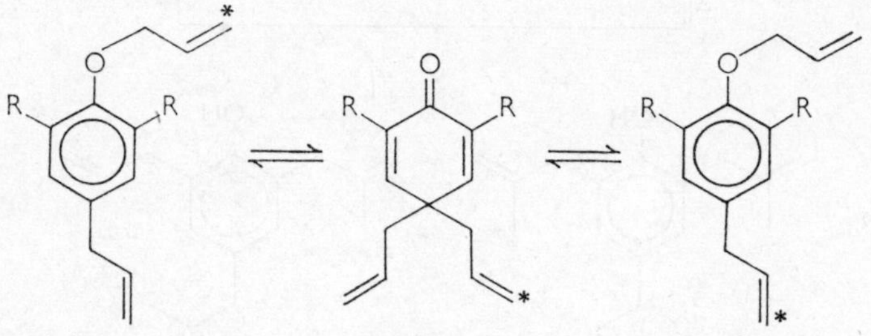

(50)

(132)   (133)   (134)

By kinetic analysis of the conversion of **121** to **124** or **125** (equation 47) Schmid calculated that the ratio of k_3/k_2 at 170° is approximately 3·0[61]. This agrees well with the earlier observation that the independently synthesized intermediate (**135**) on heating to 75–100° gives compounds **136** and **137** in a ratio of 2·7∶1 (equation 51)[51].

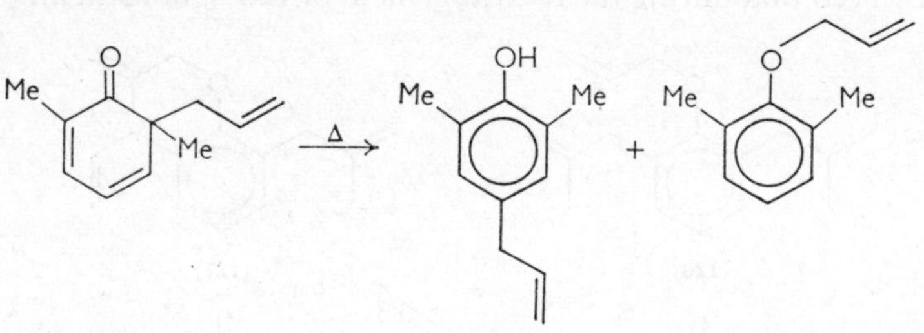

(51)

(135)   (136)   (137)

Recently it has been reported that dienone **139** is the major product of the thermolysis of **138** (equation 52)[62].

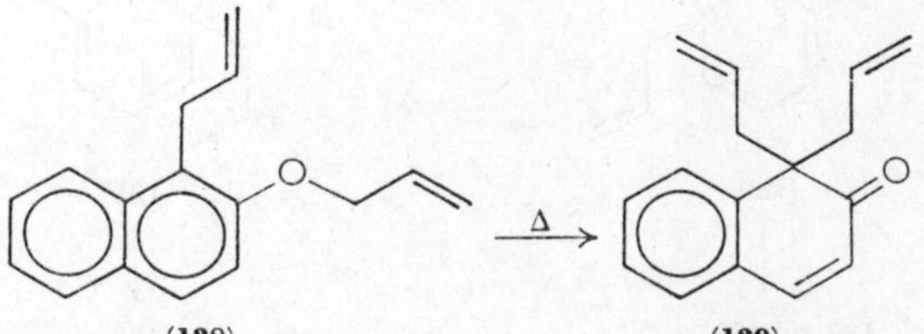

(52)

(138)   (139)

2. The cyclic nature of the rearrangement

The generality of the previously mentioned inversion process has been demonstrated by subsequent studies[58, 63–70]. The α or γ carbon of the allyl group in the ether was labeled and the position of the label in the product was determined. If the original ether was α labeled the product had the label in the γ position if an *ortho* rearrangement occurred and in the α position if a *para* isomerization took place (equation 53).

$$(53)$$

$$(140) \qquad (141) \qquad (142)$$

In addition, studies of the vapor-phase rearrangement of deuterium and carbon-14 labeled allyl vinyl ethers have shown that less than 1% of the total yield of 4-pentenal has the allyl group uninverted[71]. If the Claisen rearrangement is intramolecular, the inversion of the allyl group suggests it is a concerted cyclic process. The intramolecularity has been confirmed by experiments showing that added phenol is not alkylated during the reaction and that a mixture of two different allyl ethers does not yield cross-products during thermolysis[63, 72].

The nature of the rearrangement is, by virtue of the observed intramolecularity and inversion, concerted and cannot involve dissociation into free radicals or an ion pair. This is supported by the activation parameters for the reaction. The entropy of activation is large and negative. Thus, the vapor-phase rearrangement of allyl vinyl ether has a $\Delta S^{\ddagger}$ of $-7 \cdot 7$ e.u. at $180°$[73, 74]. This indicates that there are fewer degrees of freedom in the transition state than in the initial state. Using hydrocarbons as models and assuming a six-membered cyclic transition state, $\Delta S^{\ddagger}$ was calculated to be $-8 \cdot 1$ e.u.[73].

The volume of activation, as determined by Brower, is also relatively large and negative ($\Delta V^{\ddagger} = -18$ ml/mole), indicating that the spatial requirements of the transition state are less than those of the ground state[75]. For comparison, the difference in molar volumes of 1-hexene and cyclohexane is -17 ml. It was also observed that changes in solvent have little effect on $\Delta V^{\ddagger}$, suggesting a relatively nonpolar transition state[75, 76].

3. The nature of the transition state

Several workers have shown the existence of stereoselectivity in the formation of products from the Claisen rearrangement of *cis-* or *trans-*α,γ-dimethylallyl phenyl ether (equation 54)[77–81]. The major product

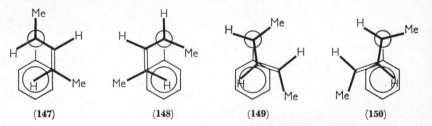

from racemic **143** or **144** was the *trans* isomer (**145**)[77,78], and the re-arrangement of (+)-*R*-**144** gave a mixture of 82% *S-trans* isomer (**145**) and 18% *R-cis* isomer (**146**)[80]. Steric interactions in the possible conformations of the six-membered cyclic transition states provide an explanation for these results. If one considers molecular models of the *R-trans* ether (*R*-**144**, Figure 1), it can be seen that the least hindered of the four possible conformers is **147**. Both **147** and **150** lead to the

FIGURE 1. Conformations of *R-trans*-α,γ-dimethylallyl phenyl ether.

S-trans form of **145**, while the less favorable forms (**148** and **149**) give the *R-cis* isomer of **146**. Using similar arguments, *trans* products from the other three isomeric ethers (*R*- and *S*-**143** and *S*-**144**) would be predicted. Several results in studies of aliphatic Claisen rearrangements can be similarly explained[77,82,83].

It has been found that *cis-γ*-substituted allyl phenyl ethers rearrange more slowly than the corresponding *trans* isomers[84, 85]. This has been taken to suggest that the 'chair-like' conformation of the transition state (**147** and **148**) is favored[85]. The argument (see Figure 2) is that if the 'boat' conformation of the transition state is favored (**151** and **152**)

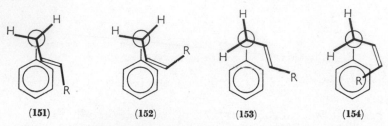

(151)   (152)   (153)   (154)

FIGURE 2. Comparison of boat and chair conformations of transition state in *cis*- and *trans*-substituted allyl phenyl ethers.

then the *cis* isomer (**152**) would be able to achieve the transition state conformation more easily because of smaller steric interactions and would rearrange more rapidly than the *trans* isomer. The opposite would be true for the 'chair' conformation (**153** against **154**). Since the *trans* isomers reacted faster than the *cis* isomers, the latter alternative was indicated. Further evidence in this regard was obtained from the rates of rearrangement of *β*-substituted allyl aryl ethers (equation 55)[86].

$$
\begin{array}{c}
\textbf{(155)} \qquad\qquad \textbf{(156)} \\
\xrightarrow[\;(C_6H_5)_2O\;]{\Delta}
\end{array}
\qquad (55)
$$

(155)   (156)

(R = H, Me, or *t*-Bu; Y = H or OMe)

The lack of any significant decrease in rate as the size of the *β* substituent was increased was taken as evidence in support of a 'chair' form of the transition state. The argument used was similar to that above (Figure 3). If the 'boat' conformation of the transition state is favored one would expect a large decrease in rate with larger R groups due to steric repulsions in **158**. Little or no such effect would be expected for

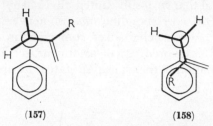

(157)   (158)

FIGURE 3. Comparison of boat and chair conformations of transition
state in β-alkyl-substituted allyl phenyl ethers.

the 'chair' form. The data obtained are consistent with the latter
picture.

Recent theoretical considerations of the electronically similar Cope
rearrangement by Woodward and Hoffmann also indicate a preference
for the 'chair' conformation of the transition state[87]. Their argument
is based on the symmetry of possible molecular orbitals involved in the
reaction. Experimental studies of the Cope rearrangement had previously led to the same conclusion[88].

Kinetic studies of the rearrangement of *para*-substituted allyl phenyl
ethers have demonstrated that the rate is increased by electron-
releasing substituents[89,90]. The use of σ^+ values in the Hammett
equation gives the best correlation of the rate constants ($r = 0.99$).
The small negative ρ (-0.6[89], -0.5[90]) is comparable to the value
observed for the Diels–Alder reaction with 1-arylbutadienes[91].

Substituent effects in the allyl group were studied using substituted
cinnamyl phenyl ethers[92]. Again the data are best correlated by σ^+
constants ($\rho = -0.40$, $r = 0.995$).

A rate study of the rearrangement of seven *meta*-substituted allyl
phenyl ethers gave data less amenable to interpretation[93]. *Ortho* rearrangement of *meta*-substituted allyl phenyl ethers (**159**) can result in
two isomeric products (**160** and **161**). The ratio of the 3- to 5-substituted
product is generally in the range 0.3 to 4, and varies with the substituent and possibly with the choice of temperature and solvent[94–104].

(159)   (160)   +   (161)   (56)

The results of several studies[94-98] in which yields and/or product ratios were determined seem to indicate a lack of significant steric hindrance in the formation of isomer **160**; even with bulky groups in the *meta* position it may be the major product. In a study by White and Slater (X = MeO, Me, Br, Cl, CN, and C_6H_5CO) the ratio of products (**161/160**) showed a slight tendency to increase as the electron-donating ability of X decreased[94]. At present insufficient data exist to suggest the true nature of this effect. Indeed, there are conflicting data where X is Me[97,102,103], OH[96,104], and MeCONH[95,101]. Many of these inconsistent results may be ascribed to the lack of modern methods of analysis, although the variance may be due in part to the differing reaction conditions. The rates observed for the *meta*-substituted allyl phenyl ethers were separated into rate coefficients for the formation of each phenolic product using the previously determined[94] product ratios. Attempts were made to correlate the reaction rates of the *meta*-substituted ethers using σ_m, σ_p, σ_p^+, and σ_p^- values; σ_p^+ gave the best line with $r = 0.964$ and $\rho = 0.664$[93].

These correlations of the substituent-rate data for the *meta*- and *para*-substituted allyl phenyl ethers and the substituted cinnamyl phenyl ethers were interpreted by the representation of the transition state given in Figure 4[93]. Properly situated substituents can interact by

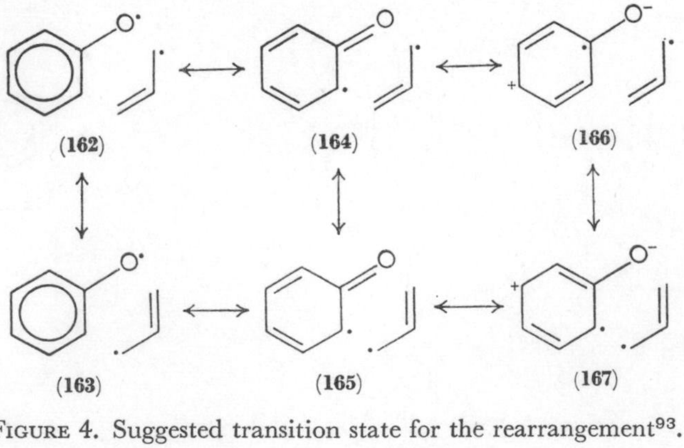

(162) (164) (166)

(163) (165) (167)

FIGURE 4. Suggested transition state for the rearrangement[93].

electron donation with the centers of unpaired electron density to reduce the latter. Hence the correlation by σ^+ values and the observed negative ρ.

Rates also increase slightly as the polarity of the solvent increases[89,105-107]. When the rearrangement is carried out in the absence of solvent, the rate increases four-fold during the course of the reaction[105]. This is presumably due to the increasing polarity of the media as it changes from ether to phenol. These solvent effects can possibly be explained by general acid catalysis of the reaction (see section III) or by the contribution of polar structures such as **166** and **167** to the transition-state hybrid.

C. Abnormal Products of the Claisen Rearrangement

It has been shown that the presence of an *ortho* substituent does not cause exclusive migration to the other *ortho* position. The isolation of both *ortho*- and *para*-rearrangement products indicates that both dienones are formed as intermediates (equation 57)[108,109]. Marvell and coworkers found that *o*-methyl-, *o*-ethyl-, *o*-isopropyl-, and *o*-*t*-butylphenyl allyl ethers (**168**) rearranged to give **173** to **172** ratios of

(57)

5·6, 9, 10, and 15, respectively[109]. This was explained as the result of a steric effect on the relative rate of formation of **169**.

The rearrangement of 2-butenyl *m*-tolyl ether (**174**, R = X = Me, Y = H) produced, in addition to the two expected *ortho* isomers (**175** and **176**), a 7% yield of *p*-(2-butenyl)-*m*-cresol (**177**) (equation 58)[110].

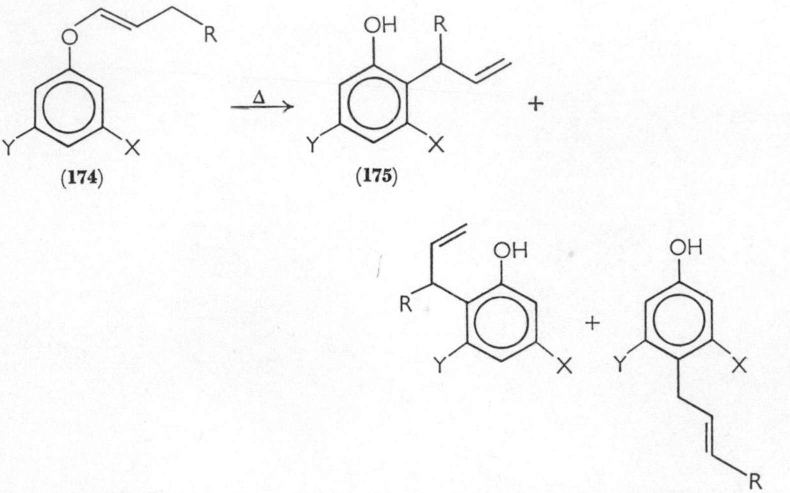

(174) (175) +

(58)

(176) (177)

Similarly, 3,5-disubstituted phenyl 2-butenyl ethers (**174**, R = Me, X = Y = MeO, Me, or Et) gave both *ortho* and *para* products[110]. As the size of the *meta* substituents increased, the relative amount of *para* isomer increased. Increasing the size of R in **174** from methyl to phenyl resulted in an even greater percentage of **177**. The *ortho* to *para* ratio was also shown to increase with the polarity of the medium. Thermolysis of **175** (R = X = Me, Y = H or Me) was shown to produce **177**. No satisfactory explanation has been suggested for the solvent dependence. However, it may be due to a polar effect on the enolization of the dienone intermediate.

Certain 2,4,6-trisubstituted phenyl allyl ethers have been observed to undergo rearrangement with displacement of either an *ortho* or *para* substituent. Thus 2,4,6-tribromophenyl allyl ether gave a 68% yield of 2,4-dibromo-6-allylphenol[111]. If only the *ortho* positions are substituted, the normal 2,6-disubstituted-4-allylphenols are obtained along with small amounts of 6-substituted 2-allylphenols[111,112]. Tarbell reported that in the rearrangement of ethers **178** and **180** carbon dioxide is the preferred leaving group as only phenols **179** and **181** were isolated (equations 59 and 60) [112]. Nothing is known about

$$\text{(178)} \xrightarrow[125°]{\Delta} \text{(179)} \tag{59}$$

$$\text{(180)} \xrightarrow[165°]{\Delta} \text{(181)} \tag{60}$$

the mechanism of the rearrangement when accompanied by loss of halogen; the reaction involves a loss of Cl^+, but no products resulting from it have been reported.

Isomerizations of the normal products of the Claisen rearrangement have been observed in several instances. The simplest of these is the formation of a coumaran (equation 61) [112,113]. The ratio of the

$$\text{(182)} \xrightarrow{\Delta} \text{(183)} \longrightarrow \text{(184)} \tag{61}$$

amounts of **184** to **183** has been shown to increase as the reaction proceeds, and its formation is probably acid-catalyzed by the phenol present.

Another type of product isomerization was discovered by Lauer and coworkers [114]. They observed that 1-(2-pentenyl) phenyl ether (**185a**) rearranged to o-4-(2-pentenyl)phenol (**187a**) in addition to the expected o-3-(1-pentenyl)phenol (**186a**) (equation 62) [115,116]. Similarly

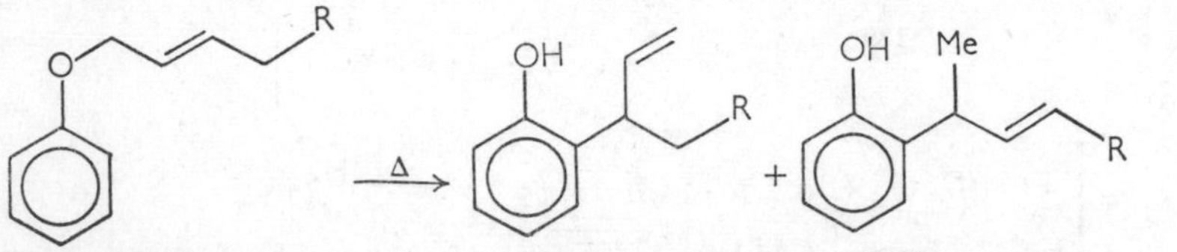

$$(62)$$

(**185**)　　　(**186**)　　　(**187**)

((**a**) R = Me; (**b**) R = Et; (**c**) R = H)

ethers **185b** and **185c** were also found to give abnormal products [117–119]. Subsequent work has shown that the abnormal product (**187**) is formed from the normal product (**186**) by a second rearrangement [120,121]. The mechanism of this reaction has been given by Marvell and coworkers (equation 63) [120]. The methyl ether of **186a** did

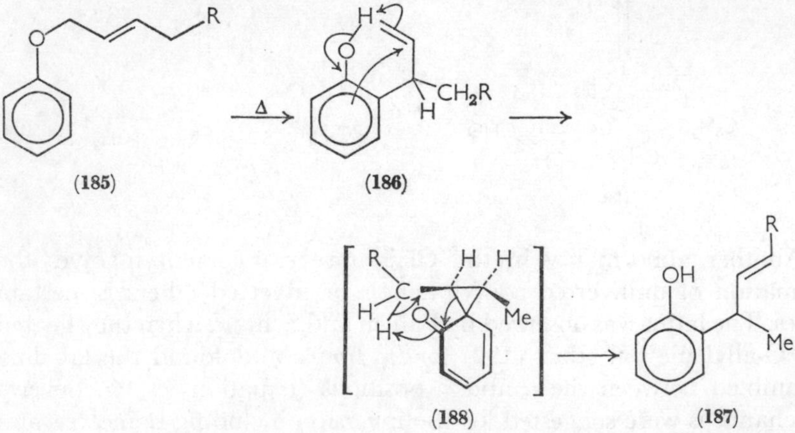

(**185**)　　　　　(**186**)

$$(63)$$

(**188**)　　　　　(**187**)

not rearrange even in the presence of added phenol [120], indicating the necessity for the phenolic proton as shown (**186**). A recent study of an analogous reaction gives strong support for this mechanism [122,123]. It was found that heating 2,2-d_2-3-methyl-4-pentenoylbenzene (**189**) resulted in deuterium exchange with the hydrogen atoms on the 5-carbon (**190**) and the methyl group in the 3-position (**191**) [123]. The mechanism in equation (64) was used to explain the results and is identical to that proposed by Marvell (equation 63).

21*

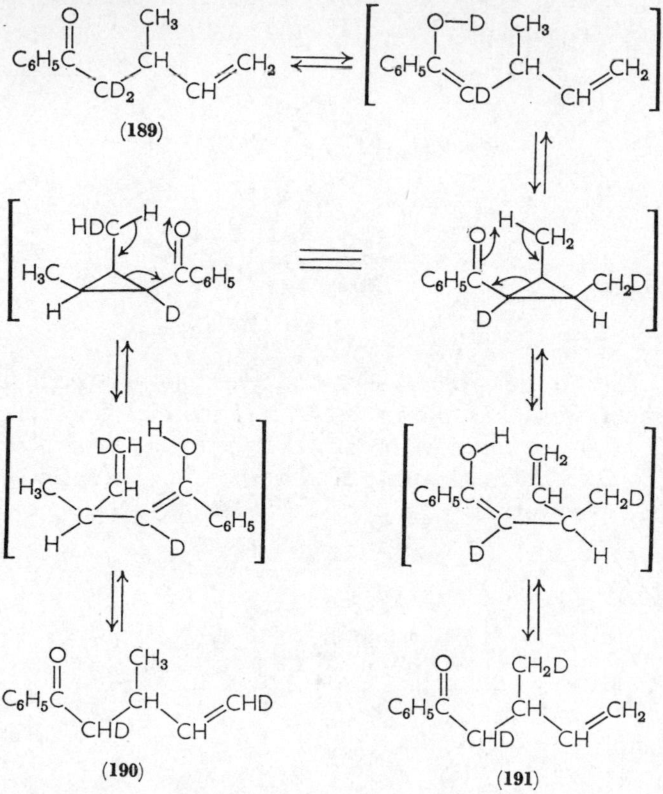

(64)

(190)   (191)

Another abnormality in the Claisen rearrangement involves the formation of uninverted *o*-allylphenols or inverted ethers in certain cases. The latter was observed by Fahrni and Schmid when they heated γ-^{14}C-allyl mesityl ether (**192**) for 96 hours and found the labeling scrambled between the α and γ positions (equation 65)[124]. Several mechanisms were suggested for the inversion including homolysis and

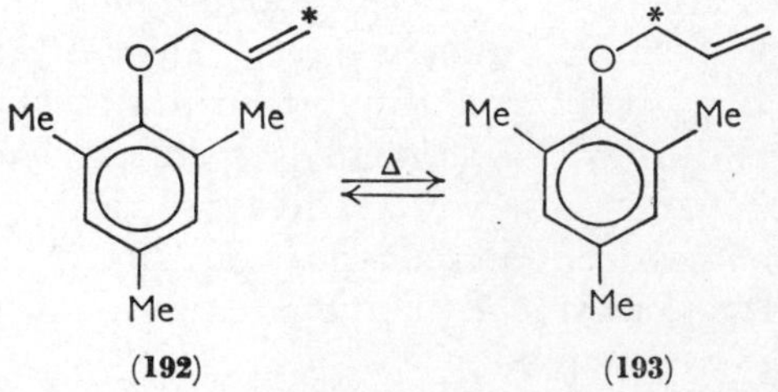

(65)

(192)   (193)

recombination, a series of inversions with a migration from the 2- to
the 6-position (**194** to **195**, equation 66), and a four-centered inversion

(**192**)   (**194**)

(**195**)   (**193**)   (66)

of the allyl group. The last mechanism was considered unlikely because
of its steric requirements, the mechanism of equation (66) was shown
to be inconsistent with the kinetics of the reaction, and an intermolecular mechanism found only slight support on the basis that
only 5–10% crossing was observed when a mixture of **192** and allyl
2,6-dimethylphenyl ether were heated together.

Ortho rearrangement without inversion was reported by Marcinkiewicz and coworkers in the thermolysis of crotyl β-tocopheryl ether
(**196**, equation 67)[125]. Similar results were obtained with crotyl

(**196**)   (**197**)
                              +

(**198**)   (67)

γ-tocopheryl ether. The mechanism of equation (66) was suggested to explain the formation of **198** since again no crossover was observed during mixed rearrangement.

Another variation of the Claisen rearrangement is the migration of an allyl group to an o- or p-vinyl side-chain (equation 68)[126]. Two

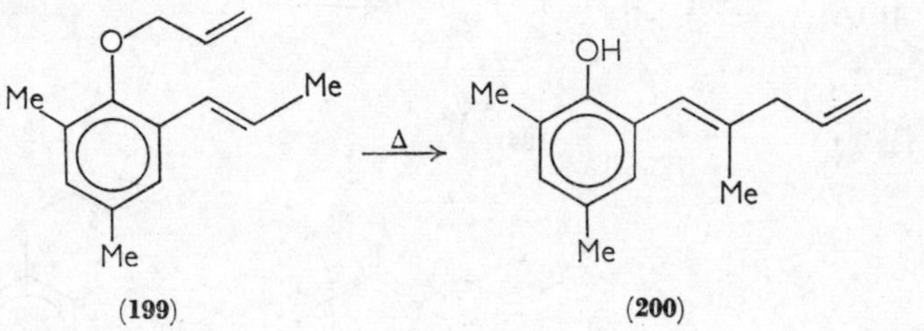

(68)

(199)   **(200)**

possible intramolecular mechanisms were suggested for this rearrangement as shown in equation (69). Using γ-^{14}C-labeled **199**, Schmid and

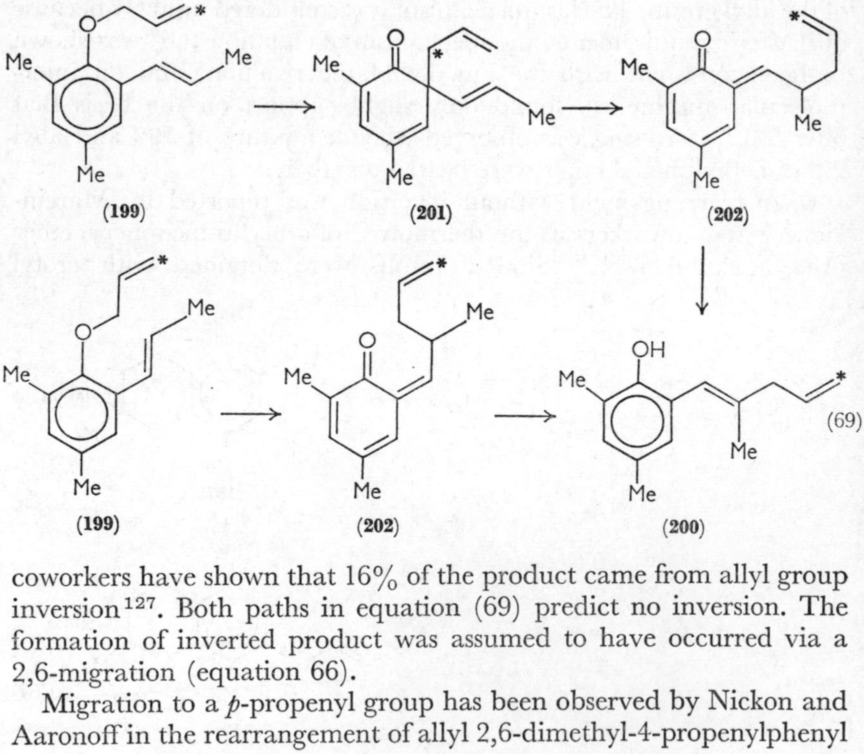

(199)   **(201)**   **(202)**

(69)

(199)   **(202)**   **(200)**

coworkers have shown that 16% of the product came from allyl group inversion[127]. Both paths in equation (69) predict no inversion. The formation of inverted product was assumed to have occurred via a 2,6-migration (equation 66).

Migration to a p-propenyl group has been observed by Nickon and Aaronoff in the rearrangement of allyl 2,6-dimethyl-4-propenylphenyl

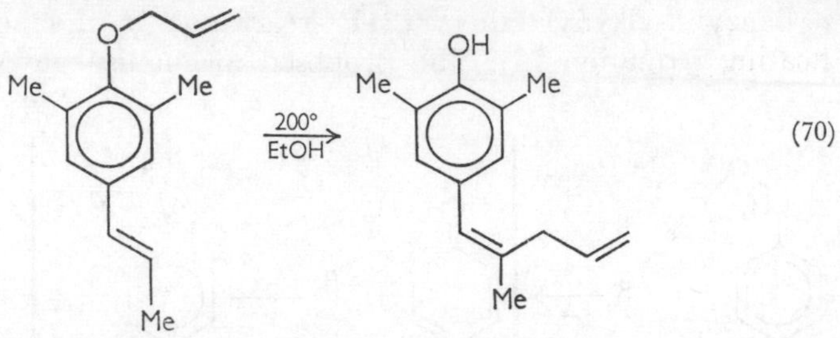

(70)

(203)   (204)

ether (**203**) (equation 70)[128]. Under similar conditions no rearrangement of allyl 4-phenyl-2,6-di-methylphenyl ether was observed.

D. Miscellaneous Claisen-like Rearrangements

A number of ether rearrangements appear to occur by mechanisms
similar to that of the Claisen rearrangement. One such process is the
formation of arylacetones (**207**) by heating certain benzyl 2-propenyl
ethers (**205**) to 240° (equation 71)[129]. Only *m*-methoxy-substituted

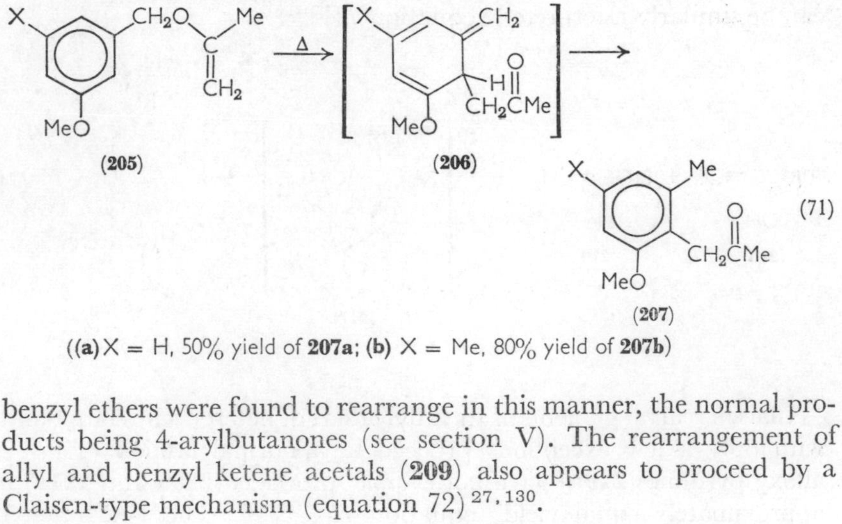

(205)   (206)   (207)

(71)

((a) X = H, 50% yield of **207a**; (b) X = Me, 80% yield of **207b**)

benzyl ethers were found to rearrange in this manner, the normal products being 4-arylbutanones (see section V). The rearrangement of
allyl and benzyl ketene acetals (**209**) also appears to proceed by a
Claisen-type mechanism (equation 72)[27,130].

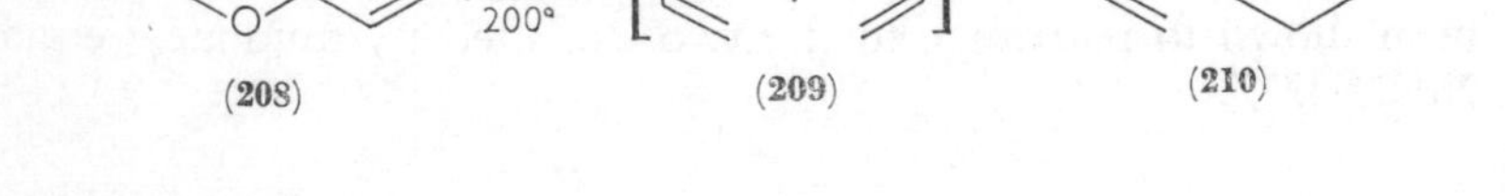

(208)   (209)   (210)

(72)

Benzyl l-alkynyl ethers (211) rearrange to indanones (214) on heating (equation 73). The proposed mechanism involves a Claisen

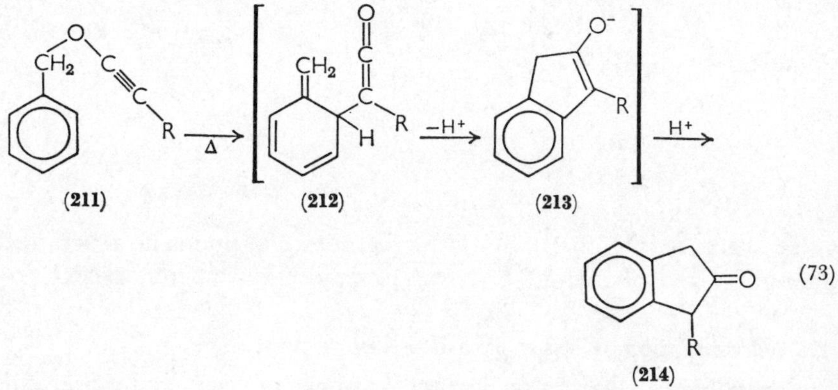

(73)

rearrangement of the ether to a ketene (212) which undergoes ring closure to give the product. The reaction of propargyl alcohols (215) with ethyl 2-propenyl ether (216) to form 4,5-hexadiene-2-ones (218) can be similarly interpreted (equation 74) [131].

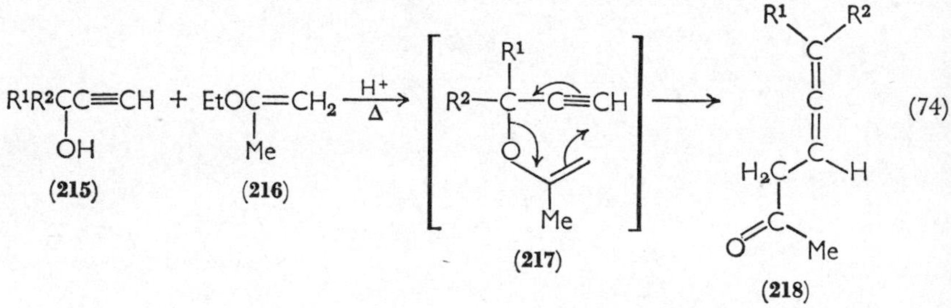

(74)

Claisen rearrangements of the allyl ethers of heterocyclic compounds with only a few exceptions proceed in a normal fashion. Thus 2-alloxy pyridine (219a) gave both 'ortho' products (220a and 221a) in approximately equal yield (equation 75) [132, 133]. The 1-(2-butenyl) ether (219c) was observed to yield an additional product, 1-(2-butenyl)-2-pyridone (220b). The formation of the latter product was not explained. Similarly, 2-substituted 4-alloxypyrimidines (222) have been shown to rearrange to the two expected pyrimidones (equation 76) [134, 135].

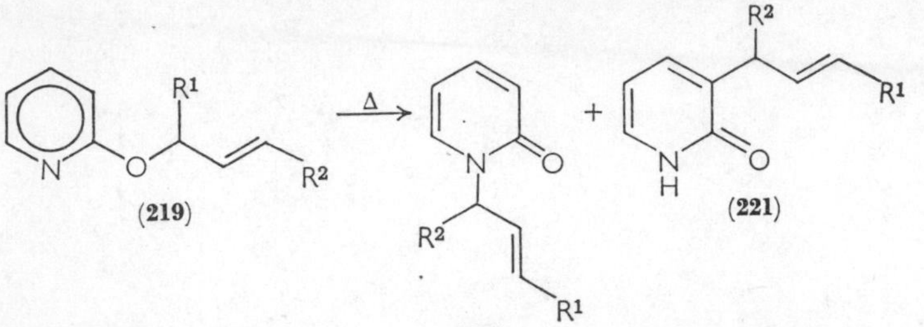

(75)

(219) (220) (221)

((a) $R^1 = R^2 = H$; (b) $R^1 = Me$, $R^2 = H$; (c) $R^1 = H$, $R^2 = Me$)

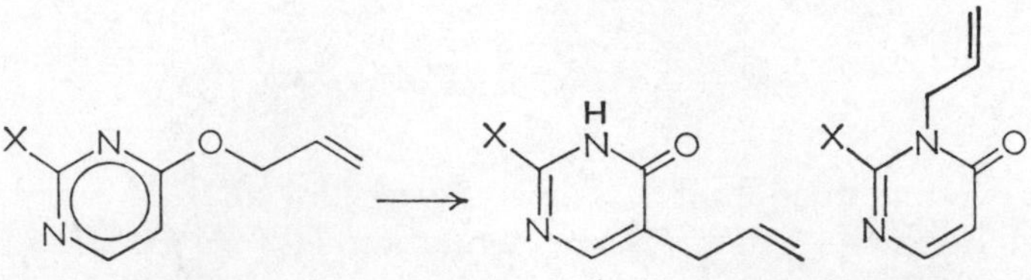

(76)

(222) (223) (224)

Thermolysis of 2-alloxy- and 2-(2-butenyloxy)quinolines (225) produced the corresponding 1-allyl-2-quinolones[136] (equation 77), indicating a similarity between 2-quinolyl and 2-naphthyl ethers[45] with respect to the direction of migration.

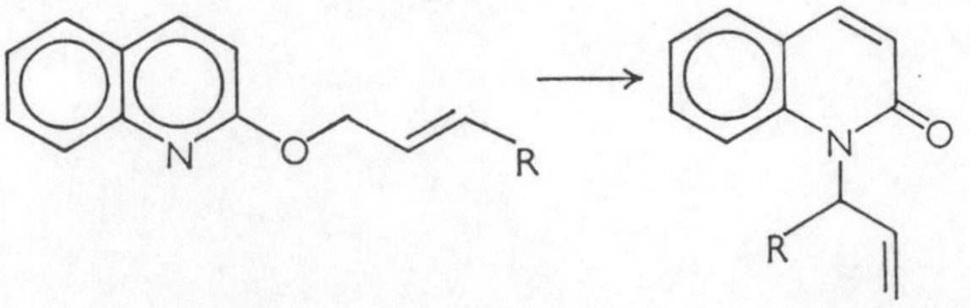

(77)

(225) (226)

(R = H or Me)

Makisumi has observed an unusual migration to a *meta* side-chain in certain heterocyclic systems. Thus, while allyl 7-(5-methyl-*s*-triazolo-[1.5-a]pyrimidyl) ether (227) gave a 50% yield of the expected product (228)[137], the 5,6-dimethyl compound (229) yielded 6-methyl-5-(3-butenyl)-7-hydroxytriazolo[1.5-a]pyrimidine (230) in 66% yield[138] (equations 78 and 79). Similar results were obtained with

$$(78)$$

$$(79)$$

allyl 4-(2,3-dimethylquinolyl) ether (**231a**) and allyl 4-(2-methyl-3-(3-butenyl)quinolyl ether (**231b**) (equation 80)[139]. *Para*-migration

products (**233**) and products (**234**) resulting from cyclization of the major product were isolated in small amounts. A mechanism involving initial *ortho* migration followed by tautomerization and a Cope rearrangement was postulated to explain these products (equation 81)[140].

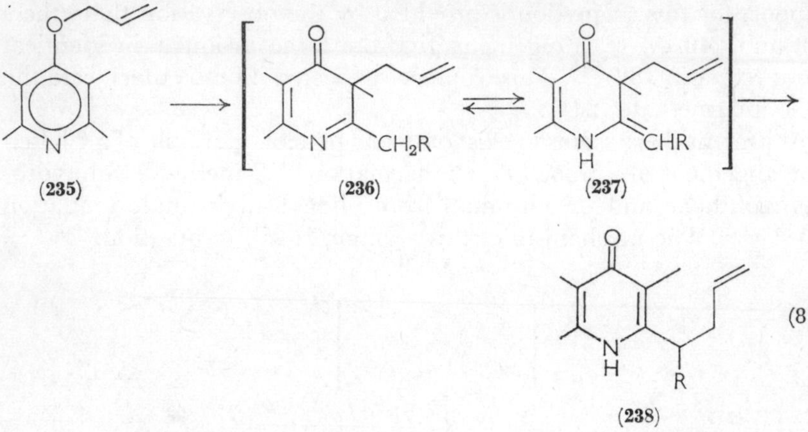
CH$_2$R
CHR
(235)
(236)
(237)
(238)

(81)

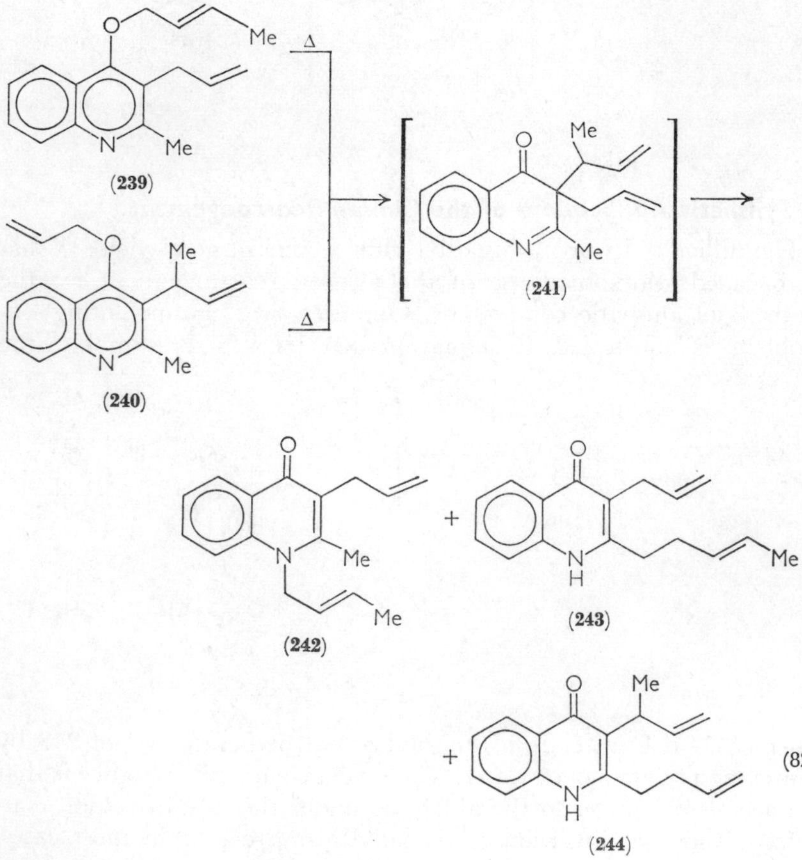
Δ
Δ
(239)
(240)
(241)
(242)
(243)
(244)

(82)

Support for this suggestion is provided by the observation that ethers **239** and **240** on rearrangement give the same products in identical ratios (equation 82)[140]. This would be expected if both ethers yield the same intermediate (**241**).

At present there seems to exist only one possible example of a Claisen rearrangement of a thioether, the formation of 2-methyl-2,3-dihydro-thianaphthene and thiachroman from phenyl allyl sulfide (equation 83)[141,142]. The mechanism of this reaction is still in question.

E. Synthetic Applications of the Claisen Rearrangement

The difficulty in preparing allyl vinyl ethers in good yields[143] has discouraged widespread use of the Claisen rearrangement for the synthesis of aliphatic compounds. One means of circumventing this problem is illustrated in equation (84)[144–146]. Presumably the

ether (**250**) is formed from the allyl acetal or hemiacetal of **248** by elimination of alcohol or water. The evidence for this sequence is that the acetal rearranges to the aldehyde under the usual reaction conditions, and that inversion of the allyl group occurs in most cases.

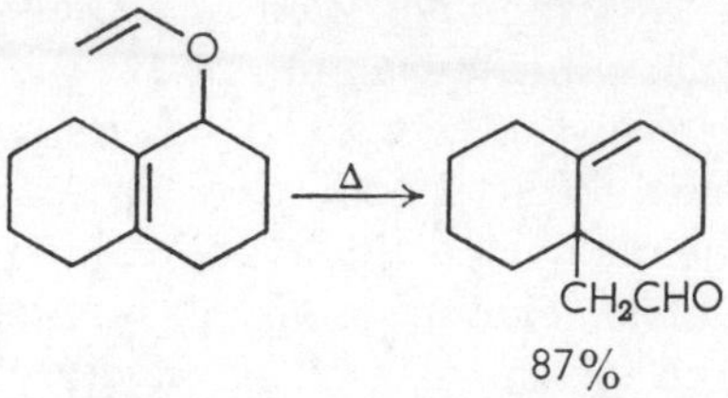

(85)

(252)   (253)

87%

(86)

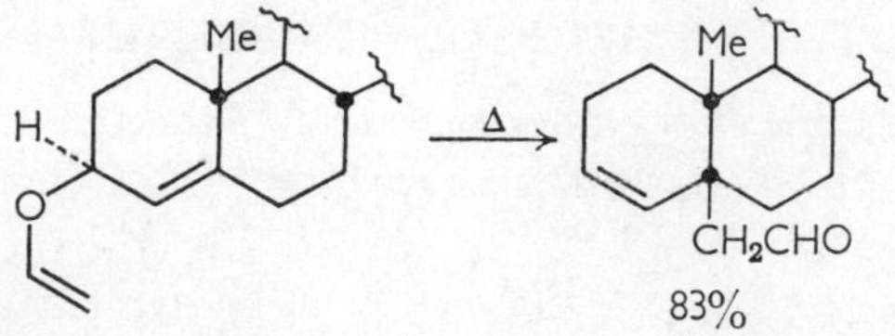

(254)   (255)

83%

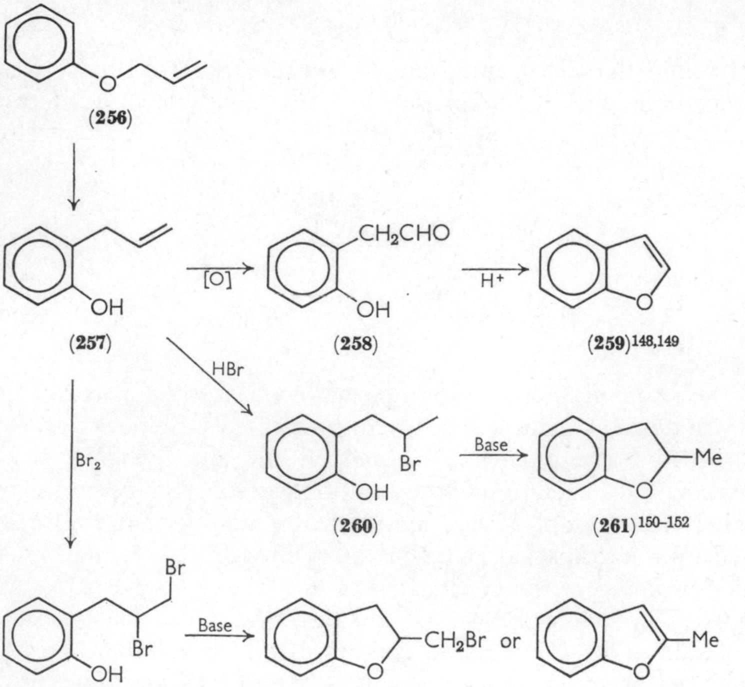

(256)

(257)   (258)   (259)[148,149]

(260)   (261)[150-152]

(262)   (263)[153]   (264)[151]

(87)

Burgstahler and Nordin have used the Claisen rearrangement for introducing angular substituents into polycyclic systems (equations 85 and 86)[147]. The vinyl ethers of Δ^4-cholestenol-3α (254) and Δ^4-cholestenol-3β have been shown to rearrange stereospecifically to 5α- and 5β-Δ^3-cholestenylacetaldehyde, respectively.

The Claisen rearrangement has also proved useful in the synthesis of various benzofuran systems[148–153]. A variety of products can be obtained from the same allyl phenol (equation 87).

V. OTHER THERMAL REARRANGEMENTS

The ability of simple enol ethers to rearrange thermally to aldehydes or ketones (equation 88) was first recognized by Staudinger and Ruzicka.

$$\text{(88)}$$

They found that the heating of 267 gave 3-ethyl-4-methyl-1,2-cyclopentanedione (268) (equation 89)[154]. Lauer and Spielman determined

$$\text{(89)}$$

that the rearrangement is intermolecular and is often complicated by side-reactions[155]. Thus, a mixture of α-methoxy-p-chlorostyrene (269) and α-(n-butoxy)styrene (270) yielded all four possible products (equation 90). Furthermore, the reaction was found to be second order in ether. Reaction of the product with the starting material was suggested by the formation of 1,2-dibenzoylpropane (277) and methane as side-products of the thermolysis of α-methoxystyrene (275) (equation 91). The source of 277 was indicated by the observations that 276 was stable under the reaction conditions and that 275 when heated with excess acetophenone (278) gave 279 and methane. The mechanism postulated at this time involved first the reaction of two molecules

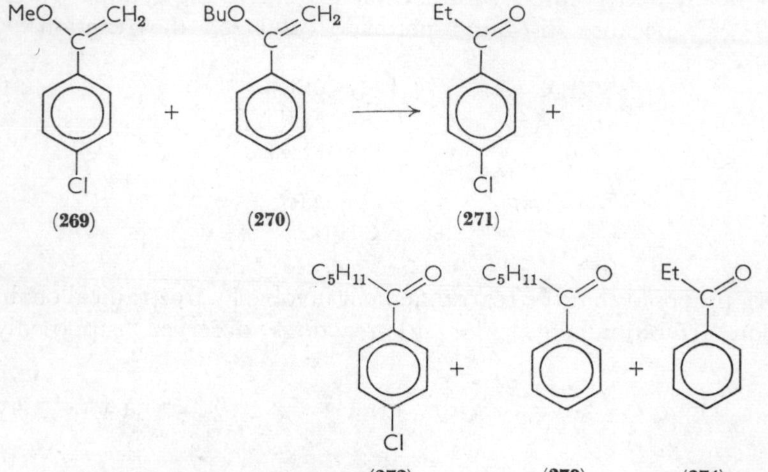

(269) (270) (271) (272) (273) (274) (90)

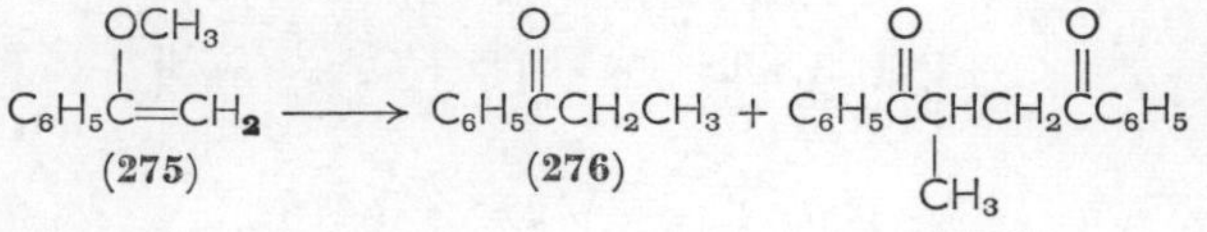

(275) (276) (277) (91)

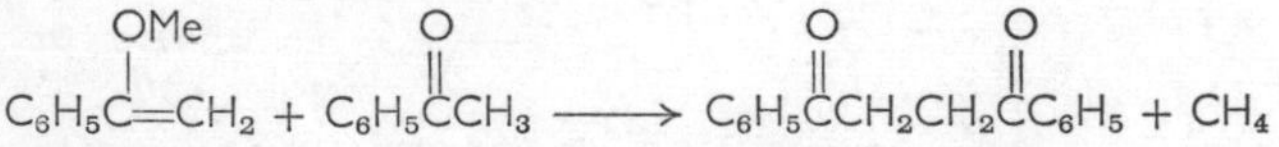

(275) (278) (279) (92)

of the ether (**280**) to form an ion-pair complex (**281**), followed by a nucleophilic displacement within the ion pair to give the product (equation 93)[155].

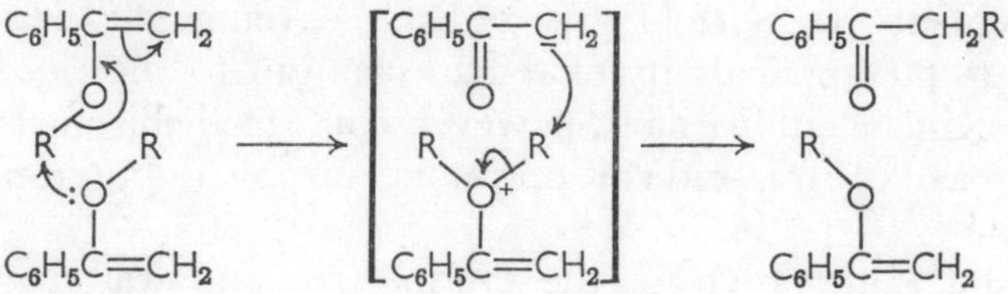

(280) (281) (282) (93)

Later studies by Wiberg and coworkers confirmed the intermolecularity of the reaction. They utilized isotopically labeled ethers[156] and optically active ethers with asymmetric migrating groups (equation 94)[157]. Because di-*t*-butyl peroxide catalyzed the reaction[157],

$$
\begin{array}{ccc}
C_6H_5C{=}CH_2 & \longrightarrow & C_6H_5CCH_2CHR \\
\ \ \ \ | & & \ \ \ \| \ \ \ \ \ | \\
O{-}CHR & & O \ \ \ Me \\
(+) \ \ \ \ \ | & & Racemic \\
Me & & \\
(283) & & (284)
\end{array}
\tag{94}
$$

$$(R = Et \text{ or } C_6H_5)$$

Wiberg proposed that the rearrangement involved a free-radical chain reaction (equation 95). The side-reactions observed supposedly

$$
C_6H_5C{=}CH_2 + R\cdot \longrightarrow C_6H_5\overset{\cdot}{C}{-}CH_2R \longrightarrow C_6H_5C{-}CH_2R + R\cdot
\tag{95}
$$

$$
\begin{array}{ccc}
\ \ | & \ \ | & \ \ \| \\
O{-}R & O{-}R & O \\
(285) & (286) & (287)
\end{array}
$$

$$
\begin{array}{cc}
C_6H_5CCH_2R + R\cdot \longrightarrow RH + C_6H_5C{-}\overset{\cdot}{C}HR \\
\ \ \ \ \| & \ \ \ \ \ \ \ \ \ \ \ \| \\
O & O
\end{array}
$$

$$
\begin{array}{cc}
(287) & (288)
\end{array}
$$

$$\Big\downarrow + 285$$

$$
\begin{array}{ccc}
\ \ \ \ \ \ \ \ R & & R \\
\ \ \ \ \ \ \ \ | & & | \\
R\cdot + C_6H_5CCHCH_2CC_6H_5 & \longleftarrow & C_6H_5CCHCH_2\overset{\cdot}{C}C_6H_5 \\
\ \ \ \ \ \ \ \ \| \ \ \ \ \ \ \ \| & & \ \ \ \| \ \ \ \ \ \ \ \ | \\
\ \ \ \ \ \ \ \ O \ \ \ \ \ \ \ O & & O \ \ \ \ \ \ O \\
& & \ \ \ \ \ \ \ \ \ \ \ \ \ \backslash R \\
(290) & & (289)
\end{array}
\tag{96}
$$

involved chain transfer (equation 96). The lack of inhibition of the rearrangement by normal free-radical scavengers[157] leaves some doubt as to the applicability of this mechanism to the pure thermal reaction. Kinetic studies have, however, confirmed this mechanism in the presence of free-radical initiators (azobis(isobutyronitrile) or $(t\text{-BuO})_2$)[158].

A possible alternative for the thermal reaction was suggested by Mortenson and Spielman[159]. They assumed a nucleophilic attack of the double bond on the alkyl group followed by path (a), or concurrent with path (b), a second similar nucleophilic attack to give the product (equation 97). However, this seems unlikely in light of

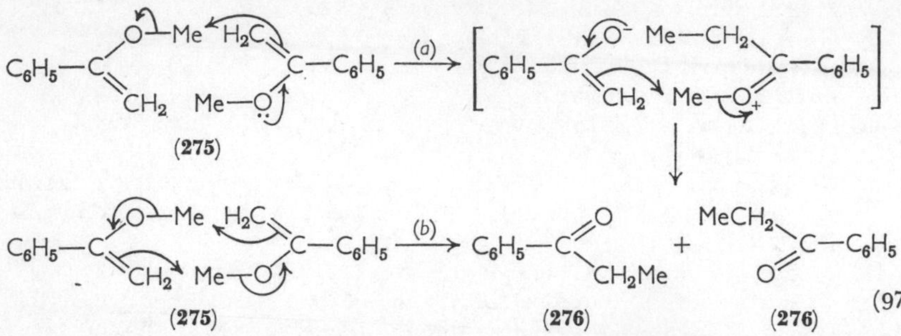

(97)

Wiberg's finding that optically active ethers were racemized. If the mechanism of equation (97) were operative, one would expect inversion of configuration.

A similar rearrangement involving alkyl aryl ethers[160,161] has been observed (equation 98). This reaction has been shown to involve

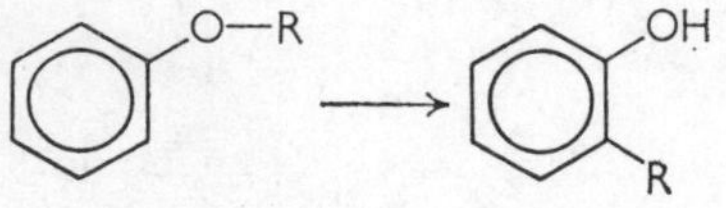

(98)

significant retention of configuration of R in **292**[160], and thus may not be strictly analogous (enol ether against phenol ether). This latter reaction has been extended to heterocyclic ethers[156,162] (equation 99), and is in this case at least partly intermolecular[156].

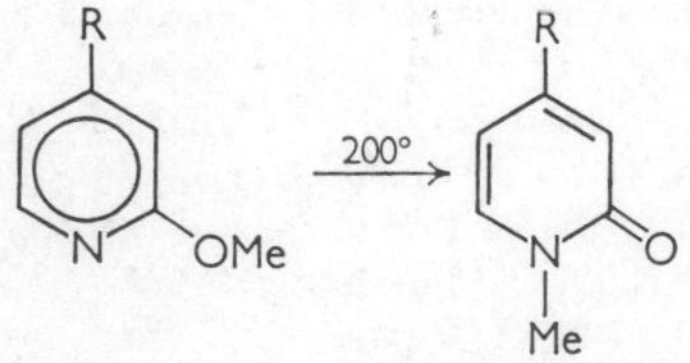

(99)

(R = Me or Et)

VI. REFERENCES

1. G. Wittig and L. Löhmann, *Ann. Chem.*, **550**, 260 (1942).
2. W. Schlenk and E. Bergmann, *Ann. Chem.*, **464**, 35 (1928).
3. G. Wittig and W. Happe, *Ann. Chem.*, **557**, 205 (1947).

4. P. Schorigin, *Chem. Ber.*, **57**, 1627, 1634 (1924).
5. G. Wittig and E. Stahnecker, *Ann. Chem.*, **605**, 69 (1957).
6. G. Wittig, H. Döser, and I. Lorenz, *Ann. Chem.*, **562**, 192 (1949).
7. C. R. Hauser and S. W. Kantor, *J. Am. Chem. Soc.*, **73**, 1437 (1951).
8. D. Y. Curtin and S. Leskowitz, *J. Am. Chem. Soc.*, **73**, 2633 (1951).
9. D. Y. Curtin and W. R. Proops, *J. Am. Chem. Soc.*, **76**, 494 (1954).
10. T. S. Stevens, *J. Chem. Soc.*, 2107 (1930); T. Thomson and T. S. Stevens, *J. Chem. Soc.*, 1932 (1932); J. L. Dunn and T. S. Stevens, *J. Chem. Soc.*, 1927 (1932).
11. T. Thomson and T. S. Stevens, *J. Chem. Soc.*, 69 (1932).
12. G. Wittig and R. Clausnizer, *Ann. Chem.*, **588**, 145 (1954).
13. J. Cast, T. S. Stevens, and J. Holmes, *J. Chem. Soc.*, 3521 (1960).
14. B. J. Millard and T. S. Stevens, *J. Chem. Soc.*, 3397 (1963).
15. J. H. Brewster and M. W. Kline, *J. Am. Chem. Soc.*, **74**, 5179 (1952).
16. U. Schöllkopf, *Angew. Chem.*, **72**, 570 (1960).
17. U. Schöllkopf and W. Fabian, *Ann. Chem.*, **642**, 1 (1961).
18. U. Schöllkopf and H. Schäfer, *Ann. Chem.*, **663**, 22 (1963).
19. U. Schöllkopf and D. Walter, *Ann. Chem.*, **654**, 27 (1962).
20. (a) P. T. Lansbury and V. A. Pattison, *J. Org. Chem.*, **27**, 1933 (1962); (b) P. T. Lansbury and V. A. Pattison, *J. Am. Chem. Soc.*, **84**, 4295 (1962).
21. J. D. Roberts and R. H. Mazur, *J. Am. Chem. Soc.*, **73**, 2509 (1951).
22. M. S. Silver, P. R. Schafer, J. E. Nordlander, C. Rüchardt and J. D. Roberts, *J. Am. Chem. Soc.*, **82**, 2646 (1960).
23. P. T. Lansbury, V. A. Pattison, J. D. Sidler, and J. B. Bieber, *J. Am. Chem. Soc.*, **88**, 78 (1966).
24. R. L. Letsinger and D. F. Pollart, *J. Am. Chem. Soc.*, **78**, 6079 (1956).
25. (a) U. Schöllkopf and M. Eisert, *Ann. Chem.*, **664**, 76 (1963); (b) U. Schöllkopf and M. Rizk, *Angew. Chem., Intern. Ed. Engl.*, **4**, 957 (1965).
26. T. J. Wallace, H. Pobiner, J. E. Hofmann, and A. Schriesheim, *Proc. Chem. Soc.*, 137 (1963).
27. H. Olsman, A. Graveland, and J. F. Arens, *Rec. Trav. Chem.*, **83**, 301 (1964).
28. G. Wittig, P. Davis, and G. Koenig, *Chem. Ber.*, **84**, 627 (1951).
29. R. A. Smith, *J. Am. Chem. Soc.*, **55**, 3718 (1933).
30. M. M. Sprung and E. S. Wallis, *J. Am. Chem. Soc.*, **56**, 1715 (1934).
31. H. Hart and R. J. Elia, *J. Am. Chem. Soc.*, **76**, 3031 (1954).
32. H. Hart and H. S. Eleuterio, *J. Am. Chem. Soc.*, **76**, 519 (1954).
33. W. I. Gilbert and E. S. Wallis, *J. Org. Chem.*, **5**, 184 (1940).
34. M. J. S. Dewar and N. A. Puttnam, *J. Chem. Soc.*, 4080 (1959).
35. M. J. S. Dewar and N. A. Puttnam, *J. Chem. Soc.*, 4086 (1959).
36. M. J. S. Dewar and N. A. Puttnam, *J. Chem. Soc.*, 4090 (1959).
37. M. J. S. Dewar and N. A. Puttnam, *J. Chem. Soc.*, 959 (1960).
38. N. M. Cullinane, R. A. Woolhouse, and G. B. Carter, *J. Chem. Soc.*, 2995 (1962).
39. D. S. Tarbell and J. C. Petropoulos, *J. Am. Chem. Soc.*, **74**, 244 (1952).
40. W. Gerrard, M. F. Lappert, and H. B. Silver, *Proc. Chem. Soc.*, 19 (1957).
41. P. Fahrni, A. Habich, and H. Schmid, *Helv. Chim. Acta*, **43**, 448 (1960).
42. H. Schmid, *Gazz. Chim. Ital.*, **92**, 968 (1962).
43. E. Piers and R. K. Brown, *Can. J. Chem.*, **41**, 329 (1963).
44. E. Piers and R. K. Brown, *Can. J. Chem.*, **41**, 2917 (1963).

45. L. Claisen, *Chem. Ber.*, **45**, 3157 (1912).
46. S. Scichilone, *Gazz. Chim. Ital.*, **12**, 449 (1882).
47. S. G. Powell and R. Adams, *J. Am. Chem. Soc.*, **42**, 646 (1920).
48. D. S. Tarbell in *Organic Reactions*, Vol. 2 (Ed. R. Adams), John Wiley and Sons, New York, 1944, pp. 1–48.
49. S. J. Rhoads in *Molecular Rearrangements*, Vol. I (Ed. P. de Mayo), John Wiley and Sons, New York, 1963, pp. 665–706.
50. L. Claisen and E. Tietze, *Chem. Ber.*, **58**, 275 (1925).
51. D. Y. Curtin and R. J. Crawford, *J. Am. Chem. Soc.*, **79**, 3156 (1957).
52. H. Conroy and R. A. Firestone, *J. Am. Chem. Soc.*, **75**, 2530 (1953).
53. H. Conroy and R. A. Firestone, *J. Am. Chem. Soc.*, **78**, 2290 (1956).
54. F. Kalberer and H. Schmid, *Helv. Chim. Acta*, **40**, 779 (1957).
55. K. Schmid, W. Haegele, and H. Schmid, *Helv. Chim. Acta*, **37**, 1080 (1954).
56. D. Y. Curtin and H. W. Johnson Jr., *J. Am. Chem. Soc.*, **76**, 2276 (1954).
57. D. Y. Curtin and H. W. Johnson Jr., *J. Am. Chem. Soc.*, **78**, 2611 (1956).
58. E. N. Marvell and R. Teranishi, *J. Am. Chem. Soc.*, **76**, 6165 (1954).
59. F. Kalberer, K. Schmid, and H. Schmid, *Helv. Chim. Acta*, **39**, 555 (1956).
60. F. Kalberer and H. Schmid, *Helv. Chim. Acta*, **40**, 13 (1957).
61. W. Haegele and H. Schmid, *Helv. Chim. Acta*, **41**, 657 (1958).
62. J. Green and D. McHale, *Chem. Ind. (London)*, 1801 (1964).
63. C. D. Hurd and L. Schmerling, *J. Am. Chem. Soc.*, **59**, 107 (1937).
64. W. M. Lauer and P. A. Sanders, *J. Am. Chem. Soc.*, **65**, 198 (1943).
65. J. P. Ryan and P. R. O'Connor, *J. Am. Chem. Soc.*, **74**, 5866 (1952).
66. H. Schmid and K. Schmid, *Helv. Chim. Acta*, **35**, 1879 (1952).
67. H. Schmid and K. Schmid, *Helv. Chim. Acta*, **36**, 489 (1953).
68. S. J. Rhoads, R. Raulins, and R. D. Reynolds, *J. Am. Chem. Soc.*, **75**, 2531 (1953).
69. E. N. Marvell, A. V. Logan, L. Friedman, and R. W. Ledeen, *J. Am. Chem. Soc.*, **76**, 1922 (1954).
70. S. J. Rhoads and R. L. Crecelius, *J. Am. Chem. Soc.*, **77**, 5183 (1955).
71. Y. Pocker, *Proc. Chem. Soc.*, 141 (1961).
72. A. S. Fomenko and E. A. Sadovnikova, *Zh. Obshch. Khim.*, **20**, 1898 (1950).
73. F. W. Shuler and G. W. Murphy, *J. Am. Chem. Soc.*, **72**, 3155 (1950).
74. L. Stein and G. W. Murphy, *J. Am. Chem. Soc.*, **74**, 1041 (1952).
75. K. R. Brower, *J. Am. Chem. Soc.*, **83**, 4370 (1961).
76. K. R. Brower, *J. Am. Chem. Soc.*, **85**, 1401 (1963).
77. A. W. Burgstahler, *J. Am. Chem. Soc.*, **82**, 4681 (1960).
78. E. N. Marvell and J. L. Stephenson, *J. Org. Chem.*, **25**, 676 (1960).
79. E. R. Alexander and R. W. Kluiber, *J. Am. Chem. Soc.*, **73**, 4304 (1951).
80. H. L. Goering and W. I. Kimoto, *J. Am. Chem. Soc.*, **87**, 1748 (1965).
81. E. N. Marvell, J. L. Stephenson, and J. Ong, *J. Am. Chem. Soc.*, **87**, 1267 (1965).
82. J. W. Ralls, R. E. Lundin, and G. F. Bailey, *J. Org. Chem.*, **28**, 3521 (1963).
83. R. K. Hill and A. G. Edwards, *Tetrahedron Letters*, 3239 (1964).
84. L. D. Huestis and L. J. Andrews, *J. Am. Chem. Soc.*, **83**, 1963 (1961).
85. W. N. White and B. E. Norcross, *J. Am. Chem. Soc.*, **83**, 1968 (1961).
86. W. N. White and B. E. Norcross, *J. Am. Chem. Soc.*, **83**, 3265 (1961).

87. R. Hoffmann and R. B. Woodward, *J. Am. Chem. Soc.*, **87**, 4389 (1965).
88. W. von E. Doering and W. R. Roth, *Tetrahedron*, **18**, 67 (1962).
89. W. N. White, D. Gwynn, R. Schlitt, C. Girard, and W. Fife, *J. Am. Chem. Soc.*, **80**, 3271 (1958).
90. H. L. Goering and R. R. Jacobson, *J. Am. Chem. Soc.*, **80**, 3277 (1958).
91. Y. Okamoto and H. C. Brown, *J. Org. Chem.*, **22**, 485 (1957).
92. W. N. White and W. K. Fife, *J. Am. Chem. Soc.*, **83**, 3846 (1961).
93. W. N. White and C. D. Slater, *J. Org. Chem.*, **27**, 2908 (1962).
94. W. N. White and C. D. Slater, *J. Org. Chem.*, **26**, 3631 (1961).
95. Z. Budesinsky and E. Rockova, *Chem. Listy*, **48**, 427 (1954).
96. K. D. Kaufman and W. E. Russey, *J. Org. Chem.*, **30**, 1320 (1965).
97. D. S. Tarbell and S. S Stradling, *J. Org. Chem.*, **27**, 2724 (1962).
98. P. G. Holton, *J. Org. Chem.*, **27**, 357 (1962).
99. E. T. McBee and E. Rapkin, *J. Am. Chem. Soc.*, **73**, 2375 (1951).
100. F. Mauthner, *J. Prakt. Chem.*, **102**, 41 (1921).
101. R. T. Arnold, J. McCool, and E. Schultz, *J. Am. Chem. Soc.*, **64**, 1023 (1942).
102. C. S. Marvel and N. A. Higgins, *J. Am. Chem. Soc.*, **70**, 2218 (1948).
103. Q. R. Bartz, R. F. Miller, and R. Adams, *J. Am. Chem. Soc.*, **57**, 371 (1935).
104. C. D. Hurd, H. Greengard, and F. D. Pilgrim, *J. Am. Chem. Soc.*, **52**, 1700 (1930).
105. J. F. Kincaid and D. S. Tarbell, *J. Am. Chem. Soc.*, **61**, 3085 (1939).
106. D. S. Tarbell and J. F. Kincaid, *J. Am. Chem. Soc.*, **62**, 728 (1940).
107. W. N. White and E. F. Wolfarth, *140th Meeting, Am. Chem. Soc.*, September 1961, p. 52Q.
108. B. D. Tiffany, *J. Am. Chem. Soc.*, **70**, 592 (1948).
109. E. N. Marvell, B. Richardson, R. Anderson, J. Stephenson, and T. Crandell, *J. Org. Chem.*, **30**, 1032 (1965).
110. J. Borgulya, H.-J. Hansen, R. Barner, and H. Schmid, *Helv. Chim. Acta*, **46**, 2444 (1963).
111. C. D. Hurd and C. N. Webb, *J. Am. Chem. Soc.*, **58**, 2190 (1936).
112. D. S. Tarbell and J. W. Wilson, *J. Am. Chem. Soc.*, **64**, 607 (1942).
113. W. M. Lauer and O. Moe, *J. Am. Chem. Soc.*, **65**, 289 (1943).
114. W. M. Lauer and W. F. Filbert, *J. Am. Chem. Soc.*, **58**, 1388 (1936).
115. W. M. Lauer and L. I. Hansen, *J. Am. Chem. Soc.*, **61**, 3039 (1939).
116. W. M. Lauer and H. E. Ungnade, *J. Am. Chem. Soc.*, **61**, 3047 (1939).
117. W. M. Lauer and R. M. Leekley, *J. Am. Chem. Soc.*, **61**, 3043 (1939).
118. C. D. Hurd and M. A. Pollack, *J. Org. Chem.*, **3**, 550 (1939).
119. W. M. Lauer, G. A. Doldouras, R. E. Hileman, and R. Liepins, *J. Org. Chem.*, **26**, 4785 (1961).
120. E. N. Marvell, D. R. Anderson, and J. Ong, *J. Org. Chem.*, **27**, 1109 (1962).
121. A. Habich, R. Barner, R. M. Roberts, and H. Schmid, *Helv. Chim. Acta*, **45**, 1943 (1962).
122. R. M. Roberts and R. G. Landolt, *J. Am. Chem. Soc.*, **87**, 2281 (1965).
123. R. M. Roberts, R. N. Greene, R. G. Landolt, and E. W. Heyer, *J. Am. Chem. Soc.*, **87**, 2282 (1965).
124. P. Fahrni and H. Schmid, *Helv. Chim. Acta*, **42**, 1102 (1959).
125. S. Marcinkiewicz, D. McHale, and J. Green, *Proc. Chem. Soc.*, 228 (1964).
126. W. M. Lauer and D. W. Wujciak, *J. Am. Chem. Soc.*, **78**, 5601 (1956).

127. K. Schmid, P. Fahrni, and H. Schmid, *Helv. Chim. Acta*, **39**, 708 (1956).
128. A. Nickon and B. R. Aaronoff, *J. Org. Chem.*, **29**, 3014 (1964).
129. W. J. le Noble, P. J. Crean, and B. Gabrielson, *J. Am. Chem. Soc.*, **86**, 1649 (1964).
130. S. M. McElvain, H. I. Anthes, and S. H. Shapiro, *J. Am. Chem. Soc.*, **64**, 2525 (1942).
131. S. Julia, M. Julia, and P. Graffin, *Bull. Soc. Chim. France*, 3218 (1964).
132. B. I. Mikhant'ev, E. I. Fedorov, A. I. Kucherova, and V. P. Potapova, *Zh. Obshch. Khim.*, **29**, 1874 (1959).
133. F. J. Dinan and H. Tieckelmann, *J. Org. Chem.*, **29**, 892 (1964).
134. H. J. Minnemeyer, J. A. Egger, J. F. Holland, and H. Tieckelmann, *J. Org. Chem.*, **26**, 4425 (1961).
135. F. J. Dinan, H. J. Minnemeyer, and H. Tieckelmann, *J. Org. Chem.*, **28**, 1015 (1963).
136. Y. Makisumi, *Tetrahedron Letters*, 2833 (1964).
137. Y. Makisumi, *Chem. Pharm. Bull. (Tokyo)*, **11**, 851 (1963).
138. Y. Makisumi, *Chem. Pharm. Bull. (Tokyo)*, **11**, 859 (1963).
139. Y. Makisumi, *Tetrahedron Letters*, 699 (1964).
140. Y. Makisumi, *Tetrahedron Letters*, 1635 (1964).
141. H. Kwart and C. M. Hackett, *J. Am. Chem. Soc.*, **84**, 1754 (1962); H. Kwart and E. R. Evans, *J. Org. Chem.*, **31**, 413 (1966).
142. C. Y. Meyers, C. Rinaldi, and L. Bonoli, *J. Org. Chem.*, **28**, 2440 (1963).
143. W. Watanabe and L. E. Conlon, *J. Am. Chem. Soc.*, **79**, 2828 (1957).
144. K. C. Brannock, *J. Am. Chem. Soc.*, **81**, 3379 (1959).
145. P. Cresson, *Bull. Soc. Chim. France*, 2618 (1964).
146. P. Cresson, *Bull. Soc. Chim. France*, 2629 (1964).
147. A. W. Burgstahler and I. C. Nordin, *J. Am. Chem. Soc.*, **83**, 198 (1961).
148. R. Aneja, S. K. Mukerjee, and T. R. Seshadri, *Chem. Ber.*, **93**, 297 (1960).
149. R. Aneja, S. K. Mukerjee, and T. R. Seshadri, *Tetrahedron*, **2**, 203 (1958).
150. A. B. Sen and R. P. Rastogi, *J. Ind. Chem. Soc.*, **30**, 355 (1953).
151. F. Scheinmann and H. Suschitzky, *Tetrahedron*, **7**, 31 (1959).
152. A. Mustafa, M. M. Sidky, S. M. A. D. Zayed, and F. M. Soliman, *Tetrahedron*, **19**, 1335 (1963).
153. A. Funke and K. von Däniken, *Bull. Soc. Chim. France*, 457 (1953).
154. H. Staudinger and L. Ruzicka, *Helv. Chim. Acta*, **7**, 377 (1924).
155. W. M. Lauer and M. A. Spielman, *J. Am. Chem. Soc.*, **55**, 4923 (1933).
156. K. B. Wiberg, T. M. Shryne, and R. R. Kintner, *J. Am. Chem. Soc.*, **79**, 3160 (1957).
157. K. B. Wiberg and B. I. Rowland, *J. Am. Chem. Soc.*, **77**, 1159 (1955).
158. K. B. Wiberg, R. R. Kintner, and E. L. Motell, *J. Am. Chem. Soc.*, **85**, 450 (1963).
159. C. W. Mortenson and M. A. Spielman, *J. Am. Chem. Soc.*, **62**, 1609 (1940).
160. H. Hart and H. S. Eleuterio, *J. Am. Chem. Soc.*, **76**, 519 (1954).
161. F. M. Elkobaisi and W. J. Hickinbottom, *J. Chem. Soc.*, 1873 (1959).
162. G. E. Hilbert and T. B. Johnson, *J. Am. Chem. Soc.*, **52**, 2001 (1930).

CHAPTER 15

Detection and estimation of ethers

JAMES S. FRITZ

Iowa State University, Ames, U.S.A.

I. INTRODUCTION

Analytical problems involving ethers are in many ways similar to those of other organic compounds. The problems encountered will usually fit into one of the following categories:

Qualitative. Isolation and (*a*) detection of a known ether, (*b*) determination of empirical formula, and (*c*) determination of structural formula.

Quantitative. Determination of amount present of a particular ether or ethers in a mixture of organic substances. Isolation of the compound(s) is often not required.

In the above, separation methods such as crystallization, distillation, gas and liquid chromatography may be invaluable for isolating a desired ether for qualitative work or for quantitative analysis. Modern spectrophotometric, nuclear magnetic resonance, and mass spectrometric analytical methods are valuable for deducing the structural formulas of organic compounds in general, including ethers. Because these methods are discussed in specialized books, the material in this chapter will deal with those spectral and chemical methods that are used specifically to determine the ether function. Most of the quantitative chemical methods described are easy to carry out, and they often yield extremely valuable information. Especially in quantitative analysis of mixtures, chemical methods usually give more precise results than are obtainable by strictly instrumental means.

II. ISOLATION AND SEPARATION OF ETHERS

Methods such as fractional distillation, gas chromatography, column chromatography, paper chromatography, and thin-layer chromatography are of course applicable to the isolation and separation of ethers as well as other organic compounds. The principles of these separation techniques are well known and need not be discussed here. Although chromatographic separations of some classes of organic compounds are well documented, comparatively few papers have dealt specifically with the separation of ethers. Ray[1] has described the separation of a number of aliphatic ethers by gas chromatography. Carruthers, Johnstone, and Plimmer[2] studied the separation of methyl aryl ethers by gas chromatography using a column containing one part of Apiezon M on 2·5 parts of Celite C22. They employed a column 260 cm long, nitrogen carrier gas, a temperature of 145°C, and a flow rate of 14 ml/min. Under these conditions the retention volumes given in Table 1 were obtained.

Some excellent separations of ethers have been obtained using salting-out chromatography or solubilization chromatography. Sargent and Rieman[3] separated ethers on a column of 200–400 mesh Dowex 50–X4 ion-exchange resin using 0·01 M to 4·0 M ammonium sulfate as the eluting agent. Lowering the concentration of ammonium sulfate decreases the 'salting-out' effect and causes the ethers to be eluted one by one.

In solubilization chromatography, using the same ion-exchange resin, the eluting (mobile) phase is a mixture of water and a miscible organic solvent such as acetic acid. The solute ethers are held in the

TABLE 1. Gas chromatographic retention volumes of ArOMe-type ethers[2].

Ar	B.p. (°c)	Retention volume compared to anisole
Phenyl	154	1·00
o-Cresyl	171	1·56
m-Cresyl	177	1·67
p-Cresyl	176	1·67
2,3-Xylyl	199	2·96
2,4-Xylyl	192	2·42
2,5-Xylyl	194	2·50
2,6-Xylyl	182	2·05
3,4-Xylyl	204	3·16
3,5-Xylyl	194	2·50
o-Methoxyphenyl	207	2·51
m-Methoxyphenyl	214	3·11

resin by interaction with the polystyrene matrix. A higher proportion of organic solvent in the eluent increases the solubility of the solutes and speeds their elution from the column. Sherma and Rieman[4] studied the following ethers: diisopropyl, di-n-propyl, ethyl n-butyl, di-n-butyl, anisole, diphenyl, diisopropyl, and di-n-propyl. A typical separation is shown in Figure 1.

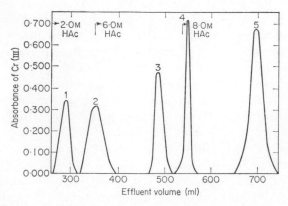

FIGURE 1. The separation of a five-component ether mixture. 102·0 cm × 2·28 cm^2 Dowex 50–X4, 200–400 mesh, hydrogen form, 0·28 cm/min. Aqueous acetic acid eluent changed at 350 ml and 540 ml. 1 diisopropyl ether; 2 ethyl n-butyl ether; 3 di-n-butyl ether; 4 anisole; 5 diphenyl ether. [Reproduced, by permission, from reference 4.]

III. DETECTION OF ETHERS BY CLASSICAL AND SPECTROPHOTOMETRIC METHODS

The classical methods for detecting ethers are often somewhat cumbersome. The presence of an ether is deduced from the solubility class, from the presence of oxygen as determined by qualitative elemental analysis, and from the absence of other oxygen functional groups of other types of compound in the same solubility class.

Identification of a particular ether by classical methods is more straightforward. The possibilities are narrowed to a short list by measurement of the melting point or boiling point (and often of the refractive index as well). Then a derivative is prepared and its melting point is determined to confirm the particular ether present. For symmetrical aliphatic ethers, the 3,5-dinitrobenzoate is a common derivative (equation 1). Picrates of aromatic ethers are often used as derivatives.

$$ROR + ClCO\!\!-\!\!\underset{NO_2}{\overset{NO_2}{\bigcirc}}\!\!\longrightarrow ROCO\!\!-\!\!\underset{NO_2}{\overset{NO_2}{\bigcirc}} + RCl \qquad (1)$$

The ether function as such does not absorb radiant energy to any extent in the visible or ultraviolet spectral regions, although specific ethers may sometimes be detected by the absorbance of other functional groups in the molecule. For example furan has an absorption maximum at 252 mμ owing to conjugated unsaturation.

In the infrared the characteristic response of the C—O—C system to stretching vibrations is not greatly different from that of the C—C—C system. For this reason these two systems absorb radiant energy in the same general wavelength regions. However, more intense infrared bands are observed for the ethers, owing to the greater changes of dipole moment in ethers. Useful for identification of ethers is a strong vibration band due to asymmetric stretching between about 8·00 and 9·45 μ (1250–1060 cm^{-1}). For aliphatic and cyclic compounds containing the C—O—C function this band occurs between 8·70 and 9·45 μ (1250–1060 cm^{-1}). For aryl, arylalkyl, and vinyl ethers this band occurs between about 7·85 and 8·35 μ (1270–1200 cm^{-1}). Carboxylic esters and lactones also absorb strongly in the region 7·85–8·15 μ. In the last-mentioned ethers there is a weaker symmetric stretching band around 9·30 to 9·80 μ (1275–1200 cm^{-1}).

Some additional infrared absorption bands that are often useful are as follows:

ArOCH$_3$ 3·51 μ (2850 cm^{-1})

3·28–3·33 μ (3050–3000 cm^{-1})
8·00 μ (1250 cm^{-1})
10·5–12·35 μ (950–810 cm^{-1})

10·8 μ (925 cm^{-1})

Books by Nakanishi[5] and by Silverstein and Bassler[6] provide useful information on the infrared behavior of ethers. Randall, Fowler, Fuson, and Dangl[7] give infrared spectra of a number of specific ethers.

IV. QUANTITATIVE CHEMICAL METHODS FOR ETHERS

A. Alkoxy Group

Compounds containing an alkoxy group in which the alkyl group is not higher than butyl (and preferably is methyl or ethyl) can be determined quantitatively by cleavage with hydroiodic acid (equation 2).

$$\text{—OR} + \text{HI} \longrightarrow \text{—OH} + \text{RI} \qquad (2)$$

After cleavage, the alkyl iodide is usually separated from the reaction mixture by distillation and is determined by gravimetric, titrimetric, or gasometric means. This method was first proposed by Zeisel[8] and was adapted to a micro scale by Pregl[9]. An excellent review of the method together with details concerning procedures and apparatus is given by Cheronis and Ma[10].

Alcohols as well as ethers react with hydroiodic acid to form an alkyl iodide. In mixed ethers, R^1OR^2, where R^1 is a long-chain group and R^2 contains one to four carbon atoms, cleavage with HI produces mostly R^2I and R^1OH. However, if the reaction goes partly in the reverse manner to produce R^2OH and R^1I, the R^2OH can further react with HI to give R^2I and H_2O. This may also happen if both R^2 and R^1 are short-chain groups. Thus diethyl ether produces two molecules of ethyl iodide (reaction 3). If the reaction produces mainly R^1OH and

$$\text{EtOEt} + \text{HI} \longrightarrow \text{EtOH} + \text{EtI} \xrightarrow{\text{HI}} 2\ \text{EtI} \qquad (3)$$

R²I, however, and only minor amounts of R¹I, correct results will be obtained provided R¹I has a sufficiently high boiling point to allow the lower boiling R²I to be separated from it by distillation.

A typical apparatus for determining alkoxy compounds is shown in Figure 2. The sample is dissolved in acetic anhydride or in xylene. Microanalytical reagent grade hydriodic acid (which is 57% HI instead of the usual 47 or 48% acid) is added and the mixture is heated to speed the reaction. A slow stream of nitrogen is bubbled into the reaction mixture to aid in volatilizing the alkyl iodide.

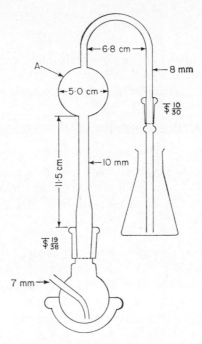

FIGURE 2. Apparatus for the determination of alkoxy compounds.
[Reproduced, by permission, from reference 12.]

In the classical methods a scrubber (not shown in Figure 2) is included in the apparatus to separate the alkyl iodide from hydrogen iodide and iodine. Pregl used a suspension of red phosphorus in water to achieve this separation (reaction 4). The hydrogen iodide is soluble

$$2\,P + 3\,I_2 \longrightarrow 2\,PI_3 \tag{4a}$$

$$PI_3 + H_2O \longrightarrow H_3PO_3 + 3\,HI \tag{4b}$$

in water while the alkyl iodide is not soluble and continues through the scrubber. However, Elek[11] employed a suspension of phosphorus and cadmium sulfate to avoid possible loss of hydrogen iodide through the scrubber (equation 5). Thus if all goes well only the alkyl iodide

$$4\,HI + 2\,CdSO_4 \longrightarrow Cd(CdI_4) + 2\,H_2SO_4 \tag{5}$$

enters the receiver where it is absorbed and determined by one of the methods discussed in the next subsection. At this point it might be stated that the cleavage reaction proceeds fairly rapidly, but the volatility of the alkyl iodide limits the method to lower alkoxy groups.

Determination of the alkyl iodide. Gravimetrically, the alkyl iodide may be absorbed by a solution of silver nitrate in 95% ethanol. A double salt is formed, but this decomposes on digestion with water so that the overall reaction is (6). Unfortunately the precipitation is not

$$RI + AgNO_3 \longrightarrow AgI(s) + RNO_3 \tag{6}$$

quite complete and a small correction factor must be employed.

The alkyl iodide may also be determined by the indirect iodine method. Bromine oxidizes the iodine in the alkyl iodide to iodic acid in acetate-buffered solution (equation 7). The excess bromine is re-

$$RI + 3\,Br_2 + 3\,H_2O \longrightarrow HIO_3 + RBr + 5\,HBr \tag{7}$$

duced by careful addition of formic acid (equation 8). Finally the iodic

$$Br_2 + HCO_2H \longrightarrow 2\,HBr + CO_2 \tag{8}$$

acid is reduced with potassium iodide, and the iodine formed is titrated with standard thiosulfate (equation 9).

$$HIO_3 + 5\,I^- + 5\,H^+ \longrightarrow 3\,I_2 + 3\,H_2O \tag{9a}$$

$$2\,S_2O_3{}^{2-} + I_2 \longrightarrow S_4O_6{}^{2-} + 2\,I^- \tag{9b}$$

The nonaqueous acid–base titrimetric method of Cundiff and Markunas[12] is unique in that it is not necessary to separate the alkyl iodide from either HI or iodine. The alkyl iodide is converted into the corresponding alkylpyridinium iodide, and a differentiating titration with tetrabutylammonium hydroxide titrates first the HI that is distilled over and next the alkyl pyridinium iodide. These authors reported excellent results for the analysis of some twenty-nine different ethers including methoxy, ethoxy, propoxy, and butoxy compounds and one thioether.

Separation and determination of alkyl iodides by gas chromatography is another possibility. Vertalier and Martin[13] successfully separated several of the lower alkyl iodides, but their results were not quantitative. Ma and Schlachter[14] reported a useful method although their procedure is somewhat involved and their apparatus rather elaborate.

B. Oxyalkylene Group

Siggia and coworkers[15] have proposed a method for quantitative determination of compounds containing the oxyalkylene group. Their method is based on reaction (10), which is thought to proceed through

$$-CH_2CH_2O- + 2\,HI \longrightarrow CH_2{=}CH_2 + I_2 + H_2O \qquad (10)$$

the formation of 1,2-diiodoethane, followed by decomposition to ethylene plus iodine. Some of the 1,2-diiodide may react with HI (reaction 11).

$$ICH_2CH_2I + HI \longrightarrow CH_3CH_2I + I_2 \qquad (11)$$

In this procedure the sample is boiled with 55–58% HI for 1·5 hours under carbon dioxide. Then the mixture is cooled, potassium iodide is added, and the iodine formed is titrated with standard thiosulfate. Good results were obtained for the following compounds: diethylene glycol monobutyl ether, ethylene glycol monomethyl ether, polyethylene glycol (Carbowax 400), dioxane, polypropylene glycol, ethylene glycol, diethylene glycol dimethyl ether, ethylene oxide, and stearic acid esters of polyethylene glycol.

C. Acetals and Ketals

Acetals and ketals are usually easy to hydrolyze in acidic solution. Methods for the quantitative chemical analysis of these compounds are generally based on the determination of the aldehyde or ketone formed.

In the method of Siggia[16] the aldehyde is determined by a quantitative formation of the bisulfite addition product.

The ketone from a ketal may, after hydrolysis, be determined by a standard oximation procedure such as that of Fritz, Yamamura, and Bradford[17].

D. Vinyl Ethers

Vinyl ethers are readily hydrolyzed to acetaldehyde (reaction 12).

The acetaldehyde can be determined quantitatively by a bisulfite addition or by an oximation procedure.

$$ROCH{=}CH_2 + H_2O \xrightarrow{\ H^+\ } ROH + CH_3CHO \tag{12}$$

A useful quantitative method for vinyl ethers is based on reaction of iodine in methanol–water (equation 13)[18]. In this method there is no

$$ROCH{=}CH_2 + I_2 + MeOH \longrightarrow \underset{\underset{OMe}{|}}{ROCHCH_2I} + HI \tag{13}$$

interference from impurities usually associated with vinyl ethers such as acetaldehyde, acetals, alcohols, acetylene, or water. The sum of acetal plus vinyl ether can be ascertained by the hydrolysis method. Then on another aliquot only the vinyl ether is measured by the iodine method.

E. Epoxides

The α-epoxide (oxirane) functional group is quite reactive toward nucleophilic reagents (reaction 14). Useful analytical methods involv-

$$\tag{14}$$

ing this type of reaction include the addition of hydrogen chloride[19], thiosulfate[20], morpholine[21], and hydrogen bromide[22]. Probably the best of these is the method of Durbetaki[22] in which the epoxide is determined by *direct titration* with anhydrous hydrogen bromide in acetic acid (reaction 15). The end point in this titration may be determined

$$\tag{15}$$

potentiometrically using glass and calomel electrodes, or with a visual indicator such as crystal violet.

Although most α-epoxy compounds titrate smoothly, Dijkstra and Dahmen[23] found the titration of glycidyl esters to be 'annoyingly slow' by this procedure. A fairly long wait was required for equilibrium to be attained after addition of each increment of titrant, especially near the equivalence point. These authors then proceeded to show how the titration could be speeded up. The mechanism of hydrogen bromide addition is one of rapid protonation, followed by slow addition of the anion (reaction 16). When the titration is performed in the presence of

$$H^+ + \underset{|}{\overset{O}{-C}}\!\!-\!\!\overset{}{\underset{|}{C}}- \longrightarrow \left(\underset{\underset{|}{-C}\overset{}{\underset{}{}}\underset{|}{C-}}{\overset{\overset{+}{H}}{\overset{|}{O}}}\right)^{+} \overset{Br^-}{\longrightarrow} \underset{|}{\overset{OH}{-C}}\!\!-\!\!\underset{\underset{Br}{|}}{\overset{}{C}}- \tag{16}$$

three equivalents of tetrabutylammonium iodide for each equivalent of epoxide, the titration proceeds much more rapidly and there is a larger potential break at the equivalence point in the titration. Addition of an excess of a quaternary ammonium bromide also speeds up the titration; the use of lithium bromide is somewhat less effective.

Operationally it is more convenient to dissolve the sample in glacial acetic acid, add an excess of a quaternary ammonium bromide or iodide, and titrate with standard perchloric acid in glacial acetic acid. This avoids the necessity of preparing and keeping a standard solution of anhydrous hydrogen bromide in glacial acetic acid.

Keen[24] has devised a method for the determination of β-epoxides (oxetanes) based on their cleavage to the 1,3-chlorohydrin by pyridinium chloride (reaction 17). The oxetane ring is considerably more

$$\underset{\underset{CH_2}{}}{\overset{CH_2}{C}}\!\!\diagdown\!\!O + HCl \underset{pyridine}{\overset{\Delta}{\longrightarrow}} \underset{\underset{CH_2Cl}{}}{\overset{CH_2OH}{C}} \tag{17}$$

stable than the oxirane ring; therefore this reaction requires the use of anhydrous pyridinium chloride and refluxing for approximately 3 hours. (A modification of this procedure employs a sealed tube and requires less time.) After the reaction is complete, water is added and the excess acidity is titrated with 0.15 M sodium hydroxide using phenolphthalein indicator.

Excellent results were obtained for approximately ten different oxetanes. This procedure also determines most oxiranes quantitatively. Esters and several olefins caused no interference, and the author feels that aromatic and noncyclic aliphatic ethers will cause no interference.

F. Miscellaneous Quantitative Methods

In strictly anhydrous media ethers can be determined by titration with a standard solution of a Lewis acid. Thus Trambouze[25] titrated dioxane with aluminum chloride in benzene using thermometric detection of the end point. Sheka[26] titrated diethyl ether, diphenyl ether, and dioxane with aluminum bromide and followed the titration by measuring the dielectric constant of the solution. Zenchelsky, Periale, and Cobb[27] studied the reaction between dioxane and stannic chloride in benzene and found a combining ratio of one to one and accuracy of $\pm 1\%$ in the titration.

Schenk, Santiago, and Wines[28] noted that 1,3-dimethoxybenzene reacts with tetracyanoethylene in acetic anhydride–chloroform to produce a color that follows Beer's law. Apparently other aryl ethers can be determined using this reaction.

Anethole and perhaps other aryl ethers can be determined quantitatively by oxidation with cerium(IV)[29]. Binary mixtures containing an ether may sometimes be analyzed by a phase titration. For example Lazzari[30] analyzed mixtures of dibutyl ether and butyl alcohol by titration with water to the formation of a permanent turbidity.

V. QUANTITATIVE DETERMINATION OF THIOETHERS (SULFIDES)

In the absence of other sulfur-containing compounds, determination of thioethers can be based on a quantitative analysis for total sulfur by standard methods. However, a much more selective method involves oxidation to sulfoxide with bromine in partly aqueous solution (equation 18). This reaction is fast enough for direct titration with

$$R_2S + Br_2 + H_2O \longrightarrow R_2S{\to}O + 2\,HBr \qquad (18)$$

bromine to be possible. Excess bromine will further oxidize the sulfoxide to the sulfone, but the latter reaction is slower. Siggia and Edsberg[31] carried out the titration in acetic acid–water containing some hydrochloric acid. The titrant used is a standard bromate–bromide solution which reacts with the hydrochloric acid in the sample solution to form bromine in situ (equation 19). The bromine then

$$BrO_3^- + 5\,Br^- + 6\,H^+ \longrightarrow 3\,Br_2 + 3\,H_2O \qquad (19)$$

oxidizes the sulfide to the sulfoxide. The end point in the titration is detected by the first lasting color of the excess free bromine.

This method also oxidizes mercaptans more or less quantitatively, but the accuracy is rather poor. Jaselskis[32] solved the problem of analyzing mixtures of sulfides and mercaptans by first treating the mercaptan with acrylonitrile in basic solution (reaction 20). The sulfide from this reaction, plus the sulfide originally present in the

$$RSH + CH_2{=}CHCN \xrightarrow{\;OH^-\;} RSCH_2CH_2CN \qquad (20)$$

sample, are titrated with bromine according to the method of Siggia and Edsberg[31]. On another aliquot of the sample only the mercaptan is determined by titration with iodine or with mercury(II)[33].

VI. REFERENCES

1. N. H. Ray, *J. Appl. Chem. (London)*, **4**, 21 (1954).
2. W. Carruthers, R. A. W. Johnstone, and J. R. Plimmer, *Chem. Ind. (London)*, 331 (1958).
3. R. Sargent and W. Rieman, *Anal. Chim. Acta*, **18**, 197 (1958).
4. J. Sherma and W. Rieman *Anal. Chim. Acta*, **20**, 357 (1959).
5. K. Nakanishi, *Infrared Absorption Spectroscopy*, Holden-Day, San Francisco, 1962.
6. R. M. Silverstein and G. C. Bassler, *Spectrometric Identification of Organic Compounds*, John Wiley and Sons, New York, 1963.
7. H. M. Randall, R. G. Fowler, N. Fuson, and J. R. Dangl, *Infrared Determination of Organic Structures*, Van Nostrand, Princeton, 1949.
8. S. Zeisel, *Monatsch. Chem.*, **6**, 989 (1885).
9. F. Pregl, *Quantitative Organic Microanalysis* (Transl. E. Fyleman), Blakiston, Philadelphia, 1924.
10. N. D. Cheronis and T. S. Ma, *Organic Functional Group Analysis by Micro- and Semimicro-Methods*, Interscience Publishers, New York, 1964, pp. 124–141.
11. A. Elek, *Ind. Eng. Chem., Anal. Ed.*, **11**, 174 (1939).
12. R. H. Cundiff and P. C. Markunas, *Anal. Chem.*, **33**, 1028 (1961).
13. S. Vertalier and F. Martin, *Chim. Anal.*, **40**, 80 (1958).
14. T. S. Ma and M. S. Schlachter in ref. 10, p. 622.
15. S. Siggia, A. C. Starke, J. J. Garis and C. R. Stahl, *Anal. Chem.*, **30**, 115 (1958).
16. S. Siggia, *Ind. Eng. Chem., Anal. Ed.*, **19**, 1025 (1947).
17. J. S. Fritz, S. S. Yamamura, and E. C. Bradford, *Anal. Chem.*, **31**, 260 (1959).
18. S. Siggia and R. L. Edsberg, *Ind. Eng. Chem., Anal. Ed.*, **20**, 762 (1948).
19. D. Swern, T. W. Findley, G. N. Billen, and J. T. Scanlan, *Anal. Chem.*, **19**, 414 (1947).
20. W. C. J. Ross, *J. Chem. Soc.*, 2257 (1950).
21. G. L. Funk in F. E. Critchfield, *Organic Functional Group Analysis*, Macmillan, New York, 1963, p. 136.
22. A. J. Durbetaki, *Anal. Chem.*, **28**, 2000 (1956).
23. R. Dijkstra and E. A. M. F. Dahmen, *Anal. Chim. Acta*, **31**, 28 (1964).
24. R. T. Keen, *Anal. Chem.*, **29**, 1041 (1957).
25. Y. Trambouze, *Compt. Rend.*, **238**, 648 (1951).
26. I. A. Sheka, *Zh. Obshch. Khim.*, **26**, 1340 (1956).
27. S. T. Zenchelsky, J. Periale, and J. C. Cobb, *Anal. Chem.*, **28**, 67 (1956).
28. G. H. Schenk, M. Santiago, and P. Wines, *Anal. Chem.*, **35**, 167 (1963).
29. D. G. M. Diaper and F. R. Richardson, *Can. J. Chem.*, **34**, 1835 (1956).
30. G. Lazzari, *Ann. Chim. (Rome)*, **38**, 287 (1948).
31. S. Siggia and R. L. Edsberg, *Ind. Eng. Chem., Anal. Ed.*, **20**, 938 (1948).
32. B. Jaselskis, *Anal. Chem.*, **31**, 928 (1959).
33. J. S. Fritz and T. A. Palmer, *Anal. Chem.*, **33**, 98 (1961).

CHAPTER **16**

Appendix on safety measures

N. V. STEERE

University of Minnesota, U.S.A.

I. INTRODUCTION

Any chemical requires certain precautions when handled, and while ethers are not especially hazardous, their use involves certain risks of fire, toxic effects, and unexpected reactions.

After a brief review of the toxic, fire, and explosion hazards of some of the ethers, reasonable protective measures will be outlined. Except for the unique problems of peroxide formation in ethers, the practices described will be suitable for preventing accidents in many other laboratory operations, particularly those involving the handling of flammable liquids.

It is not yet current practice to require that proposals for laboratory research contain statements of safety considerations[1], but, in addition to the institutional and supervisory responsibilities, there are certain individual responsibilities which must be fulfilled if laboratory accidents are to be prevented[2]. Each investigator has the responsibility to: (a) find out the health and safety hazards of the chemicals to be used and produced, and the hazards of the reactions which may occur; (b) design the experimental setup and procedures to avoid or limit unplanned occurrences; and (c) investigate and record unplanned events which occur.

II. FIRE HAZARDS OF ETHERS

Since almost all ethers will burn in air, an assessment of their potential hazards depends upon flash points and evaporation rates, vapor densities, ignition temperatures, ignition sources, and fire temperatures.

A. Flash Points and Evaporation Rates

The flash point of a liquid is the lowest temperature at which vapors are given off in sufficient quantities for the vapor–air mixture above the surface of the liquid to propagate a flame away from the source of ignition. In other words an explosive vapor–air mixture can form whenever a liquid is used or stored in an open container at a temperature above its flash point. Many laboratory fires have occurred because flammable mixtures of ether vapor and air were formed when the solvent was poured from one container to another.

The flash point of a flammable liquid is determined by heating it in standard equipment and measuring the minimal temperature at which a flash can be obtained when a small flame is introduced in the vapor above the surface of that liquid. The equipment used for liquids with a flash point below about 80° c is the Tag Closed Cup Tester, described by the American Society for Testing Materials, specification D56.

The approximate flash point of some common ethers and their relative evaporation times are shown in Table 1. The evaporation times are relative to diethyl ether as 1·0[3]. The rate for diffusion of diethyl ether in free air in the neighborhood of the source is 4·4 cc/sec[4].

TABLE 1. Flash points and relative evaporation times of ethers.

Compound	Flash point (°c)	Relative evaporation time ($Et_2O = 1·0$)
Butylcellosolve (ethylene glycol monobutyl ether)	61	85
Di-n-butyl ether	25	14·5
Cellosolve (ethylene glycol mono-ethyl ether)	40	28·1
p-Dioxane	12	5·8
Divinyl ether	−30	−
Diethyl ether	−45	1·0
Diisopropyl ether	−28	1·4
Methylcellosolve (ethylene glycol monomethyl ether)	42	21·1
Tetrahydrofuran	−14	2·0

B. Vapor Densities

Since the vapors of ethers are heavier than air, they tend to flow downwards from pouring operations and open containers. Flammable concentrations of vapors may travel a considerable distance to a source of ignition, which may result in a flame flashing back to the source of vapors or in an explosion.

Vapor densities of some of the ethers, compared to air as 1·0, are: diethyl ether, 2·6; tetrahydrofuran, 2·5; p-dioxane, 3·0; and diisopropyl ether, 3·5. Such densities and a tendency toward downward flow account for the requirement that operating room electrical equipment below 5 feet above the floor must be explosion-proof.

As pure solvent vapors become diluted in air, the vapor density of the mixture begins to approach that of air, and such mixtures may easily be carried upward by air currents within the laboratory. For example, while the vapor density of pure diethyl ether vapor is 2·6, the least possible explosive concentration of ether is 1·9% v/v and this mixture has a vapor density of 1·03.

C. Limits of Flammability

The lower limit of flammability, or the lower explosive limit, is the lowest percentage concentration by volume in which a flash will occur or a flame will travel if the mixture is ignited. The upper limit of flammability, or the upper explosive limit, is the highest percentage concentration by volume of a flammable mixture in which a flash will occur or flame will travel.

Limits of flammability for horizontal and downward propagation of flame in mixtures of diethyl ether in air and in tubes of different materials and diameters have been determined. The limits of flammability of several ethers in air, in oxygen, and in other atmospheres are included in the critical review by Coward and Jones[5] which lists flammability limits for many other materials. Limits of flammability of ether vapors are listed in Table 2.

TABLE 2. Limits of flammability of ether vapors.

Compound	Limits of flammability (% v/v)	
	Lower	Upper
Butylcellosolve	1·1	16·0
Di-n-butyl ether	1·5	7·6
Cellosolve	2·6	15·7
p-Dioxane	2·0	22
Divinyl ether	1·7	27·9
Diethyl ether	1·9	48
Diisopropyl ether	1·4	21
Methylcellosolve	2·5	19·8
Tetrahydrofuran	2·0	11·8

D. Ignition Temperatures

The ignition temperature is the minimal temperature required to initiate or cause self-sustained combustion, independent from the source of ignition. Listed temperatures should be considered as approximations since they vary with the composition of the vapor–air mixture, oxygen concentration, humidity, size of test vessel, and other parameters of the test situation (Table 3).

TABLE 3. Ignition temperatures for ethers.

Compound	Ignition temp. (°c)
Butylcellosolve	244
Di-n-butyl ether	194
p-Dioxane	180
Divinyl ether	360
Diethyl ether	180
Isopropyl ether	443
Tetrahydrofuran	321

Attention is directed to the particularly low ignition temperatures of diethyl ether and p-dioxane, especially with reference to temperatures listed for some of the ignition sources described in the next section.

The minimal energy of a capacitance spark that is just capable of igniting a nonflowing stoichiometric mixture has been determined[6], and it is claimed possible to predict the minimal energy to ignite almost any organic compound by comparison of the molecular structure to those examined.

E. Ignition Sources

Since the elimination or control of the ignition sources is a basic approach to prevention of fires and explosions where flammable liquids are transferred or stored, it is appropriate to list some of the possible sources of ignition, including both the obvious and the not so obvious.

I. Flame

Flame sources of ignition can include laboratory burners, glass-blowing equipment, gas pilot lights, welding torches, plumbers' lead pots, and matches used to light cigars, cigarettes, and pipes.

2. Heat

Electrical heating elements in furnaces and hot plates, sparks from grinding and metal tools, and lighted tobacco are heat sources which may be readily apparent as ignition sources. Less apparent ignition sources include incandescent light bulbs, high-pressure steam lines, overheated bearings, heating mantles, and low-temperature electrical ovens. Cigarette temperatures have been reported[7] to reach up to 732° c.

Perhaps, because the electrical heating coils in low-temperature ovens are not readily visible or because the coils are not heated to a bright red, such ovens have erroneously been considered safe for heating mixtures containing diethyl ether, although the resistance heating elements can be well above the ignition temperature of many flammable liquids[8]. Even the surface temperature of a steam line at 7·03 kg/cm^2 can reach 170° c[8].

3. Electric sparks

Electrical sparks may result from short circuits and arcs from electric motors, switches, thermostats, loose electrical contacts including loose light bulbs, maintenance or work on live electrical circuits, and other electrical equipment. Ordinary refrigerators have a variety of electrical ignition sources *within* the refrigeration chamber.

4. Static electricity

Static electricity may be generated by repeated contact or separation of two dissimilar substances, such as the rubbing of clothing, moving machinery, *and pouring of flammable liquids*. The *Merck Index* reports that ether is a good insulator and when shaken under absolutely dry conditions can generate enough static electricity to start a fire.

F. Fire Temperature

Some of the concern which will be expressed later in this chapter for special containers for ethers and other flammable liquids and for special fire-protected storage is based on the importance of limiting the amount of fuel contributed to the fire and minimizing fire damage.

Vaporization increases as the temperature rises, and flammable liquids at elevated temperatures are obviously much more hazardous than the same materials at standard temperature. Furthermore, flammable liquids may liberate heat up to ten times faster than, for example, wood planking[9].

Ignition of a 3·8 l of low flash point thinner produced a peak fire temperature of 471° c in exactly 1 minute from time of ignition, and one gallon of duplicating fluid adjacent to wood shelving covered with paper, cardboard boxes, and books produced a peak fire temperature of 832°c in exactly 2 minutes from time of ignition[10].

G. Report of a Laboratory Fire

Having obtained a strongly positive potassium iodide test for peroxide in a two-year-old dioxane sample, a graduate student added 5 to 6 g of lithium aluminum hydride to about 400 ml of cold dioxane to reduce the peroxide. When hydrogen evolved in small bubbles in the reaction on the bench, he carried the container with a towel to the hood at the other end of the laboratory; the hydrogen began to evolve rapidly in large bubbles and the bottle exploded, burning with first and second degree burns his face and both arms. It is not known whether the explosion was caused by ignition of hydrogen or of dioxane vapors by either static electricity or by the heat of the reaction.

III. HEALTH HAZARDS OF ETHERS

The effects of ethers (and other chemicals) due to inhalation, skin contact, or ingestion may range from drowsiness and lack of co-ordination to serious injury or death depending upon the susceptibility of the individual, the toxicity of the chemical, and the duration of exposure.

Toxic materials act on the body by physical, by chemical or physiological means, or by a combination of these. The interested reader can refer to Stokinger's excellent discussion of the modes of action of toxic substances[11].

A. Ingestion

Accidental or intentional ingestion of ethers is certainly very rare in the laboratory, particularly if such materials are in containers with legible labels containing, whenever possible, the appropriate warning[12].

Ethers are reported to have a low order of toxicity[13] although 30 to 60 cc may be fatal when swallowed[14], and a case of fatal poisoning due to the ingestion of a large quantity of Methylcellosolve (2-methoxyethanol) has been recorded[15].

B. Skin Contact

Prolonged or repeated contacts of ethers with skin will cause tissue defatting and dehydration leading to dermatitis, but there is no record of skin sensitization. Some compounds penetrate the skin in harmful amounts, e.g. it has been reported that dioxane may be absorbed through the skin in sufficient quantities to produce injury[16]. Glycol ethers are not strong skin irritants and do not penetrate the skin in harmful amounts, with the exception of butylcellosolve and hexyl-cellosolve[13]. Application of liquid tetrahydrofuran to the skin of 196 persons was found to be essentially nonirritating, although repeated exposure will delipidize and dehydrate the skin[13]. Cellosolve, Butyl-cellosolve, and Cellosolve acetates have not produced systemic intoxication in industry, but have been responsible in certain laboratory animals for central nervous system depression, renal damage, and alterations in blood elements and toxicity[11].

C. Inhalation

Inhalation is the most likely and important means by which ethers enter the body. The effects of various ethers may include narcosis, irritation of the nose, throat, and mucous membranes, and chronic or acute poisoning.

Ethers in general are central nervous system depressants with diethyl ether and divinyl ether being used as general anesthetics; it is reported that pulmonary edema may in rare instances follow acute exposure to diethyl ether. Anesthesia is produced at concentrations of 25,000 p.p.m. of tetrahydrofuran and deep narcosis at 60,000 p.p.m. and exposures to high concentrations of glycol ether vapors may cause central nervous system effects[13].

Although no cases of industrial systemic intoxications had been reported for bis(dicholoroethyl) ether, animal studies indicate that the vapor is an intense respiratory tract irritant causing pulmonary edema[11]. Exposure to vapor concentrations of dioxane averaging 470 p.p.m. for several days was judged responsible for the death of a worker who at autopsy was found to have central nervous system damage, bronchopneumonia, and severe liver and kidney injury[17].

Acute exposure to methylcellosolve R may cause pronounced neurologic effects, including headache, drowsiness, fatigue, forgetfulness, tremors, and other symptoms, while low-grade chronic exposures may cause depression of red blood cell formation[11]. The literature includes a report on five persons who suffered from methylcellosolve intoxication after an industrial exposure[18].

Systemic effects which may result from overexposure to dioxane vapors or percutaneous absorption of liquid dioxane may include severe gastric symptoms, and liver necrosis and nephritis[11].

Some ethers, such as Carbitol (diethylene glycol monoethyl ether) and Butylcarbitol (diethylene glycol monobutyl ether), may not give warning by odor or irritative properties at threshold or toxic concentrations; others are sufficiently irritating to the eyes, nose, and throat so that the 'sensory limits' for comfortable exposures may be below threshold limits for toxic exposures (see Table 4). For comparison, the

TABLE 4. Sensory limits obtained for certain solvent vapors[19, 20].

Solvent	Concentration of vapor (p.p.m.) which irritated majority of subjects			Highest concentration (p.p.m.) estimated satisfactory for 8-hour exposure
	Eyes	Nose	Throat	
Diethyl ether	–	200	–	100
Di-n-butyl ether	200	200	> 200	100
Dioxane	> 200	> 200	> 200	200
Diisopropyl ether	> 300	> 300	> 300	> 300

threshold limit values given by the American Conference of Governmental Industrial Hygienists in 1964 were 400 p.p.m. for ether, 100 p.p.m. for dioxane, and 500 p.p.m. for diisopropyl ether.

D. Threshold Limit Values

TABLE 5. Recommended threshold limit values. [Reproduced, by permission, from *Threshold Limit Values 1965*, American Conference of Industrial Hygiene.]

Ether	p.p.m.	mg/m³
[C] Allyl glycidyl ether	10	45
2-Butoxyethanol (Butylcellosolve) [skin]	50	240
n-Butyl glycidyl ether	50	270
[C] Dichloroethyl ether [skin]	15	90
[C] Diglycidyl ether	0·5	2·8
Dioxane [skin]	100	360
Dipropylene glycol methyl ether [skin]	100	600
Diethyl ether	400	1200
2-Ethoxyethanol (Cellosolve) [skin]	200	740
2-Ethoxyethylacetate (cellosolve acetate) [skin]	100	540
Isopropyl glycidyl ether	50	240
2-Methoxyethanol (Methylcellosolve) [skin]	25	80
Phenyl glycidyl ether	50	310
Diisopropyl ether	500	2100
Tetrahydrofuran	200	590

[a] [C] refers to a maximal safe concentration and [skin] refers to the need to prevent cutaneous absorption.

The threshold limit value of a chemical is the highest atmospheric concentrations to which laboratory personnel should be exposed during regular working periods, to avoid nuisance, irritation, narcosis, impaired health, or other stress. Recommended threshold limit values for many chemicals have been established (Table 5) and are reviewed and published annually by the American Conference of Governmental Industrial Hygienists, which also publishes *Documentation of Threshold Limit Values*. The meaning, use, and limitations of threshold limit values are set forth in this annual listing.

IV. REACTIVITY HAZARDS

In addition to citing some hazardous chemical reactions which have been recorded between ethers and other chemicals, this section includes information on the formation, detection, inhibition, and removal of the peroxides which may be formed in many ethers by autooxidation. Methods of disposal of waste ethers, including those containing or suspected of containing peroxides, will be discussed in section V.F.

A. Hazardous Chemical Reactions

A convenient and accessible compilation of hazardous chemical reactions was published in 1964[21] and there are plans to publish revised editions as additional information on hazardous reactions is accumulated. The Committee who prepared this work invites those who have personal knowledge of hazardous reactions or who know of references to hazardous reactions which have been omitted to send the information to the Secretary of the Sectional Committee on Hazardous Chemical Reactions, The National Fire Protection Association, 60 Batterymarch Street, Boston, Massachusetts, 02110.

The *Manual of Hazardous Chemical Reactions*[21] (copyrighted by the National Fire Protection Association and quoted here by permission) gives references to the following reactions:

Diethyl ether   Mixtures of liquid air and diethyl ether exploded spontaneously.

Solutions of bromoazide in ether are stable for a few hours, but after this or when being concentrated are likely to explode on shaking.

Explosions involving diethyl ether and lithium aluminum hydride, with aluminum chloride as a catalyst, have been traced to carbon dioxide as an impurity in the ether.

Nitrosyl perchlorate ignites and explodes with diethyl ether.

Perchloric acid explodes with ether.

Explosions can occur when permanganates that have been treated with sulfuric acid come in contact with diethyl ether.

Sodium or potassium peroxide is spontaneously flammable with diethyl ether.

Diethyl ether reacts violently when mixed with anhydrous nitric acid.

Dimethyl ether — Occasional explosions involving dimethyl ether and aluminum hydride have been traced to carbon dioxide impurity in the ether.

In the lithium aluminum hydride reduction of organic compounds [22] some substances containing active hydrogen decompose the reagent with the liberation of hydrogen [23]. Peroxides of tetrahydrofuran or their reaction products may cause vigorous reaction with lithium aluminum hydride and a subsequent fire [24].

B. Peroxides

Ethers tend to absorb and react with oxygen from the air to form unstable peroxides which may detonate with extreme violence when they become concentrated by evaporation or distillation, or when combined with other compounds that give a detonable mixture, or when disturbed by heat, shock, or friction.

Peroxides formed in organic compounds by autooxidation have caused many laboratory accidents, including unexpected explosions [25,26]. An 'empty' 250 cc bottle which had held diethyl ether exploded when the ground glass stopper was replaced; another explosion cost a graduate student the total sight of one eye and most of the sight of the other; and a third killed a research chemist when he attempted to unscrew the cap from an old bottle of diisopropyl ether [27]. Appropriate action to prevent injuries from peroxides and ethers depends not only on knowledge about formation of peroxides and methods for detection and removal, but is also helped by proper labeling and inventory procedures, by personal protective equipment, and by adequate disposal methods.

1. Formation of peroxides

Peroxides may form in freshly distilled and unstabilized ethers within less than two weeks. Peroxide formation began in tetrahydrofuran after three days and in diethyl ether after eight days[28]. Exposure to the air, as in opened and partially emptied containers, accelerates formation of peroxides in ethers[29,30], and while the effect of exposure to light does not seem to be fully understood, it is generally recommended that ethers which will form peroxides should be stored in full, air-tight, amber glass bottles, preferably in the dark.

Although diethyl ether is frequently found stored under refrigeration, there is no evidence that refrigerated storage will prevent formation of peroxides.

The storage time required for peroxides to increase from 0·5 p.p.m. to 5 p.p.m. was less than two months for a tinplate container, six months for an aluminum container, and over 17 months for a glass container[31]. Rise in peroxide content was not appreciably accelerated at temperatures about 11°c above room temperature[31]. Davies has reported[32] on the hazards of the formation of peroxides in various liquids, and the literature contains an extensive report on autooxidation of diethyl ether[32].

Diisopropyl ether seems unusually susceptible to peroxidation: a half-filled 500 ml bottle of diisopropyl ether peroxidized despite being kept over a wad of iron wool[34]. Although it may be possible to stabilize diisopropyl ether in other ways, the absence or exhaustion of a stabilizer may not always be obvious from the appearance of a sample, so that even opening a container of diisopropyl ether of uncertain age to test for peroxides may be hazardous[27].

2. Detection and estimation of peroxides

Appreciable quantities of crystalline solids have been reported[25,26] as gross evidence for the formation of peroxides, and a case is known in which peroxides formed a viscous liquid in the bottom of a glass bottle of ether. If similar viscous liquid or crystalline solids are observed in ethers, no further tests are recommended, since in disposals of such material explosions have been reported when the bottles were broken.

Chemical and physical methods for detecting and estimating peroxides are described and cited by Davies[32,35]; he comments on several methods for detecting hydroperoxides and the problems of detecting dialkyl peroxides and polymeric alkylidene peroxides.

Ferrous thiocyanate is reported to be more sensitive in detecting hydroperoxides than potassium iodide solution (recommended in the Manufacturing Chemists' Association chemical safety data sheet SD-29 for diethyl ether). The ferrous thiocyanate test is as follows:

A *fresh* solution of 5 cc of 1% ferrous ammonium sulphate, 0·5 cc of 1 N sulfuric acid and 0·5 cc of 0·1 N ammonium thiocyanate are mixed (and if necessary, decolorized with a trace of zinc dust) and shaken with an equal quantity of the liquid to be tested; if peroxides are present, a red color will develop.

Acidified ferrous thiocyanate used as a spray reagent for paper chromotography will detect 15 γ of a hydroperoxide or diacyl peroxide, as cited by Davies[35].

The MCA method of testing for peroxides in diethyl ether, as described in SD-29, is as follows:

Add 1 cc of a freshly prepared 10% solution of potassium iodide to 10 cc of diethyl ether in a 25 cc glass-stoppered cylinder of colorless glass protected from light; when viewed transversely against a white background, no color should be seen in either liquid.

If any yellow color appears when 9 cc of diethyl ether are shaken with 1 cc of a saturated solution of potassium iodide, there is more than 0·005% peroxide and the ether should be discarded[36].

A quantitative test for peroxide in tetrahydrofuran and dioxane is as follows[36]:

To 50 ml of the ether add 6 ml of glacial acetic acid, 4 ml of chloroform, and 1 g of potassium iodide; titrate with 0·1 N thiosulfate to find the percent of peroxide, equal to

$$\frac{\text{ml of } Na_2S_2O_3 \times \text{normality} \times 1·7}{\text{weight of sample}}$$

If the reaction is carried out in acetic acid, air must be excluded by an inert gas, or by the vapor of the boiling solvent to prevent autooxidation of the iodide[35]. Acetic anhydride or hot isopropanol can be used as the reaction medium.

A method for rapid detection of traces of peroxides in ethers has been developed from the use of N,N-dimethyl-p-phenylenediamine sulfate to detect quantities of benzoyl and lauroyl peroxides[37].

Davies refers to qualitative and quantitative estimations, including both chemical and instrumental methods[35].

It is also reported[35] that dialkyl peroxides can be detected only after they have been hydrolyzed to hydroperoxides under strongly acid conditions, and that no satisfactory method appears to have been developed for the estimation of alkylidene peroxides[32].

3. Inhibition of peroxides

No single method seems to be suitable for inhibiting peroxide formation in all types of ethers, although storage and handling under an inert atmosphere would be a generally useful precaution.

Some of the materials which have been used to stabilize ethers and inhibit formation of peroxide include the addition of 0·001% hydroquinone or diphenylamine[33, 35], polyhydroxyphenols, aminophenols, and arylamines. 0·001 g of pyrogallol in 100 cc ether was reported to prevent peroxide formation over a period of two years[32]. *Water will not prevent formation of peroxides in ethers,* and iron, lead, and aluminum will not inhibit the peroxidation of diisopropyl ether[38] although iron does act as an inhibitor in diethyl ether. Dowex-1 has been reported effective for inhibiting peroxide formation in diethyl ether[39]; 100 p.p.m. of 1-naphthol for diisopropyl ether[40], hydroquinone for tetrahydrofuran[41], and stannous chloride or ferrous sulfate for dioxane[40] and substituted stilbenequinones have been proposed[42] as stabilizers against oxidation of ethers and other compounds.

4. Removal of peroxides

Reagents which have been used for removing hydroperoxides from solvents are reported by Davies[32] to include sodium sulfite, sodium hydrogen sulfite, stannous chloride, lithium aluminum hydride (*caution:* see notes in sections II.G and IV.B), zinc and acid, sodium and alcohol, copper–zinc couple, potassium permanganate, silver hydroxide, and lead dioxide. Decomposition of the peroxides with ferrous sulfate is a commonly used method—454 g (1 lb) of 30% ferrous sulfate solution in water is added to each 11·4 l (30 gal)[43]. Caution is needed since the reaction may be vigorous if the solvent contains a high concentration of peroxide.

Reduction of alkylidene or dialkyl peroxides is more difficult but reduction by zinc in acetic or hydrochloric acid, sodium in alcohol (see note on case of ignition of hydrogen liberated from water), or the copper–zinc couple might be used for purifying solvents containing these peroxides[32].

Addition of one part of 23% sodium hydroxide to 10 parts of diethyl ether or tetrahydrofuran removed peroxides completely after agitation for 30 minutes; sodium hydroxide pellets reduced but did not remove the peroxide contents of teterahydrofuran after two days[28]. Addition of 30% N chloroform to tetrahydrofuran inhibited peroxide formation until the eighth day with only slight change during 15 succeeding days of tests[28]. The peroxides were removed from the mixture by agitating it with 1% aqueous sodium borohydride for 15 minutes (with no attempt made to measure temperature rise or evolution of hydrogen).

A simple method for removing peroxides from high quality ether samples without need for distillation apparatus or appreciable loss of ether consists of percolating the solvent through a column of Dowex-1 ion-exchange resin[39]. A column of alumina was used to remove peroxides and traces of water from diethyl ether, dibutyl ether, and dioxane[44] and also for removing peroxides from tetrahydrofuran and diisopropyl ether[32].

Calcium hydride can be used for obtaining anhydrous and peroxide-free p-dioxane[45], by refluxing followed by distillation. The use of sodium and potassium borohydrides to reduce peroxide in tetrahydrofuran and diethylene glycol dimethyl ether (diglyme) and to inhibit them for some time against further peroxidation has been reported[46].

For removing peroxides from ethers the need and value has been expressed[24] for an insoluble solid which can be separated by filtration or decantation. Cerous hydroxide $(Ce(OH)_3)$ fulfills these requirements[47]. Cerous hydroxide, prepared from a cerous salt solution by sodium hydroxide, changes from white to reddish brown within a minute or two after addition to an ether if peroxides are present; removal of peroxides can be completed within 15 minutes. The peroxyceric compound and unchanged cerous hydroxide can be removed by centrifugation (*caution:* flammable vapors ignite if the centrifuge is electric and not explosion-proof) and decantation. After treatment with cerous hydroxide each of twelve ethers which had previously contained peroxides gave negative potassium iodide tests. After the removal of peroxides, the ethers were tested for the presence of cerium by the benzidine test, with negative results except for allyl ethyl ether and benzyl n-butyl ether. It was noted that di-t-butyl peroxide did not liberate iodine from acidified potassium iodide solution nor did it react with cerous hydroxide[47].

V. PROTECTIVE MEASURES

A. Ventilation

Laboratory ventilation systems must effectively remove flammable and toxic materials that become airborne and at the same time exhaust a minimal volume of air, in order to meet the needs of both safety and economy. Some recommended designs for hoods, ventilation, equipment, and related subjects are treated in references 48–53.

B. Control of Sources of Ignition

Explosion-proof electrical outlets, lights, motors, blenders, centrifuges, and refrigerators are available for use in atmospheres where flammable vapors and gases may not be controlled completely by ventilation or other means. Equipment which is explosion-proof should be tested, labeled, and listed by a nationally recognized testing laboratory.

Electrical heating appliances should either not be capable of heating to the ignition temperature of flammable materials used or should be prevented from reaching that temperature by limiting devices.

Arcing contacts of autotransformers can be separated from flammable vapors and gases by immersion in oil, or by enclosing and purging with air or nitrogen[54].

C. Containers and Labeling

The volume, material, and labeling of containers for chemicals have a significant bearing on prevention and control of laboratory accidents. The duration and intensity of laboratory fires will be greatly increased if large volumes of flammable solvents become involved, which is likely to happen if there are many glass bottles or cans larger than one liter stored in the laboratory. Inadequate labeling of containers can be expected to result in problems if the contents cannot be identified quickly and positively, if the age of contents which may peroxidize cannot be determined readily, or if the fire, health, and reactivity hazards of the contents must be found in a handbook by reference to a library.

The need for adequate labeling extends far beyond the immediate requirements of the individual user, since the individual user may not be present in case of fire or explosion when containers are broken or spilled, and he may not be around years later when the containers have deteriorated or otherwise lost their value. Therefore, wax pencil markings, abbreviations, formulas only, and code names or numbers should be avoided in favor of adequate labels.

Recommendations for information that should be considered for inclusion on the label are[12]: (*a*) name of the chemical, preferably the chemical name, or the types of chemical; (*b*) signal word to indicate severity of hazard (e.g. 'danger', 'warning', or 'caution'); (*c*) statement of hazards, with most serious first; (*d*) precautionary measures to be taken to avoid injury or damage from hazards stated; and (*e*) instructions in case of contact or exposure if results are severe and immediate action may be necessary.

It is recommended that labels for laboratory chemicals are dated when issued and marked with the name of the user, particularly in the case of liquids which tend to peroxidize or which are not common. Flammable and combustible liquids should be labeled to include their flash point, as a means of recognizing needs for ventilation, ignition source control, or other precautions. A special hazard labeling has been described[55].

Whenever practicable ethers with flash points below 60° c should be stored in metal safety cans which have spring-loaded lids to prevent rupture from overheating, and which are approved by a national testing laboratory. Safety cans with flash arresters in the pouring spout will prevent flashbacks from igniting the contents.

D. Fire-protected Storage

The greatest need of fire-protected storage is for chemicals which are easily ignited, difficult to extinguish, or burn with great rapidity. Organic peroxides, azo compounds, pyrophoric metals, and flammable liquids are some of the types of chemicals which need separate and fire-protected storage[9,56,57].

E. Personal Protective Equipment

Laboratory personnel should consider both the regular and the infrequent needs for personal protective equipment, and should acquire and practice the use of such equipment, including eye protection, face and body shields, fire retardant clothing, and hand protection[58-61].

Since the most serious eye injuries in laboratories seem to have resulted from explosions, the basic eye protection should be able to stop flying objects *from the front and from the side. Spectacles with side shields seem to be the best basic protection against flying objects, and to afford a reasonable measure of protection against droplets which may be splashed up.* Although safety-glass spectacles with side shields are more expensive than plastic goggles or eyeshields, the higher initial cost seems to be justifiable on the bases of comfort and wearability, optical quality, cleaning abrasion resistance, and durability[58].

Allowing laboratory personnel to wear ordinary glasses when eye protection is required creates a false sense of security and the erroneous assumption that ordinary glasses provide a creditable degree of protection.

In a model law proposed as an eye safety legislation guide[60], the requirement for wearing eye protective devices would include every student and teacher in school, college, and university laboratories.

F. Disposal Methods

The collection, handling, transport, and final disposal of hazardous laboratory wastes is the subject of a recent book[62] and of several reports[63-65].

A good example of an excellent disposal procedure, as well as the hazards of ether peroxides, is provided by this excerpt from a report[34] on the disposal of a half-full 500 ml bottle of diisopropyl ether:

> About 5 g of a crystalline solid, presumably the peroxide, was just discernible at the bottom of the brown glass bottle, which was stoppered with a cork and had been stored in the dark. *We did not try to open the bottle.* When we broke it *by remote control behind a safety wall in an outdoor disposal unit,* the bottle exploded with a report that brought enquirers out of a nearby building.

VI. SOURCES OF INFORMATION ON HAZARDS

The American Industrial Hygiene Association (AIHA), 14125 Prevost Street, Detroit, Michigan 48227, has over 120 Hygienic Guides at the present time and regularly publishes additional guides in their journal, which concisely lists recommended maximal atmospheric concentration, severity of hazard, significant control procedures, and specific procedures which are known for first aid, biochemical assay, and special medical procedures.

The Manufacturing Chemists' Association, Inc. (MCA), 1825 Connecticut Avenue, Washington, D.C., 20009, has over 90 Chemical

TABLE 6. Chemical hazard data guides available.

Compound	AIHA	MCA	NSC
Dioxane	*	–	–
Epichlorohydrin	*	–	–
Epoxy resin systems	*	–	–
Ethylene glycol monobutyl ether (Butyl-cellosolve)	*	–	–
Ethylene glycol monoethyl ether (Cellosolve)	*	–	–
Ethylene glycol monomethyl ether (Methyl-cellosolve)	*	–	–
Ethylene oxide	*	38	–
Diethyl ether	–	29	396
Propylene oxide	*	–	–
Tetrahydrofuran	*	–	–

* Guide sheets for these chemicals are available from AIHA.

Safety Data Sheets available, as well as fourteen Chemical Safety Guides, and numerous Manuals of Standard and Recommended Practice, and an excellent film *Safety in the Chemical Laboratory*. Chemical Safety Data Sheets give the hazardous properties of chemicals and essential information for safe handling, storage, and use. They outline employee education and training, personal protective equipment recommendations, descriptions of health hazards, and methods of control and information on waste disposal.

The National Safety Council (NSC), 425 North Michigan Avenue, Chicago, Illinois 60611, publishes Data Sheets developed by its chemical section.

Table 6 lists the various data guides which are available.

VII. REFERENCES

1. H. K. Livingston, 'Safety considerations in research proposals', in *Proc. 11th Natl. Conf. Campus Safety Assoc.*, National Safety Council, Chicago, 1965.
2. N. V. Steere, 'Responsibility for accident prevention', *J. Chem. Educ.*, **41**, A27 (1964).
3. *Handbook of Organic Industrial Solvents*, 2nd ed., National Association of Mutual Casualty Companies, Chicago, 1961.
4. *International Critical Tables*, Vol. 1, McGraw-Hill Book Co., New York, 1926, p. 358.
5. H. F. Coward and G. W. Jones, *Limits of Flammability of Gases and Vapors*, U.S. Government Printing Office, Washington, D.C., 1952.
6. H. F. Calcote, C. A. Gregory, Jr., C. M. Barnett, and R. B. Gilmer, 'Spark ignition—Effect of molecular structure', *Ind. Eng. Chem.*, **44**, 2656 (1952).
7. J. R. Yockers, 'Cigarette fire mechanisms', *Quart. Natl. Fire Protection Assoc.*, **49** (No. 3), 213 (1956).
8. *Mechanical Engineers Handbook* (Ed. L. S. Marks), McGraw-Hill Book Co., New York, 1941.
9. Factory Mutual Engineering Division, *Handbook of Industrial Loss Prevention*, McGraw-Hill Book Co., New York, 1959.
10. Los Angeles Fire Department, '*Operation School Burning—No. 2*', National Fire Protection Association, Boston, 1961.
11. *Occupational Diseases* (Ed. W. M. Gafafer), Public Health Service Publication No. 1097, U.S. Government Printing Office, Washington, D.C., 1964.
12. *Guide to Precautionary Labeling of Hazardous Chemicals*, 6th ed., Manufacturing Chemists Association, Washington, D.C., 1961.
13. W. B. Deichman and H. W. Gerarde, *Symptomatology and Therapy of Toxicological Emergencies*, Academic Press, New York, 1964.
14. M. N. Gleason, R. F. Gosselin, and H. F. Hodge, *Clinical Toxicology of Commercial Products*, The Williams and Wilkins Co., Baltimore, 1957.
15. E. G. Young and L. B. Woolner, 'A case of fatal poisoning from 2-methoxyethanol', *J. Ind. Hygiene Toxicol.*, **28**, 267 (1947).

16. A. Fairley, E. C. Linton, and A. H. Ford-Moore, 'The toxicity to animals of 1,4-Dioxane', *J. of Hygiene*, **34**, 486 (1935).
17. R. T. Johnstone, 'Death due to dioxane?', *AMA Arch. Ind. Health*, **20** (No. 6), 445 (1959).
18. M. Zavon, 'Methylcellosolve intoxication', *Am. Ind. Hygiene Assoc.*, **24**, 36 (1963).
19. K. W. Nelson, J. F. Ege, M. Ross, L. E. Woodman, and L. Silverman, 'Sensory response to certain industrial solvent vapors', *J. Ind. Hygiene*, **25**, 282 (1943).
20. L. Silverman, H. F. Schulte, and M. W. First, 'Further studies on sensory response to certain industrial solvent vapors', *J. Ind. Hygiene*, **28**, 262 (1946).
21. *Manual of Hazardous Chemical Reactions*, National Fire Protection Association, Boston, 1964.
22. A. E. Finholt, A. C. Bond, Jr., and H. I. Schesinger, 'Lithium aluminum hydride, aluminum hydride and lithium gallium hydride, and some of their applications in organic and inorganic chemistry,' *J. Am. Chem. Soc.*, **69**, 1199 (1947).
23. R. F. Nystrom and W. G. Brown, 'Reduction of organic compounds by lithium aluminum hydride', *J. Am. Chem. Soc.*, **69**, 1197 (1947).
24. R. B. Moffett and B. D. Aspergren, 'Tetrahydrofuran can cause fire when used as solvent for $LiAIH_4$', *Chem. Eng. News*, **32**, 4328 (1954).
25. I. B. Douglass, *J. Chem. Educ.*, **40**, 469 (1963).
26. N. V. Steere, 'Control of hazards from peroxides in ethers', *J. Chem. Educ.*, **41**, A575 (1964).
27. *Accident Case History 603*, Manufacturing Chemists' Association, reported in part in reference 26.
28. E. Fleck, Merck, Sharp & Dohme Company Memo, May 11, 1960.
29. C. R. Noller, *Chemistry of Organic Compounds*, W. B. Saunders Co., Philadelphia, 1951.
30. J. Rosin, *Reagent Chemicals and Standards*, 4th ed., D. Van Nostrand Co., Princeton, N.J., 1961.
31. A. R. Brubaker, personal communication, December 4, 1964.
32. A. G. Davies, 'Explosion hazards of autoxidized solvents', *J. Roy. Inst. Chem.*, 386 (1956).
33. G. Lindgren, 'Autoxidation of diethyl ether and its inhibition by diphenylamine', *Acta Chir. Scand.*, **94**, 110 (1946).
34. Pajaczkowski, A., personal communication, September 29, 1964.
35. A. G. Davies, *Organic Peroxides*, Butterworths, London, 1961.
36. H. S. Brasted, personal communication, June 1, 1964.
37. P. R. Dugan, *Anal. Chem.*, **33**, 1630 (1961).
38. P. R. Dugan, *Ind. Eng. Chem.*, **56**, 37 (1964).
39. R. N. Feinstein, 'Simple method for removal of peroxides from diethyl ether', *J. Org. Chem.*, **24**, 1172 (1959).
40. *Encyclopedia of Chemical Technology*, Vol. 5 (Ed. R. E. Kirk and D. F. Othmer), Interscience Publishers, New York, 1950, pp. 871, 142.
41. *Encyclopedia of Chemical Technology*, Vol. 6 (Ed. R. E. Kirk and D. F. Othmer), Interscience Publishers, 1950, p. 1006.
42. D. G. Jones, *Brit. Pat.*, 699,079 (1953); *Chem. Abstr.*, **49**, 3262f (1955).

43. *Chemical Safety Data Sheet—SD 29, Ethyl Ether*, Manufacturing Chemists' Association, Washington, D.C., 1956.
44. W. Dasler and C. D. Bauer, 'Removal of peroxides from ethers', *Ind. Eng. Chem. Anal. Ed.*, **18**, 52 (1946).
45. E. R. Birnbaum, personal communication, August 11, 1964.
46. *Manual of Techniques*, Metal Hydrides, Inc., Beverly, Massachusetts, 1958.
47. J. B. Ramsey and F. T. Aldridge, 'Removal of peroxides from ethers with cerous hydroxide', *J. Am. Chem. Soc.*, **77**, 2561 (1955).
48. D. T. Smith, 'Shields and barricades for chemical laboratory operations', in *Proc. 11th Natl. Conf. Campus Safety Assoc.*, National Safety Council, Chicago, 1965.
49. L. Silverman and M. W. First, 'Portable laboratory scrubber unit for perchloric acid', *Am. Ind. Hygiene Assoc., J.*, **23**, 463 (1962).
50. N. V. Steere, 'Ventilation of laboratory operations', *J. Chem. Educ.*, **41**, A95, A193 (1964).
51. Campus Safety Association, 'Laboratory design consideration for safety—tenatatively approved', in *J. Chem. Educ.*, **42**, A583 (1965).
52. Committee on Industrial Ventilation, American Conference of Governmental Hygienists, *Industrial Ventilation*, 8th ed., Edward Brothers, Ann Arbor, 1964.
53. J. Halitsky, 'Estimation of stack height required to limit contamination of building air intakes', *Am. Ind. Hygiene Assoc., J.*, **26**, 106 (1965).
54. W. S. Wood, 'Use, storage, and disposal of flammable liquids', *Ind. Eng. Chem.*, **51, 87A** (1959).
55. *Recommended System for the Identification of Fire Hazards of Materials*, National Fire Protection Association, Boston, 1961.
56. N. V. Steere, 'Fire-protected storage for records and chemicals', *J. Chem. Educ.*, **41**, A859 (1964).
57. *Flammable and Combustible Liquids Code*, National Fire Protection Association, Boston, 1963.
58. N. V. Steere, 'Eye protection in laboratories', *J. Chem. Educ.*, **41**, A936 (1964).
59. I. W. Silberstein, *Natl. Safety News*, **90**, 29 (1964).
60. National Society for the Prevention of Blindness, *Wise Owl News*, Summer 1964.
61. G. N. Quam, 'Use of eye protection and body shields in college chemical laboratories', *J. Chem. Educ.*, **41**, A936 (1964).
62. P. J. Gaston, *The Care, Handling, and Disposal of Dangerous Chemicals*, Institute of Science Technology by Northern Publishers, Aberdeen, 1964.
63. R. A. Cain, 'Disposing of waste ether cans', *Anesthesiology*, **24**, 255 (1963).
64. *Safe Disposal of Empty Pesticide Containers and Surplus Pesticides*, Agricultural Research Service, U.S. Department of Agriculture, Washington, D.C., 1964.
65. D. I. Snow and H. H. Fawcett, 'Occupational health and safety' in *Laboratory Planning* (Ed. H. F. Lewis), Reinhold Publishing Corp., New York, 1962.

Author index

This author index is designed to enable the reader to locate an author's name and work with the aid of the reference numbers appearing in the text. The page numbers are printed in normal type in ascending numerical order, followed by the reference numbers in brackets. The numbers in *italics* refer to the pages on which the references are actually listed.

If reference is made to the work of the same author in different chapters, the above arrangement is repeated separately for each chapter.

23*

24—C.E.L.

Hodosan, F. 369 (60), *372*
Hoeflich, N. J. 354 (6), *371*
Hoeg, D. F. 62 (158, 159), *79*
Hoek, A. J. v. d. 489 (165), *498*
Hoffa, E. 318 (38), *347*
Hofferth, B. 62 (157), *79*
Hoffman, P. 222 (157, 159), 223 (160), *238*
Hoffmann, H. 473 (125), 483 (153), *496, 497*
Hoffmann, R. 644 (87), *666*
Hoffmeister, W. 32 (59), *76*
Hoffsommer, R. D. 360 (27), *371*
Hofman, W. 252 (31), *299*
Hofmann, J. E. 610 (190), *615*, 627 (26), *664*
Hofmann, P. 266, 267, 269 (122), *301*
Höft, E. 319 (53), *347*, 587, 589, 602, 603 (129) *613*
Hogeveen, H. 566 (60), *611*
Hogg, D. R. 28 (39), *76*
Hohmann, W. 330 (114), *349*
Hoijtink, G. J. 265 (114), *301*
Holland, J. F. 654 (134), *667*
Holland, W. 63 (166), *79*
Holliday, A. K. 274 (174), 275, 276 (185), *303*
Hollingsworth, C. A. 273 (167), *303*
Hollyhead, W. B. 153 (162a), *165*, 450 (39), *493*
Holmberg, B. 586 (121), *613*
Holmes, E. L. 147 (152), *165*
Holmquist, H. E. 326 (89), *348*
Holms, J. 621 (13), *664*
Holt, G. 117, 145 (94b), *163*
Holton, P. G. 644 (98), *666*
Homer, J. 328 (100), *348*
Homsma, T. 332 (126), *349*
Honeycutt, J. B. 62 (157), *79*
Honeycutt, J. B., Jr. 264 (104), *301*
Hooton, K. A. 111 (74a), *163*
Hoover, T. E. 73 (205), *80*
Hooz, J. 445
Hopff, H. 394 (198), *436*
Hopkins, H. B. 106 (61), *163*
Horák, V. 525, 546 (133), 547 (135, 136), *551*
Horecker, B. L. 213 (86), *236*
Horner, L. 427 (409), *442*, 473 (125), 483 (153), 484 (154), *496, 497*
Horrom, B. W. 448 (29), *493*
Horstmann, H. 542 (122), *551*
Hort, I. 427 (411), *442*
Hough, L. 377 (47), *432*

Hough, W. V. 277 (210), *304*
House, H. O. 56 (132–134), 57 (135), 58 (138), *78*, 479 (138), *496*, 555 (5), *610*
How, M. J. 208 (6), *234*
Howard, E. G. 330 (109). *349*, 606, 607 (183), *615*
Howard, J. F., Jr. 392 (177), *435*
Howard, W. L. 318 (35, 43, 46), 321 (61), 331, 337, 340 (125), *347, 349*
Howell, H. 391 (176), *435*
Howell, W. C. 447 (14), *492*
Howk, B. W. 325 (79), *348*
Hrborne, J. B. 217 (106), *237*
Hrenoff, M. K. 377 (28), *431*
Hruby, V. J. 386 (129), *434*, 599 (161), *614*
Hu, A. S. L. 227 (234), *240*
Huang, R. L. 64 (172, 174), 65 (175), 74 (214), 75 (217), *79, 80*
Huber, H. 362 (43), *372*, 428 (413), *442*
Hucho, F. 232, 233 (303), *242*
Hudson, R. F. 90, 110, 111 (28a), 131 (115), *161, 164*
Huestis, L. D. 604 (178), *615*, 643 (84), *665*
Huet, J. 391 (165), *435*
Hughes, E. D. 26 (31), 30 (55), *76*, 151 (157), *165*, 448 (18), 461 (100), *492, 495*
Hughes, G. K. 47 (91), *77*, 581 (105), 584 (116), *613*
Hughes, R. E. 519 (41), *523*
Hughes, S. R. C. 103 (57), *162*
Hughes, W. B. 336 (146), *350*
Huisgen, R. 460 (95), *495*
Humphlett, W. J. 270, 271 (141), *302*
Hung, Chang, C. 394 (202), *436*
Hünig, S. 336 (148), *350*
Hunt, D. M. 111 (74a), *163*
Hunt, P. 415, 417 (352), *441*
Hunter, A. S. 447 (13), *492*
Hunter, G. L. K. 402 (257), *438*
Hunter, W. H. 517 (40), *523*
Hurd, C. D. 73 (206), *80*, 313 (22), *346*, 447 (8), *492*, 606 (185), *615*, 641 (63), 644 (104), 647 (111), 649 (118), *665, 666*
Huston, R. C. 63 (167), *79*
Huyser, E. S. 158 (171), *166*, 345 (177), *351*, 410 (302), 428, 429 (414), *439, 443*
Hyman, H. H. 259 (72), 261 (88), *300*

Subject index

749

Acetals—*cont.*

  dependence on acidity function 318, 333

  hyperconjugative effect 333, 334

  mechanism 332, 333

  partial cleavage 334

  polar effect 333, 334

  resonance effects 333

  secondary reactions 334

  steric effects 333

  substituent effect 333

i.r. absorption 327

mass spectral determination 328, 329

n.m.r. spectra 327, 328

nucleophilic cleavage 582

peroxide formation 343

photochemical conversion into esters 369

photochemical reactions with alkenes 368, 369

polymerization 345

preparation 314–327

properties 327–329

quantitative determinations 676

radical reactions 341–345

radicals attacks on 344, 345

Raman absorption 327

reactions 329–345

  via α-alkoxy carbonium ions 332–341

  with acid chloride 336

  with anhydrides 336, 340

  with N-bromo succinamide 342, 370

  with C–C bond formation 338–340

  with diazo esters 339

  with hydroxamic acid 335

  with ketenes 339

  with Lewis acids 338–340

  with mercaptans 337

  with metal hydrides 340, 341

  with oxygen 343

  with peracids 336

  with peroxides 335

  with peroxy radicals 344, 345

  with Vilsmeier's reagent 340

  with vinyl ethers 338, 339

reduction 340, 341

stability 329–331

  in basic media 329–331

  limitations 331

  to oxidizing agents 331

  to reducing agents 330, 331

thermal decompositions 345

Acetals—*cont.*

  transition into ethers 340, 341

  u.v. absorptions 327

Acetolysis, anchimeric assistance in 119–124

Acetone, photolysis 194, 195

α-Acetoxy ethers, photochemical preparations 363, 364

Acetylation 137, 140

Acetylene oxides—*see* Oxirenes

Acetyl radicals 197, 198

Acid-catalyzed oxygen-sulfur conversion 531–533, 543–547

Acid-catalyzed reactions—*see also* Specific reactions

Acid-catalyzed rearrangements 628–635

  comparison with Friedel–Crafts alkylation 630–632

  cross products 632

  degree of intramolecularity 630–631

  mechanism 629–635

  of alkyl *o*-haloaryl ethers 634, 635

  of allyl aryl ethers 633–635

  ortho to *meta* migration 634

  ortho to *para* ratio 630–632

  solvent effects on 631

  racemization 629, 631

  side products 629–632

  stereochemistry 629–631

  temperature effect 632–635

  transalkylation 630

  versus Claisen rearrangement 633–635

Acid chlorides, photochemical reaction 368

Acid strength, substituent effect on 90, 97–107

Activating effect of ether groups 81–166

Activation energies in pyrolysis, of acetaldehyde 196

  acetone 195

  allyl ethers 191

  diethyl ether 185

  dimethyl ether 170, 177

  ethane 198, 200, 202

Activation energy of, ethyl radical decomposition 202

  methyl radical combination 194

Activation entropy—*see* Entropy of activation

Activation volume—*see* Volume of activation

Active methionine—*see* S-Adenosylmethionine

25*

Hydrolysis—*cont.*
of diazofluorenes 156
of epoxides—*see* Epoxides
of esters 125–130
alkoxy substituent effect on 126–130
mechanism, alteration of 129, 130
of thioethers 584–586
Hydroxy compounds—*see also* specific compounds
conversion into mercaptans, thiophenols and thiophene 531
β-Hydroxy cyclic thioethers, ring contraction 593
β-Hydroxy esters, from epoxides 392
β-Hydroxy ethers, conversion to *p*-halo ethers 591
reactivity 591
δ-Hydroxy δ-halo thioethers interconversions 595
ω-Hydroxy ω-halo thioethers interconversion 596
α-Hydroxy ketones, by epoxides oxidation 390
from epoxy ethers 394
t-Hydroxy peroxides, rearrangement to *p*-hydroxy peroxides 403
α-Hydroxy thioethers 588
β-Hydroxy thioethers, conversion to β-halo thioethers 591, 592, 593
reactions, with alcohols 592
with sulfides 593
with thiols 593
reactivity 591
γ-Hydroxy thioethers, conversion to γ-halo thioethers 595
δ-Hydroxy thioethers, neighboring-group interaction 595
Hyperconjugation 9
Hyperconjugation effect 120, 333, 334

Ignition temperatures 684, 685
Inductive effect 97, 100–104—*see also* Substituent effect
in nucleophilic aromatic substitution 153
in nucleophilic substitution of thioethers 578, 581, 585
in stabilizing carbonium ions 120, 556
in thioethers halogenation 603
of ether group 83, 84, 87, 97
on complexes strength 275, 289, 290, 293, 294

Inductive—*cont.*
on ether radical formation 355
related to anchimeric assistance 1119
Infrared studies, in analysis 672, 673
in determination of basicity 378
in electrophilic reactions 156
in hydrogen bonding with ethers 47, 288–293, 296
of acetals 327
of cyclic ethers 376
of cyclic hemiacetals 313
of strong complexes 247
Instantaneous dipole 246
Interaction, strong 246–248, 251, 252—*see also* Oxonium salts and Complexes
Interaction strength
correlation with association constant 251
correlation with heat of formation 246, 247
correlation with spectral data 247, 248, 283
temperature effect 250
Interactions, weak 282–293
correlation with ground state electron–donor ability 248
correlation with heat of formation 251
Mulliken theory 248, 249
strength of donor–acceptor interaction 283
Interaction types, dipole–dipole 246
dipole–induced dipole 246
instantaneous dipole 246
ion–dipole 245
London dispersion forces 246
Intermolecular condensations of thioethers 565
Intramolecular free-radical reactions 418
Intramolecular hydrogen abstraction 416, 417
Intrinsic viscosity of poly(propylene oxide) 507, 515
Inversion by glycosidases 228
Ionic character of epoxides 378
Ionization constants,
of conjugate acids 101–105
of conjugate acids of nitrogen bases 99–101
of carboxylic acids 97–98
of phenols 99–101
Ionization energy—*see* Energy of ionization